## ALSO BY THE SAME AUTHOR

# INTERNATIONAL TRANSISTOR EQUIVALENTS GUIDE

by
**ADRIAN MICHAELS**

**BERNARD BABANI (publishing) LTD
THE GRAMPIANS
SHEPHERDS BUSH ROAD
LONDON W6 7NF
ENGLAND**

Although every care is taken with the preparation of this book, the publishers or author will not be responsible in any way for any errors that might occur.

**British Library Cataloguing in Publication Data**
Michaels, Adrian
    International transistor equivalents guide
    1. Transistors
    I. Title
    621.3815'28   TK7871.9

    ISBN 0 85934 060 0

Printed and Manufactured in Great Britain by Cox & Wyman Ltd.

# NOTES ON USING THIS BOOK

It must be realised by all users of transistors, that it is impossible to guarantee absolute equivalents.

It should be noted that the equivalents quoted in columns 5 to 9 of this book, may differ slightly in electrical and/or mechanical characteristics to those shown in column 1.

It is therefore recommended, especially in critical circuits, to check against the original, the detailed characteristics of possible equivalent transistors by using the manufacturers' current specification or data sheets, before a substitution is made.

The following abbreviations for colours have been used throughout this book:

| | | | | |
|---|---|---|---|---|
| b | = | black | gn = | green |
| v | = | violet | gr = | grey |
| w | = | white | r = | red |
| br | = | brown | ye = | yellow |
| or | = | orange | bl = | blue |

| TYPE | M/S | POL | MANUFAC | EUROPEAN | | AMERICAN | | JAPANESE | USE |
|------|-----|-----|---------|----------|---|----------|---|----------|-----|
| 1 | 2 | 3 | 4 | 5 | 6 | 7 | 8 | 9 | 10 |

**1. TYPE**  Alpha-numerical transistor index

**2. M/S**  Material/Sort

| | |
|---|---|
| C | complementary transistor NPN/PNP |
| DG | dual germanium transistor |
| DJ | dual junction transistor |
| DS | dual silicon transistor |
| FET | field effect transistor |
| G | germanium transistor |
| GD | germanium Darlington transistor |
| J | junction FET (JFET) |
| M | MOSFET |
| ME | multiple-emitter transistor |
| MOS | metal oxide semiconductor |
| P | photo-transistor |
| PU | programmable unijunction transistor |
| S | silicon transistor |
| SD | silicon Darlington transistor |
| SF | silicon FET |
| TA | multiple transistor |
| U | unijunction transistor |

**3. POL**  Polarity

| | |
|---|---|
| N | NPN transistor or N-channel |
| P | PNP transistor or P-channel |
| PN | unijunction transistor |

**4. MANUFAC**  Manufacturer (see separate table)

**5, 6. EUROPEAN**  European equivalent
(. . .) near equivalent

**7, 8. AMERICAN** American equivalent
(. . .) near equivalent

**9. JAPANESE** Japanese equivalent

**10. USE**

| | |
|---|---|
| 01 | amplifier |
| 02 | high frequency amplifier |
| 03 | high power high frequency amplifier |
| 04 | light-sensitive amplifier |
| 05 | multiple amplifier |
| 06 | high power amplifier |
| 07 | switching amplifier |
| 08 | multiple switching amplifier |
| 09 | high power switching amplifier |
| 10 | switching transistor |
| 11 | high frequency switching transistor |
| 12 | chopper |
| 13 | high speed switching transistor |
| 14 | high speed high power switching transistor |
| 15 | general purpose transistor |
| 16 | high power switching transistor |
| 17 | low power switching transistor |
| 18 | television amplifier HF |
| 19 | television amplifier LF |
| 20 | special computer transistor |
| 21 | photodetector |
| 22 | radiation detector |
| 23 | matched transistor |

# MANUFACTURER

A   AMS Advanced Memory System
AE  AEI Semiconductors Ltd.
AM  Amperex Electronic Corp.
AT  Ates (SGS) Componetti SpA
BG  Bogue Electric Mfd.
BL  Bharat Electronics
BT  Burns and Towne Inc.
CA  Carter Semiconductor Inc.
CB  CBS Electronics
CE  Calvert Electronics Inc.
CI  CSR Industries Semiconductor Div.
CL  Clairex Electronics Div.
CN  Continental Semiconductor
CO  Cosem-Sescosem
CR  Crystalonics Div. Teledyne
CV  Clevite Transistor
DD  Delco Electronics Div. General Motors
DT  Delsa-Toshiba
EI  Elcoma Div.
ES  Electro-State Industries Inc.
ET  Electronic Transistor Corp. ETC
F   Fairchild Semiconductor Corp.
FE  Ferranti Ltd.
FR  Franel Corp.
FU  Fujitsu Ltd.
GE  General Electric Corp. GEC
GI  General Instrument Corp. GIC
GP  Germanium Power Devices Corp.
GX  General Sensor Inc.
HI  Hitachi Ltd.
HS  Helios Semiconductor
HW  Honeywell Semiconductor
IC  Industro Transistor Corp.
ID  International Diode Corp.
II   International Devices Inc.
IL  Intersil
IN  Intermetall/ITT Semiconductor Div.

| | |
|---|---|
| IS | Iskra |
| IT | ITT Semiconductors |
| KE | Kemtron Electronic Products |
| KM | KMC Semiconductor Corp. |
| KS | KSC Semiconductor Corp. |
| LI | Lignes Télégr. et Téléph. |
| LU | Lucas Joseph Electr. Ltd. |
| MA | Matsushita Electronic Corp. |
| MB | MBLE Manufacture Belgique de Lampes et de Matériel Electronique |
| ME | Micro Electronics Corp. |
| ML | Mistral SpA |
| MN | Miniwatt Div. of Philips Electronics |
| MO | Motorola Semiconductor Prod. |
| MT | Mitsubishi Electric Corp. |
| MU | Mullard |
| NI | Nippon Electric Comp. (NEC) |
| NP | New Jersey Semiconductor Prod. |
| NS | National Semiconductor Corp. NSC |
| NT | Newmarket Transistor Ltd. |
| NU | Nucleonic Products Co. |
| PC | Philco Corp. Micro-Electr. Div. |
| PE | Philips Electron Devices |
| PH | Philips Gloeilampenfabrieken |
| PI | Pirgo Electronics |
| PP | Power Physics Corp. |
| PT | Power Tech. Inc. |
| RA | RTC La Radiotechnique Compelec |
| RC | RCA Corp. |
| RY | Raytheon Comp. Semiconductor Div. |
| RZ | RIZ - Tvornica Poluvodica |
| S | Siemens AG |
| SA | Sanken Electric Co. Ltd. |
| SB | Société Indus. de Liaisons Electriques |
| SD | Solitron Devices |
| SE | Sescosem (Thomson - CSF) |
| SF | Silec Semiconductor |
| SG | SGS (Ates) Semiconduttori |
| SH | Shindengen Electric |
| SL | Semitron Ltd. |

| | |
|---|---|
| SM | Simicoa |
| SN | Sanyo Electric Corp. |
| SO | Sony Corp. |
| SP | Sprague Electric Corp. |
| SQ | Solid State Devices |
| SR | Semitronics Corp. |
| SS | Solid State Industrie |
| ST | Standard Telephone and Cables Ltd. |
| SU | Solid Power Corp. |
| SV | Solid State Scientific |
| SX | Siliconix Inc. |
| SY | Sylvania Electric Inc. |
| SZ | Silicon Transistor Corp. |
| Se | Semi-Elements Inc. |
| Ss | Société Européenne de Semicond. |
| St | Semiconductor Technology |
| TA | Transistor AG |
| TC | Toyo Electronic Ind. Corp. |
| TD | Tadiran |
| TE | Teledyne Semiconductor Corp. |
| TF | Telefunken - AG/AEG |
| TH | Thorn - AEI Radio |
| TJ | Tokyo Shibaura Electric |
| TK | TE-KA-DE |
| TO | Toshiba |
| TR | Transistron Electronic Corp. |
| TT | Trans-Tek Manufacturing Co. |
| TW | TRW Electronics Inc. |
| TX | Texas Instruments |
| UN | Unitrode Corp. |
| UP | UPI Semiconductor |
| UT | Uni-Tran Semiconductor |
| UK | United Kingdom |
| V | Valvo GmbH |
| W | Westinghouse Electric Corp. |
| WA | Walbern Devices |
| WE | Western Electric |
| Y | Yaou Electric Corp. |

| TYPE | M/S | POL | MANUFAC | EUROPEAN | | AMERICAN | | JAPANESE | USE |
|---|---|---|---|---|---|---|---|---|---|
| A5T3821 | J | N | TX | | | 2N4302 | | | |
| A5T3822 | J | N | TX | | | 2N4303 | | | |
| A5T3823 | J | N | TX | | | U1837E | | | |
| A5T3824 | J | N | TX | | | U1837E | | | |
| A5T5460 | J | P | TX | | | P1118E | | | |
| A5T5461 | J | P | TX | | | P1117E | | | |
| A5T5462 | J | P | TX | | | 2N4360 | | | |
| A157A | S | N | AM | BC107 | | A157 | | | |
| A157B | S | N | AM | BC107 | | A157 | | | |
| A158 | S | N | AM | BC107 | | A157 | | | |
| A158A | S | N | AM | BC107 | | A157 | | | |
| A158B | S | N | AM | BC107 | | A157 | | | |
| A158C | S | N | AM | BC107 | | A157 | | | |
| A159B | S | N | AM | BC109 | | A159 | | | |
| A159C | S | N | AM | BC109 | | A159 | | | |
| A178 | S | P | AM | BC177 | | A177 | | | |
| A178A | S | P | AM | BC177 | | A177 | | | |
| A178B | S | P | AM | BC177 | | A177 | | | |
| A179A | S | P | AM | BC179 | | A179 | | | |
| A179B | S | P | AM | BC179 | | A179 | | | |
| A192 | J | N | AM | | | 2N3823 | E304 | | |
| A610S | J | N | AM | | | MPF256 | E420 | | |
| A747A | S | N | AM | BC147 | | A747 | | | |
| A747J | S | N | AM | BC147 | | A747 | | | |
| A748B | S | N | AM | BC147 | | A747 | | | |
| A748C | S | N | AM | BC147 | | A747 | | | |
| A749B | S | N | AM | BC149 | | A749 | | | |
| A749C | S | N | AM | BC149 | | A749 | | | |
| AC105 | G | P | TF | AC173 | AC153 | 2N2706 | 2N291 | 2SB220 | 01 |
| AC105 | | | | AC153VI | AC128 | 2N2431 | 2N4106 | | 01 |
| AC106 | G | P | TF | AC131 | AC152 | | | | 01 |
| AC106 | | | | AC128 | AC131 | 2N311 | 2N2431 | 2SB220 | 01 |
| AC106 | | | | AC153 | AC153VII | 2N4106 | | | 01 |
| AC106 | | | | AC173 | | | | | 01 |
| AC107 | G | P | PH, V, MU, MB | AC125 | AC128 | 2N406 | | | 01 |
| AC107 | | | | AC151 | AC151rV | | | | 01 |
| AC107 | | | | AC122 | AC172 | | | | 01 |
| AC107N | G | P | NT | AC125 | | 2N406 | | | 01 |
| AC108 | G | P | S | AC122R | AC125 | 2N406 | 2N506 | 2SB219 | 01 |
| AC108 | | | | AC151IV | AC163 | 2N2429 | | | 01 |
| AC109 | G | P | S | AC122G | AC125 | 2N406 | 2N506 | 2SB219 | 01 |
| AC109 | | | | AC151V | AC163 | 2N2429 | | | 01 |
| AC110 | G | P | S | AC122GR | AC125 | 2N506 | 2N2429 | 2SB219 | 01 |
| AC110 | | | | AC126 | AC151VI | 2N2431 | | | 01 |
| AC110 | | | | AC151VII | AC163 | | | | 01 |
| AC110 | | | | AC173 | | | | | 01 |
| AC113 | G | P | TH, AE | AC122 | AC122R | 2N406 | | | 01 |
| AC113 | | | | AC125 | AC151 | | | | 01 |
| AC113 | | | | AC151V | AC151IV | | | | 01 |
| AC113 | | | | SFT353 | | | | | 01 |
| AC114 | G | P | TH, AE | AC122G | AC125 | | | | 01 |
| AC114 | | | | AC128 | AC151IV | | | | 01 |
| AC114 | | | | AC151V | SFT353 | | | | 01 |
| AC115 | G | P | TH, AE | AC122R | AC125 | | | | 01 |
| AC115 | | | | AC128 | AC151IV | | | | 01 |
| AC115 | | | | AC151V | AC160 | | | | 01 |
| AC116 | G | P | TF | AC121V | AC126 | 2N610 | 2N2429 | 2SB415 | 01 |
| AC116 | | | | AC151 | AC163 | | | | 01 |
| AC116 | | | | AC188K | | | | | 01 |
| AC116gn | G | P | TF | AC121VI | AC116 | | | | 01 |
| AC116gn | | | | AC125 | AC151V | | | | 01 |
| AC116yn | G | P | TF | AC116 | AC121 | 2N2429 | | 2SB75 | 01 |
| AC116ye | | | | AC125 | AC151 | | | | 01 |
| AC117 | G | P | TF | AC128 | AC128K | 2N467 | 2N2431 | 2SB370A | 01, 06 |
| AC117 | | | | AC152 | AC153 | 2N4106 | 2N249 | 2SB415 | 01, 06 |
| AC117 | | | | AC153KVII | AC188K | | | | 01, 06 |
| AC117R | G | P | TF | AC117 | AC128 | | | | 01 |
| AC117R | | | | AC153 | | | | | 01 |
| AC118 | G | P | | AC117 | AC128 | | | | 01 |
| AC118 | | | | AC153 | | | | | 01 |
| AC119 | G | P | | AC117 | AC128 | | | | 01 |
| AC119 | | | | AC153 | | | | | 01 |
| AC120 | G | P | S | AC117 | AC121 | 2N467 | 2N2431 | 2SB222 | 01 |
| AC120 | | | | AC124 | AC128 | 2N2706 | | | 01 |
| AC120 | | | | AC153 | | | | | 01 |

| TYPE | M/S | POL | MANUFAC | EUROPEAN | | AMERICAN | | | JAPANESE | USE |
|---|---|---|---|---|---|---|---|---|---|---|
| AC120IV | G | P | S | AC121IV | | | | | | 01 |
| AC120V | G | P | S | AC121V | | | | | | 01 |
| AC121 | G | P | S | AC117 | AC128 | 2N2431 | 2N2706 | | 2SB156A | 01 |
| AC121 | | | | AC152 | AC153 | | | | 2SB415 | 01 |
| AC121IV | G | P | S | AC128 | AC152IV | 2N2706 | | | | 01 |
| AC121V | G | P | S | AC128 | AC152V | 2N2706 | | | | 01 |
| AC121VI | G | P | S | AC128 | AC152VI | 2N2706 | | | | 01 |
| AC121VII | G | P | S | AC128 | AC153VII | 2N2706 | | | | 01 |
| AC122 | G | P | TF | AC122 | AC125 | 2N406 | 2N506 | | 2SB364 | 01 |
| AC122 | | | | AC150 | AC151 | 2N2429 | | | 2SB459 | 01 |
| AC122 | | | | AC162 | | | | | | 01 |
| AC122A | G | P | | AC125 | AC151IV | | | | | 01 |
| AC122A | | | | SFT353 | | | | | | 01 |
| AC122V | G | P | | AC122 | AC126 | | | | | 01 |
| AC122V | | | | AC151VII | OC305II | | | | | 01 |
| AC122V | | | | SFT353 | | | | | | 01 |
| AC122W | G | P | | AC126 | AC151 | | | | | 01 |
| AC122W | | | | SFT353 | | | | | | 01 |
| AC122gn | G | P | TF | AC122 | AC125 | | | | | 01 |
| AC122gn | | | | AC126 | AC151VI | | | | | 01 |
| AC122gn | | | | OC304III | SFT353 | | | | | 01 |
| AC122r | G | P | TF | AC122 | AC125 | | | | | 01 |
| AC122r | | | | AC151IV | SFT353 | | | | | 01 |
| AC122v | G | P | TF | AC151VII | | | | | | 01 |
| AC122w | G | P | TF | AC163 | | | | | | 01 |
| AC122ye | G | P | TF | AC122 | AC125 | | | | | 01 |
| AC122ye | | | | AC151V | SFT353 | | | | | 01 |
| AC122/30 | G | P | TF | AC126 | (AC151) | | | | | 01 |
| AC122/30 | | | | ASY48 | | | | | | 01 |
| AC122/30b | G | P | TF | AC122 | ASY48 | | | | | 01 |
| AC122/30gn | G | P | TF | (AC151VI) | ASY48VI | | | | | 01 |
| AC122/30r | G | P | TF | (AC151IV) | ASY48IV | | | | | 01 |
| AC122/30r | | | | SFT353 | | | | | | 01 |
| AC122/30v | G | P | TF | (AC151VII) | ASY48VI | | | | | 01 |
| AC122/30ye | G | P | TF | (AC151V) | ASY48V | | | | | 01 |
| AC122/30ye | | | | SFT353 | | | | | | 01 |
| AC123 | G | P | TF | AC126 | AC152 | 2N613 | 2N2429 | | 2SB56A | 01 |
| AC123 | | | | AC188K | ASY48 | | | | 2SB75A | 01 |
| AC123 | | | | ASY48V | | | | | | 01 |
| AC123gn | G | P | TF | AC123 | AC126 | | | | | 01 |
| AC123gn | | | | (AC151VI) | ASY48 | | | | | 01 |
| AC123gn | | | | ASY48VI | | | | | | 01 |
| AC123ye | G | P | TF | (AC151V) | ASY48V | | | | | 01 |
| AC124 | G | P | TF | AC128 | AC128K | 2N2431 | 2N4106 | | 2SB67 | 01, 06 |
| AC124 | | | | AC153 | (AC153KVI) | | | | | 01, 06 |
| AC124 | | | | AC188K | OC72 | | | | | 01, 06 |
| AC124K | G | P | | AC128K | AC153K | | | | | 01 |
| AC124R | G | P | TF | AC128R | AC153IV | | | | | 01 |
| AC124R | | | | AC153V | | | | | | 01 |
| AC125 | G | P | PH, V | AC122 | AC151 | 2N406 | 2N2428 | | 2SB415 | 01 |
| AC125 | | | | AC162 | AC163 | 2N2429 | | | 2SA202 | 01 |
| AC126 | G | P | PH, V | AC151 | AC163 | 2N506 | 2N2429 | | 2SB383 | 01 |
| AC126 | | | | AC171 | | | | | 2SB415 | 01 |
| AC127 | G | N | PH, MU, V, S | AC176 | AC179 | 2N2430 | | | 2SD96 | 01 |
| AC127 | | | | | | | | | 2SD105 | 01 |
| AC127z | G | N | | AC176 | | 2N2430 | | | | 01 |
| AC127/01 | G | N | PH, RA, MU | AC176 | AC176K | 2N2430 | | | | 01 |
| AC128 | G | P | PH, V, AM, BL, MN | AC117 | AC117R | 2N467 | 2N1373 | | 2SB370 | 01, 06 |
| AC128 | | | | AC124 | AC153 | 2N2431 | 2N2706 | | 2SB415 | 01, 06 |
| AC128 | | | | AC153VI | | 2N4106 | | | | 01, 06 |
| AC128 | G | P | PP, RA, MU, MO, SG | AC117 | AC117R | 2N467 | 2N1373 | | 2SB370 | 01, 06 |
| AC128 | | | | AC124 | AC153 | 2N2431 | 2N2706 | | 2SB415 | 01, 06 |
| AC128 | | | | AC153VI | | 2N4106 | | | | 01, 06 |
| AC128K | G | P | PH, V, MB | AC117K | AC128 | 2N4106 | | | 2SB415 | 01 |
| AC128K | | | | AC153K | AC153KVI | | | | | 01 |
| AC128K | | | | AC188K | OC308 | | | | | 01 |
| AC128/01 | G | P | PH, RA, MU | AC153KVI | AC188K | | | | | 01, 06 |
| AC129 | G | P | TF | AC122 | AC125 | | | | 2SB46 | 01 |
| AC129 | | | | AC151 | AC151IV | | | | | 01 |
| AC129 | | | | OC58 | OC59 | | | | | 01 |
| AC129 | | | | OC60 | | | | | | 01 |
| AC129b | G | P | TF | AC151 | | | | | | 01 |
| AC129v | G | P | TF | AC151 | | | | | | 01 |
| AC129ye | G | P | TF | AC151 | AC122 | | | | 2SB47 | 01 |
| AC129ye | | | | AC125 | | | | | | 01 |

| TYPE | M/S | POL | MANUFAC | EUROPEAN | | AMERICAN | | JAPANESE | USE |
|------|-----|-----|---------|----------|----------|----------|----------|----------|-----|
| AC130 | G | N | PH,V,RA | AC127 | AC153V | 2N2430 | | | 01 |
| AC130 | | | | AC190 | | | | | 01 |
| AC131 | G | P | TF | AC128 | AC152 | 2N1924 | 2N2431 | 2SB370A | 01, 06 |
| AC131 | | | | AC153 | AC153VI | 2N2706 | | 2SB415 | 01, 06 |
| AC131 | | | | AC180 | | | | | 01, 06 |
| AC131/30 | G | P | TF | AC128 | AC153 | | | | 01, 06 |
| AC131/30 | | | | (AC153VI) | | | | | 01, 06 |
| AC132 | G | P | PH, V, AM, BL,MN | AC125 | AC131 | 2N406 | 2N1924 | 2SB364 | 01, 06 |
| AC132 | | | | AC151VI | AC152 | | | 2SB496 | 01, 06 |
| AC132 | | | | AC162 | AC184 | | | | 01, 06 |
| AC132 | G | P | PP,RA | AC125 | AC131 | 2N406 | 2N1924 | 2SB364 | 01, 06 |
| AC132 | | | | AC151VI | AC152 | | | 2SB496 | 01, 06 |
| AC132 | | | | AC162 | AC184 | | | | 01, 06 |
| AC132/01 | G | P | PH,RA | AC153V | AC188K | 2N2706 | | | 01, 06 |
| AC134 | G | P | AT | AC121V | AC122ye | 2N406 | | | 01 |
| AC134 | | | | AC125 | AC151IV | | | | 01 |
| AC134 | | | | AC151V | AC173 | | | | 01 |
| AC134 | | | | OC71 | | | | | 01 |
| AC135 | G | P | AT | AC121V | AC122ye | 2N408 | 2N2431 | | 01 |
| AC135 | | | | AC125 | AC126 | | | | 01 |
| AC135 | | | | AC151V | AC151VI | | | | 01 |
| AC136 | G | P | AT | AC122ye | AC125 | 2N109 | 2N217 | | 01 |
| AC136 | | | | AC126 | AC131/30 | 2N2431 | | | 01 |
| AC136 | | | | ASY48VI | AC151V | | | | 01 |
| AC136 | | | | AC151VI | | | | | 01 |
| AC137 | G | P | AT | AC121VI | AC126 | 2N2431 | | | 01 |
| AC137 | | | | AC128 | AC151VII | | | | 01 |
| AC137 | | | | AC171 | | | | | 01 |
| AC138 | G | P | AT | AC122r | AC125 | 2N456 | 2N2706 | 2S42 | 01 |
| AC138 | | | | AC152 | AC153 | TA2063 | TA2065 | | 01 |
| AC138 | | | | AC151VI | AD148 | | | | 01 |
| AC138 | | | | AM54 | | | | | 01 |
| AC138H | G | P | AT | AC128 | (AC153VI) | 2N2706 | | | 01 |
| AC138-4 | G | P | AT | AC153V | | | | | 01 |
| AC138-5 | G | P | AT | AC153V | | | | | 01 |
| AC138-6 | G | P | AT | AC153VI | | | | | 01 |
| AC138-7 | G | P | AT | AC153VII | | | | | 01 |
| AC139 | G | P | AT | AC122ye | AC117R | 2N2706 | | | 01 |
| AC139 | | | | AC125 | AC128 | | | | 01 |
| AC139 | | | | AC151V | AC153 | | | | 01 |
| AC139K | G | P | AT | AC128K | AC153KVI | | | | 01 |
| AC139-4 | G | P | AT | AC153V | | | | | 01 |
| AC139-5 | G | P | AT | AC153V | | | | | 01 |
| AC139-6 | G | P | AT | AC153VI | | | | | 01 |
| AC141 | G | N | AT | AC175 | AC176 | 2N647 | 2N2430 | | 01 |
| AC141 | | | | AC181 | AM72 | | | | 01 |
| AC141 | | | | SFT377 | | | | | 01 |
| AC141B | G | N | AT | AC176 | | | | | 01 |
| AC141B4 | G | N | AT | AC176 | | | | | 01 |
| AC141B5 | G | N | AT | AC176 | | | | | 01 |
| AC141B6 | G | N | AT | AC176 | | | | | 01 |
| AC141B7 | G | N | AT | AC176 | | | | | 01 |
| AC141H | G | N | AT | (AC176) | | | | | 01 |
| AC141HK | G | N | AT | (AC176) | | | | | 01 |
| AC141K | G | N | AT | AC176K | AC187K | | | | 01 |
| AC141K4 | G | N | AT | AC176K | | | | | 01 |
| AC141K5 | G | N | AT | AC176K | | | | | 01 |
| AC141K6 | G | N | AT | AC176K | | | | | 01 |
| AC141-4 | G | N | AT | AC176 | | | | | 01 |
| AC141-5 | G | N | AT | AC176 | | | | | 01 |
| AC141-6 | G | N | AT | AC176 | | | | | 01 |
| AC142 | G | P | AT | AC117R | AC128 | 2N217 | 2N2706 | | 01 |
| AC142 | | | | AC153 | AC173 | | | | 01 |
| AC142 | | | | AM74 | | | | | 01 |
| AC142H | G | P | AT | (AC153V) | | | | | 01 |
| AC142HK | G | P | AT | (AC153V) | | | | | 01 |
| AC142K | G | P | AT | AC142 | AC153K | | | | 01, 06 |
| AC142K | | | | AC188K | | | | | 01, 06 |
| AC142K4 | G | P | AT | AC153KV | | | | | 01 |
| AC142K5 | G | P | AT | AC153KV | | | | | 01 |
| AC142K6 | G | P | AT | AC153KVI | | | | | 01 |
| AC142-4 | G | P | AT | AC153V | | | | | 01 |
| AC142-5 | G | P | AT | AC153V | | | | | 01 |
| AC142-6 | G | P | AT | AC176VI | | | | | 01 |
| AC150 | G | P | AT | AC125 | AC125R | 2N406 | 2N2429 | 2SB439 | 01 |

| TYPE | M/S | POL | MANUFAC | EUROPEAN | | AMERICAN | | JAPANESE | USE |
|------|-----|-----|---------|----------|--|----------|--|----------|-----|
| AC150 | | | | AC151 | AC151r | | | | 01 |
| AC150 | | | | AC126 | | | | | 01 |
| AC150gn | G | P | TF | AC125 | AC151rVI | 2N652 | | | 01 |
| AC150gn | | | | AC163 | | | | | 01 |
| AC150v | G | P | TF | AC151rVII | | | | | 01 |
| AC150w | G | P | TF | AC151rVII | | | | | 01 |
| AC150ye | G | P | TF | AC125 | AC151V | | | | 01 |
| AC150ye | | | | AC151rV | AC163 | | | | 01 |
| AC150ye | | | | SFT353 | | | | | 01 |
| AC151 | G | P | S | AC125 | AC126 | 2N238 | 2N2429 | 2SB430 | 01 |
| AC151 | | | | AC128 | AC173 | 2N2706 | | | 01 |
| AC151IV | G | P | S | AC122r | AC126 | 2N238 | 2N2706 | 2SB450 | 01 |
| AC151IV | | | | AC128 | | | | | 01 |
| AC151V | G | P | S | AC122ye | AC125 | 2N2706 | | | 01 |
| AC151V | | | | AC128 | | | | | 01 |
| AC151VI | G | P | S | AC122gn | AC125 | 2N2706 | | | 01 |
| AC151VI | | | | AC128 | | | | | 01 |
| AC151VII | G | P | S | AC122V | AC125 | 2N2706 | | | 01 |
| AC151VII | | | | AC128 | | | | | 01 |
| AC151r | G | P | S | AC125 | | 2N406 | | | 01 |
| AC151rIV | G | P | S | AC125 | AC128 | 2N406 | | 2SB73 | 01 |
| AC151rIV | | | | AC150 | OC306I | | | | 01 |
| AC151rV | G | P | S | AC125 | AC128 | 2N406 | | | 01 |
| AC151rV | | | | AC150 | AC151V | | | | 01 |
| AC151rV | | | | OC306II | | | | | 01 |
| AC151rVI | G | P | S | AC125 | AC128 | 2N2706 | | | 01 |
| AC151rVI | | | | AC150 | OC306III | | | | 01 |
| AC151rVII | G | P | S | AC151VII | AC160 | | | | 01 |
| AC151rVII | | | | OC307 | | | | | 01 |
| AC152 | G | P | S | AC128 | AC131/30 | 2N238 | 2N1924 | 2SB156 | 01 |
| AC152 | | | | AC132 | AC184 | 2N2431 | 2N2706 | 2SB415 | 01 |
| AC152IV | G | P | S | AC128 | AC124R | 2N610 | 2N2706 | 2S32 | 01 |
| AC152IV | | | | OC307 | OC308 | 2N4106 | | | 01 |
| AC152IV | | | | SFT322 | | | | | 01 |
| AC152V | G | P | S | AC124R | AC128 | 2N610 | 2N2706 | 2S32 | 01 |
| AC152V | | | | OC307 | OC308 | | | | 01 |
| AC152V | | | | SFT322 | | | | | 01 |
| AC152VI | G | P | S | AC117R | AC128 | 2N610 | 2N2706 | 2S32 | 01 |
| AC152VI | | | | OC307 | OC308 | | | | 01 |
| AC152VI | | | | SFT322 | | | | | 01 |
| AC153 | G | P | S | AC117 | AC124 | 2N467 | 2N2431 | 2SB415 | 01 |
| AC153 | | | | AC128 | | | | | 01 |
| AC153K | G | P | S | AC117K | AC128K | 2N4106 | | 2SB415 | 01 |
| AC153K | | | | AC180K | AC188K | | | | 01 |
| AC153KV | G | P | S | AC188K | | | | | 01 |
| AC153KVI | G | P | S | AC188K | | | | | 01 |
| AC153KVII | G | P | S | AC188K | | | | | 01 |
| AC153V | G | P | S | AC124R | AC128 | 2N467 | 2N2706 | 2SB222 | 01 |
| AC153V | | | | AC210 | ASY12 | 2N4106 | | | 01 |
| AC153V | | | | ASY24 | | | | | 01 |
| AC153VI | G | P | S | AC117R | AC128 | 2N2706 | | 2SB415 | 01 |
| AC153VI | | | | AC210 | ASY12 | | | | 01 |
| AC153VI | | | | ASY24 | | | | | 01 |
| AC153VII | G | P | S | AC117R | AC128 | 2N2706 | | | 01 |
| AC153VII | | | | AC210 | ASY12 | | | | 01 |
| AC153VII | | | | ASY24 | | | | | 01 |
| AC154 | G | P | TH, AE | AC128 | AC131 | 2N1924 | 2N2706 | | 01 |
| AC154 | | | | AC152IV | AC152V | | | | 01 |
| AC154 | | | | OC309 | | | | | 01 |
| AC155 | G | P | TH, AE | AC122r | AC122ye | 2N406 | | | 01 |
| AC155 | | | | AC125 | AC151IV | | | | 01 |
| AC155 | | | | AC151V | OC304T | | | | 01 |
| AC156 | G | P | TH, AE | AC122ye | AC125 | 2N2406 | | | 01 |
| AC156 | • | | | AC151V | OC304III | | | | 01 |
| AC157 | • | N | TH,AE | AC127 | AC175K | 2N2430 | | | 01 |
| AC157 | | | | AC176 | AC181 | | | | 01 |
| AC157 | | | | AC186 | | | | | 01 |
| AC160 | G | P | TF | AC125 | AC151r | 2N406 | | | 01 |
| AC160 | | | | AC151IV | AC161 | | | | 01 |
| AC160A | G | P | TF | AC125 | AC151r | 2N406 | | | 01 |
| AC160A | | | | AC151rV | AC151V | | | | 01 |
| AC160A | | | | AC161 | | | | | 01 |
| AC160B | G | P | TF | AC125 | AC126 | 2N406 | | | 01 |
| AC160B | | | | AC151r | AC151VI | | | | 01 |
| AC160B | | | | AC151rVI | AC161 | | | | 01 |

| TYPE | M/S | POL | MANUFAC | EUROPEAN | | AMERICAN | | JAPANESE | USE |
|---|---|---|---|---|---|---|---|---|---|
| AC160B | | | | OC307 | | | | | 01 |
| AC160K | G | P | TF | AC125R | | | | | 01 |
| AC160gn | G | P | TF | AC151rVI | AC161 | | | | 01 |
| AC160r | G | P | TF | AC125r | AC151rIV | | | 2SB73 | 01 |
| AC160r | | | | AC161 | | | | | 01 |
| | | | | | | | | | |
| AC160r | | | | OC306I | | | | | 01 |
| AC160v | G | P | TF | AC151rVII | AC161 | | | | 01 |
| AC160ve | G | P | TF | AC151rV | AC161 | | | | 01 |
| AC161 | G | P | SE | AC125r | AC151V | | | | 01 |
| AC161 | | | | AC151rV | AC151rVI | | | | 01 |
| | | | | | | | | | |
| AC161 | | | | AC160 | OC306III | | | | 01 |
| AC161 | | | | OC307 | | | | | 01 |
| AC162 | G | P | S | AC125 | AC126 | 2N37 | 2N406 | 2SB219 | 01 |
| AC162 | | | | AC128 | AC170 | 2N2429 | | 2SB459 | 01 |
| AC162 | | | | AC173 | | | | | 01 |
| | | | | | | | | | |
| AC163 | G | P | S | AC125 | AC128 | 2N406 | 2N506 | 2SB450 | 01 |
| AC163 | | | | AC171 | AC173 | 2N2429 | 2N2907 | | 01 |
| AC165 | G | P | TH, AE | AC122ve | AC125 | 2N2430 | | | 01 |
| AC165 | | | | AC151V | AC151rVI | | | | 01 |
| AC165 | | | | AC176 | AC222 | | | | 01 |
| | | | | | | | | | |
| AC166 | G | P | TH, AE | AC128 | AC131/30 | 2N1189 | 2N2706 | | 01 |
| AC166 | | | | AC152 | AC152V | 2N4106 | | | 01 |
| AC167 | G | P | TH, AE | AC128 | AC131/30 | 2N1189 | 2N2706 | | 01 |
| AC167 | | | | AC152V | | 2N4106 | | | 01 |
| AC168 | G | N | TH, AE | AC127 | AC175K | | | | 01 |
| | | | | | | | | | |
| AC168 | | | | AC179 | | | | | 01 |
| AC169 | G | P | TH | AC121V | AC122 | | | | 01 |
| AC169 | | | | AC125 | AC151 | | | | 01 |
| AC170 | G | P | TF | AC125 | AC126 | 2N406 | | 2SB54 | 01 |
| AC170 | | | | AC151VI. | AC162 | | | 2SB77A | 01 |
| | | | | | | | | | |
| AC170 | | | | AC173 | OC309 | | | | 01 |
| AC171 | G | P | TF | AC125 | AC126 | 2N406 | | 2SB439 | 01 |
| AC171 | | | | AC151VII | AC163 | | | 2SB460 | 01 |
| AC171 | | | | AC173 | | | | | 01 |
| AC172 | G | N | PH, V | AC127 | AC181 | 2N2430 | | | 01 |
| | | | | | | | | | |
| AC172 | | | | AC176 | | | | | 01 |
| AC173 | G | P | SE | AC125 | AC128 | 2N406 | 2N1189 | | 01 |
| AC173 | | | | AC131 | AC132 | | | | 01 |
| AC173 | | | | AC152 | AC152V | | | | 01 |
| AC174 | G | P | SE | AC128 | | MJ2060 | | | 01 |
| | | | | | | | | | |
| AC174 | | | | AC153 | AC153V | | | | 01 |
| AC174 | | | | AC131/30 | | | | | 01 |
| AC175 | G | N | TF | AC127 | AC181 | 2N2707 | | | 01 |
| AC175 | | | | AC187 | AC187K | | | | 01 |
| AC175K | G | N | | AC176K | AC183K | | | | 01 |
| | | | | | | | | | |
| AC176 | G | N | PH, V, S | AC181 | AC186 | 2N2430 | | | 01 |
| AC176 | | | | AC187 | | | | | 01 |
| AC176K | G | N | S | AC176 | AC181K | | | | 01 |
| AC176K | | | | AC186 | AC187K | | | | 01 |
| AC177 | G | P | TH, AE | AC128 | AC131 | 2N2706 | | | 01 |
| | | | | | | | | | |
| AC177 | | | | AC152 | AC152V | | | | 01 |
| AC177 | | | | AC173 | ASY80 | | | | 01 |
| AC178 | G | P | TF | AC122K | AC128K. | | | 2SB370 | 01 |
| AC178 | | | | AC153K | AC180K | | | | 01 |
| AC178 | | | | AC188K | | | | | 01 |
| | | | | | | | | | |
| AC179 | G | N | TF | AC176K | | | | | 01 |
| AC179 | G | N | | AC187K | | | | | 01 |
| AC179K | | | | AC181K | AC187K | | | | 01 |
| AC180 | G | P | SE | AC128 | AC131/30 | 2N1185 | 2N2706 | | 01 |
| AC180 | | | | AC153 | | 2N4106 | | | 01 |
| | | | | | | | | | |
| AC180K | G | P | SE | AC128K | AC131/30 | | | | 01 |
| AC180K | | | | AC153 | AC188K | | | | 01 |
| AC180KL | G | P | | AC188K | | | | | 01 |
| AC181 | G | N | SE | AC127 | AC176 | TLS60 | 2N2430 | | 01 |
| AC181 | | | | AC186 | | | | | 01 |
| | | | | | | | | | |
| AC181K | G | N | SE | AC176 | AC186 | | | | 01 |
| AC181K | | | | AC187K | | | | | 01 |
| AC181KL | | | | AC187K | | | | | 01 |
| AC181L | G | N | SE | AC176 | | | | | 01 |
| AC182 | G | P | SE, Ss, ML | AC125 | AC151VI | 2N406 | | | 01 |
| | | | | | | | | | |
| AC182 | | | | AC184 | | | | | 01 |
| AC183 | G | N | SE, Ss, ML | AC127 | AC176 | 2N2430 | | | 01 |
| AC184 | G | P | SE | AC128 | AC153 | MJ2060 | 2N2706 | | 01 |
| AC184 | | | | AC152 | | 2N4106 | | | 01 |
| AC184 | | | | AC131 | | | | | 01 |

| TYPE | M/S | POL | MANUFAC | EUROPEAN | | AMERICAN | | JAPANESE | USE |
|------|-----|-----|---------|----------|--|----------|--|----------|-----|
| AC185 | G | N | SE | AC127 | AC176 | 2N2430 | | | 01 |
| AC185 | | | | AC176K | AC186 | | | | 01 |
| AC186 | G | N | TF | AC176 | AC185 | 2N2430 | | | 01 |
| AC186 | | | | AC187K | | | | | 01 |
| AC187 | | | | AC175 | AC176 | 2N2430 | 2N2707 | | 01 |
| | | | | | | | | | |
| AC187K | G | N | AT, S, V, TF | AC175K | AC176K | | | | 01 |
| AC187K7 | G | N | AT | AC187K | | | | | 01 |
| AC187K8 | G | N | AT | AC187K | | | | | 01 |
| AC187K9 | G | N | AT | AC187K | | | | | 01 |
| AC187/01 | G | N | PH | AC187K | | | | | 01 |
| | | | | | | | | | |
| AC187-7 | G | N | AT | AC176 | | | | | 01 |
| AC187-8 | G | N | AT | AC176 | | | | | 01 |
| AC187-9 | G | N | AT | AC176 | | | | | 01 |
| AC188 | G | N | AT, AM, BL, MN, | AC128 | AC153VI | 2N2706 | | | 01 |
| AC188 | | | MU | AC193 | | | | | 01 |
| | | | | | | | | | |
| AC188 | G | P | PE, PH, RA, V | AC128 | AC153VI | 2N2706 | | | 01 |
| AC188 | | | | AC193 | | | | | 01 |
| AC188K | G | P | AT, S, TF, V | AC193 | | | | 2SB370 | 01, 06 |
| AC188K7 | G | P | AT | AC188K | | | | | 01 |
| AC188K8 | G | P | AT | AC188K | | | | | 01 |
| | | | | | | | | | |
| AC188K9 | G | P | AT | AC188K | | | | | 01 |
| AC188/01 | G | P | PH | AC188K | | | | | 01 |
| AC188-7 | G | P | AT | AC153VI | | | | | 01 |
| AC188-8 | G | P | AT | AC153VII | | | | | 01 |
| AC188-9 | G | P | AT | AC153VII | | | | | 01 |
| | | | | | | | | | |
| AC191 | G | P | AT | AC125 | AC151r | 2N406 | | | 01 |
| AC191-4 | G | P | AT | AC151rIV | | | | | 01 |
| AC191-5 | G | P | AT | AC151rV | | | | | 01 |
| AC191-6 | G | P | AT | AC151rVI | | | | | 01 |
| AC191-7 | G | P | AT | AC151rVI | | | | | 01 |
| | | | | | | | | | |
| AC191-8 | G | P | AT | (AC151rVI) | | | | | 01 |
| AC192 | G | P | AT | AC125 | AC151 | 2N406 | | | 01 |
| AC192 | | | | AC170 | | | | | 01 |
| AC192-4 | G | P | AT | AC151IV | | | | | 01 |
| AC192-5 | G | P | AT | AC151V | | | | | 01 |
| | | | | | | | | | |
| AC192-6 | G | P | AT | AC151VI | | | | | 01 |
| AC192-7 | G | P | AT | AC151VII | | | | | 01 |
| AC192-8 | G | P | AT | AC151VII | | | | | 01 |
| AC193 | G | P | AT | AC117 | AC128 | 2N2706 | | | 01, 06 |
| AC193 | | | | AC153 | AC153VI | | | | 01, 06 |
| | | | | | | | | | |
| AC193 | | | | AC188K | | | | | 01, 06 |
| AC193K | G | P | AT | AC117 | AC128K | | | | 01, 06 |
| AC193K | | | | AC153K | AC153KVI | | | | 01, 06 |
| AC193K | G | P | AT | AC188K | | | | | 01, 06 |
| AC193K7 | G | P | AT | AC153KVI | AC188K | | | | 01 |
| | | | | | | | | | |
| AC193K8 | G | P | AT | AC153KVII | AC188K | | | | 01 |
| AC193K9 | G | P | AT | AC153KVII | AC188K | | | | 01 |
| AC193-7 | G | P | AT | AC153VI | | | | | 01 |
| AC193-8 | G | P | AT | AC153VII | | | | | 01 |
| AC193-9 | G | P | AT | AC153VII | | | | | 01 |
| | | | | | | | | | |
| AC194 | G | N | AT | AC176 | AC181 | 2N2430 | | | 01 |
| AC194 | | | | AC186 | AC187 | | | | 01 |
| AC194 | | | | AC187K | | | | | 01 |
| AC194K | G | N | AT | AC176K | AC187K | | | | 01 |
| AC194K7 | G | N | AT | AC176K | AC187K | | | | 01 |
| | | | | | | | | | |
| AC194K8 | G | N | AT | AC176K | AC187K | | | | 01 |
| AC194K9 | G | N | AT | AC176K | AC187K | | | | 01 |
| AC194-7 | G | N | AT | AC176 | | | | | 01 |
| AC194-8 | G | N | AT | AC176 | | | | | 01 |
| AC194-9 | G | N | AT | AC176 | | | | | 01 |
| | | | | | | | | | |
| ACY16 | G | P | TF | AC128K | (AC153KV) | 2N526 | | 2SB415 | 01 |
| ACY16 | | | | ACY33V | ASY14 | | | | 01 |
| ACY17 | G | P | MU, PE, NT | (ASY48V) | | 2N1188 | 2N2207 | 2SA503 | 01 |
| ACY18 | G | P | MU, NT, PE | ACY17 | (ASY48V) | 2N1188 | 2SA504 | | 01 |
| ACY19 | G | P | MU | AC117 | AC128 | 2N249 | 2N1188 | 2S56 | 01 |
| | | | | | | | | | |
| ACY19 | | | | AC153 | ACY17 | 2N4106 | | | 01 |
| ACY19 | | | | (ASY48VII) | | | | | 01 |
| ACY20 | G | P | MU, NT, PE | AC128 | AC131/30 | 2N1188 | | 2SA504 | 01 |
| ACY20 | G | P | MU, NT, PE | AC152V | AC153 | | | | 01 |
| ACY20 | | | | ACY17 | | | | | 01 |
| | | | | | | | | | |
| ACY21 | G | P | MU, NT, PE | AC152VI | ACY17 | 2N1188 | 2N1924 | 2SB32 | 01 |
| ACY21 | | | | ACY20 | | | | | 01 |
| ACY22 | G | P | MU, NT, PE | AC152V | ACY17 | 2N1188 | 2N1924 | 2SB32 | 01 |
| ACY22 | G | P | MU, NT, PE | ACY33 | | | | | 01 |
| ACY22E | G | P | | ACY17 | | 2N1176 | | | 01 |

| TYPE | M/S | POL | MANUFAC | EUROPEAN | | AMERICAN | | JAPANESE | USE |
|---|---|---|---|---|---|---|---|---|---|
| ACY22H | G | P | | ACY17 | | 2N1176 | | | 01 |
| ACY23 | G | P | S | AC122 | AC125 | 2N37 | 2N526 | 2SB219 | 01 |
| ACY23 | | | | AC128 | ASY80 | 2N2706 | | | 01 |
| ACY23 | | | | OC71 | | | | | 01 |
| ACY23V | G | P | S | AC128 | | 2N2706 | | | 01 |
| ACY23VI | G | P | S | AC128 | | 2N2706 | | | 01 |
| ACY24 | G | P | TF | AC188K | ASY14 | 2N138 | 2N1924 | 2SB421 | 01 |
| ACY24 | | | | ASY23 | ASY48V | | | | 01 |
| ACY24 | | | | (ASY48IV) | | | | | 01 |
| ACY27 | G | P | IN, TF | AC122 | AC125 | 2N406 | 2N525 | 2S13 | 01 |
| ACY27 | | | | AC151 | ACY23 | 2N2447 | | | 01 |
| ACY27 | | | | (ASY48IV) | | | | | 01 |
| ACY28 | G | P | IN, IT | AC122 | AC125 | 2N406 | 2N526 | | 01 |
| ACY28 | | | | AC151 | ASY23 | | | | 01 |
| ACY28 | | | | ASY26 | (ASY48BV) | | | | 01 |
| ACY29 | G | P | IN, IT | AC125 | AC160 | 2N237 | 2N406 | | 01 |
| ACY29 | | | | ACY27 | ACY32 | | | | 01 |
| ACY29 | | | | (ACY48V) | | | | | 01 |
| ACY30 | G | P | IN, IT | AC122/30 | AC126 | 2N237 | 2N526 | | 01 |
| ACY30 | | | | AC128 | AC131/30 | 2N2431 | | | 01 |
| ACY30 | | | | AC153 | (ASY48VI) | | | | 01 |
| ACY31 | G | P | IN, IT | AC125 | (ASY48V) | 2N406 | | | 01 |
| ACY32 | G | P | S | AC122 | AC125 | 2N406 | 2N506 | | 01 |
| ACY32 | | | | AC125R | AC150 | 2N527 | | | 01 |
| ACY32 | | | | ASY80 | | | | | 01 |
| ACY32V | G | P | | AC125 | | 2N406 | | | 01 |
| ACY32VI | G | P | S | AC125 | | 2N406 | | | 01 |
| ACY33 | G | P | S | AC123 | AC128 | 2N527 | 2N613 | 2SA204 | 01 |
| ACY33 | | | | ACY16K | ASY14 | 2N618 | 2N2706 | | 01 |
| ACY33VI | G | P | | AC128 | | 2N2706 | | | 01 |
| ACY33VII | G | P | S | AC128 | | 2N2706 | | | 01 |
| ACY33VIII | G | P | S | AC128 | | 2N2706 | | | 01 |
| ACY34 | G | P | IN | AC122 | AC125 | 2N2431 | | | 01 |
| ACY34 | | | | ACY22 | ACY23V | | | | 01 |
| ACY34 | | | | ASY14 | ACY23 | | | | 01 |
| ACY35 | G | P | IN | AC122 | AC125 | 2N406 | | | 01 |
| ACY35 | | | | ACY23V | ASY14 | | | | 01 |
| ACY36 | G | P | IN | AC122 | AC125 | 2N406 | | | 01 |
| ACY36 | | | | ACY23V | ASY14 | | | | 01 |
| ACY38 | G | P | SE, Ss, ML | AC125 | AC125R | 2N406 | | | 01 |
| ACY38 | | | | AC151 | AC160 | | | | 01 |
| ACY38 | | | | AC160B | ACY32 | | | | 01 |
| ACY38 | | | | ASY27 | | | | | 01 |
| ACY40 | G | P | MU, NT | AC152IV | ACY17 | 2N1188 | | | 01 |
| ACY40 | | | | ACY18 | | | | | 01 |
| ACY41 | G | P | MU, NT | AC152VI | ACY17 | 2N1188 | | | 01 |
| ACY41 | | | | ACY40 | | | | | 01 |
| ACY44 | G | P | MU | ACY17 | ACY19 | 2N1188 | 2N4106 | 2S56 | 01 |
| ACY44 | | | | (ASY48V) | | | | | 01 |
| ACZ10 | G | P | TF | AC128 | AC153 | 2N467 | 2N4106 | 2SB222 | 01 |
| ACZ10 | | | | AC153V | ASY12 | | | | 01 |
| ACZ10 | | | | ASY48 | (ASY48V) | | | | 01 |
| ACZ10 | | | | ACY24K | | | | | 01 |
| AD103 | G | P | S | AD133 | ADZ11 | 2N1146 | 2N1167 | | 06 |
| AD103 | | | | AUY29/5 | SFT265 | | | | 06 |
| AD103IV | G | P | S | (AD133III) | | | | | 06 |
| AD103IV | G | P | S | (AD133IV) | | | | | 06 |
| AD103V | G | P | S | (AD133V) | | | | | 06 |
| AD103VI | G | P | S | (AD133V) | | | | | 06 |
| AD104 | G | P | S | ADZ12 | AUY21 | 2N1146A | 2N1167 | | 06 |
| AD104 | | | | AUY29/5 | SFT266 | | | | 06 |
| AD104II | G | P | S | (AUY21II) | | | | | 06 |
| AD104IV | G | P | S | (AUY21IV) | | | | | 06 |
| AD104V | G | P | S | (AUY21IV) | | | | | 06 |
| AD105 | G | P | S | ADZ12 | AU103 | 2N1146B | | | 06 |
| AD105 | | | | AUY22 | SFT266 | | | | 06 |
| AD105II | G | P | S | (AUY22II) | | | | | 06 |
| AD105III | G | P | S | (AUY22III) | | | | | 06 |
| AD105IV | G | P | S | (AUY22IV) | | | | | 06 |
| AD105V | G | P | S | (AUY22IV) | | | | | 06 |
| AD130 | G | P | S | AD129 | AD149 | TI3029 | 2N1536 | 2SB337 | 06 |
| AD130 | | | | AD153 | ASZ16 | | | 2SB426 | 06 |
| AD130III | G | P | S | AD149 | ASZ13 | TI3029 | 2N1536 | | 06 |
| AD130III | | | | OC26 | OD603 | 2N2063 | | | 06 |
| AD130III | | | | SFT213 | | | | | 06 |

| TYPE | M/S | POL | MANUFAC | EUROPEAN | | AMERICAN | | JAPANESE | USE |
|---|---|---|---|---|---|---|---|---|---|
| AD130IV | G | P | S | AD149 | AD149IV | TI3029 | 2N257 | | 06 |
| AD130IV | | | | ASZ16 | OC26 | 2N1536 | 2N2064 | | 06 |
| AD130IV | | | | SFT213 | | | | | 06 |
| AD130V | G | P | S | AD149 | AD149V | TI3029 | 2N257 | | 06 |
| AD130V | | | | ASZ16 | OC26 | 2N1536 | 2N2064 | | 06 |
| AD130V | | | | SFT213 | | | | | 06 |
| AD131 | G | P | S | AD149 | ASZ16 | 2N1536 | | 2SB425 | 06 |
| AD131 | | | | AU733 | | | | | 06 |
| AD131III | G | P | S | AD138/50 | AD149 | TI3029 | 2N1536 | 2SB471 | 06 |
| AD131III | | | | ASZ16 | OD603/50 | 2N2065 | | | 06 |
| AD131III | | | | SFT250 | | | | | 06 |
| AD131IV | G | P | S | AD138/50 | AD149IV | TI3029 | 2N268 | | 06 |
| AD131IV | | | | ASZ16 | GFT4012 | 2N1536 | 2N2066 | | 06 |
| AD131IV | | | | SFT250 | | | | | 06 |
| AD131V | G | P | S | AD138/50 | AD149V | TI3029 | 2N268 | | 06 |
| AD131V | | | | ASZ16 | GFT4012 | 2N1536 | 2N2066 | | 06 |
| AD132 | G | P | S | SFT250 | | | | | 06 |
| AD132 | | | | ASZ15 | ASZ18 | 2N1533 | | 2SB424 | 06 |
| AD132II | G | P | S | AUY32 | | | | | 06 |
| AD132II | | | | ASZ15 | OC26 | 2N1533 | 2N2065 | | 06 |
| AD132II | | | | OD603/50 | SFT250 | | | | 06 |
| AD132III | G | P | S | ASZ15 | AUY22III | 2N2065 | | 2SB472 | 06 |
| AD132III | | | | OC26 | OD603/50 | | | | 06 |
| AD132III | | | | SFT250 | | | | | 06 |
| AD132IV | G | P | S | AUY22IV | AUY28 | TI3030 | 2N268 | | 06 |
| AD132IV | | | | OC26 | SFT250 | 2N1167 | 2N2066 | | 06 |
| AD132IV | | | | GFT4012 | | | | | 06 |
| AD132V | G | P | S | AUY22IV | AUY29 | | | | 06 |
| AD133 | G | P | S | ADZ11 | ADZ12 | 2N1146 | 2N1167 | 2SB236 | 06 |
| AD133 | | | | AUY29V | SFT265 | 2N1549 | | | 06 |
| AD133III | G | P | S | ADZ11 | AUY29III | 2N1167 | 2N1549 | 2SB236 | 06 |
| AD133III | | | | AUY29V | | | | | 06 |
| AD133IV | G | P | S | AUY29IV | AUY29V | 2N1167 | | | 06 |
| AD133V | G | P | S | AUY29V | | 2N1167 | | | 06 |
| AD136 | G | P | | AD138 | AD160 | 2N1184B | 2N1536 | | 06 |
| AD136 | | | | AD211 | ASZ16 | | | | 06 |
| AD136 | | | | ASZ18 | | | | | 06 |
| AD136IV | G | P | S, TF | AD136 | | 2N1184B | | | 06 |
| AD136V | G | P | S, TF | AD136 | | 2N1184B | | | 06 |
| AD136VI | G | P | S, TF | ASZ16 | | 2N1536 | | | 06 |
| AD136/4 | G | P | S, TF | ASZ16 | | 2N1536 | | | 06 |
| AD136/5 | G | P | S, TF | ASZ16 | | 2N1536 | | | 06 |
| AD136/6 | G | P | S, TF | ASZ16 | | 2N1536 | | | 06 |
| AD138 | G | P | TF | AD133 | AD148 | 2N561 | 2N1022A | 2SB151 | 06 |
| AD138 | | | | ADZ11 | ASZ16 | 2N1536 | | 2SB425 | 06 |
| AD138 | | | | ASZ17 | ASZ18 | | | | 06 |
| AD139 | G | P | TF, V, PE, PH | AD148 | AD148V | 2N2835 | | | 06 |
| AD139 | | | | AD149 | AD150 | | | | 06 |
| AD139 | | | | AD162 | | | | | 06 |
| AD140 | G | P | PH, MU | AD149 | ASZ16 | 2N1022 | 2N1536 | | 06 |
| AD140 | | | | | | 2N2836 | | | 06 |
| AD142 | G | P | AT | AD133 | AD138/50 | 2N301A | 2N1533 | | 06 |
| AD142 | | | | AD149 | ADZ11 | | | | 06 |
| AD142 | G | P | AT | AM92 | ASZ15 | | | | 06 |
| AD142 | | | | AUY22 | SFT240 | | | | 06 |
| AD142-4 | G | P | AT | AUY22III | | | | | 06 |
| AD142-5 | G | P | AT | AUY22IV | | | | | 06 |
| AD142-6 | G | P | AT | AUY22IV | | | | | 06 |
| AD143 | G | P | AT | AD133 | AD138/50 | 2N301 | 2N1536 | | 06 |
| AD143 | | | | AD150 | ADZ11 | 2N2869 | | | 06 |
| AD143 | | | | AM91 | AUY21 | | | | 06 |
| AD143 | | | | OC26 | | | | | 06 |
| AD143R | G | P | AT | ASZ16 | AUY21 | 2N1536 | | | 06 |
| AD143R-4 | G | P | AT | AUY21III | | | | | 06 |
| AD143R-5 | G | P | AT | AUY21IV | | | | | 06 |
| AD143R-6 | G | P | AT | AUY21IV | | | | | 06 |
| AD143-4 | G | P | AT | AUY21III | | | | | 06 |
| AD143-5 | G | P | AT | AUY21IV | | | | | 06 |
| AD143-6 | G | P | AT | AUY21IV | | | | | 06 |
| AD145 | G | P | AT | AD133V | AD138 | | | | 06 |
| AD145 | | | | ASZ16 | AUY21III | | | | 06 |
| AD146 | G | P | | AD166 | | | | | 06 |
| AD148 | G | P | S, AT | AC138 | AD139 | 2N456 | 2N2835 | 2SB426 | 06 |
| AD148 | | | | AD162 | OC28 | | | | 06 |
| AD148 | | | | OC36 | | | | | 06 |

| TYPE | M/S | POL | MANUFAC | EUROPEAN | | AMERICAN | | JAPANESE | USE |
|---|---|---|---|---|---|---|---|---|---|
| AD148IV | G | P | S, AT | AD139 | AD148 | 2N456 | | 2SB426 | 06 |
| AD148IV | | | | AD156 | | | | | 06 |
| AD148V | G | P | S, AT | AD139 | AD148 | 2N2835 | | | 06 |
| AD148V | | | | AD156 | | | | | 06 |
| AD148/66 | G | P. | | AD162 | | 2N2835 | | | 06 |
| AD149 | G | P | AT, PH, S, TF | AC138 | ASZ16 | 2N456 | 2N1536 | 2SB425 | 06 |
| AD149 | | | | OC28 | OC36 | 2N2836 | | | 06 |
| AD149/01 | G | P | | AD149 | | 2N3836 | | | 06 |
| AD149/02 | G | P | | AD149 | | 2N2836 | | | 06 |
| AD149IV | G | P | AT, PH, S, TF | AD149 | AD166 | TI156 | 2N456 | 2SB471 | 06 |
| AD149IV | | | | ASZ16 | | 2N1536 | | | 06 |
| AD149V | G | P | AT, PH, S, TF | AD149 | AD166 | TI156 | 2N1536 | 2SB471 | 06 |
| AD149V | | | | ASZ16 | | | | | 06 |
| AD150 | G | P | AT, S, TF | AC138 | AD149 | 2N456 | 2N1536 | 2SB426 | 06 |
| AD150 | | | | ASZ16 | OC36 | 2N2836 | | | 06 |
| AD150IV | G | P | AT, S, TF | AD150 | AD166 | TI1156 | 2N456 | 2SB426 | 06 |
| AD150IV | | | | ASZ16 | | 2N1536 | | | 06 |
| AD150V | G | P | AT, S, TF | AD150 | AD166 | TI156 | 2N1536 | | 06 |
| AD150V | | | | ASZ16 | | | | | 06 |
| AD152 | G | P | TF | AD149 | AD156 | TI156 | 2N2835 | 2SB368 | 06 |
| AD152 | | | | AD162 | AD162V | 2N2836 | | 2SB425 | 06 |
| AD152 | | | | AD162VI | | | | | 06 |
| AD153 | G | P | SE | AD131 | AD138 | TI156 | | | 06 |
| AD153 | | | | AD149 | | | | | 06 |
| AD155 | G | P | TF | AD156 | AD162 | 2N2835 | | 2SB367 | 06 |
| AD155 | | | | AD162V | | | | 2SB426 | 06 |
| AD156 | G | P | S | AD139 | AD148 | 2N2835 | | | 06 |
| AD156 | | | | AD152 | AD162 | | | | 06 |
| AD156 | | | | AD162VII | | | | | 06 |
| AD157 | G | P | S | AD162 | AD162VII | 2N2835 | | | 06 |
| AD159 | G | P | TF | AD136 | AD136IV | | | | 06 |
| AD159 | | | | ASZ17 | | | | | 06 |
| AD160 | G | P | TF | AD136 | AD136IV | | | | 06 |
| AD160 | | | | AD136V | ASZ16 | | | | 06 |
| AD161 | G | N | PH, S, TF, V | AD165 | | 2N4077 | | | 06 |
| AD162 | G | P | PH, S, TF, V | AD262 | | 2N2835 | | 2SB367 | 06 |
| AD162 | | | | | | | | 2SB426 | 06 |
| AD162V | G | P | S | AD162 | | 2N2835 | | | 06 |
| AD162VI | G | P | S | AD162 | | 2N2835 | | | 06 |
| AD162VII | G | P | S | AD162 | | 2N2835 | | | 06 |
| AD162VIII | G | P | S | AD162 | | 2N2835 | | | 06 |
| AD163 | G | P | S | ASZ15 | ASZ18 | 2N1533 | | 2SB424 | 06 |
| AD163 | | | | AUY32 | | | | | 06 |
| AD163II | G | P | S | ASZ15 | | 2N1533 | | | 06 |
| AD163III | G | P | S | ASZ15 | | 2N1533 | | | 06 |
| AD163IV | G | P | S | ASZ15 | | 2N1533 | | | 06 |
| AD164 | G | P | TF | AD162 | AD162VI | 2N2835 | | 2SB367 | 06 |
| AD165 | G | N | TF | AD161 | | 2N4077 | | | 06 |
| AD166 | G | P | S | AD149 | (AUY21IV) | | | | 06 |
| AD167 | G | P | S | AD149 | (AUY22IV) | | | | 06 |
| AD169 | G | P | TF | AD152 | AD162 | | | 2SB368 | 06 |
| AD169 | | | | (AD162V) | | | | | 06 |
| AD262 | G | P | AT | AD148V | AD162 | 2N2835 | | | 06 |
| AD262 | | | | ASZ17 | | | | | 06 |
| AD263 | G | P | AT | (AD148V) | AD162 | 2N2835 | | | 06 |
| AD263 | | | | ASZ17 | | | | | 06 |
| ADY22 | G | P | IN, IT, ST | AD138 | ADY29 | 2N1536 | | | 06 |
| ADY22 | | | | ASZ16 | AUY21IV | | | | 06 |
| ADY22 | | | | AUY29 | | | | | 06 |
| ADY23 | G | P | IN, IT, ST | AD138 | AD138/50 | 2N1533 | | | 06 |
| ADY23 | | | | ADZ12 | ASZ15 | | | | 06 |
| ADY23 | | | | AUY22 | AUY22IV | | | | 06 |
| ADY23 | | | | AUY32 | | | | | 06 |
| ADY24 | G | P | IN, IT, ST | AD138/50 | ADZ12 | 2N1533 | | | 06 |
| ADY24 | | | | ASZ15 | AUY22 | | | | 06 |
| ADY24 | | | | AUY22IV | AUY32 | | | | 06 |
| ADY25 | G | P | IN, IT, ST | ADZ12 | ASZ15 | 2N1533 | | | 06 |
| ADY25 | | | | AUY22 | AUY28 | | | | 06 |
| ADY25 | | | | (AUY22IV) | | | | | 06 |
| ADY26 | G | P | PH, MU, V | ADZ12 | | 2N1100 | | | 06 |
| ADY27 | G | P | S | AD149 | ASZ16 | 2N1536 | | | 06 |
| ADY27IV | G | P | S | ASZ16 | | 2N1536 | | | 06 |
| ADY27V | G | P | S | ASZ16 | | 2N1536 | | | 06 |
| ADY28 | G | P | SE | ASZ15 | AUY22 | | | | 06 |
| ADY28 | | | | AUY22III | | | | | 06 |

| TYPE | M/S | POL | MANUFAC | EUROPEAN | | AMERICAN | | JAPANESE | USE |
|------|-----|-----|---------|----------|---|----------|---|----------|-----|
| ADY30 | G | P | 6 | ADZ12 | | 2N1100 | | | 06 |
| ADY31 | G | P | | ADZ12 | | 2N1100 | | | 06 |
| ADY32 | G | P | | ADZ12 | | 2N1100 | | | 06 |
| ADZ11 | G | P | PH, MU, V | AD103 | AD138 | 2N1100 | 2N1146 | | 06 |
| ADZ11 | | | | ADZ12 | AUY21 | | | | 06 |
| ADZ12 | G | P | PH, MU, V | AD104 | AD105 | 2N1100 | 2N1146A | | 06 |
| ADZ12 | | | | AUY22 | | 2N1146B | | | 06 |
| AF101 | G | P | TF | AF127 | AF131 | 2N799 | | 2S36 | 02 |
| AF101 | | | | AF106 | AF185 | | | | 02 |
| AF101 | | | | AF188 | AFY15 | | | | 02 |
| AF102 | G | P | V | AF106 | AF122 | 2N2494 | 2N2495 | | 02 |
| AF102 | | | | AF178 | AF190 | | | | 02 |
| AF105 | G | P | TF | AF126 | AF137 | 2N344 | | 2SA155 | 02 |
| AF105 | | | | AF197 | AF185 | | | | 02 |
| AF105 | | | | AF190 | | | | | 02 |
| AF105A | G | P | TF | AF126 | AF137 | | | | 02 |
| AF105A | | | | AF138 | AF190 | | | | 02 |
| AF105A | | | | AF197 | | | | | 02 |
| AF106 | G | P | S, V, TF | AF186 | AF178 | | | 2SA230 | 02 |
| AF106 | | | | AF190 | AM13 | | | | 02 |
| AF106A | G | P | AT | AF106 | | | | | 02, 18 |
| AF107 | G | P | S | AF109R | AF190 | | | | 02 |
| AF107 | | | | AFY10 | AFY11 | | | | 02 |
| AF107 | | | | AFY19 | | | | | 02 |
| AF108 | G | P | S | AF109R | AF190 | | | | 02 |
| AF108 | | | | AFY10 | AFY11 | | | | 02 |
| AF108 | | | | AFY19 | | | | | 02 |
| AF109 | G | P | V, S, TF | AF109R | AF180 | | | 2SA432 | 02 |
| AF109 | | | | AF190 | | | | | 02 |
| AF109R | G | P | AT, S, TF, V | AF180 | AF190 | | | | 02 |
| AF110 | G | P | | AF181 | AF190 | | | | 02 |
| AF111 | G | P | IN | AF127 | AF137 | 2N641 | 2N4034 | 2SA155 | 02 |
| AF111 | | | | AF185 | | | | | 02 |
| AF112 | G | P | IN | AF125 | AF126 | 2N1110 | 2N4034 | 2SA156 | 02 |
| AF112 | | | | AF136 | | | | | 02 |
| AF113 | G | P | IN | AF125 | AF135 | 2N346 | 2N2495 | 2SA116 | 02 |
| AF113 | | | | AF178 | | | | | 02 |
| AF114 | G | P | MU, PH, V, S | AF124 | AF130 | 2N346 | 2N990 | 2SA116 | 02 |
| AF114 | | | | AF134 | AF135 | 2N2495 | | | 02 |
| AF114 | | | | AF194 | | | | | 02 |
| AF114N | G | P | MN | AF124 | | | | | 02 |
| AF115 | G | P | MU, PH, V, S | AF124 | AF125 | 2N990 | 2N1110 | 2SA156 | 02 |
| AF115 | | | | AF135 | AF136 | | | | 02 |
| AF115 | | | | AF185 | | | | | 02 |
| AF115N | G | P | MN | AF125 | | | | | 02 |
| AF116 | G | P | MU, PH, V, S | AF124 | AF126 | 2N641 | 2N990 | 2SA155 | 02 |
| AF116 | | | | AF132 | AF136 | | | | 02 |
| AF116 | | | | AF137 | AF185 | | | | 02 |
| AF116N | G | P | MN | AF126 | | | | | 02 |
| AF117 | G | P | MU, PH, V, S | AF124 | AF127 | 2N642 | 2N990 | 2SA155 | 02 |
| AF117 | | | | AF133 | AF137 | | | | 02 |
| AF117 | | | | AF136 | SFT354 | | | | 02 |
| AF117N | | | MN | AF127 | | | | | 02 |
| AF118 | G | P | MU, PH, V, S | | | 2N2207 | | 2SA76 | 02 |
| AF119 | G | P | | AF127 | AF185 | | | | 02 |
| AF119 | | | | OC45 | | | | | 02 |
| AF120 | G | P | | AF126 | AF185 | | | | 02 |
| AF120 | | | | OC44 | | | | | 02 |
| AF121 | G | P | MU, PH, V, AM, PE | AF102 | AF106 | 2N2495 | 2N3588 | | 02 |
| AF121 | | | | AF201 | AF178 | | | | 02 |
| AF121 | | | | AF200U | | | | | 02 |
| AF121 | G | P | TF | AF102 | AF106 | 2N2495 | 2N3588 | | 02 |
| AF121 | | | | AF178 | AF201 | | | | 02 |
| AF121 | | | | AF200U | | | | | 02 |
| AF121S | G | P | V | (AF200U) | AF202S | | | | 02 |
| AF122 | G | P | TF | AF102 | AF106 | 2N2495 | | | 02 |
| AF122 | | | | AF178 | | | | | 02 |
| AF124 | G | P | MU, PH, V, S | AF134 | AF135 | 2N346 | 2N990 | 2SA235 | 02 |
| AF124 | | | | AF178 | AF194 | 2N2495 | 2N4035 | 2SA433 | 02 |
| AF125 | G | P | MU, PH, V, S | AF135 | AF136 | 2N990 | 2N991 | 2SA156 | 02 |
| AF125 | | | | AF124 | AF185 | 2N1110 | | 2SA433 | 02 |
| AF126 | G | P | MU, PH, V, S | AF124 | AF132 | 2N641 | 2N990 | 2SA240 | 02 |
| AF126 | | | | AF136 | AF137 | | | 2SA433 | 02 |
| AF126 | | | | SFT316 | | | | | 02 |
| AF127 | G | P | MU, PH, V, S | AF124 | AF133 | 2N642 | 2N990 | 2SA240 | 02 |

| TYPE | M/S | POL | MANUFAC | EUROPEAN | | AMERICAN | | JAPANESE | USE |
|---|---|---|---|---|---|---|---|---|---|
| AF127 | | | | AF137 | AF185 | 2N993 | 2N4034 | 2SA433 | 02 |
| AF128 | G | P | TF | ASY27 | | | | | 02 |
| AF129 | G | P | IN | AF121 | AF124 | | | | 02 |
| AF129 | | | | AF134 | | | | | 02 |
| AF130 | G | P | IN | AF124 | AF134 | 2N346 | 2N2495 | 2SA116 | 02 |
| | | | | | | | | | |
| AF130 | | | | AF178 | | 2N4035 | | | 02 |
| AF131 | G | P | IN | AF125 | AF134 | 2N1110 | | 2SA156 | 02 |
| AF131 | | | | AF135 | AF136 | | | | 02 |
| AF131 | | | | AF185 | | | | | 02 |
| AF132 | G | P | IN | AF126 | AF136 | 2N641 | | 2SA155 | 02 |
| | | | | | | | | | |
| AF132 | | | | AF138 | | | | | 02 |
| AF133 | G | P | IN | AF117 | AF127 | 2N641 | 2N4034 | 2SA155 | 02 |
| AF133 | | | | AF137 | | | | | 02 |
| AF134 | G | P | TF | AF124 | AF129 | 2N346 | 2N2495 | 2SA76 | 02 |
| AF134 | | | | AF130 | AF136 | 2N4035 | | 2SA116 | 02 |
| | | | | | | | | | |
| AF135 | G | P | TF | AF125 | AF131 | 2N1110 | | 2SA76 | 02 |
| AF135 | | | | AF136 | | | | 2SA156 | 02 |
| AF136 | G | P | TF | AF125 | AF126 | 2N1110 | 2N4034 | 2SA76 | 02 |
| AF136 | | | | AF131 | | | | 2SA156 | 02 |
| AF137 | G | P | TF | AF126 | AF127 | 2N642 | | 2SA155 | 02 |
| | | | | | | | | | |
| AF137 | | | | AF133 | SFT316 | | | 2SA433 | 02 |
| AF138 | G | P | TF | AF127 | AF132 | 2N641 | 2N4034 | 2SA155 | 02 |
| AF138 | | | | AF179 | | | | | 02 |
| AF139 | G | P | PH, S, TF, V | AF186 | AF239 | M9031 | MM139 | | 02 |
| AF139 | | | | AM18 | | 2N2244 | | | 02 |
| | | | | | | | | | |
| AF142 | | | | AF112 | AF124 | 2N4035 | | | 02 |
| AF142 | | | | AF134 | AF194 | | | | 02 |
| AF143 | G | P | AT | AF124 | AF125 | | | | 02 |
| AF143 | | | | AF135 | | | | | 02 |
| AF144 | G | P | AT | AF124 | AF126 | | | | 02 |
| | | | | | | | | | |
| AF144 | | | | AF132 | AF136 | | | | 02 |
| AF144 | | | | AF137 | | | | | 02 |
| AF146 | G | P | AT | AF125 | AF127 | | | | 02 |
| AF146 | | | | AF135 | | | | | 02 |
| AF147 | G | P | AT | AF126 | AF136 | | | | 02 |
| | | | | | | | | | |
| AF147 | | | | AF133 | | | | | 02 |
| AF148 | G | P | AT | AF126 | AF127 | 2N4034 | | | 02 |
| AF148 | | | | AF136 | AF137 | | | | 02 |
| AF149 | G | P | AT | AF126 | AF137 | | | | 02 |
| AF149 | | | | AF131 | AF136 | | | | 02 |
| | | | | | | | | | |
| AF150 | G | P | AT | AF126 | AF127 | 2N4034 | | | 02 |
| AF150 | | | | AF137 | | | | | 02 |
| AF156 | G | P | | AF127 | | | | | 02 |
| AF164 | G | P | AT | AF114 | AF124 | 2N1177 | 2N4035 | | 02 |
| AF164 | | | | AF132 | AF134 | | | | 02 |
| | | | | | | | | | |
| AF164 | | | | AF194 | | | | | 02 |
| AF165 | G | P | AT | AF124 | AF125 | 2N1178 | 2N1179 | | 02 |
| AF165 | | | | AF134 | AF135 | | | | 02 |
| AF166 | G | P | AT | AF136 | AM11 | 2N1180 | 2N4034 | | 02 |
| AF166 | | | | SFT316 | AF116 | | | | 02 |
| | | | | | | | | | |
| AF166 | | | | AF126 | | | | | 02 |
| AF168 | G | P | AT | AF125 | AF126 | 2N1183 | 2N2083 | | 02 |
| AF168 | | | | AF127 | AF135 | | | | 02 |
| AF168 | | | | AF136 | | | | | 02 |
| AF169 | G | P | AT | AF126 | AF127 | 2N1631 | 2N1632 | | 02 |
| | | | | | | | | | |
| AF169 | | | | AF129 | AF136 | 2N4034 | | | 02 |
| AF169 | | | | AF137 | | | | | 02 |
| AF170 | G | P | AT | AF127 | AF136 | 2N1426 | 2N1635 | | 02 |
| AF170 | | | | AF137 | AM14 | 2N1639 | 2N4034 | | 02 |
| AF171 | G | P | AT | AF126 | AF133 | 2N1425 | 2N4035 | | 07 |
| | | | | | | | | | |
| AF171 | | | | AF136 | | | | | 02 |
| AF172 | G | P | AT | AF117 | AF127 | 2N1633 | 2N1638 | 2SA432 | 02 |
| AF172 | | | | AF137 | AM12 | 2N4034 | | | 02 |
| AF178 | G | P | MU, PH, TF, V | AF106 | | 2N2495 | | 2SA432 | 02 |
| AF179 | G | P | MU, PH, PE | (AF106) | AF180 | 2N2654 | | | 02 |
| | | | | | | | | | |
| AF180 | G | P | MU, PH, PE, V | AF109 | (AF109R) | 2N3074 | | | 02 |
| AF180 | | | | AF133 | | | | | 02 |
| AF181 | G | P | MU, PH, TF, PE, V | AF110 | AF121 | 2N3075 | | | 02 |
| AF181 | | | | AF200 | (AF200U) | | | | 02 |
| AF182 | G | P | SE | AF121 | AF178 | | | | 02 |
| | | | | | | | | | |
| AF182 | | | | (AF201U) | | | | | 02 |
| AF185 | G | P | V, PH | AF106 | AF121 | | | | 02 |
| AF186 | G | P | PH, V | AF139 | AF239 | 2N2244 | 2N5043 | | 02 |
| AF186G | G | P | PH, PE | (AF139) | | | | | 02 |
| AF186W | G | P | PH, PE | (AF139) | | | | | 02 |

| TYPE | M/S | POL | MANUFAC | EUROPEAN | | AMERICAN | | JAPANESE | USE |
|------|-----|-----|---------|----------|---|----------|---|----------|-----|
| AF187 | G | P | SE, Ss, ML | AF121 | AF133 | 2N2244 | 2N5044 | | 02 |
| AF187 | | | | AF201 | AFY15 | | | | 02 |
| AF187 | | | | ASY70IV | | | | | 02 |
| AF188 | G | P | SE, Ss, ML | AF121 | AF133 | 2N5044 | | | 02 |
| AF188 | | | | AFY15 | ASY70VI | | | | 02 |
| AF189 | G | P | SE | AF133 | AF139 | | | | 02 |
| AF189 | | | | AFY15 | ASY70VI | | | | 02 |
| AF190 | G | P | SE | AF124 | AF133 | | | | 02 |
| AF190 | . | | | AF188 | AFY15 | | | | 02 |
| AF190 | | | | ASY70VI | | | | | 02 |
| AF191 | G | P | | SFT308 | | | | | 02 |
| AF192 | G | N | | AC130 | | | | | 02 |
| AF193 | G | P | SE | AF121 | (AF126) | 2N3323 | 2N4034 | | 02 |
| AF193 | | | | AF127 | AF132 | | | | 02 |
| AF193 | | | | AF136 | AF137 | | | | 02 |
| AF194 | G | P | SE | AF124 | AF125 | 2N3323 | 2N4035 | | 02 |
| AF194 | | | | AF134 | AF135 | | | | 02 |
| AF194 | | | | (AF200U) | | | | | 02 |
| AF195 | G | P | SE | AF125 | AF133 | 2N3323 | | | 02 |
| AF195 | | | | AF135 | | | | | 02 |
| AF196 | G | P | SE | AF125 | AF126 | 2N3323 | 2N4034 | | 02 |
| AF196 | | | | AF136 | | | | | 02 |
| AF197 | G | P | SE | AF127 | AF133 | 2N3323 | 2N3325 | | 02 |
| AF197 | | | | AF137 | | 2N4034 | | | 02 |
| AF198 | G | P | SE | AF127 | AF133 | 2N3325 | | | 02 |
| AF198 | | | | AF138 | | | | | 02 |
| AF200 | G | P | AT, S | AF121 | AF181 | | | 2SA239 | 02 |
| AF200 | | | | AF200U | | | | 2SA240 | 02 |
| AF201 | G | P | AT, S | AF121 | | | | 2SA239 | 02 |
| AF201 | | | | | | | | 2SA240 | 02 |
| AF202 | G | P | AT, S | AF121 | AF121S | | | 2SA239 | 02 |
| AF202 | | | | (AF200U) | AF202S | | | 2SA240 | 02 |
| AF202L | G | P | AT | (AF200U) | | | | | 02 |
| AF202S | G | P | S | AF121S | (AF200U) | | | 2SA240 | 02 |
| AF239 | G | P | S, TF, V | AF254 | | | | | 02 |
| AF239S | G | P | AT, S, TF, V | AF139 | | | | | 02 |
| AF240 | G | P | AT, PH, V, S | AF139 | AF239S | | | | 02 |
| AF240 | | | | AF267 | AF280 | | | | 02 |
| AF250 | G | P | | AF239S | AF267 | | | | 02 |
| AF250 | | | | AF280 | | | | | 02 |
| AF251 | G | P | TF | AF239 | AF239S | | | | 02 |
| AF252 | G | P | TF | AF239 | (AF239S) | | | | 02 |
| AF252 | | | | AF240 | | | | | 02 |
| AF253 | G | P | TF | AF109R | AF139 | | | | 02 |
| AF253 | | | | (AF240) | | | | | 02 |
| AF254 | G | P | | AF202 | | | | | 02 |
| AF256 | G | P | TF | AF106 | | | | | 02 |
| AF267 | G | P | PH, V, PE | AF239S | AF279 | | | | 02 |
| AF269 | G | P | PH, V | AF239S | AF240 | | | | 02 |
| AF269 | | | | AF280 | | | | | 02 |
| AF279 | G | P | PH, TF, S, V | AF239S | AF279S | | | | 02 |
| AF280 | G | P | PH, V, S, TF | AF257 | AF239S | | | | 02 |
| AF367 | G | P | PH, V | AF279S | | | | | 02 |
| AF369 | G | P | PH, V | AF280 | | | | | 02 |
| AFY10 | G | P | S | AFY11 | (AFY18) | | | | 02 |
| AFY10 | | | | AFY19 | | | | | 02 |
| AFY11 | G | P | S | AF106 | (AFY18) | | | 2SA431 | 02 |
| AFY11 | | | | AF121 | AFY19 | | | | 02 |
| AFY12 | G | P | AT, S, TF | AF106 | | | | 2SA431 | 02 |
| AFY12 | | | | AFZ12 | | | | | 02 |
| AFY13 | G | P | TF | AF124 | AF134 | | | | 02 |
| AFY13 | | | | (AFY12) | | | | | 02 |
| AFY14 | G | P | TF | AF124 | ASY27 | 2N990 | | 2SA72 | 02 |
| AFY14 | | | | SFT316K | | | | | 02 |
| AFY15 | G | P | TF | AF126 | AF136 | | | 2SA52 | 02 |
| AFY15 | | | | AF133 | (ASY27) | | | | 02 |
| AFY15 | | | | SFT317 | | | | | 02 |
| AFY15r | G | P | TF | (ASY26) | | | | | 02 |
| AFY15ye | G | P | TF | (ASY26) | | | | | 02 |
| AFY15V | G | P | TF | (ASY27) | | | | | 02 |
| AFY16 | G | P | AT, S, TF, V | | | M9031 | | | 02 |
| AFY18 | G | P | S | AF139 | AF240 | | | | 02 |
| AFY19 | G | P | MU, PH, V | AFY10 | AFY11 | | | | 02 |
| AFY19 | | | | AFY18 | | | | | 02 |
| AFY25 | G | P | TF | AF126 | AFY34 | | | | 02 |

| TYPE | M/S | POL | MANUFAC | EUROPEAN | | AMERICAN | | JAPANESE | USE |
|---|---|---|---|---|---|---|---|---|---|
| AFY25 | | | | (AFY42) | | | | | 02 |
| AFY26 | G | P | TF | AFY34 | (AFY42) | | | | 02 |
| AFY29 | G | P | TF | AF126 | AF133 | | | | 02 |
| AFY29 | G | P | TF | (AF200U) | SFT317 | | | | 02 |
| AFY34 | G | P | S | (AFY42) | | | | | 02 |
| | | | | | | | | | |
| AFY37 | G | P | S | AFY40 | (AFY42) | | | | 02 |
| AFY39 | G | P | S | AFY40 | (AFY42) | | | | 02 |
| AFY40 | G | P | V, PE, PH | (AFY42) | AF239S | | | | 02 |
| AFY40R | G | P | V | AF239S | (AFY42) | | | | 02 |
| AFY41 | G | P | V | (AFY42) | | | | | 02 |
| | | | | | | | | | |
| AFY42 | G | P | S | AF239S | AFY40 | | | | 02 |
| AFZ10 | G | P | TF | AFY14K | AFY19 | | | | 02 |
| AFZ11 | G | P | PH, MU | AFZ12 | | | | | 02 |
| AFZ12 | G | P | PH, MU | AF102 | AF106 | | | | 02 |
| AFZ12 | | | | AFY12 | | | | | 02 |
| | | | | | | | | | |
| AL100 | G | P | AT | AU101 | AL103 | 2N1906 | 2N2147 | | |
| AL101 | G | P | AT | AU102 | AL103 | 2N1905 | 2N2147 | | |
| AL102 | G | P | AT | AD167 | AM114 | 2N2147 | 2N5325 | | |
| AL102 | | | | AU106 | | | | | |
| AL103 | G | P | AT | AD166 | AM111 | 2N2147 | 2N2148 | | |
| | | | | | | | | | |
| AL112 | G | P | AT | AL103 | | 2N2147 | | | |
| AL113 | G | P | AT | AL103 | | 2N2147 | | | |
| ALZ10 | G | P | TF | AUY10 | | | | | 03 |
| AM11 | G | P | | AF116 | AF126 | 2N1180 | | | |
| AM11 | | | | SFT316 | | | | | |
| | | | | | | | | | |
| AM12 | G | P | | AF117 | AF127 | 2N1524 | 2N1638 | | |
| AM12 | | | | AF172 | | | | | |
| AM13 | G | P | | AF106 | AF114 | 2N1177 | | | |
| AM13 | | | | AF124 | | | | | |
| AM14 | G | P | | AF117 | AF127 | 2N1526 | 2N1639 | | |
| | | | | | | | | | |
| AM14 | | | | AF170 | | | | | |
| AM15 | G | P | | AF115 | AF125 | 2N1178 | 2N1179 | | |
| AM15 | | | | AF165 | | | | | |
| AM16 | G | P | | AF115 | AF125 | 2N2083 | | | |
| AM16 | | | | AF168 | | | | | |
| | | | | | | | | | |
| AM18 | G | P | | AF139 | | MM139 | | | |
| AM51 | G | P | | AC126 | AC137 | 2N2613 | | | |
| AM51 | | | | AC191 | | | | | |
| AM52 | G | P | | AC134 | OC71 | 2N406 | 2N215 | | |
| AM53 | G | P | | AC126 | AC161 | 2N217 | 2N2614 | | |
| | | | | | | | | | |
| AM53 | | | | AC192 | | | | | |
| AM54 | G | P | | AC138 | AC151 | TA2063 | | | |
| AM54 | | | | OC75 | | | | | |
| AM71 | G | P | | AC128 | AC139 | 40253 | | | |
| AM72 | G | N | | AC127 | AC141 | 2N647 | | | |
| | | | | | | | | | |
| AM72 | | | | SFT377 | | | | | |
| AM73 | G | P | | AC125 | AC132 | 2N109 | 2N591 | | |
| AM73 | | | | AC136 | | | | | |
| AM74 | G | P | | AC128 | AC142 | 2N217 | | | |
| AM74 | | | | AC153 | | | | | |
| | | | | | | | | | |
| AM91 | G | P | | AD143 | AD150 | 2N301 | 2N2869 | | |
| AM91 | | | | OC26 | | | | | |
| AM92 | G | P | | AD142 | AD149 | 2N301A | 2N2870 | | |
| AM92 | | | | SFT239 | | | | | |
| AM94 | G | P | | AD145 | OC16 | 40254 | | | |
| | | | | | | | | | |
| AM111 | G | P | | AD166 | AL103 | 2N2148 | | | |
| AM114 | G | P | | AD167 | AL102 | 2N2147 | | | |
| AM251 | S | N | | BC107 | BC147 | | | | |
| AM251 | | | | BC167 | BCY56 | | | | |
| AM252 | S | N | | BC108 | BC148 | | | | |
| | | | | | | | | | |
| AM252 | | | | BC168 | BCY57 | | | | |
| AM253 | S | N | | BC109 | BC149 | | | | |
| AM253 | | | | BC169 | BCY57 | | | | |
| AM254 | S | N | | BC267 | | | | | |
| AM255 | S | N | | BC268 | | | | | |
| | | | | | | | | | |
| AM256 | S | N | | BC269 | | | | | |
| AM257 | S | N | | BC270 | | | | | |
| AM258 | S | N | | BC271 | | | | | |
| AM259 | S | N | | BC272 | | | | | |
| AM260 | S | P | | BC297 | | | | | |
| | | | | | | | | | |
| AM261 | S | N | | BCY58 | BFY44 | | | | |
| AM262 | S | N | | BCY59 | | | | | |
| AM263 | S | N | | BC300 | | | | | |
| AM264 | S | N | | BC301 | | | | | |
| AM276 | S | N | | BC303 | | | | | |

| TYPE | M/S | POL | MANUFAC | EUROPEAN | | AMERICAN | | JAPANESE | USE |
|------|-----|-----|---------|----------|---|----------|---|----------|-----|
| AM291 | S | N | | BDX10 | | 2N3055 | | | |
| AM293 | S | N | | BD141 | | | | | |
| AM294 | S | N | | BD142 | | | | | |
| ASY12 | G | P | IN | AC124K | AC128 | 2N59 | 2N1924 | 2SB222 | 17 |
| ASY12 | | | | AC152 | AC153 | | | | 17 |
| ASY12 | | | | ASY23 | | | | | 17 |
| ASY12-1 | G | P | IN | (AC152IV) | | | | | 17, 10 |
| ASY12-2 | G | P | IN | (AC152IV) | | | | | 17, 10 |
| ASY13 | G | P | IN | ASY23 | ASY24 | 2N284 | 2N1926 | 2SB89 | 17, 10 |
| ASY13 | | | | (ASY48) | ASY48V | | | | 17, 10 |
| ASY13 | | | | ASY77 | | | | | 17, 10 |
| ASY13-1 | G | P | IN | (ASY48IV) | | | | | 17, 10 |
| ASY13-2 | G | P | IN | (ASY48IV) | | | | | 17, 10 |
| ASY14 | G | P | IN | ASY23 | (ASY48) | 2N284 | | 2SB89 | 17, 10 |
| ASY14 | | | | ASY48IV | | | | | 17, 10 |
| ASY14 | | | | ASY77 | | | | | 17, 10 |
| ASY14-1 | G | P | IN | (ASY48IV) | | | | | 17, 10 |
| ASY14-2 | G | P | IN | (ASY48IV) | | | | | 17, 10 |
| ASY14-3 | G | P | IN | (ASY48V) | | | | | 17, 10 |
| ASY23 | G | P | V | ASY13 | ASY14 | 2N272 | | 2SB33 | 17, 10 |
| ASY23 | | | | ASY48 | (ASY48V) | | | | 17, 10 |
| ASY24 | G | P | TF | ASY27 | (ASY48V) | | | | 17, 10 |
| ASY24 | | | | ASY56 | ASY80 | | | | 17, 10 |
| ASY24 | | | | ASZ23 | | | | | 17, 10 |
| ASY24B | G | P | TF | (ASY70V) | ASY76 | | | | 17, 10 |
| ASY26 | G | P | S, TF, V, PH | ASY24 | ASY48 | 2N799 | | 2SA155 | 17 |
| ASY26 | | | | ASY56 | | | | | 17 |
| ASY27 | G | P | S, TF, V, PH | ASY30 | ASY48 | 2N36 | 2N1305 | 2SB101 | 17 |
| ASY27 | | | | ASY58 | | | | | 17 |
| ASY28 | G | N | V, MU, PE, PH, RA | AC127) | ASY73 | 2N1304 | | | 17, 10 |
| ASY28 | G | N | TX | (AC127) | ASY73 | 2N1304 | | | 17, 10 |
| ASY29 | G | N | V, MU, PE, PH, RA | (AC127) | ASY74 | 2N211 | 2N1304 | 2SB255 | 17, 10 |
| ASY29 | G | N | TX | (AC127) | ASY74 | 2N211 | 2N1304 | 2SB255 | 17, 10 |
| ASY30 | G | P | TF | AF124 | ASY27 | 2N36 | 2N990 | 2SB101 | 17, 10 |
| ASY30 | | | | ASY32 | (ASY48V) | | | | 17, 10 |
| ASY30 | | | | ASY61 | ASY80 | | | | 17, 10 |
| ASY31 | G | P | TF, V, PH | AC163 | ACY15 | 2N506 | | 2SB219 | 17 |
| ASY31 | | | | AF125 | ASY26 | | | | 17 |
| ASY31 | | | | ASY48 | ASY56 | | | | 17 |
| ASY32 | G | P | TF, V, PH | AC122 | AFY15 | 2N506 | | 2SB219 | 17 |
| ASY32 | | | | AFY32 | ASY27 | | | | 17 |
| ASY32 | | | | ASY48 | ASY56 | | | | 17 |
| ASY48 | G | P | S | AC128 | ACY24 | 2N241 | 2N2706 | 2SB89 | 17 |
| ASY48 | | | | ASY23 | ASY81 | 2N2906 | 2N2906A | | 17 |
| ASY48 | | | | ASY77 | | | | | 17 |
| ASY50 | G | P | IN | AC122 | AC125 | 2N406 | 2N526 | | 17, 01 |
| ASY50 | | | | AC131/30 | ASY48 | | | | 17, 01 |
| ASY50 | | | | ASY70IV | ASY70V | | | | 17, 01 |
| ASY52 | G | P | IN | ASY48V | | 2N1926 | | | 17 |
| ASY53 | G | N | IN | (AC127) | | | | | 17, 01 |
| ASY54 | G | P | IN | (AC151rV) | ASY26 | 2N1303 | | | 17, 10 |
| ASY54 | | | | ASY27 | ASY48 | | | | 17, 10 |
| ASY54N | G | P | NT | OC44N | | 2N2614 | | | 17 |
| ASY55 | G | P | IN | (AC151rVI) | ASY27 | 2N1303 | | | 17, 10 |
| ASY55 | | | | TF49 | | | | | 17, 10 |
| ASY55N | G | P | NT | OC44N | | 2N2614 | | | 17 |
| ASY56 | G | P | IN | ASY27 | ASY26 | 2N1303 | | | 17, 10 |
| ASY56 | | | | TF49 | | | | | 17, 10 |
| ASY56N | G | P | NT | OC44N | | 2N2614 | | | 17 |
| ASY57 | G | P | IN | ASY26 | ASY27 | 2N1303 | 2N1305 | | 17 |
| ASY57 | | | | TF49 | | | | | 17 |
| ASY57N | G | P | NT | OC44N | | 2N2614 | | | 17 |
| ASY58 | G | P | IN | ASY27 | TF49 | 2N1303 | 2N1305 | | 17 |
| ASY58N | G | P | NT | OC44N | | 2N2614 | | | 17 |
| ASY59 | G | P | IN | ASY27 | | 2N1307 | | | 17 |
| ASY59 | | | | TF49 | | | | | 17 |
| ASY59N | G | P | NT | OC44N | | 2N2614 | | | 17 |
| ASY60 | G | P | IN | (ASY27) | | | | | 17, 02 |
| ASY61 | G | N | IN | AC127 | ASY28 | 2N1302 | | | 10, 17 |
| ASY62 | G | N | IN | AC127 | ASY29 | | | | 17, 10 |
| ASY63 | G | P | IN | AC151IV | ASY70 | 2N2614 | | | 17 |
| ASY63 | | | | OC44N | | | | | 17 |
| ASY64 | G | P | IN | (ASY26) | | | | | 17, 10 |
| ASY66 | G | P | IN | (ASY27) | | | | | 17, 10 |
| ASY70 | G | P | S | AC119 | AC124K | 2N404 | 2N467 | 2SB222 | 17 |

| TYPE | M/S | POL | MANUFAC | EUROPEAN | | AMERICAN | | JAPANESE | USE |
|------|-----|-----|---------|----------|--|----------|--|----------|-----|
| ASY70 | | | | OC74 | ASY80 | | | | 17 |
| ASY72 | G | N | IN | (AC127) | | | | | 17 |
| ASY73 | G | N | PH, V, PE, RA, AM | (AC127) | ASY29 | 2N1304 | | | 17, 20 |
| ASY73 | | | | ASY74 | | | | | 17, 20 |
| ASY74 | G | N | PH, V, PE, RA, AM | (AC127) | ASY29 | 2N1304 | | | 17, 20 |
| ASY74 | | | | ASY75 | | | | | 17, 20 |
| ASY75 | G | N | PH, V, PE, RA, AM | (AC127) | ASY29 | 2N1304 | | 2SC91 | 17, 10 |
| ASY76 | G | P | PH, V, PE, RA, AM | ACY17 | ACY16K | 2N526 | 2N1188 | | 17, 10 |
| ASY76 | | | | ASY48 | (ASY48VI) | | | | 17, 10 |
| ASY77 | G | P | PH, V, PE, RA, AM | ACY24K | ASY48 | 2N526 | 2N1188 | | 17, 10 |
| ASY77 | | | | (ASY48VI) | ASY81 | | | | 17, 10 |
| ASY80 | G | P | PH, V, AM | ACY17 | ACY24K | 2N527 | 2N1188 | | 17 |
| ASY80 | | | | ASY48 | | | | | 17 |
| ASY81 | G | P | PH, V, Ss, ML, SE | ACY17 | ACY24K | 2N11768 | | | 17, 10 |
| ASY81 | | | | (ASY48V) | ASY77 | | | | 17, 10 |
| ASY82 | G | P | TH, AE | AC152VI | | | | | 17, 01 |
| ASY83 | G | P | TH, AE | AC152VI | | | | | 17, 01 |
| ASY84 | G | P | TH, AE | AC152VI | | | | | 17, 01 |
| ASY85 | G | P | TH, AE | AC152VI | | | | | 17, 01 |
| ASY86 | G | N | TH, AE | AC127 | | | | | 17, 10 |
| ASY87 | G | N | TH, AE | AC127 | | | | | 17, 10 |
| ASY88 | G | N | TH, AE | AC127 | | | | | 17, 10 |
| ASY89 | G | N | TH, AE | AC127 | | | | | 17, 10 |
| ASY90 | G | P | AT | ASY48 | | | | | 17, 10 |
| ASY90-1 | G | P | AT | ASY48V | | | | | 17, 10 |
| ASY90-2 | G | P | AT | ASY48VI | | | | | 17, 10 |
| ASY91 | G | P | AT | ASY70 | | | | | 17 |
| ASY91-1 | G | P | AT | ASY70V | | | | | 17, 01 |
| ASY91-2 | G | P | AT | ASY70VI | | | | | 17, 01 |
| ASZ10-2 | G | P | PH, TF | AFY19 | ASY30K | | | | 17, 10 |
| ASZ10 | | | | (ASY48V) | | | | | 17, 10 |
| ASZ11 | G | P | PH, V | (AC151V) | ASY31 | | | | 17, 10 |
| ASZ12 | G | P | PH, V | (AC151V) | ASY32 | | | | 17, 10 |
| ASZ15 | G | P | SE, PH, V | AD132 | AUY28 | 2N1533 | | 2SB341 | |
| ASZ15 | | | | AUY22III | | | | 2SB424 | |
| ASZ16 | G | P | SE, V, PH | AD138/50 | AD150 | 2N1536 | | 2SB339 | 17 |
| ASZ16 | | | | AUY21IV | AUZ11 | | | 2SB425 | 17 |
| ASZ17 | G | P | SE, V, PH | AD138/50 | AD150 | 2N1536 | | 2SB339 | 17 |
| ASZ17 | | | | ASZ16 | AUY21III | | | 2SB425 | 17 |
| ASZ17 | | | | AUZ11 | | | | | 17 |
| ASZ18 | G | P | RA, PH, PE, MN, V | ASZ16 | AUY21II | 2N1536 | | 2SB340 | 17, 01 |
| ASZ18 | | | | AUY22 | (AUY22IV) | | | 2SB424 | 17, 01 |
| ASZ18 | | | | AUY28 | OC36 | | | | 17, 01 |
| ASZ18 | G | P | SE | ASZ16 | AUY21II | 2N1536 | | 2SB340 | 17, 01 |
| ASZ18 | | | | AUY22 | AUY28 | | | 2SB424 | 17, 01 |
| ASZ18 | | | | (AUY22IV) | OC36 | | | | 17, 01 |
| ASZ20 | G | P | PH | AF124 | ASY80 | 2N990 | | | 17 |
| ASZ21 | G | P | V, MU, PE, PH | (AFY11) | ASY80 | | | | 17, 01 |
| ASZ21 | G | P | V, MU, PE, PH | ASZ20 | | | | | 17, 01 |
| ASZ23 | G | P | PH | ACY24 | ASY24 | | | | 17 |
| ASZ30 | G | P | TF | ASY24 | ASY26 | 2N1925 | | | 17, 10 |
| ASZ30 | | | | (ASY48V) | | | | | 17, 10 |
| AU101 | G | P | PH | AU103 | AU106 | 2N5325 | | | 16 |
| AU101 | G | P | PH | AUY22 | | | | | 16 |
| AU102 | G | P | PH, V | AC128 | AL103 | 2N2147 | | | 16 |
| AU102 | | | | AUY21III | AUY22III | | | | 16 |
| AU103 | G | P | PH | AU105 | AU106 | 2N5325 | | 2SB468 | 16 |
| AU104 | G | P | PH | AU106 | | 2N5325 | | | 16 |
| AU105 | G | P | S | AU103 | (AUY22IV) | | | | 16, 18 |
| AU105 | | | | ASZ15 | | | | | 16, 18 |
| AU106 | G | P | AT | AU112 | | 2N5325 | | | 16 |
| AU107 | G | P | AT | AU106 | | 2N5325 | | | 16 |
| AU108 | G | P | AT | AL103 | ASZ15 | 2N2147 | | | 16 |
| AU108F | G | P | AT | AL103 | | 2N2142 | | | 16 |
| AU110 | G | P | AT | AU106 | AUY38 | 2N5325 | | | 16 |
| AU111 | G | P | AT | AU106 | | 2N5325 | | | 16 |
| AU112 | G | P | AT | AU106 | | 2N5325 | | | 16 |
| AU113 | G | P | AT | AU106 | | 2N5325 | | | 16 |
| AUY17 | G | P | PH, V | (AD132IV) | AL103 | 2N2147 | 2N4023 | | 16, 10 |
| AUY18 | G | P | S | AD148 | ASZ15 | 2N1533 | | | 16 |
| AUY18IV | G | P | S | ASZ16 | | 2N1536 | | | 16 |
| AUY18V | G | P | S | ASZ16 | | 2N1536 | | | 16 |
| AUY19 | G | P | S | AD138/50 | ASZ15 | 2N157A | 2N1044 | 2SB250 | 16 |
| AUY19 | | | | ASZ16 | AUY33 | 2N1536 | | 2SB338 | 16 |
| AUY19 | | | | OC28 | | | | | 16 |

| TYPE | M/S | POL | MANUFAC | EUROPEAN | | AMERICAN | | | JAPANESE | USE |
|---|---|---|---|---|---|---|---|---|---|---|
| AUY19III | G | P | S | ASZ16 | | 2N1536 | | | | 16 |
| AUY19IV | G | P | S | ASZ16 | | 2N1536 | | | | 16 |
| AUY19V | G | P | S | ASZ16 | | 2N1536 | | | | 16 |
| AUY20 | G | P | S | AD132 | ASZ15 | 2N157A | 2N1533 | | 2SB87 | 16 |
| | | | | ASZ18 | AUY32 | | | | 2S8341 | 16 |
| AUY20 | | | | OC36 | | | | | | 16 |
| AUY20III | G | P | S | ASZ15 | | 2N1533 | | | | 16 |
| AUY20IV | G | P | S | ASZ15 | | 2N1533 | | | | 16 |
| AUY20V | G | P | S | ASZ15 | | 2N1533 | | | | 16 |
| AUY21 | G | P | S | ASZ15 | ASZ16 | 2N352 | 2N1536 | | 2SB86 | 16 |
| AUY21 | | | | ASZ18 | AUY19IV | | | | 2SB339 | 16 |
| AUY21 | | | | AUY28 | | | | | | 16 |
| AUY21II | G | P | S | ASZ16 | | 2N1536 | | | | 16 |
| AUY21III | G | P | S | ASZ16 | | 2N1536 | | | | 16 |
| AUY21IV | G | P | S | ASZ16 | | 2N1536 | | | | 16 |
| AUY21A | G | P | AT | ASZ15 | ASZ16 | 2N1536 | | | | 16 |
| AUY21A | | | | AUY21 | | | | | | 16 |
| AUY21A-2 | G | P | AT | AUY21II | | | | | | 16 |
| AUY21A-3 | G | P | AT | AUY21III | | | | | | 16 |
| AUY21A-4 | G | P | AT | AUY21IV | | | | | | 16 |
| AUY22 | G | P | S | ASZ15 | ASZ16 | 2N174 | 2N561 | | 2SB87 | 16 |
| AUY22 | | | | AUY20IV | OC36 | 2N1533 | | | 2S8341 | 16 |
| AUY22II | G | P | S | ASZ15 | | 2N1533 | | | | 16 |
| AUY22III | G | P | S | ASZ15 | | 2N1533 | | | | 16 |
| AUY22IV | G | P | S | ASZ15 | | 2N1533 | | | | 16 |
| AUY22A | G | P | AT | ASZ15 | AUY22 | 2N1533 | | | | 16 |
| AUY22A-2 | G | P | AT | AUY22II | | | | | | 16 |
| AUY22A-3 | G | P | AT | AUY22III | | | | | | 16 |
| AUY22A-4 | G | P | AT | AUY22IV | | | | | | 16 |
| AUY28 | G | P | TF | ASZ15 | AUY22III | 2N1533 | | | 2S8340 | 16 |
| AUY28 | | | | AUY22IV | AUY30 | | | | | 16 |
| AUY29 | G | P | S | ADZ11 | ASZ16 | 2N1167 | | | | 16 |
| AUY29 | | | | AUY29IV | AUY29V | | | | | 16 |
| AUY29III | G | P | S | AUY29V | | 2N1167 | | | | 16 |
| AUY29IV | G | P | S | AUY29V | | 2N1167 | | | | 16 |
| AUY29V | G | P | S | | | 2N1167 | | | | 16 |
| AUY30 | G | P | SE | ASZ15 | ASZ16 | | | | | 16, 06 |
| AUY30 | | | | AUY22II | AUY22III | | | | | 16, 06 |
| AUY30 | | | | AUY28 | | | | | | 16, 06 |
| AUY31 | G | P | SE | ASZ16 | ASZ18 | | | | | 16 |
| AUY31 | | | | AUY21III | AUY28 | | | | | 16 |
| AUY32 | G | P | SE | ASZ15 | ASZ18 | | | | | 16, 06 |
| AUY32 | | | | AUY20 | AUY20IV | | | | | 16, 06 |
| AUY32 | | | | AUY28 | | | | | | 16, 06 |
| AUY33 | G | P | SE | AD149 | ASZ16 | | | | | 16, 06 |
| AUY33 | | | | AUY19III | AUY19IV | | | | | 16, 06 |
| AUY33 | | | | AUY28 | | | | | | 16, 06 |
| AUY34 | G | P | S | ASZ15 | ASZ18 | 2N1533 | | | | 16 |
| AUY34II | G | P | S | ASZ15 | | 2N1533 | | | | 16 |
| AUY34III | G | P | S | ASZ15 | | 2N1533 | | | | 16 |
| AUY34IV | G | P | S | ASZ15 | | 2N1533 | | | | 16 |
| AUY35 | G | P | AT | AL103 | ASZ16 | 2N2147 | | | | 16, 06 |
| AUY35 | | | | (AUY18) | AUY30 | | | | | 16, 06 |
| AUY35-4 | G | P | AT | (AUY18IV) | | | | | | 16, 06 |
| AUY35-5 | G | P | AT | (AUY18V) | | | | | | 16, 06 |
| AUY35-6 | G | P | AT | (AUY18V) | | | | | | 16, 06 |
| AUY36 | G | P | AT | AL103 | (AUY18) | 2N2147 | | | | 16 |
| AUY36 | | | | AUY35 | AUY38 | | | | | 16 |
| AUY37 | G | P | AT | ASZ15 | (AUY22) | 2N1533 | | | | 16, 06 |
| AUY37 | | | | AUY30 | AUY34II | | | | | 16, 06 |
| AUY37-4 | G | P | AT | (AUY22IV) | | | | | | 16, 06 |
| AUY37-5 | G | P | AT | (AUY22IV) | | | | | | 16, 06 |
| AUY38 | G | P | AT | ASZ15 | AU106 | 2N5325 | | | | 16 |
| AUZ11 | G | P | TF | AD150 | ASZ16 | | | | | 16 |
| AUZ11 | | | | ASZ17 | | | | | | 16 |
| B133000 | S | N | | BD221 | | | | | | |
| B133001 | S | N | | BD221 | | | | | | |
| B133002 | S | N | | BD221 | | | | | | |
| B133003 | S | N | | | | 2N6122 | | | | |
| B133004 | S | N | | | | 2N6122 | | | | |
| B133005 | S | N | | | | 2N6122 | | | | |
| B133006 | S | N | | | | 2N6123 | | | | |
| B133007 | S | N | | | | 2N6123 | | | | |
| B133008 | S | N | | | | 2N6123 | | | | |
| B170000 | S | N | SD | | | 2N6569 | | | | 06 |

| TYPE | M/S | POL | MANUFAC | EUROPEAN | | AMERICAN | JAPANESE | USE |
|---|---|---|---|---|---|---|---|---|
| B170001 | S | N | SD | | | 2N6569 | | 06 |
| B710002 | S | N | SD | | | 2N6569 | | 06 |
| B170003 | S | N | SD | | | 2N5882 | | 06 |
| B170004 | S | N | SD | | | 2N5882 | | 06 |
| B170005 | S | N | SD | | | 2N5882 | | 06 |
| | | | | | | | | |
| B170006 | S | N | SD | | | 2N5629 | | 06 |
| B170007 | S | N | SD | | | 2N5629 | | 06 |
| B170008 | S | N | SD | | | 2N5629 | | 06 |
| B170009 | S | N | SD | | | 2N6569 | | 06 |
| B170010 | S | N | SD | | | 2N6569 | | 06 |
| | | | | | | | | |
| B170011 | S | N | SD | | | 2N6569 | | 06 |
| B170012 | S | N | SD | | | 2N5882 | | 06 |
| B170013 | S | N | SD | | | 2N5882 | | 06 |
| B170014 | S | N | SD | | | 2N5882 | | 06 |
| B170015 | S | N | SD | | | 2N5629 | | 06 |
| | | | | | | | | |
| B170016 | S | N | SD | | | 2N5629 | | 06 |
| B170017 | S | N | SD | | | 2N5629 | | 06 |
| B170018 | S | N | SD | | | 2N6569 | | 06 |
| B170019 | S | N | SD | | | 2N6569 | | 06 |
| B170020 | S | N | SD | | | 2N6569 | | 06 |
| | | | | | | | | |
| B170021 | S | N | SD | | | 2N5882 | | 06 |
| B170022 | S | N | SD | | | 2N5882 | | 06 |
| B170023 | S | N | SD | | | 2N5882 | | 06 |
| B170024 | S | N | SD | | | 2N5629 | | 06 |
| B170025 | S | N | SD | | | 2N5629 | | 06 |
| | | | | | | | | |
| B170026 | S | N | SD | | | 2N5629 | | 06 |
| B176000 | S | N | SD | | | FT410 | | |
| B176001 | S | N | SD | | | FT410 | | |
| B176002 | S | N | SD | | | FT410 | | |
| B176003 | S | N | SD | | | FT410 | | |
| | | | | | | | | |
| B176004 | S | N | SD | | | FT413 | | |
| B176005 | S | N | | | | FT413 | | |
| B176006 | S | N | | | | FT423 | | |
| B176007 | S | N | | | | FT423 | | |
| B176024 | S | N | SD | | | FT423 | | |
| | | | | | | | | |
| B176025 | S | N | SD | | | FT423 | | |
| BC100 | S | N | TF | BCY49A | BD115 | | | 01 |
| BC100 | | | | (BF459) | | | | 01 |
| BC107 | S | N | IN,S, TF, V, PH | AM251 | BC147 | MPS6566 | 2N929 | 01 |
| BC107 | | | | BC167 | BC182 | | | 01 |
| | | | | | | | | |
| BC107 | | | | BC207 | BC317 | | | 01 |
| BC107 | | | | BC407 | BC547 | | | 01 |
| BC107A | S | N | IN, S, TF, V, PH | BC107 | BC147A | 2N929 | 2N2921 | 2SC458 | 01 |
| BC107A | | | | BC182A | BC407A | 2N3568 | | 01 |
| BC107A | | | | BC547A | | | | 01 |
| | | | | | | | | |
| BC107B | S | N | IN, S, TF, V, PH | BC107 | BC147B | 2N929 | | 01 |
| BC107B | | | | BC407B | BC547B | | | 01 |
| BC108 | S | N | IN, S, TF, V, PH | AM252 | BC107 | MPS6520 | 2N929 | 01 |
| BC108 | | | | BC148 | BC168 | | | 01 |
| BC108 | | | | BC183 | BC208 | | | 01 |
| | | | | | | | | |
| BC108 | | | | BC318 | BC408 | | | 01 |
| BC108 | | | | BC548 | | | | 01 |
| BC108A | S | N | IN, S, TF, V, PH | BC107 | BC148A | 2N929 | 2N3391 | 2SC458 | 01 |
| BC108A | | | | BC183A | BC408A | | | 01 |
| BC108A | | | | BC548A | BSY76 | | | 01 |
| | | | | | | | | |
| BC108B | S | N | IN, S, TF, V, PH | BC107 | BC148B | 2N929 | | 01 |
| BC108B | | | | BC183B | BC408B | | | 01 |
| BC108B | | | | BC548B | BSY80 | | | 01 |
| BC108C | S | N | IN, S, TF, V, PH | BC107 | BC148C | 2N929 | | 01 |
| BC108C | | | | BC408C | BC548C | | | 01 |
| | | | | | | | | |
| BC109 | S | N | IN, S, TF, V, PH | AM253 | BC149 | MPS6521 | 2N930 | 01 |
| BC109 | | | | BC169 | BC184 | | | 01 |
| BC109 | | | | BC209 | BC319 | | | 01 |
| BC109 | | | | BC409 | BC549 | | | 01 |
| BC109B | S | N | IN, S, TF, V, PH | BC109 | BC149B | MPS6521 | 2N930 | 2SC458 | 01 |
| | | | | | | | | |
| BC109B | | | | BC184B | BC409B | | | 01 |
| BC109B | | | | BC549B | | | | 01 |
| BC109C | S | N | IN, S, TF, V, PH | BC109 | BC149C | 2N930 | | 01 |
| BC109C | | | | BC184C | BC409C | | | 01 |
| BC109C | | | | BC549C | | | | 01 |
| | | | | | | | | |
| BC110 | S | N | S, TF | BC107 | BC174 | A157 | 2N3701 | 2SC856 | 01 |
| BC110 | | | | BF177 | BSW32 | | | 01 |
| BC111 | S | N | RA | BC182 | BC146 | | | 01 |
| BC112 | S | N | V | BC122 | BC146 | | | 01 |
| BC112 | | | | BC246 | BCW83 | | | 01 |

| TYPE | M/S | POL | MANUFAC | EUROPEAN | | | AMERICAN | | JAPANESE | USE |
|------|-----|-----|---------|----------|---|---|----------|---|----------|-----|
| BC112gn | S | N | V | (BC122bl) | | | | | | 01 |
| BC112r | S | N | V | (BC122ye) | | | | | | 01 |
| BC112ye | S | N | V | (BC122gn) | | | | | | 01 |
| BC113 | S | N | SG, ME, NS, AT, F | BC172B | BC183 | MPS6520 | 2N3568 | | 2SC458 | 01 |
| BC113 | | | | BC209 | BC237B | 2N4967 | | | | 01 |
| | | | | | | | | | | |
| BC113 | | | | BC238 | | | | | | 01 |
| BC113A | S | N | SG, AT | BC237B | | | | | | 01 |
| BC114 | S | N | SG, ME, NS, AT, F | BC173 | BC183 | MPS6521 | 2N3568 | | | 01 |
| BC114 | | | | BC184 | BC184B | 2N4967 | | | | 01 |
| BC114 | | | | BC209 | BC238B | | | | | 01 |
| | | | | | | | | | | |
| BC114 | | | | BC239 | BC239B | | | | | 01 |
| BC114 | | | | BC413C | | | | | | 01 |
| BC114A | S | N | SG, AT | BC414B | | | | | | 01 |
| BC115 | S | N | SG, F | BC107 | BC182 | MPS6566 | 2N3568 | 2SC984 | | 01 |
| BC115 | | | | BC183 | BC237 | 2N5825 | | | | 01 |
| | | | | | | | | | | |
| BC115 | | | | BC237A | | | | | | 01 |
| BC116 | S | P | SG, NS, ME, AT | BC177 | BC261 | MPS6534 | 2N2904 | 2SA565 | | 01 |
| BC116 | | | | BC212 | BC307VI | 2N5041 | 2N6015 | | | 01 |
| BC116 | | | | BC307 | | | | | | 01 |
| BC116A | S | P | SG, ME, AT | BC177 | BC212 | 2N2904 | 2N4036 | | | 01 |
| | | | | | | | | | | |
| BC116A | | | | BC261 | BFR23 | 2N5041 | | | | 01 |
| BC117 | S | N | SG, ME, AT | BC141 | BC145 | 2N1990 | 2N5831 | | | 01 |
| BC117 | | | | BF178 | (BF457) | | | | | 01 |
| BC118 | S | N | SG | BC129 | BC171 | 2N3568 | 2N4401 | | | 01 |
| BC118 | | | | BC182 | BC237 | 2N5825 | | | | 01 |
| | | | | | | | | | | |
| BC118 | | | | BC237A | | | | | | 01 |
| BC119 | S | N | SG, TX, AT, F | BC140 | BC140-6 | SX3704(SP) | 2N697 | | | 01 |
| BC119 | | | | BFY51 | | 2N2218 | 2N2297 | | | 01 |
| BC120 | S | N | SG, TX, AT | BC108 | BC140 | SX3704(SP) | 2N697 | | | 01 |
| BC120 | | | | BC140-6 | BC286 | 2N2218 | 2N3036 | | | 01 |
| | | | | | | | | | | |
| BC120 | | | | BFY51 | | 2N3665 | | | | 01 |
| BC121 | S | N | S | BC146 | BC183 | | | | | 01 |
| BC121bl | S | N | S | BC146bl | BC146G | | | | | 01 |
| BC121gn | S | N | S | BC146C | BC146ye | | | | | 01 |
| BC121w | S | N | S | BC146 | BC146r | | | | 2SC458 | 01 |
| | | | | | | | | | | |
| BC121ye | S | N | S | BC107A | BC146ye | | | | | 01 |
| BC122 | S | N | S | BC146 | BC183 | | | | | 01 |
| BC122bl | S | N | S | BC146G | | | | | | 01 |
| BC122gn | S | N | S | BC146G | | | | | | 01 |
| BC122ye | S | N | S | BC107A | BC146ye | | | | | 01 |
| | | | | | | | | | | |
| BC123 | S | N | S | BC146 | BC183 | | | | | 01 |
| BC123w | S | N | S | | | | | | 2SC458 | 01 |
| BC123ye | S | N | S | BC107A | | | | | | 01 |
| BC125 | S | N | SG, ME, AT, F | BC107 | BC107A | MPS6566 | 2N2297 | | | 01, 10 |
| BC125 | | | | BC140-6 | BC182 | | | | | 01, 10 |
| | | | | | | | | | | |
| BC125 | | | | BC337 | BFY50 | | | | | 01, 10 |
| BC125A | S | N | SG, NS | BC140-6 | | | | | | 01, 10 |
| BC125B | S | N | SG, NS, AT | BC140-6 | BFY50 | 2N2297 | | | | 01, 10 |
| BC126 | S | P | SG, ME, NS, AT, F | BC160-6 | BC261 | 2N3638A | 2N4402 | | | 01 |
| BC126 | | | | BC307 | | 2N5041 | | | | 01 |
| | | | | | | | | | | |
| BC126A | S | P | SG, NS | BC160-10 | | | | | | 01 |
| BC127 | S | N | AT | BC146r | BC146 | | | | | 01 |
| BC127 | | | | BC184 | | | | | | 01 |
| BC128 | S | N | AT | BC146 | | | | | | 01 |
| BC129 | S | N | TF | BC107 | BC182 | A157 | MPS6566 | | | 01, 02 |
| | | | | | | | | | | |
| BC129 | | | | BC207 | BC237 | | | | | 01, 02 |
| BC129 | | | | BC317 | | | | | | 01, 02 |
| BC129A | S | N | TF | BC107A | BC182A | MPS6566 | 2N3568 | 2SC281 | | 01, 02 |
| BC129A | | | | BC237A | | | | | | 01, 02 |
| BC129B | S | N | TF | BC107B | BC182B | MPS6566 | | | | 01, 02 |
| | | | | | | | | | | |
| BC129B | | | | BC237B | | | | | | 01, 02 |
| BC130 | S | N | TF | BC108 | BC183 | A157 | MPS6520 | | | 01, 02 |
| BC130 | | | | BC238 | BC107 | | | | | 01, 02 |
| BC130 | | | | BC208 | BC318 | | | | | 01, 02 |
| BC130A | S | N | TF | BC108A | BC183A | | | | 2SC281 | 01, 02 |
| | | | | | | | | | | |
| BC130A | | | | BC238B | | | | | | 01, 02 |
| BC130B | S | N | TF | BC108B | BC183B | | | | | 01 |
| BC130B | | | | BC238 | | | | | | 01 |
| BC130C | S | N | TF | BC238C | | | | | | 01, 02 |
| BC131 | S | N | TF | BC108B | BC109 | MPS6521 | SX3710 | | | 01, 02 |
| | | | | | | | | | | |
| BC131 | | | | BC184 | BC209 | 2N930 | | | | 01, 02 |
| BC131 | | | | BC239 | BC319 | | | | | 01, 02 |
| BC131B | S | N | TF | BC109B | BC184B | | | | | 01, 02 |
| BC131B | | | | BC239B | | | | | | 01, 02 |
| BC131C | S | N | TF | BC109C | BC184C | | | | | 01, 02 |

| TYPE | M/S | POL | MANUFAC | EUROPEAN | | AMERICAN | | JAPANESE | USE |
|---|---|---|---|---|---|---|---|---|---|
| BC131C | | | | BC239C | | | | | 01, 02 |
| BC132 | S | N | SG, NS, ME, AT | BC108B | BC183B | 2N966 | 2N3565 | | 01 |
| BC132 | | | | BC238A | BC237A | | | | 01 |
| BC132 | | | | BC207 | | | | | 01 |
| BC132A | S | N | SG, AT | BC237B | | | | | 01 |
| | | | | | | | | | |
| BC134 | S | N | SG, AT | BC107B | BC207 | 2N4966 | | | 01 |
| BC134 | | | | BC237B | RC184(SP) | | | | 01 |
| BC135 | S | N | SG, AT | BC107 | BC107A | MPS6566 | 2N3568 | | 01 |
| BC135 | | | | BC118 | BC182 | 2N4966 | | | 01 |
| BC135 | | | | BC182B | BC237A | | | | 01 |
| | | | | | | | | | |
| BC135A | S | N | SG, AT | BC237A | | | | | 01 |
| BC136 | S | N | SG, AT | BC125 | BC171 | MPS6566 | SX3705(SP) | | 01 |
| BC136 | | | | BC140-6 | BC182 | | | | 01 |
| BC136 | | | | BC237 | BC237A | | | | 01 |
| BC136 | | | | BC140 | | | | | 01 |
| | | | | | | | | | |
| BC137 | S | P | SG, ME, NS, AT | BC116 | BC160 | MM3726 | 2N1132 | | 01 |
| BC137 | | | | BC160-10 | BC327 | 2N5448 | | | 01 |
| BC138 | S | N | SG, AT | BC140-6 | | 2N2219 | 2N2297 | | 01 |
| BC138 | | | | BFY51 | | | | | 01 |
| BC139 | S | P | SG, TX, ME, AT | BC160 | BC160-6 | MM3726 | 2N1132 | | 01 |
| | | | | | | | | | |
| BC139 | | | | BFS95 | | 2N2904 | 2N4036 | | 01 |
| BC139 | | | | | | 2N5855 | 40406 | | 01 |
| BC140 | S | N | TF, TX, SG, S, V, F | BC286 | BC429 | 2N2218A | 2N2297 | 2SC798 | 01, 10 |
| BC140 | S | N | TF, TX, SG, S, V, F | BFY50 | BSY46 | 2N3036 | 2N5321 | | 01, 10 |
| BC140C | S | N | S | BC140-6 | | | | | 01, 10 |
| | | | | | | | | | |
| BC140D | S | N | S | BC140-16 | | | | | 01, 10 |
| BC140/6 | S | N | IN, S, V, TF, F | BFY50 | | 2N2297 | | | 01 |
| BC140/10 | S | N | IN, S, V, TF, F | BFY50 | | 2N2297 | | | 01 |
| BC140/16 | S | N | IN, S, V, TF, F | BFY50 | | 2N2297 | | | 01 |
| BC141 | S | N | F, TF, TX, SG, S, V | BC310 | BC429A | 2N2297 | 2N3036 | | 01 |
| | | | | | | | | | |
| BC141 | | | | BFY50 | | 2N3020 | 2N5320 | | 01 |
| BC141C | S | N | S | BC141-6 | | | | | 01 |
| BC141D | S | N | S | BC141-16 | | | | | 01 |
| BC141/6 | S | N | IN, S, TF, V, F | BFY50 | | 2N2297 | | | 01 |
| BC141/10 | S | N | IN, S, TF, V, F | BFY50 | | 2N2297 | | | 01 |
| | | | | | | | | | |
| BC141/16 | S | N | IN, S, TF, V, F | BFY50 | | 2N2297 | | | 01 |
| BC142 | S | N | SG, TX, ME, AT, F | BC141-6 | BC141 | 2N2219 | 2N2219A | | 01 |
| BC142 | | | | BC286 | BFY50 | 2N3020 | 2N3036 | | 01 |
| BC142 | | | | | | 40360 | | | 01 |
| BC143 | S | P | SG, TX, ME, NS, AT | BC160 | BC161-6 | MM3726 | 2N1132 | | 01 |
| | | | | | | | | | |
| BC143 | | | | BC287 | | 2N4037 | 40595 | | 01 |
| BC144 | S | N | F | BC140-6 | BC140 | 2N2218A | 2N2297 | | 01 |
| BC144 | | | SG, TX, AT | BC286 | BFY50 | 40594 | | | 01 |
| BC144 | | | | BSY44 | | | | | 01 |
| BC145 | S | N | SG, AT | BC117 | BC141 | 2N1990 | | | 01 |
| | | | | | | | | | |
| BC145 | | | | BF117 | BF178 | | | | 01 |
| BC145 | | | | BF297 | (BF457) | | | | 01 |
| BC146 | S | N | MU, PH, V, RA, AM | (BC122) | BCW83 | | | | 01 |
| BC146gn | S | N | MU, PH, V | (BC122bl) | | | | | 01 |
| BC146gr | S | N | MU, PH, V | (BC122ye) | | | | | 01 |
| | | | | | | | | | |
| BC146ye | S | N | MU, PH, V | (BC122gn) | | | | | 01 |
| BC147 | S | N | S, AT, TF, V, PH | BC171 | BC182 | A747 | MPS6566 | | 01 |
| BC147 | | | | BC107 | BC207 | | | | 01 |
| BC147 | | | | BC317 | BC407 | | | | 01 |
| BC147 | | | | BC582 | BC547 | | | | 01 |
| | | | | | | | | | |
| BC147A | S | N | AT, S, TF, V, PH | BC147 | BC171A | A747 | MPS6566 | 2SC281 | 01 |
| BC147A | | | | BC182A | BC107 | | | | 01 |
| BC147A | | | | BC407A | BC547 | | | | 01 |
| BC147B | S | N | AT, S, TF, V, PH | BC147 | BC171B | A747 | | | 01 |
| BC147B | | | | BC107B | BC182B | | | | 01 |
| | | | | | | | | | |
| BC147B | | | | BC407B | BC547B | | | | 01 |
| BC148 | S | N | AT, S, TF, V, PH | BC108 | BC147 | A747 | MPS6520 | | 01 |
| BC148 | | | | BC172 | BC183 | | | | 01 |
| BC148 | | | | BC208 | BC318 | | | | 01 |
| BC148 | | | | BC408 | BC548 | | | | 01 |
| | | | | | | | | | |
| BC148 | | | | BC583 | | | | | 01 |
| BC148A | S | N | AT, S, TF, V, PH | BC108A | BC147 | A747 | MPS6520 | 2SC281 | 01 |
| BC148A | | | | BC183A | BC172A | 2N3568 | | | 01 |
| BC148A | | | | BC408A | BC548A | | | | 01 |
| BC148B | S | N | AT, S, TF, V, PH | BC147 | BC108B | A747 | 2N3568 | | 01 |
| | | | | | | | | | |
| BC148B | | | | BC183B | BC172B | | | | 01 |
| BC148B | | | | BC408B | BC548B | | | | 01 |
| BC148C | S | N | AT, S, TF, V, PH | BC108C | BC172C | A747 | 2N3568 | | 01 |
| BC148C | | | | BC183C | BC408C | | | | 01 |
| BC148C | | | | BC54BC | | | | | 01 |

| TYPE | M/S | POL | MANUFAC | EUROPEAN | | AMERICAN | | JAPANESE | USE |
|---|---|---|---|---|---|---|---|---|---|
| BC149 | S | N | AT, S, TF, V, PH | BC109 | BC173 | A749 | MPS6521 | | 01 |
| BC149 | | | | BC184 | BC209 | | | | 01 |
| BC149 | | | | BC319 | BC409 | | | | 01 |
| BC149 | | | | BC549 | | | | | 01 |
| BC149B | S | N | AT, S, TF, V, PH | BC109B | BC149 | A749 | MPS6521 | 2SC258 | 01 |
| BC149B | | | | BC173B | BC184B | | | | 01 |
| BC149B | | | | BC409B | BC549B | | | | 01 |
| BC149C | S | N | AT, S, TF, V, PH | BC109C | BC149 | A749 | | | 01 |
| BC149C | | | | BC173C | BC409C | | | | 01 |
| BC149C | | | | BC549C | | | | | |
| BC150 | S | N | TH, AE | BC168B | | SX3707(SP) | | | 01 |
| BC151 | S | N | TH, AE | BC167 | | SX3707(SP) | | | 01 |
| BC152 | S | N | TH, AE | (BC167B) | | SX3707(SP) | | | 01 |
| BC153 | S | P | SG, ME, NS, AT, F | BC212 | BC251 | MPS6516 | 2N4966 | | 01 |
| BC153 | | | | BC307A | BC416A | 2N5041 | | | 01 |
| BC154 | S | P | SG, ME, NS, AT, F | BC158 | BC307A | MPS6522 | 2N4967 | | 01 |
| BC154 | | | | BC213 | BC252 | | | | 01 |
| BC154 | | | | BC416B | BC214(SP) | | | | 01 |
| BC155 | S | N | TF | (BC121) | BC183 | | | | 01 |
| BC155A | S | N | TF | (BC121w) | | | | | 01 |
| BC155B | S | N | TF | (BC121gn) | | | | | 01 |
| BC155C | S | N | TF | (BC121bl) | | | | | 01 |
| BC156 | S | N | TF | (BC121) | BC183 | | | | 01 |
| BC156A | S | N | TF | (BC121w) | | | | | 01 |
| BC156B | S | N | TF | BC121gn | | | | | 01 |
| BC156C | S | N | TF | (BC121bl) | | | | | 01 |
| BC157 | S | P | AT, PH, S, V | BC320 | BC212 | MPS6516 | 2N5041 | 2SA565 | 01 |
| BC157 | | | | BC307 | BC251 | | | | 01 |
| BC157 | | | | BC557 | BC204 | | | | 01 |
| BC157 | | | | BC177 | | | | | 01 |
| BC157A | S | P | AT, PH, S, V | BC157 | | | | | 01 |
| BC157B | S | P | AT, PH, S, V | BC157 | | | | | 01 |
| BC157V | S | P | S | BC157A | | | | | 01 |
| BC157VI | S | P | AT, PH, V, S | BC157A | BC157 | | | | 01 |
| BC157/6 | S | P | AT, PH, V, S | BC157A | BC157 | | | | 01 |
| BC158 | S | P | AT, PH, S, V | BC321 | BC178 | MPS6522 | | 2SA565 | 01 |
| BC158 | | | | BC252 | BC157 | | | | 01 |
| BC158 | | | | BC213 | BC308 | | | | 01 |
| BC158 | | | | BC205 | BC558 | | | | 01 |
| BC158A | S | P | AT, PH, S, V | BC178A | BC157 | | | | 01 |
| BC158A | | | | BC308A | BC558 | | | | 01 |
| BC158B | S | P | AT, PH, S, V | BC178B | BC158 | | | | 01 |
| BC158B | | | | BC308B | BC558B | | | | 01 |
| BC158V | S | P | S | BC158A | | | | | 01 |
| BC158VI | S | P | AT, PH, V, S | BC158A | BC157 | | | | 01 |
| BC158/6 | S | P | AT, PH, V, S | BC157 | BC158A | | | | 01 |
| BC159 | S | P | AT, PH, S, V | BC309 | BC214 | MPS6523 | | 2SA565 | 01 |
| BC159 | | | | BC559 | BC206 | | | | 01 |
| BC159 | | | | BC179 | BC322 | | | | 01 |
| BC159A | S | P | AT, PH, V, S | BC179A | BC159 | | | | 01 |
| BC159A | | | | BC309A | BC559A | | | | 01 |
| BC159B | S | P | AT, PH, V, S | BC179B | BC159 | | | | 01 |
| BC159B | | | | BC309B | BC559B | | | | 01 |
| BC160 | S | P | TF, TX, SQ, S, V, F | BC287 | BC143 | 2N2904 | 2N5323 | | 01 |
| BC160 | | | | | | 2N4037 | 2N1132 | | 01 |
| BC160 | | | | | | MM3726 | | | 01 |
| BC160/6 | S | P | IN, S, TF, V, F | BC143 | | 2N4037 | | | 01 |
| BC160/10 | S | P | IN, S, TF, V, F | BC143 | | 2N4037 | | | 01 |
| BC160/16 | S | P | IN, S, TF, V, F | BC143 | | 2N4037 | | | 01 |
| BC161 | S | P | TF, TX, SQ, S, V, F | BC430A | BC311 | 2N5322 | 2N4037 | | 01 |
| BC161 | | | | | | 2N2904 | | | 01 |
| BC161/6 | S | P | IN | BC143 | | 2N4037 | | | 01 |
| BC161/10 | S | P | IN, S, TF, V, F | BC143 | | 2N4037 | | | 01 |
| BC161/16 | S | P | IN, S, TF, V, F | BC143 | | 2N4037 | | | 01 |
| BC167 | S | N | S, TF | BC317 | BC171 | MPS6566 | 2N3710 | 2SC458 | 01 |
| BC167 | | | | BC237 | BC182 | | | | 01 |
| BC167 | | | | BC182L | BC207 | | | | 01 |
| BC167A | S | N | S, TF | BC182L | | 2N3710 | | | 01 |
| BC167B | S | N | S, TF | BC171B | BC182B | MPS6566 | 2N3710 | | 01 |
| BC167B | | | | BC182L | | | | | 01 |
| BC168 | S | N | S, TF | BC318 | BC172 | MPS6520 | 2N3710 | | 01 |
| BC168 | | | | BC238 | BC183 | | | | 01 |
| BC168 | | | | BC182L | BC208 | | | | 01 |
| BC168A | S | N | S, TF | BC172A | BC183A | MPS6520 | 2N3710 | 2SC458 | 01 |
| BC168A | | | | BC182L | | | | | 01 |

| TYPE | M/S | POL | MANUFAC | EUROPEAN | | AMERICAN | | JAPANESE | USE |
|------|-----|-----|---------|----------|--|----------|--|----------|-----|
| BC168B | S | N | S, TF | BC172B | BC183B | 2N3710 | | | 01 |
| BC168B | | | | BC182L | | | | | 01 |
| BC168C | S | N | S, TF | BC172C | BC183C | 2N3707 | | | 01 |
| BC168C | | | | BC184L | | | | | 01 |
| BC169 | S | N | S, TF | BC319 | BC173 | MPS6521 | 2N3707 | | 01 |
| BC169 | | | | BC239 | BC184 | | | | 01 |
| BC169 | | | | BC184L | BC209 | | | | 01 |
| BC169B | S | N | S, TF | BC173B | BC184B | MPS6521 | 2N3707 | | 01 |
| BC169B | | | | BC184L | | | | | 01 |
| BC169C | S | N | S, TF | BC173C | BC184C | 2N3707 | | | 01 |
| BC169C | | | | BC184L | | | | | 01 |
| BC170 | S | N | IN, NS | BC583 | BC169 | 2N5825 | | | 01 |
| BC170 | | | | BC237 | BC208 | | | | 01 |
| BC170 | | | | BC318 | | | | | 01 |
| BC170A | S | N | IN, ME, NS | BC168 | BC238A | 2N5825 | | 2SC458 | 01 |
| BC170A | | | | BC172 | BC148 | | | | 01 |
| BC170A | | | | BC208 | BC237 | | | | 01 |
| BC170B | S | N | IN, ME, NS | BC168 | BC237 | 2N5825 | | | 01 |
| BC170B | | | | BC238B | BC172 | | | | 01 |
| BC170B | | | | BC238A | BC183 | | | | 01 |
| BC170B | | | | BC148 | BC209 | | | | 01 |
| BC170C | S | N | IN, ME, NS | BC238C | BC237 | 2N5825 | | | 01 |
| BC171 | S | N | IN, IT, NS | BC207 | BC238 | MPS6566 | 2N2921 | 2SC458 | 01 |
| BC171 | | | | BC317 | BC182 | 2N5827 | | | 01 |
| BC171 | | | | BC582 | BC237 | | | | 01 |
| BC171A | S | N | IN, NS | BC237A | BC239 | 2N5827 | | | 01 |
| BC171B | S | N | IN, NS | BC237B | BC239 | 2N5827 | | | 01 |
| BC172 | S | N | IN, IT | BC208 | BC237 | MPS6522 | 2N5825 | 2SC458 | 01 |
| BC172 | | | | BC183 | BC238 | | | | 01 |
| BC172 | | | | BC318 | BC583 | | | | 01 |
| BC172A | S | N | IN, NS | BC238A | BC237 | 2N5925 | | | 01 |
| BC172B | S | N | IN, NS | BC238B | BC239 | 2N5827 | | | 01 |
| BC172C | S | N | IN, NS | BC238C | BC239 | 2N5827 | | | 01 |
| BC173 | S | N | IN, IT, NS | BC209 | BC238 | MPS6521 | 2N5827 | 2SC458 | 01 |
| BC173 | | | | BC319 | BC184 | | | | 01 |
| BC173B | S | N | IN, NS | BC584 | BC239 | 2N5827 | | | 01 |
| BC173C | S | N | IN, NS | BC239B | BC239 | 2N5827 | | | 01 |
| BC174 | S | N | IN, V | BC139C | BC239 | 2N5825 | | | 01 |
| BC174 | | | | BC182 | BC239E | | | | 01 |
| BC174 | | | | BC182B | BC110 | | | | 01 |
| BC174 | | | | BC237 | BCY65III | | | | 01 |
| BC174A | S | N | IN, V | BCY65EVII | BC237 | 2N5825 | | | 01 |
| BC174B | S | N | IN, V | BCY65EIX | BC237 | 2N5825 | | | 01 |
| BC175 | S | N | TH, AE | (BCY65B) | | 2N3704(SP) | | | 01 |
| BC177 | S | P | AT, S, TF, V, PH | BC320 | BC157 | MPS6517 | 2N3965 | 2SA565 | 01 |
| BC177 | | | | BC261 | BC307 | | | | 01 |
| BC177 | | | | BC212 | BC512 | | | | 01 |
| BC177 | | | | BC557 | BC204 | | | | 01 |
| BC177 | | | | BCY70 | | | | | 01 |
| BC177A | S | P | AT, S, TF, V | BCY71 | | 2N3965 | | | 01 |
| BC177B | S | P | AT, S, TF, V | BCY71 | | 2N3965 | | | 01 |
| BC177V | S | P | SE, Ss, ML, S | BC177A | | | | | 01 |
| BC177VI | S | P | AT, TF, V, Ss, ML | BC177A | BC307 | | | | 01 |
| BC177VI | S | P | NS, S | BC177A | BC307 | | | | 01 |
| BC178 | S | P | AT, S, TF, V, PH | BC321 | BC308 | MPS6518 | 2N3965 | 2SA565 | 01 |
| BC178 | | | | BC213 | BC513 | | | | 01 |
| BC178 | | | | BC558 | BC262 | | | | 01 |
| BC178 | | | | BCY70 | BC205 | | | | 01 |
| BC178 | | | | BC158 | | | | | 01 |
| BC178A | S | P | AT, S, TF, V, PH | BC558A | BCY71 | 2N3965 | | | 01 |
| BC178A | | | | BC158A | BC308A | | | | 01 |
| BC178B | S | P | AT, S, TF, V, PH | BC558B | BCY71 | 2N3965 | | | 01 |
| BC178B | | | | BC158B | BC308B | | | | 01 |
| BC178V | S | P | SE, Ss, ML, S | BC178A | | | | | 01 |
| BC179 | S | P | AT, S, TF, V, PH | BC322 | BC309 | MPS6519 | 2N3965 | | 01 |
| BC179 | | | | BC214 | BC514 | | | | 01 |
| BC179 | | | | BC559 | BC263 | | | | 01 |
| BC179 | | | | BCY70 | BC206 | | | | 01 |
| BC179 | | | | BC159 | | | | | 01 |
| BC179A | S | P | AT, TF, V, S, PH | BC559A | BCY71 | 2N3965 | | | 01 |
| BC179A | | | | BC159A | BC309A | | | | 01 |
| BC179B | S | P | AT, S, TF, V, PH | BC559B | BCY71 | 2N3965 | | | 01 |
| BC179B | | | | BC159B | BC309B | | | | 01 |
| BC179V | S | P | SE | BC179B | | | | | 01 |
| BC179VI | S | P | AT, TF, V | BC179B | | | | | 01 |

| TYPE | M/S | POL | MANUFAC | EUROPEAN | | AMERICAN | JAPANESE | USE |
|------|-----|-----|---------|----------|---|----------|----------|-----|
| BC180 | S | N | TH, AE | (BC167B) | | 2N3704(SP) | | 01 |
| BC180A | S | N | | BC237 | | 2N5825 | | 01 |
| BC181 | S | P | TX | BC157 | BC307A | | | 01 |
| BC181 | | | | BC251 | BC307VI | | | 01 |
| BC181 | | | | BC204 | BC177 | | | 01 |
| BC182 | S | N | S, SE, TF, TX | BC317 | BC171 | MPS6566 | | 01 |
| BC182 | | | | BC174 | BC237 | | | 01 |
| BC182A | | | | BC207 | | | | 01 |
| BC182A | S | N | NS, TX, S, TF | (BC167A) | | | | 01 |
| BC182K | S | N | NS | BC182 | BC237 | 2N5825 | | 01 |
| BC182KA | S | N | NS | BC182A | BC237 | 2N5825 | | 01 |
| BC182KB | S | N | NS | BC182B | BC237 | 2N5825 | | 01 |
| BC182L | S | N | NS, TX | (BC167) | | 2N5209 | | 01 |
| BC182LA | S | N | NS, TX | BC182L | | 2N5209 | | 01 |
| BC182LB | S | N | NS, TX | (BC167B) | BC182L | 2N5209 | | 01 |
| BC183 | S | N | SE, TX, NS | BC238 | BC182 | MPS6520 | | 01 |
| BC183 | | | | BC208 | (BC237) | | | 01 |
| BC183 | | | | BC318 | BC172 | | | 01 |
| BC183 | | | | BC237A | | | | 01 |
| BC183A | S | N | SE, TX, NS, S | BC182A | BC237A | | | 01 |
| BC183B | S | N | SE, TX, NS, S | BC182B | BC237B | | | 01 |
| BC183C | S | N | SE, TX, S, NS | BC182B | BC237B | | | 01 |
| BC183K | S | N | NS | BC182 | BC237 | 2N5825 | | 01 |
| BC183KA | S | N | NS | BC182A | BC237A | 2N5825 | | 01 |
| BC183KA | | | | BC237A | | | | 01 |
| BC183KB | S | N | NS | BC182B | BC237B | 2N5825 | | 01 |
| BC183KB | | | | BC237 | | | | 01 |
| BC183KC | S | N | NS | BC182B | BC237B | 2N5825 | | 01 |
| BC183KC | | | | BC237 | | | | 01 |
| BC183L | S | N | NS, TX | BC167 | BC182L | 2N5209 | | 01 |
| BC183LA | S | N | NS, TX | BC167A | BC182L | 2N5209 | | 01 |
| BC183LB | S | N | NS, TX | BC167B | BC182L | 2N5209 | | 01 |
| BC183LC | S | N | NS, TX | BC167B | BC182L | 2N5209 | | 01 |
| BC184 | S | N | SE, TX, NS | BC239 | BC550 | MPS6521 | | 01 |
| BC184 | | | | BC209 | BC413 | | | 01 |
| BC184 | | | | BC319 | BC173 | | | 01 |
| BC184 | | | | BC237 | | | | 01 |
| BC184B | S | N | SE, TX, NS | BC550B | BC413B | | | 01 |
| BC184C | S | N | SE, TX, NS | BC550C | BC413C | | | 01 |
| BC184K | S | N | NS | BC550 | BC413 | 2N5827 | | 01 |
| BC184K | | | | BC239 | | | | 01 |
| BC184KB | S | N | NS | BC550B | BC413B | 2N5827 | | 01 |
| BC184KB | | | | BC239 | | | | 01 |
| BC184KC | S | N | NS | BC550C | BC413C | 2N5827 | | 01 |
| BC184KC | | | | BC239 | | | | 01 |
| BC184L | S | N | NS, TX | (BC169) | | 2N5210 | | 01 |
| BC184LB | S | N | NS, TX | (BC169B) | BC184L | 2N5210 | | 01 |
| BC184LC | S | N | NS, TX | (BC169C) | BC184L | 2N5210 | | 01 |
| BC185 | S | N | AT, SG | BC140-6 | BC140 | 2N2219 | 2N2219A | 01 |
| BC185 | | | | BSW54 | | | | 01 |
| BC186 | S | P | MU, MN, V | BC178 | BC261 | 2N3965 | | 01 |
| BC186 | | | | BC307A | BC281 | | | 01 |
| BC186 | | | | BC177VI | | | | 01 |
| BC187 | S | P | MU, V | BC179 | BC308B | 2N3965 | | 01 |
| BC187 | | | | BC261 | BC177VI | | | 01 |
| BC187 | | | | BC181 | BC178A | | | 01 |
| BC187 | | | | BCY71 | | | | 01 |
| BC190 | S | N | IN | BCY65E | | | | 01 |
| BC190A | S | N | IN | BCY65EVII | BC107 | 2N929 | | 01 |
| BC190B | S | N | IN | BCY65EIX | BC109 | 2N930 | | 01 |
| BC192 | S | P | IN | BC328-16 | BSW24 | 2N2907 | SX3702 | 01 |
| BC194 | S | N | TF | (BC337-16) | | 2N5457 | | 01 |
| BC196 | S | P | TF | (BC258) | | | | 01 |
| BC196A | S | P | TF | (BC258A) | | | | 01 |
| BC196B | S | P | TF | (BC258B) | | | | 01 |
| BC196VI | S | P | TF | (BC258A) | | | | 01 |
| BC197 | S | N | TF | BC237B | (BC167) | | | 01 |
| BC197 | | | | BC207 | BC317 | | | 01 |
| BC197A | S | N | TF | BC107 | (BC167A) | | | 01 |
| BC197A | | | | BC171 | BC182 | | | 01 |
| BC197A | | | | BC147 | BC207 | | | 01 |
| BC197A | | | | BC123ve | | | | 01 |
| BC197B | S | N | TF | (BC167B) | | | | 01 |
| BC198 | S | N | TF | BC146ve | (BC168) | | | 01 |
| BC198 | | | | BC208 | BC318 | | | 01 |

| TYPE | M/S | POL | MANUFAC | EUROPEAN | | | AMERICAN | | | JAPANESE | USE |
|------|-----|-----|---------|----------|--|--|----------|--|--|----------|-----|
| BC198A | S | N | TF | BC(168A) | | | | | | | 01 |
| BC198B | S | N | TF | (BC168B) | | | | | | | 01 |
| BC198C | S | N | TF | (BC168C) | | | | | | | 01 |
| BC199 | S | N | TF | (BC169) | BC146C | | | | | | 01 |
| BC199B | S | N | TF | BC122gn | (BC169B) | | | | | | 01 |
| BC199B | | | | BC149 | BC209 | | | | | | 01 |
| BC199B | | | | BC109 | BC319 | | | | | | 01 |
| BC199B | | | | BC173 | | | | | | | 01 |
| BC199C | S | N | TF | (BC169C) | | | | | | | 01 |
| BC200 | S | P | MU, PH, V, AM, RA | (BC202) | BC206 | | | | | | 01 |
| BC200 | | | | BC322 | | | | | | | 01 |
| BC200gn | S | P | MU, PH, V | (BC202gn) | | | | | | | 01 |
| BC200r | S | P | MU, PH, V | (BC220r) | | | | | | | 01 |
| BC200ye | S | P | MU, PH, V | (BC202w) | | | | | | | 01 |
| BC201 | S | P | S | BC200 | BCW63 | | | | | 2SA565 | 01 |
| BC201gn | S | P | S | | | | | | | | 01 |
| BC201r | S | P | S | BC201w | | | | | | | 01 |
| BC202 | S | P | S | BC200ye | BCW63 | | | | | 2SA565 | 01 |
| BC202r | S | P | S | BC202gn | | | | | | | 01 |
| BC203 | S | P | S | BCW63 | BC200ye | | | | | | 01 |
| BC203gn | S | P | S | | | | | | | | 01 |
| BC203r | S | P | S | BC203w | | | | | | | 01 |
| BC204 | S | P | SE, AT, F | BC307 | BC307A | MPS6517 | 2N4248 | | | | 01 |
| BC204 | | | | BC177 | BC212 | | | | | | 01 |
| BC204 | | | | BC251 | | | | | | | 01 |
| BC204A | S | P | SE, Ss, ME, ML- | BC307 | BC307A | 2N6015 | | | | | 01 |
| BC204A | S | P | SG, AT, F | BC307 | BC307A | 2N6015 | | | | | 01 |
| BC204B | S | P | SE, Ss, ME, ML- | BC307B | BC309 | 2N6003 | | | | | 01 |
| BC204B | S | P | SG, AT, F | BC307B | BC309 | 2N6003 | | | | | 01 |
| BC204V | S | P | SE, Ss, ME, ML | BC307A | | | | | | | 01 |
| BC204VI | S | P | SE, Ss, ME, ML- | BC307A | | | | | | | 01 |
| BC204VI | S | P | SG, AT, F | BC307A | | | | | | | 01 |
| BC205 | S | P | SE, AT, F | BC178 | BC213 | MPS6518 | 2N4248 | | | | 01 |
| BC205 | | | | BC204 | BC252 | | | | | | 01 |
| BC205 | | | | BC308 | | | | | | | 01 |
| BC205A | S | P | SE, AT, F | BC308A | BC309 | 2N6003 | | | | | 01 |
| BC205B | S | P | SE, Ss, ME, ML- | BC308B | BC309 | 2N6003 | | | | | 01 |
| BC205B | S | P | SG, AT, F | BC308B | BC309 | 2N6003 | | | | | 01 |
| BC205V | S | P | SE | BC308A | | | | | | | 01 |
| BC205VI | S | P | SE, Ss, ME, ML | BC308A | | | | | | | 01 |
| BC206 | S | P | | BC179 | BC213 | MPS6519 | 2N4250 | | | | 01 |
| BC206 | | | | BC214 | BC253 | | | | | | 01 |
| BC206 | | | | BC309 | | | | | | | 01 |
| BC206A | S | P | SE, SG | BC309A | BC309 | 2N6003 | | | | | 01 |
| BC206B | S | P | AT, F, SG | BC309B | BC309 | 2N6003 | | | | | 01 |
| BC206B | S | P | SE, Ss, ME, ML | BC309B | BC309 | 2N6003 | | | | | 01 |
| BC206V | S | P | SE | BC309A | | | | | | | 01 |
| BC206VI | S | P | SE | BC309A | | | | | | | 01 |
| BC207 | S | N | SE, SG, AT, F | BC182 | BC237 | 2N4966 | | | | | 01 |
| BC207 | | | | BC171 | BC147 | | | | | | 01 |
| BC207A | | | | BC107 | | | | | | | 01 |
| BC207A | S | N | SE, Ss, ME, ML- | BC237A | | | | | | | 01 |
| BC207A | S | N | SG, AT, F | BC237A | | | | | | | 01 |
| BC207B | S | N | SE, Ss, ME, ML | BC237B | | | | | | | 01 |
| BC207B | S | N | SG, AT, F | BC237B | | | | | | | 01 |
| BC207C | S | N | SE | BC237B | | | | | | | 01 |
| BC208 | S | N | SE, SG, AT, F | BC183 | BC238 | | | | | | 01 |
| BC208 | | | | BC148 | BC172 | | | | | | 01 |
| BC208 | | | | BC108 | | | | | | | 01 |
| BC208A | S | N | SE, Ss, ME, ML- | BC238A | BC207 | 2N4966 | | | | | 01 |
| BC208A | S | N | SG, AT, F | BC238A | BC207 | 2N4966 | | | | | 01 |
| BC208B | S | N | SE, Ss, ME, ML- | BC238B | BC239 | 2N5827 | | | | | 01 |
| BC208B | S | N | SG, AT, F | BC238B | BC239 | 2N5827 | | | | | 01 |
| BC208C | S | N | SE, Ss, ME, ML- | BC238C | BC239 | 2N5827 | | | | | 01 |
| BC208C | S | N | SG, AT, F | BC238C | BC239 | 2N5827 | | | | | 01 |
| BC209 | S | N | SE, SG, AT, F | BC184 | BC239 | 2N4966 | | | | | 01 |
| BC209 | | | | BC173 | BC149 | | | | | | 01 |
| BC209 | | | | BC207 | BC109 | | | | | | 01 |
| BC209A | S | N | SE | BC239B | | | | | | | 01 |
| BC209B | S | N | SE, Ss, ME, ML- | BC239B | BC239 | 2N5827 | | | | | 01 |
| BC209B | S | N | SG, AT, F | BC239B | BC239 | 2N5827 | | | | | 01 |
| BC209C | S | N | SE, Ss, ME, ML- | BC239C | BC239 | 2N5827 | | | | | 01 |
| BC209C | S | N | SG, AT, F | BC239C | BC239 | 2N5827 | | | | | 01 |
| BC210 | S | N | SE | BC337-16 | BSX33 | 2N731 | | | | | 01 |
| BC211 | S | N | SE | BC140 | BFY51 | 2N2219A | 2N3020 | | | | 01 |

| TYPE | M/S | POL | MANUFAC | EUROPEAN | | AMERICAN | | JAPANESE | USE |
|---|---|---|---|---|---|---|---|---|---|
| BC211 | | | | | | 2N2218A | 2N3036 | | 01 |
| BC211A | S | N | SE | BC140-6 | | 2N2297 | | | 01 |
| BC211A | | | | BFY50 | | | | | 01 |
| BC211A-6 | S | N | SE | BC141-6 | | | | | 01 |
| BC211A-10 | S | N | SE | BC141-10 | | | | | 01 |
| | | | | | | | | | |
| BC211A-16 | S | N | SE | BC141-16 | | | | | 01 |
| BC211B | S | N | SE | BC140-6 | | | | | 01 |
| BC211C | S | N | SE | BC140-10 | | | | | 01 |
| BC211D | S | N | SE | BC140-16 | | | | | 01 |
| BC211E | S | N | SE | BC140-16 | | | | | 01 |
| | | | | | | | | | |
| BC211-6 | S | N | SE | BC140-6 | | | | | 01 |
| BC211-10 | S | N | SE | BC140-10 | | | | | 01 |
| BC211-16 | S | N | SE | BC140-16 | | | | | 01 |
| BC212 | S | P | S, TF, TX | BC157 | BC177 | 2N6015 | | | 01 |
| BC212 | | | | BC204 | BC320 | | | | 01 |
| | | | | | | | | | |
| BC212 | | | | BC251 | BC307 | | | | 01 |
| BC212A | S | P | S, TF, TX | BC307 | | 2N6015 | | | 01 |
| BC212B | S | P | S, TF, TX | BC307 | | 2N6015 | | | 01 |
| BC212K | S | P | NS, TX | BC212 | BC307 | 2N6015 | | | 01 |
| BC212KA | S | P | NS, TX | BC212A | BC307 | 2N6015 | | | 01 |
| | | | | | | | | | |
| BC212KB | S | P | NS, TX | BC212B | BC307 | 2N7015 | | | 01 |
| BC212L | S | P | NS, TX | (BC257) | | 2N5086 | | | 01 |
| BC212LA | S | P | NS, TX | (BC257A) | BC212L | 2N5086 | | | 01 |
| BC212LB | S | P | NS, TX | (BC257B) | BC212L | 2N5086 | | | 01 |
| BC212VI | S | P | S | BC212A | | | | | 01 |
| | | | | | | | | | |
| BC213 | S | P | TX, NS | BC204 | BC307 | | | | 01 |
| BC213 | | | | BC157 | BC177 | | | | 01 |
| BC213A | S | P | TX, NS | BC307A | | | | | 01 |
| BC213B | S | P | TX, NS | BC307B | | | | | 01 |
| BC213C | S | P | TX, NS | BC307B | | | | | 01 |
| | | | | | | | | | |
| BC213K | S | P | NS, TX | BC307 | BC309 | 2N6003 | | | 01 |
| BC213KA | S | P | NS, TX | BC307A | BC309 | 2N6003 | | | 01 |
| BC213KB | S | P | NS, TX | BC307B | BC309 | 2N6003 | | | 01 |
| BC213KC | S | P | NS, TX | BC307B | BC309 | 2N6003 | | | 01 |
| BC213L | S | P | NS, TX | BC257 | BC212L | 2N5086 | | | 01 |
| | | | | | | | | | |
| BC213LA | S | P | NS, TX | BC257A | BC213L | 2N5086 | | | 01 |
| BC213LB | S | P | NS, TX | BC257B | BC212L | 2N5086 | | | 01 |
| BC213LC | S | P | NS, TX | BC257B | BC212L | 2N5086 | | | 01 |
| BC214 | S | P | TX, NS | BC322 | BC253 | | | | 01 |
| BC214 | | | | BC307A | BC560 | | | | 01 |
| | | | | | | | | | |
| BC214 | | | | BC206 | BC179 | | | | 01 |
| BC214A | S | P | TX, NS | BC560A | BC415A | | | | 01 |
| BC214B | S | P | TX, NS | BC560B | BC415B | | | | 01 |
| BC214C | S | P | TX, NS | BC560C | BC415C | | | | 01 |
| BC214K | S | P | NS, TX | BC560 | BC415 | 2N6003 | | | 01 |
| | | | | | | | | | |
| BC214K | | | | BC309 | | | | | 01 |
| BC214KA | S | P | NS, TX | BC560A | BC415A | | | | 01 |
| BC214KB | S | P | NS, TX | BC560B | BC415B | 2N6003 | | | 01 |
| BC214KB | | | | BC309 | | | | | 01 |
| BC214KC | S | P | NS, TX | BC560C | BC415C | 2N6003 | | | 01 |
| | | | | | | | | | |
| BC214KC | | | | BC309 | | | | | 01 |
| BC214L | S | P | NS, TX | (BC259) | | 2N5087 | | | 01 |
| BC214LA | S | P | NS, TX | (BC259B) | | 2N5087 | | | 01 |
| BC214LB | S | P | NS, TX | (BC259B) | BC214L | 2N5087 | | | 01 |
| BC214LC | S | P | NS, TX | (BC259C) | BC239 | 2N5827 | | | 01 |
| | | | | | | | | | |
| BC215 | S | P | SE | BC231 | BC327 | 2N2907A | | | 01 |
| BC215 | | | | BC261 | BSW24 | | | | 01 |
| BC215 | | | | BC157 | | | | | 01 |
| BC215A | S | P | SE | BC327-16 | | | | | 01 |
| BC215B | S | P | SE | BC327-16 | | | | | 01 |
| | | | | | | | | | |
| BC216 | S | N | IS, AT | BC182 | | | | | 01 |
| BC217 | S | N | | BC183 | | | | | 01 |
| BC218 | S | N | IS, RZ | BC237A | | | | | 01 |
| BC218A | S | N | IS, RZ | BC237A | | | | | 01 |
| BC219 | S | N | IS, RZ | BC140-6 | | | | | 01 |
| | | | | | | | | | |
| BC220 | S | N | AT,SG | BC207 | BC183 | 2N4966 | | | 01 |
| BC220 | | | | BC237A | BC183B | | | | 01 |
| BC221 | S | P | AT, SG | BC327-16 | BC328 | 2N3638A | 2N5447 | | 01 |
| BC221 | | | | BFS95 | | 2N4036 | | | 01 |
| BC222 | S | N | AT, SG | BFY50 | BC337-16 | 2N5449 | 2N2297 | | 01 |
| | | | | | | | | | |
| BC222 | | | | BC125 | BC338 | | | | 01 |
| BC223 | S | N | TX | BC207 | BC107 | 2N3704 | 2N5449 | | 01 |
| BC223 | | | | BC337 | BC130 | 2N5825 | | | 01 |
| BC223 | | | | BC237 | BC147 | | | | 01 |
| BC223A | S | N | TX | BC337-16 | BC237 | 2N5825 | | | 01 |

| TYPE | M/S | POL | MANUFAC | EUROPEAN | | AMERICAN | | JAPANESE | USE |
|---|---|---|---|---|---|---|---|---|---|
| BC223B | S | N | TX | BC337-25 | BC239 | 2N5827 | | | 01 |
| BC224 | S | P | TX | BC158 | BC257B | 2N5087 | | | 01 |
| BC224 | | | | BC213 | BC308B | | | | 01 |
| BC224 | | | | BC205 | BC258B | | | | 01 |
| BC22b | S | P | AT, SG | BC204 | BC416A | 2N4249 | | | 01 |
| | | | | | | | | | |
| BC225 | | | | BC307A | BC212 | | | | 01 |
| BC226 | S | N | SG, AT | BC140-16 | BFY51 | 2N2297 | | | 01 |
| BC226A | S | N | IS, RZ | | | | | | 01 |
| BC231 | S | P | TX | BC179 | (BC257) | FP6535 | | | 01 |
| BC231 | | | | BC161 | BC327 | | | | 01 |
| | | | | | | | | | |
| BC231 | | | | BC137 | BC257A | | | | 01 |
| BC231A | S | P | TX | (BC257A) | BC212L | 2N5086 | | | 01 |
| BC231B | S | P | TX | (BC257B) | BC214L | 2N5087 | | | 01 |
| BC231M | S | P | TX | (BC160-16) | | | | | 01 |
| BC231bl | S | P | TX | (BC257A) | | | | | 01 |
| | | | | | | | | | |
| BC231gn | S | P | TX | (BC257B) | | | | | 01 |
| BC231gn | S | P | TX | (BC257B) | | | | | 01 |
| BC231v | S | P | TX | (BC257B) | | | | | 01 |
| BC231ye | S | P | TX | (BC257A) | | | | | 01 |
| BC232 | S | N | TX | BC147 | (BC167) | | | | 01 |
| | | | | | | | | | |
| BC232 | | | | BC207 | BC107 | | | | 01 |
| BC232 | | | | BC167A | BC130 | | | | 01 |
| BC232A | S | N | TX | (BC167A) | BC337 | FPS6532 | 2N5209 | | 01 |
| BC232A | | | | BC182L | | | | | 01 |
| BC232B | S | N | TX | (BC167B) | BC184L | 2N5210 | | | 01 |
| | | | | | | | | | |
| BC232M | S | N | TX | (BC140-16) | | | | | 01 |
| BC232bl | S | N | TX | (BC167B) | | | | | 01 |
| BC232gn | S | N | TX | (BC167A) | | | | | 01 |
| BC232gn | S | N | TX | (BC167B) | | | | | 01 |
| BC232v | S | N | TX | (BC167B) | | | | | 01 |
| | | | | | | | | | |
| BC232ye | S | N | TX | (BC167A) | | | | | 01 |
| BC234 | S | N | IS, RZ | BC237A | | | | | 01 |
| BC234A | S | N | IS, RZ | BC237A | | | | | 01 |
| BC235 | S | N | IS, RZ | BC237B | | | | | 01 |
| BC235A | S | N | IS, RZ | BC237B | | | | | 01 |
| | | | | | | | | | |
| BC236 | S | N | SE | (BF457) | BC394 | | | | 01 |
| BC237 | S | N | PH, S, TF, V | BC182 | BC171 | MPS6566 | 2N5448 | | 01 |
| BC237 | | | | BC207 | BC317 | 2N5825 | | | 01 |
| BC237A | S | N | PH, S, TF, V | BC237 | | 2N5825 | | | 01 |
| BC237B | S | N | PH, S, TF, V | BC237 | | 2N5825 | | | 01 |
| | | | | | | | | | |
| BC238 | S | N | PH, S, TF, V | BC318 | BC172 | MPS6520 | 2N5447 | | 01 |
| BC238 | | | | BC237 | BC183 | 2N5825 | | | 01 |
| BC238 | | | | BC208 | | | | | 01 |
| BC238A | S | N | PH, S, TF, V | BC237 | | 2N5825 | | | 01 |
| BC238B | S | N | PH, S, TF, V | BC237 | | 2N5825 | | | 01 |
| | | | | | | | | | |
| BC238C | S | N | PH, S, TF, V | BC237 | | | | | 01 |
| BC239 | S | N | PH, S, TF, V | BC173 | BC319 | MPS6512 | 2N5447 | | 01 |
| BC239 | | | | BC184 | BC209 | 2N5827 | | | 01 |
| BC239B | S | N | PH, S, TF, V | BC239 | | 2N5827 | | | 01 |
| BC239C | S | N | PH, S, TF, V | BC239 | | 2N5827 | | | 01 |
| | | | | | | | | | |
| BC240 | S | P | | | | 2N4058 | | | 01 |
| BC241 | S | P | | | | 2N4059 | | | 01 |
| BC242 | S | P | | | | 2N4060 | | | 01 |
| BC243 | S | P | | | | 2N4061 | | | 01 |
| BC244 | S | P | | | | 2N4062 | | | 01 |
| | | | | | | | | | |
| BC245 | S | N | | | | 2N3707 | | | 01 |
| BC246 | S | N | | | | 2N3708 | | | 01 |
| BC247 | S | N | | | | 2N3709 | | | 01 |
| BC248 | S | N | | | | 2N3710 | | | 01 |
| BC249 | S | N | | | | 2N3711 | | | 01 |
| | | | | | | | | | |
| BC250 | S | P | | BC205 | BC308VI | 2N6015 | | | 01 |
| BC250 | | | | BC308 | BC307 | | | | 01 |
| BC250 | | | | BC177 | BC231 | | | | 01 |
| BC250A | S | P | IN, TX | BC308A | BC307 | 2N6015 | | | 01 |
| BC250B | S | P | IN, TX | BC308B | BC307 | 2N6015 | | | 01 |
| | | | | | | | | | |
| BC250C | S | P | IN, TX | BC308C | BC307 | 2N6015 | | | 01 |
| BC251 | S | P | IN | BC157 | BC153 | | | | 01 |
| BC251 | | | | BC512 | | | | | 01 |
| BC251 | | | | BC320 | | | | | 01 |
| BC251A | S— | P | IN, NS, TX | BC307A | BC307 | 2N6015 | | | 01 |
| | | | | | | | | | |
| BC251B | S | P | IN, NS, TX | BC307B | BC307 | 2N6015 | | | 01 |
| BC251C | S | P | IN, TX | BC307B | BC307 | 2N6015 | | | 01 |
| BC252 | S | P | IN | BC158 | BC205 | | | 2SA565 | 01 |
| BC252 | | | | BC513 | BC213 | | | | 01 |
| BC252 | | | | BC308 | | | | | 01 |

| TYPE | M/S | POL | MANUFAC | EUROPEAN | | AMERICAN | JAPANESE | USE |
|------|-----|-----|---------|----------|---|----------|----------|-----|
| BC252A | S | P | IN, NS, TX | BC308A | BC307 | 2N6015 | | 01 |
| BC252B | S | P | IN, NS, TX | BC308B | BC307 | 2N6015 | | 01 |
| BC252C | S | P | IN, TX | BC308C | BC307 | 2N6015 | | 01 |
| BC253 | S | P | IN | BC154 | BC206 | | | 01 |
| BC253 | | | | BC179 | BC322 | | | 01 |
| BC253 | | | | BC309 | BC214 | | | 01 |
| BC253A | S | P | IN, NS, TX | BC309B | BC309 | 2N6003 | | 01 |
| BC253B | S | P | IN, NS, TX | BC309B | BC309 | 2N6003 | | 01 |
| BC253C | S | P | IN, TX | BC309C | BC309 | 2N6003 | | 01 |
| BC254 | S | N | TX | BC147 | BC207 | | | 01 |
| BC254 | | | | BC108 | BC107 | | | 01 |
| BC254 | | | | BC130 | | | | 01 |
| BC255 | S | N | TX | BC147 | BC337 | | | 01 |
| BC255 | | | | BC107 | BC108B | | | 01 |
| BC255 | | | | BC130 | | | | 01 |
| BC256 | S | P | IN | BCY77 | | 2N4250A | | 01 |
| BC256A | S | P | IN, TX | BCY77VII | BC307 | 2N6015 | | 01 |
| BC256B | S | P | IN, TX | BCY77IX | BC307 | 2N6015 | | 01 |
| BC257 | S | P | S | BC177 | BC212L | MPS6517 | 2N5086 | 2SA565 | 01 |
| BC257 | | | | BC307 | BC231 | | | 01 |
| BC257 | | | | BC204 | BC251 | | | 01 |
| BC257 | | | | BC512 | | | | 01 |
| BC257A | S | P | S | BC212L | | 2N5086 | | 01 |
| BC257B | S | P | S | BC212L | | 2N5086 | | 01 |
| BC257VI | S | P | S | BC257A | | | | 01 |
| BC258 | S | P | S | BC308 | BC178 | MPS6518 | 2N5086 | 2SA565 | 01 |
| BC258 | | | | BC205 | BC231 | | | 01 |
| BC258 | | | | BC513 | BC252 | | | 01 |
| BC258 | | | | BC212L | | | | 01 |
| BC258A | S | P | S | BC212L | | 2N5286 | | 01 |
| BC258B | S | P | S | BC212L | | 2N5086 | | 01 |
| BC258VI | S | P | S | BC258A | | | | 01 |
| BC259 | S | P | S | BC179 | BC206 | MPS6519 | 2N5087 | 01 |
| BC259 | | | | BC514 | BC253 | | | 01 |
| BC259 | | | | BC212L | BC309 | | | 01 |
| BC259A | S | P | S | BC259B | BC214L | 2N5087 | | 01 |
| BC259C | S | P | S | BC214L | | 2N5087 | | 01 |
| BC260 | S | P | IN | BC178 | BC213(SP) | 2N3964 | 2N3965 | 01 |
| BC260 | | | | BCY70 | | | | 01 |
| BC260A | S | P | IN, TX | BC178A | BCY70 | 2N3965 | | 01 |
| BC260B | S | P | IN, TX | BC178B | BCY71 | 2N3965 | | 01 |
| BC260C | S | P | IN, TX | BC178C | BCY71 | 2N3965 | | 01 |
| BC261 | S | P | IN | BC204 | BC177 | 2N3964 | 2N3965 | 01 |
| BC261 | | | | BC212 | BC157 | | | 01 |
| BC261 | | | | BCY71 | BC153 | | | 01 |
| BC261A | S | P | IN, NS, TX | BC177A | BCY71 | 2N3965 | | 01 |
| BC261B | S | P | IN, NS, TX | BC177B | BCY71 | 2N3965 | | 01 |
| BC261C | S | P | IN, TX | BC177B | BCY71 | 2N3965 | | 01 |
| BC262 | S | P | IN | BC205 | BC178 | 2N3964 | 2N3965 | 01 |
| BC262 | | | | BC204 | BC158 | | | 01 |
| BC262 | | | | BCY71 | BC213 | | | 01 |
| BC262A | S | P | IN, NS, TX | BC178A | BCY71 | 2N3965 | | 01 |
| BC262B | S | P | IN, NS, TX | BC178B | BCY71 | 2N3965 | | 01 |
| BC262C | S | P | IN, TX | BC178C | BCY71 | 2N3965 | | 01 |
| BC263 | S | P | IN | BC214 | BC179 | 2N3964 | 2N3965 | 01 |
| BC263 | | | | BC206 | BC519 | | | 01 |
| BC263 | | | | BCY71 | BC153 | | | 01 |
| BC263A | S | P | IN, NS, TX | BC179B | BCY71 | 2N3965 | | 01 |
| BC263B | S | P | IN, IT, NS, TX | BC179B | BCY71 | 2N3965 | | 01 |
| BC263C | S | P | IN, TX | BC179C | BCY71 | 2N3965 | | 01 |
| BC266 | S | P | IN | BCY77 | | 2N3962 | 2N3965 | 01 |
| BC266A | S | P | IN, TX | BCY77VII | BCY71 | 2N3965 | | 01 |
| BC266B | S | P | IN, TX | BCY77IX | BCY71 | 2N3965 | | 01 |
| BC267 | S | N | AT | BC337 | BFX95 | S7213 | 2N2222A | 01 |
| BC267 | | | | BC207 | BC317 | | | 01 |
| BC267A | S | N | AT | BC337-16 | | | | 01 |
| BC267B | S | N | AT | BC337-25 | | | | 01 |
| BC268 | S | N | AT | BFX95 | BC208 | 2N2222A | | 01 |
| BC268 | | | | BC318 | BC338 | | | 01 |
| BC268A | S | N | AT | BC338-16 | | | | 01 |
| BC268B | S | N | AT | BC338-25 | | | | 01 |
| BC268C | S | N | AT | BC338-40 | | | | 01 |
| BC269 | S | N | AT | BC109 | BC338-25 | 2N2222A | | 01 |
| BC269 | | | | BFX95 | BC209 | | | 01 |
| BC269 | | | | BC319 | | | | 01 |

| TYPE | M/S | POL | MANUFAC | EUROPEAN | | AMERICAN | | JAPANESE | USE |
|------|-----|-----|---------|----------|--|----------|--|----------|-----|
| BC269B | S | N | AT | BC338-25 | | | | | 01 |
| BC269C | S | N | AT | BC338-40 | | | | | 01 |
| BC270 | S | N | AT | BC338 | BFX95 | S7236 | 2N2222A | | 01 |
| BC270A | S | N | AT | BC338-16 | | | | | 01 |
| BC270B | S | N | AT | BC338-25 | | | | | 01 |
| BC270C | S | N | AT | BC338-40 | | | | | 01 |
| BC270-5 | S | N | AT | BC338-16 | | | | | 01 |
| BC270-6 | S | N | AT | BC338-16 | | | | | 01 |
| BC271 | S | N | AT | BC338-16 | BFX95 | 2N2222A | | | 01 |
| BC271 | | | | BC338 | | | | | 01 |
| BC272 | S | N | AT | BC337-25 | BC337 | 2N2222 | 2N2222A | | 01 |
| BC272 | | | | BFX95 | | | | | 01 |
| BC274 | S | P | CO, SE | BC307 | BC212 | | | | 01 |
| BC274A | S | P | CO, SE | BC307A | | | | | 01 |
| BC274B | S | P | CO, SE | BC307B | | | | | 01 |
| BC274V | S | P | CO, SE | BC307A | | | | | 01 |
| BC274VI | S | P | CO, SE | BC307A | | | | | 01 |
| BC275 | S | P | CO, SE | BC308 | BC213 | | | | 01 |
| BC275A | S | P | CO, SE | BC308A | | | | | 01 |
| BC275B | S | P | CO, SE | BC308B | | | | | 01 |
| BC275C | S | P | CO, SE | BC308C | | | | | 01 |
| BC275V | S | P | CO, SE | BC308A | | | | | 01 |
| BC275VI | S | P | CO, SE | BC308A | | | | | 01 |
| BC276 | S | P | CO, SE | BC309 | BC213C | | | | 01 |
| BC276A | S | P | CO, SE | BC309B | | | | | 01 |
| BC276B | S | P | CO, SE | BC309B | | | | | 01 |
| BC276C | S | P | CO, SE | BC309C | | | | | 01 |
| BC277 | S | N | CO, SE | BC237 | BC182 | | | | 01 |
| BC277A | S | N | CO, SE | BC237A | | | | | 01 |
| BC277B | S | N | CO, SE | BC237B | | | | | 01 |
| BC278 | S | N | CO, SE | BC238 | BC183 | | | | 01 |
| BC278A | S | N | CO, SE | BC238A | | | | | 01 |
| BC278B | S | N | CO, SE | BC238B | | | | | 01 |
| BC278C | S | N | CO, SE | BC238C | | | | | 01 |
| BC279 | S | N | CO, SE | BC239 | BC183C | | | | 01 |
| BC279B | S | N | CO, SE | BC239B | | | | | 01 |
| BC279C | S | N | CO, SE | BC239C | | | | | 01 |
| BC280 | S | N | SG, AT | BC414B | BC182 | 2N930 | | | 01 |
| BC280 | | | | BC109 | | | | | 01 |
| BC280A | S | N | SG, AT | BC414B | | | | | 01 |
| BC280B | S | N | SG, AT | BC414B | | | | | 01 |
| BC280C | S | N | SG, AT | BC414B | | | | | 01 |
| BC281 | S | P | SG, AT | BC416A | BC212 | 2N3964 | 2N3965 | | 01 |
| BC281 | | | | BCY70 | | | | | 01 |
| BC281B | S | P | SG, AT | BC416B | | | | | 01 |
| BC282 | S | N | SG, AT | BCX73-16 | BCW73-16 | 2N2222A | | | 01 |
| BC282 | | | | BFX95 | | | | | 01 |
| BC283 | S | P | SG, AT | BCX75-16 | BCW75-16 | 2N2906 | 2N2907A | | 01 |
| BC283 | | | | BSW24 | BC213 | | | | 01 |
| BC284 | S | N | SG, AT | BC237 | BC182 | 2N915 | 2N2222A | | 01 |
| BC284 | | | | BFX95 | | | | | 01 |
| BC284A | S | N | SG, AT | BC237A | | | | | 01 |
| BC284B | S | N | SG, AT | BC237B | | | | | 01 |
| BC285 | S | N | SG, AT | (BF457) | | 2N3114 | 2N1990R | | 01 |
| BC286 | S | N | SG, AT, F | BC141-10 | BC141-16 | 2N2302 | 2N2297 | | 01 |
| BC286 | | | | BFY60 | | | | | 01 |
| BC287 | S | P | SG, F, AT | BC161-10 | BC143 | 2N4037 | | | 01 |
| BC288 | S | N | AT, SG | (BSX63-10) | BFX34 | 2N2297 | | | 01 |
| BC288 | | | | BFY51 | | | | | 01 |
| BC289 | S | N | SG, AT | BC237 | BC107 | | | | 01 |
| BC289A | S | N | SG, AT | BC237A | | | | | 01 |
| BC289B | S | N | SG, AT | BC237B | | | | | 01 |
| BC290 | S | N | AT, SG | BC414 | | | | | 01 |
| BC290A | S | N | SG, AT | BC414B | | | | | 01 |
| BC290B | S | N | SG, AT | BC414B | | | | | 01 |
| BC290C | S | N | SG, AT | BC414C | | | | | 01 |
| BC291 | S | P | SG, AT | BC307A | | | | | 01 |
| BC291A | S | P | SG, AT | BC307A | | | | | 01 |
| BC291D | S | P | SG, AT | BC307A | | | | | 01 |
| BC292 | S | P | SG, AT | BC416 | | | | | 01 |
| BC292A | S | P | SG, AT | BC416A | | | | | 01 |
| BC292B | S | P | SG, AT | BC416B | | | | | 01 |
| BC293 | S | N | SG, AT | (BSX63-10) | BFY51 | 2N2297 | | | 01 |
| BC294 | S | P | SG, AT | BC161-16 | BFX30 | 2N2905A | | | 01 |
| BC295 | S | N | SG, AT | BC237A | | | | | 01 |

| TYPE | M/S | POL | MANUFAC | EUROPEAN | | AMERICAN | | JAPANESE | USE |
|---|---|---|---|---|---|---|---|---|---|
| BC297 | S | P | AT | BC327 | | 2N2907A | | | 01 |
| BC297-6 | S | P | AT | BC327-16 | | | | | 01 |
| BC297-7 | S | P | AT | BC327-16 | | | | | 01 |
| BC298 | S | P | AT | BC328 | | | | | 01 |
| BC298-6 | S | P | AT | BC328-16 | | | | | 01 |
| | | | | | | | | | |
| BC298-7 | S | P | AT | BC328-16 | | | | | 01 |
| BC298-8 | S | P | AT | BC328-25 | | | | | 01 |
| BC300 | S | N | AT | BSX47 | | 2N1893 | 2N3019 | | 01 |
| BC300-4 | S | N | AT | BSX47-6 | | | | | 01 |
| BC300-5 | S | N | AT | BSX47-10 | | | | | 01 |
| | | | | | | | | | |
| BC300-6 | S | N | AT | BSX47-10 | | | | | 01 |
| BC301 | S | N | AT, SG, TX | BSX46 | BC300 | 2N699 | 2N1893 | | 01 |
| BC301 | | | | BC286 | BC141-6 | | | | 01 |
| BC301-4 | S | N | AT | BSX46-6 | | | | | 01 |
| BC301-5 | S | N | AT | BSX46-10 | | | | | 01 |
| | | | | | | | | | |
| BC301-6 | S | N | AT | BSX46-16 | | | | | 01 |
| BC302 | S | N | AT, SG, TX | BSX45 | BC140-6 | 2N2270 | 2N3109 | | 01 |
| BC302 | | | | BFY50 | | 2N2297 | | | 01 |
| BC302-4 | S | N | AT | BSX45-6 | | | | | 01 |
| BC302-5 | S | N | AT | BSX45-10 | | | | | 01 |
| | | | | | | | | | |
| BC302-6 | S | N | AT | BSX45-16 | | | | | 01 |
| BC303 | S | P | AT, SG, TX | BSV17 | BC287 | 2N4314 | 2N4036 | | 01 |
| BC303 | | | | BC143 | | 2N4037 | | | 01 |
| BC303-4 | S | P | AT | BSV17-6 | | | | | 01 |
| BC303-5 | S | P | AT | BSV17-10 | | | | | 01 |
| | | | | | | | | | |
| BC303-6 | S | P | AT | BSV17-10 | | | | | 01 |
| BC304 | S | P | AT | BSV16 | BC143 | 2N4037 | | | 01 |
| BC304 | | | | BC287 | BC160-6 | | | | 01 |
| BC304-4 | S | P | AT | BSV16-6 | | | | | 01 |
| BC304-5 | S | P | AT | BSV16-10 | | | | | 01 |
| | | | | | | | | | |
| BC304-6 | S | P | AT | BSV16-16 | | | | | 01 |
| BC307 | S | P | IN, S, TF, V | BC204 | BC157 | MPS6517 | 2N6015 | | 01 |
| BC307 | | | | BC177 | BC320 | | | | 01 |
| BC307 | | | | BC212 | BC512 | | | | 01 |
| BC307 | | | | BC251 | BC557 | | | | 01 |
| | | | | | | | | | |
| BC307A | S | P | IN, S, TF, V | BC307 | | 2N6015 | | | 01 |
| BC307B | S | P | IN, S, TF, V | BC307 | | 2N6015 | | | 01 |
| BC307C | S | P | IN | BC307B | BC308 | 2N6003 | | | 01 |
| BC307VI | S | S | TF, V, SG, S, SE | BC177VI | BC307A | | | | 01 |
| BC308 | S | P | IN, S, TF, V, PH | BC205 | BC558 | MPS6518 | 2N6015 | | 01 |
| | | | | | | | | | |
| BC308 | | | | BC178 | BC321 | | | | 01 |
| BC308 | | | | BC158 | BC213 | | | | 01 |
| BC308 | | | | BC513 | BC252 | | | | 01 |
| BC308 | | | | BC307 | | | | | 01 |
| BC308A | S | P | IN, S, TF, V, PH | BC178A | BC307 | 2N6015 | | | 01 |
| | | | | | | | | | |
| BC308A | | | | BC558A | BC158A | | | | 01 |
| BC308B | S | P | IN, S, TF, V, PH | BC178B | BC307 | 2N6015 | | | 01 |
| BC308B | | | | BC558B | BC158B | | | | 01 |
| BC308C | S | P | IN, S | BC307 | | 2N6015 | | | 01 |
| BC308VI | S | S | TF, V, SG, S, SE | BC308A | BC178VI | | | | 01 |
| | | | | | | | | | |
| BC309 | S | P | IN, S, TF, V, PH | BC206 | BC559 | MPS6519 | 2N6003 | | 01 |
| BC309 | | | | BC179 | BC322 | | | | 01 |
| BC309 | | | | BC159 | BC214 | | | | 01 |
| BC309 | | | | BC178 | BC253 | | | | 01 |
| BC309 | | | | BC514 | | | | | 01 |
| | | | | | | | | | |
| BC309A | S | P | IN, S, TF, V, PH | BC179A | BC309 | 2N6003 | | | 01 |
| BC309A | | | | BC559A | BC159A | | | | 01 |
| BC309B | S | P | IN, S, TF, V, PH | BC179B | BC309 | 2N6003 | | | 01 |
| BC309B | | | | BC559B | BC159B | | | | 01 |
| BC309C | S | P | IN, S | BC309 | | 2N6003 | | | 01 |
| | | | | | | | | | |
| BC310 | S | N | SG, AT | BSX47-6 | BC286 | 2N1893 | 2N2297 | | 01 |
| BC310 | | | | BFY50 | | | | | 01 |
| BC311 | S | P | SG, AT | BSV17-6 | BC287 | 2N4314 | 2N4037 | | 01 |
| BC311 | | | | BC143 | | | | | 01 |
| BC312 | S | N | SG, AT | (BF457) | BC300 | 2N1893 | | | 01 |
| | | | | | | | | | |
| BC313 | S | P | SE, Ss, ML | BC161 | BC143 | 2N4037 | | | 01 |
| BC313A | S | P | SE | BC161-6 | BC143 | 2N4037 | | | 01 |
| BC313A-6 | S | P | SE | BSV17-6 | | | | | 01 |
| BC313A-10 | S | P | SE | BSV17-10 | | | | | 01 |
| BC313A-16 | S | P | SE | BSV17-10 | | | | | 01 |
| | | | | | | | | | |
| BC313B | S | P | SE | BC161-6 | | | | | 01 |
| BC313C | S | P | SE | BC161-10 | | | | | 01 |
| BC313D | S | P | SE | BC161-16 | | | | | 01 |
| BC313E | S | P | SE | BC161-16 | | | | | 01 |
| BC313-6 | S | P | SE | BC161-6 | | | | | 01 |

| TYPE | M/S | POL | MANUFAC | EUROPEAN | | AMERICAN | | JAPANESE | USE |
|---|---|---|---|---|---|---|---|---|---|
| BC313-10 | S | P | SE | BC161-10 | | | | | 01 |
| BC313-16 | S | P | SE | BC161-16 | | | | | 01 |
| BC314 | S | N | SG, AT | (BF457) | | 2N4390 | | | 01 |
| BC315 | S | P | TX | BC415 | BC415A | 2N5087 | 2N6003 | | 01 |
| BC315 | | | | BC309 | | | | | 01 |
| BC315A | S | P | TX | BC415A | | | | | 01 |
| BC315B | S | P | TX | BC415B | | | | | 01 |
| BC317 | S | N | MO, F | BC237 | BC167 | 2N5209 | 2N3903 | | 01 |
| BC317 | | | | BC347A | | | | | 01 |
| BC317A | S | N | MO, F | BC237A | BC167 | 2N5209 | | | 01 |
| BC317B | S | N | MO, F | BC237B | BC167 | 2N5209 | | | 01 |
| BC318 | S | N | MO, F | BC237 | BC167 | 2N5209 | | | 01 |
| BC318A | S | N | MO, F | BC237A | BC167 | 2N5209 | | | 01 |
| BC318B | S | N | MO, F | BC237B | BC167 | 2N5209 | | | 01 |
| BC318C | S | N | MO, F | BC237B | BC169 | 2N5210 | | | 01 |
| BC319 | S | N | MO, F | BC239 | BC169 | 2N5210 | | | 01 |
| BC319B | S | N | MO, F | BC239B | BC169 | 2N5210 | | | 01 |
| BC319C | S | N | MO, F | BC239C | BC169 | 2N5210 | | | 01 |
| BC320 | S | P | MO, F | BC307 | BC327 | P1119E | 2N5086 | | 01 |
| BC320A | S | P | MO, F | BC307A | BC327 | 2N5086 | | | 01 |
| BC320A | | | | BC320 | | | | | 01 |
| BC320B | S | P | MO, F | BC307B | BC327 | 2N5086 | | | 01 |
| BC320B | | | | BC320 | | | | | 01 |
| BC321 | S | P | MO, F | BC307 | BC320 | 2N5086 | | | 01 |
| BC321A | S | P | MO, F | BC307A | BC320 | 2N5086 | | | 01 |
| BC321B | S | P | MO, F | BC307B | BC320 | 2N5086 | | | 01 |
| BC322 | S | P | MO, F | BC309 | | 2N5087 | | | 01 |
| BC322B | S | P | MO, F | BC322 | BC309B | 2N5087 | | | 01 |
| BC322C | S | P | MO, F | BC322 | BC309C | 2N5087 | | | 01 |
| BC323 | S | N | AT, SG, F | (BSX63-10) | BFY50 | 2N5320 | 2N2297 | | 01 |
| BC324 | S | N | SG, AT | BC141-6 | BFY50 | 2N5320 | 2N2297 | | 01 |
| BC325 | S | P | TX | BC416A | BCY71 | 2N3965 | | | 01 |
| BC326 | S | P | TX | BC416B | BCY71 | 2N3965 | | | 01 |
| BC327 | S | P | IN, S, TF, V | | | 2N5819 | | | 01 |
| BC327-16 | S | P | IN, S, TF, V | BC327 | | 2N5819 | | | 01 |
| BC327-25 | S | P | IN, S, TF, V | BC327 | | 2N5819 | | | 01 |
| BC327-40 | S | P | IN, S, TF, V | BC327 | | 2N5819 | | | 01 |
| BC328 | S | P | IN, S, TF, V | BC327 | | 2N5819 | | | 01 |
| BC328-16 | S | P | IN, S, TF, V | BC327 | | 2N5819 | | | 01 |
| BC328-25 | S | P | IN, S, TF, V | BC327 | | 2N5819 | | | 01 |
| BC328-40 | S | P | IN, S, TF, V | BC327 | | 2N5819 | | | 01 |
| BC329 | S | N | TX | (BC414) | | 2N5210 | | | 01 |
| BC329B | S | N | TX | (BC414B) | BC329 | 2N5827 | | | 01 |
| BC329C | S | N | TX | (BC414C) | BC329 | 2N5827 | | | 01 |
| BC330 | S | N | TX | BC414 | | | | | 01 |
| BC330B | S | N | TX | BC414B | BC239 | 2N5827 | | | 01 |
| BC330C | S | N | TX | BC414C | BC239 | 2N5827 | | | 01 |
| BC331 | S | N | TX | BCY65E | | | | | 01 |
| BC331A | S | N | TX | BCY65EVII | BC237 | 2N5825 | | | 01 |
| BC331B | S | N | TX | BCY65EIX | BC237 | 2N5825 | | | 01 |
| BC331C | S | N | TX | BCY65EIX | BC237 | 2N5825 | | | 01 |
| BC332 | S | N | TX | BCY59 | | | | | 01 |
| BC332A | S | N | TX | BCY59VII | BC237 | 2N5825 | | | 01 |
| BC332B | S | N | TX | BCY59IX | BC237 | 2N5825 | | | 01 |
| BC332C | S | N | TX | BCY59X | BC237 | 2N5825 | | | 01 |
| BC333 | S | N | MO | BC238 | | | | | 01 |
| BC334 | S | P | MO | BC308 | BC320 | 2N5086 | | | 01 |
| BC335 | S | N | MO | BC239 | | | | | 01 |
| BC336 | S | P | MO | BC309 | BC322 | 2N5087 | | | 01 |
| BC337 | S | N | IN, S, TF, V | BC223 | | 2N2222A | | | 01 |
| BC337-16 | S | N | IN, S, TF, V | BC337 | | 2N5818 | | | 01 |
| BC337-25 | S | N | IN, S, TF, V | BC337 | | 2N5818 | | | 01 |
| BC337-40 | S | N | IN, S, TF, V | BC337 | | 2N5818 | | | 01 |
| BC338 | S | N | IN, S, TF, V | BC337 | | 2N5818 | | | 01 |
| BC338-16 | S | N | IN, S, TF, V | BC337 | | 2N5818 | | | 01 |
| BC338-25 | S | N | IN, S, TF, V | BC337 | | 2N5818 | | | 01 |
| BC338-40 | S | N | IN, S, TF, V | BC337 | | 2N5818 | | | 01 |
| BC340 | S | N | IN | BC140 | BFY50 | 2N3109 | 2N3110 | | 01 |
| BC340 | | | | | | 2N2297 | | | 01 |
| BC340-6 | S | N | IN | BC140-6 | BFY50 | 2N2297 | | | 01 |
| BC340-10 | S | N | IN | BC140-10 | BFY50 | 2N2297 | | | 01 |
| BC340-16 | S | N | IN | BC140-16 | BFY50 | 2N2297 | | | 01 |
| BC341 | S | N | IN | BC141 | BFY50 | 2N3107 | 2N3108 | | 01 |
| BC341 | | | | | | 2N2297 | | | 01 |
| BC341-6 | S | N | IN | BC141-6 | BFY50 | 2N2297 | | | 01 |

| TYPE | M/S | POL | MANUFAC | EUROPEAN | | AMERICAN | | JAPANESE | USE |
|------|-----|-----|---------|----------|--|----------|--|----------|-----|
| BC341-10 | S | N | IN | BC141-10 | BFY50 | 2N2297 | | | 01 |
| BC342 | S | N | MO | BC141-6 | BFY50 | 2N2297 | | | 01 |
| BC343 | S | P | MO | BC161-6 | BC143 | 2N4037 | | | 01 |
| BC344 | S | N | MO | BSX47-6 | BFY50 | 2N2297 | | | 01 |
| BC345 | S | P | MO | BSV17-6 | BC143 | 2N4037 | | | 01 |
| BC347 | S | N | MO | BC237 | BC167 | 2N5209 | | | 01 |
| BC347A | S | N | MO | BC237A | | 2N3909 | | | 01 |
| BC347B | S | N | MO | BC237B | BC347A | 2N3903 | | | 01 |
| BC347L | S | N | MO | BC237A | BC167 | 2N5209 | | | 01 |
| BC348 | S | N | MO | BC237 | BC167 | 2N5209 | 2N5555 | | 01 |
| BC348A | S | N | MO | BC237A | BC167 | 2N5209 | | | 01 |
| BC348B | S | N | MO | BC237B | BC169 | 2N5210 | | | 01 |
| BC348L | S | N | MO | BC237A | BC169 | 2N5209 | | | 01 |
| BC349 | S | N | MO | BC238 | BC169 | 2N5210 | | | 01 |
| BC349A | S | N | MO | BC238A | BC169 | 2N5210 | | | 01 |
| BC349B | S | N | MO | BC238B | BC169 | 2N5210 | | | 01 |
| BC349L | S | N | MO | BC238A | BC169 | 2N5210 | | | 01 |
| BC350 | S | P | MO | BC307 | BC320 | 2N5086 | | | 01 |
| BC350A | S | P | MO | BC307A | BC320 | 2N5086 | | | 01 |
| BC350B | S | P | MO | BC307B | BC322 | 2N5087 | | | 01 |
| BC350L | S | P | MO | BC307A | BC320 | 2N5086 | | | 01 |
| BC351 | S | P | MO | BC307 | BC320 | 2N5086 | | | 01 |
| BC351A | S | P | MO | BC307A | BC320 | 2N5086 | | | 01 |
| BC351B | S | P | MO | BC307B | BC322 | 2N5087 | | | 01 |
| BC351L | S | P | MO | BC307A | BC320 | 2N5086 | | | 01 |
| BC352 | S | P | MO | BC308 | BC322 | 2N5087 | | | 01 |
| BC352A | S | P | MO | BC308A | BC320 | 2N5086 | | | 01 |
| BC352B | S | P | MO | BC308B | BC322 | 2N5087 | | | 01 |
| BC352L | S | P | MO | BC308A | BC322 | 2N5087 | | | 01 |
| BC354 | S | P | MO | BC308 | BC320 | 2N5086 | | | 01 |
| BC355 | S | P | MO | BC308 | BC320 | 2N5086 | | | 01 |
| BC355A | S | P | MO | BC308A | BC320 | 2N5086 | | | 01 |
| BC355B | S | P | MO | BC308A | BC320 | 2N5086 | | | 01 |
| BC355C | S | P | MO | BC308B | BC322 | 2N5087 | | | 01 |
| BC357 | S | P | MO | BC308B | BC320 | 2N5086 | | | 01 |
| BC358 | S | N | MO | BC238B | | | | | 01 |
| BC360 | S | P | IN | BC160 | BFX29 | 2N5022 | 2N5023 | | 01 |
| BC360 | | | | | | 2N1132 | 2N2905A | | 01 |
| BC360-6 | S | P | IN | BC160-6 | BFX29 | 2N2905A | | | 01 |
| BC360-10 | S | P | IN | BC160-10 | BFX29 | 2N2905A | | | 01 |
| BC360-16 | S | P | IN | BC160-16 | BFX29 | 2N2905A | | | 01 |
| BC361 | S | P | IN | BC161 | BC157 | 2N4030 | 2N4031 | | 01 |
| BC361 | | | | BFX29 | | 2N2905A | | | 01 |
| BC361-6 | S | P | IN | BC161-6 | BFX29 | 2N2905A | | | 01 |
| BC361-10 | S | P | IN | BC161-10 | BFX29 | 2N2905A | | | 01 |
| BC362 | S | P | MO | (BD136-10) | BD140 | 2N4920 | | | 01 |
| BC363 | S | P | MO | (BD138-10) | BD140 | 2N4920 | | | 01 |
| BC364 | S | P | MO | (BD140-10) | BD140 | 2N4940 | | | 01 |
| BC365 | S | N | MO | (BD135-10) | BD169 | 2N4923 | | | 01 |
| BC366 | S | N | MO | (BD137-10) | BD169 | 2N4923 | | | 01 |
| BC367 | S | N | MO | (BD139-10) | BD169 | 2N4923 | | | 01 |
| BC370 | S | P | AT | BC328 | | | | | 01 |
| BC370A | S | P | AT | BC328-25 | | | | | 01 |
| BC370B | S | P | AT | BC328-40 | | | | | 01 |
| BC370-6 | S | P | AT | BC328-16 | | | | | 01 |
| BC370-7 | S | P | AT | BC328-16 | | | | | 01 |
| BC371 | S | N | AT | BC140 | BFY51 | 2N2297 | | | 01 |
| BC377 | S | N | AT | BC337 | BSW64 | 2N2222A | | | 01 |
| BC377-6 | S | N | AT | BC337-16 | | | | | 01 |
| BC377-7 | S | N | AT | BC337-25 | | | | | 01 |
| BC377-8 | S | N | AT | BC337-40 | | | | | 01 |
| BC378 | S | N | AT | BC338 | BSX33 | 2N731 | | | 01 |
| BC378-6 | S | N | AT | BC338-16 | | | | | 01 |
| BC378-7 | S | N | AT | BC338-25 | | | | | 01 |
| BC378-8 | S | N | AT | BC338-40 | | | | | 01 |
| BC381 | S | P | TX | BCX59 | BCY59 | 2N6015 | | | 01 |
| BC381 | | | | BC307 | | | | | 01 |
| BC382 | S | N | TX | BC414 | BC237 | 2N5825 | | | 01 |
| BC382B | S | N | TX | BC414B | BC239 | 2N5827 | | | 01 |
| BC382C | S | N | TX | BC414C | BC239 | 2N5827 | | | 01 |
| BC383 | S | N | TX | BC337 | BC413 | 2N5825 | | | 01 |
| BC383 | | | | BC237 | BC413B | | | | 01 |
| BC383 | | | | BCY13C | | | | | 01 |
| BC383B | S | N | TX | BC413B | BC239 | 2N5827 | | | 01 |
| BC383C | S | N | TX | BC413C | BC239 | 2N5827 | | | 01 |

| TYPE | M/S | POL | MANUFAC | EUROPEAN | | AMERICAN | JAPANESE | USE |
|------|-----|-----|---------|----------|--|----------|----------|-----|
| BC384 | S | N | TX | BC413 | BC4138 | 2N5827 | | 01 |
| BC384 | | | | BC239 | | | | 01 |
| BC384B | S | N | TX | BC413B | BC239 | 2N5827 | | 01 |
| BC384C | S | N | TX | BC414C | BC239 | 2N5827 | | 01 |
| BC385 | S | N | TX | BC237 | | 2N5825 | | 01 |
| BC385A | S | N | TX | BC237A | | | | 01 |
| BC385B | S | N | TX | BC237B | | | | 01 |
| BC386 | S | N | TX | BC238 | BC385 | 2N5825 | | 01 |
| BC386 | | | | BC237 | | | | 01 |
| BC386A | S | N | TX | BC238A | | | | 01 |
| BC386B | S | N | TX | BC238B | | | | 01 |
| BC387 | S | N | MO | BC140 | | 2N4401 | | 01 |
| BC388 | S | P | MO | BC160 | | 2N4403 | | 01 |
| BC389 | S | N | AT | BC107B | BC109 | 2N930 | | 01 |
| BC390 | S | N | AT | BC180B | BC109 | 2N930 | | 01 |
| BC391 | S | N | AT | BC108C | BC109 | 2N930 | | 01 |
| BC393 | S | P | AT | | | 2N4357 | | 01 |
| BC394 | S | N | SG, AT | (BF458) | BF337 | 2N4927 | | 01 |
| BC395 | S | N | SG, AT | BSX47 | BSW66 | 2N4001 | | 01 |
| BC396 | S | P | SG, AT | BSV17-6 | | 2N4929 | | 01 |
| BC400 | S | P | AT | BSV68 | | 2N3497 | | 01 |
| BC404 | S | P | SG, AT | (BCY77VII) | | | | 01 |
| BC404A | S | P | SG, AT | (BSY77VIII) | | | | 01 |
| BC404VI | S | P | SG, AT | (BCY77VII) | | | | 01 |
| BC405 | S | P | SG, AT | BCY77VII | | | | 01 |
| BC405A | S | P | SG, AT | BCY77VII | | | | 01 |
| BC405B | S | P | SG, AT | BCY77VIII | | | | 01 |
| BC406 | S | P | SG, AT | (BC416B) | | | | 01 |
| BC406B | S | P | SG, AT | (BC416B) | | | | 01 |
| BC407 | S | N | PH, RA, AM, V | BC147 | BC237 | 2N4966 | | 01 |
| BC407 | | | | BC107 | BC207 | | | 01 |
| BC407 | | | | BC547 | | | | 01 |
| BC407A | S | N | PH, RA, V | BC147A | BC237A | 2N4966 | | 01 |
| BC407A | | | | BC107A | BC207 | | | 01 |
| BC407A | | | | BC547A | | | | 01 |
| BC407B | S | N | PH, RA, V | BC147B | BC237B | 2N4966 | | 01 |
| BC407B | | | | BC107B | BC207 | | | 01 |
| BC407B | | | | BC547B | | | | 01 |
| BC408 | S | N | PH, RA, AM, V | BC148 | BC238 | 2N4966 | | 01 |
| BC408 | | | | BC108 | BC207 | | | 01 |
| BC408 | | | | BC548 | | | | 01 |
| BC408A | S | N | PH, RA, V | BC148A | BC238A | 2N4966 | | 01 |
| BC408A | | | | BC108A | BC207 | | | 01 |
| BC408A | | | | BC548A | | | | 01 |
| BC408B | S | N | PH, RA, V | BC148B | BC238B | 2N4966 | | 01 |
| BC408B | | | | BC108B | BC207 | | | 01 |
| BC408B | | | | BC548B | | | | 01 |
| BC408C | S | N | PH, RA, V | BC148C | BC238C | 2N4966 | | 01 |
| BC408C | | | | BC108C | BC207 | | | 01 |
| BC408C | | | | BC548C | | | | 01 |
| BC409 | S | N | PH, RA, AM, V | BC149 | BC239 | 2N4967 | | 01 |
| BC409 | | | | BC109 | BC209 | | | 01 |
| BC409 | | | | BC549 | | | | 01 |
| BC409B | S | N | PH, RA, V | BC149B | BC239B | 2N4967 | | 01 |
| BC409B | | | | BC109B | BC209 | | | 01 |
| BC409B | | | | BC549B | | | | 01 |
| BC409C | S | N | PH, RA, V | BC149C | BC239C | 2N4967 | | 01 |
| BC409C | | | | BC109C | BC209 | | | 01 |
| BC409C | | | | BC549C | | | | 01 |
| BC410 | S | N | SG, AT | BC238C | | | | 01 |
| BC411 | S | N | SG, AT | BC141-6 | | | | 01 |
| BC412 | S | N | SG, AT | BCX74-16 | BCW74-16 | | | 01 |
| BC413 | S | N | IN, S, TF, V | BC239 | | 2N5827 | | 01 |
| BC413B | S | N | IN, S, TF, V | BC239 | | 2N5827 | | 01 |
| BC413C | S | N | IN, S, TF, V | BC239 | | 2N5827 | | 01 |
| BC414 | S | N | IN, S, TF, V | BC239 | | 2N5827 | | 01 |
| BC414B | S | N | IN, S, TF, V | BC239 | | 2N5827 | | 01 |
| BC414C | S | N | IN, S, TF, V | BC239 | | 2N5827 | | 01 |
| BC415 | S | P | IN, S, TF, V | BC307 | | 2N6015 | | 01 |
| BC415A | S | P | IN, S, TF, V | BC307 | | 2N6015 | | 01 |
| BC415B | S | P | IN, S, TF, V | BC307 | | 2N6015 | | 01 |
| BC415C | S | P | IN, S, TF, V | BC309 | | 2N6003 | | 01 |
| BC416 | S | P | IN, S, TF, V | BC309 | | 2N6003 | | 01 |
| BC416A | S | P | IN, S, TF, V | BC307 | | 2N6015 | | 01 |
| BC416B | S | P | IN, S, TF, V | BC307 | | 2N6015 | | 01 |

| TYPE | M/S | POL | MANUFAC | EUROPEAN | | AMERICAN | | JAPANESE | USE |
|------|-----|-----|---------|----------|---|----------|---|----------|-----|
| BC416C | S | P | IN, S, TF, V | BC309 | | 2N6003 | | | 01 |
| BC417 | S | P | RA, AM, V | BC307 | BC204 | 2N4249 | | | 01 |
| BC417A | S | P | RA, V | BC307A | | | | | 01 |
| BC417VI | S | P | RA, V | BC307A | | | | | 01 |
| BC418 | S | P | RA, AM, V | BC308 | BC204 | 2N4249 | | | 01 |
| BC418A | S | P | RA, V | BC308A | BC204 | 2N4249 | | | 01 |
| BC418B | S | P | RA, AM, V | BC308B | BC206 | 2N4250 | | | 01 |
| BC418VI | S | P | RA, V | BC308A | | | | | 01 |
| BC419 | S | P | RA, AM, V | BC309 | BC204 | 2N4249 | | | 01 |
| BC419A | S | P | RA, V | BC309A | BC204 | 2N4249 | | | 01 |
| BC419B | S | P | RA, V | BC309B | BC206 | 2N4240 | | | 01 |
| BC420 | S | P | AT | | | 2N4357 | | | 01 |
| BC424 | S | N | MO | (BSX47) | | | | | 01 |
| BC425 | S | N | MO | (BSX46) | | | | | 01 |
| BC426 | S | P | MO | (BSV17) | | | | | 01 |
| BC427 | S | P | MO | (BSV16) | | | | | 01 |
| BC429 | S | N | TX | BD135-10 | BD169 | 2N2270 | 2N4923 | | 01 |
| BC429A | S | N | TX | BD137-10 | BD169 | 2N4923 | | | 01 |
| BC430 | S | P | TX | BD136-10 | BD140 | 40357 | 2N4920 | | 01 |
| BC430A | S | P | TX | BD138-10 | BD140 | 2N4920 | | | 01 |
| BC431 | S | N | TF | (BC141-10) | | | | | 01 |
| BC432 | S | N | TF | (BC161-10) | | | | | 01 |
| BC437 | S | N | HI | BC237 | | | | | 01 |
| BC437A | S | N | HI | BC237A | | | | | 01 |
| BC437B | S | N | HI | BC237B | | | | | 01 |
| BC438 | S | N | HI | BC238 | | | | | 01 |
| BC438A | S | N | HI | BC238A | | | | | 01 |
| BC438B | S | N | HI | BC238B | | | | | 01 |
| BC438C | S | N | HI | BC238C | | | | | 01 |
| BC439 | S | N | HI | BC239 | | | | | 01 |
| BC439B | S | N | HI | BC239B | | | | | 01 |
| BC439C | S | N | HI | BC239C | | | | | 01 |
| BC440 | S | N | AT, SG | BC140 | BFY51 | 2N5321 | 2N2297 | | 01 |
| BC440-4 | S | N | AT | BC140-6 | | | | | 01 |
| BC440-5 | S | N | AT | BC140-10 | | | | | 01 |
| BC440-6 | S | N | AT | BC140-16 | | | | | 01 |
| BC441 | S | N | AT | BC141 | BSS42 | 2N5320 | | | 01 |
| BC441-4 | S | N | AT | BC141-6 | | | | | 01 |
| BC441-5 | S | N | AT | BC141-10 | | | | | 01 |
| BC441-6 | S | N | AT | BC141-16 | | | | | 01 |
| BC460 | S | P | AT | BC160 | BSS18 | 2N5323 | | | 01 |
| BC469-4 | S | P | AT | BC160-6 | | | | | 01 |
| BC460-5 | S | P | AT | BC160-10 | | | | | 01 |
| BC460-6 | S | P | AT | BC160-16 | | | | | 01 |
| BC461 | S | P | AT, SG | BC161 | | 2N5322 | 2N4929 | | 01 |
| BC461-4 | S | P | AT | BC161-6 | | | | | 01 |
| BC461-5 | S | P | AT | BC161-10 | | | | | 01 |
| BC461-6 | S | P | AT | BC161-16 | | | | | 01 |
| BC467 | S | N | HI | BC167 | | | | | 01 |
| BC467A | S | N | HI | BC167A | | | | | 01 |
| BC467B | S | N | HI | BC167B | | | | | 01 |
| BC468 | S | N | HI | BC168 | | 2N5322 | | | 01 |
| BC468A | S | N | HI | BC168A | | | | | 01 |
| BC468B | S | N | HI | BC168B | | | | | 01 |
| BC468C | S | N | HI | BC168C | | | | | 01 |
| BC469 | S | N | HI | BC169 | | | | | 01 |
| BC469B | S | N | HI | BC169B | | | | | 01 |
| BC469C | S | N | HI | BC169C | | | | | 01 |
| BC477 | S | P | AT, SG | BCY77VII | | 2N1990R | | | 01 |
| BC477A | S | P | AT, SG | BCY77VII | | | | | 01 |
| BC477VI | S | P | AT, SG | BCY77VII | | | | | 01 |
| BC478 | S | P | AT, SG | BCY79 | BCY71 | 2N3965 | | | 01 |
| BC478A | S | P | AT, SG | BCY79VII | | | | | 01 |
| BC478B | S | P | AT, SG | BCY79IX | | | | | 01 |
| BC479 | S | P | AT, SG | BC416B | BCY71 | 2N3965 | | | 01 |
| BC479B | S | P | AT, SG | BC416B | | | | | 01 |
| BC507 | S | N | SG, AT | BC182 | | | | | 01 |
| BC507A | S | N | SG, AT | BC182A | | | | | 01 |
| BC507B | S | N | SG, AT | BC182B | | | | | 01 |
| BC507FA | S | N | SG, AT | BC182A | | | | | 01 |
| BC507FB | S | N | SG, AT | BC182B | | | | | 01 |
| BC508 | S | N | SG, AT | BC182 | | | | | 01 |
| BC508A | S | N | SG, AT | BC182A | | | | | 01 |
| BC508B | S | N | SG, AT | BC182B | | | | | 01 |
| BC508C | S | N | SG, AT | BC182B | | | | | 01 |

| TYPE | M/S | POL | MANUFAC | EUROPEAN | | AMERICAN | | JAPANESE | USE |
|------|-----|-----|---------|----------|--|----------|--|----------|-----|
| BC508BFA | S | N | SG, AT | BC182A | | | | | 01 |
| BC508FB | S | N | SG, AT | BC182B | | | | | 01 |
| BC508FC | S | N | SG, AT | BC182B | | | | | 01 |
| BC509 | S | N | SG, AT | BC414 | | | | | 01 |
| BC509B | S | N | SG, AT | BC414B | | | | | 01 |
| | | | | | | | | | |
| BC509C | S | N | SG, AT | BC414C | | | | | 01 |
| BC509FB | S | N | SG, AT | BC414B | | | | | 01 |
| BC509FC | S | N | SG, AT | BC414C | | | | | 01 |
| BC510 | S | N | SG, AT | BC413 | | | | | 01 |
| BC510B | S | N | SG, AT | BC413B | | | | | 01 |
| | | | | | | | | | |
| BC510C | S | N | SG, AT | BC413C | | | | | 01 |
| BC510FB | S | N | SG, AT | BC413B | | | | | 01 |
| BC510FC | S | N | SG, AT | BC413C | | | | | 01 |
| BC512 | S | P | TX | BC307 | | 2N6015 | | | 01 |
| BC512A | S | P | TX | BC307A | | 2N6015 | | | 01 |
| | | | | | | | | | |
| BC512B | S | P | TX | BC307B | BC309 | 2N6003 | | | 01 |
| BC513 | S | P | TX | BC308 | BC307 | 2N6015 | | | 01 |
| BC513A | S | P | TX | BC308A | BC307 | 2N6015 | | | 01 |
| BC513B | S | P | TX | BC308B | BC309 | 2N6003 | | | 01 |
| BC513C | S | P | TX | BC308C | BC309 | 2N6003 | | | 01 |
| | | | | | | | | | |
| BC514 | S | P | TX | BC309 | BC307 | 2N6015 | | | 01 |
| BC514A | S | P | TX | BC309B | BC307 | 2N6015 | | | 01 |
| BC514B | S | P | TX | BC309B | BC309 | 2N6003 | | | 01 |
| BC514C | S | P | TX | BC309C | BC309 | 2N6003 | | | 01 |
| BC520 | S | N | F | (BC414C) | | | | | 01 |
| | | | | | | | | | |
| BC520B | S | N | F | (BC414B) | | | | | 01 |
| BC520C | S | N | F | (BC414C) | | | | | 01 |
| BC521 | S | N | F | (BC414C) | | | | | 01 |
| BC521C | S | N | F | (BC414C) | | | | | 01 |
| BC521D | S | N | F | (BC414C) | | | | | 01 |
| | | | | | | | | | |
| BC522 | S | N | F | (BC413C) | | | | | 01 |
| BC522C | S | N | F | (BC413C) | | | | | 01 |
| BC522D | S | N | F | (BC413C) | | | | | 01 |
| BC522E | S | N | F | (BC413C) | | | | | 01 |
| BC523 | S | N | F | BC414B | | | | | 01 |
| | | | | | | | | | |
| BC523B | S | N | F | BC414B | | | | | 01 |
| BC523C | S | N | F | BC414C | | | | | 01 |
| BC526 | S | P | F | BC212 | | | | | 01 |
| BC526A | S | P | F | BC212A | | | | | 01 |
| BC526B | S | P | F | (BC416B) | | | | | 01 |
| | | | | | | | | | |
| BC526C | S | P | F | (BC416) | | | | | 01 |
| BC527 | S | P | F | (BSV16) | | | | | 01 |
| BC527-6 | S | P | F | (BSV16-6) | | | | | 01 |
| BC527-10 | S | P | F | (BSV16-10) | | | | | 01 |
| BC527-16 | S | P | F | (BSV16-16) | | | | | 01 |
| | | | | | | | | | |
| BC527-25 | S | P | F | (BSV16-16) | | | | | 01 |
| BC528 | S | P | F | (BSV17) | | | | | 01 |
| BC528-6 | S | P | F | (BSV17-6) | | | | | 01 |
| BC528-10 | S | P | F | (BSV17-10) | | | | | 01 |
| BC528-16 | S | P | F | (BSV17-10) | | | | | 01 |
| | | | | | | | | | |
| BC528-25 | S | P | F | (BSV17-10) | | | | | 01 |
| BC532 | S | N | F | (BF457) | | | | | 01 |
| BC533 | S | N | F | (BF458) | | | | | 01 |
| BC534 | S | P | F | (BSV17-10) | | | | | 01 |
| BC535 | S | N | F | (BSX47-10) | | | | | 01 |
| | | | | | | | | | |
| BC537 | S | N | F | (BSX46) | | | | | 01 |
| BC537-6 | S | P | F | (BSX46-6) | | | | | 01 |
| BC537-10 | S | P | F | (BXV46-10) | | | | | 01 |
| BC537-16 | S | N | F | (BSX46-16) | | | | | 01 |
| BC537-25 | S | N | F | (BSX46-16) | | | | | 01 |
| | | | | | | | | | |
| BC538 | S | N | F | (BSX47) | | | | | 01 |
| BC538-6 | S | N | F | (BSX47-6) | | | | | 01 |
| BC538-10 | S | N | F | (BSX47-10) | | | | | 01 |
| BC538-16 | S | N | F | (BSX47-10) | | | | | 01 |
| BC538-25 | S | N | F | (BSX47-10) | | | | | 01 |
| | | | | | | | | | |
| BC547 | S | N | MU, PH, S, V | BC107 | BC338 | 2N5818 | | | 01 |
| BC547 | | | | BC407 | BC147 | | | | 01 |
| BC547A | S | N | PH | BC407A | BC147A | | | | 01 |
| BC547A | | | | BC107A | | | | | 01 |
| BC547B | S | N | PH | BC407B | BC147B | | | | 01 |
| | | | | | | | | | |
| BC547B | | | | BC107B | | | | | 01 |
| BC548 | S | N | MU, PH, S, V | BC108 | BC338 | 2N5818 | | | 01 |
| BC548 | | | | BC408 | BC148 | | | | 01 |
| BC548A | S | N | PH | BC408A | BC148A | | | | 01 |
| BC548A | | | | BC108A | | | | | 01 |

| TYPE | M/S | POL | MANUFAC | EUROPEAN | | AMERICAN | | JAPANESE | USE |
|------|-----|-----|---------|----------|----|----------|----|----------|-----|
| BC548B | S | N | PH | BC408B | BC148B | | | | 01 |
| BC548B | | | | BC108B | | | | | 01 |
| BC548C | S | N | PH | BC408C | BC148C | | | | 01 |
| BC548C | | | | BC108C | | | | | 01 |
| BC549 | S | N | MU, PH, S, V | BC109 | BC338 | 2N5818 | | | 01 |
| BC549 | | | | BC409 | BC149 | | | | 01 |
| BC549B | S | N | PH | BC409B | BC149B | | | | 01 |
| BC549B | | | | BC109B | | | | | 01 |
| BC549C | S | N | PH | BC409C | BC149C | | | | 01 |
| BC549C | | | | BC109C | | | | | 01 |
| BC557 | S | P | MU, PH, S, V | BC307 | BC157 | 2N6015 | | | 01 |
| BC557 | | | | BC177 | | | | | 01 |
| BC558 | S | P | MU, PH, S, V | BC178 | BC307 | 2N6015 | | | 01 |
| BC558 | | | | BC308 | BC158 | | | | 01 |
| BC558A | S | P | PH | BC308A | BC158A | | | | 01 |
| BC558A | | | | BC178A | | | | | 01 |
| BC558B | S | P | PH | BC308B | BC158B | | | | 01 |
| BC558B | | | | BC178B | | | | | 01 |
| BC558V1 | S | P | MU, PH, V, S | BC558A | | | | | 01 |
| BC559 | S | P | MU, PH, V, S | BC309 | BC159 | 2N6003 | | | 01 |
| BC559 | | | | BC179 | | | | | 01 |
| BC559A | S | P | PH | BC159A | BC179A | | | | 01 |
| BC559A | | | | BC309A | | | | | 01 |
| BC559B | S | P | PH | BC159B | BC179A | | | | 01 |
| BC559B | | | | BC309A | | | | | 01 |
| BC582 | S | N | TX | BC237 | | | | | 01 |
| BC582A | S | N | TX | BC237A | BC237 | 2N5825 | | | 01 |
| BC582B | S | N | TX | BC237B | BC239 | 2N5827 | | | 01 |
| BC583 | S | N | TX | BC238 | | | | | 01 |
| BC583A | S | N | TX | BC238A | BC237 | 2N5825 | | | 01 |
| BC583B | S | N | TX | BC238B | BC239 | 2N5827 | | | 01 |
| BC583C | S | N | TX | BC238C | BC239 | 2N5827 | | | 01 |
| BC584 | S | N | TX | BC239 | | | | | 01 |
| BC584B | S | N | TX | BC239B | | 2N5827 | | | 01 |
| BC584C | S | N | TX | BC239C | | 2N5827 | | | 01 |
| BC612 | S | P | TX | (BCY77V11) | | | | | 01 |
| BC682 | S | N | TX | (BCY65EV11) | | | | | 01 |
| BC727 | S | P | F | BC327 | | | | | 01 |
| BC727-10 | S | P | F | BC327-16 | | | | | 01 |
| BC727-16 | S | P | F | BC327-16 | | | | | 01 |
| BC727-25 | S | P | F | BC327-25 | | | | | 01 |
| BC727-40 | S | P | F | BC327-40 | | | | | 01 |
| BC728 | S | P | F | BC328 | | | | | 01 |
| BC728-10 | S | P | F | BC328-16 | | | | | 01 |
| BC728-16 | S | P | F | BC328-16 | | | | | 01 |
| BC728-25 | S | P | F | BC328-25 | | | | | 01 |
| BC728-40 | S | P | F | BC328-40 | | | | | 01 |
| BC737 | S | N | F | BC337 | | | | | 01 |
| BC737-10 | S | N | F | BC337-16 | | | | | 01 |
| BC737-16 | S | N | F | BC337-16 | | | | | 01 |
| BC737-25 | S | N | F | BC337-25 | | | | | 01 |
| BC737-40 | S | N | F | BC337-40 | | | | | 01 |
| BC738 | S | N | F | BC338 | | | | | 01 |
| BC738-10 | S | N | F | BC338-6 | | | | | 01 |
| BC738-16 | S | N | F | BC338-16 | | | | | 01 |
| BC738-25 | S | N | F | BC338-25 | | | | | 01 |
| BC738-40 | S | N | F | BC338-40 | | | | | 01 |
| BCW10 | S | N | FE | BC338-16 | BC387 | 2N4401 | | | 01 |
| BCW10K | S | N | FE | BC338-16 | | | | | 01 |
| BCW10L | S | N | FE | BC338-16 | | | | | 01 |
| BCW10M | S | N | FE | BC338-16 | | | | | 01 |
| BCW11 | S | P | FE | BC328-16 | | | | | 01 |
| BCW11K | S | P | FE | BC328-16 | | | | | 01 |
| BCW11L | S | P | FE | BC328-16 | | | | | 01 |
| BCW11M | S | P | FE | BC328-16 | | | | | 01 |
| BCW12 | S | N | FE | BC337-16 | BC387 | 2N4401 | | | 01 |
| BCW12K | S | N | FE | BC337-16 | | | | | 01 |
| BCW12L | S | N | FE | BC337-16 | | | | | 01 |
| BCW12M | S | N | FE | BC337-16 | | | | | 01 |
| BCW13 | S | P | FE | BC327-16 | | | | | 01 |
| BCW13K | S | P | FE | BC327-16 | | | | | 01 |
| BCW13L | S | P | FE | BC327-16 | | | | | 01 |
| BCW13M | S | P | FE | BC327-16 | | | | | 01 |
| BCW14 | S | N | FE | BC337-16 | BC387 | 2N4401 | | | 01 |
| BCW14K | S | N | FE | BC337-16 | | | | | 01 |

| TYPE | M/S | POL | MANUFAC | EUROPEAN | | AMERICAN | JAPANESE | USE |
|---|---|---|---|---|---|---|---|---|
| BCW14L | S | N | FE | BC337-16 | | | | 01 |
| BCW14M | S | N | FE | BC337-16 | | | | 01 |
| BCW15 | S | P | FE | BC327-16 | | | | 01 |
| BCW15K | S | P | FE | BC327-16 | | | | 01 |
| BCW15L | S | P | FE | BC327-16 | | | | 01 |
| BCW15M | S | P | FE | BC327-16 | | | | 01 |
| BCW16 | S | N | FE | BC337-16 | BC387 | 2N4401 | | 01 |
| BCW16K | S | N | FE | BC337-16 | | | | 01 |
| BCW16L | S | N | FE | BC337-16 | | | | 01 |
| BCW16M | S | N | FE | BC337-16 | | | | 01 |
| BCW17 | S | P | FE | BC327-16 | | | | 01 |
| BCW17K | S | P | FE | BC327-16 | | | | 01 |
| BCW17L | S | P | FE | BC327-16 | | | | 01 |
| BCW17M | S | P | FE | BC327-16 | | | | 01 |
| BCW18 | S | N | FE | (BC337-16) | BC387 | 2N4401 | | 01 |
| BCW18K | S | N | FE | (BC337-16) | | | | 01 |
| BCW18L | S | N | FE | (BC337-16) | | | | 01 |
| BCW18M | S | N | FE | (BC337-16) | | | | 01 |
| BCW19 | S | P | FE | (BC327-16) | | | | 01 |
| BCW19K | S | P | FE | (BC327-16) | | | | 01 |
| BCW19L | S | P | FE | (BC327-16) | | | | 01 |
| BCW19M | S | P | FE | (BC327-16) | | | | 01 |
| BCW20 | S | N | FE | BC337-40 | BC349C | 2N3904 | | 01 |
| BCW20K | S | N | FE | BC337-40 | | | | 01 |
| BCW20L | S | N | FE | BC337-40 | | | | 01 |
| BCW20M | S | N | FE | BC337-40 | | | | 01 |
| BCW21 | S | P | FE | BC327-40 | BC309 | 2N6003 | | 01 |
| BCW21K | S | P | FE | BC327-40 | | | | 01 |
| BCW21L | S | P | FE | BC327-40 | | | | 01 |
| BCW21M | S | P | FE | BC327-40 | | | | 01 |
| BCW22 | S | N | FE | BC337-40 | BC349C | 2N3904 | | 01 |
| BCW22K | S | N | FE | BC337-40 | | | | 01 |
| BCW22L | S | N | FE | BC337-40 | | | | 01 |
| BCW22M | S | N | FE | BC337-40 | | | | 01 |
| BCW23 | S | P | FE | BC327-40 | BC309 | 2N6003 | | 01 |
| BCW23K | S | P | FE | BC327-40 | | | | 01 |
| BCW23L | S | P | FE | BC327-40 | | | | 01 |
| BCW23M | S | P | FE | BC327-40 | | | | 01 |
| BCW24 | S | N | FE, IN | BC414B | BC109 | 2N930 | | 01 |
| BCW29 | S | P | PH, V, RA | BCW618A | BFS37 | | | 01 |
| BCW29R | S | P | MU | BFS37 | | | | 01 |
| BCW30 | S | P | PH, V, RA | BCW61BC | BFS37 | | | 01 |
| BCW30R | S | P | MU | BFS37 | | | | 01 |
| BCW31 | S | N | PH, V | BFS36 | | | | 01 |
| BCW31R | S | N | MU | BFS36 | | | | 01 |
| BCW32 | S | N | PH, V, RA | BCW60AC | BFS36 | | | 01 |
| BCW32R | S | N | MU | BFS36 | | | | 01 |
| BCW33 | S | N | PH, V, RA | BCW60AD | BFS36 | | | 01 |
| BCW33R | S | N | MU | BFS36 | | | | 01 |
| BCW34 | S | N | TX | (BC337-16) | BFX95 | 2N2222A | | 01 |
| BCW35 | S | P | TX | (BC327-16) | BSW24 | 2N2907A | | 01 |
| BCW36 | S | N | TX | (BC337-16) | BSX95 | 2N2222A | | 01 |
| BCW37 | S | P | TX | (BC327-16) | BSW24 | 2N2907A | | 01 |
| BCW38 | S | N | TX | (BC337-16) | | | | 01 |
| BCW39 | S | N | TX | (BC337-16) | | | | 01 |
| BCW44 | S | N | SG, AT | BC141 | BFX85 | 40360 | 2N1893 | 01 |
| BCW45 | S | P | SG, AT | BC161 | | 40362 | | 01 |
| BCW46 | S | N | PH, V, RA | BCY65E | | SE4020 | | 01 |
| BCW46A | S | N | PH, V, RA | BCY65EVII | | | | 01 |
| BCW46B | S | N | PH, V, RA | BCY65EIX | | | | 01 |
| BCW47 | S | N | PH, V, RA | BC237 | BC207 | | | 01 |
| BCW47A | | | | BC317 | | | | 01 |
| BCW47A | S | N | PH, V, RA | BC237A | | | | 01 |
| BCW47B | S | N | PH, V, RA | BC237B | | | | 01 |
| BCW46 | S | N | PH, V, RA | BC238 | BC208 | | | 01 |
| BCW48 | | | | BC318 | | | | 01 |
| BCW48A | S | N | PH, V, RA | BC238A | | | | 01 |
| BCW48B | S | N | PH, V, RA | BC238B | | | | 01 |
| BCW48C | S | N | PH, V, RA | BC238C | | | | 01 |
| BCW49 | S | N | PH, V, RA | BC239 | BC209 | | | 01 |
| BCW49 | | | | BC319 | | | | 01 |
| BCW49B | S | N | PH, V, RA | BC239B | | | | 01 |
| BCW49C | S | N | PH, V, RA | BC239C | | | | 01 |
| BCW50 | S | N | SG, AT | (BF457) | BC285 | 2N1990R | | 01 |
| BCW51 | S | N | TX | BC182B | | | | 01 |

| TYPE | M/S | POL | MANUFAC | EUROPEAN | | AMERICAN | | JAPANESE | USE |
|------|-----|-----|---------|----------|--|----------|--|----------|-----|
| BCW51A | S | N | TX | BC182B | | | | | 01 |
| BCW51B | S | N | TX | BC182B | | | | | 01 |
| BCW52 | S | P | TX | BC212B | | | | | 01 |
| BCW54 | S | N | IN, IT | BCY65EVII | | | | | 01 |
| BCW55 | S | N | IN, IT | BCY65EIX | | | | | 01 |
| BCW56 | S | P | PH, V, RA | BCY77 | | 2N4249 | | | 01 |
| BCW56A | S | P | PH, V, RA | BCY77VII | | | | | 01 |
| BCW57 | S | P | PH, V, RA | BC307 | BC204 | | | | 01 |
| BCW57 | S | P | | BC320 | | | | | 01 |
| BCW57A | S | P | PH, V, RA | BC307A | | | | | 01 |
| BCW57B | S | P | PH, V, RA | BC307B | | | | | 01 |
| BCW58 | S | P | PH, V, RA | BC308 | BC205 | | | | 01 |
| BCW58 | S | P | | BC321 | | | | | 01 |
| BCW58A | S | P | PH, V, RA | BC308A | | | | | 01 |
| BCW58B | S | P | PH, V, RA | BC308B | | | | | 01 |
| BCW59 | S | P | PH, V, RA | BC309 | BC206 | | | | 01 |
| BCW59 | S | P | | BC322 | | | | | 01 |
| BCW59B | S | P | PH, V, RA | BC309B | | | | | 01 |
| BCW62 | S | P | TX | (BC257) | | | | | 01 |
| BCW62A | S | P | TX | (BC257A) | | | | | 01 |
| BCW62B | S | P | TX | (BC257B) | | | | | 01 |
| BCW63 | S | P | TX | (BC257) | | | | | 01 |
| BCW63A | S | P | TX | (BC257A) | | | | | 01 |
| BCW63B | S | P | TX | (BC257B) | | | | | 01 |
| BCW63C | S | P | TX | (BC257B) | | | | | 01 |
| BCW64 | S | P | TX | BC259 | | | | | 01 |
| BCW64A | S | P | TX | (BC259B) | | | | | 01 |
| BCW64B | S | P | TX | (BC259B) | | | | | 01 |
| BCW64C | S | P | TX | (BC259C) | | | | | 01 |
| BCW69 | S | P | P-I, V | BCX71BG | BFS37 | | | | 01 |
| BCW69R | S | P | MU | BFS37 | | | | | 01 |
| BCW70 | S | P | PH, V | BCX71BJ | BFS37 | | | | 01 |
| BCW70R | S | P | MU | BFS37 | | | | | 01 |
| BCW71 | S | N | PH, V | BCX70AG | BFS36 | | | | 01 |
| BCW71R | S | N | MU | BFS36 | | | | | 01 |
| BCW72 | S | N | PH, V | BCX70AJ | BFS36 | | | | 01 |
| BCW72R | S | N | MU | BFS36 | | | | | 01 |
| BCW73 | S | N | S | BFX95 | | 2N2222A | | | 01 |
| BCW73-16 | S | N | S | BFX95 | | 2N2222A | | | 01 |
| BCW73-25 | S | N | S | BFX95 | | 2N2222A | | | 01 |
| BCW73-40 | S | N | S | BFX95 | | 2N2222A | | | 01 |
| BCW74 | S | N | S | BFX95 | | 2N2222A | | | 01 |
| BCW74-16 | S | N | S | BFX95 | | 2N2222A | | | 01 |
| BCW74-25 | S | N | S | BFX95 | | 2N2222A | | | 01 |
| BCW74-40 | S | N | S | BFX95 | | 2N2222A | | | 01 |
| BCW75 | S | P | S | BSW24 | | 2N2907A | | | 01 |
| BCW75-10 | S | P | S | BSW24 | | 2N2907A | | | 01 |
| BCW75-16 | S | P | S | BSW24 | | 2N2907A | | | 01 |
| BCW75-25 | S | P | S | BSW24 | | 2N2907A | | | 01 |
| BCW76 | S | P | S | BSW24 | | 2N2907A | | | 01 |
| BCW76-10 | S | P | S | BSW24 | | 2N2907A | | | 01 |
| BCW76-16 | S | P | S | BSW24 | | 2N2907A | | | 01 |
| BCW76-25 | S | P | S | BSW24 | | 2N2907A | | | 01 |
| BCW77 | S | N | S | BFY51 | | 2N2297 | | | 01 |
| BCW77-16 | S | N | S | BFY51 | | 2N1711 | 2N2297 | | 01 |
| BCW77-25 | S | N | S | BFY51 | | 2N2297 | | | 01 |
| BCW78 | S | N | S | BFY51 | | 2N2297 | | | 01 |
| BCW78-16 | S | N | S | BFY52 | | 2N1711 | 2N2297 | | 01 |
| BCW78-25 | S | N | S | BFY50 | | 2N2297 | | | 01 |
| BCW78-40 | S | N | S | BFY51 | | 2N2297 | | | 01 |
| BCW79 | S | P | S | BFS95 | | 2N4036 | | | 01 |
| BCW79-10 | S | P | S | BFS95 | | 2N4036 | | | 01 |
| BCW79-16 | S | P | S | BFS95 | | 2N4037 | 2N4036 | | 01 |
| BCW79-25 | S | P | S | BFS95 | | 2N4036 | | | 01 |
| BCW80 | S | P | S | BFS95 | | 2N4036 | | | 01 |
| BCW80-10 | S | P | S | BFS95 | | 2N4036 | | | 01 |
| BCW80-16 | S | P | S | BFS95 | | 2N4037 | 2N4036 | | 01 |
| BCW80-25 | S | P | S | BFS95 | | 2N4036 | | | 01 |
| BCW82 | S | N | TX | (BC167) | | | | | 01 |
| BCW82A | S | N | TX | (BC167A) | | | | | 01 |
| BCW82B | S | N | TX | (BC167B) | | | | | 01 |
| BCW83 | S | N | TX | (BC167) | | | | | 01 |
| BCW83A | S | N | TX | (BC167A) | | | | | 01 |
| BCW83B | S | N | TX | (BC167B) | | | | | 01 |
| BCW83C | S | N | TX | (BC167B) | | | | | 01 |

| TYPE | M/S | POL | MANUFAC | EUROPEAN | | | AMERICAN | | JAPANESE | USE |
|------|-----|-----|---------|----------|---|---|----------|---|----------|-----|
| BCW84 | S | N | TX | (BC169) | | | | | | 01 |
| BCW84B | S | N | TX | (BC169B) | | | | | | 01 |
| BCW84C | S | N | TX | (BC169C) | | | | | | 01 |
| BCW85 | S | P | TX | BCY77VII | BC307 | 2N2907A | 2N6015 | | | 01 |
| BCW86 | S | P | TX | BCY77VIII | BC177A | 2N6015 | | | | 01 |
| | | | | | | | | | | |
| BCW86 | | | | BC307 | | | | | | 01 |
| BCW90 | S | N | SB, Ss, ML, SE | BC337 | | | | | | 01 |
| BCW90A | S | N | SB, SE | BC337-16 | BC338 | 2N5818 | | | | 01 |
| BCW90B | S | N | SB, SE | BC337-25 | BC338 | 2N5818 | | | | 01 |
| BCW90C | S | N | SE | BC338 | | 2N5818 | | | | 01 |
| | | | | | | | | | | |
| BCW90K | S | N | SB, Ss, ML, SE | (BC337) | | | | | | 01 |
| BCW90KA | S | N | SB, SE | (BC337-16) | BFY50 | 2N2297 | | | | 01 |
| BCW90KB | S | N | SB, SE | (BC337-25) | BFY50 | 2N2297 | | | | 01 |
| BCW90KC | S | N | SB, SE | (BC337-40) | BFY50 | 2N2297 | | | | 01 |
| BCW91 | S | N | SB, Ss, ML, SE | (BC337) | | | | | | 01 |
| | | | | | | | | | | |
| BCW91A | S | N | SB, SE | (BC337-16) | BC338 | 2N5818 | | | | 01 |
| BCW91B | S | N | SB, SE | (BC337-25) | BC338 | 2N5818 | | | | 01 |
| BCW91K | S | N | SB, Ss, ML, SE | (BC337) | | | | | | 01 |
| BCW91KA | S | N | SB, SE | (BC337-16) | BFY50 | 2N2297 | | | | 01 |
| BCW91KB | S | N | SB, SE | (BC337-25) | BFY50 | 2N2297 | | | | 01 |
| | | | | | | | | | | |
| BCW92 | S | P | SB, Ss, ML, SE | BC327 | | | | | | 01 |
| BCW92A | S | P | SB, SE | (BC327-16) | BC328 | 2N5819 | | | | 01 |
| BCW92B | S | P | SB, SE | BC327-25 | BC328 | 2N5819 | | | | 01 |
| BCW92K | S | P | SB, Ss, ML, SE | (BC327) | | | | | | 01 |
| BCW92KA | S | P | SB, SE | (BC327-16) | BFS95 | 2N4036 | | | | 01 |
| | | | | | | | | | | |
| BCW92KB | S | P | SB, SE | BC327-25 | BFS95 | 2N5819 | | | | 01 |
| BCW93 | S | P | SB, SE | (BC327) | | | | | | 01 |
| BCW93A | S | P | SB, SE | (BC327-16) | BC327 | 2N5819 | | | | 01 |
| BCW93B | S | P | SB, SE | (BC327-25) | BC327 | 2N5819 | | | | 01 |
| BCW93K | S | P | SB, Ss, ML, SE | (BC327) | | | | | | 01 |
| | | | | | | | | | | |
| BCW93KA | S | P | SB, SE | (BC327-16) | BFS95 | 2N4036 | | | | 01 |
| BCW93KB | S | P | SB, SE | (BC327-25) | BFS95 | 2N4036 | | | | 01 |
| BCW94 | S | N | SB, Ss, ML, SE | BC337 | | | | | | 01 |
| BCW94A | S | N | SB, SE | BC337-16 | BC337 | 2N5818 | | | | 01 |
| BCW94B | S | N | SB, SE | BC337-25 | BC337 | 2N5818 | | | | 01 |
| | | | | | | | | | | |
| BCW94C | S | N | SB, SE | BC337-40 | BC337 | 2N5818 | | | | 01 |
| BCW94K | S | N | SB, Ss, ML, SE | BC337 | | | | | | 01 |
| BCW94KA | S | N | SB, SE | BC337-16 | BFY50 | 2N2297 | | | | 01 |
| BCW94KB | S | N | SB, SE | BC337-25 | BFY50 | 2N2297 | | | | 01 |
| BCW94KC | S | N | SB, SE | BC337-40 | BFY50 | 2N2297 | | | | 01 |
| | | | | | | | | | | |
| BCW95 | S | N | SB, Ss, ML, SE | (BC337) | | | | | | 01 |
| BCW95A | S | N | SB, SE | (BC337-16) | BC337 | 2N5818 | | | | 01 |
| BCW95B | S | N | SB, SE | BC337-25 | BC338 | 2N5818 | | | | 01 |
| BCW95K | S | N | SB, Ss, ML, SE | (BC337) | | | | | | 01 |
| BCW95KA | S | N | SB, SE | (BC337-16) | BFY50 | 2N2297 | | | | 01 |
| | | | | | | | | | | |
| BCW95KB | S | N | SB, SE | (BC337-25) | BFY50 | 2N2297 | | | | 01 |
| BCW96 | S | P | SB, Ss, ML, SE | BC327 | | | | | | 01 |
| BCW96A | S | P | SB, SE | BC327-16 | BC327 | 2N5819 | | | | 01 |
| BCW96B | S | P | SB, SE | BC327-25 | BC327 | 2N5819 | | | | 01 |
| BCW96K | S | P | SB, Ss, ML, SE | BC327 | | | | | | 01 |
| | | | | | | | | | | |
| BCW96KA | S | P | SB, SE | BC327-16 | BFS95 | 2N4036 | | | | 01 |
| BCW96KB | S | P | SB, SE | BC327-25 | BFS95 | 2N4036 | | | | 01 |
| BCW97 | S | P | SB, Ss, ML, SE | (BC327) | | | | | | 01 |
| BCW97A | S | P | SB, SE | (BC327-16) | BC327 | 2N5819 | | | | 01 |
| BCW97B | S | P | SB, SE | (BC327-25) | BC327 | 2N5819 | | | | 01 |
| | | | | | | | | | | |
| BCW97K | S | P | SB, Ss, ML, SE | (BC327) | | | | | | 01 |
| BCW97KA | S | P | SB, SE | (BC327-16) | BFS95 | 2N4036 | | | | 01 |
| BCW97KB | S | P | SB, SE | (BC327-25) | BFS95 | 2N4036 | | | | 01 |
| BCW98 | S | N | TF | (BC123) | | | | | | 01 |
| BCW98A | S | N | TF | (BC123ye) | | | | | | 01 |
| | | | | | | | | | | |
| BCW98B | S | N | TF | (BC123gn) | | | | | | 01 |
| BCW98C | S | N | TF | (BC123gn) | | | | | | 01 |
| BCW98D | S | N | TF | (BC123bl) | | | | | | 01 |
| BCW99 | S | P | TF | (BC203ye) | | | | | | 01 |
| BCW99A | S | P | TF | (BC203ye) | | | | | | 01 |
| | | | | | | | | | | |
| BCW99B | S | P | TF | (BC203gn) | | | | | | 01 |
| BCW99C | S | P | TF | (BC203gn) | | | | | | 01 |
| BCX10 | S | P | AT | BC161-6 | | | | | | 01 |
| BCX17 | S | P | MU, V, PH | BCW68 | | | | | | 01 |
| BCX18 | S | P | MU, V, PH | BCW68 | | | | | | 01 |
| | | | | | | | | | | |
| BCX19 | S | N | MU, V, PH | BCW66 | | | | | | 01 |
| BCX20 | S | N | MU, V, PH | BCW66 | | | | | | 01 |
| BCX40 | S | N | AT | (BSX47) | BFX85 | 2N1893 | | | | 01 |
| BCX40-4 | S | N | AT | (BSX47-6) | | | | | | 01 |
| BCX40-5 | S | N | AT | (BSX47-10) | | | | | | 01 |

| TYPE | M/S | POL | MANUFAC | EUROPEAN | | AMERICAN | | JAPANESE | USE |
|------|-----|-----|---------|----------|---|----------|---|----------|-----|
| BCX40-6 | S | N | AT | (BSX47-10) | | | | | 01 |
| BCX60 | S | P | AT | (BSV17) | BFS93 | 2N4037 | | | 01 |
| BCX60-4 | S | P | AT | (BSV17-6) | | | | | 01 |
| BCX60-5 | S | P | AT | (BSV17-10) | | | | | 01 |
| BCX60-6 | S | P | AT | (BSV17-10) | | | | | 01 |
| | | | | | | | | | |
| BCY10 | S | P | PH, PE, V | (BC327-16) | BCY32 | 2N1475 | | | 01 |
| BCY11 | S | P | PH, PE, V | (BC327-16) | BCY32 | 2N1475 | | | 01 |
| BCY12 | S | P | PH, PE, V | (BC327-16) | BC160 | 2N1132 | 2N1475 | | 01 |
| BCY12 | | | | BCY32 | | | | | 01 |
| BCY13 | S | N | S | BCY65EVII | BSW66 | 2N2219 | 2N1893 | | 01 |
| | | | | | | | | | |
| BCY14 | S | N | S | (BF457) | BFY13 | 2N2219 | 2N1893 | | 01 |
| BCY14 | | | | BSW66 | | | | | 01 |
| BCY15 | S | N | S | BCY65EVII | BFY14 | 2N2219 | 2N1893 | | 01 |
| BCY15 | | | | BSW66 | | | | | 01 |
| BCY16 | S | N | S | (BF457) | BFY14 | 2N2219 | 2N1893 | | 01 |
| | | | | | | | | | |
| BCY16 | | | | BSY18 | BSW66 | | | | 01 |
| BCY17 | S | P | TA, S | (BC307A) | BCY12 | 2N4036 | | | 01 |
| BCY17 | | | | BCY34 | BSF95 | | | | 01 |
| BCY18 | S | P | TA, S | (BC307A) | BCY12 | 2N4036 | | | 01 |
| BCY18 | | | | BCZ11 | BSF95 | | | | 01 |
| | | | | | | | | | |
| BCY19 | S | P | TA, S | (BC212A) | BCY11 | 2N1475 | | | 01 |
| BCY19 | | | | BCY31 | BCZ12 | | | | 01 |
| BCY19 | | | | BCY32 | | | | | 01 |
| BCY20 | S | P | TA, S | (BC212A) | BCY30 | 2N1475- | | | 01 |
| BCY20 | | | | BCY32 | | | | | 01 |
| | | | | | | | | | |
| BCY21 | S | P | TA | (BC212A) | BCY32 | 2N1475 | | | 01 |
| BCY22 | S | P | TA | (BC212A) | BSV68 | 2N3497 | | | 01 |
| BCY23 | S | P | TA | (BC308A) | BCY32 | 2N1475 | | | 01 |
| BCY24 | S | P | TA | (BC308A) | BCY32 | 2N1475 | | | 01 |
| BCY25 | S | P | TA | (BC308A) | BCY32 | 2N1475 | | | 01 |
| | | | | | | | | | |
| BCY26 | S | P | TA | (BC307A) | BCY32 | 2N1475 | | | 01 |
| BCY27 | S | P | TA, S | (BC308A) | BCY31 | 2N1475 | | | 01 |
| BCY27 | | | | BCZ10 | BCY32 | | | | 01 |
| BCY28 | S | P | TA, S | (BC308A) | BCY31 | 2N1475 | | | 01 |
| BCY28 | | | | BCY32 | BCZ11 | | | | 01 |
| | | | | | | | | | |
| BCY29 | S | P | TA, S | (BC212A) | BCY30 | 2N1475 | | | 01 |
| BCY29 | | | | BCY32 | BCZ12 | | | | 01 |
| BCY30 | S | P | MU, PH, V, PE | BCW56A | (BC212A) | 2N1475 | | | 01 |
| BCY30 | | | | BCY29 | BCY32 | | | | 01 |
| BCY31 | S | P | MU, PH, V, PE | BCW56A | (BC212A) | 2N1475- | | | 01 |
| | | | | | | | | | |
| BCY31 | | | | BCY32 | BCY27 | | | | 01 |
| BCY31 | | | | BCY28 | | | | | 01 |
| BCY32 | S | P | MU, PH, V, PE, TA | (BC212A) | | 2N1475 | | | 01 |
| BCY33 | S | P | MU, PH, V, PE, TA | (BC213A) | BCY32 | 2N1475 | | | 01 |
| BCY34 | S | P | MU, PH, V, PE, TA | (BC308A) | BCY78VII | | | | 01 |
| | | | | | | | | | |
| BCY34 | | | | BC177 | BCY17 | | | | 01 |
| BCY34 | | | | BC261 | BCY27 | | | | 01 |
| BCY34 | | | | BCY32 | | | | | 01 |
| BCY38 | S | P | MU, PH, V, PE | (BC328-16) | BCY32 | 2N1475 | | | 01 |
| BCY39 | S | P | MU, PH, V, PE | (BC327-16) | BC161 | 2N2904A | 2N2904 | | 01 |
| | | | | | | | | | |
| BCY39 | | | | BCY32 | | 2N1475 | | | 01 |
| BCY40 | S | P | MU, PH, V, RA, PE | (BC328-16) | BCY32 | 2N4037 | | | 01 |
| BCY42 | S | N | F, SG, IT, TX | BC107A | BC237A | 2N929 | | | 01 |
| BCY42 | | | | BC107 | | | | | 01 |
| BCY43 | S | N | F, SG, MU, IT, TX | BC107A | BC237A | 2N930 | | | 01 |
| | | | | | | | | | |
| BCY43 | | | | BC109 | | | | | 01 |
| BCY49 | S | P | MU | (BC308A) | BCY32 | 2N1475 | | | 01 |
| BCY50 | S | N | IN, IT | BC107 | BC238A | MPS6520 | A157 | | 01 |
| BCY50 | | | | BC183 | BC108A | | | | 01 |
| BCY50 | | | | BC108B | BC183B | | | | 01 |
| | | | | | | | | | |
| BCY50i | S | N | IN, IT | BC238A | BC108B | | | | 01 |
| BCY50i | | | | BC183B | | | | | 01 |
| BCY50i | S | N | IN, IT | BC239B | BC109B | | | | 01 |
| BCY50i | | | | BC184B | | | | | 01 |
| BCY51 | S | N | IN, IT | BC108A | BC238A | MPS6520 | A157 | | 01 |
| | | | | | | | | | |
| BCY51 | | | | BC183 | BC107 | | | | 01 |
| BCY51 | | | | BC183B | BC107B | | | | 01 |
| BCY51i | S | N | IN, IT | BC238A | BC107B | | | | 01 |
| BCY51i | | | | BC182B | | | | | 01 |
| BCY51r | S | N | IN, IT | BC184 | BC239B | MPS6521 | | | 01 |
| | | | | | | | | | |
| BCY51r | | | | BC184B | BC109 | | | | 01 |
| BCY51r | | | | BC109B | | | | | 01 |
| BCY54 | S | P | MU,PH, V, RA, PE | (BC327-16) | BCY32 | 2N4036 | 2N1475 | | 01 |
| BCY55 | S | N | PH, MU, V | | | 2N2060B | 2N2642 | | 01 |
| BCY56 | S | N | PH, MN, RA, TX, V | BC414B | BC107 | FT107B | SE4021 | | 01 |

| TYPE | M/S | POL | MANUFAC | EUROPEAN | | AMERICAN | | JAPANESE | USE |
|---|---|---|---|---|---|---|---|---|---|
| BCY56 | | | | | | 2N2484 | 2N929 | | 01 |
| BCY57 | S | N | PH, V, MN, RA, TX | BC182A | BC413C | FT107A | SE4022 | 2SC648 | 01 |
| BCY57 | | | | BC109 | BCY58 | 2N3568 | 2N2921 | | 01 |
| BCY57 | | | | BC107A | | 2N930 | | | 01 |
| BCY58 | S | N | PH, S, TF, V, IN | BCY58X | AM261 | MPS6566 | SE4022 | 2SC907 | 01 |
| | | | | | | | | | |
| BCY58 | | | | BC182B | BC107B | FT107A | 2N3568 | | 01 |
| BCY58 | | | | BF Y44 | | | | | 01 |
| BCY58A | S | N | IN, TX | BCY58VII | BC107 | A157 | | | 01 |
| BCY58B | S | N | IN, TX | BCY58VIII | BC107 | A157 | | | 01 |
| BCY58C | S | N | IN, TX | BCY58IX | BC109 | 2N930 | | | 01 |
| | | | | | | | | | |
| BCY58D | S | N | PH, S, TF, V | BCY58X | BC109 | 2N930 | | | 01 |
| BCY58-7 | S | N | PH, S, TF, V | BFX95 | | 2N2222A | | | 01 |
| BCY58-8 | S | N | PH, S, TF, V | BFX95 | | 2N2222A | | | 01 |
| BCY58-9 | S | N | PH, S, TF, V | BFX95 | | 2N2222A | | | 01 |
| BCY58-10 | S | N | PH, S, TF, V | BFX95 | | 2N2222A | | | 01 |
| | | | | | | | | | |
| BCY59 | S | N | PH, S, TF, V, IN | BCY59VII | AM262 | MPS6566 | 2N2222A | 2SC907 | 01 |
| BCY59 | | | | BC182B | BC107B | SE4021 | FT107B | | 01 |
| BCY59 | | | | BFX95 | | | | | 01 |
| BCY59A | S | N | IN, SG, TX | BCY59VII | BC107 | A157 | | | 01 |
| BCY59B | S | N | IN, SG, TX | BCY59VIII | BC107 | A157 | | | 01 |
| | | | | | | | | | |
| BCY59C | S | N | IN, SG, TX | BCY59IX | BC109 | 2N930 | | | 01 |
| BCY59D | S | N | IN, SG, TX | BCY59X | BC109 | 2N930 | | | 01 |
| BCY59-7 | S | N | PH, S, TF, V | BFX95 | | 2N2222A | | | 01 |
| BCY59-8 | S | N | PH, S, TF, V | BFX95 | | 2N2222A | | | 01 |
| BCY59-9 | S | N | PH, S, TF, V | BFX95 | | 2N2222A | | | 01 |
| | | | | | | | | | |
| BCY59-10 | S | N | PH, S, TF, V | BFX95 | | 2N2222A | | | 01 |
| BCY65 | S | N | V, TX | BCY65E | BC107B | 2N2484 | 2N2483 | 2SC648 | 01 |
| BCY65 | | | | BFX95 | | FT107C | SE4020 | | 01 |
| BCY65E | S | N | S | BFX95 | | 2N2222A | | | 01 |
| BCY65E7 | S | N | S | BFX95 | | 2N2222A | | | 01 |
| | | | | | | | | | |
| BCY65E8 | S | N | S | BFX95 | | 2N2222A | | | 01 |
| BCY65E9 | S | N | S | BFX95 | | 2N2222A | | | 01 |
| BCY65VII | S | N | V | BCY65EVII | | | | | 01 |
| BCY65VIII | S | N | V | BCY65EVIII | | | | | 01 |
| BCY65IX | S | N | V | BCY65EIX | | | | | 01 |
| | | | | | | | | | |
| BCY66 | S | N | S | BC109 | BC107 | FT107B | SE4021 | 2SC648 | 01 |
| BCY66 | | | | BCY59VII | BC107B | 2N930 | | | 01 |
| BCY67 | S | P | S | BCY71 | | 2N3965 | | | 01 |
| BCY69 | S | N | SB, Ss, ML, SE | BC238C | BC109 | 2N930 | | | 01 |
| BCY70 | | P | MU, PH, V, TX, ME- | BCY77 | BC177 | 2N3964 | 2N2907 | 2SA549 | 01 |
| | | | | | | | | | |
| BCY70 | | | NS, NT, PE, RA, SG | BC261 | BC212 | 2N3965 | | | 01 |
| BCY70 | | | IT | BCY79 | BC204 | | | | 01 |
| BCY71 | S | P | MU, PH, V, IT, ME- | BC416A | | 2N2907 | 2N3964 | | 01 |
| BCY71 | | | NS, NT, PE, RA, TX | | | 2N3965 | | | 01 |
| BCY71 | | | SG | | | | | | 01 |
| | | | | | | | | | |
| BCY71A | S | P | MU, PH, V, IT, ME- | BC416B | BCY71 | 2N3965 | | | 01 |
| BCY71A | | | NS | | | | | | 01 |
| BCY72 | S | P | MU, PH, V, IT, ME- | BCY78VII | BCY70 | 2N3964 | 2N2907 | | 01 |
| BCY72 | | | NS, NT, PE, RA, SG- | | | 2N3965 | | | 01 |
| BCY72 | | | TX | | | | | | 01 |
| | | | | | | | | | |
| BCY78 | S | P | S, PH, TF, V | BC213B | BC177 | 2N3964 | 2N3965 | | 01 |
| BCY78A | S | P | IN | BCY78VII | BC177 | 2N3964 | | | 01 |
| BCY78B | S | P | IN | BCY78VIII | BC179 | 2N3965 | | | 01 |
| BCY78C | S | P | IN | BCY78IX | BC179 | 2N3965 | | | 01 |
| BCY78D | S | P | IN | BCY78X | BC179 | 2N3965 | | | 01 |
| | | | | | | | | | |
| BCY78-7 | S | P | PH, S, TF, V | BC177 | | 2N3965 | | | 01 |
| BCY78-8 | S | P | PH, S, TF, V | BC179 | | 2N3965 | | | 01 |
| BCY78-9 | S | P | PH, S, TF, V | BC179 | | 2N3965 | | | 01 |
| BCY78-10 | S | P | PH, S, TF, V | BC179 | | 2N3965 | | | 01 |
| BCY79 | S | P | PH, S, TF, V | BC177 | | 2N3964 | 2N3965 | | 01 |
| | | | | | | | | | |
| BCY79A | S | P | IN | BCY79VII | BC177 | 2N3965 | | | 01 |
| BCY79B | S | P | IN | BCY79VIII | BC179 | 2N3965 | | | 01 |
| BCY79C | S | P | IN | BCY79IX | BC179 | 2N3965 | | | 01 |
| BCY79-7 | S | P | PH, S, TF, V | BC177 | | 2N3965 | | | 01 |
| BCY79-8 | S | P | PH, S, TF, V | BC179 | | 2N3965 | | | 01 |
| | | | | | | | | | |
| BCY79-9 | S | P | PH, S, TF, V | BC179 | | 2N3965 | | | 01 |
| BCY85 | S | N | TX | (BCY65EVII) | | | | | 01 |
| BCY85A | S | N | TX | (BCY65EVII) | | | | | 01 |
| BCY85B | S | N | TX | BCY65EIX | | | | | 01 |
| BCY86 | S | N | TX | BCY65EVIII | | | | | 01 |
| | | | | | | | | | |
| BCY86A | S | N | TX | (BCY65EVIII) | | | | | 01 |
| BCY86B | S | N | TX | (BCY65EIX) | | | | | 01 |
| BCY90 | S | P | TA | (BC307A) | | | | | 01 |
| BCY90B | S | P | TA | BC307A | | | | | 01 |
| BCY91 | S | P | TA | (BC307A) | | | | | 01 |

| TYPE | M/S | POL | MANUFAC | EUROPEAN | | AMERICAN | | JAPANESE | USE |
|---|---|---|---|---|---|---|---|---|---|
| BCY91B | S | P | IA | (BC307A) | | | | | 01 |
| BCY92 | S | P | TA | (BC307A) | | | | | 01 |
| BCY92B | S | P | TA | (BC307A) | | | | | 01 |
| BCY93 | S | P | TA | (BCY77VII) | | | | | 01 |
| BCY93B | S | P | TA | (BCY77VII) | | | | | 01 |
| BCY94 | S | P | TA | (BCY77VII) | | | | | 01 |
| BCY94B | S | P | TA | (BCY77VII) | | | | | 01 |
| BCY95 | S | P | TA | (BCY77VII) | | | | | 01 |
| BCY95B | S | P | TA | (BCY77VII) | | | | | 01 |
| BCY96 | S | P | TA | (BCY77VII) | | | | | 01 |
| BCY96B | S | P | TA | (BCY77VII) | | | | | 01 |
| BCY97 | S | P | TA | (BCY77VII) | | | | | 01 |
| BCY97B | S | P | TA | (BCY77VII) | | | | | 01 |
| BCY98B | S | P | TA | (BC307A) | | | | | 01 |
| BCZ10 | S | P | MU, PE, RA, V, PH | BCY34 | BCY32 | 2N1475 | | | 01 |
| BCZ10 | | | | BCY17 | (BC308A) | | | | 01 |
| BCZ10 | | | | BC261 | BCY27 | | | | 01 |
| BCZ10 | | | | BC212 | | | | | 01 |
| BCZ11 | S | P | MU, PH, PE, RA, V | BC177 | BCY32 | 2N1475 | | | 01 |
| BCZ11 | | | | (BC308A) | BC261 | | | | 01 |
| BCZ11 | | | | BCY18 | BC212 | | | | 01 |
| BCZ11 | | | | BCY28 | BC204 | | | | 01 |
| BCZ12 | S | P | MU, PH, PE, RA, V | BCY31 | (BCY77VII) | 2N1475 | | | 01 |
| BCZ12 | | | | BCY32 | BCY19 | | | | 01 |
| BCZ12 | | | | BCY29 | | | | | 01 |
| BCZ13 | S | P | V | BCY33 | (BC308A) | | | | 01 |
| BCZ13 | | | | BC178 | BCY27 | | | | 01 |
| BCZ13 | | | | BC261 | BC213 | | | | 01 |
| BCZ14 | S | P | V | BC178 | (BC308A) | | | | 01 |
| BCZ14 | | | | BC261 | BCY28 | | | | 01 |
| BCZ14 | | | | BC213 | | | | | 01 |
| BCZ14 | | | | BC205 | | | | | 01 |
| BD106 | S | N | IN, IT | BDY12 | BD107 | 2N4910 | | | 06 |
| BD106A | S | N | IN, IT | BD124 | BDY12-10 | 2N3054 | | 2SC830 | 06 |
| BD106A | | | | BD109C | BCY47A | | | | 06 |
| BD106A | | | | BD106 | BDY34 | | | | 06 |
| BD106A | | | | BD107 | | | | | 06 |
| BD106B | S | N | IN, IT | BD124 | BDY12-16 | | | 2SC830 | 06 |
| BD106B | | | | BCY47A | BD109D | | | | 06 |
| BD106B | | | | BD106 | BDY34 | | | | 06 |
| BD106B | | | | BD107 | | | | | 06 |
| BD107 | S | N | IN, IT | BDY13 | BD107 | 2N4911 | 2N4912 | | 06 |
| BD107A | S | N | IN | BCY47A | BDY13-10 | 2N3054 | | 2SC830 | 06 |
| BD107A | | | | BD107 | BDY34 | | | | 06 |
| BD107A | | | | BD124 | | | | | 06 |
| BD107B | S | N | IN | BDY13-16 | BD107 | | | 2SC830 | 06 |
| BD109 | S | N | S | BD124 | BDY12 | 2N3054 | | 2SC830 | 06 |
| BD109 | | | | BD107 | BDY39 | | | | 06 |
| BD109 | | | | BDY34 | | | | | 06 |
| BD109B | S | N | S | BDY12-6 | | | | | 06 |
| BD109C | S | N | S | BDY12-10 | | | | | 06 |
| BC109D | S | N | S | BDY12-16 | | | | | 06 |
| BD109-6 | S | N | S | BDY12-6 | | | | | 06 |
| BD109-10 | S | N | S | BDY12-10 | | | | | 06 |
| BD109-16 | S | N | S | BDY12-16 | | | | | 06 |
| BD111 | S | N | AT, SG | BDY72 | (BU310) | 2N3054 | | 2SC681A | 06 |
| BD111 | | | | BD107 | BDY39 | | | | 06 |
| BD111 | | | | BDY34 | | | | | 06 |
| BD111A | S | N | AT, SG | (BU310) | | 2N3715 | | | 06 |
| BD112 | S | N | SG, AT | (BU310) | BDY39 | | | 2SC830 | 06 |
| BD113 | S | N | SG, AT | (BU310) | BDY39 | | | | 06 |
| BD113 | | | | BD145 | | | | | 06 |
| BD115 | S | N | MU, PH, V, RT, TX | BF179C | (BF458) | | | 2SC1546 | 06 |
| BD115 | S | N | AM, PE, RA | BD127 | BF258 | | | | 06 |
| BD115 | | | | BF115 | SFB258 | | | | 06 |
| BD116 | S | N | SG, AT | BD145 | (BU310) | 2N3055 | | | 06 |
| BD116 | | | | BD117 | BDY13 | | | | 06 |
| BD116 | | | | AM291 | BD127 | | | | 06 |
| BD117 | S | N | AT, SG | AM291 | (BU310) | 2N3713 | 2N3055 | 2SC1030 | 06 |
| BD117 | | | | BDY39 | BD127 | | | | 06 |
| BD118 | S | N | SG, AT | BD145 | (BU310) | 2N3055 | | | 06 |
| BD118 | | | | AM291 | BD130 | | | | 06 |
| BD118 | | | | BD127 | | | | | 06 |
| BD119 | S | N | SG, AT | BU111 | BD127 | | | | 06 |
| BD120 | S | N | SG, AT | (BU114) | BU110 | | | | 06 |

| TYPE | M/S | POL | MANUFAC | EUROPEAN | | AMERICAN | | JAPANESE | USE |
|---|---|---|---|---|---|---|---|---|---|
| BD121 | S | N | MU, SQ, V | AM291 | (BU310) | 2N3055 | | | 06 |
| BD121 | | | | BD130 | BD111 | | | | 06 |
| BD123 | S | N | MU, SQ, V | (BU310) | BD130 | 2N3055 | | | 06 |
| BD123 | | | | AM291 | | | | | 06 |
| BD124 | S | N | MU, PH, PE, RA, V | (BU310) | BDY13 | 2N3054 | 2N3055 | | 06 |
| BD124 | | | | BD107 | | | | | 06 |
| BD127 | S | N | TF | BD232 | (BF459) | FT48 | | | 06 |
| BD127 | | | | BU111 | BF458 | | | | 06 |
| BD128 | S | N | TF | (BF459) | BU111 | FT49 | | | 06 |
| BD128 | | | | BD232 | | | | | 06 |
| BD129 | S | N | TF | (BF459) | BU111 | FT50 | | | 06 |
| BD129 | | | | BD232 | | | | | 06 |
| BD130 | S | N | S | AM291 | BDX10 | 2N3055 | | 2SC1030 | 06 |
| BD130 | | | | BDY20 | | | | | 06 |
| BC131 | S | N | MU, PH, V, AM | (BD441) | BD237 | 2N4923 | | | 06 |
| BD132 | S | P | MU, PH, V, AM | (BD438) | BD238 | 2N4920 | | | 06 |
| BD133 | S | N | MU, PH, RA | (BD441) | BD237 | 2N4923 | | | 06 |
| BD135 | S | N | IN, S, TF, V | BD169 | SDA345 | 2N4923 | | | 06 |
| BD135 | | | | BD137 | BC429 | | | | 06 |
| BD136 | S | P | IN, S, TF, V, AM | SDA445 | BD430 | TIP30 | 2N4920 | | 06 |
| BD136 | S | P | MU, PH, RA | BD140 | | | | | 06 |
| BD137 | S | N | IN, S, TF, V, AM | SDA345 | BC429A | TIP29A | 2N4923 | | 06 |
| BD137 | S | N | MU, PH, RA | BD169 | BD169 | | | | 06 |
| BD138 | S | P | IN, S, TF, V, AM | SDB445 | BC430A | TIP30A | 2N4920 | | 06 |
| BD138 | S | P | MU, PH, RA | BD140 | | | | | 06 |
| BD139 | S | N | MU, PH, RA | SD345 | BD169 | TIP29B | 2N4923 | | 06 |
| BD139 | S | N | IN, S, TF, V, AM | | | | | | 06 |
| BD140 | S | P | IN, S, TF, V, AM | SD445 | | TIP30B | 2N4920 | | 06 |
| BD140 | S | P | MU, PH, RA | | | | | | 06 |
| BD141 | S | N | AT | | | 2N5631 | 2N4347 | | 06 |
| BD141 | | | | | | 2N3442 | | | 06 |
| BD142 | S | N | AT, MO | AM291 | BDX10 | 2N6569 | 2N3055 | | 06 |
| BD142 | | | | BDY20 | | | | | 06 |
| BD142-4 | S | N | AT | | | 2N3055 | | | 06 |
| BD142-5 | S | N | AT | | | 2N3055 | | | 06 |
| BD142-6 | S | N | AT | | | 2N3055 | | | 06 |
| BD142-7 | S | N | AT | | | 2N3055 | | | 06 |
| BD144 | S | N | MU, PH, V, AM | BUY77 | BUX18C | | | | 06 |
| BD145 | S | N | V, RA, MU | (BU310) | | | | | 06 |
| BD148 | S | N | S | BDY71 | | 2N3054 | | | 06 |
| BD148-6 | S | N | S | | | 2N3054 | | | 06 |
| BD148-10 | S | N | S | | | 2N3054 | | | 06 |
| BD148-16 | S | N | S | | | 2N3054 | | | 06 |
| BD149 | S | N | S | BDY71 | | 2N3054 | | | 06 |
| BD149-6 | S | N | S | | | 2N3054 | | | 06 |
| BD149-10 | S | N | S | | | 2N3054 | | | 06 |
| BD150 | S | N | SG | (BF459) | | 2N3440 | | | 06 |
| BD150A | S | N | SG, AT | (BF458) | | | | | 06 |
| BD150B | S | N | SG, AT | (BF458) | | | | | 06 |
| BD150C | S | N | SG, AT | (BF459) | | | | | 06 |
| BD151 | S | P | MO | BD436 | BD238 | 2N4920 | | | 06 |
| BD152 | S | P | MO | BD440 | | | | | 06 |
| BD153 | S | N | MO | BD441 | BD589 | 2N6123 | | | 06 |
| BD154 | S | N | MO | BD435 | BD589 | 2N6123 | | | 06 |
| BD155 | S | N | MO | BD439 | BD589 | 2N6123 | | | 06 |
| BD156 | S | P | MO | BD442 | BD238 | 2N4920 | | | 06 |
| BD157 | S | N | MO, SB, SE | (BF459) | BD410 | FT47 | | | 06 |
| BD158 | S | N | MO, SB, SE | BD410 | (BF459) | FT48 | | | 06 |
| BD158 | | | | BD232 | | | | | 06 |
| BD159 | S | N | MO, SB, SE | (BF459) | BD410 | FT49 | | | 06 |
| BD159 | | | | BD232 | | | | | 06 |
| BD160 | S | N | MU, PH, RT | BUY77 | | 2N6510 | | | 06 |
| BD161 | S | N | AT | | | 2N3054 | | | 06 |
| BD162 | S | N | AT, SG | | | 2N3054 | 40250 | | 06 |
| BD162 | | | | | | 2N4910 | | | 06 |
| BD163 | S | N | AT, SG | | | 2N5054 | 2N3054 | | 06 |
| BD163 | | | | | | 2N6260 | 2N4910 | | 06 |
| BD165 | S | N | MO, TF, V | BD437 | BC429 | TIP29 | | | 06 |
| BD165 | | | | BD169 | | | | | 06 |
| BD166 | S | P | MO, TF, V | BD438 | BC430 | TIP30 | 2N4920 | | 06 |
| BD166 | | | | BD140 | | | | | 06 |
| BD167 | S | N | MO, TF, V | BD439 | BD169 | TIP29A | 2N4923 | | 06 |
| BD168 | S | N | MO, TF, V | BD440 | BD140 | TIP30A | 2N4920 | | 06 |
| BD169 | S | N | MO, TF, V | BD441 | BD169 | TIP29B | 2N4923 | | 06 |
| BD170 | S | P | MO, TF, V | BD442 | BD238 | TIP30B | 2N4920 | | 06 |

| TYPE | M/S | POL | MANUFAC | EUROPEAN | | AMERICAN | | JAPANESE | USE |
|------|-----|-----|---------|----------|---|----------|---|----------|-----|
| BD171 | S | N | MO | (BF457) | BD232 | | | | 06 |
| BD172 | S | N | MO | (BF457) | BD232 | | | | 06 |
| BD173 | S | N | MO | (BF458) | BD232 | | | | 06 |
| BD175 | S | N | MO, TF | BD437 | BD237 | 2N6121 | 2N4923 | | 06 |
| BD176 | S | P | MO, TF | BD438 | BD238 | 2N6124 | 2N4920 | | 06 |
| BD177 | S | N | MO, TF | BD439 | BD237 | TIP29A | 2N4923 | | 06 |
| BD178 | S | P | MO, TF | BD440 | BD238 | TIP30A | 2N4920 | | 06 |
| BD179 | S | N | MO, TF | BD441 | BD237 | TIP29B | 2N4923 | | 06 |
| BD180 | S | P | MO, TF | BD442 | BD238 | TIP30B | 2N4920 | | 06 |
| BD181 | S | N | MU, PH, V | BDY20 | | 2N4913 | 2N3055 | | 06 |
| BD182 | S | N | MU, PH, V | BDY20 | | 2N3055 | | | 06 |
| BD183 | S | N | MU, PH, V, AM | BDX50 | | 2N3442 | 2N3716 | | 06 |
| BD183 | | | | | | 2N3773 | | | 06 |
| BD184 | S | N | MU | | | 2N3442 | | | 06 |
| BD185 | S | N | MO, TF | BD441 | BD221 | 2N5192 | | | 06 |
| BD185 | | | | BD239 | BD437 | | | | 06 |
| BD186 | S | P | MO, TF | BD442 | BD224 | 2N5195 | | | 06 |
| BD186 | | | | BD438 | BD240 | | | | 06 |
| BD187 | S | N | MO, TF | BD439 | BD239 | 2N6121 | 2N5192 | | 06 |
| BD187 | | | | BD441 | | | | | 06 |
| BD188 | S | P | MO, TF | BD440 | BD240 | 2N6124 | 2N5195 | | 06 |
| BD188 | | | | BD442 | | | | | 06 |
| BD189 | S | N | MO, TF | BD222 | BD239A | 2N5192 | | | 06 |
| BD189 | | | | BD441 | | | | | 06 |
| BD190 | S | P | MO, TF | BD442 | BD225 | 2N5195 | | | 06 |
| BD190 | | | | BD240A | BD240 | | | | 06 |
| BD191 | S | N | AT, SG | | | (2N3055) | 2N3054 | | 06 |
| BD191-4 | S | N | AT | | | (2N3055) | | | 06 |
| BD191-5 | S | N | AT | | | (2N3055) | | | 06 |
| BD191-6 | S | N | AT | | | (2N3055) | | | 06 |
| BD191-7 | S | N | AT | | | (2N3055) | | | 06 |
| BD192 | S | N | AT | | | (2N3055) | 2N6260 | | 06 |
| BD192-4 | S | N | AT | | | (2N3055) | | | 06 |
| BD192-5 | S | N | AT | | | (2N3055) | | | 06 |
| BD192-6 | S | N | AT | | | (2N3055) | | | 06 |
| BD192-7 | S | N | AT | | | (2N3055) | | | 06 |
| BD193 | S | N | AT | | | (2N3442) | | | 06 |
| BD193-4 | S | N | AT | | | (2N3442) | | | 06 |
| BD193-5 | S | N | AT | | | (2N3442) | | | 06 |
| BD193-6 | S | N | AT | | | (2N3442) | | | 06 |
| BD193-7 | S | N | AT | | | (2N3442) | | | 06 |
| BD195 | S | N | MO | (BD437) | BD243 | 2N6129 | 2N6123 | | 06 |
| BD195 | | | | BD589 | | | | | 06 |
| BD196 | S | P | MO | (BD438) | BD244 | 2N6132 | 2N6134 | | 06 |
| BD196 | | | | BDX78 | | | | | 06 |
| BD197 | S | N | MO | BD439 | BD243A | 2N6129 | 2N6123 | | 06 |
| BD197 | | | | BD589 | | | | | 06 |
| BD198 | S | P | MO | (BD440) | BD244A | 2N6132 | 2N6134 | | 06 |
| BD198 | | | | BDX78 | | | | | 06 |
| BD199 | S | N | MO | (BD441) | BD243B | 2N6130 | 2N6123 | | 06 |
| BD199 | | | | BD589 | | | | | 06 |
| BD200 | S | P | MO | (BD442) | BD244B | 2N6133 | 2N6134 | | 06 |
| BD200 | | | | BDX78 | | | | | 06 |
| BD201 | S | N | MU, PH, V, RA | (BD439) | BD243 | 2N6101 | | | 06 |
| BD201 | | | | BDX73 | | | | | 06 |
| BD202 | S | P | MU, PH, V, RA | (BD440) | BD244 | 2N6134 | | | 06 |
| BD202 | | | | BDX78 | | | | | 06 |
| BD203 | S | N | MU, PH, V, RA | (BD439) | BD243A | 2N6101 | | | 06 |
| BD203 | | | | BDX73 | | | | | 06 |
| BD204 | S | P | MU, PH, V, RA | (BD440) | BD244A | 2N6134 | | | 06 |
| BD204 | | | | BDX78 | | | | | 06 |
| BD205 | S | N | MO | BDX73 | | 2N6569 | 2N6486 | | 06 |
| BD205 | | | | | | 2N6101 | | | 06 |
| BD206 | S | P | MO | BDX78 | | 2N6489 | 2N6134 | | 06 |
| BD207 | S | N | MO | BDX73 | | FT3055 | 2N6487 | | 06 |
| BD207 | | | | | | 2N6101 | | | 06 |
| BD208 | S | P | MO | BDX78 | | 2N6490 | FT2955 | | 06 |
| BD208 | | | | | | 2N6134 | | | 06 |
| BD213 | S | N | TF | BD213-8 | | | | | 06 |
| BD213-45 | S | N | TF | BD213-8 | | 2N6486 | | | 06 |
| BD213-60 | S | N | TF | BD213-8 | | FT3055 | 2N6487 | | 06 |
| BD213-80 | S | N | TF | BD213-8 | | | | | 06 |
| BD214 | S | P | TF | BD214-8 | | | | | 06 |
| BD214-45 | S | P | TF | BD214-8 | | 2N6489 | | | 06 |
| BD214-60 | S | P | TF | BD214-8 | | FT2955 | 2N6490 | | 06 |

| TYPE | M/S | POL | MANUFAC | EUROPEAN | | AMERICAN | | JAPANESE | USE |
|---|---|---|---|---|---|---|---|---|---|
| BD214-80 | S | P | TF | BD214-8 | | 2N6419 | | | 06 |
| BD215 | S | N | SG, AT | (BUY78) | | 2N3584 | | | 06 |
| BD216 | S | N | SG, AT | (BUY77) | | 2N3585 | | | 06 |
| BD220 | S | N | F | BD441 | BD589 | 2N6123 | | | 06 |
| BD221 | S | N | F | BD439 | BD589 | 2N6123 | | | 06 |
| | | | | | | | | | |
| BD222 | S | N | F | BD441 | BD589 | 2N6123 | | | 06 |
| BD223 | S | P | F | BD442 | BD590 | 2N6126 | | | 06 |
| BD224 | S | P | F | BD440 | BD590 | 2N6126 | | | 06 |
| BD225 | S | P | F | BD442 | BD590 | 2N6126 | | | 06 |
| BD226 | S | N | PH, V, AM | BD135 | BD589 | 2N6123 | | | 06 |
| | | | | | | | | | |
| BD227 | S | P | PH, V, AM | BD136 | BD590 | 2N6126 | | | 06 |
| BD228 | S | N | PH, V, AM | BD137 | BD589 | 2N6123 | | | 06 |
| BD229 | S | P | PH, V, AM | BD138 | BD590 | 2N6126 | | | 06 |
| BD230 | S | N | PH, V, AM | BD139 | BD589 | 2N6123 | | | 06 |
| BD231 | S | P | PH, V, AM | BD140 | BD590 | 2N6126 | | | 06 |
| | | | | | | | | | |
| BD232 | S | N | MU, PH, V, AM | (BF459) | | | | | 06 |
| BD233 | S | N | PH, TF, V, S, MO | BD437 | BD237 | TIP29 | 2N4923 | | 06 |
| BD234 | S | N | PH, TF, V, S, MO | BD438 | BD238 | TIP30 | 2N4920 | | 06 |
| BD235 | S | N | PH, TF, V, S, MO | BD439 | BD237 | TIP29A | 2N4923 | | 06 |
| BD236 | S | P | PH, TF, V, S, MO | BD440 | BD238 | TIP30A | 2N4920 | | 06 |
| | | | | | | | | | |
| BD237 | S | N | PH, TF, V, S, MO | BD441 | | TIP29B | 2N4923 | | 06 |
| BD238 | S | P | PH, TF, V, S, MO | BD442 | | TIP30B | 2N4920 | | 06 |
| BD239 | S | N | TX | BD437 | | 2N6121 | | | 06 |
| BD239A | S | N | TX | BD439 | | 2N6122 | | | 06 |
| BD239B | S | N | TX | BD441 | | 2N6123 | | | 06 |
| | | | | | | | | | |
| BD239C | S | N | TX | (BD441) | | | | | 06 |
| BD240 | S | P | TX | BD438 | | 2N6124 | | | 06 |
| BD240A | S | P | TX | BD440 | | 2N6125 | | | 06 |
| BD240B | S | P | TX | BD442 | | 2N6126 | | | 06 |
| BD240C | S | P | TX | (BD442) | | | | | 06 |
| | | | | | | | | | |
| BD241 | S | N | TX | BD437 | | 2N6121 | | | 06 |
| BD241A | S | N | TX | BD439 | | 2N6122 | | | 06 |
| BD241B | S | N | TX | BD441 | | 2N6123 | | | 06 |
| BD241C | S | N | TX | (BD441) | | | | | 06 |
| BD242 | S | P | TX | BD438 | | 2N6124 | | | 06 |
| | | | | | | | | | |
| BD242A | S | P | TX | BD440 | | 2N6125 | | | 06 |
| BD242B | S | P | TX | BD442 | | 2N6126 | | | 06 |
| BD242C | S | P | TX | (BD442) | | | | | 06 |
| BD243 | S | N | TX | (BD437) | | | | | 06 |
| BD243A | S | N | TX | (BD439) | | | | | 06 |
| | | | | | | | | | |
| BD243B | S | N | TX | (BD441) | | | | | 06 |
| BD243C | S | N | TX | (BD441) | | | | | 06 |
| BD244 | S | P | TX | (BD438) | | | | | 06 |
| BD244A | S | P | TX | (BD440) | | | | | 06 |
| BD244B | S | P | TX | (BD442) | | | | | 06 |
| | | | | | | | | | |
| BD244C | S | P | TX | (BD442) | | | | | 06 |
| BD245 | S | N | TX | | | 2N6486 | | | 06 |
| BD245A | S | N | TX | | | 2N6487 | | | 06 |
| BD245B | S | N | TX | | | 2N6488 | | | 06 |
| BD246 | S | P | TX | | | 2N6489 | | | 06 |
| | | | | | | | | | |
| BD246A | S | P | TX | | | 2N6490 | | | 06 |
| BD246B | S | P | TX | | | 2N6491 | | | 06 |
| BD251 | S | N | SG, AT | (BU310) | | | | | 06 |
| BD253 | S | N | TX | BUY77 | BUX18B | | | | 06 |
| BD253A | S | N | TX | BUY78 | BUX18C | | | | 06 |
| | | | | | | | | | |
| BD253B | S | N | TX | BUY79 | BU126 | | | | 06 |
| BD253C | S | N | TX | (BUY79) | | TA8764 | | | 06 |
| BD257 | S | N | TF | BD257-1 | | | | | 06 |
| BD257-45 | S | N | TF | BD257-1 | | | | | 06 |
| BD257-60 | S | N | TF | BD257-1 | | | | | 06 |
| | | | | | | | | | |
| BD257-80 | S | N | TF | BD257-1 | | | | | 06 |
| BD257-100 | S | N | TF | BD257-1 | | | | | 06 |
| BD258 | S | P | TF | BD258-1 | | | | | 06 |
| BD258-45 | S | P | TF | BD258-1 | | | | | 06 |
| BD258-60 | S | P | TF | BD258-1 | | | | | 06 |
| | | | | | | | | | |
| BD258-80 | S | P | TF | BD258-1 | | | | | 06 |
| BD258-100 | S | P | TF | BD258-1 | | | | | 06 |
| BD260 | S | N | AT, SG | (BU310) | | FT401 | 2N3584 | | 06 |
| BD261 | S | N | AT, SG | (BU310) | | FT411 | 2N3584 | | 06 |
| BD262 | SD | P | MU, PH, V, RA | BD646 | | | | | 06 |
| | | | | | | | | | |
| BD262A | SD | P | MU, PH, V, RA | BD648 | | | | | 06 |
| BD262B | SD | P | RA, V, PH | BD650 | | | | | 06 |
| BD262L | SD | P | RA | | | | | | 06 |
| BD264 | SD | P | MU, PH, V, RA | BD646 | | RCA8203A | | | 06 |
| BD264A | SD | P | MU, PH, V, RT, RA | BD648 | | RCA8203B | | | 06 |

| TYPE | M/S | POL | MANUFAC | EUROPEAN | | AMERICAN | | JAPANESE | USE |
|------|-----|-----|---------|----------|---|----------|---|----------|-----|
| BD264B | SD | P | RA, PH, MU, V | BD650 | BDX34C | | | | 06 |
| BD264L | SD | P | RA | BD644 | | | | | 06 |
| BD265 | SD | N | MU, PH, V, RA | BD647 | | 2N6387 | | | 06 |
| BD265A | SD | N | MU, PH, V, RA | BD647 | | 2N6388 | | | 06 |
| BD265B | SD | N | RA, PH, V | BD649 | BDX33C | | | | 06 |
| | | | | | | | | | |
| BD265L | SD | N | RA | BD645 | | | | | 06 |
| BD266 | SD | P | MU, PH, V, RA | BD646 | BDX34A | | | | 06 |
| BD266A | SD | P | MU, PH, V, RA | BD648 | BDX34B | | | | 06 |
| BD266B | SD | P | RA, PH, V | BD650 | BDX34C | | | | 06 |
| BD266L | SD | P | RA | BD644 | | | | | 06 |
| | | | | | | | | | |
| BD267 | SD | N | MU, PH, V, RA | BD647 | BDX33A | | | | 06 |
| BD267A | SD | N | MU, PH, V, RA | BD647 | BDX33B | | | | 06 |
| BD267B | SD | N | RA, PH, V | BD649 | BDX33C | | | | 06 |
| BD267L | SD | N | RA | BD645 | | | | | 06 |
| BD268 | SD | P | RA | BDX34A | | | | | 06 |
| | | | | | | | | | |
| BD268A | SD | P | RA | BDX34B | | | | | 06 |
| BD269 | SD | N | RA | BDX33A | | | | | 06 |
| BD269A | SD | N | RA | BDX33B | | | | | 06 |
| BD271 | S | N | PH, V, RA | BD439 | BD241 | | | | 06 |
| BD272 | S | P | PH, V, RA | BD440 | BD242 | | | | 06 |
| | | | | | | | | | |
| BD273 | S | N | PH, V, RA | BD441 | BD241A | | | | 06 |
| BD274 | S | P | PH, V, RA | BD442 | BD242A | | | | 06 |
| BD275 | S | N | PH, V, RA | BD441 | BD241B | | | | 06 |
| BD276 | S | P | PH, V, RA | BD442 | BD242B | | | | 06 |
| BD281 | S | N | AT | BD433 | | | | | 06 |
| | | | | | | | | | |
| BD282 | S | P | AT | BD434 | | | | | 06 |
| BD283 | S | N | AT | BD221 | BD435 | | | | 06 |
| BD284 | S | P | AT | BD224 | BD436 | | | | 06 |
| BD285 | S | N | AT | BD437 | | 2N6121 | | | 06 |
| BD286 | S | P | AT | BD438 | | 2N6124 | | | 06 |
| | | | | | | | | | |
| BD291 | S | N | PH, V | BD243 | | | | | 06 |
| BD292 | S | P | PH, V | BD244 | | | | | 06 |
| BD293 | S | N | PH, V | BD243A | | | | | 06 |
| BD294 | S | P | PH, V | BD244A | | | | | 06 |
| BD301 | S | N | SB, SE | (BD439) | BD243 | 2N6123 | | | 06 |
| | | | | | | | | | |
| BD301 | | | | BD589 | | | | | 06 |
| BD302 | S | P | SB, SE | (BD440) | BD244 | 2N6126 | | | 06 |
| BD302 | | | | BD590 | | | | | 06 |
| BD303 | S | N | SB, SE | (BD439) | BD243A | 2N6123 | | | 06 |
| BD303 | | | | BD589 | | | | | 06 |
| | | | | | | | | | |
| BD304 | S | P | SB, SE | (BD440) | BD244A | 2N6126 | | | 06 |
| BD304 | | | | BD590 | | | | | 06 |
| BD306 | S | N | IN | (BD437) | | | | | 06 |
| BD306A | S | N | IN | (BD437) | BD237 | 2N4923 | | | 06 |
| BD306B | S | N | IN | (BD437) | BD237 | 2N4923 | | | 06 |
| | | | | | | | | | |
| BD307 | S | N | IN | (BD439) | | | | | 06 |
| BD307A | S | N | IN | (BD439) | BD237 | 2N4923 | | | 06 |
| BD307B | S | N | IN | (BD439) | BD237 | 2N4923 | | | 06 |
| BD311 | S | N | MO | | | 2N5881 | 2N6471 | | 06 |
| BD312 | S | P | MO | | | 2N5879 | 2N6246 | | 06 |
| | | | | | | | | | |
| BD313 | S | N | MO | | | 2N5882 | 2N6474 | | 06 |
| BD314 | S | P | MO | | | 2N5880 | 2N6247 | | 06 |
| BD315 | S | N | MO | | | 2N5882 | 2N6472 | | 06 |
| BD316 | S | P | MO | | | 2N5880 | 2N6247 | | 06 |
| BD317 | S | N | MO | | | 2N5629 | 2N6472 | | 06 |
| | | | | | | | | | |
| BD318 | S | P | MO | | | 2N6020 | 2N6248 | | 06 |
| BD361 | S | N | MO | BD437 | | TIP29 | | | 06 |
| BD361A | S | N | MO | BD437 | | TIP29 | | | 06 |
| BD362 | S | P | MO | BD438 | | TIP30 | | | 06 |
| BD362A | S | P | MO | BD438 | | TIP30 | | | 06 |
| | | | | | | | | | |
| BD363A | S | N | AT | (BD439) | | | | | 06 |
| BD363B | S | N | AT | (BD439) | | | | | 06 |
| BD375 | S | N | SG, AT | BD239 | | | | | 06 |
| BD376 | S | P | SG, AT | BD240 | | | | | 06 |
| BD377 | S | N | SG, AT | BD239A | | | | | 06 |
| | | | | | | | | | |
| BD378 | S | P | SG, AT | BD240A | | | | | 06 |
| BD379 | S | N | SG, AT | BD239B | | | | | 06 |
| BD380 | S | P | SG, AT | BD240B | | | | | 06 |
| BD400 | S | N | TX | BD169 | | 2N4923 | | | 96 |
| BD410 | S | N | TX | BD232 | | RCP111D | | | 06 |
| | | | | | | | | | |
| BD433 | S | N | PH, S, TF, V | BD441 | | 2N5192 | | | 06 |
| BD433A | S | N | S | BD441 | | 2N5192 | | | 06 |
| BD433B | S | N | S | BD441 | | 2N5192 | | | 06 |
| BD433C | S | N | S | BD441 | | 2N5192 | | | 06 |
| BD434 | S | P | PH, S, TF, V | BD442 | | 2N5195 | | | 06 |

| TYPE | M/S | POL | MANUFAC | EUROPEAN | AMERICAN | JAPANESE | USE |
|------|-----|-----|---------|----------|----------|----------|-----|
| BD434A | S | P | S | BD442 | 2N5195 | | 06 |
| BD434B | S | P | S | BD442 | 2N5195 | | 0G |
| BD434C | S | P | S | BD442 | 2N5195 | | 06 |
| BD435 | S | N | PH, S, TF, V | BD441 | 2N5192 | | 06 |
| BD435A | S | N | S | BD441 | 2N5192 | | 06 |
| BD435B | S | N | S | BD441 | 2N5192 | | 06 |
| BD435C | S | N | S | BD441 | 2N5192 | | 06 |
| BD436 | S | P | PH, S, TF, V | BD442 | 2N5195 | | 06 |
| BD436A | S | P | S | BD442 | 2N5195 | | 06 |
| BD436B | S | P | S | BD442 | 2N5195 | | 06 |
| BD436C | S | P | S | BD442 | 2N5195 | | 06 |
| BD437 | S | N | PH, S, TF, V | BD441 | 2N5192 | | 06 |
| BD438 | S | P | PH, S, TF, V | BD442 | 2N5195 | | 06 |
| BD439 | S | N | S | BD441 | 2N5192 | | 06 |
| BD440 | S | P | S | BD442 | 2N5195 | | 06 |
| BD441 | S | N | S | | 2N5192 | | 06 |
| BD442 | S | P | S | | 2N5195 | | 06 |
| BD461 | S | N | TX | BD437 | | | 06 |
| BD462 | S | P | TX | BD438 | | | 06 |
| BD463 | S | N | TX | BD437 | | | 06 |
| BD464 | S | P | TX | BD438 | | | 06 |
| BD505 | S | N | MO | (BD135-16) | | | 06 |
| BD505-1 | S | N | MO | (BD135-16) | | | 06 |
| BD505-5 | S | N | MO | (BD135-16) | | | 06 |
| BD506 | S | P | MO | (BD136-16) | | | 06 |
| BD506-1 | S | P | MO | (BD136-16) | | | 06 |
| BD506-5 | S | P | MO | (BD136-16) | | | 06 |
| BD507 | S | N | MO | (BD135-16) | | | 06 |
| BD507-1 | S | N | MO | (BD135-16) | | | 06 |
| BD507-5 | S | N | MO | (BD135-16) | | | 06 |
| BD508 | S | P | MO | (BD136-16) | | | 06 |
| BD508-1 | S | P | MO | (BD136-16) | | | 06 |
| BD508-5 | S | P | MO | (BD136-16) | | | 06 |
| BD509 | S | N | MO | (BD137-10) | | | 06 |
| BD509-1 | S | N | MO | (BD137-10) | | | 06 |
| BD509-5 | S | N | MO | (BD137-10) | | | 06 |
| BD510 | S | P | MO | (BD138-10) | | | 06 |
| BD510-1 | S | P | MO | (BD138-10) | | | 06 |
| BD510-5 | S | P | MO | (BD138-10) | | | 06 |
| BD515 | S | N | MO | (BD135-10) | RCP701A | | 06 |
| BD515-1 | S | N | MO | (BD135-10) | | | 06 |
| BD515-5 | S | N | MO | (BD135-10) | | | 06 |
| BD516 | S | P | MO | (BD136-10) | RCP700A | | 06 |
| BD516-1 | S | P | MO | (BD136-10) | | | 06 |
| BD516-5 | S | P | MO | (BD136-10) | | | 06 |
| BD517 | S | N | MO | (BD137-10) | RCP701B | | 06 |
| BD517-1 | S | N | MO | (BD137-10) | | | 06 |
| BD517-5 | S | N | MO | (BD137-10) | | | 06 |
| BD518 | S | P | MO | (BD138-10) | RCP700B | | 06 |
| BD518-1 | S | P | MO | (BD138-10) | | | 06 |
| BD518-5 | S | P | MO | (BD138-10) | | | 06 |
| BD519 | S | N | MO | (BD139-10) | RCP701C | | 06 |
| BD519-1 | S | N | MO | (BD139-10) | | | 06 |
| BD519-5 | S | N | MO | (BD139-10) | | | 06 |
| BD520 | S | P | MO | (BD140-10) | RCP700C | | 06 |
| BD520-1 | S | P | MO | (BD140-10) | | | 06 |
| BD520-5 | S | P | MO | (BD140-10) | | | 06 |
| BD525 | S | N | MO | (BD137-10) | RCP701B | | 06 |
| BD525-1 | S | N | MO | (BD137-10) | | | 06 |
| BD525-5 | S | N | MO | (BD137-10) | | | 06 |
| BD526 | S | P | MO | (BD138-10) | RCP700B | | 06 |
| BD526-1 | S | P | MO | (BD138-10) | | | 06 |
| BD526-5 | S | P | MO | (BD138-10) | | | 06 |
| BD527 | S | N | MO | (BD139-10) | RCP701C | | 06 |
| BD527-1 | S | N | MO | (BD139-10) | | | 06 |
| BD527-5 | S | N | MO | (BD139-10) | | | 06 |
| BD528 | S | P | MO | (BD140-10) | RCP700C | | 06 |
| BD528-1 | S | P | MO | (BD140-10) | | | 06 |
| BD528-5 | S | P | MO | (BD140-10) | | | 06 |
| BD529 | S | N | MO | (BD139-10) | RCP701D | | 06 |
| BD529-1 | S | N | MO | (BD139-10) | | | 06 |
| BD529-5 | S | N | MO | (BD139-10) | | | 06 |
| BD530 | S | P | MO | (BD140-10) | RCP700D | | 06 |
| BD530-1 | S | P | MO | (BD140-10) | | | 06 |
| BD530-5 | S | P | MO | (BD140-10) | | | 06 |

| TYPE | M/S | POL | MANUFAC | EUROPEAN | | AMERICAN | | JAPANESE | USE |
|------|-----|-----|---------|----------|--|----------|--|----------|-----|
| BD533 | S | N | S, AT | (BD437) | | | | | 06 |
| BD534 | S | P | S, AT | (BD438) | | | | | 06 |
| BD535 | S | N | S, AT | (BD439) | | | | | 06 |
| BD536 | S | P | S, AT | (BD440) | | | | | 06 |
| BD537 | S | N | S, AT | (BD441) | | | | | 06 |
| BD538 | S | P | S, AT | (BD442) | | | | | 06 |
| BD561 | S | N | MO | BD437 | | 2N2161 | | | 06 |
| BD562 | S | P | MO | BD438 | | 2N2164 | | | 06 |
| BD575 | SD | N | MO | BD437 | BD241 | TIP29 | | | 06 |
| BD576 | SD | P | MO | BD438 | BD242 | TIP30 | | | 06 |
| BD577 | SD | N | MO | BD439 | BD241A | TIP29A | | | 06 |
| BD578 | SD | P | MO | BD440 | BD242A | TIP30A | | | 06 |
| BD579 | SD | N | MO | BD441 | BD241B | TIP29B | | | 06 |
| BD580 | SD | P | MO | BD442 | BD242B | TIP30B | | | 06 |
| BD581 | SD | N | MO | (BD441) | | | | | 06 |
| BD582 | SD | P | MO | (BD442) | BD242C | | | | 06 |
| BD585 | S | N | MO, TF | BD437 | BD241 | 2N6121 | 2N6123 | | 06 |
| BD585 | | | | BD589 | | | | | 06 |
| BD586 | S | P | MO, TF | BD438 | BD242 | 2N6124 | 2N6126 | | 06 |
| BD586 | | | | BD590 | | | | | 06 |
| BD587 | S | N | MO, TF | BD439 | BD241A | 2N6122 | 2N6123 | | 06 |
| BD587 | | | | BD589 | | | | | 06 |
| BD588 | S | N | MO, TF | BD440 | BD242A | 2N6125 | 2N6126 | | 06 |
| BD588 | | | | BD590 | | | | | 06 |
| BD589 | S | N | MO, TF | BD441 | BD241B | 2N6123 | | | 06 |
| BD590 | S | N | MO, TF | BD442 | BD242B | 2N6126 | | | 06 |
| BD591 | S | P | MO | (BD441) | BD241C | | | | 06 |
| BD592 | S | P | MO | (BD442) | BD242C | | | | 06 |
| BD595 | S | N | MO, TF | (BD437) | BD243 | 2N6101 | 2N6129 | | 06 |
| BD595 | | | | BDX73 | | | | | 06 |
| BD596 | S | P | MO, TF | (BD438) | BD244 | 2N6132 | 2N6134 | | 06 |
| BD597 | S | N | MO, TF | (BD439) | BD243A | 2N6130 | 2N6101 | | 06 |
| BD597 | | | | BDX73 | | | | | 06 |
| BD598 | S | P | MO, TF | (BD440) | BD244A | 2N6133 | 2N6104 | | 06 |
| BD598 | | | | BDX78 | | | | | 06 |
| BD599 | S | N | MO, TF | (BD441) | BD243B | 2N6131 | 2N6101 | | 06 |
| BD599 | | | | BDX73 | | | | | 06 |
| BD600 | S | P | MO, TF | (BD442) | BD244B | 2N6134 | | | 06 |
| BD600 | | | | BDX78 | | | | | 06 |
| BD601 | S | N | MO | (BD441) | BD243C | | | | 06 |
| BD602 | S | P | MO | (BD442) | BD244C | | | | 06 |
| BD605 | S | N | MO, TF | | | 2N6486 | | | 06 |
| BD606 | S | P | MO, TF | | | 2N6489 | | | 06 |
| BD607 | S | N | MO, TF | | | FT3055 | 2N6487 | | 06 |
| BD608 | S | P | MO, TF | | | FT2955 | 2N6490 | | 06 |
| BD609 | S | N | TF, MO | | | 2N6488 | | | 06 |
| BD610 | S | P | MO, TF | | | 2N6491 | | | 06 |
| BD633 | S | N | TX | | | 40979 | | | 06 |
| BD634 | S | P | TX | | | 40980 | | | 06 |
| BD635 | S | N | TX | | | 40871 | | | 06 |
| BD636 | S | P | TX | | | 40872 | | | 06 |
| BD637 | S | N | TX | | | 40871 | | | 06 |
| BD638 | S | P | TX | | | 40872 | | | 06 |
| BD643 | SD | N | PH, S, V | BDX33 | | | | | 06 |
| BD644 | SD | P | PH, S, V | BDX34 | | | | | 06 |
| BD645 | SD | N | PH, S, V | BDX33A | | | | | 06 |
| BD646 | SD | P | S, V | BDX34A | | | | | 06 |
| BD647 | SD | N | PH, S, V | BDX33B | | | | | 06 |
| BD648 | SD | P | PH, S, V | BDX34B | | | | | 06 |
| BD661 | S | N | SG, S, V | | | 2N6486 | | | 06 |
| BD662 | S | P | SG, S, V | | | 2N6489 | | | 06 |
| BD663 | S | N | SG | | | 2N6486 | | | 06 |
| BD663A | S | N | SG | | | 2N6486 | | | 06 |
| BD663B | S | N | SG, AT | | | 2N6486 | | | 06 |
| BD664 | S | P | SG | | | 2N6489 | | | 06 |
| BD675A | SD | N | MO, AT | BD675 | | | | | 06 |
| BD676A | SD | P | MO, AT | BD676 | | | | | 06 |
| BD677A | SD | N | MO, AT | BD677 | | | | | 06 |
| BD678 | SD | P | MO, S, TF, AT | | | | | | 06 |
| BD678A | SD | P | MO, AT | BD678 | | | | | 06 |
| BD679A | SD | N | MO, AT | BD679 | | | | | 06 |
| BD680 | SD | P | MO, S, TF, AT | | | | | | 06 |
| BD680A | SD | P | MO, AT | BD680 | | | | | 06 |
| BD695 | SD | N | MO, TF | BD643 | BDX33 | | | | 06 |
| BD695 | | | | | | | | | 06 |

| TYPE | M/S | POL | MANUFAC | EUROPEAN | | AMERICAN | | JAPANESE | USE |
|------|-----|-----|---------|----------|--|----------|--|----------|-----|
| BD695A | SD | N | MO | BD643 | BDX33 | | | | 06 |
| BD696 | SD | P | MO, TF | BD644 | BDX34 | | | | 06 |
| BD696A | SD | P | MO | BD644 | BDX34 | | | | 06 |
| BD697 | SD | N | MO, TF | BD645 | BDX33A | SE9300 | 2N6101 | | 06 |
| BD697 | | | | | | | | | 06 |
| BD697A | SD | N | MO | BD645 | BDX33A | SE9300 | | | |
| BD698 | SD | P | MO, TF | BD646 | BDX34A | | | | 06 |
| BD698A | SD | P | MO | BD646 | BDX34A | | | | 06 |
| BD699 | SD | N | MO, TF | BD647 | BDX33B | SE9301 | | | 06 |
| BD699 | | | | | | | | | 06 |
| BD699A | SD | N | MO | BD647 | BDX33B | SE9301 | | | 06 |
| BD700 | SD | P | MO, TF | BD648 | BDX34B | SE9401 | | | 06 |
| BD700A | SD | P | MO | BD648 | BDX34B | SE9401 | | | 06 |
| BD701 | SD | N | MO | BD649 | BDX33C | | | | 06 |
| BD701 | | | | | | | | | 06 |
| BD702 | SD | P | MO | BD650 | BDX34C | 2N5195 | | | 06 |
| BD702 | | | | BD442 | | | | | 06 |
| BD705 | S | N | SG, AT | | | 2N6486 | | | 06 |
| BD706 | S | P | SG, AT | | | 2N6489 | | | 06 |
| BD707 | S | N | SG, AT | | | 2N6487 | | | 06 |
| BD708 | S | P | SG, AT | | | 2N6490 | | | 06 |
| BD709 | S | N | SG, AT | | | 2N6488 | | | 06 |
| BD710 | S | P | SG, AT | | | 2N6491 | | | 06 |
| BD733 | S | N | TX | BD433 | | | | | 06 |
| BD734 | S | P | TX | BD434 | | | | | 06 |
| BD735 | S | N | TX | BD435 | | | | | 06 |
| BD736 | S | P | TX | BD436 | | | | | 06 |
| BD737 | S | N | TX | BD437 | | | | | 06 |
| BD738 | S | P | TX | BD438 | | | | | 06 |
| BDX10 | S | N | AT | AM291 | | 2N3055 | | | 06 |
| BDX10-4 | S | N | AT | | | 2N3055 | | | 06 |
| BDX10-5 | S | N | AT | | | 2N3055 | | | 06 |
| BDX10-6 | S | N | AT | | | 2N3055 | | | 06 |
| BDX10-7 | S | N | AT | | | 2N3055 | | | 06 |
| BDX11 | S | N | AT | | | 2N5631 | 2N3442 | | 06 |
| BDX11-4 | S | N | AT | | | 2N3442 | | | 06 |
| BDX11-5 | S | N | AT | | | 2N3442 | | | 06 |
| BDX11-6 | S | N | AT | | | 2N3442 | | | 06 |
| BDX11-7 | S | N | AT | | | 2N3442 | | | 06 |
| BDX12 | S | N | AT | | | 2N4347 | | | 06 |
| BDX13 | S | N | AT | BDY38 | | 2N6569 | 2N3055 | | 06 |
| BDX13 | | | | | | 2N5301 | 40251 | | 06 |
| BDX13-4 | S | N | AT | | | 2N3055 | | | 06 |
| BDX13-5 | S | N | AT | | | 2N3055 | | | 06 |
| BDX13-6 | S | N | AT | | | 2N3055 | | | 06 |
| BDX13-7 | S | N | AT | | | 2N3055 | | | 06 |
| BDX14 | S | P | SE, Ss, ML | | | 2N3740 | | | 06 |
| BDX16 | S | P | SE, Ss, ML | BUX66 | | | | | 06 |
| BDX18 | S | P | PH, MU | | | 2N3792 | | | 06 |
| BDX18N | S | P | SE | BDX18 | | 2N3792 | | | 06 |
| BDX22 | S | N | AT | | | (2N3442) | SE9051 | | 06 |
| BDX22-4 | S | N | AT | | | (2N3442) | | | 06 |
| BDX22-5 | S | N | AT | | | (2N3442) | | | 06 |
| BDX22-6 | S | N | AT | | | (2N3442) | | | 06 |
| BDX23 | S | N | AT | BUY57 | | 2N5629 | | | 06 |
| BDX23-4 | S | N | AT | BUY57 | | | | | 06 |
| BDX23-5 | S | N | AT | BUY57 | | | | | 06 |
| BDX23-6 | S | N | AT | BUY57 | | | | | 06 |
| BDX23-7 | S | N | AT | BUY57 | | | | | 06 |
| BDX24 | S | N | AT | | | 2N4913 | 2N3054 | | 06 |
| BDX24 | | | | | | 2N5878 | | | 06 |
| BDX24-4 | S | N | AT | | | 2N3054 | | | 06 |
| BDX24-5 | S | N | AT | | | 2N3054 | | | 06 |
| BDX24-6 | S | N | AT | | | 2N3054 | | | 06 |
| BDX24-7 | S | N | AT | | | 2N3054 | | | 06 |
| BDX27 | S | P | S | | | 2N3879 | | | 06 |
| BDX28 | S | P | S | | | 2N3879 | | | 06 |
| BDX30 | S | P | S | | | 2N6500 | | | 06 |
| BDX31 | S | N | TX | (BU208) | | | | | 06 |
| BDX32 | S | N | TX | (BU208) | | | | | 06 |
| BDX35 | S | N | MU | BD441 | | 2N5192 | | | 06 |
| BDX36 | S | N | MU | BD441 | | 2N5192 | | | 06 |
| BDX37 | S | N | MU | BD441 | | 2N5192 | | | 06 |
| BDX40 | S | N | AT | | | 2N3772 | (2N3055) | | 06 |
| BDX40 | | | | | | 2N5302 | | | 06 |

| TYPE | M/S | POL | MANUFAC | EUROPEAN | | AMERICAN | | JAPANESE | USE |
|------|-----|-----|---------|----------|---|----------|---|----------|-----|
| BDX40-4 | S | N | AT | | | (2N3055) | | | 06 |
| BDX40-5 | S | N | AT | | | (2N3055) | | | 06 |
| BDX40-6 | S | N | AT | | | (2N3055) | | | 06 |
| BDX40-7 | S | N | AT | | | (2N3055) | | | 06 |
| BDX41 | S | N | AT | | | 2N5301 | | | 06 |
| BDX50 | S | N | AT | | | 2N5631 | (2N3442) | | 06 |
| BDX50 | | | | | | 2N3773 | | | 06 |
| BDX50-4 | S | N | AT | | | (2N3442) | | | 06 |
| BDX50-5 | S | N | AT | | | (2N3442) | | | 06 |
| BDX50-6 | S | N | AT | | | (2N3442) | | | 06 |
| BDX50-7 | S | N | AT | | | (2N3442) | | | 06 |
| BDX51 | S | N | AT | | | 2N5630 | 2N3773 | | 06 |
| BDX51 | | | | | | 2N4348 | | | 06 |
| BDX53 | SD | N | AT | BDX33 | | | | | 06 |
| BDX53A | SD | N | SG, AT | BDX33A | | | | | 06 |
| BDX53B | SD | N | SG, AT | BDX33B | | | | | 06 |
| BDX53C | SD | N | SG, AT | BDX33C | | | | | 06 |
| BDX54 | SD | P | SG, AT | BDX34 | | | | | 06 |
| BDX54A | SD | P | SG, AT | BDX34A | | | | | 06 |
| BDX54B | SD | P | SG, AT | BDX34B | | | | | 06 |
| BDX54C | SD | P | SG, AT | BDX34C | | | | | 06 |
| BDX60 | S | N | AT, SG | | | 2N5629 | (2N3055) | | 06 |
| BDX60 | | | | | | 2N6254 | | | 06 |
| BDX60-4 | S | N | AT | | | (2N3055) | | | 06 |
| BDX60-5 | S | N | AT | | | (2N3055) | | | 06 |
| BDX60-6 | S | N | AT | | | (2N3055) | | | 06 |
| BDX60-7 | S | N | AT | | | (2N3055) | | | 06 |
| BDX61 | S | N | AT, SG | | | 2N5886 | (2N3055) | | 06 |
| BDX61-4 | S | N | AT | | | (2N3055) | | | 06 |
| BDX61-5 | S | N | AT | | | (2N3055) | | | 06 |
| BDX61-6 | S | N | AT | | | (2N3055) | | | 06 |
| BDX61-7 | S | N | AT | | | (2N3055) | | | 06 |
| BDX62 | SD | P | PH, RA, MU, V | | | RCA8350A | | | 06 |
| BDX62A | SD | P | PH, RA, MU, V | | | RCA8350B | | | 06 |
| BDX63 | SD | N | PH, RA, MU, V | | | 2N6384 | | | 06 |
| BDX63A | SD | N | PH, RA, MU, V | | | 2N6385 | | | 06 |
| BDX64 | SD | P | PH, RA, MU, V | BDX84B | | | | | 06 |
| BDX64A | SD | P | PH, RA, MU, V | BDX84B | | | | | 06 |
| BDX64B | SD | P | PH, RA, MU, V | BDX84C | | | | | 06 |
| BDX65 | SD | N | PH, RA, MU, V | BDX83A | | | | | 06 |
| BDX65A | SD | N | PH, RA, MU, V | BDX83B | | | | | 06 |
| BDX65B | SD | N | PH, RA, MU, V | BDX83C | | | | | 06 |
| BDX70 | S | N | AT | BDX72 | | FT3055 | 2N6098 | | 06 |
| BDX70 | | | | | | 2N6100 | | | 06 |
| BDX71 | S | N | AT | BDX73 | | FT3055 | 2N6099 | | 06 |
| BDX71 | | | | | | 2N6101 | | | 06 |
| BDX72 | S | N | AT | | | 2N6100 | | | 06 |
| BDX73 | S | N | AT | | | 2N6101 | | | 06 |
| BDX74 | S | N | AT | | | 2N6100 | | | 06 |
| BDX75 | S | N | AT | | | 2N6103 | | | 06 |
| BDX77 | S | N | RA, PH, V | (BD441) | BD243B | 2N6101 | | | 06 |
| BDX78 | S | P | RA, PH, V | (BD442) | BD244B | | | | 06 |
| BDX78 | | | | | | 2N6134 | | | 06 |
| BDY10 | S | N | RA, AM, MU, PE, PH, V | BDY38 | BDY30 | 2N6253 | 2N4907 | | 06 |
| BDY10 | | | | | | 2N3055 | | | 06 |
| BDY11 | S | N | MU, PH | BDX50 | | 2N4909 | 2N3773 | | 06 |
| BDY12 | S | N | SE, S | BUX16 | BD124 | 2N4910 | 2N3054 | 2SC830H | 06 |
| BDY12 | | | | BLY47A | | | | | 06 |
| BDY12B | S | N | S | BDY12-6 | | | | | 06 |
| BDY12C | S | N | S | BDY12-10 | | | | | 06 |
| BDY12D | S | N | S | BDY12-16 | | | | | 06 |
| BDY13 | S | N | SE, S | BUX16 | BD124 | 2N3054 | 2N3055 | 2SC830H | 06 |
| BDY13 | | | | | | 2N3050 | | | 06 |
| BDY13B | S | N | S | BDY13-6 | | | | | 06 |
| BDY13C | S | N | S | BDY13-10 | | | | | 06 |
| BDY13D | S | N | S | BDY13-16 | | | | | 06 |
| BDY15 | S | N | IN, SE | BDY12 | BUX16 | 2N4910 | 2N3054 | 2SC830H | 06 |
| BDY15 | | | | BLY47A | BD107 | | | | 06 |
| BDY15 | | | | BD124 | | | | | 06 |
| BDY15A | S | N | IN, IT | BDY12-10 | BD107 | | | | 06 |
| BDY15B | S | N | IN, IT | BDY12-16 | BD107 | | | | 06 |
| BDY15C | S | N | IN, IT | BDY12-16 | BD107 | | | | 06 |
| BDY16 | S | N | IN | BDY13 | BD124 | 2N4911 | 2N4912 | | 06 |
| BDY16 | | | | BD107 | | 2N3055 | | | 06 |
| BDY16A | S | N | IN, IT | BDY13-10 | BD107 | | | | 06 |

| TYPE | M/S | POL | MANUFAC | EUROPEAN | | AMERICAN | | JAPANESE | USE |
|------|-----|-----|---------|----------|---|----------|---|----------|-----|
| BDY16B | S | N | IN, IT | BDY13-16 | BD107 | | | | 06 |
| BDY17 | S | N | MU, PH, SE, RA, V | BUX16 | | 2N3055 | 2N3771 | | 06 |
| BDY17 | | | | | | 2N5301 | | | 06 |
| BDY18 | S | N | MU, PH, PE, RA, V | BUY57 | BD130 | 2N3772 | 2N3055 | | 06 |
| BDY18 | | | | | | 2N5302 | | | 06 |
| BDY19 | S | N | MU, PH, PE, V | BUY57 | BD130 | 2N3773 | 2N3055 | | 06 |
| BDY20 | S | N | SE, MU, PH | BUX16 | BD130 | 2N3055 | | | 06 |
| BDY20 | | | | BDX10 | AM291 | | | | 06 |
| BDY23 | S | N | SE, Ss, ML | BUY55 | BDY92 | 2N4914 | 2N3448 | | 06 |
| BDY23A | S | N | SE | BUY55 | BDY24 | 2N3448 | | | 06 |
| BDY23B | S | N | SE | BUY55 | BDY24 | 2N3448 | | | 06 |
| BDY23C | S | N | SE | BUY55 | BDY24 | 2N3448 | | | 06 |
| BDY24 | S | N | SE, Ss, ML | BUY55 | BDY91 | 2N4915 | 2N3448 | | 06 |
| BDY24A | S | N | AT, SE | BUY55 | BDY24 | 2N3448 | | | 06 |
| BDY24B | S | N | SE | BUY55 | BDY24 | 2N3448 | | | 06 |
| BDY24C | S | N | SE | BUY55 | BDY24 | 2N3448 | | | 06 |
| BDY25 | S | N | SE, Ss, ML | BUY56 | | 2N4347 | 2N3442 | | 06 |
| BDY25 | | | | | | 2N3055 | | | 06 |
| BDY25A | S | N | SE | BUY56 | BUX16 | | | | 06 |
| BDY25B | S | N | SE | BUX16 | BUY56 | | | | 06 |
| BDY25C | S | N | SE | BUY56 | BUX16 | | | | 06 |
| BDY26 | S | N | SE, Ss, ML | BUY72 | BDY28 | 2N5157 | | | 06 |
| BDY26A | S | N | SE | BUY72 | BUX16 | | | | 06 |
| BDY26B | S | N | SE | BUY72 | BUX16 | | | | 06 |
| BDY26C | S | N | SE | BUY72 | BUX16 | | | | 06 |
| BDY27 | S | N | SE, Ss, ML | BUY77 | BDY28 | 2N5157 | | | 06 |
| BDY27A | S | N | SE | BUY77 | BUX16 | | | | 06 |
| BDY27B | S | N | SE | BUY77 | BUX16 | | | | 06 |
| BDY27C | S | N | SE | BUY77 | BUX16 | | | | 06 |
| BDY28 | S | N | SE, Ss, ML | BUY78 | | 2N5157 | | | 06 |
| BDY28A | S | N | SE | BUY78 | BUX16A | | | | 06 |
| BDY28B | S | N | SE | BUY78 | BUX16A | | | | 06 |
| BDY28C | S | N | SE | BUY78 | BUX16A | | | | 06 |
| BDY34 | S | N | TF | BDY12 | | | | | 06 |
| BDY38 | S | N | PH, RA, AM, MU, | BD130 | BDY20 | 2N6253 | 2N4914 | 2SC665H | 06 |
| BDY38 | | | PE, V | | | 2N3055 | | | 06 |
| BDY39 | S | N | S | AM291 | BDX10 | 2N3055 | | | 06 |
| BDY53 | S | N | SE, Ss, ML | BUY57 | BDY56 | | | | 06 |
| BDY54 | S | N | SE, Ss, ML | BUY58 | BDY56 | | | | 06 |
| BDY55 | S | N | SE, Ss, ML | BUY57 | BDY56 | 2N3055 | | | 06, 14 |
| BDY55 | | | | AM291 | BDX10 | | | | 06, 14 |
| BDY56 | S | N | SE, SG, Ss, ML | BUY57 | | 2N5038 | 2N4347 | | 06, 14 |
| BDY56 | | | | | | 2N3055 | | | 06, 14 |
| BDY57 | S | N | SE, Ss, ML | (BUY57) | BDY58 | 41012 | 2N5403 | | 06, 14 |
| BDY58 | S | N | SE, SG, ML, Ss | (BUY57) | | 41013 | 2N4348 | | 06, 14 |
| BDY60 | S | N | PH, MU, V | BDY13 | | | | | 06 |
| BDY61 | S | N | PH, MU, V | BDY13 | | | | | 06 |
| BDY62 | S | N | PH, MU, V | BDY13 | | | | | 06 |
| BDY71 | S | N | SE | BUY38 | | 2N3054 | | | 06 |
| BDY72 | S | N | SE, ML, Ss | | | (2N3442) | 2N3441 | | 06 |
| BDY73 | S | N | SE | BDY20 | | 2N3715 | 2N3055 | | 06 |
| BDY74 | S | N | SE, ML, Ss | BDX50 | | 2N3442 | 2N4347 | | 06 |
| BDY74 | | | | | | 2N3773 | | | 06 |
| BDY75 | S | N | | | | 2N3771 | | | 06 |
| BDY76 | S | N | SE, ML, Ss | | | (2N3055) | 2N3772 | | 06 |
| BDY76 | | | | | | 2N5302 | | | 06 |
| BDY77 | S | N | SE, ML, Ss | | | 2N3773 | 2N2773 | | 06 |
| BDY78 | S | N | SE, ML, Ss | | | 2N6373 | 2N3054 | | 06 |
| BDY79 | S | N | SE, ML, Ss | | | (2N3442) | 2N3583 | | 06 |
| BDY79 | | | | | | 2N5050 | 2N3441 | | 06 |
| BDY80 | S | N | SE | BD437 | | | | | 06 |
| BDY80A | S | N | SE | BD437 | BD589 | 2N5296 | 2N6123 | | 06 |
| BDY80B | S | N | SE | BD437 | BD589 | 2N6123 | | | 06 |
| BDY80C | S | N | SE | BD437 | BD589 | 2N6123 | | | 06 |
| BDY81 | S | N | SE | BD439 | | | | | 06 |
| BDY81A | S | N | SE | BD439 | BD589 | 2N5298 | 2N6123 | | 06 |
| BDY81B | S | N | SE | BD439 | BD589 | 2N6123 | | | 06 |
| BDY81C | S | N | SE | BD439 | BD589 | 2N6123 | | | 06 |
| BDY82 | S | P | SE | BD438 | | | | | 06 |
| BDY82A | S | P | SE | BD438 | BD590 | 2N6111 | 2N6126 | | 06 |
| BDY82B | S | P | SE | BD438 | BD590 | 2N6126 | | | 06 |
| BDY82C | S | P | SE | BD438 | BD590 | 2N6126 | | | 06 |
| BDY83 | S | P | SE | BD440 | | | | | 06 |
| BDY83A | S | P | SE | BD440 | BD590 | 2N6109 | 2N6126 | | 06 |
| BDY83B | S | P | SE | BD440 | BD590 | 2N6126 | | | 06 |

| TYPE | M/S | POL | MANUFAC | EUROPEAN | | AMERICAN | JAPANESE | USE |
|------|-----|-----|---------|----------|---|----------|----------|-----|
| BDY83C | S | P | SE | BD440 | BD590 | 2N6126 | | 06 |
| BDY90 | S | N | MU, PH, V, AM | BUY57 | | | | 06 |
| BDY91 | S | N | MU, PH, V, RA, AM | BUY57 | | 2N5038 | | 06 |
| BDY92 | S | N | MU, PH, V, RA, AM | BUY57 | | 2N5039 | | 06 |
| BDY93 | S | N | MU, PH, V, RA, AM | BUY79 | BU126 | | | 06, 14 |
| BDY94 | S | N | MU, PH, V, RA, AM | BUY79 | BU126 | | | 06 |
| BDY95 | S | N | MU, PH, V, RA, AM | BUY77 | BU126 | | | 06 |
| BDY96 | S | N | MU, PH, V, RA, AM | BUY76 | | 2N6513 | | 06, 14 |
| BDY97 | S | N | MU, PH, V, RA, AM | BUY76 | | 2N6512 | | 06 |
| BDY98 | S | N | MU, PH, V, RA, AM | BUY75 | | 2N6511 | | 06 |
| BDY99 | S | N | RA, PH, AM | BUY76 | | 2N6511 | | 06 |
| BF108 | S | N | SE, NU | BF117 | BF109 | | | 02 |
| BF108 | | | | BF114 | (BF457) | | | 02 |
| BF108 | | | | BF178 | | | | 02 |
| BF109 | S | N | PH, V, MU, PE | BF178 | (BF457) | | | 02 |
| BF109 | | | | BFY43 | BF114 | | | 02 |
| BF109 | | | | BF117 | | | | 02 |
| BF110 | S | N | TF, S, V | BF140 | (BF457) | | | 02 |
| BF110 | | | | BF111 | BF114 | | | 02 |
| BF110 | | | | BF178 | BF117 | | | 02 |
| BF111 | S | N | S | BF179C | BF456 | 2N3440 | 2SC154C | 02 |
| BF111 | | | | BD127 | (BF458) | | | 02 |
| BF111 | | | | S8F178 | BF257 | | | 02 |
| BF111 | | | | BD115 | BF178 | | | 02 |
| BF114 | S | N | TF, S, V | BF117 | (BF457) | | | 02 |
| BF114 | | | | BF178 | BF108 | | | 02 |
| BF114 | | | | BF257 | BF115 | | | 02 |
| BF114 | | | | BFY43 | | | | 02 |
| BF115 | S | N | PH, MU, V, S, TF | BF224 | BF117 | SE5056 | 2SC445 | 02 |
| BF115 | | | | BF185 | BF194 | | | 02 |
| BF115 | | | | BF225 | | | | 02 |
| BF117 | S | N | IN, IT, TX | BF179 | (BF457) | SE7001 | 2SC154 | 02 |
| BF117 | | | | BF178 | BF257 | | | 02 |
| BF118 | S | N | IN, TX | BF179C | (BF458) | 2N4927 | 2SC154C | 02 |
| BF118 | | | | BF178 | SFB258 | | | 02 |
| BF118 | | | | BF258 | BF338 | | | 02 |
| BF118 | | | | BF337 | | | | 02 |
| BF119 | S | N | IN, TX | BF456-7 | (BF457) | 2N4927 | | 02 |
| BF119 | | | | BF337 | BF178 | | | 02 |
| BF120 | S | N | IN | (BF458) | BF179 | SE7055 | 2N5833 | 02 |
| BF120 | | | | BF337 | | 2N4927 | | 02 |
| BF121 | S | N | IN | BF224 | (BF198) | SE5056 | 2SC454 | 02 |
| BF121 | | | | BF167 | BF196 | | | 02 |
| BF123 | S | N | IN | BF197 | BF173 | SE5030B | 2SC464 | 02 |
| BF123 | | | | BF196 | | | | 02 |
| BF125 | S | N | IN, TX | BF314 | (BF199) | SE5031 | | 02 |
| BF125 | | | | BF237 | BF197 | | | 02 |
| BF125 | | | | BF225 | BF173 | | | 02 |
| BF127 | S | N | IN, TX | BF224 | (BF198) | SE5056 | 2SC682 | 02 |
| BF127 | | | | BF167 | BF196 | | | 02 |
| BF130 | S | N | | BC107A | BFY39 | | | 02 |
| BF131 | S | N | | BFY39 | | | | 02 |
| BF132 | S | N | | BFY37 | BCY58 | | | 02 |
| BF133 | S | N | | BSX48 | BFY37 | | | 02 |
| BF134 | S | N | IN | BFX62 | BF173 | | | 02 |
| BF134 | | | | BF115 | | | | 02 |
| BF136 | S | N | IN | (BF198) | BFX60 | | | 02 |
| BF136 | | | | BF167 | | | | 02 |
| BF137 | S | N | IN, IT | BF115 | (BF457) | | | 02 |
| BF137 | | | | BF173 | BF257 | | | 02 |
| BF137 | | | | BF179 | BF194 | | | 02 |
| BF138 | S | N | IN | BF136 | (BF198) | | | 02 |
| BF138 | | | | BFX60 | BF167 | | | 02 |
| BF140 | S | N | SE | BFY43 | (BF457) | 2N257 | | 02 |
| BF140 | | | | BF114 | BF178 | | | 02 |
| BF140A | S | N | SE | (BF457) | BF179 | | | 02 |
| BF140D | S | N | SE | BF118 | (BF458) | | 2SC154C | 02 |
| BF140D | | | | BF179 | BF178 | | | 02 |
| BF140D | | | | BF179B | | | | 02 |
| BF140R | S | N | NU | (BF457) | BF178 | | | 02 |
| BF140S | S | N | NU | (BF457) | BF178 | | | 02 |
| BF152 | S | N | AT, SG | BF183 | BFX62 | | | 02 |
| BF152 | | | | BF224 | | | | 02 |
| BF153 | S | N | AT, SG | BF194 | BF255 | 2N5363 | | 02 |
| BF153 | | | | BF121 | BF185 | | | 02 |

| TYPE | M/S | POL | MANUFAC | EUROPEAN | | AMERICAN | | JAPANESE | USE |
|------|-----|-----|---------|----------|----|---------|----|----------|-----|
| BF153 | | | | BF224 | BF254 | | | | 02 |
| BF153 | | | | BF167 | | | | | 02 |
| BF154 | S | N | SG, AT | BC238A | BF224 | MPS6565 | 2N3564 | | 02 |
| BF154 | | | | (BF241) | BF196 | | | | 02 |
| BF154 | | | | BC172A | BF185 | | | | 02 |
| BF154 | | | | BC183A | BF255 | | | | 02 |
| BF155 | S | N | SG, AT | BF225 | (BFX62) | 2N4134 | | | 02 |
| BF155 | | | | BF180 | | | | | 02 |
| BF155R | S | N | NU | (BF457) | BF178 | | | | 02 |
| BF155S | S | N | NU | (BF457) | BF178 | | | | 02 |
| BF156 | S | N | SG, AT | BF178 | (BF457) | SE7002 | | | 02 |
| BF156 | | | | BF257 | BF117 | | | | 02 |
| BF156 | | | | BFY43 | BF140 | | | | 02 |
| BF156 | | | | BF179 | | | | | 02 |
| BF157 | S | N | SG, AT | BF173 | BF179C | | | | 02 |
| BF157 | | | | (BF457) | SFB257 | | | | 02 |
| BF157 | | | | BF257 | BF179 | | | | 02 |
| BF157 | | | | BF170 | BF179A | | | | 02 |
| BF157B | S | N | SG, AT | (BF458) | BF179C | | | | 02 |
| BF158 | S | N | SG, AT | BF224 | BF173 | 2N3563 | 40478 | | 02 |
| BF158 | | | | BF199 | BF237 | | | | 02 |
| BF159 | S | N | SG, AT | BF224 | BF173 | 40478 | | | 02 |
| BF159 | | | | BF199 | BF237 | | | | 02 |
| BF160 | S | N | SG, ME, NS, AT | BF237 | (BF199) | 40478 | | | 02 |
| BF160 | | | | BF173 | BF185 | | | | 02 |
| BF160 | | | | BF224 | BF255 | | | | 02 |
| BF161 | S | N | SG, AT | BF225 | BF181 | 2N4134 | | 2SC707 | 02 |
| BF161 | | | | BF183 | BFX62 | | | | 02 |
| BF161 | | | | BF255 | | | | | 02 |
| BF162 | S | N | SG, AT | BF225 | (BF240) | | | | 02 |
| BF162 | | | | BF200 | BFX62 | | | | 02 |
| BF163 | S | N | SG, AT | BF198 | (BF240) | | | | 02 |
| BF163 | | | | BF225 | BF167 | | | | 02 |
| BF163 | | | | BF196 | | | | | 02 |
| BF164 | S | N | SG, AT | BF224 | (BF240) | | | | 02 |
| BF164 | | | | BF225 | BF167 | | | | 02 |
| BF164 | | | | BF198 | | | | | 02 |
| BF165 | S | N | SG, AT | BF185 | (BF255) | MPS6565 | 2N3564 | | 02 |
| BF165 | | | | BC108A | BC182A | | | | 02 |
| BF165 | | | | BC107A | BF195 | | | | 02 |
| BF165 | | | | BC207A | | | | | 02 |
| BF166 | S | N | SG, AT | BF167 | BF173 | 2N4134 | | | 02 |
| BF166 | | | | BF237 | BF200 | | | | 02 |
| BF166 | | | | BF225 | BFX62 | | | | 02 |
| BF167 | S | N | MU, S, TF, V, AM- | BF237 | (BF198) | SE5056 | | | 02 |
| BF167 | | | Ss, MN, ML, PE, | BF224 | BF189 | | | | 02 |
| BF167 | | | PH, RA, SG, TX | BF200 | | | | | 02 |
| BF168 | S | N | TF, V, S | BF224 | (BF199) | | | | 02 |
| BF168 | | | | BF185 | BF173 | | | | 02 |
| BF168 | | | | BF167 | | | | | 02 |
| BF169 | S | N | SE | BC183A | BC237B | MPS6520 | | | 02 |
| BF169 | | | | BF115 | BC108 | | | | 02 |
| BF169 | | | | BC208A | BC108C | | | | 02 |
| BF169 | | | | BF185 | | | | | 02 |
| BF169A | S | N | | BF115 | | | | | 02 |
| BF169R | S | N | SE | BC237B | | | | | 02 |
| BF170 | S | N | SE | BF173 | BF178 | | | | 02 |
| BF170 | | | | BF182C | | | | | 02 |
| BF173 | S | N | MU, S, TF, V, AM- | BF306 | (BF199) | FT129 | SE5031 | 2SC464 | 02 |
| BF173 | | | AT, Ss, MN, ML, | BF224 | BF117 | | | | 02 |
| BF173 | | | PE, PH, RA, TX | BF384 | BF140 | | | | 02 |
| BF174 | S | N | SG, TX, AT | BF170 | BF179B | | | 2SC154C | 02 |
| BF174 | | | | (BF457) | BF178 | | | | 02 |
| BF174 | | | | BF457-9 | BF257 | | | | 02 |
| BF174 | | | | SFB257 | BF114 | | | | 02 |
| BF174 | | | | BF179A | | | | | 02 |
| BF175 | S | N | SG, AT | (BF241) | BF167 | 2N4134 | 2N4012 | | 02 |
| BF175 | | | | BF225 | | | | | 02 |
| BF176 | S | N | SG, AT | BF224 | (BF241) | SE5025 | | | 02 |
| BF176 | | | | BF173 | BF311 | | | | 02 |
| BF177 | S | N | MU, PH, V, TF, TX, | BF257 | (BF457) | 40360 | SE7002 | 2SC856 | 02 |
| BF177 | | | RA, AT, S, SMN, PE | BF179A | BF108 | | | | 02 |
| BF177 | | | | BFY43 | BF117 | | | | 02 |
| BF177 | | | | BF179C | | | | | 02 |
| BF178 | S | N | MU, PH, V, TF, TX | BF140D | (BF458) | 40412 | | 2SC856 | 02 |

| TYPE | M/S | POL | MANUFAC | EUROPEAN | | AMERICAN | | JAPANESE | USE |
|---|---|---|---|---|---|---|---|---|---|
| BF178 | | | HA, ML, AT, Ss, | BF457-9 | BF108 | | | | 02 |
| BF178 | | | MN, PE, S | BF179C | SFB178 | | | | 02 |
| BF179 | S | N | S, RA, AT, Ss, MN, | SFB258 | (BF458) | | | | 02 |
| BF179 | | | MU, PH, V, TF, TX, | BF179C | BF257 | | | | 02 |
| BF179 | | | ML, PE | BF148 | | | | | 02 |
| | | | | | | | | | |
| BF179A | S | N | TF, SG, PH, RA, | BF118 | (BF457) | | | 2SC154C | 02 |
| BF179A | | | ML, S, Ss | BF179C | BF257 | | | | 02 |
| BF179A | | | | BF179 | | | | | 02 |
| BF179B | S | N | TF, SG, PH, RA, | BF118 | (BF457) | | | 2SC154C | 02 |
| BF179B | | | ML, S, Ss | BF258 | BF179C | | | | 02 |
| | | | | | | | | | |
| BF179C | S | N | TF, SG, PH, RA. | (BF458) | BF258 | | | 2SC154C | 02 |
| BF179C | | | | BF118 | | | | | 02 |
| BF180 | S | N | MU, PH, V, AT, Ss | (BFX62) | BF225 | MT1061 | | | 02 |
| BF180 | | | MN, ML, PE, RA, | | | | | | 02 |
| BF180 | | | TX | | | | | | 02 |
| | | | | | | | | | |
| BF181 | S | N | MU, PH, AT, MN, | (BFX62) | BF224 | SE3005 | | | 02 |
| BF181 | | | ML, V, Ss, PE, RA, | BF180 | | | | | 02 |
| BF181 | | | TX | | | | | | 02 |
| BF182 | S | N | PH, MU, V | BFX62 | | SE3005 | | | 02 |
| BF183 | S | N | PH, MU, V | BFX62 | | SE3005 | | | 02 |
| | | | | | | | | | |
| BF184 | S | N | MU, TF, V, AT, BL | BF234 | (BF194) | SE5056 | | 2SC460 | 02 |
| BF184 | | | MN, PE, PH, RA, S | BF238 | BF115 | | | | 02 |
| BF184 | | | | BF167 | | | | | 02 |
| BF185 | S | N | MU, PH, TF, V, AT, | BF235 | (BF195) | SE5056 | 40478 | 2SC535 | 02 |
| BF185 | | | BL, MN, PE, RA, S | BF237 | BF115 | | | | 02 |
| | | | | | | | | | |
| BF185 | | | | BF125 | BF167 | | | | 02 |
| BF186 | S | N | MU, PH, V, AT | BF178 | (BF458) | | | 2SC1545 | 02 |
| BF186 | | | | BF225 | SFB258 | | | | 02 |
| BF186 | | | | BF118 | BF111 | | | | 02 |
| BF188 | S | N | SE | BF200 | | | | | 02 |
| | | | | | | | | | |
| BF189 | S | N | SE | BF224 | BF115 | | | | 02 |
| BF189 | | | | BF167 | BF173 | | | | 02 |
| BF189 | | | | BF200 | BF184 | | | | 02 |
| BF191 | S | N | | BF225 | | | | | 02 |
| BF192 | S | N | | BF225 | | | | | 02 |
| | | | | | | | | | |
| BF193 | S | N | | BF225 | | | | | 02 |
| BF194 | S | N | MU, S, TF, V | BF184 | BF237 | SE5056 | | 2SC460 | 02 |
| BF194 | | | | BF115 | BF234 | | | | 02 |
| BF194 | | | | BF173 | BF224 | | | | 02 |
| BF194 | | | | BF163 | BF189 | | | | 02 |
| | | | | | | | | | |
| BF196 | S | N | MU, PH, TF, V, AT | BF225 | (BF198) | SE5056 | | 2SC682 | 02 |
| BF196 | | | PE, RA | BF329 | BF167 | | | | 02 |
| BF196-01 | S | N | EI | (BF198) | | | | | 02 |
| BF197 | S | N | MU, PH, TF, V, AT | BF224 | (BF199) | SE5030B | | 2SC464 | 02 |
| BF197 | | | PE, RA, S | BF330 | BF173 | | | | 02 |
| | | | | | | | | | |
| BF197-01 | | | EI | (BF199) | | | | | 02 |
| BF198 | S | N | MU, S, TF, V | BF163 | BF167 | SE5056 | | | 02 |
| BF198 | | | | BF225 | | | | | 02 |
| BF199 | S | N | MU, S, TF, V | BF197 | BF173 | SE5030B | | | 02 |
| BF199 | | | | BF224 | | | | | 02 |
| | | | | | | | | | |
| BF200 | S | N | MU, PH, V, AT, PE | BF237 | (BFX62) | SE5020 | SE5024 | | 02 |
| BF200 | | | MN, ML, RA, Ss | BF238 | BF162 | | | | 02 |
| BF200 | | | | BF224 | | | | | 02 |
| BF206 | S | N | SE | (BFX62) | BF384 | | | | 02 |
| BF206 | | | | BF200 | | | | | 02 |
| | | | | | | | | | |
| BF207 | S | N | SE | (BF198) | BF224 | | | | 02 |
| BF207 | | | | BF200 | | | | | 02 |
| BF208 | S | N | SE | (BF199) | BF224 | | | | 02 |
| BF208 | | | | BF200 | | | | | 02 |
| BF209 | S | N | SE | (BFX62) | BF224 | | | | 02 |
| | | | | | | | | | |
| BF209 | | | | BF200 | | | | | 02 |
| BF210 | S | N | | BF224 | | | | | 02 |
| BF211 | S | N | | BF224 | | | | | 02 |
| BF212 | S | N | SE | (BFX62) | BF384 | | | | 02 |
| BF212 | | | | BF200 | | | | | 02 |
| | | | | | | | | | |
| BF213 | S | N | SE | (BFX62) | BF384 | | | | 02 |
| BF213 | | | | BF180 | | | | | 02 |
| BF214 | S | N | SE | BF183 | (BF254) | | | | 02 |
| BF214 | | | | BF184 | BF194 | | | | 02 |
| BF215 | S | N | SE | (BF255) | BF185 | | | | 02 |
| | | | | | | | | | |
| BF215 | | | | BF195 | | | | | 02 |
| BF216 | S | N | TH, AE | (BF255) | | | | | 02 |
| BF217 | S | N | TH, AE | (BF254) | | | | | 02 |
| BF218 | S | N | TH, AE | (BF255) | | | | | 02 |
| BF219 | S | N | TH, AE | (BF254) | | | | | 02 |

| TYPE | M/S | POL | MANUFAC | EUROPEAN | | AMERICAN | | JAPANESE | USE |
|------|-----|-----|---------|----------|---|----------|---|----------|-----|
| BF220 | S | N | TH, AE | (BF255) | | | | | 02 |
| BF222 | S | N | AT | BF225 | SFB222 | | | | 02 |
| BF222 | | | | BF200 | BFX62 | | | | 02 |
| BF222 | | | | BF195 | | | | | 02 |
| BF223 | S | N | TF | BF224 | (BF199) | SE5030B | | | 02 |
| | | | | | | | | | |
| BF223 | | | | BF169 | BF197 | | | | 02 |
| BF223 | | | | BF523 | BF232 | | | | 02 |
| BF223 | | | | BF173 | | | | | 02 |
| BF224 | S | N | TX | (BF199) | BF173 | SE5030B | | 2SC682 | 02 |
| BF224J | S | N | | BF173 | | | | | 02 |
| | | | | | | | | | |
| BF224JF | S | N | | BF173 | | | | | 02 |
| BF225 | S | N | TX | BF163 | (BF198) | SE5056 | 40487 | 2SC682 | 02 |
| BF225 | | | | BF196 | BF167 | | | | 02 |
| BF225 | | | | BF224 | | | | | 02 |
| BF225J | S | N | | BF167 | | | | | 02 |
| | | | | | | | | | |
| BF225JF | S | N | | BF167 | | | | | 02 |
| BF226 | S | N | SE | (BF225) | BF185 | | | | 02 |
| BF227 | S | N | TF | BFR27 | BF199 | 2N5830 | | | 02 |
| BF227 | | | | BF224 | BF137 | | | | 02 |
| BF227 | | | | BF384 | BF173 | | | | 02 |
| | | | | | | | | | |
| BF228 | S | N | TF | BSX21 | BF177 | 2N5830 | 2N1990R | | 02 |
| BF228 | | | | BSW69 | BSW32 | | | | 02 |
| BF229 | S | N | TF | BF194 | BF254 | SE5056 | | | 02 |
| BF229 | | | | BF184 | BF163 | | | | 02 |
| BF229 | | | | BF254 | | | | | 02 |
| | | | | | | | | | |
| BF230 | S | N | TF | BF185 | BF255 | SE5056 | | | 02 |
| BF230 | | | | BF163 | BF195 | | | | 02 |
| BF231 | S | N | IS, AT, S, TX | (BF199) | | | | | 02 |
| BF232 | S | N | SG, S, RZ, TX | (BF199) | BF173 | | | 2SC464 | 02 |
| BF232 | | | | BF224 | | | | | 02 |
| | | | | | | | | | |
| BF233 | S | N | SE, SG, RZ | BF184 | BF254 | | | 2SC464 | 02 |
| BF233 | | | | BF237 | BF238 | | | | 02 |
| BF233-2 | S | N | SE, SG, AT | BF254 | BF184 | | | | 02 |
| BF233-3 | S | N | SE, SG, AT | BF254 | BF184 | | | | 02 |
| BF233-4 | S | N | SE, SG, AT | BF254 | BF184 | | | | 02 |
| | | | | | | | | | |
| BF233-5 | S | N | SE, SG, AT | BF254 | BF184 | | | | 02 |
| BF233-6 | S | N | SE, SG, AT | (BF254) | BF184 | | | | 02 |
| BF234 | S | N | SE, SG | BF254 | BF184 | | | | 02 |
| BF234 | | | | BF194 | BF229 | | | | 02 |
| BF235 | S | N | SE, SG | BF184 | BF185 | | | | 02 |
| | | | | | | | | | |
| BF235 | | | | BF255 | | | | | 02 |
| BF236 | S | N | SE, SG | BF185 | BF255 | | | | 02 |
| BF237 | S | N | TX | BF241 | (BF199) | SE5056 | | | 02 |
| BF237 | | | | BF115 | BF163 | | | | 02 |
| BF237 | | | | BF195 | BF194 | | | | 02 |
| | | | | | | | | | |
| BF237 | | | | BF185 | | | | | 02 |
| BF238 | S | N | TX | BF240 | (BF199) | SE5056 | | | 02 |
| BF238 | | | | BF115 | BF163 | | | | 02 |
| BF238 | | | | BF194 | BF195 | | | | 02 |
| BF238 | | | | BF184 | | | | | 02 |
| | | | | | | | | | |
| BF240 | S | N | S, TF, TX, V | BF167 | BF238 | SE5056 | | | 02 |
| BF241 | S | N | S, TF, TX, V | BF173 | BF237 | SE5030B | | | 02 |
| BF241 | | | | BF167 | | | | | 02 |
| BF241A | S | N | IS, RZ | BCY65EVII | | | | | 02 |
| BF242 | S | N | IS, RZ | BCY59VII | | | | | 02 |
| | | | | | | | | | |
| BF242A | S | N | IS, RZ | BCY65EVII | | | | | 02 |
| BF243 | J | P | RZ | | | | | | 02 |
| BF244 | J | N | RZ | BF245 | | 2N3588 | | | 02 |
| BF245 | J | N | MU, V, TX | BF244 | | | | | 02 |
| BF246 | J | N | V, TX | BF247 | | | | | 02 |
| | | | | | | | | | |
| BF247 | J | N | TX | BF246 | | | | | 02 |
| BF248 | S | N | TX | BC338-16 | BSW64 | 2N2222A | | | 02 |
| BF248-1 | S | N | TX | BC338-16 | | | | | 02 |
| BF248-2 | S | N | TX | BC338-16 | | | | | 02 |
| BF248-3 | S | N | TX | BC338-16 | | | | | 02 |
| | | | | | | | | | |
| BF248-4 | S | N | TX | BC338-25 | | | | | 02 |
| BF249 | S | P | TX | BC328-16 | BSW24 | 2N2907A | | | 02 |
| BF249-1 | S | P | TX | BC328-16 | | | | | 02 |
| BF249-2 | S | P | TX | BC328-16 | | | | | 02 |
| BF249-3 | S | P | TX | BC328-16 | | | | | 02 |
| | | | | | | | | | |
| BF249-4 | S | P | TX | BC328-25 | | | | | 02 |
| BF250 | S | N | TX | BC338-16 | BC109 | 2N930 | | | 02 |
| BF251 | S | N | SG, AT | (BF240) | BF167 | SE5056 | | | 02 |
| BF252 | S | N | SG, AT | (BF240) | BF185 | | | | 02 |
| BF253 | S | N | TX, SE | (BF254) | BF184 | | | | 02 |

| TYPE | M/S | POL | MANUFAC | EUROPEAN | | AMERICAN | JAPANESE | USE |
|------|-----|-----|---------|----------|---|----------|----------|-----|
| BF254 | S | N | S, TF, TX, V | BF184 | BF163 | SE5056 | | 02 |
| BF254 | | | | BF194 | BF237 | | | 02 |
| BF255 | S | N | S, TF, TX, V | BF238 | BF163 | SE5056 | | 02 |
| BF255 | | | | BF185 | BF195 | | | 02 |
| BF257 | S | N | PH, TF, TX, V, IT | (BF457) | SFB257 | | | 02 |
| BF257 | | | S, IN. PE, F | BD115 | | | | 02 |
| BF257A | S | N | TX | (BF458) | | | | 02 |
| BF257B | S | N | TX | (BF458) | | | | 02 |
| BF257C | S | N | TX | (BF458) | | | | 02 |
| BF257D | S | N | TX | (BF457) | | | | 02 |
| BF257G | S | N | TX | (BF458) | | | | 02 |
| BF257N | S | N | TX | (BF458) | | | | 02 |
| BF257S | S | N | TX | (BF457) | | | | 02 |
| BF258 | S | N | PH, TF, TX, V, IT | BF259 | (BF458) | | | 02 |
| BF258 | | | IN, PE, S, F | SBF258 | BF338 | | | 02 |
| BF258A | S | N | TX | (BF459) | | | | 02 |
| BF259 | S | N | PH, TF, TX, V, IT, | (BF459) | BF258 | SE7056 | | 02 |
| BF259 | | | IN, PE, S, F | BF338 | | | | 02 |
| BF259A | S | N | TX | (BF459) | | | | 02 |
| BF259G | S | N | TX | (BF459) | | | | 02 |
| BF260 | S | N | AT | BF199 | BF167 | SE5056 | | 02 |
| BF260 | | | | BF173 | BF200 | | | 02 |
| BF261 | S | N | AT | BF167 | BF173 | SE5056 | | 02 |
| BF261 | | | | BF199 | | | | 02 |
| BF262 | S | N | MU | BF362 | | | | 02 |
| BF263 | S | N | MU | BF363 | | | | 02 |
| BF264 | S | N | MU | BF363 | | | | 02 |
| BF266 | S | N | IS, RZ | (BF240) | | | | 02 |
| BF267 | S | N | IS, RZ | (BF198) | | | | 02 |
| BF268 | S | N | | BFY90 | | 2N2857 | | 02 |
| BF270 | S | N | SG, AT | BF164 | BF198 | SE5056 | | 02 |
| BF271 | S | N | SG, AT | BF173 | BF199 | FT129 | SE5030B | 02 |
| BF273 | S | N | SG, ME, AT | (BF255) | BF200 | | | 02 |
| BF273C | S | N | SG, AT | (BF254) | BF200 | | | 02 |
| BF273D | S | N | SG, AT | (BF255) | BF200 | | | 02 |
| BF274 | S | N | SG, ME, AT | (BF254) | BF173 | | | 02 |
| BF274B | S | N | SG, AT | (BF254) | BF173 | | | 02 |
| BF274C | S | N | SG, AT | (BF254) | BF173 | | | 02 |
| BF275 | S | N | IS, RZ | (BF240) | | | | 02 |
| BF287 | S | N | SG, AT | (BF241) | BF167 | 2N4134 | | 02 |
| BF287 | | | | BF200 | | | | 02 |
| BF288 | S | N | SG, AT | (BF240) | BF163 | SE5056 | | 02 |
| BF288 | | | | BF200 | | | | 02 |
| BF290 | S | N | SG, AT | (BF198) | BF183 | SE5031 | | 02 |
| BF291 | S | N | SG, AT | BC237A | BFX93 | 2N915 | 2N918 | 02 |
| BF291A | S | N | SG, AT | BC237A | BFX93 | 2N918 | | 02 |
| BF291B | S | N | SG, AT | BC237A | BFX93 | 2N918 | | 02 |
| BF292 | S | N | SG, AT, TX | (BF458) | BF258 | | | 02 |
| BF292A | S | N | SG, AT, TX | (BF457) | BF257 | SE7001 | | 02 |
| BF292B | S | N | SG, AT, TX | (BF458) | | | | 02 |
| BF292B1 | | | | SBF178 | BF258 | | | 02 |
| BF292C | S | N | SG, AT, TX | (BF458) | BF258 | SE7055 | | 02 |
| BF293 | S | N | AG, AT | BC237A | BSW64 | 2N2222A | | 02 |
| BF293A | S | N | SG, AT | BC237A | BSW64 | 2N2222A | | 02 |
| BF293D | S | N | SG, AT | BC237A | BSW64 | 2N2222A | | 02 |
| BF294 | S | N | SG, AT | (BF457) | BF257 | | | 02 |
| BF297 | S | N | TX | (BF457) | BF118 | | | 02 |
| BF297 | | | | BF257 | | | | 02 |
| BF298 | S | N | TX | (BF458) | BF118 | | | 02 |
| BF298 | | | | BF258 | | | | 02 |
| BF299 | S | N | TX | (BF459) | BF259 | | | 02 |
| BF302 | S | N | AT | (BF199) | BF160 | FT129 | | 02 |
| BF302 | | | | BF167 | | | | 02 |
| BF303 | S | N | AT | (BF199) | BF184 | FT129 | SE5031 | 02 |
| BF304 | S | N | AT | (BF199) | BF173 | FT129 | SE5031 | 02 |
| BF304 | | | | BF167 | | | | 02 |
| BF305 | S | N | AT, SG | (BF458) | BF257 | | | 02 |
| BF305 | | | | SBF257 | | | | 02 |
| BF306 | S | N | AT | (BF199) | BF173 | FT129 | SE5031 | 02 |
| BF308 | S | N | SG, AT | (BF199) | BFY90 | 2N2857 | | 02 |
| BF309 | S | N | SG, AT | (BF199) | BFY90 | 2N2857 | | 02 |
| BF310 | S | N | S, TF | BF181 | BF173 | SE5030B | | 02 |
| BF311 | S | N | TF, V | (BF199) | BF173 | SE5030B | 2SC856 | 02 |
| BF311 | | | | BF224 | | | | 02 |
| BF314 | S | N | S, TF | BF200 | | | | 02 |

| TYPE | M/S | POL | MANUFAC | EUROPEAN | | AMERICAN | | JAPANESE | USE |
|------|-----|-----|---------|----------|--|----------|--|----------|-----|
| BF321 | S | N | SE | (BF255) | | | | | 02 |
| BF321A | S | N | SE | (BF255) | BF200 | | | | 02 |
| BF321B | S | N | SE | (BF254) | BF200 | | | | 02 |
| BF321C | S | N | SE | (BF254) | BF200 | | | | 02 |
| BF321D | S | N | SE | (BF254) | BF200 | | | | 02 |
| BF321E | S | N | SE | (BF254) | BF200 | | | | 02 |
| BF321F | S | N | SE | (BF254) | BF200 | | | | 02 |
| BF322 | S | N | TX | BCW77-16 | BSW54 | 40317 | 2N2219A | | 02 |
| BF322-1 | S | N | TX | BCW77-16 | | | | | 02 |
| BF322-2 | S | N | TX | BCW77-16 | | | | | 02 |
| BF322-3 | S | N | TX | BCW77-16 | | | | | 02 |
| BF322-4 | S | N | TX | BCW25 | | | | | 02 |
| BF323 | S | P | TX | BCW79-16 | BFX29 | 40319 | 2N2905A | | 02 |
| BF323-1 | S | P | TX | BCW79-16 | | | | | 02 |
| BF323-2 | S | P | TX | BCW79-16 | | | | | 02 |
| BF323-3 | S | N | TX | BCW79-16 | | | | | 02 |
| BF323-4 | S | N | TX | BCW79-25 | | | | | 02 |
| BF325 | S | N | TX | (BF240) | BF200 | | | | 02 |
| BF329 | S | N | AT | (BF198) | BF167 | SE5056 | | | 02 |
| BF329 | | | | BF196 | BF225 | | | | 02 |
| BF330 | S | N | AT | (BF199) | BF173 | SE5031 | | | 02 |
| BF330 | | | | BF197 | BF224 | | | | 02 |
| BF332 | S | N | AT | BF184 | BF194 | | | | 02 |
| BF332 | | | | BF152 | BF384 | | | | 02 |
| BF332B | S | N | AT | BF194 | BF184 | | | | 02 |
| BF333 | S | N | AT | BF185 | BF195 | | | | 02 |
| BF333 | | | | BF160 | BF224 | | | | 02 |
| BF333C | S | N | AT | BF195 | BF184 | | | | 02 |
| BF333D | S | N | AT | BF195 | | | | | 02 |
| BF334 | S | N | PH, V, PE | BF199 | BF224 | SE5056 | | | 02 |
| BF334 | | | | BF184 | | | | | 02 |
| BF335 | S | N | PH, V, PE | BF198 | BF185 | SE5056 | | | 02 |
| BF336 | S | N | MU, PH, V, TX, RA | (BF458) | BF258 | 2N4927 | | | 02 |
| BF336 | S | N | AM, PE, F | | | | | | 02 |
| BF337 | S | N | MU, PH, V, TX, RA | (BF458) | BF258 | 2N4927 | | | 02 |
| BF337 | S | N | AM, PE, F | (BF259) | | | | | 02 |
| BF338 | S | N | MU, PH, V, AM, PE | (BF459) | BF258 | 2N4927 | | | 02 |
| BF338 | S | N | F | (BF459) | BF258 | 2N4927 | | | 02 |
| BF339 | S | P | TX | (BF324) | | | | | 02 |
| BF340 | S | P | TX | (BF451) | | | | | 02 |
| BF341 | S | P | TX | (BF450) | | | | | 02 |
| BF342 | S | P | TX | (BF451) | | | | | 02 |
| BF343 | S | P | TX | (BF450) | | | | | 02 |
| BF344 | S | N | AT | (BF254) | BF184 | | | | 02 |
| BF345 | S | N | AT | (BF255) | BF185 | | | | 02 |
| BF355 | S | N | RA, MU | | | 2N3440 | | | 02 |
| BF357 | S | N | TX | BFY90 | | 2N2857 | | | 02 |
| BF357K | S | N | TX | BFY90 | | 2N2857 | | | 02 |
| BF365 | S | N | LI, RA | BF254 | | | | | 02 |
| BF366 | S | N | MO | (BF198) | BF200 | | | | 02 |
| BF367 | S | N | MO | BF198 | BF200 | | | | 02 |
| BF368 | S | N | MO | (BF255) | BF200 | | | | 02 |
| BF368K | S | N | MO | BF255 | BF200 | | | | 02 |
| BF369 | S | N | MO | (BF254) | BF200 | | | | 02 |
| BF369K | S | N | MO | BF254 | BF200 | | | | 02 |
| BF371 | S | N | MO | (BF199) | BF173 | | | | 02 |
| BF373 | S | N | MO | (BF241) | BF173 | | | | 02 |
| BF377 | S | N | TF | (BFX89) | BF183 | | | | 02 |
| BF378 | S | N | TF | (BFX89) | BF183 | | | | 02 |
| BF379 | S | P | TF | (BF451) | | | | | 02 |
| BF380 | S | N | MO | BF258 | | RCP113A | | | 02 |
| BF381 | S | N | MO | BF258 | | RCP113B | | | 02 |
| BF382 | S | N | MO | BF259 | | RCP113C | | | 02 |
| BF384 | S | N | TX | (BF254) | BF184 | | | | 02 |
| BF385 | S | N | TX | (BF255) | BF185 | | | | 02 |
| BF387 | S | N | AT | (BF457) | BF257 | | | | 02 |
| BF388 | S | N | AT | (BF457) | BF257 | | | | 02 |
| BF389B | S | N | AT | (BF458) | BF258 | | | | 02 |
| BF389C | S | N | AT | (BF458) | BF258 | | | | 02 |
| BF390 | S | N | AT | BF259 | | | | | 02 |
| BF394 | S | N | MO | BF254 | BF184 | SE7056 | | | 02 |
| BF394A | S | N | MO | BF184 | | | | | 02 |
| BF394B | S | N | MO | BF184 | | | | | 02 |
| BF394C | S | N | MO | BF184 | | | | | 02 |
| BF395 | S | N | MO | BF255 | BF185 | | | | 02 |

| TYPE | M/S | POL | MANUFAC | EUROPEAN | | AMERICAN | | JAPANESE | USE |
|------|-----|-----|---------|----------|---|----------|---|----------|-----|
| BF395C | S | N | MO | BF184 | | | | | 02 |
| BF411 | S | N | TF | (BF457) | | | | | 02 |
| BF412 | S | N | TF | (BF457) | | | | | 02 |
| BF413 | S | N | TF | (BF458) | | | | | 02 |
| BF414 | S | P | TF | BF324 | | | | | 02 |
| BF440 | S | P | TF | BF450 | | | | | 02 |
| BF441 | S | P | TF | BF451 | | | | | 02 |
| BF454 | S | N | S, AT, V, IN | BF240 | | | | | 02 |
| BF454B | S | N | AT | BF240 | | | | | 02 |
| BF455 | S | N | AT | BF241 | | | | | 02 |
| BF455C | S | N | AT | BF241 | | | | | 02 |
| BF455D | S | N | AT | BF241 | | | | | 02 |
| BF456 | S | N | TX | BF457 | BD232 | | | | 02 |
| BF457 | S | N | TX, S, V | BD232 | BD115 | | | | 02 |
| BF458 | S | N | TX, S, V | BD115 | BD232 | | | | 02 |
| BF459 | S | N | TX, S, V | BF338 | BD232 | | | | 02 |
| BF494 | S | N | PH, V | BF254 | | | | | 02 |
| BF495 | S | N | PH, V | BF255 | | | | | 02 |
| BF497 | S | N | SG, AT | (BF199) | BF173 | | | | 02 |
| BF523 | S | N | TX | (BF240) | BC107C | | | | 02 |
| BF540 | S | P | TX | (BF451) | | | | | 02 |
| BF541 | S | P | TX | (BF450) | | | | | 02 |
| BF542 | S | P | TX | (BF450) | | | | | 02 |
| BF594 | S | N | TX | BF254 | BF184 | | | | 02 |
| BF595 | S | N | TX | BF255 | BF185 | | | | 02 |
| BF596 | S | N | TX | (BF198) | BF167 | | | | 02 |
| BF597 | S | N | TX | (BF199) | BF173 | | | | 02 |
| BF597A | S | N | TX | (BF199) | | | | | 02 |
| BF597B | S | N | TX | (BF199) | | | | | 02 |
| BF694 | S | N | TX | (BF199) | | | | | 02 |
| BF694A | S | N | TX | (BF199) | | | | | 02 |
| BF694B | S | N | TX | (BF199) | | | | | 02 |
| BFJ45 | S | N | IS, RZ | BSX45-6 | | | | | 02 |
| BFJ46 | S | N | IS, RZ | BSX45-16 | | | | | 02 |
| BFJ47 | S | N | IS, RZ | BSX47-10 | | | | | 02 |
| BFJ48 | S | N | IS, RZ | BSX47-6 | | | | | 02 |
| BFJ49 | S | N | IS, RZ | BSX47-10 | | | | | 02 |
| BFJ50 | S | N | IS, RZ | BSX47-6 | | | | | 02 |
| BFJ57 | S | N | IS, RZ | (BF457) | | | | | 02 |
| BFJ64 | S | P | IS, RZ | (BCW80-16) | | | | | 02 |
| BFJ70 | S | N | IS, RZ | (BF199) | | | | | 02 |
| BFJ72 | S | N | IS, RZ | BCY59VII | | | | | 02 |
| BFJ73 | S | N | IS, RZ | BCY59VIII | | | | | 02 |
| BFJ74 | S | N | IS, RZ | (BC182A) | | | | | 02 |
| BFJ75 | S | N | IS, RZ | (BC182A) | | | | | 02 |
| BFJ77 | S | N | IS, RZ | BFY90 | | | | | 02 |
| BFJ78 | S | N | IS, RZ | BFY90 | | | | | 02 |
| BFJ79 | S | N | IS, RZ | BFY90 | | | | | 02 |
| BFJ92 | S | N | IS, RZ | BCY59VII | | | | | 02 |
| BFJ93 | S | N | IS, RZ | BCY59VIII | | | | | 02 |
| BFJ98 | S | N | IS, RZ | (BF457) | | | | | 02 |
| BFR10 | S | N | SG, AT, TX | (BCW78-16) | | | | | 02 |
| BFR11 | S | N | SG, AT, TX | (BCW74-10) | | | | | 02 |
| BFR14 | S | N | S | BFR14A | | | | | 02 |
| BFR16 | S | N | SG, S, AT, TX | (BC414B) | BC109 | 2N930 | | | 02 |
| BFR17 | S | N | SG, AT, TX | (BC414C) | BC109C | 2N930 | | | 02 |
| BFR18 | S | N | SG, AT, TX | BSX46-10 | BSX88 | 2N731 | | | 02 |
| BFR19 | S | N | SG, AT, TX | BSX45-6 | BFY51 | 2N1613 | 2N2297 | | 02 |
| BFR20 | S | N | SG, AT, TX | BSX45-16 | BFY51 | 2N1711 | 2N2297 | | 02 |
| BFR21 | S | N | SG, AT, TX | BSX47-6 | BFY65 | 2N1893 | 2N1990 | | 02 |
| BFR22 | S | N | AT, TX | BSX47-6 | BSW66 | 2N2102 | 2N4001 | | 02 |
| BFR23 | S | P | AT, TX | BSV17-6 | | 2N4036 | | | 02 |
| BFR24 | S | P | AT, TX | BSV16-10 | BFR23 | 2N4037 | 2N4036 | | 02 |
| BFR25 | S | N | AT, TX | (BF457) | | 2N4390 | | | 02 |
| BFR27 | S | N | LI | | | | | | 02 |
| BFR36 | S | N | SG, AT | (BFW16A) | | | | | 02 |
| BFR45 | J | N | | | | 2N4416 | | | 02 |
| BFR50 | S | N | TX | (BSX46-6) | BFY51 | 2N2297 | | | 02 |
| BFR51 | S | N | TX | (BSX46-6) | BFY50 | 2N2297 | | | 02 |
| BFR52 | S | N | TX | (BSX45-10) | BFY50 | 2N2297 | | | 02 |
| BFR53 | S | N | PH, V | (BFR35) | | | | | 02 |
| BFR56 | S | N | TX | (BSY34) | BFY51 | 2N5321 | 2N2297 | | 02 |
| BFR57 | S | N | TX | (BF457) | BF257 | | | | 02 |
| BFR58 | S | N | TX | (BF458) | BF258 | | | | 02 |
| BFR59 | S | N | TX | (BF459) | BF259 | | | | 02 |

| TYPE | M/S | POL | MANUFAC | EUROPEAN | | AMERICAN | JAPANESE | USE |
|---|---|---|---|---|---|---|---|---|
| BFR60 | S | P | TX | BSV17-6 | | | | 02 |
| BFR61 | S | P | TX | BSV16-6 | | | | 02 |
| BFR62 | S | P | TX | BSV15-10 | | | | 02 |
| BFR67 | S | N | SG, AT | (BC167) | | | | 02 |
| BFR67A | S | N | SG,AT | (BC167A) | | | | 02 |
| BFR67B | S | N | SG, AT | (BC167B) | | | | 02 |
| BFR68 | S | N | SG, AT | (BC168) | | | | 02 |
| BFR68A | S | N | SG,AT | (BC168A) | | | | 02 |
| BFR68B | S | N | SG, AT | (BC168B) | | | | 02 |
| BFR68C | S | N | SG, AT | (BC168C) | | | | 02 |
| BFR69 | S | P | SG, AT | (BC257) | | | | 02 |
| BFF69A | S | P | SG, AT | (BC257A) | | | | 02 |
| BF I69B | S | P | SG, AT | (BC257B) | | | | 02 |
| BFR69V1 | S | P | SG, AT | (BC257A) | | | | 02 |
| BFR70 | S | P | SG, AT | (BC258) | | | | 02 |
| BFR70A | S | P | SG, AT | (BC258A) | | | | 02 |
| BFR70B | S | P | SG, AT | (BC258B) | | | | 02 |
| BFR70V1 | S | P | SG, AT | (BC258A) | | | | 02 |
| BFR71 | S | N | SG, AT | (BC167A) | | | | 02 |
| BFR72 | S | N | SG, AT | (BC167A) | | | | 02 |
| BFR73 | S | P | SG, AT | (BC257A) | | | | 02 |
| BFR74 | S | P | SG, AT | (BC257A) | | | | 02 |
| BFR77 | S | N | SG, AT | BSX47-6 | | 2N1893 | | 02 |
| BFR78 | S | N | SG, AT | BSX47-6 | | 2N2405 | | 02 |
| BFR79 | S | P | TX | (BSV17-10) | | | | 02 |
| BFR80 | S | P | TX | (BSV17-10) | | | | 02 |
| BFR81 | S | P | TX | (BSV16-16) | | | | 02 |
| BFR86 | S | N | TX | (BF457) | | | | 02 |
| BFR87 | S | N | TX | (BF457) | | | | 02 |
| BFR88 | S | N | TX | (BF458) | | | | 02 |
| BFR89 | S | N | TX | (BF459) | | | | 02 |
| BFR90 | S | N | MU, PH, V | (BFR34A) | | | | 02 |
| BFR91 | S | N | MU, PH, V | (BFR34A) | | | | 02 |
| BFR92 | S | N | MU, PH, V | (BFR35A) | | | | 02 |
| BFR93 | S | N | MU, PH, V | (BFR35A) | BFR92 | | | 02 |
| BFS10 | S | N | SG, AT | (BFX55) | | 2N3866 | | 02 |
| BFS11 | S | N | AT | (BF198) | | | | 02 |
| BFS12 | S | P | SG, AT | BSV15-16 | | 2N5042 | | 02 |
| BFS13E | S | N | SG, AT | (BC123ye) | | | | 02 |
| BFS14E | S | P | SG, AT | (BC203ye) | | | | 02 |
| BFS18 | S | N | PH, V, RA | (BFS20) | BFS20R | | | 02 |
| BFS18B | S | N | | BFS20R | | | | 02 |
| BFS19 | S | N | PH, V, RA, S | (BFS20) | BFS20R | | | 02 |
| BFS19R | S | N | MU | BFS20R | | | | |
| BFS20 | S | N | PH, S, V | BFS20R | | | | |
| BFS21 | S | N | PH, V, MU | | | 2N5199 | | |
| BFS21A | S | N | PH, V, MU | | | 2N5199 | | |
| BFS37A | S | P | FE | BFS37 | | | | |
| BFS38A | S | N | FE | BFS38 | | | | |
| BFS39 | S | N | FE | BFS38 | | | | |
| BFS40A | S | P | FE | BFS40 | | | | |
| BFS41 | S | P | FE | BFS40 | | | | |
| BFS42 | S | N | FE | BFS43 | | | | |
| BFS44 | S | P | FE | BFS45 | | | | |
| BFS46A | S | N | FE | BFS46 | | | | |
| BFS47 | S | N | | BSX21 | | | | |
| BFS48 | S | P | | | | 2N4031 | | |
| BFS50 | S | N | TF | (BFX55) | | | | |
| BFS52 | S | P | | | | 2N2904 | | 02 |
| BF S53 | 3 | P | | | | 2N2905 | | |
| BFS59 | S | N | FE | BCX73-16 | BC387 | 2N4401 | | |
| BFS59K | S | N | FE | BCX73-16 | | | | 02 |
| BFS59L | S | N | FE | BCX73-16 | | | | 02 |
| BFS59M | S | N | FE | BCX73-16 | | | | 02 |
| BFS60 | S | N | FE | BCX74-16 | BC387 | 2N4401 | | 02 |
| BFS60K | S | N | FE | BCX74-16 | | | | 02 |
| BFS60L | S | N | | BCX74-16 | | | | 02 |
| BFS60M | S | N | FE | BCX74-16 | | | | 02 |
| BFS61 | S | N | FE | BC387 | | | | 02 |
| BFS62 | S | N | TF | (BF199) | | 2N4401 | | 02 |
| BFS65 | S | N | LI | BFS69 | | | | |
| BFS67 | S | P | | | | 2N3821 | | |
| BFS67P | J | N | TX | | | 2N4303 | | |
| BFS68 | J | N | TX | | | 2N3823 | | |
| BFS68P | J | N | TX | | | UI837E | | |

| TYPE | M/S | POL | MANUFAC | EUROPEAN | | AMERICAN | | JAPANESE | USE |
|------|-----|-----|---------|----------|--|----------|--|----------|-----|
| BFS70 | J | N | TX | | | 2N3821 | | | |
| BFS71 | J | N | TX | | | 2N3822 | | | |
| BFS72 | J | N | TX | | | 2N3823 | | | |
| BFS73 | J | N | TX | | | 2N3824 | 2N3821 | | |
| BFS74 | J | N | TX | | | 2N4856 | | | |
| BFS75 | J | N | TX | | | 2N4857 | | | |
| BFS76 | J | N | TX | | | 2N4858 | | | |
| BFS77 | J | N | TX | | | 2N4859 | | | |
| BFS78 | J | N | TX | | | 2N4860 | | | |
| BFS79 | J | N | TX | | | 2N4861 | | | |
| BFS80 | J | N | TX | | | 2N4416A | | | |
| BFS85 | S | N | FE | BFS88 | | | | | 02 |
| BFS89 | S | N | TX, AT | (BF459) | BD115 | | | | 02 |
| BFS89 | S | | | BF259 | | | | | 02 |
| BFS90 | S | P | TX | | | 40987 | | | 02 |
| BFS90A | S | P | TX | | | 40987 | | | 02 |
| BFS91 | S | P | TX | | | 40999 | | | 02 |
| BFS91A | S | P | TX | | | 40999 | | | 02 |
| BFS92 | S | P | PH, V, RA, PE, MU | BSV17-6 | | 2N4036 | 2N4929 | | 02 |
| BFS93 | S | P | PH, V, RA, PE, MU | BSV17-10 | | 2N4314 | 2N4929 | | 02 |
| BFS94 | S | P | PH, V, RA, PE, MU, | BSV17-6 | BFS95 | 2N4037 | 2N4036 | | 02 |
| BFS94 | S | P | TX | | | | | | 02 |
| BFS95 | S | P | PH, V, RA, PE, MU, | BSV15-10 | | 2N4037 | 2N4036 | | 02 |
| BFS95 | S | P | TX | | | | | | 02 |
| BFS96 | S | P | FE | BCX76-10 | | 2N4036 | 2N4403 | | 02 |
| BFS96K | S | P | FE | BCX76-16 | | | | | 02 |
| BFS96L | S | P | FE | BCX76-16 | | | | | 02 |
| BFS96M | S | P | FE | BCX76-16 | | | | | 02 |
| BFS97 | S | P | FE | BCX76-16 | | 2N4403 | | | 02 |
| BFS97K | S | P | FE | BCX76-16 | | | | | 02 |
| BFS97L | S | P | FE | BCX76-16 | | | | | 02 |
| BFS97M | S | P | FE | BCX76-16 | | | | | 02 |
| BFS98 | S | P | FE | | | 2N4403 | | | |
| BFS99 | S | N | AT, TX | (BF457) | BC394 | 2N5830 | 2N4390 | | 02 |
| BFT20 | S | P | TX | (BCX76-16) | | | | | 02 |
| BFT21 | S | P | TX | (BCX75-16) | | | | | 02 |
| BFT22 | S | P | TX | (BCX75-16) | | | | | 02 |
| BFT23 | S | N | MU | (BFR35) | | | | | 02 |
| BFT29 | S | N | TX | | | | | | 02 |
| BFT30 | S | N | TX | | | | | | 02 |
| BFT31 | S | N | TX | | | | | | 02 |
| BFT32 | S | N | TX | | | 40635 | | | 02 |
| BFT33 | S | N | TX | | | 40409 | | | 02 |
| BFT34 | S | N | TX | | | 2N2405 | | | 02 |
| BFT35 | S | P | TX | | | 2N4314 | | | 02 |
| BFT36 | S | N | TX | | | 40410 | | | 02 |
| BFT39 | S | N | TX | BSX47-10 | BSW54 | 40409 | 2N2219A | | 02 |
| BFT40 | S | N | TX | BSX46-10 | BSW54 | 40628 | 2N2219A | | 02 |
| BFT41 | S | N | TX | BSX46-16 | BSW54 | 40628 | 2N2219A | | 02 |
| BFT47 | S | N | SE | (BF457) | BF257 | | | | 02 |
| BFT48 | S | N | SE | (BF458) | BF258 | | | | 02 |
| BFT49 | S | N | SE | (BF459) | BF259 | | | | 02 |
| BFT53 | S | N | TX | (BCXJ4-16) | | | | | 02 |
| BFT54 | S | N | TX | (BCX73-16) | | | | | 02 |
| BFT55 | S | N | TX | (BCX73-16) | | | | | 02 |
| BFT60 | S | P | TX | BSV17-10 | BFS95 | 2N4037 | 2N4036 | | 02 |
| BFT61 | S | P | TX | BSV16-6 | BFS95 | 2N4037 | 2N4036 | | 02 |
| BFT62 | S | P | TX | BSV15-10 | BFS95 | 40815 | 2N4036 | | 02 |
| BFT69 | S | P | TX | (BSV17-10) | | | | | 02 |
| BFT70 | S | P | TX | (BSV17-10) | | | | | 02 |
| BFT71 | S | P | TX | (BSV16-16) | | | | | 02 |
| BFT79 | S | P | TX | BSV17-10 | BFS93 | 2N4037 | | | 02 |
| BFT80 | S | P | TX | BSV17-10 | BFS93 | 40815 | 2N4037 | | 02 |
| BFT81 | S | P | TX | BSV16-16 | BFS95 | 2N4036 | | | 02 |
| BFV56 | S | N | TX | (BSX49) | | (2N3252) | | | 02 |
| BFV56A | S | N | TX | (BSX49) | | (2N3253) | | | 02 |
| BFV57 | S | N | TX | (BSX49) | | (2N4013) | | | 02 |
| BFV57A | S | N | TX | (BSX49) | | (2N4014) | | | 02 |
| BFV63 | S | N | TX | BCW73-16 | | (2N2222) | | | 02 |
| BFV63A | S | N | TX | BCW74-16 | | (2N2222A) | | | 02 |
| BFV63B | S | N | TX | BCW73-16 | | (2N2221) | | | 02 |
| BFV64 | S | P | TX | BCW76-16 | | (2N2907A) | | | 02 |
| BFV64A | S | P | TX | (BCW76-16) | | (2N2907A) | | | 02 |
| BFV64B | S | P | TX | BCW76-16 | | (2N2906) | | | 02 |
| BFV65 | S | N | TX | (BSY63) | | (2N914) | | | 02 |

| TYPE | M/S | POL | MANUFAC | EUROPEAN | | AMERICAN | | JAPANESE | USE |
|------|-----|-----|---------|----------|--|----------|--|----------|-----|
| BFV65A | S | N | TX | (BSY63) | | (2N2369) | | | 02 |
| BFV65B | S | N | TX | (BSY63) | | (2N2369A) | | | 02 |
| BFV66 | S | N | TX | (BSX49) | | (2N2539) | | | 02 |
| BFV66A | S | N | TX | (BSX49) | | (2N2540) | | | 02 |
| BFV67 | S | N | TX | (BSY17) | | (2N709) | | | 02 |
| | | | | | | | | | |
| BFV68 | S | N | TX | BC414B | | (2N930) | | | 02 |
| BFV68A | S | N | TX | BC414B | | (2N2484) | | | 02 |
| BFV69 | S | N | TX | (BFX89) | | (2N918) | | | 02 |
| BFV69A | S | N | TX | (BFX89) | | (2N2865) | | | 02 |
| BFV90 | S | N | TX | (BSY34) | | | | | 02 |
| | | | | | | | | | |
| BFV90A | S | N | TX | (BSY34) | BSW54 | 2N2219A | | | 02 |
| BFV90B | S | N | TX | (BSY34) | BSW54 | 2N2219A | | | 02 |
| BFV99 | S | N | TX | (BSX46-6) | | | | | 02 |
| BFW10 | J | N | PH, MU, V | | | 2N4416 | 2N3823 | | |
| BFW11 | J | N | PH, MU, V | | | 2N4416 | 2N3822 | | |
| | | | | | | | | | |
| BFW16 | S | N | PH, MU, V, AM, PE | BFW16A | | 2N4875 | 2N4878 | | |
| BFW16A | S | N | PH, MU, V, S | BFY39 | BFY40 | 2N918 | | | 02 |
| BFW17 | S | N | MU, PH, V, AM, PE | BFW16A | | 2N3866 | 2N4876 | | |
| BFW17A | S | N | MU, PH, V, RA, PE | BFW16A | BFY39 | 2N918 | | | 02 |
| BFW19 | S | N | AT | | | 2N3137 | | | |
| | | | | | | | | | |
| BFW20 | S | P | MO, SG, TX, TD | (BC416B) | BCY71 | 2N3962 | 2N3965 | | 02 |
| BFW21 | S | P | TX, TD | BCY70 | | 2N3963 | 2N3965 | | |
| BFW22 | S | P | MO, SG, TX, TD | BC416C | BCY70 | 2N3964 | 2N3965 | | 02 |
| BFW23 | S | P | MO, SG, TX, TD | (BC416C) | BCY70 | 2N3965 | | | 02 |
| BFW24 | S | N | MO, SG, TX, TD | BSX46-6 | BFX85 | 2N2193 | 2N2102 | | 02 |
| | | | | | | | | | |
| BFW24 | | | | | | 2N1893 | 2N3108 | | 02 |
| BFW24 | | | | | | 2N2193A | | | 02 |
| BFW25 | S | N | MO, SG, TD | BSX45-16 | BFY51 | 2N2192 | 2N1711 | | 02 |
| BFW25 | | | | | | 2N2297 | 2N3109 | | 02 |
| BFW25 | | | | | | 2N2192A | | | 02 |
| | | | | | | | | | |
| BFW26 | S | N | MO, SG, TD | BSX45-6 | | 2N2193 | 2N697 | | 02 |
| BFW26 | | | | | | 2N2297 | 2N3110 | | 02 |
| BFW26 | | | | | | 2N2193A | | | 02 |
| BFW29 | S | N | TX, LI, TD | BSX45-6 | | 2N2219A | | | 02 |
| BFW30 | S | N | MU, S, PH, V | BFY69 | BFY37 | 2N918 | MT1061A | | |
| | | | | | | | | | |
| BFW31 | S | P | TX, TD | BCW76-16 | BSW24 | 2N2907 | 2N2907A | | 02 |
| BFW32 | S | P | TX, TD | BCW73-16 | | 2N2222 | | | 02 |
| BFW33 | S | N | TX, SG, TD | BSX47-6 | BFX85 | 2N1893 | | | 02 |
| BFW34 | S | N | LI | BSX45 | BSX45-6 | 2N4432 | 2N2297 | | 02 |
| BFW34 | | | | BFY51 | | | | | 02 |
| | | | | | | | | | |
| BFW35 | S | N | LI | BSX45 | BSX45-10 | 2N5203 | 2N2297 | | 02 |
| BFW35 | | | | BFY51 | | | | | 02 |
| BFW36 | S | N | LI, TD | (BF458) | | 2N5073 | 2N3114 | | 02 |
| BFW36 | | | | | | 2N5059 | | | 02 |
| BFW37 | S | N | LI, TD | (BF457) | | 2N3114 | | | 02 |
| | | | | | | | | | |
| BFW38 | S | N | LI | (BF458) | | | | | 02 |
| BFW39 | S | N | TD | | | 2N2915 | | | |
| BFW39A | S | N | TD | | | 2N2919A | | | |
| BFW40 | S | N | TD | | | 2N2916 | | | |
| BFW40A | S | N | TD | | | 2N2916 | | | |
| | | | | | | | | | |
| BFW41 | S | N | LI, TD | BFY90 | | 2N918 | | | 02 |
| BFW42 | S | N | LI | (BFW16A) | | | | | 02 |
| BFW43 | S | P | TX, AT | | | 2N4357 | 2N3494 | | |
| BFW43 | | | | | | 2N5059 | | | |
| BFW44 | S | P | S, SG, TX, AT | BFT19 | | 2N4358 | 2N3495 | | 02 |
| | | | | | | | | | |
| BFW45 | S | N | MU, PH, V, RA, AM | (BF457) | BF257 | 2N5059 | | | 02 |
| BFW45 | | | | BF174 | | SE7001 | | | 02 |
| BFW46 | S | N | MO, TX, V, PH | BSX72 | | 2N3924 | 2N3553 | | |
| BFW47 | S | N | MO, TX, V, PH | | | 2N3553 | 2N719A | | |
| | | | | | | | | | |
| BFW47 | | | | | | 40478 | | | |
| BFW51 | S | N | TD | | | 2N2974 | 2N2639 | | |
| BFW51A | S | N | TD | | | 2N2978 | | | |
| BFW52 | S | N | TD | | | 2N2975 | 2N2642 | | |
| BFW52A | S | N | TD | | | 2N2979 | | | |
| | | | | | | | | | |
| BFW54 | J | N | TX | | | 2N3822 | | | |
| BFW55 | J | N | TX | | | 2N3822 | | | |
| BFW56 | J | N | TX | | | 2N5393 | | | |
| BFW57 | S | N | MU, PH, MN, PE | (BC337-16) | | SE6020 | | | 02 |
| BFW58 | S | N | MU, PH, MN, PE | (BC337-16) | BFW57 | SE6020 | | | 02 |
| | | | | | | | | | |
| BFW59 | S | N | MU, PH, MN, PE | BC337-16 | BFW57 | SE6020 | | | 02 |
| BFW60 | S | N | MU, PH, MN, PE | BC337-16 | BC147A | SE6020 | | | 02 |
| BFW60 | | | | BFW57 | | | | | 02 |
| BFW61 | S | N | PH, MU, V | | | 2N4222 | | | |
| BFW63 | S | N | SG, AT | (BF198) | | FT129 | | | 02 |

| TYPE | M/S | POL | MANUFAC | EUROPEAN | | AMERICAN | | JAPANESE | USE |
|------|-----|-----|---------|----------|---|----------|---|----------|-----|
| BFW64 | S | N | SG, AT | (BF198) | | MT1061 | | | 02 |
| BFW66 | S | N | SG, AT | (BSY34) | | 2N2219A | | | 02 |
| BFW67 | S | N | SG, AT | (BF459) | | 2N5058 | | | 02 |
| BFW68 | S | N | SG, AT, TX | (BSX49) | | 2N2222A | | | 02 |
| BFW69 | S | N | SG, AT | (BFX55) | | | | | 02 |
| | | | | | | | | | |
| BFW70 | S | N | SG, AT | (BF199) | | | | | 02 |
| BFW71 | S | N | SG, AT | (BSX49) | | | | | 02 |
| BFW80 | S | N | LI | (BCW78-16) | BFY51 | 2N2297 | | | 02 |
| BFW87 | S | P | MU | (BC327-16) | | | | | 02 |
| BFW88 | S | P | MU | (BC327-16) | BFW87 | | | | 02 |
| | | | | | | | | | |
| BFW89 | S | P | MU | (BC327-16) | BFW87 | | | | 02 |
| BFW90 | S | P | MU | BC327-16 | BFW87 | | | | 02 |
| BFW91 | S | P | MU | BC327-16 | BFW87 | | | | 02 |
| BFW96 | S | N | MU | | | 2N4416 | | | |
| BFW97 | S | N | FE | (BFX89) | BFX73 | 2N918 | | | 02 |
| | | | | | | | | | |
| BFW97K | S | N | FE | (BFX89) | | | | | 02 |
| BFW97L | S | N | FE | (BFX89) | | | | | 02 |
| BFW97M | S | N | FE | (BFX89) | | | | | 02 |
| BFW99 | S | N | S | BFR15 | | | | | 02 |
| BFW99S | S | N | S | (BFS55) | | | | | |
| | | | | | | | | | |
| BFX11 | S | P | TX, AT | | | 2N3726 | 2N3350 | | |
| BFX11 | | | | | | 2N3351 | | | |
| BFX12 | S | P | MU, V, SG, TX | BC178 | BCY78VII | 2N3965 | MPS6518 | 2SA548 | 02 |
| BFX12 | | | | BC262 | BC178VI | 2N2894 | 2N2411 | | 02 |
| BFX12 | | | | BC213 | BC205 | | | | 02 |
| | | | | | | | | | |
| BFX12 | | | | BCY71 | | | | | 02 |
| BFX13 | S | P | MU, V, SG, TX | BC262 | BCY78VII | 2N2907A | MPS6518 | 2SA548 | 02 |
| BFX13 | | | | BC213 | BC178VI | 2N2412 | 2N2894 | | 02 |
| BFX13 | | | | BSW24 | BC178 | | | | 02 |
| BFX14 | S | N | SG, TX, AT | BSY58 | BSW54 | 2N2883 | 2N2219A | | 02 |
| | | | | | | | | | |
| BFX15 | S | N | AT | | | 2N2060 | 2N2919 | | |
| BFX17 | S | N | SG, AT, TX | | | (2N3553) | 2N3053 | | 02 |
| BFX17 | | | | | | 2N3725 | 2N2863 | | 02 |
| BFX18 | S | N | SG, TX, AT | BFX60 | (BF198) | 2N918 | 2N4134 | | 02 |
| BFX18 | | | | BF173 | BF225 | | TIS85 | | 02 |
| | | | | | | | | | |
| BFX19 | S | N | SG, AT | BFX60 | (BF198) | 2N918 | 2N4135 | | 02 |
| BFX19 | | | | BC109 | BF173 | TIS84 | | | 02 |
| BFX20 | S | N | SG, AT | (BF198) | BF173 | 2N918 | 2N4135 | | 02 |
| BFX20 | | | | BFX60 | | TIS84 | | | 02 |
| BFX21 | S | N | SG, AT | (BF198) | BF173 | 2N918 | 2N4135 | | 02 |
| | | | | | | | | | |
| BFX21 | | | | BFX59 | | | | | 02 |
| BFX25 | S | P | | | | 2N3504 | | | |
| BFX29 | S | P | MU, V, TX, SG, ME | (BCW80-16) | BC161 | 2N4036 | 2N2905A | 2SA537 | 02 |
| BFX29 | S | P | MN, NS, NT, PE, TD | | | 2N2905 | | | 02 |
| BFX30 | S | P | MU, V, TX, SG, NT | (BCW80-16) | BC161 | 2N4036 | 2N2905 | 2SA537 | 02 |
| | | | | | | | | | |
| BFX30 | | | TD | BFX29 | | 2N3503 | | | 02 |
| BFX31 | S | N | AT, SG | (BF198) | BFX60 | 2N4134 | | | 02 |
| BFX31 | | | | BC173 | | | | | 02 |
| BFX32 | S | N | TF, TD | (BF199) | | | | | 02 |
| BFX33 | S | N | TF | (BFX55) | | 2N2218 | | | 02 |
| | | | | | | | | | |
| BFX34 | S | N | MU, PH, TF, V, PE | (BSX63-10) | BUY47 | | | | 02 |
| BFX34 | S | N | SG, AT, F | | | | | | 02 |
| BFX35 | S | P | SG, TX | BCY79VIII | BCY71 | 2N3504 | 2N3505 | | 02 |
| BFX35 | | | | | | 2N3965 | | | 02 |
| BFX36 | S | P | TX, AT | | | 2N4024 | 2N3810 | | |
| | | | | | | | | | |
| BFX37 | S | P | MU, SG, TX, NS, AT | BCY77VII | | 2N2907A | 2N3962 | | |
| BFX38 | S | P | SG, TX, AT, F | BSV16-16 | BC161 | 2N4032 | 2N4036 | | 02 |
| BFX38 | | | | BFS95 | | | | | 02 |
| BFX39 | S | P | SG, TX, AT, F | BSV16-16 | BFS95 | 2N4030 | 2N4036 | | 02 |
| BFX40 | S | P | SG, TX, AT, F | BSV17-10 | BC161 | 2N4031 | 2N4033 | | 02 |
| | | | | | | | | | |
| BFX40 | | | | BFS93 | | 2N4037 | | | 02 |
| BFX41 | S | P | SG, TX, AT, F | BSV17-6 | BC161 | 2N4031 | 2N4030 | | 02 |
| BFX41 | | | | BFS93 | | 2N4037 | | | 02 |
| BFX43 | S | N | MU, PH, AM, RA, PE | (BSY63) | | 2N2369 | 2N2368 | | 02 |
| BFX43 | S | N | TX | | | | | | 02 |
| | | | | | | | | | |
| BFX44 | S | N | MU, PH, AM, PE | (BSY63) | | 2N2368 | 2N2369 | | 02 |
| BFX44 | S | N | RA, TX | | | | | | 02 |
| BFX45 | S | N | V, RA | (BC238B) | BCW49 | 2N2222 | | 2SC907 | 02 |
| BFX45 | | | | BC148 | | | | | 02 |
| BFX47 | S | N | V | BFY90 | | | | | 02 |
| | | | | | | | | | |
| BFX48 | S | P | TX, AT | | | 2N2905 | 2N4034 | | |
| BFX50 | S | N | RA, TX | (BSX46-6) | BSX33 | 2N2222A | 2N731 | | 02 |
| BFX51 | S | N | RA, TX | (BSX47-6) | BSX33 | 2N2222A | 2N731 | | 02 |
| BFX52 | S | N | RA, TX | (BSX48) | BSX33 | 2N2222A | 2N731 | | 02 |
| BFX53 | S | N | TF | BFY90 | | | | | |

| TYPE | M/S | POL | MANUFAC | EUROPEAN | | AMERICAN | | JAPANESE | USE |
|---|---|---|---|---|---|---|---|---|---|
| BFX55 | S | N | S | BFS23 | | 2N3866 | | | |
| BFX59 | S | N | S | BFX89 | | 2N918 | FT129 | | |
| BFX60 | S | N | S | BF173 | | FT129 | 2N918 | | |
| BFX61 | S | N | SE | BSX47-6 | SFT443 | 2N1893 | | | |
| BFX62 | S | N | S | BF180 | | | | | 02 |
| BFX63 | S | N | V, MU | | | | | | |
| BFX65 | S | P | TF, TX | BC179 | | 3SK20 | | | |
| BFX66 | S | N | MO, AT | | | 2N3965 | | | |
| BFX67 | S | N | MO, AT | | | 2N998 | | | |
| BFX68 | S | N | SG, TX, AT, MO | BSX45-16 | BFY51 | 2N997 | | | |
| | | | | | | 2N1711 | 2N2297 | | 02 |
| BFX68A | S | N | SG, AT, TX | BSX45-16 | BFY51 | 2N1711 | 2N2297 | | 02 |
| BFX69 | S | N | SG, TX, MO, AT | BSX45-6 | BFY51 | 2N697 | 2N1613 | | 02 |
| BFX69A | | | | | | 2N2297 | | | 02 |
| BFX69A | S | N | SG, TX, MO, AT | BSX45-6 | BFY51 | 2N1613 | 2N3110 | | 02 |
| | | | | | | 2N2297 | | | 02 |
| BFX70 | S | N | MO, TX, AT | | | | | | |
| BFX71 | S | N | MO, TX, AT | | | 2N2060 | | | |
| BFX72 | S | N | MO, TX, AT | | | 2N2223 | | | |
| BFX73 | S | N | SG, TX, AT, MO | BFY90 | | 2N2223A | | | |
| BFX74 | S | P | SG, TX, MO, AT | BSV16-6 | BFS95 | 2N918 | | | 02 |
| BFX74 | | | | | | 2N4037 | 2N1131 | | 02 |
| BFX74A | S | P | SG, TX, MO, AT | BSV16-6 | BFX29 | 2N4036 | | | 02 |
| BFX74A | | | | | | 2N4314 | 2N1132 | | 02 |
| BFX77 | S | N | SE, TD | (BF198) | BF115 | 2N2905A | | | 02 |
| BFX77 | | | | BF173 | | 2N918 | | | 02 |
| BFX82 | S | P | AT | | | 2N4381 | | | |
| BFX83 | S | P | AT | | | 2N4382 | | | |
| BFX84 | S | N | MU, FE, ME, MN | BSX46-6 | BFY50 | 2N3108 | 2N2297 | | 02 |
| BFX84 | S | N | NS, NT, SG, TX | | | | | | 02 |
| BFX85 | S | N | MU, TX, SG, FE | BSX46-10 | BSW66 | 2N2405 | 2N3107 | | 02 |
| BFX85 | S | N | ME, MN, NS, NT | | | 2N4001 | | | |
| BFX86 | S | N | MU, TX, SG, ME | BSX45-10 | BFX85 | 2N1711 | 2N3109 | | 02 |
| BFX86 | S | N | MN, NS, NT | | | 2N2297 | | | 02 |
| BFX87 | S | P | MU, TX, SG, ME | BSV16-10 | BFX30 | 2N4036 | 2N2904A | | 02 |
| BFX87 | S | P | MN, NS, NT, V, TD | | | 2N2905A | | | 02 |
| BFX88 | S | P | MU, TX, SG, ME | BSV15-10 | BFX30 | 2N4037 | 2N2904 | | 02 |
| BFX88 | S | P | MN, NS, NT, V, TD | | | 2N2905A | | | 02 |
| BFX89 | S | N | MU, S, TF, V | | | 2N918 | MT1061 | 2SC707 | |
| BFX89N | S | N | | BF384 | BF385 | | | | |
| BFX90 | S | P | MO, AT | | | 2N3930 | | | |
| BFX91 | S | P | MO, SG, AT | BFT28B | | 2N3931 | | | |
| BFX92 | S | N | SG, TX | BC414B | BC109 | 2N929 | 2N930 | | 02 |
| BFX92A | S | N | SG, TX | (BC414B) | | 2N2483 | | | 02 |
| BFX93 | S | N | SG, TX | BC414B | | 2N930 | | | 02 |
| BFX93A | S | N | SG, TX | (BC414B) | | 2N2484 | | | 02 |
| BFX94 | S | N | SG, TX, AT | (BCW73-16) | BSW64 | 2N2221 | 2N2222A | | 02 |
| BFX94A | S | N | SG, TX, AT | (BCW73-16) | | | | | 02 |
| BFX95 | S | N | SG, TX, AT | (BCW73-16) | BSW64 | 2N2222 | 2N2222A | | 02 |
| BFX95A | S | N | SG, TX, AT | (BCW73-16) | | | | | 02 |
| BFX96 | S | N | SG, AT, TX | BCW77-16 | BSW54 | 2N2218 | 2N2219A | | 02 |
| BFX96A | S | N | SG, TX, AT | BCW77-16 | | | | | 02 |
| BFX97 | S | N | SG, TX, AT | BCW77-16 | BSW54 | 2N2219 | 2N2219A | | 02 |
| BFX97A | S | N | SG, TX, AT | BCW77-16 | | | | | 02 |
| BFX98 | S | N | SG, AT, TX | (BF457) | BF257 | 2N3114 | | | 02 |
| BFX98 | | | | BF258 | | | | | 02 |
| BFX99 | S | N | MO, TX, AT | | | 2N2060B | | | 02 |
| BFY10 | S | N | MU, PH, V, TX, AM | BFY33 | BC237A | 40814 | 2N929 | | |
| BFY10 | S | N | PE, RA | BFY55 | BSX45 | 2N1565 | | | 02 |
| BFY10 | S | N | | BFX45 | BC107 | | | | 02 |
| BFY11 | S | N | MU, PH, V, TX, AM | BSX45 | BC237A | 40814 | 2N1566 | | 02 |
| BFY11 | S | N | PE, RA | BFY50 | BC107 | 2N929 | 2N930 | | 02 |
| BFY11 | | | | BFY33 | | | | | 02 |
| BFY12 | S | N | S | BFY11 | BSX45 | 2N2219 | 2N2218A | 2SC579 | 02 |
| BFY12 | S | | | BSX73 | BCY13 | 2N2219A | | | 02 |
| BFY12 | | | | BFY10 | | | | | 02 |
| BFY12B | S | N | S | BSX45-6 | | 2N2218A | | | |
| BFY12C | S | N | S | BSX45-10 | | 2N2218A | | | 02 |
| BFY12D | S | N | S | BSX45-16 | | 2N2219A | | | 02 |
| BFY13 | S | N | S | BSX46 | BCY14 | 2N2219 | 2N2219A | | 02 |
| BFY13B | S | N | S | BSX46-6 | | 2N2218A | | | 02 |
| BFY13C | S | N | S | BSX46-10 | | 2N2218A | | | 02 |
| BFY13D | S | N | S | BSX46-16 | | 2N2219A | | | 02 |
| BFY14 | S | N | S | BSX47 | BFY43 | | | | 02 |
| BFY14 | | | | BCY15 | BF140 | | | | 02 |
| BFY14B | S | N | S | BSX47-6 | | | | | 02 |

| TYPE | M/S | POL | MANUFAC | EUROPEAN | | AMERICAN | | JAPANESE | USE |
|---|---|---|---|---|---|---|---|---|---|
| BFY14C | S | N | S | BSX47-10 | | | | | 02 |
| BFY14D | S | N | S | BSX47-10 | | | | | 02 |
| BFY15 | S | N | IN | BFY67 | (BCW77-16) | 2N697 | 2N2219 | | 02 |
| BFY15 | | | | BFY33 | | 2N930 | | | 02 |
| BFY16 | S | N | IN | (BCW77-16) | BFY12 | 2N697 | 2N2219 | | 02 |
| BFY17 | S | N | IN, TX | BFX55, | BCY59VII | 40317 | 2N708 | | 02 |
| BFY17 | | | | BSX72 | BFY10 | 2N2219 | 2N2222 | | 02 |
| BFY17 | | | | BFY12 | | 2N3014 | 2N2218 | | 02 |
| BFY18 | S | N | ST, TX, SG, IN | BSY93 | BCY59VII | 2N2222 | 2N708 | | 02 |
| BFY18 | | | | BCY59 | BSX75 | 2N3014 | 2N2222A | | 02 |
| BFY18 | | | | BFY87 | BSY63 | | | | 02 |
| BFY18 | | | | BSW64 | | | | | 02 |
| BFY19 | S | N | ST, TX, SG, IN | BFY33 | BCY58VII | 2N708 | 2N3014 | | 02 |
| BFY19 | | | | BSY19 | BSY63 | 2N753 | 2N930 | | 02 |
| BFY19 | | | | BC108A | BSW64 | | | | 02 |
| BFY20 | S | N | IN | BF173 | | 2N2218 | 2N2640 | | 02 |
| BFY22 | S | N | IN | BFY87ye | (BC121w) | 2N930 | | 2SC475 | 02 |
| BFY22 | | | | BC146r | BC121 | | | | 02 |
| BFY22 | | | | BF224 | BFY47r | | | | 02 |
| BFY23 | S | N | IN | BFY87ye | (BC121w) | 2N930 | | 2SC476 | 02 |
| BFY23 | | | | BC146r | BC121ye | | | | 02 |
| BFY23 | | | | BF224 | BFY47ye | | | 2SC476 | 02 |
| BFY23A | S | N | IN | BC146br | (BC121gn) | | | | 02 |
| BFY23A | | | | BF224 | BC146gn | | | | 02 |
| BFY23A | | | | BFY87w | | | | | 02 |
| BFY24 | S | N | IN | BFY87A | (BC121w) | 2N930 | 2N918 | | 02 |
| BFY24 | | | | BC146r | BC121 | | | | 02 |
| BFY24 | | | | BFY47r | BC146r | | | | 02 |
| BFY25 | S | N | IN, ST | (BCW78-16) | BSY29 | 2N2219 | | | 02 |
| BFY26 | S | N | IN, SG, TX, ST | (BCW74-16) | BSY63 | 2N708 | 2N2219A | | 02 |
| BFY27 | S | N | IN, TD, TF, TX | (BCW74-16) | BFY28 | 2N915 | 2N918 | | 02 |
| BFY27 | | | | BF167 | | 2N2221A | 2N2222A | | 02 |
| BFY27N | S | N | | BCY86 | | | | | 02 |
| BFY28 | S | N | IN, ST | BC182A | BSY34 | 2N2221 | | | 02 |
| BFY29 | S | N | IN | BC123 | (BC123w) | 2N930 | | | 02 |
| BFY29 | | | | BFY49r | BC146r | | | | 02 |
| BFY30 | S | N | IN | BC130 | (BC123ye) | 2N930 | | | 02 |
| BFY30 | | | | BFY49r | BC146r | | | | 02 |
| BFY31 | S | N | S | BSX45-6 | | | | | 02 |
| BFY33 | S | N | S, TX | BSX46 | BSX45-6 | 2N697 | 2N1613 | 2SC479 | 02 |
| BFY33 | | | | BFX33 | BSY92 | | | | 02 |
| BFY33 | | | | BSX95 | | | | | 02 |
| BFY34 | S | N | S, TX, MO, SG, AT | BSX45 | BSX45-6 | 2N697 | 2N1613 | 2SC479 | 02 |
| BFY34 | | | | BFY51 | BSY44 | 2N2297 | | | 02 |
| BFY34 | | | | BSX95 | | | | | 02 |
| BFY37 | S | N | IN, TX, ST | BSY95A | BSW64 | 2N2222 | 2N2222A | 2SC907 | 02 |
| BFY37 | | | | BC238A | BC108A | 2N2218 | | | 02 |
| BFY37 | | | | BSY70 | BSX48 | | | | 02 |
| BFY37 | | | | BSX93 | BC107 | | | | 02 |
| BFY37i | S | N | IN | BC108A | BC238A | 2N2218 | | 2SC907 | 02 |
| BFY37i | | | | BC107 | BSX48 | | | | 02 |
| BFY37i | | | | BFY37 | BSY70 | | | | 02 |
| BFY37i | | | | BC238 | | | | | 02 |
| BFY39 | S | N | IN, NS, TX | BSY39 | BC237A | 2N930 | 2N929 | | 02 |
| BFY39 | | | | BC183 | BC107 | | | | 02 |
| BFY39 | | | | BFY27 | | | | | 02 |
| BFY39i | S | N | IN | BC237A | BC107A | | | 2SC284 | 02 |
| BFY39i | | | | BFY39 | BC182 | | | | 02 |
| BFY39I | S | N | IN, NS, TX, V | BC107A | BC182 | | | | 02 |
| BFY39II | S | N | IN, NS, TX, V | BC237A | BC107A | | | | 02 |
| BFY39II | | | | BC107B | | | | | 02 |
| BFY39III | S | N | IN, NS, TX, V | BC237A | BC107B | | | | 02 |
| BFY39III | | | | BC107C | | | | | 02 |
| BFY40 | S | N | TX, IN, ST | BSY92 | BF178 | 2N1313 | 40320 | 2SC708 | 02 |
| BFY40 | | | | BSX45-6 | BFY51 | 2N2297 | 2N1613 | | 02 |
| BFY40 | | | | BFY34 | BSY44 | 2N2218 | | | 02 |
| BFY40 | | | | BSX44 | BC140 | | | | 02 |
| BFY41 | S | N | TX, SG, IN, ST | BF258 | BSX47-6 | 2N1893 | 2N2218A | 2SC708A | 02 |
| BFY41 | | | | BF140 | BF111 | 2N698 | | | 02 |
| BFY41 | | | | BF257 | BSY45 | | | | 02 |
| BFY42 | S | N | | BC107 | | 2N697 | | | 02 |
| BFY43 | S | N | TX, SG, IN | BF140 | BF257 | 2N3114 | | 2SC154C | 02 |
| BFY43 | | | | (BF457) | BSW68 | | | | 02 |
| BFY43 | | | | BF110 | BF178 | | | | 02 |
| BFY43 | | | | BF114 | BF258 | | | | 02 |

| TYPE | M/S | POL | MANUFAC | EUROPEAN | | AMERICAN | | JAPANESE | USE |
|---|---|---|---|---|---|---|---|---|---|
| BFY44 | S | N | MU, PH, V, TX, - | BFY12 | SFT443 | 2N3553 | 2N2102 | | 02 |
| BFY44 | S | N | AM, RA | | | 2N3725 | | | 02 |
| BFY45 | S | N | S, TX | BF178 | (BF457) | 4O48O | 2N1990 | 2SC857 | 02 |
| BFY45 | | | | BF156 | BFY65 | SE7002 | | | 02 |
| BFY45 | | | | BSW66 | | | | | 02 |
| BFY46 | S | N | S, AT, TX | BSX45 | BSX45-16 | 2N1711 | | | 02 |
| BFY46 | | | | BSY71 | BSX96 | | | 2SC479 | 02 |
| BFY47 | S | N | S | (BC121w) | BC121 | | | | 02 |
| BFY47b | S | N | S | (BC121w) | | | | | 02 |
| BFY47r | S | N | S | (BC121w) | | | | | 02 |
| BFY48 | S | N | S | (BC122w) | BC122 | 2N930 | | | 02 |
| BFY48b | S | N | S | (BC121w) | | | | | 02 |
| BFY48r | S | N | S | (BC121w) | | | | | 02 |
| BFY49 | S | N | S | (BC123w) | | 2N930 | | | 02 |
| BFY49b | S | N | S | (BC123w) | | | | | 02 |
| BFY49r | S | N | S | (BC123w) | | | | | 02 |
| BFY50 | S | N | MU, AM, PH, NS, IT | BSY85 | BSX45-6 | 2N1893 | 2N697 | 2SC798 | 02 |
| BFY50 | | | TX, V, AT, ME, MN | BSX46 | BSY46 | 2N4047 | 2N2193 | | 02 |
| BFY50 | | | NT, PE, RA, SG | | | 2N2222 | 2N3253 | | 02 |
| BFY50E | | | LI | BSX45-6 | BFY51 | 2N2297 | | | 02 |
| BFY50I | S | N | IN | BC238A | | | | | 02 |
| BFY51 | S | N | MU, AM, PH, AT, IT | BSY85 | BSX45-6 | 2N2297 | 2N697 | 2SC708 | 02 |
| BFY51 | | | V, TX, ME, MN, NS | BSY95 | BSY46 | 2N4046 | 2N2193 | | 02 |
| BFY51 | | | NT, PE, RA, SG | | | 2N3053 | 2N3252 | | 02 |
| BFY51I | S | N | IN | BC238A | | | | | 02 |
| BFY52 | S | N | MU, PH, AM, MN | BFY56 | BSX45-10 | 2N2219 | 2N3252 | 2SC708 | 02 |
| BFY52 | | | AT, V, TX, ME, NS | BFY51 | BSX45 | 2N3053 | 2N3724 | | 02 |
| BFY52 | | | NT, PE, RA, SG | BSY46 | | 2N2192 | 2N2297 | | 02 |
| BFY53 | S | N | MU, PH, MN, NT, | BFY51 | BSX45-6 | 2N2192 | 2N2297 | | 02 |
| BFY53 | | | V, TX | BSX46 | BSY46 | | | | 02 |
| BFY55 | S | N | MU, PH, V, TX, MO | BSX45-6 | BSY46 | 2N2193 | 2N697 | 2SC708 | 02 |
| BFY55 | | | | BFY51 | | 2N3253 | 2N2297 | | 02 |
| BFY56 | S | N | SG, TX, MO, ME, | BSY83 | BSX45-10 | 2N3110 | 2N699 | | 02 |
| BFY56 | | | NS, AT | BSX61 | BSX46 | 2N2294 | 2N3252 | | 02 |
| BFY56 | | | | BFY51 | BSY50 | | | | 02 |
| BFY56A | S | N | SG, TX, AT, TF | BSX45-6 | BSW65 | 2N3108 | 2N2297 | | 02 |
| BFY56A | | | | BFY51 | | | | | 02 |
| BFY56B | S | N | SG, AT | BSX45-6 | | | | | 02 |
| BFY57 | S | N | SG, TX | BF140 | (BF457) | SE7002 | 2N5059 | | 02 |
| BFY57 | | | | BF117 | BF257 | 2N3114 | | | 02 |
| BFY57 | | | | BF110 | | | | | 02 |
| BFY63 | S | N | SG, LI, AT, TD | (BFX55) | | 2N3137 | 2N3866 | | 02 |
| BFY63 | | | | | | 2N2883 | | | 02 |
| BFY64 | S | P | SG, ME, TX, AT, TD | (BCW80-16) | BFX29 | 2N2905 | 2N2905A | | 02 |
| BFY65 | S | N | TF, TX | BC141 | (BF457) | 2N2243 | 2N1990 | 2SC145 | 02 |
| BFY65 | | | | BSY65 | BFY80 | 2N1893 | 2N3036 | | 02 |
| BFY65 | | | | BC255 | BF177 | | | | 02 |
| BFY65 | | | | BF156 | | | | | 02 |
| BFY66 | S | N | TF, AT, MO, TX | BFY90 | BFX62 | 2N918 | S8528 | | 02 |
| BFY66 | | | | BF180 | | | | | 02 |
| BFY67 | S | N | V, PH, TX, MO, AM | BFY51 | BSX45-6 | 2N3053 | 2N1613 | 2SC708A | 02 |
| BFY67 | | | MN, PE, RA | BSY44 | BSY52 | 2N2297 | | | 02 |
| BFY67A | S | N | V, TX | BSX45-6 | | 2N1613 | 2N2219 | 2SC708 | 02 |
| BFY67C | S | N | V, TX | BSX45-6 | | 2N2219 | | 2SC708 | 02 |
| BFY68 | S | N | PH, V, TX | BSX45-16 | BSY71 | 2N1711 | 2N2297 | | 02 |
| BFY68 | | | | BFY51 | | | | | 02 |
| BFY68A | S | · | V | BSX46-16 | | 2N2219 | | | 02 |
| BFY69 | S | N | TF | BC386 | (BC122) | 2N706A | | | 02 |
| BFY69 | | | | BC146 | | | | | 02 |
| BFY69gn | S | N | TF | (BC122w) | | | | | 02 |
| BFY69gr | S | N | TF | (BC122bl) | | | | | 02 |
| BFY69r | S | N | TF | (BC122w) | | | | | 02 |
| BFY69ye | S | N | TF | (BC122w) | | | | | 02 |
| BFY69v | S | N | TF | (BC122ye) | | | | | 02 |
| BFY69w | S | N | TF | (BC122gn) | | | | | 02 |
| BFY69A | S | N | TF | (BC122) | BC146 | | | | 02 |
| BFY69Agn | S | N | TF | (BC122w) | | | | | 02 |
| BFY69Agr | S | N | TF | (BC122bl) | | | | | 02 |
| BFY69Aye | S | N | TF | (BC122w) | | | | | 02 |
| BFY69Av | S | N | TF | (BC122ye) | | | | | 02 |
| BFY69Aw | S | N | TF | (BC122gn) | | | | | 02 |
| BFY69B | S | N | TF | (BC122) | | | | | 02 |
| BFY69Bgn | S | N | TF | (BC122w) | | | | | 02 |
| BFY69Bgr | S | N | TF | (BC122bl) | | | | | 02 |
| BFY69Br | S | N | TF | (BC122w) | | | | | 02 |

| TYPE | M/S | POL | MANUFAC | EUROPEAN | | AMERICAN | | JAPANESE | USE |
|------|-----|-----|---------|----------|--|----------|--|----------|-----|
| BFY69Bye | S | N | TF | (BC122w) | | | | | 02 |
| BFY69Bv | S | N | TF | (BC122ye) | | | | | 02 |
| BFY69Bw | S | N | TF | (BC122gn) | | | | | 02 |
| BFY70 | S | N | MU, PH, V, TX | SFT443 | | 2N3553 | 2N3053 | | 02 |
| BFY70 | S | N | AM, RA | | | 2N3724 | | | 02 |
| BFY72 | S | N | SG, NS, TX, AT | (BSY34) | | 2N2218 | 2N2219 | | 02 |
| BFY73 | S | N | SG, AT, TX | (BSY34) | | 2N2219 | | | 02 |
| BFY74 | S | N | SG, AT, MO, TX | BC182A | BSW64 | 2N2221 | 2N915 | | 02 |
| BFY74 | S | N | | | | 2N2222A | | | 02 |
| BFY75 | S | N | SG, AT, MO, TX | BC182B | BSW64 | 2N2221 | 2N2222A | | 02 |
| BFY75 | S | N | | | | 2N915 | | | 02 |
| BFY76 | S | N | SG, NS, TX, AT | BC414B | BC109 | 2N929 | 2N930 | | 02 |
| BFY76 | S | N | | | | 2N2483 | | | 02 |
| BFY77 | S | N | SG, TX, TD | BC414B | BC109 | 2N929 | 2N930 | | 02 |
| BFY78 | S | N | SG, TX, MO, TD | (BFY90) | BC109 | 2N918 | 2N2865 | | 02 |
| BFY79 | S | N | | | | 2N3737 | TLS84 | | 02 |
| BFY79 | S | N | | | | 2N4390 | | | 02 |
| BFY80 | S | N | TF, TX | BSW32 | (BF457) | 2N2896 | 2N1990 | | 02 |
| BFY80 | S | N | | BC394 | BF177 | 2N2243 | 2N719A | | 02 |
| BFY80 | S | N | | BSY56 | | 2N3036 | | | 02 |
| BFY81 | S | N | TX, TD, AT | | | 2N2917 | 2N2642 | | 02 |
| BFY81 | S | N | | | | 2N2643 | | | 02 |
| BFY82 | S | N | TX, TD, AT | | | 2N2982 | 2N2060 | | 02 |
| BFY83 | S | N | TX, TD, AT | | | 2N2223 | | | 02 |
| BFY84 | S | N | TX, TD, AT | | | 2N3423 | | | 02 |
| BFY85 | S | N | TF | BCY87 | BF184 | 2N2640 | 2N3036 | 2SC280 | 02 |
| BFY85 | S | N | | BFY19 | | 2N2896 | | | 02 |
| BFY86 | S | N | TF | BCY89 | BF185 | 2N2639 | 2N3036 | | 02 |
| BFY86 | S | N | | BFY19 | | | | | 02 |
| BFY87 | S | N | TF | BFY19 | BC146 | 2N930 | 2N5181 | | 02 |
| BFY87 | S | N | | BCY83 | BC122 | | | | 02 |
| BFY87 | S | N | | BF185 | | | | | 02 |
| BFY87gn | S | N | TF | (BC122w) | | | | | 02 |
| BFY87gr | S | N | TF | (BC122bl) | | | | | 02 |
| BFY87r | S | N | TF | (BC122w) | | | | | 02 |
| BFY87ye | S | N | TF | (BC122w) | | | | | 02 |
| BFY87v | S | N | TF | (BC122ye) | | | | | 02 |
| BFY87w | S | N | TF | (BC122gn) | | | | | 02 |
| BFY87A | S | N | TF | BC146 | BC122 | | | | 02 |
| BFY87Agn | S | N | TF | (BC122w) | | | | | 02 |
| BFY87Agr | S | N | TF | (BC122bl) | | | | | 02 |
| BFY87Aye | S | N | TF | (BC122w) | | | | | 02 |
| BFY87Av | S | N | TF | (BC122ye) | | | | | 02 |
| BFY87Aw | S | N | TF | (BC122gn) | | | | | 02 |
| BFY88 | S | N | TF | BF185 | (BF199) | FT129 | SE5030B | 2SC707 | 02 |
| BFY88 | S | N | | BFY19 | BFX89 | 2N5181 | | | 02 |
| BFY88 | S | N | | BF224 | BFX60 | | | | 02 |
| BFY88 | S | N | | BF180 | | | | | 02 |
| BFY90 | S | N | | BF169 | BF357 | 2N2857 | MT1061 | | 02 |
| BFY90 | S | N | | | | 2N3013 | 2N2222 | | 02 |
| BFY90B | S | N | MU | BFY90 | | | | | 02 |
| BFY91 | S | N | TX, MO, IN | BCY59VII | BFY86 | 2N2642 | 2N2915 | 2SC280 | 02 |
| BFY91 | S | N | | BF169 | | | | | 02 |
| BFY92 | S | N | TX, MO, IN | BCY59VII | BFY85 | 2N2643 | 2N2917 | 2SC280 | 02 |
| BFY92 | S | N | | BF169 | | | | | 02 |
| BFY93 | S | N | | | | 2N2920 | | | 02 |
| BFY94 | S | P | SG, TX | BCW80-16 | | 40594 | 2N2904 | | 02 |
| BFY95 | S | P | | | | 2N2906 | | | 02 |
| BFY99 | S | N | S | SFT443 | | 2N3553 | 2N706A | | 02 |
| BFZ10 | S | P | | BCZ11 | | | | | 02 |
| BLW11 | S | N | TX | (BFW16A) | | | | | 03 |
| BLY10 | S | N | IN | (BDY12-6) | | | | | 03 |
| BLY11 | S | N | IN | (BDY12-6) | | | | | 03 |
| BLY12 | S | N | IN, IT | (BDY12-10) | | | | | 03 |
| BLY14 | S | N | PH, MU, V | SFT443 | | 2N3553 | | | 03 |
| BLY15 | S | N | IN | (BDY13-6) | SFT443A | | | | 03 |
| BLY15A | S | N | IN | (BDY13-6) | | 2N3632 | | | 03 |
| BLY16 | S | N | IN | (BDY13-6) | SFT443A | | | | 03 |
| BLY17 | S | N | MU | SFT441A | BLY16 | | | | 03 |
| BLY20 | S | N | V | BLY16 | SFT443A | 2N3375 | | | 03 |
| BLY21 | S | N | V | BLY16 | SFT443A | 2N3632 | | | 03 |
| BLY22 | S | N | S | SFT440 | | 2N3375 | 2N3632 | | 03 |
| BLY25 | S | N | AT | | | 2N4116 | | | 03 |
| BLY26 | S | N | AT | | | 2N4115 | | | 03 |
| BLY27 | S | N | SE | SFT440 | | 2N3375 | | | 03 |

| TYPE | M/S | POL | MANUFAC | EUROPEAN | | AMERICAN | | JAPANESE | USE |
|------|-----|-----|---------|----------|--|----------|--|----------|-----|
| BLY28 | S | N | SE | SFT443A | BLY16 | | | | 03 |
| BLY29 | S | N | AT | | | | | | 03 |
| BLY30 | S | N | AT | | | 2N4075 | | | 03 |
| BLY36 | S | N | MU | | | 2N4076 | | | 03 |
| BLY40 | S | N | LI | | | MSA8506 | 2N3375 | | 03 |
| | | | | | | 2N5072 | | | 03 |
| BLY47 | S | N | TX | BUY55 | | 2N4915 | | | 03 |
| BLY47A | S | N | TX | (BUY55) | | 2N3054 | | | 03 |
| BLY48 | S | N | TX | BUY55 | | | | | 03 |
| BLY48A | S | N | TX | (BUY55) | | | | | 03 |
| BLY49 | S | N | TX | BUY56 | | | | | 03 |
| BLY49A | S | N | TX | (BUY56) | | | | | 03 |
| BLY50 | S | N | TX | BUY56 | | | | | 03 |
| BLY50A | S | N | TX | (BUY56) | | | | | 03 |
| BLY55 | S | N | MU | | | | | | 03 |
| BLY57 | S | N | V | | | MSA8507 | | | 03 |
| | | | | | | 2N3926 | 2N3632 | | 03 |
| BLY58 | S | N | V | | | 2N3937 | 2N3632 | | 03 |
| BLY59 | S | N | V | | | 2N3375 | | | 03 |
| BLY60 | S | N | V | | | 2N3927 | 2N3632 | | 03 |
| BLY62 | S | N | TX | | | MSA8507 | | | 03 |
| BLY63 | S | N | TX | | | MSA8506 | | | 03 |
| BLY64 | S | N | AT | | | 2N5002 | | | 03 |
| BLY65 | S | P | AT | | | 2N5003 | | | 03 |
| BLY66 | S | N | AT | | | 2N5004 | | | 03 |
| BLY68 | S | N | SG, AT | (BU310) | | 2N5069 | | | 03 |
| BLY70 | S | N | SG, AT | (BU310) | | 2N4915 | | | 03 |
| BLY75 | S | N | | | | 2N5025 | | | 03 |
| BSJ61 | S | N | IS, RZ | BSY62A | | | | | 17 |
| BSJ62 | S | N | IS, RZ | BSY62A | | | | | 17 |
| BSJ63 | S | N | IS, RZ | BSY63 | | | | | 17 |
| BSJ65 | S | N | IS, RZ | BSY62A | | | | | 17 |
| BSJ66 | S | N | IS, RZ | (BSY63) | | | | | 17 |
| BSJ67 | S | N | IS, RZ | (BSY63) | | | | | 17 |
| BSJ68 | S | N | IS, RZ | (BSY63) | | | | | 17 |
| BSS10 | S | N | AT | (BSY63) | BSX20 | 2N3261 | 2N2222A | | 17 |
| BSS10 | S | N | | BSW64 | | | | | 17 |
| BSS11 | S | N | AT | (BSY63) | BSX20 | 2N2369 | 2N2369A | | 17 |
| BSS12 | S | N | AT | (BSY18) | BSX20 | 2N3011 | 2N2369 | | 17 |
| BSS13 | S | N | AT | BSY34 | BSS27 | 2N5189 | 2N3053 | | 17 |
| BSS13 | | | | | | 2N5262 | | | 17 |
| BSS14 | S | N | AT | (BSY34) | BFX34 | 2N5262 | | | 17 |
| BSS14 | | | | BSS27 | | | | | 17 |
| BSS15 | S | N | AT | (BSX47-10) | BSV94 | 2N5320 | | | 17 |
| BSS15 | | | | BSS42 | | | | | 17 |
| BSS16 | S | N | AT | BSX46 | BSV93 | 2N5321 | 2N5320 | | 17 |
| BSS16 | | | | BSS42 | | | | | 17 |
| BSS17 | S | P | AT | (BSV17-10) | | 2N5322 | 2N4036 | | 17 |
| BSS17 | | | | | | 2N4929 | | | 17 |
| BSS18 | S | P | AT | (BSV17) | | 2N5323 | 2N4036 | | 17 |
| BSS19 | S | N | TX | BSW69 | | | | | 17 |
| BSS20 | S | N | TX | BSW69 | | | | | 17 |
| BSS21 | S | N | TX | (BSY18) | | | | | 17 |
| BSS23 | S | N | TF, TX | BSX49 | BSX33 | 2N731 | | | 17 |
| BSS26 | S | N | AT, SG, TX | BSX49 | BSX33 | 2N731 | | | 17 |
| BSS27 | S | N | MU, PH, V, PE, TX | (BSY34) | BSX59 | 2N3444 | | | 17 |
| BSS28 | S | N | MU, PH, V, PE | (BSY34) | BSS27 | 2N5262 | | | 17 |
| BSS29 | S | N | MU, PH, V, PE, TX | (BSY34) | BSS27 | 2N5262 | | | 17 |
| BSS30 | S | N | AT, TX | BSX46-6 | BSW33 | 2N2102 | 2N4001 | | 17 |
| BSS31 | S | N | AT, TX | BSX46-16 | BF156 | 2N1990 | | | 17 |
| BSS32 | S | N | AT, TX | BSX47-6 | BSW66 | 2N2405 | 2N4001 | | 17 |
| BSS33 | S | N | LI, TX | (BF458) | | | | | 17 |
| BSS34 | S | N | TX | (BF457) | | | | | 17 |
| BSS35 | S | N | TX | (BF457) | | | | | 17 |
| BSS38 | S | N | V, MU, S | (BF457) | BSX21 | 2N1990R | | | 17 |
| BSS40 | S | N | V, TX | BSX49 | BSX33 | 2N731 | | | 17 |
| BSS41 | S | N | V, TX | BSX49 | BSX33 | 2N731 | | | 17 |
| BSS42 | S | N | TF | | | 2N5320 | | | 17 |
| BSS43 | S | N | TF | BSS42 | | 2N5320 | | | 17 |
| BSS45 | S | N | TF | | | 2N5320 | | | 17 |
| BSS46 | S | P | TF | | | 2N5322 | | | 17 |
| BSS48 | S | N | TF | | | 2N3440 | | | 17 |
| BSS49 | S | N | TF | | | 2N3439 | | | 17 |
| BSS68 | S | P | V, MU, S | | | 2N3497 | | | 17 |
| BSV15 | S | S | TF, SG, PH, S, V | BFR23 | | 2N2905 | 2N4037 | | 17 |
| BSV15 | | | | | | 2N4036 | 2N4030 | | 17 |
| BSV15-6 | S | P | V, TF, S | BFS93 | | 2N4037 | | | 17 |

| TYPE | M/S | POL | MANUFAC | EUROPEAN | | AMERICAN | | JAPANESE | USE |
|---|---|---|---|---|---|---|---|---|---|
| BSV15-10 | S | P | V, TF, S | BFS93 | | 2N4037 | | | 17 |
| BSV15-16 | S | P | V, TF, S | BFS93 | | 2N4037 | | | 17 |
| BSV16 | S | P | TF, SG, PH, S, TX | BFR23 | | 2N2905 | 2N4314 | | 17 |
| BSV16 | S | P | V | | | 2N4036 | 2N4030 | | 17 |
| BSV16-6 | S | P | ML, SG, S, TF, V | BFS93 | | 2N4314 | 2N4037 | | 17 |
| BSV16-10 | S | P | ML, SG, S, TF, V | BFS93 | | 2N4314 | 2N4037 | | 17 |
| BSV16-16 | S | P | V, TF, S | BFS93 | | 2N4037 | | | 17 |
| BSV17 | S | P | PH, S, V | | | 2N5322 | 2N4929 | | 17 |
| BSV17-6 | S | P | S, V | BFS93 | | 2N4037 | | | 17 |
| BSV17-10 | S | P | S, V | BFS93 | | 2N4037 | | | 17 |
| BSV22 | J | N | V | | | 2N4416 | | | 17 |
| BSV23 | S | N | FE | (BSY62) | BSX20 | 2N2369 | | | 17 |
| BSV23K | S | N | FE | (BSY62) | | | | | 17 |
| BSV23L | S | N | FE | (BSY62) | | | | | 17 |
| BSV23M | S | N | FE | (BSY62) | | | | | 17 |
| BSV24 | S | N | FE | (BSY62) | BSX20 | 2N2369 | | | 17 |
| BSV24K | S | N | FE | (BSY62) | | | | | 17 |
| BSV24L | S | N | FE | (BSY62) | | | | | 17 |
| BSV24M | S | N | FE | (BSY62) | | | | | 17 |
| BSV25 | S | N | FE | (BSY18) | BSX20 | 2N2369 | | | 17 |
| BSV25K | S | N | FE | (BSY18) | | | | | 17 |
| BSV25M | S | N | FE | (BSY18) | | | | | 17 |
| BSV26 | S | N | FE | (BSY63) | BSX20 | 2N2369 | | | 17 |
| BSV26K | S | N | FE | (BSY63) | | | | | 17 |
| BSV26L | S | N | FE | (BSY63) | | | | | 17 |
| BSV26M | S | N | FE | (BSY63) | | | | | 17 |
| BSV27 | S | N | FE | (BSY63) | BSX20 | 2N2369 | | | 17 |
| BSV27K | S | N | FE | (BSY63) | | | | | 17 |
| BSV27L | S | N | FE | (BSY63) | | | | | 17 |
| BSV27M | S | N | FE | (BSY63) | | | | | 17 |
| BSV28 | S | N | FE | (BF457) | BSX21 | 2N1990R | | | 17 |
| BSV28K | S | N | FE | (BF457) | | | | | 17 |
| BSV28L | S | N | FE | (BF457) | | | | | 17 |
| BSV28M | S | N | FE | (BF457) | | | | | 17 |
| BSV29 | S | N | FE | (BF457) | BSX21 | 2N1990R | | | 17 |
| BSV29K | S | N | FE | (BF457) | | | | | 17 |
| BSV29L | S | N | FE | (BF457) | | | | | 17 |
| BSV29M | S | N | FE | (BF457) | | | | | 17 |
| BSV33 | S | P | FE | BSW25 | | 2N3546 | | | 17 |
| BSV36 | S | N | FE | BSW35 | | | | | 17 |
| BSV40 | S | N | IN, IT, ST | (BSY63) | BSW64 | 2N2222A | | | 17 |
| BSV41 | S | N | IN, IT, ST | (BSY63) | BSW64 | 2N2222A | | | 17 |
| BSV42 | S | N | IN, IT, ST | BSV17-10 | BFS95 | 2N4036 | | | 17 |
| BSV43 | S | P | IN, ST | BSV16-10 | | | | | 17 |
| BSV43A | S | P | IN, IT, ST | BSV16-6 | BFS95 | 2N4036 | | | 17 |
| BSV43B | S | P | IN, IT, ST | BSV16-16 | BFS95 | 2N4036 | | | 17 |
| BSV44 | S | P | IN, ST | BSV16-10 | | | | | 17 |
| BSV44A | S | P | IN, IT, ST | BSV16-6 | BFS95 | 2N4036 | | | 17 |
| BSV44B | S | P | IN, IT, ST | BSV16-16 | BFS95 | 2N4036 | | | 17 |
| BSV45 | S | P | IN, ST | BSV15-10 | | | | | 17 |
| BSV45A | S | P | IN, IT, ST | BSV15-6 | BFS95 | 2N4036 | | | 17 |
| BSV45B | S | P | IN, IT, ST | BSV15-16 | BFS95 | 2N4036 | | | 17 |
| BSV46 | S | P | IN, IT, ST | (BSV17-10) | BSW24 | 2N2907A | | | 17 |
| BSV47 | S | P | IN, ST | (BSV16-10) | | | | | 17 |
| BSV47A | S | P | IN, IT, ST | (BSV16-6) | BSW24 | 2N2907 | | | 17 |
| BSV47B | S | P | IN, IT, ST | (BSV16-16) | BSW24 | 2N2907A | | | 17 |
| BSV48 | S | P | IN, ST | (BSV16-10) | | | | | 17 |
| BSV48A | S | P | IN, IT, ST | (BSV16-6) | BSW24 | 2N2907A | | | 17 |
| BSV48B | S | P | IN, IT, ST | (BSV16-16) | BSW24 | 2N2907A | | | 17 |
| BSV49 | S | P | IN, ST | (BSV15-10) | | | | | 17 |
| BSV49A | S | P | IN, IT, ST | (BSV15-6) | BSW24 | 2N2907A | | | 17 |
| BSV49B | S | P | IN, IT, ST | (BSV15-16) | BSW24 | 2N2907A | | | 17 |
| BSV51 | S | N | IN, TF | (BF457) | BSX21 | 2N4416 | | | 17 |
| BSV52 | S | N | MU, PH, V | BSV65FA | BC122 | | | | 17 |
| BSV52 | | | | BSV35 | | | | | 17 |
| BSV52R | S | N | MU | BSV35 | | | | | 17 |
| BSV59 | S | N | AT, SG | BSX49 | | | | | 17 |
| BSV60 | S | N | TF | BSX62 | BSV64 | 2N4877 | | | 17 |
| BSV62 | S | N | RA | | | 2N4393 | | | 17 |
| BSV64 | S | N | MU, PH, V, PE | (BSX46-10) | BFX34 | 2N4877 | | | 17 |
| BSV64 | | | | BSX63-6 | | | | | 17 |
| BSV68 | S | P | MU, PH, V, PE | | | 2N3497 | | | 17 |
| BSV68 | S | N | TF | BSY34 | BSS14 | 2N5321 | 2N3735 | | 17 |
| BSV69 | S | N | TF | (BSY34) | BSW54 | 2N5321 | 2N2219A | | 17 |
| BSV77 | S | N | SG, AT | | | 2N5321 | | | 17 |
| BSV78 | S | N | V, MU, PH | | | 2N4856 | | | 17 |

| TYPE | M/S | POL | MANUFAC | EUROPEAN | | AMERICAN | | JAPANESE | USE |
|------|-----|-----|---------|----------|--|----------|--|----------|-----|
| BSV79 | S | N | MU, V, PH | | | 2N4857A | | | 17 |
| BSV80 | S | N | V, MU, PH | | | 2N4858A | | | 17 |
| BSV82 | S | P | AT | (BSV17-6) | BFS93 | 2N4037 | | | 17 |
| BSV83 | S | P | AT | BSV17-6 | BFS93 | 2N4037 | | | 17 |
| BSV84 | S | N | AT | (BSX47-6) | BFX85 | 2N1893 | | | 17 |
| BSV85 | S | N | AT | BSX49 | BSX33 | 2N731 | | | 17 |
| BSV86 | S | N | V, PE | (BCW74-16) | | | | | 17 |
| BSV87 | S | N | V, PE | (BCW74-16) | | | | | 17 |
| BSV88 | S | N | V, PE | (BCW73-16) | | | | | 17 |
| BSV89 | S | N | SG, AT | (BSY62) | | | | | 17 |
| BSV90 | S | N | SG, AT | (BSY62) | | | | | 17 |
| BSV91 | S | N | SG, AT | (BSY63) | | | | | 17 |
| BSV92 | S | N | SG, AT | (BSY63) | | | | | 17 |
| BSV96 | S | P | V, PE | BC327-16 | | | | | 17 |
| BSV97 | S | P | V, PE | BC327-16 | | | | | 17 |
| BSV98 | S | P | V, PE | BC327-16 | | | | | 17 |
| BSV99 | S | N | TX | (BSY18) | | | | | 17 |
| BSW10 | S | N | TF | BF177 | BSX46-6 | 2N2218A | 2N3722 | | 17 |
| BSW10 | | | | BSX46 | BSX23 | 2N699 | | | 17 |
| BSW11 | S | N | TF | BSW59 | BSW13 | SE3646 | 2N3646 | | 17 |
| BSW12 | S | N | TF | BSX69 | BSW13 | S9506 | 2N3646 | | 17 |
| BSW12 | | | | BF173 | | SE3646 | 2N914 | | 17 |
| BSW13 | S | N | S | BC146 | | | | | 17 |
| BSW19 | S | P | TF, TX | BCY70 | BCY78VII | 2N2906 | 2N3965 | 2SA548 | 17 |
| BSW19 | | | | BC177A | BCW52 | 40406 | 2N3504 | | 17 |
| BSW19 | | | | | | 2N3014 | | | 17 |
| BSW19VI | S | P | TF, TX | BCY78VII | BC177A | | | | 17 |
| BSW19A | S | P | TF, TX | BCY78VIII | BC177A | 2N3965 | | | 17 |
| BSW19A | | | | BCY70 | | | | | 17 |
| BSW20 | S | P | TF | BCY78VIII | BC307A | | | | 17 |
| BSW20 | | | | BC307 | | | | | 17 |
| BSW20VI | S | P | TF | BCY78VIII | BC307A | | | | 17 |
| BSW20A | S | P | TF | BCY78VIII | BC307A | | | | 17 |
| BSW21 | S | P | MO, SE, TX, ML, Ss | BCY70 | BC308A | 2N2906 | 2N3965 | | 17 |
| BSW21 | | | | BCY72 | BCY78 | | | | 17 |
| BSW21A | S | P | MO, SE, TX, Ss, ML | BC307A | BCY71 | 2N3965 | | | 17 |
| BSW21A | | | | BCY70 | | | | | 17 |
| BSW22 | S | P | MO, Se, TX, Ss, ML | BCY70 | BC308B | 2N2907 | 2N3965 | | 17 |
| BSW22 | | | | BC178B | BCY78 | | | | 17 |
| BSW22A | S | P | MO, SE, TX, Ss, ML | BC307B | BCY79VIII | 2N3965 | | | 17 |
| BSW22A | | | | BCY70 | | | | | 17 |
| BSW23 | S | P | TX, MO, SG | (BCW80-16) | BSX29 | 2N4037 | 2N2904 | | 17 |
| BSW23 | | | | | | 2N2905A | | | 17 |
| BSW24 | S | P | TX, SG | (BCW78-16) | | 2N2906 | 2N2907A | | 17 |
| BSW25 | S | P | TX, AT | BCY72 | | 2N2894A | 2N3546 | | 17 |
| BSW26 | S | N | TX | (BSX49) | BSX59 | 2N4047 | 2N731 | | 17 |
| BSW26 | | | | BSX33 | | | | | 17 |
| BSW27 | S | N | TX | (BSY34) | BSX59 | 2N4047 | 2N2219A | | 17 |
| BSW27 | | | | BSW54 | | | | | 17 |
| BSW28 | S | N | TX | (BSY34) | BSX59 | 2N4047 | 2N2219A | | 17 |
| BSW28 | | | | BSW54 | | | | | 17 |
| BSW29 | S | N | TX | (BSY34) | BSX60 | 2N4046 | 2N2219A | | 17 |
| BSW32 | S | N | TX | (BF457) | BSX21 | 2N5830 | | | 17 |
| BSW33 | S | N | V, RA | BC237A | BC147A | | | 2SC641 | 17 |
| BSW34 | S | N | V, RA | BC237A | BCW47 | | | | 17 |
| BSW35 | S | N | V, RA | BCY65EVII | BCW46 | | | | 17 |
| BSW36 | S | P | TX | (BCW79-16) | BFX29 | 2N2905 | 2N2905A | | 17 |
| BSW37 | S | P | TX | | | 2N2894 | | | 17 |
| BSW38 | S | N | TX | (BSY62) | | | | | 17 |
| BSW39 | S | N | TF, TX | BSX47 | BSW66 | 2N1893 | 2N4001 | | 17 |
| BSW39-6 | S | N | TF | BSX47-6 | | | | | 17 |
| BSW39-10 | S | N | TF | BSX47-10 | | | | | 17 |
| BSW39-16 | S | N | TF | BSX47-10 | | | | | 17 |
| BSW40 | S | P | TF, TX | BSV17 | | 2N4929 | | | 17 |
| BSW40-6 | S | P | TF | BSV17-6 | | | | | 17 |
| BSW40-10 | S | P | TF | BSV17-10 | | | | | 17 |
| BSW40-16 | S | P | TF | BSV17-10 | | | | | 17 |
| BSW40-25 | S | P | TF | (BSV17-10) | | | | | 17 |
| BSW41 | S | N | MU, PH, V, AM | BSX48 | BSW64 | 2N2222A | 2N2221 | 2SC321 | 17 |
| BSW41 | S | N | PE, TX | | | 2N3866 | | | 17 |
| BSW42 | S | N | SE, ML, Ss | BC317 | BC237A | 2N4966 | | | 17 |
| BSW42 | | | | BC163A | BC238A | | | | 17 |
| BSW42 | | | | BC207 | | | | | 17 |
| BSW42A | S | N | SE | BC237A | BC207 | 2N4966 | | | 17 |
| BSW42B | S | N | SE, ML, Ss | BCY65EVII | BC207 | 2N4966 | | | 17 |

| TYPE | M/S | POL | MANUFAC | EUROPEAN | | AMERICAN | JAPANESE | USE |
|---|---|---|---|---|---|---|---|---|
| BSW43 | S | N | SE, ML, Ss | BC318 | BC237B | 2N4967 | | 17 |
| BSW43 | | | | BC183A | BC238B | | | 17 |
| BSW43 | | | | BC209 | BC208 | | | 17 |
| BSW43A | S | N | SE, ML, Ss | BC237B | | 2N4967 | | 17 |
| BSW43A | | | | BC209 | | | | 17 |
| BSW43B | S | N | SE | BCY65EIX | BC209 | 2N4967 | | 17 |
| BSW44 | S | P | SE, ML, Ss | BC321 | BC307A | | | 17 |
| BSW44 | | | | BC213A | BC308VI | | | 17 |
| BSW44 | | | | BC204 | BC205 | | | 17 |
| BSW44A | S | P | SE | BC204 | | 2N4249 | | 17 |
| BSW44B | S | P | SE | BCY77VII | | | | 17 |
| BSW45 | S | P | SE, ML, Ss | BC322 | BC307B | 2N4250 | | 17 |
| BSW45 | | | | BC213A | BC308B | | | 17 |
| BSW45 | | | | BC206 | | | | 17 |
| BSW45A | S | P | SE, ML, Ss | BC307B | BC327 | 2N4250 | | 17 |
| BSW45A | | | | BC206 | | | | 17 |
| BSW45B | S | P | SE | BCY771X | | | | 17 |
| BSW49 | S | N | LI, TX | BSY58 | | 2N2219A | | 17 |
| BSW51 | S | N | V, MO, TX | BCW77-16 | BSY34 | 2N2218 | 2N2219A | 2SC479 | 17 |
| BSW51 | | | | BSW54 | | | | 17 |
| BSW52 | S | N | V, MO, TX | BCW77-16 | BSY34 | 2N2219 | 2N2219A | | 17 |
| BSW52 | | | | BSW54 | | | | 17 |
| BSW53 | S | N | V, MO, TX | BCW78-16 | BSY34 | 2N2218A | 2N2219A | 2SC479 | 17 |
| BSW53 | | | | BSW54 | | | | 17 |
| BSW54 | S | N | V, MO, TX | BCW78-16 | BSY34 | 2N2219A | | 17 |
| BSW58 | S | N | V, TX | (BSY63) | | 2N2369 | | 17 |
| BSW59 | S | N | V, TX | (BSY62) | | 2N2369 | | 17 |
| BSW61 | S | N | V, MO, TX | BCW73-16 | BSX49 | 2N2221 | 2N2221A | 17 |
| BSW61 | | | | BSW64 | | | | 17 |
| BSW62 | S | N | V, MO, TX | BCW73-16 | BSX49 | 2N2222 | 2N2221A | 17 |
| BSW62 | | | | BSW64 | | | | 17 |
| BSW63 | S | N | V, MO, TX | BCW74-16 | BSX49 | 2N2221A | | 17 |
| BSW63 | | | | BSW64 | | | | 17 |
| BSW64 | S | N | V, MO, TX | BCW74-16 | BSX49 | 2N2222A | 2N2221A | 17 |
| BSW65 | S | N | MU, V, PH | BSW66 | (BSX47-10) | 2N3019 | 2N3725 | 17 |
| BSW65 | | | | BSX63-6 | BSW10 | 2N4001 | | 17 |
| BSW66 | S | N | MU, V, PH | (BSX47-10) | BSX46 | 2N3019 | 2N3712 | 17 |
| BSW66 | | | | | | 2N4001 | | 17 |
| BSW67 | S | N | PH, MU, V | | | 2N3712 | 2N3440 | 17 |
| BSW68 | S | N | PH, MU, V | | | 2N3712 | 2N3440 | 17 |
| BSW69 | S | N | MU, PH, V, AM, RA | (BF457) | BFY45 | 2N3712 | | 17 |
| BSW69 | S | N | PE | BF297 | | | | 17 |
| BSW70 | S | N | MU | (BF457) | | 2N2222 | | 17 |
| BSW72 | S | P | IN, TX | BCW75-10 | BC327-16 | 2N2906 | 2N2906A | 17 |
| BSW72 | | | | BSW24 | | | | 17 |
| BSW73 | S | P | IN, TX | BCW75-16 | BC327-25 | 2N2907 | 2N2906A | 17 |
| BSW73 | | | | BSW24 | | | | 17 |
| BSW74 | S | P | IN, TX | BCW76-10 | BC327-16 | 2N2906 | 2N2906A | 17 |
| BSW74 | | | | BSW24 | | | | 17 |
| BSW75 | S | P | IN, TX | BCW76-16 | BC327-25 | 2N2907 | 2N2906A | 17 |
| BSW75 | | | | BSW24 | | | | 17 |
| BSW78 | S | N | IN | (BSY63) | | | | 17 |
| BSW79 | S | N | IN | (BSY63) | | | | 17 |
| BSW80 | S | N | IN | (BSY63) | | | | 17 |
| BSW82 | S | N | IN, IT, TX | BCW73-16 | BSX48 | 2N2221 | | 17 |
| BSW83 | S | N | IN, IT, TX | BCW73-16 | BSX48 | 2N2222 | | 17 |
| BSW84 | S | N | IN, IT, TX | BCW74-16 | BSX49 | 2N2221A | | 17 |
| BSW85 | S | N | IN, IT, TX | BCW74-16 | BSX49 | 2N2222A | | 17 |
| BSW88 | S | N | TF | BC183 | BC167 | 2N3692 | | 17 |
| BSW88 | | | | BSW33 | BC167A | | | 17 |
| BSW88A | S | N | TF | BC167A | | | | 17 |
| BSW88B | S | N | TF | BC167B | | | | 17 |
| BSW89 | S | N | TF | BCW51 | BC237 | 2N3692 | | 17 |
| BSW89 | | | | BSW33 | BC167A | | | 17 |
| BSW89A | S | N | TF | BC237A | | | | 17 |
| BSW89B | S | N | TF | (BC237B) | | | | 17 |
| BSW92 | S | N | SE | BC238A | | | | 17 |
| BSW93 | S | P | SG, AT | BSV15-6 | | 2N5023 | | 17 |
| BSW96 | S | N | | | | 2N2193A | | 17 |
| BSW97 | S | P | | | | 2N2906 | | 17 |
| BSW98 | S | N | | | | 2N2193 | | 17 |
| BSW99 | S | P | | | | 2N2904 | | 17 |
| BSX12 | S | N | PH, V, AT | BSY58 | | 2N3303 | | 17 |
| BSX12A | S | N | V, PH | BSX12 | | 2N3303 | | 17 |
| BSX19 | S | N | MU, PH, V, PE | (BSY63) | BSX48 | 2N2368 | 2N2369 | 2SC689 | 17 |

| TYPE | M/S | POL | MANUFAC | EUROPEAN | | AMERICAN | | JAPANESE | USE |
|---|---|---|---|---|---|---|---|---|---|
| BSX19 | S | N | SG, TX | BSX20 | | 2N2369 | 2N2369A | 2SC689 | 17 |
| BSX20 | S | N | MU, PH, V, SG | (BSY63) | BSX48 | | | | 17 |
| BSX20 | S | N | PE, TX | BSY19 | | | | | 17 |
| BSX21 | S | N | IN, TX, AM, MU | BC394 | (BF457) | 2N1990R | 2N1893 | 2SC857 | 17 |
| BSX21 | S | N | NS, PE, PH, V | BFY45 | BFY80 | 2N4390 | | | 17 |
| | | | | | | | | | 17 |
| BSX22 | S | N | IN, TX, IT | BSX62 | (BSX45-10) | 2N4231 | 2N5321 | | 17 |
| BSX22 | | | | BSW26 | BSX45 | 2N2297 | 2N1613 | | 17 |
| BSX22 | | | | BFY51 | BFY50 | 2N3724 | | | 17 |
| BSX23 | S | N | IN, TX, IT | BSW26 | (BSX46-10) | 2N2297 | 2N5320 | | 17 |
| BSX23 | | | | BFY51 | BFX34 | 2N1613 | 2N3725 | | 17 |
| BSX23 | | | | BSX62 | | | | | 17 |
| BSX24 | S | N | TX | BCY58 | BC237A | 2N2221 | A157A | 2SC907 | 17 |
| BSX24 | | | | BSW27 | BSX51A | | | | 17 |
| BSX24 | | | | BC107 | BSW41 | | | | 17 |
| BSX24C | S | N | | | | S7136 | | | 17 |
| | | | | | | | | | 17 |
| BSX25 | S | N | TF, TX | BSW41 | BC223 | 2N731 | 2N2222 | | 17 |
| BSX25 | | | | BCW73-16 | BSX33 | 2N913 | TS2222 | | 17 |
| BSX25 | | | | BSX24 | BCY59 | | | | 17 |
| BSX25 | | | | BSX51A | BSW82 | | | | 17 |
| BSX26 | S | N | TX, AT, SG | BSY19 | BSY63 | 2N2369 | 2N708 | | 17 |
| | | | | | | | | | 17 |
| BSX26 | | | | BSY20 | | 2N2368 | 2N3013 | | 17 |
| BSX27 | S | N | SG, TX, AT | (BSY17) | BSX20 | 2N2369 | 2N2368 | | 17 |
| BSX27 | | | | | | 2N709 | 2N3010 | | 17 |
| BSX28 | S | N | SG, TX, AT | (BSY62) | BSX20 | 2N2368 | 2N2369 | | 17 |
| BSX28 | | | | | | 2N3011 | | | 17 |
| | | | | | | | | | 17 |
| BSX29 | S | P | TX, AT | | | 2N3546 | 2N2906 | | 17 |
| BSX29 | | | | | | 2N2894 | 2N3012 | | 17 |
| BSX30 | S | N | SG, TX, AT | BSY34 | | 2N2410 | 2N2846 | | 17 |
| BSX32 | S | N | SG, TX, AT | (BSY34) | | 2N2218 | 2N3725 | | 17 |
| BSX33 | S | N | SG, TX, AT | BSY46-6 | | 2N731 | 2N2218A | | 17 |
| | | | | | | | | | 17 |
| BSX33 | | | | | | 2N3110 | 2N2193 | | 17 |
| BSX35 | S | N | TX, AT | BSX20 | | | | | 17 |
| BSX36 | S | P | SG, TX, AT | BC327-16 | | 2N2906 | 2N2907 | | 17 |
| BSX38 | S | N | TF, TX | BCY58VII | BCY59 | 2N2222 | 2N708 | 2SC907 | 17 |
| BSX38 | | | | BSY19 | BSX24 | | | | 17 |
| | | | | | | | | | 17 |
| BSX38 | | | | BSY58 | BSX51 | | | | 17 |
| BSX38 | | | | BCW51 | | | | | 17 |
| BSX38A | S | N | TF | BCY59VII | BSW64 | 2N2221A | | | 17 |
| BSX38B | S | N | TF | BCY59IV | BSW64 | 2N2221A | | | 17 |
| BSX39 | S | N | SG, TX, AT | (BSY63) | BSX20 | 2N708 | 2N2369 | | 17 |
| | | | | | | | | | 17 |
| BSX40 | S | P | TX, IT, IN | BSV15-6 | BFX29 | 2N4037 | 2N2904 | 2SA537 | 17 |
| BSX40 | | | | | | 2N2905A | | | 17 |
| BSX41 | S | P | TX, IN | BSV15-16 | BFX29 | 2N2905 | 2N2905A | | 17 |
| BSX44 | S | N | MU, PH, AM, PE | (BSY17) | BSX20 | 2N2369 | 2N2228A | | 17 |
| BSX44 | S | N | TX | | | 2N2475 | 2N709 | | 17 |
| | | | | | | | | | |
| BSX45 | S | N | TF, TX, ML, S | BSX22 | BFX85 | 2N2297 | 2N3063 | | 17 |
| BSX45 | S | N | SG, V | | | 2N3252 | 2N4231 | | 17 |
| BSX45-6 | S | N | S, TF, V | BFY51 | | 2N3110 | 2N2297 | | 17 |
| BSX45-10 | S | N | S, TF, V | BFY51 | | 2N3110 | 2N2297 | | 17 |
| BSX45-16 | S | N | S, TF, V | BFY51 | | 2N3109 | 2N2297 | | 17 |
| | | | | | | | | | |
| BSX46 | S | N | TF, TX, ML, S, SG | BSV64 | BFX85 | 2N2102 | 2N3252 | | 17 |
| BSX46 | S | N | V | | | 2N2297 | | | 17 |
| BSX46-6 | S | N | S, TF, V | BFX55 | | 2N3108 | 2N1893 | | 17 |
| BSX46-10 | S | N | S, TF, V | BFX85 | | 2N3108 | 2N1893 | | 17 |
| BSX46-16 | S | N | S, TF, V | BFX85 | | 2N3107 | 2N1893 | | 17 |
| | | | | | | | | | |
| BSX47 | S | N | S, V | BFX85 | | 2N1893 | | | 17 |
| BSX47-6 | S | N | S, V | BFX85 | | 2N1893 | | | 17 |
| BSX47-10 | S | N | S, V | BFX85 | | 2N1893 | | | 17 |
| BSX48 | S | N | S | BSW64 | | 2N2221A | 2N2221 | | 17 |
| BSX48 | | | | | | 2N4013 | 2N2539 | | 17 |
| | | | | | | | | | |
| BSX49 | S | N | S | BSX59 | | 2N2222A | 2N4013 | | 17 |
| BSX49 | | | | | | 2N3444 | | | 17 |
| BSX51 | S | N | SE, ML, Ss, TX | BSW64 | BCY58 | 2N2222 | 2N2221A | | 17 |
| BSX51 | | | | BCY58III | BCW51 | | | | 17 |
| BSX51A | S | N | SE, Ss, ML, TX | BSW64 | BCY59VII | 2N2222A | 2N2221A | | 17 |
| | | | | | | | | | 17 |
| BSX51A | | | | SFT14A | BC107A | | | | 17 |
| BSX51B | S | N | SE | BCY65EVII | BSW64 | 2N2221A | | | 17 |
| BSX52 | S | N | SE, ML, Ss, TX | BCY58IX | BCY58VIII | 2N2222 | 2N2221A | | 17 |
| BSX52 | | | | BSW64 | | | | | 17 |
| BSX52A | S | N | SE, ML, Ss, TX | BCY59IX | BC107B | 2N2222A | 2N2221A | | 17 |
| | | | | | | | | | 17 |
| BSX52A | | | | BSW64 | | | | | 17 |
| BSX52B | S | N | SE | BCY65EIV | BSW64 | 2N2221A | | | 17 |
| BSX53 | S | N | SE, TX, TF | BCW51 | BCY58 | 2N2222 | 2N1613 | 2SC907 | 17 |
| BSX53 | | | | BSX51 | BCY58VIII | | | | 17 |
| BSX53A | S | N | SE, TF | BCY58VII | BSW64 | 2N2221A | | | 17 |
| | | | | | | | | | 17 |

| TYPE | M/S | POL | MANUFAC | EUROPEAN | | AMERICAN | | JAPANESE | USE |
|------|-----|-----|---------|----------|--|----------|--|----------|-----|
| BSX53B | S | N | SE, TF | BCY58IX | BSW64 | 2N2221A | | | 17 |
| BSX54 | S | N | SE, TX, TF | BCY86 | BCY59 | 2N2222A | 2N1711 | | 17 |
| BSX54 | | | | BSX51A | BC107A | | | | 17 |
| BSX54A | S | N | SE' TF | BCY59VII | BSW64 | 2N2221A | | | 17 |
| BSX54B | S | N | SE, TF | BCY59IX | BSW64 | 2N2221A | | | 17 |
| BSX59 | S | N | MU, PH, V, TX, RA | (BSY34) | BSX45 | 2N3444 | 2N5321 | 2SC479 | 17 |
| BSX59 | S | N | AM, FE, PE | | | 2N3725 | 2N2218A | | 17 |
| BSX60 | S | N | MU, PH, V, TX, RA | (BSY34) | BSX45 | 2N3725 | 2N5321 | 2SC479 | 17 |
| BSX60 | S | N | AM, FE, NT, PE | BSX56 | | 2N3724 | 2N2219A | | 17 |
| BSX61 | S | N | MU, PH, V, TX, RA | (BSX34) | BSX45 | 2N5321 | 2N3725 | 2SC479 | 17 |
| BSX61 | S | N | AM, FE, NT, PE | BSX56 | | 2N2219A | | | 17 |
| BSX62 | S | N | S, V | BSW65 | BFX34 | 2N1889 | | | 17 |
| BSX63 | S | N | S, V | BSW65 | BFX34 | 2N1893 | | | 17 |
| BSX63B | S | N | S | BSX63-6 | | | | | 17 |
| BSX63C | S | N | S | BSX63-10 | | | | | 17 |
| BSX66 | S | N | V, TD | BCY58VII | BC108A | 2N743 | | | 17 |
| BSX67 | S | N | V, TD | BCY58VII | BC108A | 2N744 | | | 17 |
| BSX68 | S | N | TF, V | BC238A | BC148 | 2N2884 | S9518 | 2SC641 | 17 |
| BSX69 | S | N | TF, V | BC238A | BC148 | 2N2884 | | | 17 |
| BSX69 | | | | BFY39 | | | | | 17 |
| BSX70 | S | N | V, TD, TX | BCW74-16 | | 2N2222 | 2N718A | | 17 |
| BSX71 | S | N | V, TD, TX | BCW74-25 | | 2N2222 | 2N956 | | 17 |
| BSX72 | S | N | TF, TX, TD | BCW77-16 | BSY78 | 2N3724 | 2N3053 | 2SC479 | 17 |
| BSX72 | | | | | | 2N2219A | 2N2218 | | 17 |
| BSX72 | | | | | | 2N2219 | | | 17 |
| BSX73 | S | N | TF | | | 2N2218 | | | 17 |
| BSX74 | S | N | TF | | | 2N2219 | | | 17 |
| BSX75 | S | N | TF, TX, TD | BSX33 | BCW73-16 | 2N2222 | 2N2218 | | 17 |
| BSX75 | | | | BSW41 | BSX48 | 2N4013 | 2N3704A | | 17 |
| BSX75 | | | | | | 2N731 | | | 17 |
| BSX76 | | N | MU, TX, TD | (BCY58VII) | | 2N2369 | 2N3014 | | 17 |
| BSX77 | | N | MU, TX, TD | (BCY59VII) | | 2N2369 | 2N3014 | | 17 |
| BSX78 | | N | MU, TX, TD | (BCY59VIII) | | 2N2369 | 2N3014 | | 17 |
| BSX79 | S | N | TF, TX | BCY59VII | BSX51A | 2N2222 | 2N2219 | | 17 |
| BSX79 | | | | BSY74 | | | | | 17 |
| BSX79A | S | N | TF | BCY59VII | | | | | 17 |
| BSX79B | S | N | TF | BCY59IV | | | | | 17 |
| BSX80 | S | N | TF | (BSY63) | BSX68 | 2N708 | S9506 | 2SC641 | 17 |
| BSX81 | S | N | TF | BCW83 | BC147 | 2N718 | 2N2410 | | 17 |
| BSX81 | | | | BSW33 | BSY58 | | | | 17 |
| BSX81A | S | N | TF | BC147A | | | | | 17 |
| BSX81B | S | N | TF | BC147B | | | | | 17 |
| BSX87 | S | N | MO, SG, TX, AT | (BSY63) | BSX20 | 2N914 | 2N2369 | | 17 |
| BSX87A | S | N | MO, SG, TX, AT | (BSY63) | BSX20 | 2N708 | 2N2369 | | 17 |
| BSX88 | S | N | MO, SG, TX, NS, AT | (BSY63) | BSX20 | 2N708 | 2N2369 | | 17 |
| BSX88A | S | N | MO, SG, TX, AT | (BSY63) | BSX20 | 2N914 | 2N2369 | | 17 |
| BSX89 | S | N | MO, SG, TX, AT | (BSY62) | BSX20 | 2N706A | 2N2369 | | 17 |
| BSX90 | S | N | MO, SG, TX, TD | BSY17 | BSX20 | 2N743 | 2N2369 | | 17 |
| BSX91 | S | N | MO, SG, TX, TD | BSY18 | BC232 | 2N744 | 2N2369 | | 17 |
| BSX91 | | | | BSX20 | | | | | 17 |
| BSX92 | S | N | MO, SG, TX, TD | (BSY63) | BSX20 | 2N2368 | 2N2369 | | 17 |
| BSX93 | S | N | MO, SG, TX, AT | (BSY63) | | 2N2369 | | | 17 |
| BSX94A | S | P | SG, AT | | BSX20 | 2N4207 | | | 17 |
| BSX95 | S | N | V, TX | BCW78-16 | BSX45 | 2N1613 | 2N698 | 2SC479 | 17 |
| BSX95 | | | | BFX97 | | 2N2219A | | | 17 |
| BSX96 | S | N | V, TX | BCW78-16 | BSX45 | 2N1711 | 2N698 | 2SC479 | 17 |
| BSX96 | | | | BFX97 | | 2N2219A | | | 17 |
| BSX97 | S | N | SE | (BC337-16) | BSX48 | 2N2218 | | | 17 |
| BSX99 | S | N | S | (BSY62A) | | | | | 17 |
| BSY10 | S | N | MU, V, AM, PE | BF177 | (BCY66) | 2N2219A | 2N735 | | 17 |
| BSY10 | S | N | PH, RA, TX | BCY65E | BSY45 | 2N2222 | 2N2218A | | 17 |
| BSY10 | S | N | | BSY44 | BFY50 | | | | 17 |
| BSY10 | | | | BSW54 | | | | | 17 |
| BSY11 | S | N | MU, V, AM, PE | BCY59VII | BCY66 | 2N2219A | 2N736 | | 17 |
| BSY11 | S | N | PH, RA, TX | BSW54 | BSY44 | 2N2218 | 2N2222 | | 17 |
| BSY11 | | | | BFY50 | | | | | 17 |
| BSY17 | S | N | TX, MO, S | BSY70 | BSY21 | 2N2369 | 2N743 | 2SC321 | 17 |
| BSY17 | | | | BSX20 | | 2N2368 | 2N914 | | 17 |
| BSY18 | S | N | TX, MO, S | BSY21 | BCY16 | 2N744 | 2N2368 | 2SC321 | 17 |
| BSY18 | | | | BSX20 | BSY70 | 2N2369 | | | 17 |
| BSY19 | S | N | TX, MO, V | BSY63 | BSX20 | 2N708 | 2N2369 | 2SC321 | 17 |
| BSY20 | S | N | TX, MO, V, IN | BSY18 | BSY62 | 2N706B | 2N2369 | | 17 |
| BSY20 | | | | BSY70 | | | | | 17 |
| BSY21 | S | N | TX, MO, IN | BSX20 | BSY10 | 2N914 | 2N2369 | | 17 |
| BSY21 | | | | BSY18 | BSY63 | | | | 17 |

| TYPE | M/S | POL | MANUFAC | EUROPEAN | | AMERICAN | | JAPANESE | USE |
|------|-----|-----|---------|----------|---|----------|---|----------|-----|
| BSY22 | S | N | MO, IN | BF115 | BSY63 | 2N916 | 2N3014 | | 17 |
| BSY22 | | | | BSX20 | | 2N2369 | | | 17 |
| BSY23 | S | N | MO, IN | BSY63 | BSX20 | 2N834 | 2N2369 | | 17 |
| BSY23 | | | | | | 2N2368 | 2N3014 | | 17 |
| BSY24 | S | N | IN, IT, ST, TX | BSY91 | BC337-16 | 2N2218 | 2N2219 | | 17 |
| BSY24 | | | | | | | | | 17 |
| BSY25 | | | | BSX72 | BSX62 | | | | 17 |
| BSY25 | S | N | IN, TX, ST | BSY58 | | | | | 17 |
| BSY25 | | | | BSY58 | BC337-16 | 2N697 | 2N2218 | | 17 |
| BSY26 | S | N | IN, MU, IT, ST, TX | BSX72 | BSY46 | 2N2219 | | | 17 |
| BSY26 | | | | BSY39 | BSY62A | 2N706A | 2N708 | | 17 |
| BSY26 | | | | | | | | | 17 |
| BSY27 | S | N | IN, MU, IT, SG | BSY18 | BSY19 | | | | 17 |
| BSY27 | S | N | ST, TX | BSX20 | BSY62B | 2N753 | 2N708 | | 17 |
| BSY28 | S | N | IN, IT, ST, TX | BSY18 | BSY39 | 2N2369 | | | 17 |
| BSY28 | | | | BSY21 | BSY17 | 2N708 | 2N2369 | | 17 |
| BSY29 | | | | BSY19 | BSY38 | 2N914 | 2N743 | | 17 |
| BSY29 | S | N | IN, IT, ST, TX | BSY39 | BSY18 | 2N708 | 2N2369 | | 17 |
| BSY29 | | | | BSX70 | BSY21 | 2N744 | 2N914 | | 17 |
| BSY30 | S | N | S | BSY62A | | | | | 17 |
| BSY31 | S | N | S | BSY62B | | | | | |
| BSY32 | S | N | | BSX70 | BSY29 | 2N743 | | | 17 |
| BSY32 | | | | | | | | | 17 |
| BSY33 | S | N | | BSY38 | BSY29 | 2N744 | | | 17 |
| BSY33 | | | | BSX70 | | | | | 17 |
| BSY34 | S | N | TX, S | BSY39 | BFY44 | 2N3725 | 2N2218 | 2SC479 | 17 |
| BSY34 | | | | BSX59 | BSX73 | 2N3724 | 2N2219A | | 17 |
| BSY34 | | | | BSX61 | | | | | 17 |
| BSY36 | S | N | | BSY21 | BSY38 | 2N708 | 2N743 | | 17 |
| BSY36 | | | | BSY70 | | | | | 17 |
| BSY37 | S | N | | BSY21 | BSY38 | 2N708 | 2N743 | | 17 |
| BSY37 | S | N | | BSY70 | | | | | 17 |
| BSY38 | S | N | MU, V, AM, BL, TX | BSX20 | BSY62A | 2N708 | 2N2363 | | 17 |
| BSY38 | S | N | MN, NS, PE, PH, RA | BSY21 | BSY19 | 2N2369 | 2N743 | | 17 |
| BSY38A | S | N | | BSX20 | | 2N2369 | | | 17 |
| BSY39 | S | N | MU, V, AM, BL, NS | BSX20 | BSY62B | 2N708 | 2N744 | | 17 |
| BSY39 | S | N | ME, MN, RA, TX | BSY19 | BSY21 | 2N2369 | | | 17 |
| BSY39A | S | N | | BSX20 | | 2N2369 | | | 17 |
| BSY40 | S | P | TX, MU, V | BCY78 | BCY70 | 2N3965 | 2N2894 | 2SA548 | 17 |
| BSY40 | | | | | | 2N2411 | | | 17 |
| BSY41 | S | P | TX, MU, V | BCY78 | BCY70 | 2N2894 | 2N2412 | 2SA548 | 17 |
| BSY41 | | | | | | 2N3965 | | | 17 |
| BSY42 | S | N | | BFY12 | BSX73 | 2N2219 | | | 17 |
| BSY43 | S | N | | BFY12 | BSX73 | 2N2219 | | | 17 |
| BSY44 | S | N | MO, TX, TD, TF | BSW66 | BSX45-6 | 2N699 | 2N1613 | 2SC708A | 17 |
| BSY44 | | | | BSX45 | BSX95 | 2N1893 | | | 17 |
| BSY45 | S | N | MO, TX, TD, TF | BSX47-6 | BC141-6 | 2N1893 | 2N3498 | 2SC708A | 17 |
| BSY45 | | | | BSW66 | | 2N1613 | | | 17 |
| BSY46 | S | N | MO, TX, TD, TF | BSW66 | BSX46-6 | 2N699 | 2N1893 | 2SC708A | 17 |
| BSY46 | | | | BFY55 | BSX46 | 2N1613 | 2N2193 | | 17 |
| BSY47 | S | N | | BSY20 | BDY62 | 2N706A | | | 17 |
| BSY47 | S | N | | BSY70 | | | | | 17 |
| BSY48 | S | N | S | BSY20 | BSY62 | 2N706A | | | 17 |
| BSY48 | | | | BSY70 | | | | | 17 |
| BSY50 | S | N | | BSY20 | BSY62 | 2N706A | | | 17 |
| BSY50 | | | | BSY70 | | | | | 17 |
| BSY51 | S | N | IN, SE, ML, IT, TX | BFY50 | BSX45-6 | 2N697 | 2N2297 | 2SC479 | 17 |
| BSY51 | S | N | ME, V, NS, SG, Ss | BFY34 | BSX45 | | | | 17 |
| BSY51 | S | N | MO | | | | | | 17 |
| BSY52 | S | N | IN, V, MO, SG, ME | BSW54 | BSX45-16 | 2N2219A | 2N1420 | 2SC479 | 17 |
| BSY52 | S | N | SE, Ss, IT, ML, NS, | BFY34 | BSX45 | 2N1711 | 2N2219 | | 17 |
| BSY52 | S | N | TX | | | | | | 17 |
| BSY53 | S | N | IN, SE, SG, IT, V, Ss | BSY67 | BSX45-6 | 2N697 | 2N1613 | 2SC479 | 17 |
| BSY53 | S | N | TX, MO, ML, ME | BSX46-6 | BFY34 | 2N2219A | | | 17 |
| BSY53 | S | N | NS | BSY44 | BSX45 | | | | 17 |
| BSY53 | | | | BSW54 | | | | | 17 |
| BSY54 | S | N | IN, SE, V, Ss, IT | BSY71 | BSX45-16 | 2N1711 | 2N2219A | | 17 |
| BSY54 | S | N | ME, ML, NS, SG | BSX46-10 | BFY46 | | | | 17 |
| BSY54 | S | N | TX, MO | BSX45 | | | | | 17 |
| BSY55 | S | N | IN, SE, V, IT, ME | BSX46-6 | BSX47-6 | 2N1893 | 2N3498 | | 17 |
| BSY55 | S | N | TF, TX | BSW66 | BFY14C | | | | 17 |
| BSY55 | | | | BSY45 | | | | | 17 |
| BSY56 | S | N | IN, SE, V, IT, ME | BSW66 | BSX47-10 | 2N1890 | 2N1893 | | 17 |
| BSY56 | S | N | SG, FE, TX | BFY14D | BSX46-10 | | | | 17 |
| BSY58 | S | N | TX, S | BFY44 | BSX73 | 2N2218 | 2N3725 | 2SC479 | 17 |
| BSY58 | | | | BSX59 | | 2N3724 | 2N2537 | | 17 |

| TYPE | M/S | POL | MANUFAC | EUROPEAN | | AMERICAN | | JAPANESE | USE |
|---|---|---|---|---|---|---|---|---|---|
| BSY59 | S | P | S | BC327-16 | BC238 | 2N2905 | | | 17 |
| BSY60 | S | N | | | | 2N706A | | | 17 |
| BSY61 | S | N | S | (BSY62B) | BC238A | 2N706 A | | | 17 |
| BSY62 | S | N | | BSY70 | BSX20 | 2N706 | 2N2369 | | 17 |
| BSY62 | | | | BFX20 | | 2N706A | 2N708 | | 17 |
| BSY62A | S | N | | BSY62 | BSY70 | 2N706A | | 2SC321 | 17 |
| BSY62A | | | | BSX20 | | | | | 17 |
| BSY62B | S | N | S | BSY62 | BSX20 | 2N706A | | 2SC321 | 17 |
| BSY63 | S | N | TX, S | BSY19 | BSX20 | 2N708 | 2N2369 | 2SC321 | 17 |
| BSY63 | | | | BFX20 | | | | | 17 |
| BSY68 | S | N | RA, TX | (BF457) | BFY65 | 2N2405 | 2N1990 | | 17 |
| BSY68 | | | | | | 2N3114 | | | 17 |
| BSY70 | S | N | MO, TX, TD, TF | BSX20 | BSY62A | 2N706 | 2N2369 | 2SC321 | 17 |
| BSY70 | | | | BSX19 | BSY62 | | | | 17 |
| BSY71 | S | N | MO, TX, TD, TF | BSW66 | BSX45-16 | 2N1893 | 2N1711 | | 17 |
| BSY71 | | | | BFY46 | | 2N2219A | 2N2219 | | 17 |
| BSY72 | S | N | TX, IN, ST | BC182A | BC239B | A157A | MPS6520 | 2SC648 | 17 |
| BSY72 | | | | BCY58VII | BC108A | 2N930 | 2N3014 | | 17 |
| BSY72 | | | | BC130A | | | | | 17 |
| BSY72 | | | | BC107 | | | | | 17 |
| BSY73 | S | N | TX, IN, ST | BC182A | BC107 | A157A | MPS6520 | 2SC907 | 17 |
| BSY73 | | | | BC238A | BC108A | 2N2221 | 2N3014 | | 17 |
| BSY73 | | | | BSX53 | BSY63 | | | | 17 |
| BSY73 | | | | BC130A | BC59VII | | | | 17 |
| BSY74 | S | N | TX, IN, ST | BC182A | BC238A | A157A | MPS6520 | 2SC907 | 17 |
| BSY74 | | | | BC108A | BFY46 | 2N929 | 2N3014 | | 17 |
| BSY74 | | | | BCY58VII | BSX53 | | | | 17 |
| BSY74 | | | | BC130A | | | | | 17 |
| BSY75 | S | N | TX, IN, ST | BSX79 | BC237A | 2N2221 | 2N2222 | 2SC907 | 17 |
| BSY75 | | | | BC59VII | BFY33 | A157 | | | 17 |
| BSY75 | | | | BC107 | BSX51A | | | | 17 |
| BSY76 | S | N | TX, TD, IN, ST | BCY59VII | BC237A | 2N2221 | 2N2222 | 2SC907 | 17 |
| BSY76 | | | | BCW51 | BFY12C | A157 | | | 17 |
| BSY76 | | | | BC107 | BSX45 | | | | 17 |
| BSY76B | S | N | | BC108A | | | | | 17 |
| BSY77 | S | N | TX, IN, ST | BSX21 | BCY65EVII | A157 | 2N2219 | | 17 |
| BSY77 | | | | BCY65E | BFY34 | 2N2221A | 2N2222A | | 17 |
| BSY77 | | | | BSY56 | BSX45 | | | | 17 |
| BSY77 | | | | BC107 | | | | | 17 |
| BSY78 | S | N | TX, IN, ST | BC107 | | | | | 17 |
| BSY78 | | | | BCY65EVII | | 2N2222A | 2N3019 | | 17 |
| BSY78 | | | | BFY46 | BSX45 | A157 | | | 17 |
| BSY79 | S | N | IN, TX, IT, RA, V | BSX45 | (BF457) | 2N4390 | 2N1990R | 2SC857 | 17 |
| BSY79 | | | | BC394 | BFY45 | S7013 | 2N3114 | | 17 |
| BSY79 | | . | | BFY80 | | | | | 17 |
| BSY80 | S | N | TX, IN, ST | BC108A | (BC238C) | 2N930 | MPS6520 | 2SC987 | 17 |
| BSY80 | | | | BCY58VIII | BC108 | | | | 17 |
| BSY80 | | | | BC130C | BC109 | | | | 17 |
| BSY80 | | | | BC184 | | | | | 17 |
| BSY81 | S | N | IN, TX, IT, ME, ST | BFY51 | BSX45-6 | 2N2193 | 2N697 | 2SC708 | 17 |
| BSY81 | | | | BSX65-6 | BSX72 | 2N2297 | 2N2218 | | 17 |
| BSY81 | | | | | | 2N3110 | | | 17 |
| BSY82 | S | N | IN, IT, TX, ME, ST | BFY51 | BSX45-16 | 2N2192 | 2N1711 | | 17 |
| BSY82 | | | | BSX45-10 | BSY72 | 2N2297 | 2N2219 | | 17 |
| BSY82 | | | | | | 2N3109 | | | 17 |
| BSY83 | S | N | IN, IT, TX, ME, SG | BFY50 | BSX45-6 | 2N2218A | 2N697 | 2SC708 | 17 |
| BSY83 | S | N | ST | BSY40 | BSY46 | 2N3110 | 2N1613 | | 17 |
| BSY83 | | | | | | 2N2193 | 2N2297 | | 17 |
| BSY84 | S | N | IN, IT, TX, ME, ST | BSX45-16 | BSX45-10 | 2N2192 | 2N1711 | | 17 |
| BSY84 | | | | BFY50 | | 2N3109 | 2N2297 | | 17 |
| BSY85 | S | N | IN, IT, ME, TX, ST | BSX47-6 | BSY46 | 2B2193A | 2N1889 | 2SC708A | 17 |
| BSY85 | | | | BSW66 | | 2N1893 | 2N3108 | | 17 |
| BSY86 | S | N | IN, IT, ME, TX, ST | BSX47-10 | BSX46-10 | 2N2192A | 2N1893 | | 17 |
| BSY86 | | | | BSW66 | | 2N1890 | 2N3019 | | 17 |
| BSY86 | | | | | | 2N3107 | | | 17 |
| BSY87 | S | N | IN, IT, TX, ME, ST | BSW66 | BSX46-6 | 2N1889 | 2N2102 | | 17 |
| BSY87 | S | N | MO | BFY14C | BC141-6 | 2N1893 | 2N3108 | | 17 |
| BSY88 | S | N | IN, IT, ME, TX, MO | BSW66 | BSX46-16 | 2N1890 | 2N1893 | | 17 |
| BSY88 | S | N | ST | BFY14D | BC141-10 | 2N3019 | 2N3107 | | 17 |
| BSY89 | S | N | IN, IT, TX | BC238B | BC107 | 2N2432 | A157A | | 17 |
| BSY90 | S | N | IN, IT, TX, ST | BSW54 | BCW77-16 | 2N1711 | 2N2219 | | 17 |
| BSY90 | | | | BFY46 | BC140-16 | 2N2219A | | | 17 |
| BSY91 | S | N | TF, TX | BSX51A | BCW77-16 | 2N2297 | 2N697 | 2SC708 | 17 |
| BSY91 | | | | BSX60 | BFY33 | 2N2218 | TS2219 | | 17 |
| BSY91 | | | | BSX48 | BSX25 | | | | 17 |

| TYPE | M/S | POL | MANUFAC | EUROPEAN | | AMERICAN | | | JAPANESE | USE |
|---|---|---|---|---|---|---|---|---|---|---|
| BSY91 | S | N | TF, TX | BFY51 | | | | | | 17 |
| BSY92 | S | N | TF, TX | BFY51 | BCW78-16 | 2N2297 | 2N1711 | 2SC479 | | 17 |
| BSY92 | | | | BFY34 | BSX45-6 | 2N2219 | 2N2219A | | | 17 |
| BSY93 | S | N | TF, TX | BCW74-16 | BCY65E | 2N2222 | 2N2222A | | | 17 |
| BSY93 | | | | BC107 | | A157A | | | | 17 |
| BSY95 | S | N | MU, TX, ME, ST | BSY62B | BSX20 | 2N2369 | | | | 17 |
| BSY95A | S | N | FE, IN, MU, IT, NS | BC108A | BSY62B | | | | | 17 |
| BSY95A | S | N | ME, NT, SG, TX, | BSY62 | BSX20 | 2N2218 | 2N2369 | 2SC321 | | 17 |
| BSY95A | S | N | ST | BSX73 | BSY58 | | | | | 17 |
| BSY149A | S | N | | BSX66 | | | | | | 17 |
| BSY149B | S | N | | BSX67 | | | | | | 17 |
| BSY152A | S | N | | BSX19 | | | | | | 17 |
| BSY152B | S | N | | BSX20 | | | | | | 17 |
| BU100 | S | N | SG, AT | BUY55 | | | | | | 17 |
| BU100A | S | N | AT, SG | BUY55 | | 2N5629 | | | | 16 |
| BU102 | S | N | AT, SG | BUY74 | BUX18B | 2N5631 | | | | 16 |
| BU103A | S | N | SE | | | 2N4912 | | | | 16 |
| BU104 | S | N | SE, ML, Ss | BUY74 | BU108 | | | | | 16 |
| BU105 | S | N | MU, PH, TF, V, AM | BU208 | | | | | | 16 |
| BU105 | S | N | MO, PE, RA | | | | | 2SC937 | | 16 |
| BU106 | S | N | TX, RA | BU110 | | | | | | 16 |
| BU107 | S | N | TX | BUY73 | | | | | | 16 |
| BU108 | S | N | PH, TF, V, AM, PE | BU208 | | | | | | 16 |
| BU108 | S | N | MO | | | | | | | 16 |
| BU109 | S | N | SE, ML, Ss | BU110 | BU108 | | | | | 16 |
| BU111 | S | N | S | | | | | | | 16 |
| BU112 | S | N | SE, ML, Ss | BU126 | | 2N6512 | | | | 16 |
| BU113 | S | N | SE, ML, Ss | BUY75 | | | | | | 16 |
| BU113S | S | N | SE | BUY76 | | | | | | 16 |
| BU114 | S | N | S | BUY76 | | 2N6510 | | | | 16 |
| BU115 | S | N | AT | BUY76 | | | | | | 16 |
| BU116 | S | N | AT | BUY75 | | | | | | 16 |
| BU117 | S | N | AT | BUY74 | | | | | | 16 |
| BU120 | S | N | AT | BUY74 | BDY98 | 2N6249 | | | | 16 |
| BU121 | S | N | AT, SG | BUY74 | BUX18 | | | | | 16 |
| BU122 | S | N | AT | BU111 | | | | | | 16 |
| BU123 | S | N | AT | BU111 | | | | | | 16 |
| BU125 | S | N | SG, AT | BUY47 | | 2N4895 | | | | 16 |
| BU126A | S | N | MO | BU126 | | | | | | 16 |
| BU127 | S | N | AT, SG | BUY58 | | 2N5630 | | | | 16 |
| BU128 | S | N | AT, SG | BUY73 | | 2N6249 | | | | 16 |
| BU129 | S | N | SE, ML | BU111 | BUX18C | | | | | 16 |
| BU130 | S | N | AM | BU111 | | | | | | 16 |
| BU131 | S | N | V, PH | BUY76 | | | | | | 16 |
| BU132 | S | N | PH, V | (BUY79) | | | | | | 16 |
| BU133 | S | N | PH | BUY79 | | | | | | 16 |
| BU134 | S | N | SE, ML | BUY79 | | | | | | 16 |
| BU134 | S | N | | BDY28 | BU126 | | | | | 16 |
| BU135 | S | N | MO | | | 2N6510 | | | | 16 |
| BU136 | S | N | MO | | | 2N6510 | | | | 16 |
| BU204 | S | N | PH, SE, MU, TF | BU208 | | | | | | 16 |
| BU205 | S | N | PH, V, SE, MU, TF | BU208 | | | | | | 16 |
| BU206 | S | N | PH, MU, TF | (BU208) | | | | | | 16 |
| BU207 | S | N | PH, V, SE, MU, TF | BU208 | | | | | | 16 |
| BU209 | S | N | PH, V, MU, TF | (BU208) | | | | | | 16 |
| BU210 | S | N | S | BUY74 | | | | | | 16 |
| BU211 | S | N | S | BUY75 | | | | | | 16 |
| BU212 | S | N | S | BUY76 | | | | | | 16 |
| BU221 | S | N | AT | BUY75 | | | | | | 16 |
| BU310 | S | N | S | BUX17 | | | | | | 16 |
| BU311 | S | N | S | BUX17 | | | | | | 16 |
| BU312 | S | N | S | BUX17 | | | | | | 16 |
| BU409 | S | N | SG | | | | | | | 16 |
| BUX10 | S | N | SE | (BUY58) | | TA8863J | | | | 16 |
| BUX11 | S | N | SE | (BUY73) | | | | | | 16 |
| BUX14 | S | N | SE | (BUY76) | | | | | | 16 |
| BUX15 | S | N | SE | (BUY76) | | | | | | 16 |
| BUX26 | S | N | S | | | | | | | 16 |
| BUX27 | S | N | S | | | 2N6510 | | | | 16 |
| BUX28 | S | N | SE, ML | BUX18C | | | | | | 16 |
| BUX39 | S | N | SE, ML | (BUY57) | | 2N5038 | | | | 16 |
| BUX40 | S | N | SE, ML | BUY73 | | 2N6354 | | | | 16 |
| BUX41 | S | N | SE, ML | BUY74 | BUX17A | | | | | 16 |
| BUX42 | S | N | SE, ML | BUY75 | BUX17B | | | | | 16 |
| BUX43 | S | N | SE, ML | BUY76 | BUX17C | | | | | 16 |
| BUX44 | S | N | SE, ML | (BUY76) | BUX18C | | | | | 16 |

| TYPE | M/S | POL | MANUFAC | EUROPEAN | | AMERICAN | | JAPANESE | USE |
|------|-----|-----|---------|----------|---|----------|---|----------|-----|
| BUX45 | S | N | SE | (BUY76) | | | | | 16 |
| BUX84 | S | N | PH | | | TA8863A | | | 16 |
| BUY10 | S | N | IN, IT, ST | BDY12-6 | | | | | 16 |
| BUY11 | S | N | IN, IT, ST | BDY12-6 | | | | | 16 |
| BUY12 | S | N | S | BUY58 | BDY91 | | | | 16 |
| BUY12S | S | N | SE | BUY58 | | | | | 16 |
| BUY13 | S | N | S | BUY57 | BDY91 | | | 2SC665 | 16 |
| BUY13 | | | | BDY93 | | | | | 16 |
| BUY13S | S | N | SE | BUY57 | | | | 2SD125A | 16 |
| BUY14 | S | N | | BDY61 | | 2N4911 | | | 16 |
| BUY16 | S | N | AT | BDY90 | | | | | 16 |
| BUY17 | S | N | AT | BDY60 | | | | | 16 |
| BUY18 | S | N | SG, AT | BUY77 | BU110 | | | | 16 |
| BUY19 | S | N | AT | | | 2N5730 | | | 16 |
| BUY20 | S | N | TX | BUY58 | | | | | 16 |
| BUY21 | S | N | TX | BUY73 | | | | | 16 |
| BUY21A | S | N | TX | BUY74 | | | | | 16 |
| BUY22 | S | N | TX | BUY75 | | | | | 16 |
| BUY23 | S | N | TX | BUY75 | | | | | 16 |
| BUY23A | S | N | TX | BUY76 | | | | | 16 |
| BUY23B | S | N | TX | BUY76 | | | | | 16 |
| BUY24 | S | N | SG, AT | (BUY55) | | 2N5068 | 2N5069 | | 16 |
| BUY26 | S | N | S | | | 2N3442 | | | 16 |
| BUY35 | S | N | S | | | 2N6511 | | | 16 |
| BUY38 | S | N | AT | | | 2N3054 | | | 16 |
| BUY38-4 | S | N | AT | | | 2N3054 | | | 16 |
| BUY38-5 | S | N | AT | | | 2N3054 | | | 16 |
| BUY38-6 | S | N | AT | | | 2N3054 | | | 16 |
| BUY38-7 | S | N | AT | | | 2N3054 | | | 16 |
| BUY43 | S | N | S | BDY71 | | 2N3054 | | | 16 |
| BUY43-6 | S | N | S | | | 2N3054 | | | 16 |
| BUY43-10 | S | N | S | | | 2N3054 | | | 16 |
| BUY43-16 | S | N | S | | | 2N3054 | | | 16 |
| BUY44 | S | N | S | BU110 | | | | | 16 |
| BUY46 | S | N | AT, S, MO | | | 2N3054 | 2N3045 | | 16 |
| BUY46-4 | S | N | AT, S | | | 2N3054 | | | 16 |
| BUY46-6 | S | N | AT, S | | | 2N3054 | | | 16 |
| BUY48 | S | N | AT | BUY47 | | | | | 16 |
| BUY51A | S | N | TX | | | 2N3772 | | | 16 |
| BUY55 | S | N | S | | | 2N5239 | | | 16 |
| BUY56 | S | N | S | | | 2N5239 | | | 16 |
| BUY60 | S | N | TX | | | 2N3439 | | | 16 |
| BUY66 | S | N | TX | BUY74 | BU126 | | | | 16 |
| BUY67 | S | N | TX | BUY74 | BU126 | | | | 16 |
| BUY68 | S | N | SG, AT | | | 2N4895 | 2N4896 | | 16 |
| BUY69 | S | N | TX | (BUY76) | | | | | 16 |
| BUY69A | S | N | TX | (BUY76) | | | | | 16 |
| BUY69B | S | N | TX | BUY76 | BU126 | | | | 16 |
| BUY69C | S | N | TX | BUY75 | BU126 | | | | 16 |
| BUY70 | S | N | TX | (BUY76) | | | | | 16 |
| BUY70A | S | N | TX | (BUY76) | | | | | 16 |
| BUY70B | S | N | TX | BUY76 | BU126 | | | | 16 |
| BUY70C | S | N | TX | BUY75 | BU126 | | | | 16 |
| BUY71 | S | N | TX | (BU208) | | | | | 16 |
| BUY72 | S | N | S | | | 2N5239 | | | 16 |
| BUY74 | S | N | S | BUX18A | | | | | 16 |
| BUY75 | S | N | S | BUX18C | | | | | 16 |
| BUY76 | S | N | S | BU126 | | | | | 16 |
| BUY77 | S | N | S | BUX18A | | | | | 16 |
| BUY78 | S | N | S | BUX18C | | | | | 16 |
| BUY79 | S | N | S | BU126 | | | | | 16 |
| BUY84 | S | N | AT | BUY76 | | | | | 16 |
| BUY85 | S | N | AT | BUY75 | | | | | 16 |
| C94 | SF | N | SL | | | 2N5457 | | | |
| C94E | SF | N | SL | | | 2N5457 | | | |
| C95 | SF | N | SL | | | 2N5457 | | | |
| C95A | SF | N | SL | | | 2N5457 | | | |
| C95E | SF | N | SL | | | 2N5459 | | | |
| C96E | SF | N | SL | | | 2N5459 | | | |
| C413N | J | N | CR | | | 2N4091 | 2N4859 | | |
| C413N | | | | | | 2N6451 | | | |
| C413E | J | N | | | | MPF4391 | | | |
| C610 | J | N | | | | 2N4092 | | | |
| C611 | J | N | | | | MFE2095 | 2N5360 | | |
| C612 | J | N | | | | MFE2095 | 2N5360 | | |

| TYPE | M/S | POL | MANUFAC | EUROPEAN | | AMERICAN | | JAPANESE | USE |
|------|-----|-----|---------|----------|--|----------|--|----------|-----|
| C613 | J | N | | | | MFE2095 | 2N5360 | | |
| C614 | J | N | | | | MFE2093 | 2N5360 | | |
| C615 | J | N | | | | MFE2095 | 2N5360 | | |
| C620 | J | N | | | | MFE2093 | 2N5358 | | |
| C621 | J | N | | | | MFE2093 | 2N5358 | | |
| C622 | J | N | | | | MFE2093 | 2N5358 | | |
| C623 | J | N | | | | MFE2093 | 2N5358 | | |
| C624 | J | N | | | | MFE2093 | 2N5358 | | |
| C625 | J | N | | | | MFE2093 | 2N5358 | | |
| C650 | J | N | | | | MFE2093 | 2N5358 | | |
| C651 | J | N | SG | | | MFE2093 | 2N5358 | | |
| C652 | J | N | SG | | | MFE2093 | 2N5358 | | |
| C653 | J | N | | | | MFE2093 | 2N5358 | | |
| C673 | J | N | | | | MFE2093 | 2N5358 | | |
| C674 | J | N | | | | 2N5361 | TN4341 | | |
| C680 | J | N | CR | | | MFE2093 | TN4338 | | |
| C680A | J | N | CR | | | MFE2093 | TN4338 | | |
| C681 | J | N | CR | | | MFE2093 | TN4338 | | |
| C681A | J | N | CR | | | MFE2093 | TN4338 | | |
| C682 | J | N | CR | | | MFE2094 | 2N3460 | | |
| C682A | J | N | CR | | | MFE2094 | 2N3460 | | |
| C683 | J | N | CR | | | MFE2094 | 2N2460 | | |
| C683A | J | N | CR | | | MFE2094 | 2N3460 | | |
| C684 | J | N | CR | | | MFE2095 | 2N3459 | | |
| C684A | J | N | CR | | | MFE2095 | 2N3459 | | |
| C685 | J | N | CR | | | MFE2095 | 2N3459 | | |
| C685A | J | N | CR | | | MFE2095 | 2N3459 | | |
| C6690 | J | N | CR | | | 2N4220 | 2N3458 | | |
| C6691 | J | N | CR | | | 2N4220 | 2N3458 | | |
| C6692 | J | N | CR | | | MFE2095 | 2N3459 | | |
| CDT1310 | G | P | ST, KS | (AUY21IV) | | | | | 06 |
| CDT1311 | G | P | ST, KS, IN | (AUY22IV) | AUY21IV | | | | 06 |
| CDT1311 | | | | ASZ17 | AD131 | | | | 06 |
| CDT1311 | | | | AUY28 | AD151 | | | | 06 |
| CDT1311 | | | | ASZ18 | | | | | 06 |
| CDT1312 | G | P | ST, KS | (AUY22IV) | | | | | 06 |
| CDT1313 | G | P | KS | AUY22IV | AD132 | 2N1100 | | | |
| CDT1313 | | | | ASZ16 | ASZ15 | | | | |
| CDT1313 | | | | ASZ18 | | | | | |
| CDT1319 | G | P | ST, KS | (AUY21III) | | | | | |
| CDT1320 | G | P | ST, KS | (AUY22III) | | | | | |
| CDT1321 | G | P | ST, KS | (AUY22III) | | | | | |
| CF2386 | SF | N | CR | | | 2N5459 | | | |
| CK13 | G | P | | ASY27 | | | | | |
| CK14 | G | P | | | | 2N1307 | | | |
| CK17 | G | P | | | | 2N1309 | | | |
| CK22 | G | P | | AC125 | | | | | |
| CK65 | G | P | | ASY27 | | | | | |
| CK66 | G | P | | AC125 | | | | | |
| CK721 | G | P | | AC125 | AC126 | 2N2429 | | | |
| CK721 | | | | OC71 | | | | | |
| CK722 | G | P | | AC125 | AC126 | 2N2429 | | | |
| CK722 | | | | OC71 | | | | | |
| CK724 | G | P | | AC125 | AC126 | 2N2429 | | | |
| CK725 | G | P | | AC125 | AC126 | 2N2429 | | | |
| CK725 | | | | OC71 | | | | | |
| CK727 | G | P | | AC125 | AC126 | 2N2429 | | | |
| CK727 | | | | OC71 | | | | | |
| CK751 | G | P | | AC128 | AC132 | 2N2431 | 2N281 | | |
| CK751 | | | | OC72 | | | | | |
| CK759 | G | P | | AF127 | AF185 | | | | |
| CK759 | | | | OC45 | | | | | |
| CK760 | G | P | | AF127 | AF185 | | | | |
| CK760 | | | | OC45 | | | | | |
| CK761 | G | P | | AF126 | AF127 | | | | |
| CK761 | | | | AF185 | | | | | |
| CK762 | G | P | | AF126 | AF185 | | | | |
| CK762 | | | | OC44 | | | | | |
| CK766 | G | P | | AF126 | AF185 | | | | |
| CK766 | | | | OC44 | | | | | |
| CK766A | G | P | | AF126 | AF185 | | | | |
| CK766A | | | | OC44 | | | | | |
| CK790 | S | P | | BCZ10 | | | | | |
| CK791 | S | P | | BCZ11 | | | | | |
| CK793 | G | P | | ASY77 | OC77 | | | | |

| TYPE | M/S | POL | MANUFAC | EUROPEAN | | AMERICAN | | JAPANESE | USE |
|------|-----|-----|---------|----------|---|----------|---|----------|-----|
| CK870 | G | P | | AC125 | AC126 | 2N2429 | | | |
| CK871 | G | P | | AC125 | AC126 | 2N2429 | | | |
| CK872 | G | P | | AC128 | AC132 | 2N2431 | | | |
| CK872 | | | | OC72 | | | | | |
| CK878 | G | P | | AC128 | OC74 | 2N2431 | | | |
| CK882 | G | P | | AC128 | AC312 | 2N2431 | | | |
| CK882 | | | | OC72 | | | | | |
| CK888 | G | P | | AC128 | AC132 | 2N2431 | | | |
| CK888 | | | | OC72 | | | | | |
| CK891 | G | P | | AC125 | | | | | |
| CK892 | G | P | | AC125 | | | | | |
| CK896 | G | P | | OC57 | | | | | |
| CK896A | G | P | | OC57 | OC58 | | | | |
| CK897 | G | P | | OC58 | | | | | |
| CK897A | G | P | | OC58 | | | | | |
| CK898 | G | P | | OC59 | | | | | |
| CK898A | G | P | | OC59 | OC77 | | | | |
| CL1020 | | | | | | TCR5297 | | | |
| CL1520 | | | | | | TCR5302 | | | |
| CL2210 | | | | | | TCR5283 | | | |
| CL2220 | | | | | | TCR5306 | | | |
| CL3310 | | | | | | TCR5287 | | | |
| CL3320 | | | | | | TCR5310 | | | |
| CL4710 | | | | | | TCR5290 | | | |
| CL4720 | | | | | | TCR5314 | | | |
| CL6810 | | | | | | TCR5293 | | | |
| CLT2010 | P | N | CL | | | TIL81 | | | |
| CLT2020 | P | N | CL | | | TIL81 | | | |
| CLT2030 | P | N | CL | | | TIL81 | | | |
| CLT2130 | P | N | CL | | | TIL81 | | | |
| CLT2140 | P | N | CL | | | TIL81 | | | |
| CLT2150 | P | N | CL | | | TIL81 | | | |
| CLT2160 | P | N | CL | | | TIL81 | | | |
| CLT3020 | P | N | CL | | | TIL605 | | | |
| CLT3030 | P | N | CL | | | TIL606 | | | |
| CLT3160 | P | N | CL | | | TIL602 | | | |
| CLT3170 | P | N | CL | | | TIL604 | | | |
| CLT4020 | P | N | CL | | | TIL613 | | | |
| CLT4030 | P | N | CL | | | TIL614 | | | |
| CLT4160 | P | N | CL | | | TIL610 | | | |
| CLT4170 | P | N | CL | | | TIL612 | | | |
| CM600 | J | N | CR | | | 2N4392 | 2N4857 | | |
| CM601 | J | N | CR | | | 2N4091 | 2N4856 | | |
| CM601 | | | | | | 2N4092 | | | |
| CM602 | J | N | CR | | | 2N4091 | 2N4856 | | |
| CM602 | | | | | | 2N4092 | | | |
| CM603 | J | N | CR | | | 2N4091 | 2N4856 | | |
| CM640 | SF | N | CR | | | 2N3824 | 2N4093 | | |
| CM641 | SF | N | CR | | | 2N4393 | 2N4858 | | |
| CM641 | | | | | | 2N4093 | | | |
| CM642 | SF | N | CR | | | 2N4092 | 2N4858 | | |
| CM643 | SF | N | CR | | | 2N4391 | 2N4857 | | |
| CM643 | | | | | | 2N4091 | | | |
| CM644 | SF | N | CR | | | 2N4092 | 2N4858 | | |
| CM644 | | | | | | 2N4093 | | | |
| CM645 | SF | N | CR | | | 2N4092 | 2N4857 | | |
| CM646 | SF | N | CR | | | 2N4091 | 2N4856 | | |
| CM646 | | | | | | 2N4092 | | | |
| CM647 | SF | N | CR | | | 2N4391 | 2N4856 | | |
| CM650 | J | N | | | | MFE2012 | 2N4446 | | |
| CM651 | J | N | | | | MFE2012 | SFC1784 | | |
| CM651 | | | | | | 2N4446 | | | |
| CM652 | J | N | | | | SFC1783 | | | |
| CM653 | J | N | | | | SFC1785 | | | |
| CM697 | J | N | CR | | | MPF4392 | | | |
| CM710 | P | | | | | TIL132sp | | | |
| CM712 | P | | | | | TIL135 | | | |
| CMX740 | SF | N | CR | | | MPF4391 | | | |
| CP650 | SF | N | CR, IL | | | 2N3970 | MPF4391 | | |
| CP650 | | | | | | 2N5432 | | | |
| CP651 | J | N | CR, IL | | | 2N3970 | MPF4391 | | |
| CP651 | | | | | | 2N5433 | | | |
| CP652 | J | N | CR, IL | | | 2N3970 | MPF4392 | | |
| CP652 | | | | | | 2N4447 | | | |
| CP653 | J | N | CR, IL | | | 2N4091 | MPF4392 | | |

| TYPE | M/S | POL | MANUFAC | EUROPEAN | | AMERICAN | | JAPANESE | USE |
|---|---|---|---|---|---|---|---|---|---|
| CP653 | | | | | | 2N4448 | | | |
| CR022 | J | | | | | TCR5283 | | | |
| CR024 | J | | | | | TCR5284 | | | |
| CR027 | J | | | | | TCR5285 | | | |
| CR030 | J | | | | | TCR5286 | | | |
| CR033 | J | | | | | TCR5287 | | | |
| CR039 | J | | | | | TCR5288 | | | |
| CR043 | J | | | | | TCR5289 | | | |
| CR047 | J | | | | | TCR5290 | | | |
| CR056 | J | | | | | TCR5291 | | | |
| CR062 | J | | | | | TCR5292 | | | |
| CR068 | J | | | | | TCR5293 | | | |
| CR075 | J | | | | | TCR5294 | | | |
| CR082 | J | | | | | TCR5295 | | | |
| CR091 | J | | | | | TCR5296 | | | |
| CR100 | J | | | | | TCR5297 | | | |
| CR110 | J | | | | | TCR5298 | | | |
| CR120 | J | | | | | TCR5299 | | | |
| CR130 | J | | | | | TCR5300 | | | |
| CR140 | J | | | | | TCR5301 | | | |
| CR150 | J | | | | | TCR5302 | | | |
| CR160 | J | | | | | TCR5303 | | | |
| CR180 | J | | | | | TCR5304 | | | |
| CR200 | J | | | | | TCR5305 | | | |
| CR220 | J | | | | | TCR5306 | | | |
| CR240 | J | | | | | TCR5307 | | | |
| CR270 | J | | | | | TCR5308 | | | |
| CR300 | J | | | | | TCR5309 | | | |
| CR330 | J | | | | | TCR5310 | | | |
| CR360 | J | | | | | TCR5311 | | | |
| CR430 | J | | | | | TCR5313 | | | |
| CR470 | J | | | | | TCR5314 | | | |
| CS1654 | S | N | | BC338 | | | | | |
| CS1655 | S | N | | BF494 | | | | | |
| CS1660 | S | N | | BF494 | | | | | |
| CS1744 | S | N | | BC548 | | | | | |
| CS9003 | S | N | | BC547 | | | | | |
| CS9010 | S | N | | BC547B | | | | | |
| CS9011 | S | N | | BC547B | | | | | |
| CS9011H | S | N | | BF494 | | | | | |
| CS9013 | S | N | | BC547B | | | | | |
| CS9014 | S | N | | BC548 | | | | | |
| CS9015 | S | P | | BC558 | | | | | |
| CS9016 | S | N | | BF495 | | | | | |
| CS9017 | S | N | | BF495 | | | | | |
| CS9018 | S | N | | BF495 | | | | | |
| CS9021D | S | N | | BF495 | | | | | |
| CS9021E | S | N | | BF495 | | | | | |
| CS9021F | S | N | | BC549 | | | | | |
| CS9022 | S | N | | BC549B | | | | | |
| CS9126 | S | N | | BC548 | | | | | |
| CS9127 | S | N | | BC558 | | | | | |
| CTP1002 | G | P | IN | (AD131III) | ASZ15 | | | | |
| CTP1003 | G | P | IN | (AD131III) | | | | | |
| CTP1003 | | | | OC28 | | | | | |
| CTP1004 | G | P | IN | (AD131III) | AD149 | 2N2836 | | | |
| CTP1004 | | | | OC26 | | | | | |
| CTP1005 | G | P | IN | (AD131III) | AD149 | 2N2836 | | | |
| CTP1005 | | | | OC26 | OC27 | | | | |
| CTP1006 | G | P | IN | (AD131III) | ASZ16 | | | | |
| CTP1006 | | | | OC29 | | | | | |
| CTP1032 | G | P | IN | (AC151IV) | AC125 | 2N2429 | | | |
| CTP1032 | | | | AC126 | | | | | |
| CTP1033 | G | P | IN | (AC151IV) | AC125 | 2N2429 | | | |
| CTP1033 | | | | AC126 | | | | | |
| CTP1034 | G | P | IN | (AC151V) | AC125 | 2N2429 | | | |
| CTP1034 | | | | AC126 | | | | | |
| CTP1035 | G | P | IN | (AC151V) | AC125 | 2N2429 | | | |
| CTP1035 | | | | AC126 | | | | | |
| CTP1036 | G | P | IN | (AC151VI) | AC126 | 2N2429 | | | |
| CTP1102 | G | P | IN | (AUY19IV) | | | | | |
| CTP1104 | G | P | IN | AD130III | OC26 | 2N2062A | 2N2836 | | |
| CTP1104 | | | | AD149 | OC30 | | | | |
| CTP1106 | G | P | IN | (AUY19V) | | | | | |
| CTP1108 | G | P | IN | AD130IV | AD130III | 2N2061A | 2N2836 | | |

| TYPE | M/S | POL | MANUFAC | EUROPEAN | | AMERICAN | | JAPANESE | USE |
|------|-----|-----|---------|----------|----|----------|----|----------|-----|
| CTP1108 | G | P | IN | OC26 | AD130 | | | | |
| CTP1108 | | | | AD149 | | | | | |
| CTP1109 | G | P | IN | AD130V | AD150IV | 2N2061A | 2N2836 | | |
| CTP1109 | | | | OC26 | AD130III | | | | |
| CTP1109 | | | | AD149 | AD150 | | | | |
| CTP1109 | | | | TI156 | | | | | |
| CTP1111 | G | P | IN | (AUY21III) | ASZ15 | 2N2065A | | 2SB472 | |
| CTP1111 | | | | AD132II | AD131 | | | | |
| CTP1111 | | | | AD132III | | | | | |
| CTP1112 | G | P | IN | (AD163III) | | | | | |
| CTP1117 | G | P | IN | (AD131III) | | | | | |
| CTP1119 | G | P | IN | (AD131III) | | | | | |
| CTP1127 | G | P | IN | (AD162III) | | | | | |
| CTP1133 | G | P | IN | (AD131III) | | | | | |
| CTP1135 | G | P | IN | (AD131III) | | | | | |
| CTP1137 | G | P | IN | (AD131III) | | | | | |
| CTP1265 | G | P | IN | (AUY21IV) | | | | | |
| CTP1266 | G | P | IN | (AUY21IV) | | | | | |
| CTP1296 | G | P | IN | (AUY22IV) | | | | | |
| CTP1297 | G | P | IN | (AUY22IV) | | | | | |
| CTP1306 | G | P | IN | (AUY21IV) | | | | | |
| CTP1307 | G | P | IN | (AUY21IV) | | | | | |
| CTP1320 | G | P | IN | (AC151IV) | AC125 | 2N2429 | | | |
| CTP1320 | | | | AC126 | | | | | |
| CTP1330 | G | P | IN | (AC151IV) | AC125 | 2N2429 | | | |
| CTP1330 | | | | AC126 | | | | | |
| CTP1340 | G | P | IN | (AC151IV) | AC125 | 2N2429 | | | |
| CTP1340 | | | | AC126 | | | | | |
| CTP1350 | G | P | IN | (AC151V) | AC125 | 2N2429 | | | |
| CTP1350 | | | | AC126 | | | | | |
| CTP1360 | G | P | IN | (AC151VI) | AC126 | 2N2429 | | | |
| CTP1390 | G | P | IN | (AC121IV) | AF127 | | | | |
| CTP1390 | | | | AF185 | OC45 | | | | |
| CTP1400 | G | P | IN | (AC121V) | AF127 | | | | |
| CTP1400 | | | | AF185 | OC45 | | | | |
| CTP1410 | G | P | IN | (AC121VI) | AF126 | | | | |
| CTP1410 | | | | AF185 | OC44 | | | | |
| CTP1500 | G | P | KS | AUY22III | AD138 | 2N1100 | 2N1556 | | 06 |
| CTP1500 | | | | ASZ16 | ADZ12 | | | | 06 |
| CTP1500 | | | | AUY21 | | | | | 06 |
| CTP1503 | G | P | KS | AUY22III | AD104 | 2N1100 | 2N1555 | | 06 |
| CTP1503 | | | | ASZ16 | AD138 | | | | 06 |
| CTP1503 | | | | ADZ12 | | | | | 06 |
| CTP1504 | G | P | IN, ST, KS | AD153III | (AUY22IV) | 2N1554 | | | |
| CTP1504 | | | | AUY21III | AD133 | | | | |
| CTP1504 | | | | AUY28 | AD138 | | | | |
| CTP1504 | | | | ASZ18 | | | | | |
| CTP1505 | G | P | IN | (AUY29III) | | | | | |
| CTP1506 | G | P | IN | (AUY29IV) | | | | | |
| CTP1507 | G | P | IN | (AUY29III) | | | | | |
| CTP1508 | G | P | IN, ST, KS | AD138 | (AUY21IV) | 2N1553 | | | |
| CTP1508 | | | | AD133III | AD133 | | | | |
| CTP1508 | | | | ADZ11 | AD136 | | | | |
| CTP1509 | G | P | IN | (AUY29III) | ADZ12 | | | | |
| CTP1513 | G | P | IN | (AUY29V) | | | | | |
| CTP1514 | G | P | IN | (AUY29V) | AD149 | 2N2836 | | | |
| CTP1514 | | | | OC26 | | | | | |
| CTP1550 | G | P | IN | (AUY21IV) | | | | | |
| CTP1551 | G | P | IN | (AUY22IV) | ASZ15 | | | | |
| CTP1728 | G | P | IN | (AUY19IV) | | | | | |
| CTP1729 | G | P | IN | (AUY20IV) | | | | | |
| CTP1730 | G | P | IN | (AUY34IV) | | | | | |
| CTP1731 | G | P | IN | (AUY19V) | | | | | |
| CTP1732 | G | P | IN | (AUY20V) | | | | | |
| CTP1733 | G | P | IN | (AUY34V) | | | | | |
| CTP1735 | G | P | IN | (AUY19V) | | | | | |
| CTP1736 | G | P | IN | (AUY19V) | | | | | |
| CTP1739 | G | P | IN | (AUY19III) | | | | | |
| CTP3500 | G | P | KS | ADZ12 | | | | | 06 |
| CTP3503 | G | P | KS | ADZ12 | | | | | 06 |
| CTP3504 | G | P | IN, ST, KS | (AUY22IV) | | | | | 06 |
| CTP3508 | G | P | IN, ST, KS | (AUY21IV) | | | | | 06 |
| CTP3550 | G | P | IN | (AUY21IV) | | | | | |
| CTP3551 | G | P | IN | (AUY22IV) | | | | | |
| CV2389 | G | P | UK | GET114 | V10/30A | | | | |

| TYPE | M/S | POL | MANUFAC | EUROPEAN | | AMERICAN | JAPANESE | USE |
|---|---|---|---|---|---|---|---|---|
| CV2389 | | | | OC71 | | | | |
| CV2400 | G | P | UK | GET106 | V10/30A | | | |
| CV2400 | | | | OC71 | | | | |
| CV5105 | G | P | UK | OC45 | | | | |
| CV5321 | G | P | UK | | | 2N456 | | |
| | | | | | | | | |
| CV5328 | G | P | UK | OC35X2 | | | | |
| CV5329 | G | P | UK | OC28X2 | | | | |
| CV5334 | S | P | UK | OC450 | | | | |
| CV5337 | G | P | UK | OC73 | | | | |
| CV5352 | G | P | UK | OC47C | | | | |
| | | | | | | | | |
| CV5359 | G | P | UK | XS101 | | | | |
| CV5411 | G | P | UK | GET110X | | | | |
| CV5416 | G | P | UK | OC84 | | | | |
| CV5439 | G | P | UK | OC75 | | | | |
| CV5445 | G | P | UK | NKT203 | | | | |
| | | | | | | | | |
| CV5457 | G | P | UK | ASZ20 | OC70 | | | |
| CV5459 | G | P | UK | GET104 | | | | |
| CV5465 | G | P | UK | | | 2N512A | | |
| CV5620 | G | N | UK | | | 2N78 | | |
| CV5621 | G | N | UK | | | 2N144/13 | | |
| | | | | | | | | |
| CV5622 | G | P | UK | | | 2N158 | | |
| CV5623 | G | P | UK | | | 2N247 | | |
| CV5624 | G | P | UK | | | 2N274 | | |
| CV5625 | S | N | UK | | | 2N332 | | |
| CV5626 | S | N | UK | | | 2N337 | | |
| | | | | | | | | |
| CV5627 | S | N | UK | | | 2N339 | | |
| CV5628 | G | P | UK | | | 2N344 | | |
| CV5629 | G | P | UK | | | 2N357 | | |
| CV5630 | G | P | UK | | | 2N384 | | |
| CV5631 | G | P | UK | | | 2N404 | | |
| | | | | | | | | |
| CV5632 | G | P | UK | | | 2N457 | | |
| CV5633 | G | P | UK | | | 2N458 | | |
| CV5634 | U | PN | UK | | | 2N489 | | |
| CV5635 | U | PN | UK | | | 2N491 | | |
| CV5636 | S | N | UK | | | 2N498 | | |
| | | | | | | | | |
| CV5637 | S | N | UK | | | 2N452 | | |
| CV5638 | S | N | UK | | | 2N550 | | |
| CV5639 | G | N | UK | | | 2N585 | | |
| CV5640 | G | P | UK | | | 2N527 | | |
| CV5641 | G | P | UK | | | 2N651 | | |
| | | | | | | | | |
| CV5642 | G | P | UK | | | 2N670 | | |
| CV5643 | G | P | UK | | | 2N674 | | |
| CV5644 | S | N | UK | | | 2N697 | | |
| CV5645 | G | P | UK | | | 2N1044/1 | | |
| CV5646 | G | P | UK | | | 2N1100 | | |
| | | | | | | | | |
| CV5647 | S | P | UK | | | 2N1131 | | |
| CV5648 | S | N | UK | | | 2N1139 | | |
| CV5649 | G | P | UK | | | 2N1184 | | |
| CV5650 | S | P | UK | | | 2N1196 | | |
| CV5651 | G | P | UK | | | 2N1285 | | |
| | | | | | | | | |
| CV5652 | S | N | UK | | | 2N1149 | | |
| CV5653 | S | N | UK | | | 2N1150 | | |
| CV5654 | S | N | UK | | | 2N1152 | | |
| CV5655 | S | N | UK | | | 2N1155 | | |
| CV5661 | S | N | UK | | | 2N1253 | | |
| | | | | | | | | |
| CV5663 | G | P | UK | | | 2N502 | | |
| CV5703 | G | P | UK | | | 2N173 | | |
| CV5710 | G | P | UK | OC44 | | | | |
| CV5711 | G | P | UK | OC77 | | | | |
| CV5712 | G | P | UK | OC71 | | | | |
| | | | | | | | | |
| CV5713 | G | P | UK | OC72 | | | | |
| CV5733 | G | P | UK | | | 2N277 | | |
| CV5740 | S | P | UK | OC202 | | | | |
| CV5761 | S | P | UK | | | 2N1132 | | |
| CV5762 | G | P | UK | | | 2N601 | | |
| | | | | | | | | |
| CV5773 | G | P | UK | | | 2N174 | | |
| CV5774 | G | P | UK | GT35 | | | | |
| CV5775 | G | P | UK | | | 2N11368 | | |
| CV5776 | G | N | UK | | | 2N144/13 | | |
| CV5778 | G | P | UK | | | 2N525 | | |
| | | | | | | | | |
| CV5781 | G | N | UK | | | 2N35 | | |
| CV5782 | G | N | UK | | | 2N440 | | |
| CV5784 | G | N | UK | | | 2N377 | | |
| CV5785 | G | N | UK | | | 2N169A | | |
| CV5789 | S | N | UK | | | 2N333 | | |

| TYPE | M/S | POL | MANUFAC | EUROPEAN | | AMERICAN | | JAPANESE | USE |
|------|-----|-----|---------|----------|---|----------|---|----------|-----|
| CV5792 | S | N | UK | | | | | 2S702 | |
| CV5804 | G | P | UK | OC170 | | | | | |
| CV5806 | G | P | UK | | | 2N1123 | | | |
| CV5813 | G | P | UK | OC123 | | | | | |
| CV5814 | | | UK | TK300 | | | | | |
| CV5818 | S | P | UK | ASZ23 | | | | | |
| CV5826 | G | P | UK | OC206 | | | | | |
| CV5832 | G | P | UK | | | 2N599 | | | |
| CV5833 | G | P | UK | GET875 | | | | | |
| CV5844 | S | P | UK | OC201 | | | | | |
| CV5848 | S | P | UK | BCZ11 | | | | | |
| CV5849 | S | P | UK | OC202 | | | | | |
| CV5850 | S | P | UK | OC203 | | | | | |
| CV5851 | G | P | UK | GET573 | | | | | |
| CV5856 | G | P | UK | GET110 | | | | | |
| CV5857 | G | P | UK | OC42 | | | | | |
| CV5858 | G | P | UK | OC201 | | | | | |
| CV5860 | S | N | UK | ZT23 | | | | | |
| CV5861 | G | P | UK | | | 2G401 | | | |
| CV5863 | S | N | UK | ZT21 | | | | | |
| CV5865 | S | P | UK | OC205 | | | | | |
| CV5878 | G | P | UK | GET102 | | | | | |
| CV5879 | G | P | UK | GET111 | | | | | |
| CV5885 | | | UK | TK420 | | | | | |
| CV5887 | G | P | UK | | | 2N2048 | | | |
| CV5888 | G | P | UK | | | 2N2048 | | | |
| CV5902 | G | P | UK | GET104 | | | | 2S005 | |
| CV5909 | S | N | UK | | | | | | |
| CV5910 | S | N | UK | | | | | 2S109 | |
| CV5913 | S | N | UK | | | 2N1718 | | | |
| CV5942 | G | P | UK | | | 2N1742 | | | |
| CV5949 | S | P | UK | | | 2G220 | | | |
| CV5951 | S | P | UK | BCY32 | | | | | |
| CV5960 | S | N | UK | | | | | 2S002 | |
| CV5967 | G | P | UK | | | 2G403 | | | |
| CV5970 | S | P | UK | OC701K | | | | | |
| CV5974 | S | N | UK | | | | | 2S102 | |
| CV5975 | S | N | UK | | | | | 2S103 | |
| CV5978 | S | P | UK | | | 2N1255 | | | |
| CV5980 | S | P | UK | OC206 | | | | | |
| CV5994 | G | P | UK | | | 2G225 | | | |
| CV5995 | S | N | UK | | | | | 2S703 | |
| CV5996 | S | P | UK | | | 2N1744 | | | |
| CV7001 | G | P | UK | ACY31 | GET103 | 2G303 | | | |
| CV7002 | G | P | UK | GET116 | | 2G382 | | | |
| CV7003 | G | P | UK | ASY55 | OC44 | 2G302 | | | |
| CV7004 | G | P | UK | ASY54 | GET873 | | | | |
| CV7004 | | | | OC45 | | | | | |
| CV7005 | G | P | UK | GET103 | OC71 | 2G371 | 2N280 | | |
| CV7006 | G | P | UK | GET103 | OC72 | 2N281 | 2N374 | | |
| CV7006 | | | | V10/50A | | | | | |
| CV7007 | G | P | UK | GET111 | OC77 | 2G377 | | | |
| CV7008 | G | P | UK | GET106 | V10/50A | | | | |
| CV7009 | G | P | UK | GET110 | V60/201P | | | | |
| CV7010 | G | P | UK | OC16 | OC26 | 2N1314 | | | |
| CV7010 | | | | V30/30P | | | | | |
| CV7011 | G | P | UK | V60/30P | | | | | |
| CV7012 | G | P | UK | V60/30P | | | | | |
| CV7042 | G | P | UK | ASY63 | GET872 | 2G302 | TK298 | | |
| CV7043 | S | P | UK | BCZ10 | OC200 | | | 2S322 | |
| CV7044 | S | P | UK | BCZ11 | OC201 | | | 2S323 | |
| CV7054 | G | P | UK | OC23 | | | | | |
| CV7056 | S | N | UK | | | | | 2S002 | |
| CV7057 | S | N | UK | | | | | 2S003 | |
| CV7058 | S | N | UK | | | | | 2S004 | |
| CV7059 | S | N | UK | | | | | 2S005 | |
| CV7060 | S | N | UK | | | | | 2S014 | |
| CV7061 | S | N | UK | | | | | 2S012A | |
| CV7062 | S | N | UK | | | | | 2S017 | |
| CV7063 | S | N | UK | | | | | 2S018 | |
| CV7064 | S | N | UK | | | | | 2S019 | |
| CV7065 | S | N | UK | | | | | 2S020 | |
| CV7066 | S | N | UK | | | | | 2S013A | |
| CV7074 | G | P | UK | GET103 | | | | | |
| CV7075 | S | P | UK | OC201 | | | | 2S323 | |

| TYPE | M/S | POL | MANUFAC | EUROPEAN | | AMERICAN | JAPANESE | USE |
|------|-----|-----|---------|----------|---|----------|----------|-----|
| CV7080 | G | P | UK | GET571 | | | | |
| CV7081 | G | P | UK | GET572 | | | | |
| CV7082 | G | P | UK | GET573 | | | | |
| CV7083 | G | P | UK | NKT402 | OC29 | | | |
| CV7084 | G | P | UK | NKT404 | OC35 | | | |
| CV7085 | G | P | UK | NKT401 | OC28 | | | |
| CV7086 | G | P | UK | OC36 | | | | |
| CV7087 | G | P | UK | GET875 | | | | |
| CV7089 | G | P | UK | OC171 | | 2G306 | | |
| CV7107 | G | P | UK | ACY31 | | 2G401 | | |
| CV7111 | G | N | UK | OC139 | | | | |
| CV7112 | G | N | UK | OC140 | | | | |
| CV7117 | S | P | UK | OC203 | | | | |
| CV7118 | G | P | UK | XB114 | | | | |
| CV7131 | S | N | UK | ZT20 | | 2N1564 | | |
| CV7132 | S | N | UK | | | | | |
| CV7133 | S | N | UK | ZT21 | | 2N1565 | | |
| CV7134 | S | N | UK | ZT22 | | | | |
| CV7149 | S | P | UK | ZT23 | | 2N1564 | | |
| CV7151 | S | N | UK | BCY32 | | | 2S302 | |
| | | | | | | | 2S303 | |
| CV7152 | S | P | UK | | | | 2S301 | |
| CV7154 | S | N | UK | ZT43 | | | 2S103 | |
| CV7185 | G | P | UK | ASY66 | | | | |
| CV7186 | S | N | UK | ZT45 | | | | |
| CV7187 | S | N | UK | ZT46 | | | | |
| CV7188 | S | P | UK | OC205 | | | | |
| CV7321 | G | P | UK | OC72X2 | | | | |
| CV7326 | G | P | UK | GET111 | | 2G377 | | |
| CV7327 | G | P | UK | GET102 | | 2G371 | | |
| CV7328 | S | N | UK | | | | 2S104 | |
| CV7333 | S | N | UK | | | | 2S025 | |
| CV7334 | S | N | UK | | | | 2S026 | |
| CV7335 | G | N | UK | AFZ12 | | | | |
| CV7336 | S | N | UK | | | 2N743 | 2S131 | |
| CV7337 | S | N | UK | | | 2N744 | 2S131 | |
| CV7388 | G | P | UK | ASZ21 | | | | |
| CV7341 | S | P | UK | BCY32 | | | | |
| CV7342 | S | P | UK | BCY32 | | | 2S300 | |
| CV7343 | S | P | UK | BCY32 | | | 2S300 | |
| CV7344 | S | P | UK | BCY32 | | | 2S300 | |
| | | | | | | | 2S300 | |
| CV7345 | S | P | UK | BCY32 | | | 2S300 | |
| CV7346 | S | P | UK | BCY32 | | | 2S300 | |
| CV7348 | G | N | UK | | | 2N1302 | | |
| CV7349 | G | N | UK | | | 2N1304 | | |
| CV7350 | G | N | UK | | | 2N1306 | | |
| CV7351 | G | N | UK | | | 2N1308 | | |
| CV7352 | G | P | UK | | | 2N1303 | | |
| CV7353 | G | P | UK | | | 2N1305 | | |
| CV7354 | G | P | UK | | | 2N1307 | | |
| CV7355 | G | P | UK | | | 2N1309 | | |
| CV7361 | S | N | UK | BUY11 | | | | |
| CV7362 | S | N | UK | BSY25 | | | | |
| CV7363 | S | P | UK | BCZ11 | | 2N2217 | | |
| CV7365 | G | P | UK | GET115 | | | 2S305 | |
| CV7366 | S | P | UK | | | | | |
| | | | | | | | 2S305 | |
| CV7370 | G | P | UK | | | 2N501 | | |
| CV7371 | S | N | UK | ZT83 | | 2N2220 | | |
| CV7372 | G | N | UK | ZT84 | | 2N2221 | | |
| CV7373 | S | N | UK | ZT86 | | | | |
| CV7376 | G | P | UK | ACY17 | | | | |
| CV7379 | S | N | UK | | | 2N916 | | |
| CV7390 | G | P | UK | | | 2G102 | | |
| CV7392 | G | N | UK | GET116 | | | | |
| CV7393 | G | P | UK | | | 2N705 | | |
| CV7394 | G | P | UK | | | 2N711 | | |
| CV7396 | S | P | UK | | | | | |
| CV7404 | S | N | UK | | | | 2S307 | |
| CV7430 | S | N | UK | BSY26 | | 2N1893 | | |
| CV7431 | S | N | UK | BSY27 | | | | |
| CV7436 | G | P | UK | ACY18 | | 2N753 | | |
| CV7437 | G | P | UK | ACY19 | | | | |
| CV7438 | G | P | UK | ACY20 | | | | |
| CV7439 | G | P | UK | ACY21 | | | | |
| CV7440 | S | N | UK | BFY19 | | | | |
| CV7448 | G | P | UK | ASY60 | | 2N1613 | | |

| TYPE | M/S | POL | MANUFAC | EUROPEAN | | AMERICAN | | JAPANESE | USE |
|------|-----|-----|---------|----------|---|----------|---|----------|-----|
| CV7451 | S | N | UK | | | 2N1479 | | | |
| CV7452 | S | N | UK | | | 2N1480 | | | |
| CV7453 | S | N | UK | | | 2N1481 | | | |
| CV7454 | S | N | UK | | | 2N1482 | | | |
| CV7455 | S | N | UK | | | 2N1483 | | | |
| CV7456 | S | N | UK | | | 2N1484 | | | |
| CV7457 | S | N | UK | | | 2N1485 | | | |
| CV7458 | S | N | UK | | | 2N1486 | | | |
| CV7459 | S | P | UK | OC205 | | | | 2S300 | |
| CV7460 | G | P | UK | AUY10 | | | | | |
| CV7461 | S | N | UK | | | | | 2S103 | |
| CV7462 | S | P | UK | | | 2N2411 | | | |
| CV7463 | S | N | UK | | | 2N2412 | | | |
| CV7464 | S | N | UK | | | 2N706A | | | |
| CV7477 | S | N | UK | C63 | | | | | |
| CV7478 | S | N | UK | | | 2N918 | | | |
| CV7479 | S | N | UK | | | 2N2060 | | | |
| CV7480 | S | N | UK | | | 2N1511 | | | |
| CV7481 | S | N | UK | | | 2N1512 | | | |
| CV7482 | S | N | UK | | | 2N1513 | | | |
| CV7483 | G | P | UK | | | 2N1514 | | | |
| CV7490 | S | N | UK | BFY17 | | | | | |
| CV7491 | S | N | UK | BFY18 | | | | | |
| CV7492 | S | N | UK | | | 2N929 | | | |
| CV7493 | S | N | UK | | | 2N930 | | | |
| CV7494 | G | P | UK | OC20 | | | | | |
| CV7495 | S | N | UK | | | 2N696 | | | |
| CV7496 | S | N | UK | | | 2N697 | | | |
| CV7497 | S | N | UK | C64 | | | | | |
| CV7527 | S | N | UK | ZT1487 | | | | | |
| CV7528 | S | N | UK | ZT1488 | | | | | |
| CV7529 | S | N | UK | ZT1489 | | | | | |
| CV7530 | S | N | UK | ZT1490 | | | | | |
| CV7554 | S | N | UK | | | 2N2475 | | | |
| CV7555 | S | N | UK | | | 2N2369A | | | |
| CV7580 | S | P | UK | | | 2N1131 | | | |
| CV7581 | S | P | UK | | | 2N1132 | | | |
| CV7588 | S | N | UK | | | | | 2S104P | |
| CV7593 | S | N | UK | | | 2N2477 | | | |
| CV7594 | S | P | UK | | | 2N2894 | | | |
| CV7595 | S | P | UK | | | 2N3209 | | | |
| CV7596 | S | N | UK | | | | | 2S103 | |
| CV7597 | G | P | UK | | | 2N501 | | | |
| CV7598 | S | P | UK | | | | | 2S301 | |
| CV7602 | S | P | UK | ZT152 | | | | | |
| CV7603 | S | P | UK | ZT153 | | | | | |
| CV7604 | S | P | UK | ZT154 | | | | | |
| CV7605 | S | N | UK | | | 2N916 | | | |
| CV7606 | G | P | UK | ADZ11 | | | | | |
| CV7607 | G | P | UK | ADZ12 | | | | | |
| CV7608 | G | P | UK | ADY26 | | | | | |
| CV7609 | S | N | UK | BFY19 | | | | | |
| CV7610 | S | N | UK | BFY19 | | | | | |
| CV7627 | | | UK | BSX15 | | | | | |
| CV7628 | | | UK | BSX16 | | | | | |
| CV7629 | S | N | UK | | | | | 2S024 | |
| CV7630 | S | P | UK | | | 2N2696 | | | |
| CV7631 | S | P | UK | | | 2N2904 | 2N2927 | | |
| CV7632 | S | N | UK | ZT192 | | | | | |
| CV7633 | S | N | UK | ZT192 | | | | | |
| CV7639 | S | N | UK | ZT190 | | | | | |
| CV7644 | S | P | UK | ZT189 | | | | | |
| CV7646 | S | N | UK | | | 2N708 | | | |
| CV7647 | S | P | UK | | | | | 2S322 | |
| CV7648 | S | N | UK | BSY95A | | | | | |
| CV7669 | S | P | UK | | | 2N2904 | | | |
| CV7670 | S | P | UK | | | 2N2905 | | | |
| CV7671 | S | P | UK | | | 2N2904A | | | |
| CV7672 | S | P | UK | | | 2N2905A | | | |
| CV7673 | S | P | UK | | | 2N2906 | | | |
| CV7674 | S | P | UK | | | 2N2907 | | | |
| CV7675 | S | P | UK | | | 2N2906A | | | |
| CV7676 | S | P | UK | | | 2N2907A | | | |
| CV7722 | S | N | UK | BFY50 | | | | | |
| CV7723 | S | N | UK | BFY51 | | | | | |

| TYPE | M/S | POL | MANUFAC | EUROPEAN | | AMERICAN | | JAPANESE | USE |
|------|-----|-----|---------|----------|---|----------|---|----------|-----|
| CV7724 | S | N | UK | BFY52 | | | | | |
| CV7725 | S | N | UK | BFY50 | | | | | |
| CV7726 | S | N | UK | BFY51 | | | | | |
| CV7750 | S | N | UK | ZT81 | | | | | |
| CV7751 | | | UK | ZT811 | | | | | |
| CV7752 | S | N | UK | ZT82 | | | | | |
| CV7753 | S | P | UK | ZT182 | | | | | |
| CV7754 | S | N | UK | ZT87 | | | | | |
| CV7755 | S | P | UK | ZT187 | | | | | |
| CV8007 | S | P | UK | OC702K | | | | | |
| CV8015 | S | N | UK | | | | | 2S08 | |
| CV8111 | G | P | UK | GET105 | | | | | |
| CV8119 | G | N | UK | | | 2N1302 | | | |
| CV8126 | G | P | UK | NKT124 | | | | | |
| CV8130 | G | P | UK | ACY18 | | | | | |
| CV8150 | G | P | UK | GET880 | | | | | |
| CV8252 | G | P | UK | OC42 | | | | | |
| CV8259 | G | P | UK | ACY21 | | | | | |
| CV8288 | G | P | UK | TK13 | | | | | |
| CV8314 | G | P | UK | OC76 | | | | | |
| CV8315 | G | P | UK | OC44 | | | | | |
| CV8316 | G | P | UK | OC45 | | | | | |
| CV8322 | G | P | UK | | | 2G220X2 | | | |
| CV8333 | S | N | UK | | | 2N1492 | | | |
| CV8335 | G | P | UK | | | 2G210X2 | | | |
| CV8341 | G | P | UK | OC24 | | | | | |
| CV8342 | G | P | UK | OC28 | | | | | |
| CV8344 | G | P | UK | OC71 | | | | | |
| CV8345 | G | N | UK | OC140 | | | | | |
| CV8346 | G | P | UK | OC77 | | | | | |
| CV8347 | S | P | UK | OC201 | | | | | |
| CV8349 | S | P | UK | OC203 | | | | | |
| CV8354 | G | P | UK | OC170 | | | | | |
| CV8355 | G | P | UK | OC22 | | | | | |
| CV8356 | G | P | UK | OC29 | | | | | |
| CV8359 | G | P | UK | | | 2G306 | | | |
| CV8360 | S | N | UK | ZT23 | | | | | |
| CV8361 | G | P | UK | | | 2G104 | | | |
| CV8362 | G | P | UK | GET103 | | | | | |
| CV8363 | G | P | UK | GET102 | | | | | |
| CV8366 | G | P | UK | GET573 | | | | | |
| CV8368 | G | P | UK | | | 2G221 | | | |
| CV8369 | G | P | UK | | | 2G140 | | | |
| CV8370 | S | N | UK | | | | | 2S005 | |
| CV8371 | G | N | UK | | | 2N388 | | | |
| CV8372 | G | P | UK | | | 2G304 | | | |
| CV8373 | | | UK | | | | | 2S108 | |
| CV8389 | G | P | UK | OC71 | | | | | |
| CV8393 | S | P | UK | | | | | 2S301 | |
| CV8396 | S | N | UK | | | | | 2S026 | |
| CV8397 | G | N | UK | | | 2N1308 | | | |
| CV8398 | G | P | UK | | | 2N1307 | | | |
| CV8399 | G | P | UK | | | 2N1309 | | | |
| CV8400 | G | N | UK | | | 2G220 | | | |
| CV8414 | S | N | UK | DT1121 | | | | | |
| CV8415 | S | N | UK | DT1111 | | | | | |
| CV8416 | S | N | UK | DT1112 | | | | | |
| CV8417 | S | N | UK | | | | | 2S002 | |
| CV8421 | S | N | UK | | | | | 2S004 | |
| CV8422 | S | N | UK | | | | | 2S020 | |
| CV8424 | S | N | UK | DT4111 | | | | | |
| CV8425 | S | P | UK | OC450 | | | | | |
| CV8426 | S | P | UK | OC470 | | | | | |
| CV8427 | S | P | UK | OC470 | | | | | |
| CV8439 | G | P | UK | | | 2N174X2 | | | |
| CV8440 | G | P | UK | OC72 | | | | | |
| CV8447 | S | P | UK | OC200 | | | | | |
| CV8448 | G | P | UK | OC23 | | | | | |
| CV8451 | S | N | UK | | | | | 2S019 | |
| CV8453 | S | N | UK | | | | | 2S002 | |
| CV8455 | S | N | UK | | | | | 2S003 | |
| CV8467 | S | N | UK | | | 2N930 | | | |
| CV8473 | S | P | UK | | | | | 2S324X2 | |
| CV8480 | G | P | UK | OC36 | | | | | |
| CV8484 | S | N | UK | | | 2N1721 | | | |

| TYPE | M/S | POL | MANUFAC | EUROPEAN | AMERICAN | JAPANESE | USE |
|---|---|---|---|---|---|---|---|
| CV8500 | S | P | | | | 2S321 | |
| CV8501 | G | P | UK | NKT403 | | | |
| CV8509 | G | P | UK | | 2N441 | | |
| CV8541 | U | P | UK | | 2N1671A | | |
| CV8542 | S | N | UK | | 2N334A | | |
| CV8543 | S | P | UK | | 2N685 | | |
| CV8549 | S | P | UK | BCZ11 | | | |
| CV8551 | S | P | UK | OC480K | | | |
| CV8558 | G | P | UK | GET111 | | | |
| CV8559 | G | P | UK | NKT223 | | | |
| CV8560 | G | P | UK | OC26 | | | |
| CV8565 | S | P | UK | OC450K | | | |
| CV8568 | S | N | UK | | 2N916 | | |
| CV8582 | | | UK | GT42 | | | |
| CV8593 | G | P | UK | | 2N1536 | | |
| CV8597 | S | P | UK | | 2N876 | | |
| CV8598 | | | UK | | 2N877 | | |
| CV8600 | G | P | UK | | 2N396 | | |
| CV8601 | S | N | UK | | 2N719A | | |
| CV8602 | S | N | UK | | 2N1990 | | |
| CV8603 | S | N | UK | | 2N2297 | | |
| CV8607 | G | P | UK | GET113 | | | |
| CV8609 | S | N | UK | BFY16 | | | |
| CV8611 | S | N | UK | | | 2S024 | |
| CV8612 | S | N | UK | | | 2S323 | |
| CV8613 | S | N | UK | | | 2S712 | |
| CV8615 | S | N | UK | BSY95A | | | |
| CV8618 | G | P | UK | GET885 | | | |
| CV8635 | G | P | UK | AFZ11 | | | |
| CV8638 | G | P | UK | AFZ12A | | | |
| CV8639 | G | P | UK | AFZ12B | | | |
| CV8641 | G | P | UK | GET890 | | | |
| CV8642 | G | P | UK | GET887 | | | |
| CV8643 | S | N | UK | | | 2S701 | |
| CV8645 | S | N | UK | | | 2S017 | |
| CV8647 | S | N | UK | ZT92 | | | |
| CV8649 | S | N | UK | ZT86 | | | |
| CV8661 | G | P | UK | | 2N1204 | | |
| CV8662 | G | P | UK | | 2N1499A | | |
| CV8668 | G | P | UK | | 2N513A | | |
| CV8673 | G | P | UK | | 2G227 | | |
| CV8677 | | | UK | ZT227C | | | |
| CV8686 | G | P | UK | NKT401X2 | | | |
| CV8696 | S | N | UK | | | 2S711 | |
| CV8700 | | | UK | ASY64 | | | |
| CV8702 | G | P | UK | | 2N976 | | |
| CV8710 | S | N | UK | | 2N1889 | | |
| CV8712 | J | | UK | | 2N2398 | | |
| CV8718 | S | P | UK | BCY39 | | | |
| CV8722 | S | P | UK | | | 2S306 | |
| CV8723 | J | P | UK | | 2N2498 | | |
| CV8724 | G | P | UK | OC83 | | | |
| CV8725 | G | P | UK | | 2N257 | | |
| CV8728 | S | N | UK | | 2N715 | | |
| CV8729 | S | N | UK | | 2N706A | | |
| CV8756 | G | P | UK | OC122 | | | |
| CV8758 | S | P | UK | | 2N1720 | | |
| CV8760 | S | P | UK | BCY31 | | | |
| CV8762 | S | P | UK | | | 2S322 | |
| CV8765 | G | P | UK | NKT213 | | | |
| CV8767 | U | PN | UK | | 2N2160 | | |
| CV8775 | G | P | UK | ADZ12 | | | |
| CV8781 | S | N | UK | | | 2S020 | |
| CV8782 | S | N | UK | | | 2S026 | |
| CV8783 | S | P | UK | | | 2S304 | |
| CV8785 | G | P | UK | | 2N1309 | | |
| CV8786 | G | P | UK | | 2N1309 | | |
| CV8789 | G | P | UK | | 2N458AX2 | | |
| CV8792 | G | P | UK | CTP1109 | | | |
| CV8794 | G | P | UK | NKT226 | | | |
| CV8798 | G | N | UK | | 2N1302 | | |
| CV8799 | G | P | UK | | 2N1303 | | |
| CV8800 | G | P | UK | | 2N1184B | | |
| CV8801 | G | P | UK | NKT301 | | | |
| CV8802 | G | P | UK | NKT127 | | | |

| TYPE | M/S | POL | MANUFAC | EUROPEAN | | AMERICAN | | JAPANESE | USE |
|------|-----|-----|---------|----------|---|----------|---|----------|-----|
| CV8803 | G | P | UK | | | 2N268 | | | |
| CV8804 | G | P | UK | | | 2N1021 | | | |
| CV8806 | S | N | UK | | | 2N1481 | | | |
| CV8807 | S | P | UK | OC700 | | | | | |
| CV8810 | G | P | UK | NKT304 | | | | | |
| CV8817 | G | P | UK | | | 2N1692 | | | |
| CV8818 | S | N | UK | | | | | | |
| CV8819 | G | N | UK | | | 2N1030 | | 2S722 | |
| CV8826 | S | P | UK | OC203 | | | | | |
| CV8827 | S | N | UK | | | | | 2S017 | |
| CV8828 | G | P | UK | | | 2N677B | | | |
| CV8830 | S | P | UK | OC440 | | | | | |
| CV8831 | S | P | UK | OC460 | | | | | |
| CV8832 | G | P | UK | | | 2N499 | | | |
| CV8837 | G | N | UK | NKT713 | | | | | |
| CV8838 | G | P | UK | NKT32 | | | | | |
| CV8843 | S | N | UK | | | 2N1613 | | | |
| CV8844 | S | N | UK | | | 2N708 | | | |
| CV8845 | S | N | UK | | | 2N2223 | | | |
| CV8846 | S | P | UK | | | 2N869 | | | |
| CV8847 | S | P | UK | | | 2N995 | | | |
| CV8848 | G | P | UK | | | 2N227C | | | |
| CV8849 | G | P | UK | | | 2N1038 | | | |
| CV8850 | G | P | UK | | | 2N1907 | | | |
| CV8856 | S | P | UK | | | 2N1131 | | | |
| CV8857 | S | P | UK | | | 2N2233 | | | |
| CV8863 | S | N | UK | BLY12 | | | | | |
| CV8864 | G | P | UK | | | 2N645 | | | |
| CV8874 | S | N | UK | | | 2N2432 | | | |
| CV8875 | S | N | UK | | | 2N1410 | | | |
| CV8876 | S | N | UK | | | 2N1506 | | | |
| CV8881 | S | N | UK | | | 2N1716 | | | |
| CV8883 | S | N | UK | | | 2N2846 | | | |
| CV8886 | S | N | UK | | | | | 2S025 | |
| CV8887 | S | P | UK | | | | | 2S017X2 | |
| CV8889 | S | N | UK | | | 2N3055 | | | |
| CV8890 | S | N | UK | | | 2N3053 | | | |
| CV8891 | S | P | UK | OC701 | | | | | |
| CV8894 | S | P | UK | OC204 | | | | | |
| CV8899 | G | P | UK | | | 2N458X2 | | | |
| CV8901 | S | N | UK | | | 2N2739 | | | |
| CV8902 | S | N | UK | | | 2N3054 | | | |
| CV8903 | S | N | UK | | | 2N1016 | | | |
| CV8909 | S | N | UK | | | 2N708A | | | |
| CV8910 | S | N | UK | | | | | 2S025 | |
| CV8911 | S | N | UK | | | 2N1700 | | | |
| CV8913 | S | N | UK | | | 2N2218 | | | |
| CV8915 | S | N | UK | BFY19 | | | | | |
| CV8916 | S | N | UK | BSY26 | | | | | |
| CV8923 | G | N | UK | | | 2N444A | | | |
| CV8924 | G | P | UK | | | 2N456A | | | |
| CV8925 | G | P | UK | | | 2N457A | | | |
| CV8941 | S | N | UK | | | 2N1483 | | | |
| CV8942 | S | P | UK | | | | | | |
| CV8950 | S | P | UK | | | 2N1259 | | 2S303 | |
| CV8966 | G | N | UK | OC139 | | | | | |
| CV8968 | S | P | UK | | | 2N1254 | | | |
| CV8970 | S | P | UK | | | | | 2S302 | |
| CV8972 | S | P | UK | | | 2N2800 | | | |
| CV8979 | G | P | UK | | | 2N1396 | | | |
| CV8981 | J | | UK | | | 2N1742X2 | | | |
| CV8982 | G | P | UK | OC25 | | | | | |
| CV9000 | G | P | UK | | | 2N386 | | | |
| CV9001 | | | UK | ASY67 | | | | | |
| CV9002 | S | P | UK | | | | | 2S320 | |
| CV9004 | S | P | UK | | | 2N727 | | | |
| CV9008 | G | P | UK | | | 2N1907 | | | |
| CV9017 | S | N | UK | | | 2N1701 | | | |
| CV9020 | G | P | UK | | | 2N1225 | | | |
| CV9021 | S | P | UK | BSY25 | | | | | |
| CV9029 | S | P | UK | | | 2N721 | | | |
| CV9031 | G | N | UK | | | 2N797 | | | |
| CV9033 | S | N | UK | BUY11 | | | | | |
| CV9035 | S | N | UK | | | | | 2S721 | |
| CV9039 | G | P | UK | GET882 | | | | | |

| TYPE | M/S | POL | MANUFAC | EUROPEAN | | AMERICAN | | JAPANESE | USE |
|---|---|---|---|---|---|---|---|---|---|
| CV9040 | G | N | UK | ASY29 | | | | | |
| CV9047 | S | P | UK | | | 2N2894 | | | |
| CV9048 | S | P | UK | | | 2N2696 | | | |
| CV9055 | S | N | UK | | | 2N698 | | | |
| CV9058 | S | P | UK | | | | | 2S324 | |
| CV9059 | S | P | UK | BCY40 | | | | | |
| CV9068 | G | P | UK | OC71 | | | | | |
| CV9069 | G | P | UK | GET881 | | | | | |
| CV9070 | G | P | UK | GET889 | | | | | |
| CV9071 | G | P | UK | GET892 | | | | | |
| CV9074 | S | N | UK | BSY29 | | | | | |
| CV9075 | S | N | UK | | | 2N915 | | | |
| CV9083 | S | N | UK | | | 2N2243A | | | |
| CV9098 | G | P | UK | | | 2N458A | | | |
| CV9101 | S | N | UK | | | 2N2040 | | | |
| CV9104 | S | P | UK | BCY32X2 | | | | | |
| CV9106 | G | P | UK | GT46 | | | | | |
| CV9111 | G | P | UK | GT43 | | | | | |
| CV9114 | S | N | UK | | | | | 2S732 | |
| CV9128 | U | | UK | | | 2N494 | | | |
| CV9129 | S | N | UK | | | 2N1016B | | | |
| CV9139 | S | N | UK | | | 2N1893 | | | |
| CV9131 | S | N | UK | | | 2N2150 | | | |
| CV9132 | S | N | UK | | | 2N2219 | | | |
| CV9133 | S | N | UK | | | 2N2484 | | | |
| CV9134 | S | P | UK | | | 2N2905 | | | |
| CV9157 | S | P | UK | | | 2N1918 | | | |
| CV9177 | G | P | UK | | | 2G4035 | | | |
| CV9183 | G | P | UK | TS13 | | | | | |
| CV9184 | G | P | UK | | | 2N597 | | | |
| CV9190 | G | P | UK | NKT271 | | | | | |
| CV9192 | S | P | UK | | | 2N2905A | | | |
| CV9209 | S | N | UK | | | | | 2S018 | |
| CV9211 | S | N | UK | | | 2N706 | | | |
| CV9212 | S | N | UK | | | 2N703 | | | |
| CV9215 | S | N | UK | BSY95 | | | | | |
| CV9216 | S | N | UK | | | 2N3447 | | | |
| CV9218 | S | N | UK | | | 40251 | | | |
| CV9235 | G | P | UK | | | 2N711 | | | |
| CV9243 | | | UK | | | 4011C | | | |
| CV9247 | S | P | UK | BCY31 | | | | | |
| CV9249 | G | P | UK | | | 2G401 | | | |
| CV9250 | G | P | UK | | | 2N297 | | | |
| CV9251 | G | P | UK | | | 2N397 | | | |
| CV9255 | S | N | UK | | | 2N3553 | | | |
| CV9256 | S | N | UK | | | 2N3263 | | | |
| CV9258 | G | P | UK | GET103X2 | | | | | |
| CV9259 | G | P | UK | OC83 | | | | | |
| CV9261 | G | N | UK | | | 2N1304 | | | |
| CV9264 | G | P | UK | OC35 | | | | | |
| CV9266 | G | P | UK | GET538 | | | | | |
| CV9267 | G | P | UK | GET888 | | | | | |
| CV9290 | S | N | UK | | | 2N2893 | | | |
| CV9291 | S | N | UK | | | 2N914 | | | |
| CV9294 | | | UK | XK575 | | | | | |
| CV9296 | S | N | UK | | | 2N549 | | | |
| CV9300 | S | N | UK | | | 2N2021 | | | |
| CV9308 | G | P | UK | NKT405 | | | | | |
| CV9313 | G | P | UK | | | 2N525A | | | |
| CV9314 | U | | UK | | | 2N1671A | | | |
| CV9318 | G | P | UK | | | 2N1553 | | | |
| CV9320 | S | N | UK | | | 2N2368 | | | |
| CV9321 | S | N | UK | | | | | 2S104 | |
| CV9324 | G | P | UK | | | 2N6698 | | | |
| CV9342 | G | N | UK | NKT404 | | | | | |
| CV9347 | S | N | UK | | | SE3001 | | | |
| CV9351 | G | P | UK | AFZ12 | | | | | |
| CV9352 | U | | UK | | | 2N1671B | | | |
| CV9354 | S | P | UK | | | 2N2861 | | | |
| CV9359 | S | N | UK | BUY10 | | | | | |
| CV9360 | | | UK | BLY11 | | | | | |
| CV9364 | S | N | UK | | | 2N2223A | | | |
| CV9366 | S | P | UK | | | 2N3072 | | | |
| CV9367 | S | N | UK | | | 2N3442 | | | |
| CV9368 | S | N | UK | | | 2N2484 | | | |

| TYPE | M/S | POL | MANUFAC | EUROPEAN | AMERICAN | JAPANESE | USE |
|------|-----|-----|---------|----------|----------|----------|-----|
| CV9372 | G | P | UK | NKT218 | | | |
| CV9373 | G | P | UK | GET872 | | | |
| CV9375 | G | P | UK | ACY30 | | | |
| CV9378 | S | N | UK | BFX21 | | | |
| CV9379 | S | N | UK | BSY95A | | | |
| CV9384 | S | N | UK | | 2N3235 | | |
| CV9392 | J | N | UK | ZT2474 | | | |
| CV9395 | S | N | UK | | 2N2194 | | |
| CV9400 | S | N | UK | | 2N163 | | |
| CV9407 | G | P | UK | | 2N539 | | |
| CV9415 | G | P | UK | | 2G302 | | |
| CV9420 | S | P | UK | BCY18 | | | |
| CV9426 | S | S | UK | BFY50 | | | |
| CV9430 | S | P | UK | BCY30 | | | |
| CV9431 | S | P | UK | BCY34 | | | |
| CV9436 | S | N | UK | | 2N3441 | | |
| CV9437 | S | N | UK | | 2N3442 | | |
| CV9447 | G | P | UK | OC77 | | | |
| CV9449 | S | N | UK | | 2N3858X2 | | |
| CV9456 | G | P | UK | AU130 | | | |
| CV9457 | G | P | UK | ACY39 | | | |
| CV9463 | S | N | UK | | 2N1711 | | |
| CV9477 | S | N | UK | | 2N2338 | | |
| CV9481 | G | P | UK | | 2N1309 | | |
| CV9483 | G | P | UK | ACY20 | | | |
| CV9484 | G | P | UK | ACY17 | | | |
| CV9486 | S | N | UK | | 2N709 | | |
| CV9487 | G | P | UK | | 2N1534 | | |
| CV9496 | G | N | UK | | 2N1311 | | |
| CV9498 | G | P | UK | | 2N2656 | | |
| CV9508 | S | P | UK | BFY64 | | | |
| CV9512 | S | N | UK | | 2N2979 | | |
| CV9513 | J | S | UK | | 2N3278 | | |
| CV9515 | S | N | UK | | 2N2824 | | |
| CV9516 | S | P | UK | ZT211 | | | |
| CV9518 | S | P | UK | | 2N2890 | | |
| CV9526 | G | P | UK | | 2N1754 | | |
| CV9538 | S | P | UK | BCY54 | | | |
| CV9562 | S | N | UK | | 2N699 | | |
| CV9563 | G | P | UK | | 2N1305 | | |
| CV9564 | | | UK | | 2N1369A | | |
| CV9565 | S | N | UK | | 2S733 | | |
| CV9566 | S | P | UK | | 2S305 | | |
| CV9577 | G | P | UK | | 2N1531 | | |
| CV9578 | G | P | UK | | 2N1748A | | |
| CV9585 | S | N | UK | BFY20 | | | |
| CV9588 | S | P | UK | | 2N3906 | | |
| CV9589 | S | N | UK | | 40250 | | |
| CV9590 | S | N | UK | | 40231 | | |
| CV9602 | U | | UK | | 2N492A | | |
| CV9603 | S | N | UK | | 2N2892 | | |
| CV9604 | S | N | UK | | 2N2102 | | |
| CV9605 | J | | UK | | 2N3993 | | |
| CV9606 | J | | UK | | 2N3824 | | |
| CV9611 | G | P | UK | | 2N1147 | | |
| CV9623 | S | P | UK | | 2N3467 | | |
| CV9624 | S | N | UK | | 2N3252 | | |
| CV9628 | S | N | UK | | 2N3252 | | |
| CV9667 | S | N | UK | | 2N3236 | | |
| CV9668 | S | N | UK | | 2N706B | | |
| CV9669 | S | N | UK | | 2N2538 | | |
| CV9670 | G | P | UK | | 2N966 | | |
| CV9697 | S | N | UK | | 2N3108 | | |
| CV9699 | S | N | UK | | 2N2369 | | |
| CV9700 | G | P | UK | | 2N1147B | | |
| CV9701 | S | N | UK | | 2N3501 | | |
| CV9702 | S | P | UK | | 2N3637 | | |
| CV9703 | S | N | UK | | 2N1052 | | |
| CV9705 | S | N | UK | | 2N3503 | | |
| CV9706 | S | N | UK | | 2N3375 | | |
| CV9707 | S | N | UK | | 2N3478 | | |
| CV9716 | S | N | UK | | 2N3419 | | |
| CV9717 | S | N | UK | | 2N1506A | | |
| CV9719 | S | N | UK | ZT2876 | | | |
| CV9724 | S | N | UK | BSY26 | | | |

| TYPE | M/S | POL | MANUFAC | EUROPEAN | | AMERICAN | JAPANESE | USE |
|------|-----|-----|---------|----------|----|----------|----------|-----|
| CV9730 | G | P | UK | ASY26 | | | | |
| CV9734 | S | N | UK | | | 2N342 | | |
| CV9735 | S | N | UK | | | 2N341 | | |
| CV9736 | S | N | UK | | | 2N332 | | |
| CV9737 | S | N | UK | | | 2N333 | | |
| CV9741 | S | N | UK | | | 2N1488 | | |
| CV9742 | S | N | UK | | | 2N1483 | | |
| CV9760 | S | N | UK | ZT1483 | | | | |
| CV9761 | S | N | UK | ZT1484 | | | | |
| CV9762 | S | N | UK | ZT1485 | | | | |
| CV9763 | S | N | UK | ZT1486 | | | | |
| CV9766 | G | N | UK | | | 2N656 | | |
| CV9767 | G | P | UK | | | 2N174A | | |
| CV9777 | G | P | UK | AD161 | AD162 | | | |
| CV9778 | G | P | UK | AC126 | | | | |
| CV9780 | S | N | UK | BC107 | | | | |
| CV9786 | S | N | UK | | | 2N3584 | | |
| CV9791 | S | P | UK | | | 2N3121 | | |
| CV9792 | S | N | UK | | | 2N2193 | | |
| CV9793 | S | N | UK | | | 2N3418 | | |
| CV9794 | S | N | UK | BSX23 | | | | |
| CV9797 | G | P | UK | OC83X2 | | | | |
| CV9798 | G | P | UK | | | 2N1755 | | |
| CV9807 | G | P | UK | | | 2N2067 | | |
| CV9808 | S | N | UK | | | 2N1899 | | |
| CV9811 | G | P | UK | GM3788 | | | | |
| CV9815 | G | P | UK | OC20X2 | | | | |
| CV9829 | S | N | UK | | | 2N422 | | |
| CV9830 | S | N | UK | | | 2N917 | | |
| CV9831 | G | P | UK | | | 2N2287 | | |
| CV9832 | G | P | UK | | | 2N158A | | |
| CV9861 | S | N | UK | ZT1479 | | | | |
| CV9862 | S | N | UK | ZT1480 | | | | |
| CV9863 | S | N | UK | ZT1481 | | | | |
| CV9864 | S | N | UK | ZT1482 | | | | |
| CV9865 | S | N | UK | ZT1487 | | | | |
| CV9866 | S | N | UK | ZT1488 | | | | |
| CV9867 | S | N | UK | ZT1489 | | | | |
| CV9868 | S | N | UK | ZT1490 | | | | |
| CV9869 | S | N | UK | | | 2N1973 | | |
| CV9872 | S | N | UK | | | 2N2033 | | |
| CV9873 | U | | UK | | | 2N489 | | |
| CV9888 | S | N | UK | | | 2N3019 | | |
| CV9895 | S | N | UK | BSY11 | | | | |
| CV9909 | S | N | UK | | | 2N1016A | | |
| CV9913 | G | N | UK | | | 2N338 | | |
| CV9914 | S | P | UK | | | 2N1131A | | |
| CV9925 | G | P | UK | | | 2N711A | | |
| CV9927 | G | P | UK | OC71X2 | | | | |
| CV9928 | G | P | UK | OC44X2 | | | | |
| CV9939 | S | N | UK | BFY11 | | | | |
| CV9944 | G | P | UK | | | 2N526 | | |
| CV9955 | S | N | UK | BUY11 | | | | |
| CV9956 | S | N | UK | BFY18 | | | | |
| CV9957 | S | N | UK | BSY25 | | | | |
| CV9958 | S | N | UK | BSY27 | | | | |
| CV9959 | | | UK | ASY60 | | | | |
| CV9961 | G | P | UK | ASZ21 | | | | |
| CV9962 | S | N | UK | ZT43 | | | | |
| CV9975 | S | N | UK | | | 2N947 | | |
| CV9977 | S | N | UK | | | | 2S033 | |
| CV9978 | S | N | UK | | | | 2S034 | |
| CV9979 | S | N | UK | | | | 2S035 | |
| CV9980 | S | N | UK | | | | 2S036 | |
| CV9986 | S | N | UK | | | 2N335 | | |
| CV9988 | S | N | UK | | | 2N1647 | | |
| CV10018 | S | N | UK | | | 2N910 | | |
| CV10037 | G | P | UK | | | 2N10318 | | |
| CV10040 | S | N | UK | | | | 2S731 | |
| CV10044 | S | N | UK | | | 2N2916 | | |
| CV10046 | S | N | UK | | | 2N3866 | | |
| CV10047 | S | N | UK | | | 2N3632 | | |
| CV10048 | J | P | UK | | | 2N2497 | | |
| CV10053 | J | N | UK | ZFT14 | | | | |
| CV10060 | S | N | UK | | | 2N743 | | |

| TYPE | M/S | POL | MANUFAC | EUROPEAN | AMERICAN | JAPANESE | USE |
|------|-----|-----|---------|----------|----------|----------|-----|
| CV10061 | G | N | UK | OC141 | | | |
| CV10063 | G | P | UK | NKT677 | | | |
| CV10068 | G | P | UK | OC171 | | | |
| CV10075 | S | N | UK | | 2N1485 | | |
| CV10082 | S | N | UK | | | 2S104 | |
| CV10085 | S | P | UK | OC205 | | | |
| CV10086 | S | P | UK | | | 2S307 | |
| CV10094 | S | P | UK | BCY32 | | | |
| CV10095 | G | N | UK | | 2N1308 | | |
| CV10109 | G | P | UK | ASY66 | | | |
| CV10139 | S | P | UK | OC466 | | | |
| CV10140 | S | N | UK | | 2N3572 | | |
| CV10141 | S | N | UK | | 2N3110 | | |
| CV10142 | S | N | UK | | 2N2891 | | |
| CV10143 | S | N | UK | | 40422 | | |
| CV10150 | S | N | UK | ZT82 | | | |
| CV10159 | S | N | UK | BFY52 | | | |
| CV10160 | G | P | UK | ADZ11 | | | |
| CV10161 | S | N | UK | ZDT21 | | | |
| CV10162 | G | N | UK | | 2N1672 | | |
| CV10164 | G | P | UK | | 2G387 | | |
| CV10166 | S | P | UK | | 40321 | | |
| CV10168 | S | P | UK | | 2N2945 | | |
| CV10180 | S | P | UK | | | 2S325 | |
| CV10181 | | | UK | | | 2S720 | |
| CV10183 | G | P | UK | ACY19 | | | |
| CV10190 | S | P | UK | | 2N2904 | | |
| CV10202 | G | P | UK | NKT128 | | | |
| CV10209 | G | P | UK | NKT404X2 | | | |
| CV10215 | S | N | UK | | 2N1613 | | |
| CV10235 | S | P | UK | BCY72 | | | |
| CV10236 | S | N | UK | BFY72 | | | |
| CV10238 | S | N | UK | | 2N3543 | | |
| CV10240 | S | N | UK | ZT1514 | | | |
| CV10243 | S | N | UK | BF115 | | | |
| CV10244 | S | N | UK | ZT1513 | | | |
| CV10266 | G | P | UK | OC20 | | | |
| CV10267 | G | P | UK | | 2N3731 | | |
| CV10268 | S | N | UK | | 2N3643 | | |
| CV10269 | S | P | UK | | 2N3638 | | |
| CV10270 | S | N | UK | | 2N3566 | | |
| CV10271 | S | N | UK | | 2N3565 | | |
| CV10272 | S | N | UK | | 2N3251 | | |
| CV10273 | G | P | UK | OC43 | | | |
| CV10274 | G | P | UK | | 2N711 | | |
| CV10275 | G | P | UK | ASY27 | | | |
| CV10276 | G | P | UK | AF118 | | | |
| CV10279 | | | UK | ZT1072 | | | |
| CV10280 | S | P | UK | BCY38 | | | |
| CV10283 | G | P | UK | ADY26 | | | |
| CV10288 | G | P | UK | | 2N2068 | | |
| CV10292 | G | P | UK | | 2G303 | | |
| CV10304 | S | N | UK | | 2N718 | | |
| CV10309 | S | N | UK | | 2N2410 | | |
| CV10336 | G | P | UK | | 2N222A | | |
| CV10337 | S | N | UK | BSY38 | | | |
| CV10338 | S | N | UK | BSY39 | | | |
| CV10345 | S | N | UK | BDY10 | | | |
| CV10350 | G | P | UK | | 2N2063 | | |
| CV10351 | S | N | UK | | 2N3302 | | |
| CV10352 | S | N | UK | | 2N3045 | | |
| CV10353 | S | P | UK | | 2N3051 | | |
| CV10357 | S | N | UK | | 2N424 | | |
| CV10376 | G | P | UK | GET880 | | | |
| CV10379 | S | N | UK | BFY57 | | | |
| CV10381 | G | P | UK | NKT401 | | | |
| CV10384 | G | P | UK | | 2N140 | | |
| CV10391 | S | N | UK | | 2N2479 | | |
| CV10393 | S | N | UK | | 2N2405 | | |
| CV10394 | G | P | UK | | 2G382 | | |
| CV10396 | S | N | UK | | | 2S502 | |
| CV10409 | S | N | UK | | | 2S327 | |
| CV10410 | J | P | UK | | 2N2386 | | |
| CV10411 | S | N | UK | | 2N2865 | | |
| CV10412 | S | N | UK | | 2N2950 | | |

| TYPE | M/S | POL | MANUFAC | EUROPEAN | AMERICAN | JAPANESE | USE |
|------|-----|-----|---------|----------|----------|----------|-----|
| CV10413 | S | N | UK | | 2N2951 | | |
| CV10414 | G | P | UK | | 2N2998 | | |
| CV10415 | S | N | UK | | 2N657 | | |
| CV10416 | S | N | UK | | 2N930 | | |
| CV10419 | S | N | UK | | 2N1566A | | |
| CV10420 | S | N | UK | | 2N1049A | | |
| CV10432 | S | P | UK | | 2N1132 | | |
| CV10440 | S | N | UK | BC107 | | | |
| CV10441 | S | N | UK | | 2N3440 | | |
| CV10467 | G | P | UK | NKT12 | | | |
| CV10471 | S | N | UK | BFY52 | | | |
| CV10509 | S | N | UK | | 2N2218 | | |
| CV10511 | S | N | UK | | 2N743X2 | | |
| CV10520 | S | N | UK | BFY79 | | | |
| CV10531 | S | N | UK | BFY44 | | | |
| CV10532 | S | N | UK | | 2N3018 | | |
| CV10533 | S | N | UK | BFY90 | | | |
| CV10540 | S | N | UK | BFX84 | | | |
| CV10541 | S | N | UK | BC108 | | | |
| CV10544 | S | N | UK | | | 2S002 | |
| CV10547 | S | N | UK | | 2N3234 | | |
| CV10548 | S | P | UK | | 2N4036 | | |
| CV10550 | G | P | UK | ACY22 | | | |
| CV10552 | S | N | UK | | 2N3262 | | |
| CV10556 | S | N | UK | | 2N1489 | | |
| CV10557 | S | N | UK | | 2N497 | | |
| CV10558 | S | N | UK | | 2N3118 | | |
| CV10560 | S | N | UK | | 2N3935 | | |
| CV10561 | S | P | UK | | 2N3202 | | |
| CV10562 | S | P | UK | | 2N3636 | | |
| CV10563 | G | P | UK | | 2N2078 | | |
| CV10564 | S | P | UK | | 2N3702 | | |
| CV10575 | J | N | UK | | 2N3935 | | |
| CV10576 | G | P | UK | | 2G309 | | |
| CV10577 | G | P | UK | | 2N3323 | | |
| CV10580 | G | P | UK | | 2N383 | | |
| CV10581 | G | P | UK | | 2N1373 | | |
| CV10582 | G | P | UK | | 2N2189 | | |
| CV10583 | G | P | UK | | 2N2635 | | |
| CV10584 | S | N | UK | | 2N3391 | | |
| CV10585 | S | N | UK | | 2N2218A | | |
| CV10588 | S | P | UK | | 2N2185 | | |
| CV10595 | J | N | UK | | 2N3436 | | |
| CV10601 | S | N | UK | | 2N657A | | |
| CV10602 | S | N | UK | | 2N1481 | | |
| CV10618 | S | N | UK | BC108 | | | |
| CV10627 | G | P | UK | | 2N1146 | | |
| CV10629 | S | P | UK | BFX88 | | | |
| CV10675 | G | N | UK | AC176 | | | |
| CV10680 | S | N | UK | | 2N2192 | | |
| CV10681 | S | N | UK | BFY63 | | | |
| CV10682 | S | P | UK | | 2N3703 | | |
| CV10683 | S | N | UK | | 2N3704 | | |
| CV10684 | J | N | UK | | 2N3819 | | |
| CV10686 | G | N | UK | | 2N1306 | | |
| CV10692 | S | N | UK | | | 2S024 | |
| CV10697 | U | PN | UK | | 2N491B | | |
| CV10715 | S | N | UK | | 40354 | | |
| CV10718 | G | P | UK | OC36X2 | | | |
| CV10720 | S | N | UK | BFY17 | | | |
| CV10732 | G | P | UK | | 2N1762 | | |
| CV10736 | S | N | UK | | 2N2243 | | |
| CV10739 | S | N | UK | ZT1708 | | | |
| CV10740 | S | P | UK | ZT183 | | | |
| CV10741 | S | P | UK | ZT184 | | | |
| CV10747 | S | P | UK | | 2N3504 | | |
| CV10750 | S | N | UK | ZT90 | | | |
| CV10751 | G | P | UK | | 2G386 | | |
| CV10766 | J | N | UK | | 2N4.193 | | |
| CV10767 | S | N | UK | BF185 | | | |
| CV10768 | S | N | UK | BF184 | | | |
| CV10769 | S | N | UK | BC109 | | | |
| CV10778 | S | N | UK | BFY72X2 | | | |
| CV10779 | S | P | UK | | 2N3063 | | |
| CV10786 | S | N | UK | | 2N6998 | | |

| TYPE | M/S | POL | MANUFAC | EUROPEAN | | AMERICAN | | JAPANESE | USE |
|------|-----|-----|---------|----------|--|----------|--|----------|-----|
| CV10787 | S | N | UK | | | 2N3998 | | | |
| CV10788 | S | N | UK | | | 2N3420 | | | |
| CV10789 | S | N | UK | | | 2N3570 | | | |
| CV10806 | S | N | UK | BC109 | | | | | |
| CV10809 | G | P | UK | OC71 | | | | | |
| CV10814 | S | P | UK | BCY71 | | | | | |
| CV10815 | S | N | UK | BSX21 | | | | | |
| CV10821 | S | P | UK | BFX39 | | | | | |
| CV10824 | G | P | UK | | | 2N2996 | | | |
| CV10827 | S | N | UK | BFY81 | | | | | |
| CV10828 | S | P | UK | | | 2N3905 | | | |
| CV10834 | S | N | UK | | | | | 2S501 | |
| CV10836 | S | N | UK | BDY11 | | | | | |
| CV10837 | S | N | UK | BCY55 | | | | | |
| CV10838 | S | P | UK | | | 2N2274 | | | |
| CV10845 | S | N | UK | | | | | 2S033 | |
| CV10846 | S | N | UK | | | | | | |
| CV10850 | S | N | UK | BSX19 | | 2N3773 | | | |
| CV10855 | G | P | UK | NKT228 | | | | | |
| CV10862 | S | N | UK | ZT81 | | | | | |
| CV10863 | S | N | UK | ZT403P | | | | | |
| CV10866 | S | N | UK | ZT42 | | | | | |
| CV10879 | | | UK | | | | | 2S300 | |
| CV10885 | G | P | UK | OC35X3 | | | | | |
| CV10886 | S | N | UK | BCY42 | | | | | |
| CV10893 | G | P | UK | | | 2N2444 | | | |
| CV10895 | G | P | UK | | | 2N512B | | | |
| CV10898 | G | P | UK | | | 2N652A | | | |
| CV10899 | G | P | UK | | | 2N1183B | | | |
| CV10900 | G | P | UK | | | 2N2048 | | | |
| CV10901 | S | P | UK | | | 2N2043 | | | |
| CV10905 | S | N | UK | BSY39/2 | | | | | |
| CV10908 | G | P | UK | AF124 | | | | | |
| CV10909 | G | G | UK | ASZ15 | | | | | |
| CV10910 | G | P | UK | | | 2N1041 | | | |
| CV10911 | S | P | UK | | | 2N495 | | | |
| CV10912 | S | N | UK | | | 2N718A | | | |
| CV10918 | S | N | UK | BCY55 | | | | | |
| CV10930 | S | P | UK | | | 2N4399 | | | |
| CV10944 | S | N | UK | | | 2N2641 | | | |
| CV10945 | S | P | UK | | | 2N727 | | | |
| CV10946 | S | N | UK | | | 2N3712 | | | |
| CV10971 | G | P | UK | NKT143 | | | | | |
| CV10980 | S | N | UK | | | 2N2034 | | | |
| CV10981 | S | N | UK | | | 2N2452 | | | |
| CV10986 | S | N | UK | BSX30 | | | | | |
| CV10990 | S | P | UK | BCY70 | | | | | |
| CV10992 | G | P | UK | GET875 | | | | | |
| CV10993 | S | N | UK | BD121 | | | | | |
| CV10995 | G | P | UK | GET872 | | | | | |
| CV10996 | S | P | UK | | | 2N705 | | | |
| CV10999 | G | P | UK | | | 2N1554 | | | |
| CV11000 | S | N | UK | | | 2N2977 | | | |
| CV11007 | S | N | UK | | | 2N3585 | | | |
| CV11010 | S | P | UK | | | 2N5416 | | | |
| CV11011 | G | P | UK | | | 2N2613 | | | |
| CV11012 | S | N | UK | BD123 | | | | | |
| CV11013 | S | N | UK | BSX27 | | | | | |
| CV11014 | S | N | UK | BCY43 | | | | | |
| CV11023 | S | N | UK | | | 2N2857 | | | |
| CV11034 | S | P | UK | BSW25 | | | | | |
| CV11040 | S | N | UK | | | 2N2925 | | | |
| CV11041 | S | N | UK | | | 2N3904 | | | |
| CV11042 | G | P | UK | | | 2N2207 | | | |
| CV11043 | G | P | UK | | | 2N967 | | | |
| CV11044 | S | N | UK | | | 2N2501 | | | |
| CV11045 | G | P | UK | | | 2N2148 | | | |
| CV11046 | S | N | UK | | | 2N2923 | | | |
| CV11047 | S | N | UK | | | 2N2924 | | | |
| CV11054 | S | P | UK | BFX35 | | | | | |
| CV11056 | S | P | UK | | | 2N3741 | | | |
| CV11058 | S | N | UK | BFY82 | | | | | |
| CV11060 | S | N | UK | ZT88 | | | | | |
| CV11062 | S | P | UK | | | 2N2604 | | | |
| CV11070 | S | N | UK | | | | | 2S024 | |

| TYPE | M/S | POL | MANUFAC | EUROPEAN | | AMERICAN | | JAPANESE | USE |
|---|---|---|---|---|---|---|---|---|---|
| CV11071 | S | N | UK | | | | | 2S025 | |
| CV11072 | S | N | UK | | | | | 2S026 | |
| CV11078 | S | P | UK | BFX11 | | | | | |
| CV11089 | S | P | UK | ZT152 | | | | | |
| CV11091 | S | P | UK | ZT210 | | | | | |
| CV11092 | S | N | UK | ZDT42 | | | | | |
| CV11095 | S | N | UK | ZT1484 | | | | | |
| CV11096 | S | N | UK | ZT91 | | | | | |
| CV11099 | S | N | UK | | | 2N845 | | | |
| CV11113 | S | N | UK | | | 2N3439 | | | |
| CV11123 | G | P | UK | ACY17 | | 2N2907A | | | |
| CV11135 | S | P | UK | | | 2N722 | | | |
| CV11137 | S | N | UK | | | 2N720A | | | |
| CV11139 | S | N | UK | | | 2N4401 | | | |
| CV11143 | S | N | UK | | | | | | |
| CV11144 | S | P | UK | | | 2N4403 | | | |
| CV11145 | S | N | UL | | | 40346 | | | |
| CV11147 | S | N | UK | | | 40348 | | | |
| CV11149 | S | N | UK | | | 2N3791 | | | |
| CV11151 | S | P | UK | | | 2N1275 | | | |
| CV11152 | S | N | UK | | | | | 2S512 | |
| CV11153 | S | P | UK | | | 2N3133 | | | |
| CV11155 | G | P | UK | | | 2N2147 | | | |
| CV11227 | S | P | UK | | | 2N2944 | | | |
| CV11228 | S | P | UK | BFX48 | | | | | |
| CV11229 | S | N | UK | ZT1479 | | | | | |
| CV11236 | S | P | UK | BCY71 | | | | | |
| CV11238 | S | N | UK | BFY51 | | | | | |
| CV11241 | S | N | UK | | | 2N4348 | | | |
| CV11242 | S | N | UK | | | 2N3240 | | | |
| CV11243 | G | P | UK | | | 2N1396 | | | |
| CV11248 | G | P | UK | | | 2N1905 | | | |
| CV11152 | G | P | UK | | | | | 2S512 | |
| D40D | S | N | GE | | | 2N6121 | | | 06, 16 |
| D40D1 | S | N | GE, NP | | | RCP707 | TIP29 | | 06, 16 |
| D40D1 | | | | | | 2N6288 | | | 06, 16 |
| D40D2 | S | N | GE, NP | | | RCP707 | TIP29 | | 06, 16 |
| D40D2 | | | | | | 2N6288 | | | 06, 16 |
| D40D3 | S | N | GE, NP | | | RCP707 | TIP29 | | 06, 16 |
| D40D4 | S | N | GE, NP | | | RCP707 | TIP29 | | 06, 16 |
| D40D4 | | | | | | TIP29A | 2N6290 | | 06, 16 |
| D40D5 | S | N | GE, NP | | | RCP707 | TIP29 | | 06, 16 |
| D40D5 | | | | | | TIP29A | 2N6290 | | 06, 16 |
| D40D6 | S | N | GE | | | RCP701B | | | 06, 16 |
| D40D7 | S | N | GE, NP | | | RCP701B | TIP29A | | 06, 16 |
| D40D7 | | | | | | 2N6292 | | | 06, 16 |
| D40D8 | S | N | GE, NP | | | RCP701B | TIP29A | | 06, 16 |
| D40D8 | | | | | | 2N6292 | | | 06, 16 |
| D40D10 | S | N | GE | | | RCP701C | TIP29B | | 06, 16 |
| D40D10 | | | | | | 2N6175 | | | 06, 16 |
| D40D11 | S | N | GE | | | RCP701C | TIP29B | | 06, 16 |
| D40D11 | | | | | | 2N6175 | | | 06, 16 |
| D40E1 | S | N | GE | | | RCP705 | | | 06, 16 |
| D40E5 | S | N | GE | | | RCP701B | | | 06, 16 |
| D40E7 | S | N | GE | | | RCP701C | | | 06, 16 |
| D40N1 | S | N | GE | | | RCP113B | TIP47 | | 06, 16 |
| D40N1 | | | | | | 2N6175 | | | 06, 16 |
| D40N2 | S | N | GE | | | RCP111B | TIP47 | | 06, 16 |
| D40N2 | | | | | | 2N6175 | | | 06, 16 |
| D40N3 | S | N | GE | | | RCP113C | TIP48 | | 06, 16 |
| D40N3 | | | | | | 2N6175 | | | 06, 16 |
| D40N4 | S | N | GE | | | RCP111C | TIP48 | | 06, 16 |
| D40N4 | | | | | | 2N6175 | | | 06, 16 |
| D40P1 | S | N | GE | | | TIP47 | 2N6175 | | 06, 16 |
| D40P3 | S | N | GE | | | TIP47 | 2N6175 | | 06, 16 |
| D40P5 | S | N | GE | | | TIP47 | 2N6175 | | 06, 16 |
| D41D | S | P | GE | | | 2N6124 | | | 06, 16 |
| D41D1 | S | P | GE, NP | | | RCP706 | TIP30 | | 06, 16 |
| D41D1 | | | | | | 2N6111 | | | 06, 16 |
| D41D2 | S | P | GE, NP | | | RCP706 | TIP30 | | 06, 16 |
| D41D2 | | | | | | 2N6111 | | | 06, 16 |
| D41D4 | S | P | GE, NP | | | RCP700B | TIP30A | | 06, 16 |
| D41D4 | | | | | | TIP30 | 2N6109 | | 06, 16 |
| D41D5 | S | P | GE, NP | | | RCP700B | TIP30 | | 06, 16 |
| D41D5 | | | | | | TIP30A | 2N6109 | | 06, 16 |

| TYPE | M/S | POL | MANUFAC | EUROPEAN | | AMERICAN | | JAPANESE | USE |
|------|-----|-----|---------|----------|--|----------|--|----------|-----|
| D41D6 | S | P | | | | RCP700B | | | 06, 16 |
| D41D7 | S | P | GE, NP | | | RCP700B | TIP30A | | 06, 16 |
| D41D7 | | | | | | 2N6107 | | | 06, 16 |
| D41D8 | S | P | GE, NP | | | RCP700B | TIP30A | | 06, 16 |
| D41D8 | | | | | | 2N6107 | | | 06, 16 |
| D41D10 | S | P | GE | | | RCP700B | RCP700C | | 06, 16 |
| D41D10 | | | | | | TIP30B | 2N6107 | | 06, 16 |
| D41D11 | S | P | GE | | | RCP700B | RCP700C | | 06, 16 |
| D41D11 | | | | | | TIP30B | 2N6107 | | 06, 16 |
| D41D13 | S | P | GE | | | RCP700C | | | 06, 16 |
| D41E1 | S | P | GE | | | RCP704 | | | 06, 16 |
| D41E5 | S | P | GE | | | RCP700B | | | 06, 16 |
| D41E7 | S | P | GE | | | RCP700C | | | 06, 16 |
| D42C | S | N | | | | 2N6121 | | | 06, 16 |
| D42C1 | S | N | GE, NP | | | 2N6288 | RCP707 | | 06, 16 |
| D42C1 | S | N | GE, NP | | | TIP31 | 2N6121 | | 06, 16 |
| D42C2 | | | | | | RCP705 | TIP31 | | 06, 16 |
| D42C2 | S | N | GE, NP | | | 2N6121 | 2N6288 | | 06, 16 |
| D42C3 | | | | | | RCP705 | TIP31 | | 06, 16 |
| D42C3 | S | N | GE, NP | | | 2N6121 | 2N6288 | | 06, 16 |
| D42C4 | S | N | GE, NP | | | RCP703A | TIP31A | | 06, 16 |
| D42C4 | | | | | | TIP31 | 2N6121 | | 06, 16 |
| D42C5 | | | | | | 2N6290 | | | 06, 16 |
| D42C5 | S | N | GE, NP | | | RCP701A | TIP31 | | 06, 16 |
| D42C5 | | | | | | TIP31A | 2N6121 | | 06, 16 |
| D42C6 | | | | | | 2N6290 | | | 06, 16 |
| D42C6 | S | N | GE, NP | | | RCP701A | TIP31 | | 06, 16 |
| D42C6 | | | | | | TIP31A | 2N6222 | | 06, 16 |
| D42C7 | S | N | GE, NP | | | 2N6290 | | | 06, 16 |
| D42C7 | | | | | | RCP703B | TIP31A | | 06, 16 |
| D42C8 | | | | | | 2N6222 | 2N6292 | | 06, 16 |
| D42C8 | S | N | GE, NP | | | RCP701B | TIP31A | | 06, 16 |
| D42C9 | | | | | | 2N6222 | 2N6292 | | 06, 16 |
| D42C9 | S | N | GE | | | RCP701B | TIP31A | | 06, 16 |
| D42C9 | | | | | | 2N6292 | 2N6122 | | 06, 16 |
| D42C10 | S | N | GE | | | RCP703C | TIP31B | | 06, 16 |
| D42C10 | | | | | | 2N6292 | 2N6123 | | 06, 16 |
| D42C11 | S | N | GE | | | RCP701C | TIP31B | | 06, 16 |
| D42C11 | | | | | | 2N6292 | 2N6123 | | 06, 16 |
| D42C12 | S | N | GE | | | RCP701C | | | 06, 16 |
| D43C | S | P | | | | 2N6124 | | | 06, 16 |
| D43C7 | S | P | GE, NP | | | RCP706 | TIP32 | | 06, 16 |
| D43C2 | | | | | | 2N6124 | 2N6111 | | 06, 16 |
| D43C2 | S | P | GE, NP | | | RCP704 | TIP32 | | 06, 16 |
| D43C2 | | | | | | 2N6124 | 2N6111 | | 06, 16 |
| D43C3 | S | P | GE, NP | | | RCP704 | TIP32 | | 06, 16 |
| D43C3 | | | | | | 2N6124 | 2N6111 | | 06, 16 |
| D43C4 | S | P | GE, NP | | | RCP702A | TIP32A | | 06, 16 |
| D43C4 | | | | | | TIP32 | 2N6124 | | 06, 16 |
| D43C4 | | | | | | 2N6109 | | | 06, 16 |
| D43C5 | S | P | GE, NP | | | RCP700A | TIP32A | | 06, 16 |
| D43C5 | | | | | | TIP32 | 2N6124 | | 06, 16 |
| D43C5 | | | | | | 2N6109 | | | 06, 16 |
| D43C6 | S | P | GE, NP | | | RCP700A | | | 06, 16 |
| D43C7 | S | P | GE, NP | | | RCP702B | TIP32A | | 06, 16 |
| D43C7 | | | | | | 2N6109 | 2N6125 | | 06, 16 |
| D43C8 | S | P | GE, NP | | | RCP700B | TIP32A | | 06, 16 |
| D43C8 | | | | | | 2N6125 | 2N6107 | | 06, 16 |
| D43C9 | S | P | GE | | | RCP700B | 2N6125 | | 06, 16 |
| D43C9 | | | | | | 2N6107 | TIP32A | | 06, 16 |
| D43C10 | S | P | GE | | | RCP702C | 2N6107 | | 06, 16 |
| D43C10 | | | | | | 2N6126 | TIP32B | | 06, 16 |
| D43C11 | S | P | GE | | | RCP700C | 2N6107 | | 06, 16 |
| D43C11 | | | | | | 2N6126 | TIP32B | | 06, 16 |
| D43C12 | S | P | GE | | | RCP700C | | | 06, 16 |
| D44C | S | N | | | | | | | 06, 16 |
| D44C1 | S | N | GE, NP | BD221 | BD239 | 2N6121 | | | 06, 16 |
| D44C1 | | | | | | 2N6288 | 2N6121 | | 06, 16 |
| D44C2 | S | N | GE, NP | BD221 | BD239 | TIP31 | | | 06, 16 |
| D44C2 | | | | | | 2N6288 | 2N6121 | | 06, 16 |
| D44C2 | | | | | | TIP31 | | | 06, 16 |
| D44C3 | S | N | GE, NP | BD221 | BD239 | 2N6288 | 2N6121 | | 06, 16 |
| D44C3 | | | | | | TIP31 | | | 06, 16 |
| D44C4 | S | N | GE, NP | BD239 | | 2N6290 | 2N6121 | | 06, 16 |
| D44C4 | | | | | | TIP31 | | | 06, 16 |

| TYPE | M/S | POL | MANUFAC | EUROPEAN | | AMERICAN | | JAPANESE | USE |
|------|-----|-----|---------|----------|--|----------|--|----------|-----|
| D44C5 | S | N | GE, NP | | | TIP31 | | | 06, 16 |
| D44C6 | S | N | GE, NP | BD239 | | 2N6292 | 2N6121 | | 06, 16 |
| D44C6 | | | | | | TIP31 | | | 06, 16 |
| D44C7 | S | N | GE, NP | BD239A | | 2N6292 | 2N6122 | | 06, 16 |
| D44C7 | | | | | | TIP31A | | | 06, 16 |
| D44C8 | S | N | GE, NP | BD239A | | 2N6292 | 2N6122 | | 06, 16 |
| D44C8 | | | | | | TIP31A | | | 06, 16 |
| D44C9 | S | N | GE, NP | BD239A | | 2N6292 | 2N6122 | | 06, 16 |
| D44C9 | | | | | | TIP31A | | | 06, 16 |
| D44C10 | S | N | GE | BD239B | | 2N6292 | 2N6123 | | 06, 16 |
| D44C10 | | | | | | TIP31B | | | 06, 16 |
| D44C11 | S | N | GE | BD239B - | | 2N6292 | 2N6123 | | 06, 16 |
| D44C11 | | | | | | TIP31B | | | 06, 16 |
| D44C12 | S | N | GE | BD239B | | 2N6123 | | | 06, 16 |
| D44E1 | SD | N | GE | | | SE9300 | 2N6386 | | 06, 16 |
| D44E2 | SD | N | GE | | | SE9300 | 2N6387 | | 06, 16 |
| D44E3 | SD | N | GE | | | SE9301 | 2N6388 | | 06, 16 |
| D44H1 | S | N | GE | | | 2N6288 | 2N6129 | | 06, 16 |
| D44H1 | | | | | | TIP41 | | | 06, 16 |
| D44H2 | S | N | GE | | | 2N6288 | 2N6129 | | 06, 16 |
| D44H2 | | | | | | TIP41 | | | 06, 16 |
| D44H4 | S | N | GE | | | 2N6290 | 2N6129 | | 06, 16 |
| D44H4 | | | | | | TIP41 | | | 06, 16 |
| D44H5 | S | N | GE | | | 2N6290 | 2N6129 | | 06, 16 |
| D44H5 | | | | | | TIP41 | | | 06, 16 |
| D44H7 | S | N | GE | | | 2N6292 | 2N6130 | | 06, 16 |
| D44H7 | | | | | | TIP41A | | | 06, 16 |
| D44H8 | S | N | GE | | | 2N6292 | 2N6130 | | 06, 16 |
| D44H8 | | | | | | TIP41A | | | 06, 16 |
| D44H10 | S | N | GE | | | 2N6131 | 2N6292 | | 06, 16 |
| D44H10 | | | | | | TIP41B | | | 06, 16 |
| D44H11 | S | N | GE | | | 2N6131 | 2N6292 | | 06, 16 |
| D44H11 | | | | | | TIP41B | | | 06, 16 |
| D44R1 | S | N | GE | | | TA8863B | TIP47 | | 18 |
| D44R2 | S | N | GE | | | TA8863B | TIP47 | | 18 |
| D44R3 | S | N | GE | | | TA8863B | TIP48 | | 18 |
| D44R4 | S | N | GE | | | TA8863B | TIP48 | | 18 |
| D44R5 | S | N | GE | | | TA8863F | | | 18 |
| D44R6 | S | N | GE | | | TA8863F | | | 18 |
| D45C | S | P | | | | 2N6124 | | | 06, 16 |
| D45C1 | S | P | GE, NP | BD224 | BD240 | 2N6111 | 2N6124 | | 06, 16 |
| D45C1 | | | | | | TIP32 | | | 06, 16 |
| D45C2 | S | P | GE, NP | BD224 | BD240 | 2N6111 | 2N6124 | | 06, 16 |
| D45C2 | | | | | | TIP32 | | | 06, 16 |
| D45C3 | S | P | GE, NP | BD224 | BD240 | 2N6111 | 2N6124 | | 06, 16 |
| D45C3 | | | | | | TIP32 | | | 06, 16 |
| D45C4 | S | P | GE, NP | BD240 | | 2N6109 | 2N6124 | | 06, 16 |
| D45C4 | | | | | | TIP32 | | | 06, 16 |
| D45C5 | S | P | GE, NP | BD240 | | 2N6109 | 2N6124 | | 06, 16 |
| D45C5 | | | | | | TIP32 | | | 06, 16 |
| D45C6 | S | P | GE, NP | BD240 | | 2N6109 | 2N6124 | | 06, 16 |
| D45C6 | | | | | | TIP32 | | | 06, 16 |
| D45C7 | S | P | GE, NP | BD240A | | 2N6125 | 2N6107 | | 06, 16 |
| D45C7 | | | | | | 2N6124 | TIP32A | | 06, 16 |
| D45C8 | S | P | GE, NP | BD240A | | 2N6107 | 2N6125 | | 06, 16 |
| D45C8 | | | | | | TIP32A | | | 06, 16 |
| D45C9 | S | P | GE, NP | BD240A | | 2N6107 | 2N6125 | | 06, 16 |
| D45C9 | | | | | | TIP32A | | | 06, 16 |
| D45C10 | S | P | GE | BD240B | | 2N6107 | 2N6126 | | 06, 16 |
| D45C10 | | | | | | TIP32B | | | 06, 16 |
| D45C11 | S | P | GE | BD240B | | 2N6107 | 2N6126 | | 06, 16 |
| D45C11 | | | | | | TIP32B | | | 06, 16 |
| D45C12 | S | P | GE | BD240B | | 2N6126 | | | 06, 16 |
| D45E1 | SD | P | GE | | | SE9400 | RCA8203 | | 06, 16 |
| D45E2 | SD | P | GE | | | SE9400 | RCA8203A | | 06, 16 |
| D45E3 | SD | P | GE | | | SE9401 | RCA8203B | | 06, 16 |
| D45H1 | S | P | GE | | | 2N6111 | 2N6132 | | 06, 16 |
| D45H1 | | | | | | TIP42 | | | 06, 16 |
| D45H2 | S | P | GE | | | 2N6111 | 2N6132 | | 06, 16 |
| D45H2 | | | | | | TIP42 | | | 06, 16 |
| D45H4 | S | P | GE | | | 2N6109 | 2N6132 | | 06, 16 |
| D45H4 | | | | | | TIP42 | | | 06, 16 |
| D45H5 | S | P | GE | | | 2N6109 | 2N6132 | | 06, 16 |
| D45H5 | | | | | | TIP42 | | | 06, 16 |
| D45H7 | S | P | GE | | | 2N6109 | 2N6107 | | 06, 16 |

| TYPE | M/S | POL | MANUFAC | EUROPEAN | | AMERICAN | | JAPANESE | USE |
|------|-----|-----|---------|----------|---|----------|---|----------|-----|
| D45H7 | | | | | | 2N6133 | TIP42A | | 06, 16 |
| D45H8 | S | P | GE | | | 2N6107 | 2N6133 | | 06, 16 |
| D45H8 | | | | | | TIP42A | | | 06, 16 |
| D45H9 | S | P | GE | | | 2N6133 | | | 06, 16 |
| D45H10 | S | P | GE | | | 2N6107 | 2N6134 | | 06, 16 |
| | | | | | | | | | |
| D45H10 | | | | | | TIP42B | | | 06, 16 |
| D45H11 | S | P | GE | | | 2N6134 | 2N6107 | | 06, 16 |
| D45H11 | | | | | | TIP42B | | | 06, 16 |
| D1101 | J | N | | | | 2N4220A | 2N3070 | | |
| D1102 | J | N | | | | MFE2094 | 2N3070 | | |
| | | | | | | | | | |
| D1103 | J | N | | | | MFE2093 | 2N3071 | | |
| D1177 | J | N | | | | MFE2095 | 2N3070 | | |
| D1178 | J | N | | | | MFE2094 | 2N3070 | | |
| D1179 | J | N | | | | MFE2093 | 2N3071 | | |
| D1180 | J | N | | | | 2N4221A | 2N4222A | | |
| | | | | | | | | | |
| D1181 | | | | | | 2N3069 | | | |
| D1182 | J | N | | | | 2N4220A | 2N3070 | | |
| D1183 | J | N | | | | 2N4220A | 2N3071 | | |
| D1184 | J | N | | | | 2N4223 | TN4341 | | |
| | | | | | | 2N4220A | TN4340 | | |
| | | | | | | | | | |
| D1185 | J | N | | | | 2N4220A | TN4399 | | |
| D1201 | J | N | | | | 2N4224 | | | |
| D1202 | J | N | | | | 2N3821 | | | |
| D1203 | J | N | | | | MFE2093 | 2N5358 | | |
| D1301 | J | N | | | | 2N4222A | | | |
| | | | | | | | | | |
| D1302 | J | N | | | | 2N4220A | | | |
| D1303 | J | N | | | | 2N4220A | | | |
| DE1004 | | | | | | MFE3003 | | | |
| DN3066A | J | N | | | | MFE2095 | 2N3070 | | |
| DN3067A | J | N | | | | MFE2094 | 2N3071 | | |
| | | | | | | | | | |
| DN3068A | J | N | | | | MFE2093 | 2N3071 | | |
| DN3069A | J | N | | | | 2N4221A | 2N3069 | | |
| DN3070A | J | N | | | | 2N4220A | 2N3070 | | |
| DN3071A | J | N | | | | 2N4220A | 2N3071 | | |
| DN3356A | J | N | | | | 2N4091 | | | |
| | | | | | | | | | |
| DN3366A | J | N | | | | 2N4091 | | | |
| DN3367A | J | N | | | | 2N4091 | | | |
| DN3368A | J | N | | | | 2N4221A | | | |
| DN3369A | J | N | | | | 2N4220A | | | |
| DN3370A | J | N | | | | MFE2093 | | | |
| | | | | | | | | | |
| DN3436A | J | N | | | | 2N3436 | | | |
| DN3437A | J | N | | | | 2N3437 | | | |
| DN3438A | J | N | | | | 2N3438 | | | |
| DN3458 | J | N | | | | 2N4222A | | | |
| DN3459A | J | N | | | | 2N4220A | | | |
| | | | | | | | | | |
| DN3460A | J | N | | | | 2N4220A | | | |
| DNX1 | J | N | | | | 2N3822 | 2N3069 | | |
| DNX1A | J | N | | | | 2N3822 | | | |
| DNX2 | J | N | | | | MFE2093 | MFE2094 | | |
| DNX2 | | | | | | 2N3070 | | | |
| | | | | | | | | | |
| DNX2A | J | N | | | | MFE2093 | MFE2094 | | |
| DNX3 | J | N | | | | MFE2093 | 2N3071 | | |
| DNX3A | J | N | | | | MFE2093 | | | |
| DNX4 | J | N | | | | 2N3822 | | | |
| DNX4A | J | N | | | | 2N3822 | | | |
| | | | | | | | | | |
| DNX5 | J | N | | | | 2N3821 | | | |
| DNX5A | J | N | | | | 2N3821 | | | |
| DNX6 | J | N | | | | MFE2093 | | | |
| DNX6A | J | N | | | | MFE2093 | | | |
| DNX7 | J | N | | | | 2N3824 | TN4341 | | |
| | | | | | | | | | |
| DNX7A | J | N | | | | 2N3824 | | | |
| DNX8 | J | N | | | | 2N3821 | TN4340 | | |
| DNX8A | J | N | | | | 2N3821 | | | |
| DNX9 | J | N | | | | 2N3821 | TN4339 | | |
| DNX9A | J | N | | | | 2N3821 | | | |
| | | | | | | | | | |
| DR100 | G | P | | TS1 | TS14 | | | | |
| DR101 | G | P | | TS1 | | | | | |
| DR102 | G | P | | TS2 | TS14 | | | | |
| DR108 | G | P | | TS1 | | | | | |
| DR109 | G | P | | TS1 | TS14 | | | | |
| | | | | | | | | | |
| DR110 | G | P | | TS3 | | | | | |
| DR126 | G | P | | TS14 | OC66 | 2N465 | | | |
| DR127 | G | P | | TS2 | TS14 | | | | |
| DR128 | G | P | | OC65 | OC66 | 2N465 | | | |
| DR129 | G | P | | TS2 | TS14 | 2N465 | | | |

| TYPE | M/S | POL | MANUFAC | EUROPEAN | | AMERICAN | | JAPANESE | USE |
|---|---|---|---|---|---|---|---|---|---|
| DR130 | G | P | | TS1 | | | | | |
| DR131 | G | P | | TS1 | | | | | |
| DS25 | G | P | | AF185 | | | | | |
| DS26 | G | P | | AC128 | | 2N2431 | | | |
| DS34 | G | P | | AF178 | | 2N2495 | | | |
| DS41 | G | P | | AF178 | | 2N2495 | | | |
| DS44 | G | N | | AC127 | | 2N2430 | | | |
| DS46 | G | N | | | | | | | |
| DT80 | G | P | | CTP1502 | | 2N677C | 2N1031B | | |
| DT100 | G | P | | CTP1500 | | 2N677C | 2N1031C | | |
| DT1003 | S | N | LU | BFY44 | | | | | |
| DT1111 | S | N | LU | ZT1479 | | | | | |
| DT1112 | S | N | LU | ZT1480 | | | | | |
| DT1121 | S | N | LU | ZT1481 | | | | | |
| DT1122 | S | N | LU | ZT1482 | BDY11 | | | | |
| DT1511 | S | N | LU | ZT1700 | | | | | |
| DT1521 | S | N | LU | ZT2270 | | | | | |
| DT4110 | S | N | | BDY10 | | | | | |
| DT4111 | S | N | | ZT1488 | | | | | |
| DT4121 | S | N | | ZT1490 | | | | | |
| DTS401 | S | N | DD, SF, SU | | | FT401 | | | |
| DTS402 | S | N | DD, SF, SU | | | FT402 | | | |
| DTS403 | S | N | DD | | | FT402 | | | |
| DTS409 | S | N | | | | FT402 | | | |
| DTS410 | S | N | DD, SF, SU, SD | | | FT410 | RCA410 | | |
| DTS411 | S | N | DD, SU, SD, SF | | | FT411 | RCA411 | | |
| DTS413 | S | N | DD, IC, SF, SD, SU | | | FT413 | RCA413 | | |
| DTS423 | S | N | DD, SF, SD, SU | | | FT423 | RCA423 | | |
| DTS424 | S | N | DD, SU | | | 2N6251 | | | |
| DTS430 | S | N | DD, SF, SU | | | FT430 | | | |
| DTS431 | S | N | DD, SF, SU | | | FT431 | RCA431 | | |
| DTS515 | S | N | | | | 2N6250 | | | |
| DTS516 | S | N | | | | 2N6250 | | | |
| DTS517 | S | N | | | | 2N6250 | | | |
| DTS519 | S | N | | | | FT430 | | | |
| DTS1010 | S | N | DD | | | SE9304 | | | |
| DTS1020 | S | N | DD | | | SE9304 | | | |
| DTS4010 | S | N | | | | FT430 | | | |
| DU4339 | J | N | | | | TD5905 | | | |
| DU4340 | J | N | | | | 2N5047 | SU2369 | | |
| DW6208 | S | N | | BC107B | | | | | |
| DW6577 | S | N | | BC107A | | | | | |
| DW6737 | S | N | | BC107A | | | | | |
| DW7000 | S | N | | BC167 | | | | | |
| DW7035 | S | N | | BC167B | BC113 | | | | |
| DW7035 | | | | BC182B | BC171B | | | | |
| DW7039 | S | N | | BF110 | BF178 | | | | |
| DW7039 | | | | BF156 | BF117 | | | | |
| DW7050 | S | N | | BF232 | BF176 | | | | |
| E100 | J | N | IL, NS, SX | | | MPF102 | 2N5950 | | |
| E100 | | | | | | 2N5163 | | | |
| E101 | J | N | IL, NS, SX | | | 2N5457 | 2N4302 | | |
| E102 | J | N | IL, NS, SX | | | 2N5457 | 2N5953 | | |
| E102 | | | | | | 2N4302 | | | |
| E103 | J | N | IN, NS, SX | | | 2N5459 | 2N5950 | | |
| E103 | | | | | | U1837E | | | |
| E105 | J | N | | | | MPF4391 | 2N4445 | | |
| E106 | J | N | | | | MPF4391 | 2N4447 | | |
| E107 | J | N | | | | MPF4391 | 2N5434 | | |
| E108 | J | N | IL, SX | | | MPF4391 | | | |
| E109 | J | N | IL, SX | | | MPF4391 | | | |
| E110 | J | N | IL, SX | | | MPF4391 | | | |
| E111 | J | N | IL, SX | | | MPF4391 | TIS73 | | |
| E111 | | | | | | U1897E | | | |
| E112 | J | N | IL, SX | | | MPF4392 | TIS74 | | |
| E112 | | | | | | U1898E | | | |
| E113 | J | N | IL, SX | | | MPF4393 | TIS75 | | |
| E113 | | | | | | U1899E | | | |
| E114 | J | N | | | | 2N5486 | U2047E | | |
| E174 | J | P | | | | MPF970 | P1086E | | |
| E175 | J | P | | | | MPF970 | P1086E | | |
| E176 | J | P | | | | MPF971 | P1086E | | |
| E201 | J | N | | | | 2N5457 | ITE4338 | | |
| E202 | J | N | | | | 2N5458 | ITE4340 | | |
| E203 | J | N | | | | 2N5459 | U1837E | | |

| TYPE | M/S | POL | MANUFAC | EUROPEAN | AMERICAN | | JAPANESE | USE |
|------|-----|-----|---------|----------|----------|---|----------|-----|
| E210 | J | N | | | 2N5484 | | | |
| E211 | J | N | | | 2N5485 | | | |
| E212 | J | N | | | 2N5486 | U2047E | | |
| E230 | J | N | | | 2N5457 | ITE4868 | | |
| E231 | J | N | | | 2N5458 | ITE4869 | | |
| E232 | J | N | | | 2N5459 | ITE4860 | | |
| E270 | J | P | | | MPF970 | P1087E | | |
| E271 | J | P | | | MPF970 | P1087E | | |
| E300 | J | N | IL, SX | | 2N5486 | U1994E | | |
| E300 | J | N | | | 2N5245 | | | |
| E304 | J | N | | | 2N5486 | U1994E | | |
| E305 | J | N | | | 2N5485 | 2N5484 | | |
| E308 | J | N | | | 2N5486 | | | |
| E309 | J | N | | | 2N5486 | | | |
| E310 | J | N | | | 2N5486 | | | |
| E400 | J | N | | | 2N5197 | | | |
| E401 | J | N | | | 2N5198 | | | |
| E402 | J | N | | | 2N5199 | | | |
| E413 | J | N | | | 2N5198 | | | |
| E414 | J | N | | | 2N5199 | | | |
| E415 | J | N | | | 2N5046 | | | |
| E420 | J | N | | | 2N5046 | | | |
| E421 | J | N | | | 2N5047 | | | |
| ED1401A | S | N | | BC548A | | | | |
| ED1401B | S | N | | BC548B | | | | |
| ED1401C | S | N | | BC548C | | | | |
| ED1402A | S | N | | BC548 | | | | |
| ED1402B | S | N | | BC548A | | | | |
| ED1402C | S | N | | BC548B | | | | |
| ED1402D | S | N | | BC548B | | | | |
| ED1402E | S | N | | BC548C | | | | |
| ED1501A | S | N | | BF495 | | | | |
| ED1501B | S | N | | BF495 | | | | |
| ED1501C | S | N | | BF495 | | | | |
| ED1502A | S | N | | BF495 | | | | |
| ED1502B | S | N | | BF495 | | | | |
| ED1502C | S | N | | BF495 | | | | |
| ED1502D | S | N | | BF494 | | | | |
| ED1502E | S | N | | BF494 | | | | |
| ED1601A | S | P | | BC558 | | | | |
| ED1601B | S | P | | BC558A | | | | |
| ED1601C | S | P | | BC558B | | | | |
| ED1602A | S | P | | BC558 | | | | |
| ED1602B | S | P | | BC558 | | | | |
| ED1602C | S | P | | BC558A | | | | |
| ED1602D | S | P | | BC558A | | | | |
| ED1602E | S | P | | BC558B | | | | |
| ED1701 | S | N | | BC338 | | | | |
| ED1801 | S | N | | BC328 | | | | |
| EMS113 | S | N | ML | | 2N6384 | | | |
| EMS114 | S | N | ML | | 2N6385 | | | |
| EMS159 | S | P | ML | | RCA8350A | | | |
| EMS160 | S | P | ML | | RCA8350B | | | |
| EMS213 | S | N | ML | | 2N6387 | | | |
| EMS214 | S | B | ML | | 2N6388 | | | |
| EMS217 | S | N | ML | | 2N6387 | | | |
| EMS218 | S | N | ML | | 2N6388 | | | |
| EMS259 | S | P | ML | | RCA8203A | | | |
| EMS260 | S | P | ML | | RCA8203B | | | |
| EMS261 | S | P | ML | | RCA8203A | | | |
| EMS262 | S | P | ML | | RCA8203B | | | |
| EN697 | S | N | BT, F, NS | | 2N697 | | | |
| EN706 | S | N | F | | 2N706 | | | |
| EN708 | S | N | F, NS | | 2N708 | | | |
| EN718A | S | N | F | | 2N718A | | | |
| EN722 | S | P | F, NS | | 2N722 | | | |
| EN744 | S | N | F, NS | | 2N744 | | | |
| EN870 | S | N | F | | 2N870 | | | |
| EN871 | S | N | F | | 2N871 | | | |
| EN914 | S | N | F | | 2N914 | FX914 | | |
| EN915 | S | N | F | | 2N915 | | | |
| EN916 | S | B | F, NS | | 2N916 | | | |
| EN918 | S | N | F, NS | | 2N918 | FX918 | | |
| EN930 | S | N | F, NS | | 2N930 | | | |
| EN956 | S | N | F, NS | | 2N956 | | | |

| TYPE | M/S | POL | MANUFAC | EUROPEAN | AMERICAN | | JAPANESE | USE |
|------|-----|-----|---------|----------|----------|---|----------|-----|
| EN1132 | S | P | BT, F, NS | | 2N1132 | | | |
| EN1613 | S | N | BT, F, NS | | 2N1613 | | | |
| EN1711 | S | N | BT, F, NS | | 2N1711 | | | |
| EN2219 | S | N | BT, F, NS | | 2N2219 | | | |
| EN2222 | S | N | BT, F, NS | | 2N2222 | FX2222 | | |
| EN2369A | S | N | F, ME, NS | | 2N2369A | FX2369A | | |
| EN2484 | S | N | F, ME, NS | | PN2484-18 | 2N2484 | | |
| EN2484 | | | | | FX2484 | | | |
| EN2894A | S | P | F | | 2N2894A | FX2894A | | |
| EN2905 | S | P | BT, F, NS | | 2N2905 | | | |
| EN2907 | S | P | BT, F, NS | | 2N2907 | FX2907 | | |
| EN3009 | S | N | F | | 2N3009 | | | |
| EN3011 | S | N | F, NS | | 2N3011 | | | |
| EN3013 | S | N | F | | 2N3013 | FX3013 | | |
| EN3014 | S | N | F | | 2N3014 | FX3014 | | |
| EN3250 | S | P | F, NS | | 2N3250 | | | |
| EN3502 | S | P | F, NS | | 2N3502 | FX3502 | | |
| EN3504 | S | P | F, NS | | 2N3504 | | | |
| EN3903 | S | N | F | | 2N3903 | FT3903 | | |
| EN3903 | | | | | FX3903 | | | |
| EN3904 | S | N | F | | 2N3904 | FT3904 | | |
| EN3904 | | | | | FX3904 | | | |
| EN3905 | S | P | F | | 2N3905 | FT3905 | | |
| EN3905 | | | | | FX3905 | | | |
| EN3906 | S | P | F | | 2N3906 | FT3906 | | |
| EN3906 | | | | | FX3906 | | | |
| EN3962 | S | P | F | | PN3692-18 | 2N3962 | | |
| EN3962 | | | | | FX3962 | | | |
| EN4123 | S | N | F | | 2N4123 | | | |
| EN4124 | S | N | F | | 2N4124 | | | |
| EN4125 | S | P | F | | 2N4125 | | | |
| EN4126 | S | P | F | | 2N4126 | | | |
| FE100 | J | N | | | MFE2095 | 2N3452 | | |
| FE100A | J | N | | | MFE2095 | 2N3455 | | |
| FE102 | J | N | | | MFE2094 | 2N3453 | | |
| FE102A | J | N | | | MFE2094 | 2N3456 | | |
| FE104 | J | N | | | MFE2093 | 2N3454 | | |
| FE104A | J | N | | | MFE2093 | 2N3457 | | |
| FE200 | J | N | | | 2N3070 | | | |
| FE202 | J | N | | | MFE2093 | 2N3070 | | |
| FE204 | J | N | | | MFE2093 | 2N3070 | | |
| FE300 | J | N | | | 2N4220A | 2N4222A | | |
| FE300 | | | | | 2N3069 | | | |
| FE302 | J | N | | | 2N4220A | 2N4222A | | |
| FE302 | | | | | 2N3070 | | | |
| FE304 | J | N | | | MFE2093 | 2N4220A | | |
| FE304 | | | | | 2N3070 | | | |
| FE400 | J | N | | | 2N3436 | 2N3069 | | |
| FE400A | J | N | | | 2N3069 | | | |
| FE402 | J | N | | | 2N3437 | 2N3070 | | |
| FE402A | J | N | | | 2N3070 | | | |
| FE404 | J | N | | | 2N3436 | 2N3070 | | |
| FE404A | J | N | | | 2N3070 | | | |
| FE0654A | J | N | F, IL | | 2N5486 | 2N5950 | | |
| FE0654A | | | | | U1837E | | | |
| FE0654B | J | N | F, IL | | 2N5485 | 2N5951 | | |
| FE0654B | | | | | 2N4303 | | | |
| FE0654C | J | N | F | | 2N5484 | 2N4302 | | |
| FE0655A | J | N | | | 2N5638 | KE4859 | | |
| FE0655B | J | N | | | 2N5639 | KE4861 | | |
| FE0655C | J | N | | | 2N5640 | KE4393 | | |
| FE3819 | J | N | F, IL | | 2N5458 | 2N5953 | | |
| FE3819 | | | | | U1837E | | | |
| FE4302 | J | N | F | | 2N5953 | 2N4302 | | |
| FE4303 | J | N | F | | 2N5952 | 2N4303 | | |
| FE4304 | J | N | F | | 2N5951 | 2N4304 | | |
| FE5245 | J | N | F, IL | | 2N5486 | 2N5245 | | |
| FE5246 | J | N | F, IL | | 2N5486 | 2N5246 | | |
| FE5247 | J | N | F, IL | | 2N5486 | 2N5247 | | |
| FE5457 | J | N | F, IL | | 2N5953 | 2N5457 | | |
| FE5458 | J | N | F, IL | | 2N5952 | 2N5458 | | |
| FE5459 | J | N | F, IL | | 2N5950 | 2N5459 | | |
| FE5484 | J | N | F, IL | | 2N5953 | 2N5484 | | |
| FE5485 | J | N | F, IL | | 2N5952 | 2N5485 | | |
| FE5486 | J | N | F, IL | | 2N5949 | 2N5486 | | |

| TYPE | M/S | POL | MANUFAC | EUROPEAN | AMERICAN | | JAPANESE | USE |
|------|-----|-----|---------|----------|----------|---|----------|-----|
| FI0049 | M | P | F | | MFE3020 | MFE3021 | | |
| FI100 | M | P | | | 2N4352 | | | |
| FM1100 | J | | NS | | SU2098B | | | |
| FM1100A | J | | | | TD5906A | | | |
| FM1101 | J | | NS | | SU2098B | | | |
| FM1101A | J | | | | TD5906A | | | |
| FM1102 | J | | NS | | SU2098B | | | |
| FM1102A | J | | | | TD5906A | | | |
| FM1103 | J | N | NS | | 2N5198 | | | |
| FM1103A | J | N | | | TD5908A | | | |
| FM1104 | J | N | NS | | 2N5199 | | | |
| FM1104A | J | N | | | TD5909A | | | |
| FM1105 | J | | NS | | SU2098B | | | |
| FM1105A | J | | | | TD5906A | | | |
| FM1106 | J | | NS | | SU2098B | | | |
| FM1106A | J | | | | TD5906A | | | |
| FM1107 | J | | NS | | SU2098B | | | |
| FM1107A | J | | | | TD5906A | | | |
| FM1108 | J | N | NS | | 2N5198 | | | |
| FM1108A | J | N | | | TD5908A | | | |
| FM1109 | J | N | NS | | 2N5199 | | | |
| FM1109A | J | N | | | TD5905A | | | |
| FM1110 | J | | NS | | SU2098B | | | |
| FM1110A | J | | | | TD5908A | | | |
| FM1111 | J | | NS | | SU2098B | | | |
| FM1111A | J | | | | SU2079 | | | |
| FM1200 | J | N | NS | | 2N5561 | | | |
| FM1201 | J | N | NS | | 2N5561 | | | |
| FM1202 | J | N | NS | | 2N5561 | | | |
| FM1203 | J | | NS | | SU2367A | | | |
| FM1204 | J | | NS | | SU2369 | | | |
| FM1205 | J | N | NS | | 2N5561 | | | |
| FM1206 | J | N | NS | | 2N5561 | | | |
| FM1207 | J | N | NS | | 2N5561 | | | |
| FM1208 | J | | NS | | SU2367A | | | |
| FM1209 | J | | NS | | SU2369 | | | |
| FM1210 | J | | NS | | SU2367 | | | |
| FM1211 | J | | NS | | SU2369 | | | |
| FM3954 | J | N | NS | | 2N3954 | | | |
| FM3954A | J | N | NS | | 2N3954A | | | |
| FM3955 | J | N | NS | | 2N3955 | | | |
| FM3955A | J | N | NS | | 2N3955 | | | |
| FM3956 | J | N | NS | | 2N3956 | | | |
| FM3957 | J | N | NS | | 2N3957 | | | |
| FM3958 | J | N | NS | | 2N3958 | | | |
| FP4339 | J | N | SX | | MATCHED | 2N4220 | | |
| FP4340 | J | N | SX | | MATCHED | 2N4220A | | |
| FPF110 | P | | | | TIL63* | | | |
| FPF110A | P | | | | TIL66* | | | |
| FPF110B | P | | | | TIL66* | | | |
| FPF130 | P | | | | TIL67* | | | |
| FPF130A | P | | | | TIL67* | | | |
| FPF130B | P | | | | TIL67* | | | |
| FPM100 | P | | | | TIL613* | | | |
| FPO100 | P | | | | TIL613* | | | |
| FPS6507 | S | N | | | 2N5770 | 2N4275 | | |
| FPS6507 | S | | | | TIS86 | 2N4996 | | |
| FPS6511 | S | N | | | MPS6511 | TIS87 | | |
| FPS6512 | S | N | F | | MPS6512 | TIS99 | | |
| FPS6513 | S | N | F | | MPS6513 | TIS99 | | |
| FPS6514 | S | N | F | | MPS6514 | TIS98 | | |
| FPS6515 | S | N | F | | MPS6515 | TIS97 | | |
| FPS6516 | S | P | F | | MPS6516 | 2N5447 | | |
| FPS6517 | S | P | F | | MPS6517 | 2N5447 | | |
| FPS6518 | S | P | F | | MPS6518 | 2N5447 | | |
| FPS6519 | S | P | F | | MPS6519 | 2N5447 | | |
| FPS6520 | S | N | F | | MPS6520 | TIS98 | | |
| FPS6521 | S | N | F | | MPS6521 | TIS97 | | |
| FPS6522 | S | P | F | | MPS6522 | 2N5447 | | |
| FPS6523 | S | P | F | | MPS6523 | 2N5447 | | |
| FPS6530 | S | N | F | | MPS6530 | TIS92 | | |
| FPS6531 | S | N | F | | MPS6531 | TIS92 | | |
| FPS6532 | S | N | F | | MPS6532 | TIS92 | | |
| FPS6533 | S | P | F | | MPS6533M | 2N3644 | | |
| FPS6534M | S | P | F | | MPS6534M | 2N3644 | | |

| TYPE | M/S | POL | MANUFAC | EUROPEAN | | AMERICAN | | JAPANESE | USE |
|------|-----|-----|---------|----------|--|----------|--|----------|-----|
| FPS6534M | | P | F | | | TIS93 | | | |
| FPS6535M | S | P | F | | | MPS6535M | 2N3638 | | |
| FPS6535M | | | | | | TIS93 | | | |
| FPS6539 | S | N | | | | PE4030B | SE5032 | | |
| FPS6540 | S | N | | | | PE5030B | SE5030B | | |
| FPS6543 | S | N | | | | PE5030B | SE5030B | | |
| FPS6544 | S | N | | | | PE5030B | SE5030B | | |
| FPS6546 | S | N | | | | PE5030B | SE5030B | | |
| FPS6547 | S | N | | | | PE5030B | SE5030B | | |
| FPS6548 | S | N | | | | PE5030B | SE5030B | | |
| FPS6560 | S | N | F | | | | | | |
| FPS6561 | S | N | F | | | MPS6561 | | | |
| FPS6562 | S | P | F | | | SE6562 | | | |
| FPS6563 | S | P | F | | | SE6563 | | | |
| FPS6565 | S | N | F | | | FPS6566 | | | |
| FPS6566 | S | N | F | | | | | | |
| FPS6567 | S | N | | | | PE5030B | SE5030B | | |
| FPS6568 | S | N | | | | SE5052 | | | |
| FPS6569 | S | N | | | | FPS6570 | | | |
| FPS6570 | S | N | | | | FPS6569 | | | |
| FPS6571 | S | N | F | | | 2N5133 | | | |
| FPSA12 | SD | N | F | | | MPSA12 | | | |
| FPSA13 | SD | N | F | | | MPSA13 | | | |
| FPSA14 | SD | N | | | | MPSA14 | | | |
| FPSA65 | S | P | | | | MPSA65 | | | |
| FPSA66 | S | P | | | | MPSA66 | | | |
| FPT100 | P | | | | | TIL63* | | | |
| FPT100A | P | | | | | TIL67* | | | |
| FPT100B | P | | | | | TIL67* | | | |
| FPT120 | P | | | | | TIL78* | | | |
| FPT120A | P | | | | | TIL67* | | | |
| FPT120B | P | | | | | TIL67* | | | |
| FT57 | M | N | F | | | MFE3004 | MFE3006 | | |
| FT107A | S | N | F | (BC413C) | | SE4022 | FX107A | | |
| FT107B | S | N | F | BC414C | | SE4021 | FX107B | | |
| FT107C | S | N | F | (BC414C) | | SE4020 | FX107C | | |
| FT0650 | J | N | | | | 2N4416 | | | |
| FT0654A | J | N | F, IL | | | 2N3824 | | | |
| FT654A | J | N | | | | 2N4392 | | | |
| FT0654B | J | N | | | | 2N3824 | | | |
| FT654B | J | N | | | | 2N4092 | | | |
| FT0654C | J | N | F, IL | | | 2N4221 | | | |
| FT654C | J | N | | | | 2N4393 | | | |
| FT0654D | J | N | F, IL | | | 2N4221 | | | |
| FT654D | J | N | | | | 2N3972 | | | |
| FT0654E | J | N | F, IL | | | 2N4220 | | | |
| FT654E | J | N | | | | TN4340 | | | |
| FT0655A | J | N | | | | 2N4091 | | | |
| FT655A | J | N | | | | 2N4856A | | | |
| FT0655B | J | N | | | | 2N4092 | | | |
| FT655B | J | N | | | | 2N4858A | | | |
| FT0655C | J | N | | | | 2N4093 | | | |
| FT655C | J | N | | | | 2N3972 | | | |
| FT701 | M | P | F, IL | | | MFE3021 | | | |
| FT703 | M | P | | | | MFE3003 | 3N160 | | |
| FT704 | M | P | F, IL | | | 2N4352 | 3N174 | | |
| FT709 | S | N | F | (BSY17) | | 2N709 | | | |
| FT1746 | S | P | F | (BCY78VII | | | | | |
| FT2974 | S | N | F | | | 2N2974 | | | |
| FT2975 | S | N | F | | | 2N2975 | | | |
| FT2978 | S | N | F | | | 2N2978 | | | |
| FT2979 | S | N | F | | | 2N2979 | | | |
| FT3567 | S | N | F | BSX45-6 | | | | | |
| FT3568 | S | N | F | BSX46-6 | | | | | |
| FT3569 | S | N | F | BSX45-16 | | | | | |
| FT3641 | S | N | F | (BSY34) | | | | | |
| FT3642 | S | N | F | (BSY34) | | | | | |
| FT3643 | S | N | F | (BSY34) | | | | | |
| FT3820 | J | P | F | | | AST5460 | P1069E | | |
| FT3820 | | | | | | 2N4360 | | | |
| FT3903 | S | N | | | | FX3903 | 2N3946 | | |
| FT3904 | S | N | | | | DN3904 | 2N3947 | | |
| FT3904 | | | | | | FX3904 | | | |
| FT3905 | S | P | | | | 2N3250 | FX3905 | | |
| FT3906 | S | P | | | | DN3906 | 2N3251 | | |

| TYPE | M/S | POL | MANUFAC | EUROPEAN | | AMERICAN | | JAPANESE | USE |
|---|---|---|---|---|---|---|---|---|---|
| FT3906 | | | | | | FX3906 | | | |
| FT3909 | J | P | | | | 2N2608 | 2N3909 | | |
| FT3909 | | | | | | 2N4360 | | | |
| FT4017 | S | P | F | | | 2N4017 | | | |
| FT4018 | S | P | F | | | 2N4018 | | | |
| FT4019 | S | P | F | | | 2N4019 | | | |
| FT4020 | S | P | F | | | 2N4020 | | | |
| FT4021 | S | P | F | | | 2N4021 | | | |
| FT4022 | S | P | F | | | 2N4022 | | | |
| FT4023 | S | P | F | | | 2N4023 | | | |
| FT4024 | S | P | F | | | 2N4024 | | | |
| FT4025 | S | P | F | | | 2N4025 | | | |
| FT5040 | S | P | F | BSV15-10 | | | | | |
| FT5041 | S | P | F | BSV15-10 | | | | | |
| FX107A | S | N | | | | FT107A | | | |
| FX107B | S | N | | | | FT107B | | | |
| FX107C | S | N | | | | FT107C | | | |
| FX709 | S | N | | | | FT709 | | | |
| FX914 | S | N | | | | EN914 | 2N914 | | |
| FX918 | S | N | | | | EN918 | 2N918 | | |
| FX2368 | S | N | | | | 2N2368 | FX2369A | | |
| FX2368 | | | | | | 2N2369A | | | |
| FX2369A | S | N | | | | EN2369A | 2N2369A | | |
| FX2369A | | | | | | 2N2369 | | | |
| FX2483 | S | N | | | | 2N2483 | FX2484 | | |
| FX2484 | | | | | | 2N2484 | | | |
| FX2484 | S | N | | | | EN2484 | 2N2484 | | |
| FX2894 | S | P | | | | 2N2894 | | | |
| FX2894A | S | P | | | | 2N2894A | EN2894A | | |
| FX2907 | S | P | | | | EN2907 | | | |
| FX3013 | S | N | | | | EN3013 | 2N3013 | | |
| FX3013 | | | | | | EN3014· | 2N3014 | | |
| FX3014 | S | N | | | | EN3014 | 2N3014 | | |
| FX3299 | S | N | | | | 2N3299 | 2N3299 | | |
| FX3299 | | | | | | FX3300 | | | |
| FX3300 | S | N | | | | 2N3300 | 2N3302 | | |
| FX3502 | S | P | | | | EN3502 | 2N3502 | | |
| FX3503 | S | P | | | | 2N3503 | 2N3645 | | |
| FX3724 | S | N | | | | 2N3724 | 2N4013 | | |
| FX3725 | S | N | | | | 2N3725 | 2N4047 | | |
| FX3903 | S | N | | | | 2N3903 | EN3903 | | |
| FX3903 | | | | | | FT3903 | | | |
| FX3904 | S | N | | | | 2N3904 | EN3904 | | |
| FX3904 | | | | | | FT3904 | | | |
| FX3905 | S | P | | | | 2N3905 | EN3905 | | |
| FX3905 | | | | | | FT3905 | | | |
| FX3906 | S | P | | | | 2N3906 | EN3906 | | |
| FX3906 | | | | | | FT3906 | | | |
| FX3962 | S | P | | | | EN3962 | 2N3962 | | |
| FX3963 | S | P | | | | 2N3963 | | | |
| FX3964 | S | P | | | | 2N3964 | | | |
| FX3965 | S | P | | | | 2N3965 | | | |
| FX4034 | S | P | | | | 2N4034 | 2N4121 | | |
| FX4046 | S | N | | | | 2N4046 | 2N4047 | | |
| FX4046 | | | | | | FX4047 | | | |
| FX4047 | S | N | | | | 2N4047 | 2N4014 | | |
| FX4047 | | | | | | 2N3724 | FX3724 | | |
| FX4207 | S | P | | | | 2N4207 | | | |
| FX4960 | S | N | | | | 2N4960 | 2N4961 | | |
| FX4960 | | | | | | 2N4962 | 2N4963 | | |
| GA004 | G | P | | ASY27 | | | | | |
| GA52829 | G | P | | AC126 | | 2N2429 | | | |
| GE26 | S | N | | | | 2N6122 | | | |
| GE28 | S | N | | | | 2N6122 | | | |
| GE29 | S | P | | | | 2N6125 | | | |
| GEMR | S | N | | | | 2N6121 | | | |
| GET3 | G | P | GE | AC125 | AC126 | 2N185 | 2N2429 | | |
| GET3 | | | | V10/50A | | | | | |
| GET4 | G | P | GE | AC125 | AC126 | 2N185 | 2N2429 | | |
| GET4 | | | | NKT228 | | | | | |
| GET5 | G | P | GE | AC125 | NKT304 | | | | |
| GET5 | | | | V30/201P | | | | | |
| GET6 | G | P | GE | NKT226 | TS3 | 2N185 | | | |
| GET6 | | | | V10/50A | | | | | |
| GET7 | G | P | GE | V15/30NP | | | | | |

| TYPE | M/S | POL | MANUFAC | EUROPEAN | | AMERICAN | | JAPANESE | USE |
|------|-----|-----|---------|----------|--|----------|--|----------|-----|
| GET8 | G | P | GE | V30/30NP | | | | | |
| GET9 | G | P | GE | NKT401 | | | | | |
| GET15 | G | P | GE | V15/201P | | | | | |
| GET16 | G | P | GE | V30/201P | | | | | |
| GET20 | G | P | GE | V30/201P | | | | | |
| GET102 | | | | AC126 | AC132 | 2N2429 | | | |
| GET102 | G | P | GE | AC156 | | | | | |
| GET103 | | | | AC126 | AC132 | 2N2429 | | | |
| GET103 | G | P | GE | ASY58 | | | | | |
| GET104 | G | P | GE | AC126 | ASY59 | 2G303 | 2N2429 | | |
| GET105 | G | P | GE | NKT304 | V60/201P | | | | |
| GET106 | G | P | GE | AC126 | AC128 | 2N2429 | | | |
| GET106 | | | | AC132 | | | | | |
| GET110 | G | P | GE | ASY80 | V60/201P | | | | |
| GET110 | | | | NKT303 | | | | | |
| GET111 | G | P | GE | ACY30 | NKT227 | 2G377 | | | |
| GET113 | G | P | GE | ACY30 | AC128 | 2G301 | | | |
| GET114 | G | P | GE | AC128 | ACY30 | 2G301 | 2N2431 | | |
| GET115 | G | P | GE | NKT304 | NKT351 | | | | |
| GET115 | | | | V15/201P | | | | | |
| GET116 | G | P | GE | NKT304 | V30/201P | | | | |
| GET120 | G | P | GE | NKT303 | V30/201P | | | | |
| GET535 | G | P | GE | NKT228 | | | | | |
| GET536 | G | P | GE | NKT228 | | | | | |
| GET538 | G | P | GE | NKT227 | | | | | |
| GET571 | G | P | GE | NKT404 | V15/30NP | 2N456 | | | |
| GET572 | G | P | GE | NKT404 | OC35 | 2N456 | | | |
| GET572 | | | | XC141 | | | | | |
| GET573 | G | P | GE | NKT403 | V60/30NP | 2N457 | | | |
| GET574 | G | P | GE | NKT403 | | | | | |
| GET581 | G | P | GE | NKT401 | | | | | |
| GET582 | G | P | GE | NKT403 | | | | | |
| GET583 | G | P | GE | NKT404 | | | | | |
| GET584 | G | P | GE | NKT402 | | | | | |
| GET870 | G | P | GE | AC170 | | | | | |
| GET871 | G | P | GE | OC41 | XA151 | 2G301 | | | |
| GET872 | G | P | GE | OC42 | XA152 | 2G302 | | | |
| GET873 | G | P | GE | AF127 | AF185 | OC45 | | | |
| GET874 | G | P | GE | AF126 | AF185 | | | | |
| GET874 | | | | OC44 | | | | | |
| GET875 | G | P | GE | ASY27 | OC43 | 2G306 | | | |
| GET880 | G | P | MU, GE | ASY26 | ASY27 | | | | |
| GET883 | G | P | GE | AF127 | AF185 | | | | |
| GET884 | G | P | GE | AF126 | | | | | |
| GET885 | G | P | MU, GE | | | 2N1309 | | | |
| GET889 | G | P | MU, GE | ASY27 | | | | | |
| GET891 | G | P | MU, GE | | | 2G303 | | | |
| GET892 | G | P | MU, GE | | | 2G304 | | | |
| GET896 | G | P | MU, GE | ASY27 | | | | | |
| GET897 | G | P | GE | NKT142 | | | | | |
| GET898 | G | P | MU, GE | NKT141 | | | | | |
| GFT20 | G | P | TK | AC125 | AC151 | 2N2429 | 2N63 | 2SB220 | |
| GFT20 | | | | AC162 | AC151IV | 2N1190 | 2N238 | 2SB459 | |
| GFT20 | | | | AC122r | AC126 | | | | |
| GFT20R | G | P | TK, NU | AC150 | AC162 | 2N44 | | 2SB32 | |
| GFT20R | | | | AC151IV | | | | | |
| GFT20/15 | G | P | TK, IN | AC151IV | | | | | |
| GFT20/30 | G | P | TK | AC151IV | | | | | |
| GFT20/60 | G | P | TK | ASY48IV | | | | | |
| GFT21 | G | P | TK | AC126 | AC151 | 2N66 | 2N2429 | 2SB219 | |
| GFT21 | | | | AC162 | AC151V | | | | |
| GFT21 | | | | AC122ve | AC125 | | | | |
| GFT21R | G | P | TK | AC151V | | | | | |
| GFT21/15 | G | P | TK | AC151V | AC125 | | | | |
| GFT21/15 | | | | OC604 | | | | | |
| GFT21/30 | G | P | TK | AC151V | | | | | |
| GFT21/60 | G | P | TK | ASY48V | | | | | |
| GFT22 | G | P | TK | AC151VII | | | | | |
| GFT22R | G | P | TK | AC151VII | | | | | |
| GFT22/15 | G | P | TK | AC151VII | | | | | |
| GFT22/30 | G | P | TK | AC151VII | | | | | |
| GFT22/60 | G | P | TK | ASY48VI | | | | | |
| GFT25 | G | P | TK | AC122 | AC125 | 2N36 | 2N2429 | 2SB101 | |
| GFT25 | | | | AC163 | AC151IV | 2N1190 | 2N238 | 2SB459 | |
| GFT25 | | | | AC122r | AC126 | | | | |

| TYPE | M/S | POL | MANUFAC | EUROPEAN | | AMERICAN | | JAPANESE | USE |
|---|---|---|---|---|---|---|---|---|---|
| GFT25R | G | P | TK | AC151IV | | | | | |
| GFT25/15 | G | P | | AC125 | AC151 | | | | |
| GFT25/15 | | | | AC171 | AC151IV | | | | |
| GFT25/30 | G | P | TK | AC125 | AC151 | | | | |
| GFT25/30 | | | | AC171 | AC151IV | | | | |
| GFT25/60 | G | P | TK | ASY48IV | | | | | |
| GFT26 | G | P | NU, TK | (AD130III) | AD149 | | | | |
| GFT26 | | | | OC26 | | | | | |
| GFT30 | G | P | TK | (AD130IV) | | | | | |
| GFT31 | G | P | TK | AC121IV | AC126 | 2N44 | | 2SB220 | |
| GFT31 | | | | AC131 | AC152 | | | | |
| GFT31/15 | G | P | TK | AC121IV | AC128 | | | | |
| GFT31/30 | G | P | TK | AC152IV | | | | | |
| GFT31/60 | G | P | TK | ASY48IV | ACY24 | 2N24A | | 2SB89 | |
| GFT31/60 | | | | ACZ10 | ASY48 | | | | |
| GFT32 | G | P | TK, IN | AC121IV | AC128 | 2N59 | 2N2429 | 2SB222 | |
| GFT32 | | | | AC132 | AC153 | 2N4106 | | | |
| GFT32 | | | | AC152IV | AC124R | | | | |
| GFT32/15 | G | P | TK | AC121IV | AC124 | | | | |
| GFT32/15 | | | | AC12B | AC152IV | | | | |
| GFT32/30 | G | P | TK | AC124 | AC128 | | | | |
| GFT32/30 | | | | AC152IV | | | | | |
| GFT32/60 | G | P | TK | ASY48IV | | | | | |
| GFT33 | G | P | TK | AC152V | AC124R | 2N610 | | 2SB32 | |
| GFT33 | | | | AC128 | | | | | |
| GFT33/15 | G | P | TK | AC152V | | | | | |
| GFT33/30 | G | P | TK | AC152V | | | | | |
| GFT33/60 | G | P | TK | ASY48V | | | | | |
| GFT34 | G | P | TK | AC121V | AC160 | | | | |
| GFT34 | | | | AC124 | AC128 | | | | |
| GFT34/15 | G | P | TK | AC121V | AC128 | 2N138 | | 2SA219 | |
| GFT34/15 | G | P | TK | AC152 | AC153 | | | | |
| GFT34/30 | G | P | TK | AC152V | | | | | |
| GFT34/60 | G | P | TK | ASY48V | | | | | |
| GFT41 | G | P | TK | AF106 | AF178 | 2N2495 | | 2SA230 | |
| GFT42 | G | P | TK | AF190 | | | | | |
| GFT42A | G | P | TK | (AF125) | | | | | |
| GFT42A | | | | (AF126) | AF132 | 2N2495 | 2N384 | 2SA116 | |
| GFT42A | | | | AF178 | SFT358 | | | | |
| GFT42B | G | P | TK | (AF127) | AF134 | 2N384 | | 2SA116 | |
| GFT42B | | | | AF135 | AF185 | | | | |
| GFT43 | G | P | TK | (AF125) | | | | | |
| GFT43A | G | P | TK | (AF126) | AF136 | 2N310 | | 2SA154 | |
| GFT43A | | | | AF137 | AF185 | | | | |
| GFT43B | G | P | TK | (AF127) | AF136 | 2N370 | | | |
| GFT43B | | | | AF137 | AF185 | | | | |
| GFT43D | G | P | TK | AF126 | | | | | |
| GFT43/15 | G | P | TK | AC124 | AC128 | | | | |
| GFT43/15 | | | | AC152V | | | | | |
| GFT44 | G | P | TK | (AC121V) | AF132 | | | | |
| GFT44 | | | | AF137 | AF185 | | | | |
| GFT44/15 | G | P | | AF126 | AF127 | 2N137 | | HJ23D | |
| GFT44/15 | | | | AF185 | | | | | |
| GFT44/15E | G | P | TK | (AC121V) | | | | | |
| GFT44/30 | G | P | TK | (AC151V) | | | | | |
| GFT45 | G | P | | (AC121IV) | AF132 | 2N136 | | 2SA206 | |
| GFT45 | | | | AF137 | AF185 | | | | |
| GFT45/30 | G | P | TK | (AC151IV) | | | | | |
| GFT2006 | G | P | TK, IN | AD130III | OC16 | TI156 | 2N456 | 2SB471 | |
| GFT2006 | | | | AD149 | | | | | |
| GFT2006/30 | G | P | TK | AD130III | AD149 | 2N68 | 2N2836 | 2SB240 | |
| GFT2006/30 | | | | OC30 | | | | | |
| GFT2006/60 | G | P | TK | AD131III | | | | | |
| GFT2006/90 | G | P | TK | AD163III | | | | | |
| GFT3008 | G | P | TK | AD130IV | | | | | |
| GFT3008/20 | G | P | TK | AD130IV | AD130III | 2N2836 | | 2SB86 | |
| GFT3008/20 | | | | AD149 | OC30 | | | | |
| GFT3008/40 | G | P | TK | AD131IV | AD139 | 2N2836 | TI3029 | 2SB86 | |
| GFT3008/40 | | | | AD149 | AD131III | | | 2SB471 | |
| GFT3008/40 | | | | AD138/50 | | | | | |
| GFT3008/60 | G | P | TK | AD131IV | AD131 | | | 2SB86 | |
| GFT3008/60 | | | | AD139 | AD148 | | | | |
| GFT3008/60 | | | | AD131III | | | | | |
| GFT3008/80 | | | | AD132IV | AD132III | | | 2SB86 | |
| GFT3008/80 | | | TK | CTP1111 | | | | | |

| TYPE | M/S | POL | MANUFAC | EUROPEAN | | AMERICAN | | JAPANESE | USE |
|---|---|---|---|---|---|---|---|---|---|
| GFT3108 | G | P | TK | AD130III | | | | | |
| GFT3108/20 | G | P | TK | AD132III | | | | | |
| GFT3108/40 | G | P | TK | AD130III | AD149 | 2N2065 | | 2SB478 | |
| GFT3108/40 | | | TK | AD132III | ASZ15 | | | | |
| GFT3108/60 | | | TK | AD131III | AD139 | | | | |
| GFT3108/80 | | | TK | AD132III | AD132II | | | | |
| GFT3408 | | | TK | AD130V | | | | | |
| GFT3408/20 | G | P | TK | AD130V | AD149 | 2N2836 | | | |
| GFT3408/20 | | | TK | OC26 | AD130IV | | | | |
| GFT3408/40 | G | P | TK | AD131V | AD149 | 2N2836 | 2N1295 | 2SB83 | |
| GFT3408/40 | | | | OC26 | AD131VI | TI3029 | 2N2065 | | |
| GFT3408/40 | | | | AD138/50 | | | | | |
| GFT3408/60 | G | P | TK | AD131V | AD105 | 2N268 | | | |
| GFT3408/60 | G | P | TK | AD131IV | ASZ18 | | | | |
| GFT3408/80 | G | P | TK | AD132V | AD132IV | | | | |
| GFT3708 | G | P | TK | AD131V | | | | | |
| GFT3708/20 | G | P | TK | AD130V | | | | | |
| GFT3708/40 | G | P | | AD131V | ASZ16 | TI3029 | 2N2066 | | |
| GFT3708/40 | | | | AD138/50 | | | | | |
| GFT3708/60 | G | P | TK | AD131V | AD131V | | | | |
| GFT3708/80 | G | P | TK | AD132V | AD132IV | | | | |
| GFT4012 | G | P | TK | AD131IV | OC26 | | | | |
| GFT4012/15 | G | P | TK | AD131 | AD149 | 2N1295 | | 2SB83 | |
| GFT4012/15 | | | | OC26 | | | | | |
| GFT4012/30 | G | P | TK | AD130IV | AD130III | 2N1295 | 2N2836 | 2SB83 | |
| GFT4012/30 | | | | AD149 | OC26 | 2N2063 | | | |
| GFT4012/60 | G | P | TK | AD131IV | AD131III | 2N268 | | | |
| GFT4012/60 | | | | OC60V | SFT240 | | | | |
| GFT4012/60 | | | | AD131V | | | | | |
| GFT4112/30 | G | P | TK | AD131III | | | | | |
| GFT4112/60 | G | P | TK | AD131III | | | | | |
| GFT4308 | G | P | TK | AD131IV | | | | | |
| GFT4308/40 | G | P | TK | AD131IV | AD130IV | TI3029 | 2N257 | | |
| GFT4308/40 | | | TK | AD149IV | AD149 | | | | |
| GFT4308/60 | G | P | TK | AD132IV | | | | | |
| GFT4308/80 | G | P | TK | AD163IV | AD132IV | | | | |
| GFT4412 | G | P | TK | AD131V | | | | | |
| GFT4412/30 | G | P | TK | AD130V | AD130IV | TI3029 | 2N257 | | |
| GFT4412/30 | | | TK | AD149IV | AD149 | | | | |
| GFT4412/60 | G | P | TK | AD131V | AD131IV | | | | |
| GFT4608 | G | P | TK | AD131V | | | | | |
| GFT4608/40 | G | P | TK | AD131V | | | | | |
| GFT4608/60 | G | P | TK | AD132V | AD138/50 | TI3029 | 2N2066 | | |
| GFT4608/60 | | | TK | AD131V | | | | | |
| GFT4608/80 | G | P | TK | AD163IV | | | | | |
| GFT4712 | G | P | TK | AD130V | | | | | |
| GFT4712/30 | G | P | TK | AD130V | | | | | |
| GFT4712/60 | G | P | TK | AD131V | AD138/50 | TI3029 | 2N2066 | | |
| GFT8024 | G | P | TK | [AUY21III] | AD149 | 2N2836 | | | |
| GFT8024 | | | | CTP1514 | OC26 | | | | |
| GM0290 | G | P | | AF139 | | 2N5043 | MM139 | M9031 | |
| GM029A | G | P | | AF139 | | 2N5043 | MM139 | M9031 | |
| GM0760 | P | P | | AF109 | AF106 | | | 2SA432 | |
| GM0760 | | | | AF180 | AF190 | | | | |
| GM0761 | G | P | | AF106 | AF190 | | | 2SA230 | |
| GS100 | P | | GX | | | TIL606 | | | |
| GS300 | P | | GX | | | TIL58 | | | |
| GS400 | P | | GX | | | LS400 | | | |
| GS420 | P | | GX | | | LS400 | | | |
| GS600 | P | | GX | | | TIL81* | | | |
| GS610 | P | | GX | | | TIL81* | | | |
| GT3 | G | P | | AC125 | AC126 | 2N2429 | | | |
| GT4A | G | P | | AC128 | AC132 | 2N2431 | | | |
| GT11 | G | P | | AF127 | AF185 | | | | |
| GT11 | | | | OC45 | | | | | |
| GT12 | G | P | | AF127 | AF185 | | | | |
| GT12 | | | | OC45 | | | | | |
| GT13 | G | P | | AF126 | AF185 | | | | |
| GT13 | | | | OC44 | | | | | |
| GT14 | G | P | | AC128 | ASY77 | 2N2431 | | | |
| GT14 | | | | OC72 | | | | | |
| GT14H | G | P | | OC58 | OC66 | | | | |
| GT20 | G | P | | AC128 | AC132 | 2N2431 | | | |
| GT20 | | | | OC72 | | | | | |
| GT20H | G | P | | OC58 | OC66 | | | | |

| TYPE | M/S | POL | MANUFAC | EUROPEAN | | AMERICAN | | JAPANESE | USE |
|---|---|---|---|---|---|---|---|---|---|
| GT31 | G | P | | AC125 | AC126 | 2N2429 | | | |
| GT32 | G | P | | AC128 | AC132 | 2N2431 | | | |
| GT33 | G | P | | AC128 | AC132 | 2N2431 | | | |
| GT34 | G | P | GI | AC125 | AC126 | 2N2429 | | | |
| GT34H | G | P | | ASY77 | OC77 | | | | |
| GT34S | G | P | | AC125 | | | | | |
| GT38 | G | P | | AC125 | AC126 | 2N2429 | | | |
| GT38 | | | | OC71 | | | | | |
| GT41 | G | P | | AF185 | ASY27 | | | | |
| GT42 | G | P | | AF185 | ASY27 | | | | |
| GT43 | G | P | | AF185 | ASY27 | | | | |
| GT45 | G | P | | ASY26 | ASY27 | | | | |
| GT70 | G | P | | ASY26 | | | | | |
| GT74 | G | P | GI | AC126 | | 2N2429 | | | |
| GT81 | G | P | GI | AC126 | AC128 | 2N2429 | 2N2431 | | |
| GT81 | | | | OC72 | | | | | |
| GT81H | G | P | | AC126 | OC58 | 2N2429 | | | |
| GT81H | | | | OC66 | | | | | |
| GT81HS | G | P | | AC126 | | 2N2429 | | | |
| GT81R | G | P | | AC128 | AC132 | 2N2431 | | | |
| GT83 | G | P | | AC125 | AC126 | 2N2429 | | | |
| GT87 | G | P | | AC125 | AC126 | 2N2429 | | | |
| GT88 | G | P | | ASY26 | | | | | |
| GT109 | G | P | | AC128 | OC72 | 2N2431 | | | |
| GT109R | G | P | | AC128 | AC132 | 2N2431 | | | |
| GT122 | G | P | GI | AC126 | OC76 | 2N2429 | | | |
| GT161 | G | P | | AF126 | AF185 | | | | |
| GT222 | G | P | GI | AC125 | AC126 | 2N2429 | | | |
| GT222 | | | | OC71 | | | | | |
| GT310 | G | P | | AC128 | | 2N2431 | | | |
| GT759 | G | P | | AF127 | OC45 | | | | |
| GT760 | G | P | | AF127 | AF185 | | | | |
| GT760 | | | | OC45 | | | | | |
| GT760R | G | P | | AF127 | AF185 | | | | |
| GT760R | | | | OC45 | | | | | |
| GT761 | G | P | | AF126 | AF127 | | | | |
| GT761 | | | | AF185 | | | | | |
| GT761R | G | P | | AF126 | AF185 | | | | |
| GT761R | | | | OC44 | | | | | |
| GT762 | G | P | | AF185 | OC44 | | | | |
| GT949 | G | N | GI | | | | | | |
| H2 | G | P | | AD149 | | 2N2836 | | | |
| H3 | G | P | | AD149 | | 2N2836 | | | |
| H4 | G | P | | AD149 | | 2N2836 | | | |
| H8DEF | G | P | | AF185 | | | | | |
| HA1 | G | P | | AC126 | OC66 | 2N2429 | | | |
| HA1 | | | | OC71 | | | | | |
| HA2 | G | P | | AC126 | OC66 | 2N2429 | | | |
| HA2 | | | | OC71 | | | | | |
| HA3 | G | P | | AC126 | OC66 | 2N2429 | | | |
| HA3 | | | | OC71 | | | | | |
| HA8 | G | P | | OC66 | OC58 | | | | |
| HA8 | | | | OC59 | OC60 | | | | |
| HA9 | G | P | | OC58 | OC59 | | | | |
| HA9 | | | | OC60 | OC66 | | | | |
| HA10 | G | P | | OC58 | OC59 | | | | |
| HA10 | | | | OC60 | OC66 | | | | |
| HA2000 | M | P | | | | 3N156A | | | |
| HA2001 | M | P | | | | 3N155 | | | |
| HA2010 | M | P | | | | 3N156A | | | |
| HC1 | G | P | | AC126 | | 2N2429 | | | |
| HD197 | G | P | | AC128 | | 2N2431 | | | |
| HEP801 | J | N | MO | | | 2N4221 | | | |
| HEP802 | J | N | MO | | | 2N3819 | U1837E | | |
| HEP803 | J | P | MO | | | 2N3330 | | | |
| HEPF0021 | J | N | MO | | | 2N3819 | U1837E | | |
| HEPF1035 | J | P | MO | | | 2N3330 | | | |
| HEPF2004 | J | N | MO | | | 2N5397 | | | |
| HEPF2005 | J | N | MO | | | 2N3822 | | | |
| HF1 | G | P | | AF185 | | | | | |
| HF2 | G | P | | AF185 | | | | | |
| HJ15 | G | P | | AC126 | AC117 | 2N362 | 2N2429 | | |
| HJ15 | | | | AC153 | | | | | |
| HJ17 | G | P | | AC128 | | 2N2431 | | | |
| HJ17D | G | P | | AC124 | AC128 | 2N632 | 2N2431 | | |

| TYPE | M/S | POL | MANUFAC | EUROPEAN | | AMERICAN | | JAPANESE | USE |
|------|-----|-----|---------|----------|---|----------|---|----------|-----|
| HJ17D | G | P | | AC153J | | | | | |
| HJ22 | G | P | | AF185 | | | | | |
| HJ22D | G | P | | AF131 | AF137 | 2N482 | 2N483 | | |
| HJ22D | | | | AF185 | | | | | |
| HJ23 | G | P | | AF126 | AF136 | 2N140 | 2N412 | | |
| HJ23 | | | | AF185 | | | | | |
| HJ23D | G | P | | AF126 | AF127 | 2N411 | 2N485 | | |
| HJ23D | | | | AF185 | | | | | |
| HJ32 | G | P | | AF131 | AF135 | 2N370 | | | |
| HJ32 | | | | AF136 | | | | | |
| HJ34 | G | P | | AC128 | 2N2431 | | | | |
| HJ34A | G | P | | AC128 | | 2N2431 | | | |
| HJ35 | G | P | | ASZ16 | | | | | |
| HJ37 | G | P | | AF126 | AF132 | 2N371 | | | |
| HJ37 | | | | AF137 | | | | | |
| HJ50 | G | P | | AC122 | AC126 | 2N215 | 2N2429 | | |
| HJ50 | | | | AC163 | | | | | |
| HJ51 | G | P | | AC128 | AC153 | 2N408 | 2N2431 | | |
| HJ51 | | | | AC180 | | | | | |
| HJ54 | G | P | | | | 2N139 | | | |
| HJ55 | G | P | | AF132 | AF136 | 2N219 | | | |
| HJ55 | | | | AF185 | | | | | |
| HJ56 | G | P | | AF133 | AF137 | 2N410 | | | |
| HJ56 | | | | AF185 | | | | | |
| HJ57 | G | P | | AF132 | AF136 | 2N412 | | | |
| HJ57 | | | | AF185 | | | | | |
| HJ60 | G | P | | AF132 | AF136 | 2N139 | | | |
| HJ60 | | | | AF185 | | | | | |
| HJ61 | G | P | | AF127 | AF133 | 2N219 | | | |
| HJ61 | | | | AF137 | | | | | |
| HJ62 | G | P | | AC125 | AF185 | | | | |
| HJ70 | G | P | | AF132 | AF135 | | | | |
| HJ70 | | | | AF185 | | | | | |
| HJ71 | G | P | | AF132 | AF137 | 2N140 | 2N371 | | |
| HJ71 | | | | AF185 | | | | | |
| HJ72 | G | P | | AF132 | AF137 | 2N140 | 2N372 | | |
| HJ72 | | | | AF185 | | | | | |
| HJ73 | G | P | | AF132 | AF137 | 2N373 | | | |
| HJ73 | | | | AF185 | | | | | |
| HJ74 | G | P | | AF132 | AF136 | 2N374 | | | |
| HJ74 | | | | AF137 | | | | | |
| HJ75 | G | P | | AF132 | AF137 | 2N544 | | | |
| HJ75 | | | | AF185 | | | | | |
| HLS400 | P | | | | | 2S400 | | | |
| HRN1020 | M | P | | | | MFE3003 | | | |
| HRN1030 | M | P | | | | MFE3003 | | | |
| HRN8318D | M | P | | | | MFE3003 | | | |
| HRN8338D | M | P | | | | 3N155 | | | |
| HRN8346D | M | P | | | | MFE3003 | | | |
| HRN8350 | M | P | | | | MFE3003 | | | |
| HRN8353 | M | P | | | | MFE3003 | | | |
| HRN8360 | M | P | | | | 2N4352 | | | |
| HRN8363 | M | P | | | | 3N155 | | | |
| HS3 | G | P | | ASY27 | OC47 | | | | |
| HS4 | G | P | | ASY27 | OC47 | | | | |
| HS15 | G | P | | | | 2N109 | | | |
| HS17D | G | P | | | | 2N109 | | | |
| HS22D | G | P | | | | 2N139 | | | |
| HS23D | G | P | | | | 2N140 | | | |
| HT700 | P | | | | | TIL78* | | | |
| IF1 | G | P | | AF185 | | | | | |
| IF2 | G | P | | AF185 | | | | | |
| IF3 | G | P | | AF185 | | | | | |
| IMF3954 | J | N | IL | | | 2N5545 | 2N5197 | | |
| IMF3954A | J | N | IL | | | 2N5196 | | | |
| IMF3955 | J | N | IL | | | 2N5547 | 2N5198 | | |
| IMF3955A | J | N | IL | | | 2N5546 | 2N5198 | | |
| IMF3956 | J | N | IL | | | 2N5547 | 2N5199 | | |
| IMF3957 | J | N | IL | | | 2N5547 | 2N5199 | | |
| IMF3958 | J | N | IL | | | 2N5045 | 2N5199 | | |
| IT108 | J | N | IL | | | 2N5486 | 2N5245 | | |
| IT108 | | | | | | U1994E | | | |
| IT109 | J | N | IL | | | 2N5486 | 2N5397 | | |
| IT1700 | M | P | IL | | | MFE3003 | 3N163 | | |
| IT1701 | M | P | IL | | | MFE3003 | 3N163 | | |

| TYPE | M/S | POL | MANUFAC | EUROPEAN | | AMERICAN | | JAPANESE | USE |
|---|---|---|---|---|---|---|---|---|---|
| IT1702 | M | P | IL | | | MFE3003 | 3N163 | | |
| IT1750 | M | P | IL | | | 3N155 | | | |
| IT2700 | | | IL | | | 3N170 | | | |
| IT2701 | | | IL | | | 3N170 | | | |
| ITE3066 | J | N | IL | | | 2N5639 | 2N5953 | | |
| ITE3066 | | | | | | 2N4302 | | | |
| ITE3067 | J | N | IL | | | 2N5639 | 2N3460 | | |
| ITE3067 | | | | | | 2N4302 | | | |
| ITE3068 | J | N | IL | | | 2N5639 | ITE4118 | | |
| ITE4117 | J | N | IL | | | 2N5640 | TN4117 | | |
| ITE4118 | J | N | IL | | | 2N5640 | TN4118 | | |
| ITE4119 | J | N | IL | | | 2N5640 | TN4119 | | |
| ITE4338 | J | N | IL | | | 2N5486 | 2N3460 | | |
| ITE4338 | | | | | | E101 | | | |
| ITE4339 | J | N | IL | | | 2N5486 | 2N3460 | | |
| ITE4340 | | | | | | 2N4302 | | | |
| ITE4340 | J | N | IL | | | 2N5486 | 2N5953 | | |
| ITE4341 | | | | | | 2N4302 | | | |
| ITE4341 | J | N | IL | | | 2N5486 | 2N5953 | | |
| ITE4342 | | | | | | 2N4303 | | | |
| ITE4342 | J | N | | | | 2N5486 | | | |
| ITE4391 | J | N | IL | | | MPF4391 | TIS73 | | |
| ITE4391 | | | | | | U1897E | | | |
| ITE4392 | J | N | IL | | | MPF4392 | TIS74 | | |
| ITE4392 | | | | | | U1898E | | | |
| ITE4393 | J | N | IL | | | MPF4393 | TIS75 | | |
| ITE4393 | | | | | | U1899E | | | |
| ITE4416 | J | N | IL | | | 2N5486 | 2N5245 | | |
| ITE4416 | | | | | | U1994E | | | |
| ITE4867 | J | N | IL | | | 2N5457 | 2N3460 | | |
| ITE4867 | | | | | | 2N4867 | | | |
| ITE4868 | J | N | IL | | | 2N5458 | 2N3459 | | |
| ITE4868 | | | | | | 2N4868 | | | |
| ITE4869 | J | N | IL | | | 2N5459 | 2N5953 | | |
| ITE4869 | | | | | | 2N4869 | | | |
| IW8377 | S | N | | BFX62 | BF155 | | | | |
| IW8377 | | | | BF180 | | | | | |
| J1 | G | P | | OC72 | | | | | |
| J2 | G | P | | OC72 | | | | | |
| J3 | G | P | | OC72 | | | | | |
| J309 | J | N | | | | 2N5486 | | | |
| J310 | J | N | | | | 2N5486 | | | |
| JP1 | G | P | | AC128 | OC72 | 2N2431 | | | |
| K1001 | M | N | | | | MFE3004 | MFE3005 | | |
| K1003 | M | N | | | | MFE3004 | MFE3005 | | |
| K1004 | J | N | | | | MFE3001 | | | |
| K1201 | M | N | | | | MFE3005 | | | |
| K1202 | M | N | | | | MFE3004 | | | |
| K1501 | M | P | | | | 3N157A | | | |
| K1502 | M | P | | | | 3N157A | | | |
| K1504 | M | P | | | | 2N4352 | | | |
| KE510 | J | N | | | | 2N5640 | | | |
| KE511 | J | N | | | | 2N5640 | | | |
| KE3684 | J | N | IL | | | 2N5457 | 2N5953 | | |
| KE3684 | | | | | | 2N4303 | | | |
| KE3685 | J | N | IL | | | 2N5458 | AST3821 | | |
| KE3685 | | | | | | 2N4302 | | | |
| KE3686 | J | N | | | | E101 | | | |
| KE3687 | J | N | IL | | | 2N5457 | E101 | | |
| KE3823 | J | N | | | | 2N5668 | AST3823 | | |
| KE3823 | | | | | | U1837E | | | |
| KE3970 | J | N | IL | | | 2N5638 | TIS73 | | |
| KE3970 | | | | | | U1897E | | | |
| KE3971 | J | N | IL | | | 2N5639 | TIS74 | | |
| KE3971 | | | | | | U1898E | | | |
| KE3972 | J | N | IL | | | 2N5640 | TIS75 | | |
| KE3972 | | | | | | U1899E | | | |
| KE4091 | J | N | IL | | | 2N5638 | TIS73 | | |
| KE4091 | | | | | | U1897E | | | |
| KE4092 | J | N | IL | | | 2N5639 | TIS74 | | |
| KE4092 | | | | | | U1899E | | | |
| KE4093 | J | N | IL | | | 2N5640 | TIS75 | | |
| KE4093 | | | | | | U1899E | | | |
| KE4220 | J | N | IL | | | 2N5457 | AST3821 | | |
| KE4220 | | | | | | 2N4302 | | | |

| TYPE | M/S | POL | MANUFAC | EUROPEAN | | AMERICAN | | JAPANESE | USE |
|---|---|---|---|---|---|---|---|---|---|
| KE4221 | J | N | IL | | | 2N5458 | AST3822 | | |
| KE4221 | | | | | | 2N4303 | | | |
| KE4222 | J | N | IL | | | 2N5459 | AST3822 | | |
| KE4222 | | | | | | U1837E | | | |
| KE4223 | J | N | IL | | | MPF102 | 2N5950 | | |
| | | | | | | | | | |
| KE4223 | | | | | | U1837E | | | |
| KE4224 | J | | IL | | | MPF102 | 2N5949 | | |
| KE4224 | | | | | | 2N5163 | | | |
| KE4391 | J | N | IL | | | MPF4391 | TIS73 | | |
| KE4391 | | | | | | U1897E | | | |
| KE4392 | J | N | IL | | | MPF4392 | TIS74 | | |
| KE4392 | | | | | | U1898E | | | |
| KE4393 | J | N | IL | | | MPF4393 | TIS75 | | |
| KE4393 | | | | | | U1899E | | | |
| KE4416 | J | N | IL | | | 2N5486 | 2N5245 | | |
| | | | | | | | | | |
| KE4416 | | | | | | U1994E | | | |
| KE4856 | J | N | IL | | | MPF4391 | TIS73 | | |
| KE4856 | | | | | | U1897E | | | |
| KE4857 | J | N | IL | | | MPF4392 | TIS74 | | |
| KE4857 | | | | | | U1898E | | | |
| KE4858 | J | N | IL | | | MPF4393 | TIS75 | | |
| KE4858 | | | | | | U1899E | | | |
| KE4859 | J | N | IL | | | MPF4391 | 2N4859 | | |
| KE4859 | | | | | | TIS73 | U1897E | | |
| KE4860 | J | N | IL | | | MPF4392 | 2N4860 | | |
| | | | | | | | | | |
| KE4860 | | | | | | TIS74 | U1898E | | |
| KE4861 | J | N | IL | | | MPF4393 | 2N4861 | | |
| KE4861 | | | | | | TIS74 | U1899E | | |
| KE5103 | J | N | IL | | | 2N5668 | 2N3823 | | |
| KE5103 | | | | | | 2N5952 | 2N4302 | | |
| KE5104 | J | N | IL | | | 2N5669 | 2N3823 | | |
| KE5104 | | | | | | 2N5953 | 2N4303 | | |
| KE5105 | J | N | IL | | | 2N5670 | 2N3823 | | |
| KE5105 | | | | | | 2N5245 | U1994E | | |
| L148 | P | | | | | LS869 | | | |
| | | | | | | | | | |
| LA-600 | P | | | | | TIL601* | | | |
| LA-700 | P | | | | | TIL63* | | | |
| LDF603 | J | N | AM | | | 2N4221A | | | |
| LDF604 | J | N | AM | | | 2N4221A | | | |
| LDF605 | J | N | AM | | | 2N4222A | | | |
| | | | | | | | | | |
| LDF691 | J | N | AM | | | 2N4391 | | | |
| LDF692 | J | N | AM | | | 2N4392 | | | |
| LDF693 | J | N | | | | 2N4393 | | | |
| LM390 | S | P | | BC328 | | | | | |
| LM399 | S | N | | BC338 | | | | | |
| | | | | | | | | | |
| LM596 | S | N | | BC548C | | | | | |
| M10H | G | P | | AF178 | | 2N2495 | | | |
| M10L | G | N | | AC176 | | 2N2495 | | | |
| M12H | G | P | | AF178 | | | | | |
| M100 | M | N | SX | | | 2N3796 | | | |
| | | | | | | | | | |
| M101 | M | N | SX | | | | | | |
| M103 | M | P | IL, SX | | | MFE3003 | 3N161 | | |
| M104 | M | P | IL, SX | | | 3N158 | 3N174 | | |
| M106 | M | P | IL, SX | | | 2N4067 | | | |
| M107 | M | P | IL, SX | | | 2N4067 | | | |
| | | | | | | | | | |
| M108 | M | P | IL, SX | | | 2N4067 | | | |
| M113 | M | P | IL, SX | | | 3N155 | | | |
| M114 | M | P | IL, SX | | | 2N4352 | 3N160 | | |
| M116 | M | P | SX | | | 3N161 | | | |
| M117 | M | P | IL, SX | | | 3N160 | | | |
| | | | | | | | | | |
| M119 | M | P | SX | | | MFE3003 | 3N161 | | |
| M163 | M | P | SX | | | 3N163 | | | |
| M164 | M | P | SX | | | 3N164 | | | |
| M200 | S | N | | BC548 | | | | | |
| M200E | S | N | | BC548B | | | | | |
| | | | | | | | | | |
| M290 | G | P | | AC128 | | | | | |
| M299 | S | N | | BC338 | | | | | |
| M511 | M | P | IL, SX | | | MFE3003 | 3N161 | | |
| M511A | M | P | IL, SX | | | MFE3003 | 3N161 | | |
| M517 | M | P | SX | | | 3N161 | | | |
| | | | | | | | | | |
| M3016 | G | P | | AC128 | | | | | |
| MA100 | G | P | MO | | | MA881 | | | |
| MA112 | G | P | MO | | | MA113 | | | |
| MA113 | G | P | MO | | | MA114 | | | |
| MA114 | G | P | MO | | | MA883 | | | |

| TYPE | M/S | POL | MANUFAC | EUROPEAN | | AMERICAN | | JAPANESE | USE |
|------|-----|-----|---------|----------|--|----------|--|----------|-----|
| MA115 | G | P | MO | | | MA113 | | | |
| MA116 | G | P | MO | | | MA114 | | | |
| MA117 | G | P | MO | | | MA116 | | | |
| MA200 | G | P | MO | | | MA202 | | | |
| MA201 | G | P | MO | | | MA201 | | | |
| | | | | | | | | | |
| MA202 | G | P | MO | | | MA200 | | | |
| MA203 | G | P | MO | | | MA203 | | | |
| MA204 | G | P | MO | | | MA201 | MA203 | | |
| MA205 | G | P | MO | | | MA204 | | | |
| MA206 | G | P | MO | | | MA205 | | | |
| | | | | | | | | | |
| MA286 | G | P | MO | | | MA287 | | | |
| MA287 | G | P | MO | | | MA117 | | | |
| MA288 | G | P | MO | | | MA887 | | | |
| MA881 | G | P | MO | | | MA882 | | | |
| MA882 | G | P | MO | | | MA883 | | | |
| | | | | | | | | | |
| MA883 | G | P | MO | | | MA884 | | | |
| MA884 | G | P | MO | | | MA889 | | | |
| MA885 | G | P | MO | | | MA881 | MA886 | | |
| MA886 | G | P | MO | | | MA887 | | | |
| MA887 | G | P | MO | | | MA888 | | | |
| | | | | | | | | | |
| MA888 | G | P | MO | | | MA889 | | | |
| MA889 | G | P | MO | | | MA884 | | | |
| MA909 | G | P | MO | | | MA910 | | | |
| MA910 | G | P | MO | | | | | | |
| MA1703 | G | P | MO | | | | | | |
| | | | | | | | | | |
| MA1703 | G | P | MO | | | MA1704 | | | |
| MA1704 | G | P | MO | | | MA1705 | | | |
| MA1705 | G | P | MO | | | | | | |
| MA1706 | G | P | MO | | | MA1707 | | | |
| MA1707 | G | P | MO | | | MA1708 | | | |
| | | | | | | | | | |
| MA1708 | G | P | MO | | | | | | |
| MC101 | G | P | | AF185 | | | | | |
| MEO411 | S | P | ME | BC307VI | | | | | |
| MEO412 | S | P | ME | BC307A | | | | | |
| MEM511 | M | P | GI, IL | | | MFE3003 | SFB3082 | | |
| | | | | | | | | | |
| MEM511A | M | P | | | | MFE3003 | | | |
| MEM511C | M | P | GI, IL | | | 3N161 | | | |
| MEM517A | M | P | GI | | | MFE3003 | | | |
| MEM520 | M | P | GI, IL | | | 2N5352 | 3N174 | | |
| MEM520C | M | P | GI, IL | | | 2N5352 | 3N174 | | |
| | | | | | | | | | |
| MEM550 | M | P | GI, IL | | | SFC5418 | | | |
| MEM550C | M | P | GI, IL | | | SFC5418 | | | |
| MEM551 | M | P | GI, IL | | | SFC5417 | | | |
| MEM551C | M | P | GI, IL | | | SFC5417 | | | |
| MEM554 | M | N | GI | | | MFE3006 | 3N201 | | |
| | | | | | | | | | |
| MEM554C | M | N | GI | | | MFE3006 | 3N201 | | |
| MEM556 | M | P | GI | | | 3N158A | 3N174 | | |
| MEM556C | M | P | GI | | | 3N158A | 3N174 | | |
| MEM557 | M | N | GI | | | 3N128 | | | |
| MEM557C | M | N | GI | | | 3N128 | | | |
| | | | | | | | | | |
| MEM560 | M | P | GI | | | 3N158A | 3N161 | | |
| MEM560C | M | P | GI | | | 3N158A | 3N161 | | |
| MEM561C | M | P | | | | 3N158A | | | |
| MEM562 | M | N | GI | | | 2N4351 | | | |
| MEM562C | M | N | GI | | | 2N4351 | | | |
| | | | | | | | | | |
| MEM563 | M | N | GI | | | 2N4351 | | | |
| MEM563C | M | N | | | | 2N4351 | | | |
| MEM564C | M | N | GI | | | 3N140 | | | |
| MEM571C | M | N | GI | | | 3N128 | | | |
| MEM575 | M | P | GI | | | 3N158A | | | |
| | | | | | | | | | |
| MEM614 | M | N | GI | | | 3N140 | 3N203 | | |
| MEM615A | M | N | | | | 3N140 | | | |
| MEM616 | M | N | | | | 3N140 | | | |
| MEM617 | M | N | | | | 3N140 | | | |
| MEM618 | M | N | | | | 3N140 | | | |
| | | | | | | | | | |
| MEM655 | M | N | GI | | | 3N128 | | | |
| MEM656A | M | N | | | | 3N128 | | | |
| MEM660 | M | N | GI | | | 3N128 | SFC3260 | | |
| MEM780 | M | P | | | | MFE5000 | | | |
| MEM803 | M | P | GI | | | 3N158A | | | |
| | | | | | | | | | |
| MEM804 | M | P | GI | | | 3N158A | | | |
| MEM806 | M | P | GI | | | 3N158A | | | |
| MEM806A | M | P | | | | 3N158A | | | |
| MEM807 | M | P | GI | | | 3N158A | | | |
| MEM807A | M | P | | | | 3N158A | | | |

| TYPE | M/S | POL | MANUFAC | EUROPEAN | | AMERICAN | | JAPANESE | USE |
|------|-----|-----|---------|----------|--|----------|--|----------|-----|
| MEM809 | M | P | | | | 3N158A | | | |
| MEM819 | M | P | | | | 3N158A | | | |
| MEM857 | M | P | | | | MFE5000 | | | |
| MFE120 | M | N | MO | | | | | | |
| MFE121 | M | N | MO | | | | | | |
| MFE122 | M | N | MO | | | | | | |
| MFE2000 | J | N | MO | | | SFB182 | 2N3823 | | |
| MFE2001 | J | N | MO | | | SFB6183 | 2N3823 | | |
| MFE2002 | J | N | MO | | | SFB6184 | | | |
| MFE2004 | J | N | MO, IL | | | 2N4860 | 2N4093 | | |
| MFE2005 | J | N | MO, IL | | | 2N4859 | 2N4092 | | |
| MFE2006 | J | N | MO, IL | | | 2N4859 | 2N4091 | | |
| MFE2007 | J | N | MO, IL | | | 2N4860 | 2N3970 | | |
| MFE2008 | J | N | MO, IL | | | 2N4859 | 2N3970 | | |
| MFE2009 | J | N | MO, IL | | | 2N4859 | 2N4878 | | |
| MFE2010 | J | N | MO, IL | | | 2N4859 | | | |
| MFE2011 | J | N | MO, IL | | | SFC1785 | 2N4977 | | |
| MFE2012 | J | N | MO, IL | | | SFC1785 | 2N4446 | | |
| MFE2093 | J | N | MO, IL | | | 2N5358 | | | |
| MFE2094 | J | N | MO, IL | | | 2N5359 | | | |
| MFE2095 | J | N | MO, IL | | | 2N5360 | | | |
| MFE2097 | J | N | MO | | | 2N4093 | 2N4092 | | |
| MFE2098 | J | N | MO | | | 2N4091 | | | |
| MFE2133 | J | N | MO | | | 2N4860 | 2N4092 | | |
| MFE3003 | M | P | MO, IL | | | SFC4047 | | | |
| MFE3006 | M | N | MO | | | | | | |
| MFE3007 | M | N | MO | | | | | | |
| MFE3008 | M | N | MO | | | | | | |
| MFE4007 | J | P | MO, IL | | | 2N2608 | | | |
| MFE4008 | J | P | MO, IL | | | 2N2608 | | | |
| MFE4009 | J | P | MO, IL | | | 2N2498 | | | |
| MFE4010 | J | P | MO | | | 2N2498 | | | |
| MFE4011 | J | P | MO | | | 2N3331 | | | |
| MFE4012 | J | P | MO | | | 2N3331 | | | |
| MFT122 | G | P | | AC128 | | 2N2431 | | | |
| MFT123 | G | P | | AC128 | | 2N2431 | | | |
| MHT5501 | S | N | HW | | | 2N4300 | | | |
| MHT5502 | S | N | HW | | | 2N4300 | | | |
| MHT5503 | S | N | HW | | | 2N4300 | | | |
| MHT5504 | S | N | HW | | | 2N4300 | | | |
| MHT5505 | S | N | HW | | | 2N4300 | | | |
| MHT5506 | S | N | HW | | | 2N4300 | | | |
| MHT5507 | S | N | HW | | | 2N4300 | | | |
| MHT5508 | S | N | HW | | | 2N4300 | | | |
| MHT6408 | S | N | HW | | | 2N3996 | | | |
| MHT6409 | S | N | HW | | | 2N3996 | | | |
| MHT6410 | S | N | HW | | | 2N3996 | | | |
| MHT6411 | S | N | HW | | | 2N3996 | | | |
| MHT6412 | S | N | HW | | | 2N3996 | | | |
| MHT6413 | S | N | HW | | | 2N3996 | | | |
| MHT6414 | S | N | HW | | | 2N3996 | | | |
| MHT6415 | S | N | HW | | | 2N3996 | | | |
| MHT6416 | S | N | HW | | | 2N3996 | | | |
| MHT7011 | S | N | HW | | | 2N4301 | | | |
| MHT7012 | S | N | HW | | | 2N4301 | | | |
| MHT7013 | S | N | HW | | | 2N4301 | | | |
| MHT7014 | S | N | HW | | | 2N4301 | | | |
| MHT7015 | S | N | HW | | | 2N4301 | | | |
| MHT7016 | S | N | HW | | | 2N4301 | | | |
| MHT7017 | S | N | HW | | | 2N4301 | | | |
| MHT7018 | S | N | HW | | | 2N4301 | | | |
| MHT7019 | S | N | HW | | | 2N4301 | | | |
| MHT7401 | S | N | HW | | | 2N3421 | | | |
| MHT7402 | S | N | HW | | | 2N3421 | | | |
| MHT7403 | S | N | HW | | | 2N3421 | | | |
| MHT7404 | S | N | HW | | | 2N3421 | | | |
| MHT7405 | S | N | HW | | | 2N3421 | | | |
| MHT7406 | S | N | HW | | | 2N3421 | | | |
| MHT7407 | S | N | HW | | | 2N3421 | | | |
| MHT7408 | S | N | HW | | | 2N3421 | | | |
| MHT7409 | S | N | HW | | | 2N3421 | | | |
| MHT7410 | S | N | HW | | | 2N3421 | | | |
| MHT7411 | S | N | HW | | | 2N3421 | | | |
| MHT7412 | S | N | HW | | | 2N3421 | | | |
| MHT7413 | S | N | HW | | | 2N3421 | | | |

| TYPE | M/S | POL | MANUFAC | EUROPEAN | | AMERICAN | | JAPANESE | USE |
|------|-----|-----|---------|----------|---|----------|---|----------|-----|
| MHT7414 | S | N | HW | | | 2N3421 | | | |
| MHT7415 | S | N | HW | | | 2N3421 | | | |
| MHT7416 | S | N | HW | | | 2N3421 | | | |
| MHT7417 | S | N | HW | | | 2N3421 | | | |
| MHT7418 | S | N | HW | | | 2N3421 | | | |
| MHT7419 | S | N | HW | | | 2N3421 | | | |
| MHT7801 | S | N | HW | | | 2N5381 | | | |
| MHT7802 | S | N | HW | | | 2N5387 | | | |
| MHT7803 | S | N | HW | | | 2N5387 | | | |
| MHT7804 | S | N | HW | | | 2N5387 | | | |
| MHT7805 | S | N | HW | | | 2N5387 | | | |
| MHT7806 | S | N | HW | | | 2N5387 | | | |
| MHT7807 | S | N | HW | | | 2N5387 | | | |
| MHT7808 | S | N | HW | | | 2N5387 | | | |
| MHT7809 | S | N | HW | | | 2N5387 | | | |
| MHT8002 | S | N | HW | | | 2N4002 | | | |
| MHT8004 | S | N | HW | | | 2N4002 | | | |
| MHT9001 | S | N | HW | | | 2N4002 | | | |
| MHT9002 | S | N | HW | | | 2N4002 | | | |
| MHT9003 | S | N | HW | | | 2N4002 | | | |
| MHT9004 | S | N | HW | | | 2N4002 | | | |
| MHT9005 | S | N | HW | | | 2N4002 | | | |
| MHT9006 | S | N | HW | | | 2N4002 | | | |
| MHT9007 | S | N | HW | | | 2N4002 | | | |
| MHT9008 | S | N | HW | | | 2N4002 | | | |
| MHT9009 | S | N | HW | | | 2N4002 | | | |
| MHT9010 | S | N | HW | | | 2N4002 | | | |
| MHT9011 | S | N | HW | | | 2N4002 | | | |
| MHT9012 | S | N | HW | | | 2N4002 | | | |
| MJ400 | S | N | MO | (BUY79) | | 2N5338 | TIP49 | | 06 |
| MJ400 | | | | | | 2N3585 | | | 06 |
| MJ410 | S | N | MO | BUY74 | | FT410 | RCA410 | | 06 |
| MJ411 | S | N | MO | BUY75 | | FT411 | RCA411 | | 06 |
| MJ413 | S | N | MO | BUY76 | | FT413 | TIP54 | | 16 |
| MJ413 | | | | | | RCA413 | | | 16 |
| MJ420 | S | N | MO | BF258 | (BF459) | 2N5059 | 2N3440 | | 06 |
| MJ421 | S | N | MO | (BF459) | | 2N3439 | | | 06 |
| MJ423 | S | N | MO | BUY76 | BDY96 | FT423 | TIP54 | | 16 |
| MJ423 | | | | | | RCA423 | | | 16 |
| MJ424 | S | N | MO | BUX16C | BUY76 | 2N6251 | | | 06 |
| MJ425 | S | N | MO | BUX18C | BUY76 | | | | 06 |
| MJ430 | | | MO | | | FT430 | | | |
| MJ431 | S | N | MO | BUY76 | BDY96 | FT431 | TIP54 | | 16 |
| MJ431 | | | | | | RCA431 | | | 16 |
| MJ450 | S | P | MO | | | 2N6469 | 2N4398 | | 09 |
| MJ450 | | | | | | TIP32 | 2N6246 | | 09 |
| MJ480 | S | N | MO | | | 2N6470 | 2N3055 | | 06 |
| MJ480 | | | | | | 2N4913 | 2N3713 | | 06 |
| MJ480 | | | | | | 2N5067 | | | 06 |
| MJ481 | S | N | MO | | | 2N6471 | 2N3055 | | 06 |
| MJ481 | | | | | | 2N4914 | 2N3714 | | 06 |
| MJ481 | | | | | | 2N5068 | | | 06 |
| MJ490 | S | P | MO | | | 2N6469 | 2N4904 | | 06 |
| MJ490 | | | | | | TIP34 | 2N4901 | | 06 |
| MJ490 | | | | | | 2N6246 | | | 06 |
| MJ491 | S | P | MO | | | 2N4905 | TIP34 | | 06 |
| MJ491 | | | | | | 2N4902 | 2N6246 | | 06 |
| MJ500 | S | P | MO | | | TIP42 | | | 09 |
| MJ501 | S | P | MO | | | TIP42A | | | 09 |
| MJ802 | S | N | MO | | | 2N3716 | 2N6258 | | 06 |
| MJ900 | S | P | MO | | | RCA8350A | 2N3789 | | 06 |
| MJ901 | S | P | MO | | | RCA8350B | 2N3790 | | 06 |
| MJ920 | S | P | MO | | | RCA8350A | | | 06 |
| MJ921 | S | P | MO | | | RCA8350B | | | 06 |
| MJ1000 | S | N | MO | | | SE9303 | RCA1000 | | 06 |
| MJ1000 | | | | | | 2N3713 | | | 06 |
| MJ1001 | S | N | MO | | | SE9304 | RCA1001 | | 06 |
| MJ1001 | | | | | | 2N3714 | | | 06 |
| MJ1200 | S | N | MO | | | 2N6384 | | | 06 |
| MJ1201 | S | N | MO | | | 2N6385 | | | 06 |
| MJ1800 | S | N | MO | BUX16C | BUY74 | 2N6250 | TIP51 | | 09 |
| MJ1800 | | | | BDY98 | | 2N5838 | | | 09 |
| MJ2249 | S | N | MO | BDX25-6 | | 2N3766 | 2N3878 | | 09 |
| MJ2249 | | | | | | MJ2250 | TIP31A | | 09 |
| MJ2249 | | | | | | 2N3879 | | | 09 |

| TYPE | M/S | POL | MANUFAC | EUROPEAN | | AMERICAN | | JAPANESE | USE |
|------|-----|-----|---------|----------|---|----------|---|----------|-----|
| MJ2250 | S | N | MO | BDX25-6 | | 2N3767 | TIP31B | | 09 |
| MJ2250 | | | | | | 2N3879 | | | |
| MJ2251 | S | N | MO | BUX67C | (BUY78) | MJ2252 | TIP47 | | 06 |
| MJ2251 | | | | | | 2N2584 | | | 06 |
| MJ2252 | S | N | MO | BUX67C | (BUY78) | TIP48 | 2N3584 | | 06 |
| | | | | | | | | | |
| MJ2253 | S | P | MO | | | MJ2254 | TIP32 | | |
| MJ2253 | | | | | | 2N4899 | 2N5955 | | |
| MJ2254 | S | P | MO | | | TIP32B | 2N5954 | | 09 |
| MJ2254 | | | | | | 2N4900 | | | 09 |
| MJ2255 | S | N | MO | | | 2N3713 | | | |
| | | | | | | | | | |
| MJ2257 | S | N | MO | | | 2N3714 | | | 09 |
| MJ2267 | S | P | MO | | | 2N6469 | 2N4901 | | 09 |
| MJ2267 | | | | | | 2N3789 | 2N3791 | | 09 |
| MJ2267 | | | | | | 2N6246 | | | 09 |
| MJ2268 | S | P | MO | | | 2N5879 | 2N4902 | | 09 |
| | | | | | | | | | |
| MJ2268 | | | | | | 2N3790 | 2N6246 | | 09 |
| MJ2500 | S | P | MO | | | RCA8350A | TIP145 | | 06 |
| MJ2501 | S | P | MO | | | RCA8350B | TIP146 | | 06 |
| MJ2801 | S | N | MO | | | 2N6569 | 2N6371 | | 09 |
| MJ2801 | | | | | | 2N3055 | 2N3713 | | 09 |
| | | | | | | | | | |
| MJ2801 | | | | | | 40251 | | | 09 |
| MJ2802 | S | N | MO | | | 2N3714 | | | |
| MJ2804 | S | N | MO | | | 2N5881 | 2N4347 | | 06 |
| MJ2840 | S | N | MO | | | 2N3715 | TIP41A | | 06 |
| MJ2840 | | | | | | 2N3055 | | | 06 |
| | | | | | | | | | |
| MJ2840 | | | | | | 2N5882 | 2N4347 | | 06 |
| MJ2841 | S | N | MO | | | 2N3716 | TIP41B | | 06 |
| MJ2841 | | | | | | 2N6254 | | | 06 |
| MJ2862 | S | P | MO | | | 2N3791 | | | |
| MJ2901 | S | P | MO | | | 2N6469 | 2N4901 | | 09 |
| | | | | | | | | | |
| MJ2901 | | | | | | 2N6246 | | | 09 |
| MJ2940 | S | P | MO | BDX18N | | 2N6254 | 2N5879 | | 06 |
| MJ2940 | | | | | | 2N3791 | | | 06 |
| MJ2941 | S | P | MO | | | 2N5880 | 2N6247 | | 06 |
| MJ2941 | | | | | | 2N3792 | 2N6246 | | 06 |
| | | | | | | | | | |
| MJ2955 | S | P | MO | BDX18N | | FT2955 | 2N6247 | | 09 |
| MJ3000 | S | N | MO | | | SE9300 | TIP140 | | 06 |
| MJ3001 | S | N | MO | | | SE9304 | TIP141 | | 06 |
| MJ3010 | S | N | MO | BUX16B | | TIP51 | MJ3011 | | |
| MJ3011 | S | N | MO | BUX16B | | TIP53 | | | |
| | | | | | | | | | |
| MJ3026 | S | N | MO | BUY78 | BUY79 | 2N5839 | | | 06 |
| MJ3027 | S | N | MO | BU126 | BUY78 | FT401 | 2N5840 | | 06 |
| MJ3028 | S | N | MO | BU126 | BUY78 | FT402 | | | 06 |
| MJ3029 | S | N | MO | BUX16A | BUY74 | FT411 | TIP51 | | 06 |
| MJ3029 | | | | BDY95 | | | | | 06 |
| | | | | | | | | | |
| MJ3030 | S | N | MO | BUX16C | BUY79 | FT413 | TIP53 | | 06 |
| MJ3101 | S | N | MO | BDX25-6 | | 2N3878 | TIP31 | | 09 |
| MJ3201 | S | N | MO | BUX67A | (BF458) | SE9331 | TIP47 | | 06 |
| MJ3202 | S | N | MO | BUX67B | (BF459) | SE9331 | TIP48 | | 06 |
| MJ3202 | | | | | | 2N3585 | | | 06 |
| | | | | | | | | | |
| MJ3260 | S | N | MO | | | 2N6250 | | | 10 |
| MJ3430 | S | N | MO | BUX18B | BUY75 | FT411 | 2N5840 | | 06 |
| MJ3583 | S | P | MO | | | 2N6211 | | | 06 |
| MJ3584 | S | P | MO | | | 2N6212 | | | 09 |
| MJ3585 | S | P | MO | | | 2N6212 | | | 09 |
| | | | | | | | | | |
| MJ3701 | S | P | MO | | | 2N5956 | 2N4898 | | 09 |
| MJ3701 | | | | | | TIP32 | 2N5456 | | 09 |
| MJ3760 | S | N | MO | BU126 | | | | | |
| MJ3761 | S | N | MO | BU126 | | | | | |
| MJ3771 | S | N | MO | | | 2N3771 | 2N5301 | | 09 |
| | | | | | | | | | |
| MJ3772 | S | N | MO | | | 2N3772 | 2N5301 | | 09 |
| MJ3773 | S | N | MO | | | 2N5630 | 2N3773 | | 09 |
| MJ3801 | S | N | MO | | | TIP33B | | | |
| MJ3802 | S | N | MO | | | TIP33B | | | |
| MJ4000 | S | N | MO | | | SE9303 | 2N6384 | | 06 |
| | | | | | | | | | |
| MJ4000 | | | | | | TIP120 | | | 06 |
| MJ4001 | S | N | MO | | | SE9304 | 2N6385 | | 06 |
| MJ4001 | | | | | | TIP121 | | | 06 |
| MJ4010 | S | P | MO | | | RCA8350A | TIP125 | | 06 |
| MJ4011 | S | P | MO | | | RCA8350B | TIP126 | | 06 |
| | | | | | | | | | |
| MJ4030 | S | P | MO | | | TIP145 | | | 06 |
| MJ4031 | S | P | MO | | | TIP146 | | | 06 |
| MJ4032 | S | P | MO | | | TIP147 | | | 06 |
| MJ4033 | S | N | MO | | | | | | 06 |
| MJ4034 | S | N | MO | | | | | | 06 |

| TYPE | M/S | POL | MANUFAC | EUROPEAN | | AMERICAN | | JAPANESE | USE |
|------|-----|-----|---------|----------|--|----------|--|----------|-----|
| MJ4035 | S | N | MO | | | | | | 09 |
| MJ4101 | S | N | MO | | | | | | |
| MJ4240 | S | P | MO | | | TIP31 | | | 09 |
| MJ4502 | S | P | MO | | | 2N6212 | | | 06 |
| MJ4545 | | | MO | | | 2N4399 | 2N6248 | | |
| | | | | | | FT5415 | | | |
| MJ4645 | S | P | MO | | | FT5416 | | | 06 |
| MJ4647 | S | P | MO | | | FT5416 | | | 06 |
| MJ4648 | S | P | MO | | | FT5416 | | | 06 |
| MJ5038 | S | N | MO | | | 2N5038 | | | |
| MJ5415 | S | P | MO | | | 2N5415 | | | 06 |
| MJ5416 | S | P | MO | | | 2N5416 | | | 06 |
| MJ5600 | S | N | MO | | | 2N3772 | | | |
| MJ5601 | S | N | MO | | | 2N6258 | | | |
| MJ5602 | S | N | MO | | | 2N3773 | | | |
| MJ5603 | S | N | MO | | | 2N3773 | | | |
| MJ6000 | S | N | MO | | | 2N3772 | | | |
| MJ6001 | S | N | MO | | | 2N6258 | | | |
| MJ6002 | S | N | MO | | | 2N3773 | | | |
| MJ6003 | S | N | MO | | | 2N6258 | | | |
| MJ6004 | S | N | MO | | | 2N6259 | | | |
| MJ6257 | S | N | MO | | | 2N3771 | | | 09 |
| MJ6302 | S | N | MO | | | 2N5631 | 2N3773 | | 09 |
| MJ6700 | S | P | MO | | | | | | 06 |
| MJ6701 | S | P | MO | | | | | | 09 |
| MJ7000 | S | N | MO | | | 2N3265 | 2N5303 | | 09 |
| MJ7160 | S | N | MO | | | FT430 | | | |
| MJ8100 | S | P | MO | | | | | | 09 |
| MJ8101 | S | P | MO | | | | | | 09 |
| MJ9000 | S | N | MO | | | 2N6805 | | | 06 |
| MJE29 | S | N | MO | BD239 | | TIP29 | | | |
| MJE29A | S | N | MO | BD239A | | TIP29A | | | |
| MJE29B | S | N | MO | BD239B | | TIP29B | | | |
| MJE29C | S | N | MO | BD239C | | TIP29C | | | |
| MJE30 | S | P | MO | BD240 | | TIP30 | | | |
| MJE30A | S | P | MO | BD240A | | TIP30A | | | |
| MJE30B | S | P | MO | BD240B | | TIP30B | | | |
| MJE30C | S | P | MO | BD240C | | TIP30C | | | |
| MJE31 | S | N | MO | BD241 | | TIP31 | | | |
| MJE31A | S | N | MO | BD241A | | TIP31A | | | |
| MJE31B | S | N | MO | BD241B | | TIP31B | | | |
| MJE31C | S | N | MO | BD241C | | TIP31C | | | |
| MJE32 | S | P | MO | BD242 | | TIP32 | | | |
| MJE32A | S | P | MO | BD242A | | TIP32A | | | |
| MJE32B | S | P | MO | BD242B | | TIP32B | | | |
| MJE32C | S | P | MO | BD242C | | TIP32C | | | |
| MJE33 | S | N | MO | | | 2N6486 | TIP33 | | |
| MJE33A | S | N | MO | | | 2N6487 | TIP33A | | |
| MJE33B | S | N | MO | | | 2N6488 | TIP33B | | |
| MJE34 | S | P | MO | | | 2N6489 | TIP34 | | |
| MJE34A | S | P | MO | | | 2N6490 | TIP34A | | |
| MJE34B | S | P | MO | | | 2N6491 | TIP34B | | |
| MJE41 | S | N | MO | BD243 | | TIP41 | | | |
| MJE41A | S | N | MO | BD243A | | TIP41A | | | |
| MJE41B | S | N | MO | BD243B | | TIP41B | | | |
| MJE41C | S | N | MO | BD243C | | TIP41C | | | |
| MJE42 | S | P | MO | BD244 | | TIP42 | | | |
| MJE42A | S | P | MO | BD244A | | TIP42A | | | |
| MJE42B | S | P | MO | BD244B | | TIP42B | | | |
| MJE42C | S | P | MO | BD244C | | TIP42C | | | |
| MJE47 | S | N | MO | | | TA8863C | | | |
| MJE48 | S | N | MO | | | TA8863B | | | |
| MJE49 | S | N | MO | | | TA8863A | | | |
| MJE101 | S | P | MO | BD132 | | TIP34 | RCA101 | | |
| MJE102 | S | P | MO | | | TIP34A | RCA102 | | |
| MJE103 | S | P | MO | | | TIP34A | RCA103 | | |
| MJE103 | | | | | | TIP34 | | | |
| MJE104 | S | P | MO | | | TIP34B | RCA104 | | |
| MJE104 | | | | | | TIP34A | | | |
| MJE105 | S | P | MO | (BD440) | | TIP32A | 2N6133 | | |
| MJE105 | | | | | | TIP34A | RCA105 | | |
| MJE105K | S | P | MO | | | TIP32A | 2N6133 | | |
| MJE170 | S | P | MO | | | TIP30 | 2N5323 | | 07 |
| MJE171 | S | P | MO | | | TIP30A | 2N5323 | | 07 |
| MJE172 | S | P | MO | | | TIP32B | 2N5322 | | 07 |
| MJE180 | S | N | MO | | | TIP29 | 2N5321 | | 07 |

| TYPE | M/S | POL | MANUFAC | EUROPEAN | | AMERICAN | | JAPANESE | USE |
|---|---|---|---|---|---|---|---|---|---|
| MJE181 | S | N | MO | | | TIP29A | 2N5321 | | 07 |
| MJE182 | S | N | MO | | | TIP29B | 2N5320 | | 07 |
| MJE200 | S | N | MO | | | TIP31 | 2N4895 | | 01 |
| MJE201 | S | N | MO | BD131 | | TIP33 | RCA201 | | |
| MJE202 | S | N | MO | | | TIP33A | RCA202 | | |
| MJE203 | | | | | | TIP33A | RCA203 | | |
| MJE203 | S | N | MO | | | TIP33 | | | |
| MJE204 | S | N | MO | | | TIP33A | TIP33P | | |
| MJE204 | | | | | | RCA204 | | | |
| MJE205 | S | N | MO | (BD439) | | TIP31A | TIP33 | | 06 |
| MJE205 | | | | | | TIP33A | 2N6130 | | 06 |
| MJE205 | | | | | | RCA205 | | | 06 |
| MJE205K | S | N | MO | (BD439) | | TIP31A | 2N6130 | | 06 |
| MJE210 | S | P | MO | | | TIP32 | | | 01 |
| MJE220 | S | N | MO | BD221 | | 2N5321 | | | 07 |
| MJE221 | S | N | MO | BD221 | | 2N5320 | | | 07 |
| MJE222 | S | N | MO | BD221 | | 2N5321 | | | 07 |
| MJE223 | S | N | MO | BD222 | | 2N5321 | | | 07 |
| MJE224 | S | N | MO | BD222 | | 2N5320 | | | 07 |
| MJE225 | S | N | MO | BD222 | | 2N5321 | | | 07 |
| MJE230 | S | P | MO | | | 2N5323 | | | 07 |
| MJE231 | S | P | MO | | | 2N5322 | | | 07 |
| MJE232 | S | P | MO | | | 2N5323 | | | 07 |
| MJE233 | S | P | MO | | | 2N5323 | | | 07 |
| MJE234 | S | P | MO | | | 2N5322 | | | 07 |
| MJE235 | S | P | MO | | | 2N5323 | | | 07 |
| MJE240 | S | N | MO | | | 2N5320 | | | 07 |
| MJE241 | S | N | MO | | | 2N5320 | | | 07 |
| MJE242 | S | N | | | | 2N5320 | | | 07 |
| MJE243 | S | N | MO | | | 2N5681 | | | 07 |
| MJE244 | S | N | MO | | | 2N5682 | | | 07 |
| MJE250 | S | P | MO | | | 2N5322 | | | 07 |
| MJE251 | S | P | MO | | | 2N5322 | | | 07 |
| MJE252 | S | P | MO | | | 2N5322 | | | 07 |
| MJE253 | S | P | MO | | | 2N5679 | | | 07 |
| MJE254 | S | P | MO | | | 2N5679 | | | 07 |
| MJE305 | S | N | MO | AM291 | BDX10 | 2N3055 | | | |
| MJE340 | S | N | MO | (BF459) | BD410 | FT48 | TIP48 | | 06 |
| MJE340 | | | | BD144 | | | | | |
| MJE340K | S | N | MO | (BF459) | | FT48 | TA8863B | | 06 |
| MJE341 | S | N | MO | (BF458) | | | | | 06 |
| MJE341K | S | N | MO | (BF458) | | TA8863J | | | 06 |
| MJE344 | S | N | MO | (BF458) | | FT47 | | | 06 |
| MJE344K | S | N | MO | (BF458) | | FT47 | | | 06 |
| MJE350 | S | P | MO | | | FT48 | | | 01 |
| MJE370 | S | P | MO | BD436 | | TIP30 | 2N6124 | | 06 |
| MJE370 | | | | | | TIP32 | RCA370 | | 06 |
| MJE370 | | | MO, NP | | | SDA445 | | | 06 |
| MJE370K | S | P | MO | BD242 | BD436 | TIP30 | 2N6124 | | 06 |
| MJE371 | S | P | MO, NP | BD224 | BD438 | 2N6124 | TIP32 | | 06 |
| MJE371 | | | | | | RCA371 | SDA445 | | 06 |
| MJE371K | S | P | MO | BD224 | BD438 | 2N6124 | | | 06 |
| MJE520 | S | N | MO, NP | BD435 | | TIP29 | TIP31 | | 06 |
| MJE520 | | | | | | 2N6121 | RCA520 | | 06 |
| MJE520 | | | | | | SDA345 | | | 06 |
| MJE520K | S | N | MO | BD241 | BD435 | TIP29 | 2N6121 | | 06 |
| MJE521 | S | N | MO, NP | BD221 | BD437 | TIP31 | RCA521 | | 06 |
| MJE521 | | | | | | SDA345 | 2N6121 | | 06 |
| MJE521K | S | N | MO | BD221 | BD437 | 2N6121 | | | 06 |
| MJE700 | S | P | MO | BD646 | | RCA8203A | | | |
| MJE701 | S | P | MO | BD646 | | RCA8203A | TIP119 | | 06 |
| MJE702 | S | P | MO | BD648 | | RCA8203B | TIP116 | | 06 |
| MJE703 | S | P | MO | BD648 | | RCA8203B | TIP116 | | 06 |
| MJE710 | S | P | MO | (BD438) | | TIP30 | 2N5323 | | 09 |
| MJE711 | S | P | MO | (BD440) | | TIP30A | 2N5323 | | 09 |
| MJE712 | S | P | MO | (BD442) | | TIP30B | 2N5322 | | 09 |
| MJE720 | S | N | MO | (BD437) | | TIP29 | 2N5321 | | 09 |
| MJE721 | S | N | MO | (BD439) | | TIP29A | 2N5321 | | 09 |
| MJE722 | S | N | MO | (BD441) | | TIP29B | | | 09 |
| MJE800 | S | N | MO | BD645 | | SE9300 | 2N6387 | | 06 |
| MJE800 | | | | | | TIP110 | | | 06 |
| MJE801 | S | N | MO | (BD645) | | 2N6387 | TIP110 | | 06 |
| MJE801 | | | | | | SE9301 | | | 06 |
| MJE802 | S | N | MO | BD647 | | SE9300 | 2N6388 | | 06 |
| MJE802 | | | | | | TIP111 | | | 06 |

| TYPE | M/S | POL | MANUFAC | EUROPEAN | | AMERICAN | | JAPANESE | USE |
|---|---|---|---|---|---|---|---|---|---|
| MJE803 | S | N | MO | BD647 | | SE9301 | 2N6388 | | 06 |
| MJE803 | | | | | | TIP111 | | | 06 |
| MJE1090 | S | P | MO | BDX34A | BD646 | TIP125 | | | 06 |
| MJE1091 | S | P | MO | BDX34A | BD646 | TIP125 | | | 06 |
| MJE1092 | S | P | MO | BDX34B | BD648 | TIP126 | | | 06 |
| MJE1093 | S | P | MO | BDX34B | BD648 | TIP126 | | | 06 |
| MJE1100 | S | N | MO | BDX33A | BD645 | SE9300 | TIP120 | | 06 |
| MJE1101 | S | N | MO | BDX33A | BD645 | SE9300 | TIP120 | | 06 |
| MJE1102 | S | N | MO | BDX33B | BD647 | SE9301 | TIP121 | | 06 |
| MJE1103 | S | N | MO | BDX33B | BD647 | SE9301 | TIP121 | | 06 |
| MJE1290 | S | P | MO | | | 2N6489 | 2N6109 | | 09 |
| MJE1290 | | | | | | TIP34 | | | 09 |
| MJE1291 | S | P | MO | | | FT2955 | 2N6490 | | 09 |
| MJE1291 | S | N | MO | | | 2N6107 | TIP34A | | 09 |
| MJE1660 | | | | | | 2N6486 | 2N6103 | | 09 |
| MJE1660 | | | | | | TIP33 | | | 09 |
| MJE1661 | S | N | MO | | | FT3055 | 2N6487 | | 09 |
| MJE1661 | | | | | | 2N6101 | TIP33A | | 09 |
| MJE2010 | S | P | MO | BD244 | (BD438) | TIP32 | TIP34 | | 09 |
| MJE2010 | | | | | | 2N6124 | | | 09 |
| MJE2011 | S | P | MO | BD244A | (BD440) | TIP32A | TIP34A | | 09 |
| MJE2011 | | | | | | 2N6125 | | | 09 |
| MJE2020 | S | N | MO | BD243 | (BD437) | TIP31 | TIP33 | | 09 |
| MJE2021 | S | N | MO | BD243A | (BD439) | TIP31A | TIP33A | | 09 |
| MJE2021 | | | | | | 2N6122 | | | 09 |
| MJE2050 | S | N | MO | | | 2N6121 | 40979 | | 06 |
| MJE2060 | S | N | MO | | | TIP54 | | | |
| MJE2061 | S | N | MO | | | TIP54 | | | |
| MJE2090 | S | P | MO | BDX34A | BD646 | | | | 06 |
| MJE2091 | S | P | MO | BDX34A | BD646 | | | | 06 |
| MJE2092 | S | P | MO | BDX34B | BD648 | | | | 06 |
| MJE2093 | S | P | MO | BDX34B | BD648 | | | | 06 |
| MJE2100 | S | N | MO | BDX33A | BD645 | | | | 06 |
| MJE2101 | S | N | MO | BDX33A | BD645 | | | | 06 |
| MJE2102 | S | N | MO | BDX33B | BD647 | | | | 06 |
| MJE2103 | S | N | MO | BDX33B | BD647 | | | | 06 |
| MJE2150 | S | | MO | | | TIP32 | | | 06 |
| MJE2160 | S | N | MO | | | TA8863B | | | 01 |
| MJE2360 | S | N | MO | | | FT49 | TA8863E | | 06 |
| MJE2361 | S | N | MO | | | FT49 | TA8863A | | 06 |
| MJE2370 | S | P | MO | BD240 | BD438 | TIP30 | TIP34 | | 09 |
| MJE2370 | | | | | | 2N5320 | TIP34 | | 09 |
| MJE2371 | S | P | MO | BD240A | BD440 | 2N6107 | 2N523 | | 09 |
| MJE2371 | | | | | | TIP34A | | | 09 |
| MJE2480 | S | N | MO | BD221 | BD243 | 2N6290 | 2N6121 | | 09 |
| MJE2480 | | | | (BD437) | | TIP33 | | | 09 |
| MJE2481 | S | N | MO | BD222 | BD243A | 2N6282 | 2N6121 | | 09 |
| MJE2481 | | | | (BD439) | | TIP33A | | | 09 |
| MJE2482 | S | N | MO | BD221 | BD243 | 2N6290 | 2N6129 | | 09 |
| MJE2482 | | | | (BD437) | | TIP33 | | | 09 |
| MJE2483 | S | N | MO | BD222 | BD243A | 2N6202 | 2N6130 | | 09 |
| MJE2483 | | | | (BD439) | | TIP33A | | | 09 |
| MJE2490 | S | P | MO | BD224 | BD244 | 2N6109 | 2N6124 | | 09 |
| MJE2490 | | | | BD438 | | TIP34 | | | 09 |
| MJE2491 | S | P | MO | BD225 | BD244A | 2N6107 | 2N6125 | | 09 |
| MJE2491 | | | | BD440 | | TIP34A | | | 09 |
| MJE2520 | S | N | MO | BD239 | BD437 | TIP29 | TIP33 | | 09 |
| MJE2520 | | | | | | 2N6290 | 2N5321 | | 09 |
| MJE2521 | S | N | MO | BD239A | BD439 | 2N6292 | 2N5321 | | 09 |
| MJE2521 | | | | | | TIP33A | | | 09 |
| MJE2522 | S | N | MO | BD241 | BD437 | 2N6121 | TIP33 | | 09 |
| MJE2523 | S | N | MO | BD241A | BD439 | 2N6122 | TIP33A | | 09 |
| MJE2801 | S | N | MO | | | FT3055 | 2N6487 | | 09 |
| MJE2801 | | | | | | TIP33A | TIP41A | | 09 |
| MJE2801K | S | N | MO | | | FT3055 | 2N6487 | | 06 |
| MJE2901 | S | P | MO | | | FT2955 | 2N6490 | | 06 |
| MJE2901 | | | | | | TIP42A | 2N3789 | | 06 |
| MJE2901 | | | | | | TIP34 | | | 06 |
| MJE2901K | S | P | MO | | | FT2955 | 2N6490 | | 06 |
| MJE2901K | | | | | | 2N3789 | | | 06 |
| MJE2955 | S | P | MO | | | FT2955 | 40878 | | 09 |
| MJE2955 | | | | | | 2N3791 | TIP34 | | 09 |
| MJE2955 | | | | | | TIP2955 | | | 09 |
| MJE2955K | S | P | MO | | | FT2955 | 40878 | | 09 |

| TYPE | M/S | POL | MANUFAC | EUROPEAN | | AMERICAN | | JAPANESE | USE |
|------|-----|-----|---------|----------|---|----------|---|----------|-----|
| MJE2955K | | | | | | 2N3791 | | | 09 |
| MJE3050 | S | N | MO | | | TIP33A | | | 09 |
| MJE3054 | S | N | MO | (BD441) | | RCA3054 | 2N6123 | | 09 |
| MJE3055 | S | N | MO | AM291 | BDX10 | FT3055 | RCA3055 | | 09 |
| MJE3055 | | | | | | 2N6099 | TIP3055 | | 09 |
| | | | | | | | | | |
| MJE3055 | | | | | | 2N3055 | TIP33A | | 09 |
| MJE3055K | S | N | MO | | | FT3055 | RCA3055 | | 09 |
| MJE3370 | S | P | MO | BD242 | (BD436) | TIP30 | TIP32 | | 06 |
| MJE3370 | | | | | | 2N6124 | | | 06 |
| MJE3371 | S | P | MO | BD224 | (BD438) | 40980 | 2N6124 | | 06 |
| | | | | | | | | | |
| MJE3371 | | | | | | TIP32 | | | 06 |
| MJE3439 | S | N | MO | | | FT49 | RCP11D | | 06 |
| MJE3439 | | | | | | 2N3439 | TIP51 | | 06 |
| MJE3440 | S | N | MO | | | FT47 | 2N3440 | | 06 |
| MJE3440 | | | | | | TIP52 | | | 06 |
| | | | | | | | | | |
| MJE3520 | S | N | MO | (BD435) | | TIP29 | TIP33 | | 06 |
| MJE3521 | S | N | MO | BD221 | (BD437) | 2N6121 | TIP33 | | 06 |
| MJE3738 | S | N | MO | (BF458) | | FT43 | TIP51 | | 06 |
| MJE3739 | S | N | MO | (BF459) | | TIP52 | | | 06 |
| MJE3740 | S | P | MO | BD440 | | 2N6125 | 2N6107 | | 16 |
| | | | | | | | | | |
| MJE3740 | | | | | | TIP34A | | | 16 |
| MJE3741 | S | P | MO | BD442 | | 2N6107 | 2N6126 | | 16 |
| MJE3741 | | | | | | TIP34B | | | 16 |
| MJE3839 | | | MO | | | FT48 | | | |
| MJE4916 | S | P | MO | | | 2N6124 | | | |
| | | | | | | | | | |
| MJE4918 | S | P | MO | BD240 | BD438 | TIP30 | | | 06 |
| MJE4919 | S | P | MO | BD240A | BD440 | TIP30A | 2N6125 | | 06 |
| MJE4920 | S | P | MO | BD240B | BD442 | TIP30B | 2N6126 | | 06 |
| MJE4921 | S | N | MO | BD239 | BD437 | TIP29 | 2N6121 | | 06 |
| MJE4922 | S | N | MO | BD239A | BD439 | TIP29A | 2N6122 | | 06 |
| | | | | | | | | | |
| MJE4923 | S | N | MO | BD239B | BD441 | TIP29B | 2N6123 | | 06 |
| MJE5120 | S | N | MO | | | 2N6121 | | | |
| MJE5190 | S | N | MO | BD221 | (BD437) | 2N6121 | | | 06 |
| MJE5191 | S | N | MO | BD222 | (BD439) | 2N6122 | | | 06 |
| MJE5192 | S | N | MO | (BD441) | | 2N6123 | | | 06 |
| | | | | | | | | | |
| MJE5193 | S | P | MO | BD224 | (BD438) | 2N6124 | | | 06 |
| MJE5194 | S | P | MO | BD225 | (BD440) | 2N6125 | | | 06 |
| MJE5195 | S | P | MO | (BD442) | | 2N6126 | | | 06 |
| MJE5655 | S | N | MO | | | FT47 | TA8863J | | 06 |
| MJE5656 | S | N | MO | | | FT48 | TA8863F | | 06 |
| | | | | | | | | | |
| MJE5657 | S | N | MO | | | FT49 | TA8863F | | 06 |
| MJE5974 | S | P | MO | (BD440) | | TIP32 | 2N6489 | | 06 |
| MJE5974 | | | | | | 2N6132 | | | 06 |
| MJE5975 | S | P | MO | (BD442) | | TIP32A | 2N6490 | | 06 |
| MJE5975 | | | | | | 2N6133 | | | 06 |
| | | | | | | | | | |
| MJE5976 | S | P | MO | (BD442) | | TIP32B | 2N6491 | | 06 |
| MJE5976 | | | | | | 2N6134 | | | 06 |
| MJE5977 | S | N | MO | (BD439) | | TIP31 | 2N6486 | | 06 |
| MJE5977 | | | | | | 2N6129 | | | 06 |
| MJE5978 | S | N | MO | (BD441) | | TIP31A | 2N6487 | | 06 |
| | | | | | | | | | |
| MJE5978 | | | | | | 2N6130 | | | 06 |
| MJE5979 | S | N | MO | (BD441) | | TIP31B | 2N6488 | | 06 |
| MJE5979 | | | | | | 2N6131 | | | 06 |
| MJE5980 | S | P | MO | | | 2N6132 | 2N6489 | | 06 |
| MJE5981 | S | P | MO | | | 2N6133 | 2N6490 | | 06 |
| | | | | | | | | | |
| MJE5982 | S | P | MO | | | 2N6134 | 2N6491 | | 06 |
| MJE5983 | S | N | MO | | | 2N6129 | 2N6486 | | 06 |
| MJE5984 | S | N | MO | | | 2N6130 | 2N6487 | | 06 |
| MJE5985 | S | N | MO | | | 2N6131 | 2N6488 | | 06 |
| MJE6040 | S | P | MO | BDX34A | | | | | 06 |
| | | | | | | | | | |
| MJE6041 | S | P | MO | BDX34B | | | | | 06 |
| MJE6042 | S | P | MO | BDX34C | | | | | 06 |
| MJE6043 | S | N | MO | BDX33A | | SE9300 | | | 06 |
| MJE6044 | S | N | MO | BDX33B | | SE9301 | | | 06 |
| MJE6045 | S | N | MO | BDX33C | | SE9302 | | | 06 |
| | | | | | | | | | |
| MM1812 | S | N | MO | | | 2N3440 | | | |
| MM2090 | J | N | MO | | | 3N124 | | | |
| MM2091 | J | N | MO | | | 3N125 | | | |
| MM2092 | J | N | MO | | | 3N126 | | | |
| MM2102 | M | N | MO | | | 2N4351 | | | |
| | | | | | | | | | |
| MM2103 | M | P | MO | | | 2N4352 | | | |
| MM3005 | S | N | MO | | | 40635 | 2N5681 | | 07 |
| MM3006 | S | N | MO | | | 2N5681 | | | 07 |
| MM3007 | S | N | MO | | | 2N5681 | | | 07 |
| MM4000 | S | P | MO | BFT28 | | | | | 02 |

| TYPE | M/S | POL | MANUFAC | EUROPEAN | | AMERICAN | | JAPANESE | USE |
|------|-----|-----|---------|----------|---|----------|---|----------|-----|
| MM4001 | S | P | MO | BFT28A | | | | | 02 |
| MM4002 | S | P | MO | BFT28B | | | | | 02 |
| MM4003 | S | P | MO | BFT28C | | | | | 02 |
| MM5005 | S | P | MO | | | 40634 | 2N5679 | | 11 |
| MM5006 | S | P | MO | | | 2N5679 | | | 11 |
| MM5007 | S | P | MO | | | 2N5679 | | | 11 |
| MMF1 | J | N | MO | | | 2N5197 | | | |
| MMF2 | J | N | MO | | | 2N3921 | | | |
| MMF3 | J | N | MO | | | 2N5198 | | | |
| MMF4 | J | N | MO | | | 2N3922 | | | |
| MMF5 | J | N | MO | | | 2N5199 | | | |
| MMF6 | J | N | MO | | | SU2080 | | | |
| MMR6/1 | G | P | | AC126 | | 2N2429 | | | |
| MMR6/2 | G | P | | AF178 | | 2N2495 | | | |
| MMR6/3 | G | P | | AF185 | | | | | |
| MMR6/11 | G | P | | AC128 | | 2N2431 | | | |
| MMR6/12 | G | P | MO | AD149 | | 2N2836 | | | |
| MMT3823 | J | N | MO | | | 2N3823 | | | |
| MN24 | G | P | | AD149 | OC16 | 2N2836 | | | |
| MN25 | G | P | | AD149 | OC16 | 2N2836 | | | |
| MN26 | G | P | | AD149 | OC16 | 2N2836 | | | |
| MP500 | G | P | MO | | | MP504 | | | 06 |
| MP501 | G | P | MO | | | MP505 | | | 06 |
| MP502 | G | P | MO | | | MP506 | | | 06 |
| MP504 | G | P | MO | | | MP500 | | | 06 |
| MP505 | G | P | MO | | | MP501 | | | 06 |
| MP506 | G | P | MO | | | | | | 06 |
| MP525 | G | P | MO | | | | | | 06 |
| MP939 | G | P | | AU105 | AU103 | | | | |
| MP1612 | G | P | MO | | | MP1612A | | | 06 |
| MP1612A | G | P | MO | | | MP1612B | | | 06 |
| MP1612B | G | P | MO | | | | | | 06 |
| MP1613 | G | P | MO | | | | | | 06 |
| MP2060 | G | P | MO | | | MP2061 | | | 06 |
| MP2061 | G | P | MO | | | MP2062 | | | 06 |
| MP2062 | G | P | MO | | | MP2063 | | | 06 |
| MP2063 | G | P | MO | | | | | | 06 |
| MPF102 | J | N | MO, IL, NS, SX | | | 2N3819 | 2N5486 | | |
| MPF103 | J | N | IL, MO, NS | | | 2N5457 | 2N5953 | | |
| MPF104 | J | N | IL, MO, NS | | | 2N5458 | 2N5952 | | |
| MPF105 | J | N | IL, MO, NS | | | 2N5459 | 2N5951 | | |
| MPF106 | J | N | IL, NS, MO | | | 2N5485 | 2N5952 | | |
| MPF107 | J | N | IL, NS, MO | | | 2N5486 | 2N5950 | | |
| MPF108 | J | N | MO, SX | | | 2N3819 | 2N5486 | | |
| MPF109 | J | N | MO, SX | | | 2N3819 | 2N5163 | | |
| MPF111 | J | N | MO, IL, NS, SX | | | 2N3819 | 2N5163 | | |
| MPF112 | J | N | MO, IL, NS, SX | | | 2N3819 | 2N5163 | | |
| MPF120 | J | N | MO | | | 3N203 | | | |
| MPF121 | J | N | MO | | | 3N201 | | | |
| MPF122 | J | N | MO | | | 3N203 | | | |
| MPF151 | J | P | MO | | | 2N5460 | | | |
| MPF152 | J | P | MO | | | 2N5461 | | | |
| MPF153 | J | P | MO | | | 2N5462 | | | |
| MPF154 | J | P | MO | | | 2N5463 | | | |
| MPF155 | J | P | MO | | | 2N5464 | | | |
| MPF156 | J | P | MO | | | 2N5465 | | | |
| MPF157 | M | N | MO | | | MFE3004 | | | |
| MPF158 | M | N | MO | | | MFE3005 | | | |
| MPF159 | M | N | MO | | | 2N4351 | | | |
| MPF160 | M | P | MO | | | 2N4352 | | | |
| MPF161 | J | P | IL, MO | | | 2N5462 | P1069E | | |
| MPS292 | S | N | MO | BC238B | | | | | |
| MPS370 | S | N | MO | BC238 | | | | | |
| MPS404 | S | P | MO | (BC238A) | | | | | 10 |
| MPS404A | S | P | MO | (BC237A) | | | | | 10 |
| MPS653 | S | N | MO | BC237A | | | | | |
| MPS706 | S | N | MO, F, NS | BSY62A | | 2N5772 | 2N4275 | | 13 |
| MPS706A | S | N | MO, F | BSY62A | | 2N5772 | 2N4275 | | 13 |
| MPS834 | S | N | MO, F, NS | BSY63 | | 2N5772 | 2N4275 | | 13 |
| MPS918 | S | N | MO, NS | (BFX89) | | TIS62 | 2N5770 | | 01 |
| MPS918 | | | | | | EN918 | | | 01 |
| MPS2369 | S | N | MO, F, NS | (BSX63) | | 2N5770 | 2N4275 | | 13 |
| MPS2711 | S | N | MO, F, NS | BC238A | | 2N2711 | 2N5135 | | 01 |
| MPS2711 | | | | | | 2N3691 | | | 01 |
| MPS2712 | S | N | MO, F, NS | BC238A | | 2N2712 | 2N5135 | | 01 |

| TYPE | M/S | POL | MANUFAC | EUROPEAN | AMERICAN | | JAPANESE | USE |
|---|---|---|---|---|---|---|---|---|
| MPS2712 | | | | | 2N3692 | | | 01 |
| MPS2713 | S | N | MO, F | (BSY62) | 2N2713 | 2N5135 | | 10 |
| MPS2713 | | | | | 2N4275 | | | 10 |
| MPS2714 | S | N | MO, F, NS | (BSY62) | 2N2714 | 2N5135 | | 10 |
| MPS2714 | | | | | 2N4275 | | | 10 |
| | | | | | | | | |
| MPS2715 | S | N | MO, NS | | MPS2711 | 2N5135 | | |
| MPS2716 | S | N | MO, NS | | MPS2712 | 2N5135 | | |
| MPS2716 | | | | | 2N3692 | | | |
| MPS2894 | S | P | MO | | | | | |
| MPS2923 | S | N | MO, F, NS | BC238A | TIS99 | 2N2923 | | 07 |
| | | | | | | | | |
| MPS2923 | | | | | 2N5135 | | | 07 |
| MPS2924 | S | N | MO, F, NS | BC238B | TIS98 | 2N2924 | | 07 |
| MPS2924 | | | | | 2N5135 | | | 07 |
| MPS2925 | S | N | MO, F, N | BC238B | TIS98 | 2N3565 | | 07 |
| MPS2926 | S | N | MO, F, NS | BC238B | 2N3691 | 2N3692 | | 07 |
| | | | | | | | | |
| MPS2926br | S | N | MO | BC238A | | | | 07 |
| MPS2926gn | S | N | MO | BC238B | | | | 07 |
| MPS2926r | S | N | MO | BC238A | | | | 07 |
| MPS2926or | S | N | MO | BC238A | | | | 07 |
| MPS2926ye | S | N | MO | BC238B | | | | 07 |
| | | | | | | | | |
| MPS3392 | S | N | MO, F, NS | BC238B | 2N3392 | SE6002 | | 01 |
| MPS3392 | | | | | EN4124 | | | 01 |
| MPS3393 | S | N | MO, F, NS | BC238B | 2N3393 | SE6002 | | 01 |
| MPS3393 | | | | | SE1001 | | | 01 |
| MPS3394 | S | N | MO, F, NS | BC238A | 2N4123 | EN4123 | | 01 |
| | | | | | | | | |
| MPS3395 | S | N | MO, F, NS | BC238C | 2N3395 | SE6002 | | 01 |
| MPS3396 | S | N | MO, NS | | | | | |
| MPS3397 | S | N | MO, NS | | MPS3396 | | | |
| MPS3398 | S | N | MO, NS | | | | | |
| MPS3563 | S | N | F, MO, NS | | TIS62 | 2N3563 | | 02 |
| | | | | | | | | |
| MPS3638 | S | P | MO, F, NS | BC328-16 | 2N5354 | 2N3638 | | 11 |
| MPS3638 | | | | | 2N5355 | 2N5448 | | 11 |
| MPS3638A | S | P | MO, F, NS | BC328-16 | 2N5355 | 2N3638A | | 11 |
| MPS3638A | | | | | 2N5447 | | | 11 |
| MPS3638-5 | S | P | F | | 2N3638 | | | 11 |
| | | | | | | | | |
| MPS3638A-5 | S | P | F | | 2N3638A | | | 11 |
| MPS3639 | S | P | MO | | 2N3639 | | | 10 |
| MPS3640 | S | P | MO | | 2N3640 | | | 10 |
| MPS3646 | S | N | MO, F, NS | (BSY63) | 2N3646 | | | 13 |
| MPS3646-18 | S | N | F | | 2N3646 | | | 13 |
| | | | | | | | | |
| MPS3693 | S | N | MO, F, NS | (BC414A) | 2N3826 | 2N3903 | | 02 |
| MPS3693 | | | | | EN3903 | 2N3693 | | 02 |
| MPS3694 | S | N | MO, F, NS | (BC414) | 2N3827 | 2N3904 | | 02 |
| MPS3694 | | | | | EN3904 | 2N3694 | | 02 |
| MPS3702 | S | P | MO, F, NS | BC307B | 2N3638A | | | 02 |
| | | | | | | | | |
| MPS3703 | S | P | MO, F, NS | BC307A | 2N3638 | | | 02 |
| MPS3704 | S | N | MO, F, NS | BC337-16 | 2N3704 | 2N3566 | | 02 |
| MPS3705 | S | N | MO, F, NS | | 2N3705 | 2N3566 | | 02 |
| MPS3705 | | | | | SE6001 | | | 02 |
| MPS3706 | S | N | MO, F, NS | BC337-25 | 2N3706 | 2N3566 | | 02 |
| | | | | | | | | |
| MPS3707 | S | N | MO, F, NS | BC413B | 2N3707 | SE4010 | | 01 |
| MPS3707 | | | | | EN4124 | | | 01 |
| MPS3708 | S | N | MO, F, NS | BC237B | 2N3708 | EN4123 | | 01 |
| MPS3708 | | | | | EN4124 | | | 01 |
| MPS3709 | S | N | MO, F, NS | BC237A | 2N3709 | EN4123 | | 01 |
| | | | | | | | | |
| MPS3710 | S | N | MO, F, NS | BC237A | 2N3710 | EN4124 | | 01 |
| MPS3711 | S | N | MO, F, NS | BC237B | 2N3711 | EN3904 | | 01 |
| MPS3711 | | | | | 2N3565 | | | 01 |
| MPS3721 | S | N | MO, F | BC238B | 2N3721 | 2N5135 | | 07 |
| MPS3721 | | | | | 2N3692 | | | 07 |
| | | | | | | | | |
| MPS3725 | S | N | MO | (BSX49) | | | | 09 |
| MPS4354 | S | P | MO, F | (BSV16-6) | | | | 09 |
| MPS4355 | S | P | MO, F | (BSV16-16) | | | | 09 |
| MPS4356 | S | P | MO, F | (BSV17-6) | | | | 09 |
| MPS5172 | S | N | MO, F | BC238B | 2N2134 | | | 02 |
| | | | | | | | | |
| MPS5551M | S | N | F | | | | | |
| MPS6506 | S | N | MO | | TIS86 | 2N4996 | | |
| MPS6507 | S | N | MO | | TIS86 | 2N4996 | | 01 |
| MPS6507 | | | | | 2N5770 | SE3002 | | 01 |
| MPS6508 | S | N | MO | | TIS86 | 2N4996 | | |
| | | | | | | | | |
| MPS6509 | S | N | MO | | TIS84 | | | |
| MPS6510 | S | N | MO | | TIS84 | | | |
| MPS6511 | S | N | MO, F | | TIS87 | SE3005 | | 02 |
| MPS6511 | | | | | FPS6511 | | | 02 |
| MPS6512 | S | N | MO, F, NS | | TIS99 | 2N4123 | | 02 |

| TYPE | M/S | POL | MANUFAC | EUROPEAN | | AMERICAN | | JAPANESE | USE |
|------|-----|-----|---------|----------|--|----------|--|----------|-----|
| MPS6512 | S | N | MO, F, NS | | | 2N4124 | FPS6512 | | 02 |
| MPS6513 | S | N | MO, F, NS | BC237A | | TIS99 | EN4124 | | 02 |
| MPS6513 | | | | | | FPS6513 | | | 02 |
| MPS6514 | S | N | MO, F, NS | BC237B | BC207 | TIS98 | FPS6514 | | 02 |
| MPS6515 | S | N | MO, F, NS | BC237B | BC207 | TIS97 | FPS6515 | | 02 |
| | | | | | | | | | |
| MPS6515 | | | | BC209 | | | | | 02 |
| MPS6516 | S | P | MO, F, NS | BC307A | | 2N5447 | EN3905 | | 02 |
| MPS6516 | | | | | | FPS6516 | | | 02 |
| MPS6517 | S | P | MO, F, NS | BC307A | | FPS6517 | 2N5447 | | 02 |
| MPS6517 | | | | | | EN3905 | | | 02 |
| | | | | | | | | | |
| MPS6518 | S | P | MO, F, NS | BC307B | | 2N5447 | EN3906 | | 02 |
| MPS6518 | | | | | | FPS6518 | | | 02 |
| MPS6519 | S | P | MO, F | BC308B | | 2N5447 | EN4126 | | 02 |
| MPS6519 | | | | | | FPS6519 | | | 02 |
| MPS6520 | S | N | MO, F, NS | BC413B | | TIS98 | SE4020 | | 02 |
| | | | | | | | | | |
| MPS6520 | | | | | | FPS6520 | | | 02 |
| MPS6521 | S | N | MO, F, NS | BC413C | | TIS97 | SE4020 | | 02 |
| MPS6521 | | | | | | FPS6521 | | | 02 |
| MPS6522 | S | P | MO, F, NS | BC415B | | 2N5447 | EN4126 | | 02 |
| MPS6522 | | | | | | FPS6522 | | | 02 |
| | | | | | | | | | |
| MPS6523 | S | P | MO, F | BC415C | | 2N5447 | EN4126 | | 02 |
| MPS6523 | | | | | | FPS6523 | | | 02 |
| MPS6528 | S | N | MO | | | TIS84 | | | |
| MPS6529 | S | N | MO | | | TIS108 | | | |
| MPS6530 | S | N | MO, F, NS | BC337-16 | | TIS92 | 2N4944 | | 02 |
| | | | | | | | | | |
| MPS6530 | | | | | | FPS6530 | | | 02 |
| MPS6531 | S | N | MO, F, NS | BC337-16 | | TIS92 | 2N4946 | | 02 |
| MPS6531 | | | | | | FPS6531 | | | 02 |
| MPS6532 | S | N | MO, F, NS | BC337-16 | BC237A | TIS92 | 2N3566 | | 02 |
| MPS6532 | | | | | | FPS6532 | | | 02 |
| | | | | | | | | | |
| MPS6533 | S | P | MO, NS | BC327-16 | BC177A | TIS93 | MPS6533M | | 02 |
| MPS6533 | | | | | | 2N3644 | | | 02 |
| MPS6533M | S | P | F | BC327-16 | | FPS6533M | | | 02 |
| MPS6534 | S | P | MO, NS | BC327-16 | BC177A | TIS93 | MPS6534M | | 02 |
| MPS6534 | | | | | | 2N3644 | | | 02 |
| | | | | | | | | | |
| MPS6534M | S | P | F, MO | BC327-16 | | FPS6534M | | | 02 |
| MPS6535 | S | P | MO, NS | BC327-16 | BC177IV | TIS93 | MPS6535M | | 02 |
| MPS6535M | S | P | F, MO | BC327-16 | | FPS6535M | | | 02 |
| MPS6539 | S | N | MO | (BF199) | | PE4030B | SE5032 | | 02 |
| MPS6539 | | | | | | 2N3690 | FPS6539 | | 02 |
| | | | | | | | | | |
| MPS6540 | S | N | MO | (BF198) | | PE5030B | SE5030B | | 02 |
| MPS6540 | | | | | | FPS6540 | | | 02 |
| MPS6541 | S | N | MO | | | TIS86 | 2N4996 | | 02 |
| MPS6542 | S | N | MO | | | TIS62 | PE5030B | | 02 |
| MPS6542 | | | | | | SE5030B | | | 02 |
| | | | | | | | | | |
| MPS6543 | S | N | MO | | | TIS86 | PE5030B | | 02 |
| MPS6543 | | | | | | SE5030B | FPS6543 | | 02 |
| MPS6544 | S | N | MO | | | TIS87 | PE5030B | | 02 |
| MPS6544 | | | | | | SE5030B | FPS6544 | | 02 |
| MPS6545 | S | N | MO | | | TIS87 | PE5030B | | 02 |
| | | | | | | | | | |
| MPS6545 | | | | | | SE5030B | | | 02 |
| MPS6546 | S | N | MO | (BF199) | | TIS86 | PE5030B | | 01 |
| MPS6546 | | | | | | SE5030B | FPS6546 | | 01 |
| MPS6547 | S | N | MO | (BF199) | | TIS86 | PE5030B | | 01 |
| MPS6547 | | | | | | SE5030B | FPS6547 | | 01 |
| | | | | | | | | | |
| MPS6548 | S | N | MO | | | PE5030B | SE5030B | | 01 |
| MPS6548 | | | | | | FPS6548 | | | 01 |
| MPS6552 | S | N | MO | | | TIS98 | | | |
| MPS6553 | S | N | MO | | | TIS97 | | | |
| MPS6554 | S | N | MO | | | TIS97 | | | |
| | | | | | | | | | |
| MPS6555 | S | N | MO | | | TIS97 | | | |
| MPS6560 | S | N | MO, F | BC338-16 | | TIS92 | SE6560 | | 02 |
| MPS6560 | | | | | | FPS6560 | | | 02 |
| MPS6561 | S | N | MO, F | | | TIS92 | SE6561 | | 02 |
| MPS6561 | | | | | | FPS6561 | | | 02 |
| | | | | | | | | | |
| MPS6562 | S | P | MO, F | | | TIS93 | SE6562 | | 02 |
| MPS6562 | | | | | | FPS6562 | | | 02 |
| MPS6563 | S | P | MO, F | BC328-16 | | TIS93 | SE6563 | | 02 |
| MPS6563 | | | | | | FPS6563 | | | 02 |
| MPS6564 | S | N | MO | | | 2N4994 | | | |
| | | | | | | | | | |
| MPS6565 | S | N | MO, F, NS | BC237A | | TIS99 | EN3909 | | 02 |
| MPS6565 | | | | | | FPS6565 | | | 02 |
| MPS6566 | S | N | MO, F, NS | BC237B | | TIS98 | EN3904 | | 02 |
| MPS6566 | | | | | | FPS6566 | | | 02 |
| MPS6567 | S | N | MO | (BF241) | | TIS86 | PE5030B | | 02 |

| TYPE | M/S | POL | MANUFAC | EUROPEAN | | AMERICAN | | JAPANESE | USE |
|---|---|---|---|---|---|---|---|---|---|
| MPS6567 | S | N | MO | | | SE5030B | FPS6567 | | 02 |
| MPS6568 | S | N | MO | (BF198) | | FPS6568 | | | 02 |
| MPS6568A | S | N | MO | (BF198) | | | | | 02 |
| MPS6569 | S | N | MO | (BF198) | | FPS6569 | | | 02 |
| MPS6570 | S | N | MO | (BF198) | | FPS6570 | | | 02 |
| MPS6571 | S | N | F, MO, NS | BC413C | | SE4020 | FPS6571 | | 02 |
| MPS6579 | S | P | MO | | | TIS37 | | | |
| MPS6590 | S | N | MO | | | MPSA06 | | | 01 |
| MPS6591 | S | N | MO | | | MPSA05 | | | 01 |
| MPS9600/1 | S | N | MO | BF495 | | | | | |
| MPS9600/2 | S | N | MO | BF495 | | | | | |
| MPS9600/3 | S | N | MO | BF495 | | | | | |
| MPS9600/4 | S | N | MO | BC549B | | | | | |
| MPS9603 | S | N | MO | BF494 | | | | | |
| MPS9606 | S | N | MO | BC548 | | | | | |
| MPS9607 | S | N | MO | BC548 | | | | | |
| MPS9608 | S | N | MO | BC548A | | | | | |
| MPS9610 | S | N | MO | BC549B | | | | | |
| MPS9616 | S | N | MO | BC338 | | | | | |
| MPS9636 | S | N | MO | BC548B | | | | | |
| MPS9644 | S | N | MO | BC548A | | | | | |
| MPS9656 | S | P | MO | BC558 | | | | | |
| MPS9657 | S | P | MO | BC558 | | | | | |
| MPS9658 | S | P | MO | BC558 | | | | | |
| MPS9666 | S | P | MO | BC328 | | | | | |
| MPS9696 | S | N | MO | BC548 | | | | | |
| MPS-A05 | S | N | F, MO | (BSX46-10) | | 2N3404 | 2N5856 | | |
| MPS-A05 | | | | | | 2N3416 | 2N6010 | | |
| MPS-A06 | S | N | F, MO | (BSX47-10) | | 2N3405 | 2N5856 | | |
| MPS-A06 | | | | | | 2N3417 | 2N6012 | | |
| MPS-A09 | S | N | F, MO | BC414B | | 2N5209 | SE4020 | | |
| MPS-A10 | S | N | MO, F | | | MPSA20 | 2N3903 | | |
| MPS-A10 | | | | | | 2N3693 | | | |
| MPS-A12 | S | N | MO, F | | | FPSA12 | | | |
| MPS-A13 | S | N | MO, F | | | FPSA13 | | | |
| MPS-A14 | S | N | MO, F | | | FPSA14 | | | |
| MPS-A16 | S | N | MO | BC237B | | | | | |
| MPS-A17 | S | N | MO | BC237B | | | | | |
| MPS-A18 | S | N | MO | (BC414C) | | | | | |
| MPS-A20 | S | N | F, MO | BC237B | | 2N3903 | | | |
| MPS-A42 | S | N | F, MO | (BF459) | | | | | |
| MPS-A43 | S | N | F, MO | (BF458) | | | | | |
| MPS-A55 | S | P | F, MO | (BSV16-10) | | 2N6011 | 2N5857 | | |
| MPS-A55 | | | | | | 2N6015 | 2N6017 | | |
| MPS-A56 | S | P | MO, F | (BSV17-10) | | 2N5857 | 2N3645 | | |
| MPS-A65 | S | P | MO, F | | | FPSA65 | | | |
| MPS-A66 | S | P | MO, F | | | MPSA65 | FPSA66 | | |
| MPS-A70 | S | P | F, MO | BC307A | | 2N3905 | | | |
| MPS-H02 | S | N | MO | | | | | | |
| MPS-H10 | S | N | MO, NS | | | 2N5770 | SE3003 | | |
| MPS-H10 | | | | | | SE3005 | | | |
| MPS-H11 | S | N | MO, NS | | | 2N5770 | SE3003 | | |
| MPS-H11 | | | | | | SE3005 | | | |
| MPS-H32 | S | N | MO, NS | | | PE5010 | SE5056 | | |
| MPS-H37 | S | N | MO, NS | | | PE5030B | SE5030B | | |
| MPS-L01 | S | N | F, MO, NS | (BF457) | | 2N5831 | | | |
| MPS-L07 | S | P | MO, F | | | 2N5771 | | | |
| MPS-L08 | S | P | MO, F | | | 2N5771 | | | |
| MPS-L51 | S | P | MO, F, NS | | | 2N4889 | | | |
| MPS-U01 | S | N | MO | (BD135-10) | | | | | |
| MPS-U01A | S | N | MO | (BD135-10) | | | | | |
| MPS-U02 | S | N | MO | (BD137-10) | | | | | |
| MPS-U05 | S | N | MO | (BD137-10) | BD137 | | | | |
| MPS-U06 | S | N | MO | (BD139-10) | BD139 | | | | |
| MPS-U07 | S | N | MO | (BD139-10) | | | | | |
| MPS-U51 | S | P | MO | (BD136-10) | | | | | |
| MPS-U51A | S | P | MO | (BD136-10) | | | | | |
| MPS-U52 | S | P | MO | (BD138-10) | | | | | |
| MPS-U55 | S | P | MO | (BD138-10) | | 2N6125 | | | |
| MPS-U56 | S | P | MO | (BD140-10) | | 2N6126 | | | |
| MPS-U57 | S | P | MO | (BD140-10) | | 2N6126 | | | |
| MRD100 | P | N | MO | | | TIL78* | | | |
| MRD150 | P | N | MO | | | TIL78* | | | 22 |
| MRD300 | P | N | MO | | | TIL81* | | | 22 |
| MRD310 | P | N | MO | | | TIL81* | | | 22 |

| TYPE | M/S | POL | MANUFAC | EUROPEAN | | AMERICAN | | JAPANESE | USE |
|------|-----|-----|---------|----------|--|----------|--|----------|-----|
| MRD450 | P | N | MO | | | TIL78* | | | 22 |
| MRD600 | P | | MO | | | TIL601* | | | |
| MRD810 | P | N | MO | | | TIL81* | | | 22 |
| MRD3050 | P | N | MO | | | TIL81* | | | 22 |
| MRD3051 | P | N | MO | | | TIL81* | | | 22 |
| MRD3052 | P | N | MO | | | TIL81* | | | 22 |
| MRD3053 | P | N | MO | | | TIL81* | | | 22 |
| MRD3054 | P | N | MO | | | TIL81* | | | 22 |
| MRD3055 | P | N | MO | | | TIL81* | | | 22 |
| MRD3056 | P | N | MO | | | TIL81* | | | 22 |
| MT1 | P | | | | | TIL81* | | | |
| MT2 | P | | | | | TIL81* | | | |
| MT1038 | S | N | F | (BFR15) | | | | | |
| MT1038A | S | N | F | (BFR15) | | | | | |
| MT1039 | S | N | F | (BFR15) | | | | | |
| MT1060 | S | N | F | (BFR15) | | | | | |
| MT1060A | S | N | F | (BFR15) | | | | | |
| MT1061 | S | N | F | (BFR15) | | | | | |
| MT1061A | S | N | F | (BFR15) | | | | | |
| MT1062 | S | N | F | (BFW92) | | | | | |
| MT3833 | S | N | F | (BFW92) | | | | | |
| MT3834 | S | N | F | (BFW92) | | | | | |
| MTC70 | G | P | | AC128 | | 2N2431 | | | |
| MTC71 | G | P | | AC126 | | 2N2429 | | | |
| MTC72 | G | P | | AC128 | | 2N2431 | | | |
| MTC76 | G | P | | AC128 | | 2N2431 | | | |
| NF500 | J | N | IL, NS | | | MPF102 | 2N3823 | | |
| NF500 | | | | | | 2N4224 | | | |
| NF501 | J | N | IL, NS | | | MPF102 | 2N3823 | | |
| NF501 | | | | | | 2N4224 | | | |
| NF506 | J | N | IL, NS | | | MPF102 | 2N4416 | | |
| NF506 | | | | | | 2N3823 | | | |
| NF510 | J | N | IL, NS | | | 2N4093 | 2N4861 | | |
| NF510 | | | | | | 2N3970 | | | |
| NF511 | J | N | IL, NS | | | 2N4093 | 2N4861 | | |
| NF511 | | | | | | 2N3970 | | | |
| NF520 | J | N | IL, NS | | | 2N5639 | 2N3822 | | |
| NF520 | | | | | | 2N4224 | | | |
| NF521 | J | N | IL, NS | | | 2N3970 | 2N3821 | | |
| NF521 | | | | | | 2N4220 | | | |
| NF522 | J | N | IL, NS | | | 2N5640 | 2N3822 | | |
| NF522 | | | | | | 2N4224 | | | |
| NF523 | J | N | IL, NS | | | 2N3971 | 2N3821 | | |
| NF523 | | | | | | 2N4220 | | | |
| NF530 | J | N | IL, NS | | | 2N5638 | 2N3459 | | |
| NF530 | | | | | | 2N3069 | | | |
| NF531 | J | N | IL, NS | | | 2N5639 | 2N3460 | | |
| NF531 | | | | | | 2N3070 | | | |
| NF532 | J | N | IL, NS | | | 2N5640 | 2N3459 | | |
| NF532 | | | | | | 2N3069 | | | |
| NF533 | J | N | IL, NS | | | 2N5640 | 2N3460 | | |
| NF533 | | | | | | 2N3070 | | | |
| NF550 | J | N | NS | — | | 2N3958 | | | |
| NF580 | J | N | | | | MFE2012 | SFC1783 | | |
| NF580 | | | | | | 2N4445 | | | |
| NF581 | J | N | | | | MFE2012 | SFC1783 | | |
| NF581 | | | | | | 2N4447 | | | |
| NF582 | J | N | | | | MFE2012 | SFC1785 | | |
| NF582 | | | | | | 2N5434 | | | |
| NF583 | J | N | | | | MFE2011 | SFC1785 | | |
| NF583 | | | | | | 2N5434 | | | |
| NF584 | J | N | | | | MFE2012 | SFC1785 | | |
| NF584 | | | | | | 2N4446 | | | |
| NF585 | J | N | | | | MFE2011 | SFC1785 | | |
| NF585 | | | | | | 2N5433 | | | |
| NF3819 | J | N | | | | FE3819 | | | |
| NF4302 | J | N | NS | | | 2N5458 | 2N3459 | | |
| NF4302 | | | | | | 2N4302 | | | |
| NF4303 | J | N | NS | | | 2N5458 | 2N3458 | | |
| NF4303 | | | | | | 2N4303 | | | |
| NF4304 | J | N | NS | | | 2N5458 | 2N3458 | | |
| NF4304 | | | | | | 2N4304 | | | |
| NF4445 | J | N | | | | MFE2012 | SFC1783 | | |
| NF4445 | | | | | | 2N4445 | | | |
| NF4446 | J | N | | | | SFC1785 | 2N4446 | | |

| TYPE | M/S | POL | MANUFAC | EUROPEAN | | AMERICAN | | JAPANESE | USE |
|------|-----|-----|---------|----------|---|----------|---|----------|-----|
| NF4447 | J | N | | | | SFC1783 | 2N4447 | | |
| NF4448 | J | N | | | | SFC1785 | 2N4448 | | |
| NF5163 | J | N | | | | 2N5163 | | | |
| NF5457 | J | N | | | | 2N3459 | 2N5457 | | |
| NF5458 | J | N | | | | 2N3459 | 2N5458 | | |
| NF5459 | J | N | | | | 2N3458 | 2N5459 | | |
| NF5485 | J | N | | | | 2N4416 | 2N5485 | | |
| NF5486 | J | N | | | | 2N4416 | 2N5486 | | |
| NF5555 | J | N | | | | 2N5555 | | | |
| NF5638 | J | N | | | | 2N4391 | 2N5638 | | |
| NF5639 | J | N | | | | 2N4393 | 2N5639 | | |
| NF5640 | J | N | | | | 2N4393 | 2N5640 | | |
| NF5653 | J | N | | | | 2N4856 | 2N5653 | | |
| NF5654 | J | N | | | | 2N4857 | 2N5654 | | |
| NKT52 | G | P | | NKT72 | | | | | |
| NKT53 | G | P | | NKT73 | | | | | |
| NKT54 | G | P | | NKT73 | | | | | |
| NKT62 | G | P | | NKT72 | | | | | |
| NKT63 | G | P | | NKT73 | | | | | |
| NKT64 | G | P | | NKT73 | | | | | |
| NKT74 | G | P | | NKT73 | | | | | |
| NKT122 | G | P | | 2GT102 | | | | | |
| NKT123 | G | P | | 2GT102 | | | | | |
| NKT124 | G | P | NT | | | 2N1309 | | | |
| NKT125 | G | P | NT | 2GT102 | | 2N1305 | | | |
| NKT126 | G | P | NT | 2GT102 | | | | | |
| NKT127 | G | P | | | | 2N1309 | | | |
| NKT128 | G | P | | 2GT102 | | 2N1305 | | | |
| NKT129 | G | P | | 2GT102 | | | | | |
| NKT132 | G | P | | AF185 | | | | | |
| NKT133 | G | P | | AF185 | | | | | |
| NKT142 | G | P | | 2GT102 | | | | | |
| NKT143 | G | P | | 2GT102 | | | | | |
| NKT152 | G | P | | NKT162 | | | | | |
| NKT152C | G | P | | NKT162 | | | | | |
| NKT153 | G | P | | NKT163 | | | | | |
| NKT153A | G | P | | NKT163 | | | | | |
| NKT153B | G | P | | NKT163 | | | | | |
| NKT153/25 | G | P | | NKT163 | | | | | |
| NKT153/25B | G | P | | NKT163 | | | | | |
| NKT153/25C | G | P | | NKT163 | | | | | |
| NKT154 | G | P | | NKT164 | | | | | |
| NKT154A | G | P | | NKT164 | | | | | |
| NKT154B | G | P | | NKT164 | | | | | |
| NKT154R | G | P | | NKT164 | | | | | |
| NKT154/25 | G | P | | NKT164 | | | | | |
| NKT154/25B | G | P | | NKT164 | | | | | |
| NKT154/25C | G | P | | NKT164 | | | | | |
| NKT162 | G | P | | 2GT102 | | | | | |
| NKT163Z/25 | G | P | | NKT163 | | | | | |
| NKT163/25 | G | P | | NKT163 | | | | | |
| NKT163/25B | G | P | | NKT163 | | | | | |
| NKT164Z/25 | G | P | | NKT164 | | | | | |
| NKT164/25 | G | P | | NKT164 | | | | | |
| NKT164/25B | G | P | | NKT164 | | | | | |
| NKT172 | G | P | | NKT162 | | | | | |
| NKT173 | G | P | | NKT163 | 2G371 | | | | |
| NKT174 | G | P | | NKT164 | | | | | |
| NKT182 | G | P | | NKT162 | | | | | |
| NKT183 | G | P | | NKT163 | | | | | |
| NKT184 | G | P | | NKT164 | | | | | |
| NKT202 | G | P | | AC126 | | 2N2429 | | | |
| NKT203 | G | P | | AC126 | | 2N2429 | | | |
| NKT204 | G | P | | AC126 | | 2N2429 | | | |
| NKT205 | G | P | | AC126 | | 2N2429 | | | |
| NKT206 | G | P | | AC126 | | 2N2429 | | | |
| NKT208 | G | P | | AC128 | | 2N2431 | | | |
| NKT212 | G | P | NT | 2G303 | | | | | |
| NKT213 | C | P | NT | 2G347 | | | | | |
| NKT214 | G | P | NT | 2G371 | | | | | |
| NKT215 | G | P | NT | 2G371 | | | | | |
| NKT216 | G | P | NT | 2G374 | | | | | |
| NKT217 | G | P | NT | 2G377 | | | | | |
| NKT222 | G | P | | 2G182 | | | | | |
| NKT223 | G | P | NT | AC156 | | | | | |

| TYPE | M/S | POL | MANUFAC | EUROPEAN | | AMERICAN | | JAPANESE | USE |
|------|-----|-----|---------|----------|--|----------|--|----------|-----|
| NKT250 | G | P | | NKT274 | | | | | |
| NKT251 | G | P | | AC128 | NKT271 | 2N2431 | | | |
| NKT251A | G | P | | NKT271 | | 2N2429 | | | |
| NKT252 | G | P | | AC126 | NKT274 | | | | |
| NKT252A | G | P | | NKT274 | | | | | |
| NKT253 | G | P | | NKT271 | | | | | |
| NKT254 | G | P | | NKT274 | | | | | |
| NKT254A | G | P | | NKT274 | | | | | |
| NKT255 | G | P | | NKT275 | | | | | |
| NKT255A | G | P | | NKT275 | | | | | |
| NKT255E | G | P | | NKT275 | | | | | |
| NKT255J | G | P | | NKT275 | | | | | |
| NKT258 | G | P | | NKT274 | | | | | |
| NKT260 | G | P | | NKT274 | | | | | |
| NKT261 | G | P | NT | NKT271 | | | | | |
| NKT261A | G | P | | NKT271 | | | | | |
| NKT262 | G | P | NT | NKT274 | | | | | |
| NKT262A | G | P | | NKT274 | | | | | |
| NKT263 | G | P | | NKT271 | | | | | |
| NKT264 | G | P | NT | NKT274 | | | | | |
| NKT265 | G | P | NT | NKT275 | | | | | |
| NKT265A | G | P | | NKT275 | | | | | |
| NKT265E | G | P | | NKT275 | | | | | |
| NKT265J | G | P | | NKT275 | | | | | |
| NKT268 | G | P | | NKT274 | | | | | |
| NKT270 | G | P | NT | NKT274 | | | | | |
| NKT271 | G | P | NT | AC154 | 2G302 | | | | |
| NKT271A | G | P | | NKT271 | | | | | |
| NKT272 | G | P | NT | AC113 | NKT274 | | | | |
| NKT272A | G | P | | NKT274 | | | | | |
| NKT273 | G | P | | NKT271 | | | | | |
| NKT277 | G | P | | NKT271 | | | | | |
| NKT278 | G | P | | NKT274 | | | | | |
| NKT403 | G | P | NT | AD140 | | | | | |
| NKT450 | G | P | | NKT452 | | | | | |
| NKT453 | G | P | NT | NKT452 | | | | | |
| NKT713 | G | N | NT | AC157 | | | | | |
| NKT751 | G | N | | NKT773 | | | | | |
| NKT80111 | J | N | NT | | | 2N5457 | | | |
| NKT80112 | J | N | NT | | | 2N5457 | | | |
| NKT80113 | J | N | NT | | | 2N5457 | | | |
| NKT80114 | J | N | NT | | | 2N5459 | | | |
| NKT80211 | J | N | NT | | | 2N5459 | | | |
| NKT80212 | J | N | NT | | | 2N5459 | | | |
| NKT80213 | J | N | NT | | | 2N5459 | | | |
| NKT80215 | J | N | NT | | | 2N5458 | | | |
| NKT80216 | J | N | NT | | | 2N5458 | | | |
| NPC108 | J | N | NU | | | 2N5485 | | | |
| NPC108A | J | N | NU | | | 2N5485 | | | |
| NPC211N | J | N | NU | | | 2N5457 | | | |
| NPC212N | J | N | NU | | | 2N5457 | | | |
| NPC213N | J | N | NU | | | 2N5458 | | | |
| NPC214N | J | N | NU | | | 2N5457 | | | |
| NPC215N | J | N | NU | | | 2N5457 | | | |
| NPC216N | J | N | NU | | | 2N5458 | | | |
| NSL610 | P | N | | | | TIL81* | | | |
| OC13 | G | P | | AC126 | AC125 | 2N2429 | | | |
| OC13 | | | | OC71 | | | | | |
| OC14 | G | P | | OC4 | OC74 | | | | |
| OC16 | G | P | | AD149 | AD130III | 2N2836 | 2N2063 | 2SB83 | |
| OC16 | | | | AD162 | OC26 | TI3029 | 2N1314 | | |
| OC22 | | | MU, PH, V | AUY19V | AD149 | 2N157A | 2N301A | 2SB338 | |
| OC22 | | | | AD148IV | OD603 | SFT213 | | 2SB42 | |
| OC23 | G | P | MU, PH, V | AUY19V | AD149 | 2N157A | | 2SB338 | |
| OC23 | | | | AD148 | OD603 | | | | |
| OC23 | | | | GFT4012 | | | | | |
| OC24 | G | P | MU, PH, V | AUY19V | AD148V | 2N157A | | 2SB338 | |
| OC24 | | | | AD149 | CTO1111 | | | | |
| OC25 | G | P | MN, MU | AD149 | | 2N2836 | | | |
| OC26 | G | P | PE, PH, V | AD149 | AD150IV | 2N2836 | TI156 | 2SB83 | |
| OC26 | | | | AD150 | AD153 | 2N456 | 2N1314 | | |
| OC27 | G | P | | AD149 | V30/30P | 2N353 | 2N1315 | | |
| OC28 | G | P | MN, MU, PE | AUY22II | AUY22III | 2N174 | 2N456 | 2SB341 | |
| OC28 | | | | AUY28 | ASZ15 | | | 2SB424 | |
| OC28 | | | | AD148 | | | | | |

| TYPE | M/S | POL | MANUFAC | EUROPEAN | | AMERICAN | | JAPANESE | USE |
|------|-----|-----|---------|----------|---|----------|---|----------|-----|
| OC29 | G | P | MN, MU, PE, V | AUY21III | AD138/50 | 2N174 | 2N457 | 2SB341 | |
| OC29 | | | | ASZ16 | AD150 | | | 2SB425 | |
| OC29 | | | | AUY31 | | | | | |
| OC30 | G | P | MU, PH, V | AD148V | AD139 | 2N141 | | 2SB86 | |
| OC30 | | | | AD149 | AD155 | | | | |
| | | | | | | | | | |
| OC30 | | | | AD152 | AD162 | | | | |
| OC30 | | | | AD148 | | | | | |
| OC30A | G | P | V | AD148 | AD152 | | | | |
| OC30A | | | | AD148IV | AD148V | | | | |
| OC308 | G | P | V | | | | | | |
| | | | | | | | | | |
| OC32 | G | P | | OC57 | OC58 | | | | |
| OC32 | | | | OC65 | | | | | |
| OC33 | G | P | | AC125 | AC126 | 2N2429 | | | |
| OC33 | | | | OC65 | | | | | |
| OC34 | G | P | | AC126 | AC125 | 2N2429 | | | |
| | | | | | | | | | |
| OC34 | | | | OC66 | | | | | |
| OC35 | G | P | MN, MU, PE, V | AUY21III | AD138/50 | 2N352 | | 2SB339 | |
| OC35 | | | | ASZ17 | AUY31 | | | 2SB425 | |
| OC35 | | | | SFT214 | | | | | |
| OC36 | G | P | MN, MU, PE, V | AUY22II | AUY28 | 2N174 | 2N157A | 2SB341 | |
| | | | | | | | | | |
| OC36 | | | | ASZ18 | AD132 | | | 2SB424 | |
| OC37 | G | P | | ASY76 | OC76 | | | | |
| OC38 | G | P | | AC126 | AC128 | 2N2429 | | | |
| OC38 | | | | AC132 | | | | | |
| OC41 | G | P | MU | (AC121IV) | ASY26 | | | | |
| | | | | | | | | | |
| OC41 | | | | ASY27 | | | | | |
| OC42 | G | P | MU | (AC121V) | ASY26 | | | | |
| OC42 | | | | AC125 | AC125 | | | | |
| OC43 | G | P | MU | (AC121VI) | ASY27 | | | | |
| OC44 | G | P | MU, PH, V, PE | (AC121VI) | AF185 | 2N36 | | 2SB101 | |
| | | | | | | | | | |
| OC44 | | | | ASY27 | AF126 | | | 2SB44 | |
| OC44 | | | | AF132 | AF188 | | | | |
| OC44 | | | | AFY15 | | | | | |
| OC45 | G | P | MU, PH, V, PE | (AC121VI) | AF185 | 2N36 | 2N218 | 2SB101 | |
| OC45 | | | | ASY27 | AFY15 | | | 2SB845 | |
| | | | | | | | | | |
| OC45 | | | | AF126 | AF133 | | | | |
| OC45 | | | | AF187 | | | | | |
| OC46 | G | P | PH, V | ASY46 | ASY26 | 2N269 | | 2SA212 | |
| OC46 | | | | ASY27 | AF133 | | | 2S40 | |
| OC46 | | | | SFT226 | | | | | |
| | | | | | | | | | |
| OC47 | G | P | PH, V | ASY47 | ASY27 | 2N269 | | 2SA217 | |
| OC47 | | | | AF188 | SFT227 | | | 2S40 | |
| OC50 | G | P | PH | (AC151VII) | | | | | |
| OC53 | G | P | AM | (AF139) | | | | | |
| OC54 | G | P | AM | (AF239) | | | | | |
| | | | | | | | | | |
| OC55 | G | P | AM | (AF239) | | | | | |
| OC56 | G | P | AM | (AC151V) | | | | | |
| OC57 | G | P | PH, V | (AC151IV) | OC58 | 2N1190 | 2N106 | 2SB47 | |
| OC57 | | | | AC151 | AC122ye | | | 2SB168 | |
| OC57 | | | | AC125 | AC129r | | | | |
| | | | | | | | | | |
| OC57 | | | | OC330 | | | | | |
| OC58 | G | P | PH, V | (AC151V) | AC122v | 2N106 | | 2SB168 | |
| OC58 | | | | AC129 | OC341 | | | | |
| OC58 | | | | OC624ye | AC151 | | | | |
| OC59 | G | P | PH, V | (AC151V) | AC151 | 2N106 | | 2SB168 | |
| | | | | | | | | | |
| OC59 | | | | AC122b | AC129 | | | | |
| OC59 | | | | AF129b | OC342 | | | | |
| OC60 | G | P | PH, V | AC151 | AC151V | 2N108 | | 2SB169 | |
| OC60 | | | | AC122ye | AC125 | | | | |
| OC60 | | | | AC129 | AF129b | | | | |
| | | | | | | | | | |
| OC60 | | | | OC342 | | | | | |
| OC65 | G | P | | OC57 | AC125 | | | ST301 | |
| OC65 | | | | OC330 | OC622 | | | | |
| OC66 | G | P | | AC126 | OC58 | 2N2429 | | ST302 | |
| OC66 | | | | OC340 | OC624 | | | | |
| | | | | | | | | | |
| OC70 | G | P | MU, PH, V | AC126 | AC151IV | 2N2429 | 2N279 | 2SB75 | |
| OC70 | | | | AC122 | AC125 | | | | |
| OC70 | | | | AC163 | | | | | |
| OC71 | G | P | MU, PH, V, PE | AC126 | AC151IV | 2N2429 | 2N280 | 2SB77 | |
| OC71 | | | | AC151V | AC122 | | | | |
| | | | | | | | | | |
| OC71 | | | | AC163 | OC3041 | | | | |
| OC71N | G | P | NT | AC126 | | | | | |
| OC72 | G | P | MU, PH, V, PE | AC151IV | AC151V | 2N2431 | 2N282 | 2SB89 | |
| OC72 | | | | AC128 | AC151IV | | | | |
| OC72 | | | | AC151V | AC153 | | | | |

| TYPE | M/S | POL | MANUFAC | EUROPEAN | | AMERICAN | | JAPANESE | USE |
|---|---|---|---|---|---|---|---|---|---|
| OC72 | | | | | | | | | |
| OC73 | | | | AC131 | AC132 | | | | |
| OC73 | G | P | | AC151IV | AC126 | | | | |
| OC74 | | | | GFT34 | OC75 | | | | |
| OC74 | G | P | PH, V, PE | AC128 | AC151V | 2N2431 | 2N1501 | 2SB156 | |
| | | | | AC117 | AC124 | | | | |
| OC74 | | | | OC318 | AC153 | | | | |
| OC74N | G | P | MN, NT | AC121V | AC121VI | | | | |
| OC75 | G | P | PH, MU, V | AC126 | AC151VI | 2N2429 | 2N466 | 2SB89 | |
| OC75 | | | | AC151V | AC116 | | | | |
| OC75 | | | | AC131 | OC304III | | | | |
| OC75N | G | P | NT | AC151VI | | | | | |
| OC76 | G | P | MU, PH, V, PE | AC151IV | ASY48IV | 2N284 | 2N395 | 2SB89 | |
| OC76 | | | | AC131 | ASY76 | | | | |
| OC76 | | | | AC125 | AC152 | | | | |
| OC77 | G | P | MU,PH,V,PE | ASY48IV | ASY77 | 2N24A | 2N284A | 2SB89 | |
| OC77 | | | | AC128 | ACY24 | | | | |
| OC77 | | | | ASY81 | | | | | |
| OC77N | G | P | NT | ASY48IV | | | | | |
| OC78 | G | | | AC128 | | | | | |
| OC79 | G | P | PH,V,PE | AC128 | AC152V | 2N2431 | 2N223 | 2SB156 | |
| OC79 | | | | AC152VI | AC124 | | | | |
| OC79 | | | | AC125 | AC151V | | | | |
| OC80 | G | P | PH,V,PE | AC152VI | AC121VI | | | | |
| OC80 | | | | AC126 | AC124 | | | | |
| OC80 | | | | AC128 | | | | | |
| OC80A | G | P | | AC152VI | AC152VII | | | | |
| OC81 | G | P | | AC153 | AC117R | | | | |
| OC81 | | | | AC128 | | | | | |
| OC82 | G | P | | AC128 | | | | | |
| OC83 | G | P | PH,MU | AC152V | AC131 | | | | |
| OC83 | | | | AC128 | AC124K | | | | |
| OC84 | G | P | PH,MU | AC153V | AC128 | 2N4106 | 2N467 | 2SB222 | |
| OC84 | | | | AC131 | AC124K | | | | |
| OC110 | G | P | | AC126 | AC125 | 2N2429 | | | |
| OC120 | G | P | | AC128 | AC125 | 2N2429 | | | |
| OC122 | G | P | PH,V,PE | AC153V | ASY80 | 2N4106 | 2N467 | 2SB222 | |
| OC122 | | | | AC180 | AC124K | | | | |
| OC122 | | | | AC152V | | | | | |
| OC123 | G | P | PH,V,PE | ASY48V | ASY24 | 2N241 | | | |
| OC123 | | | | ASY77 | ASY81 | | | | |
| OC123 | | | | ASY48 | | | | | |
| OC130 | G | P | | AC126 | AC125 | 2N2429 | | | |
| OC139 | G | N | MU,PH,V,PE,RA | AC127 | ASY73 | 2N1090 | | 2SC89 | |
| OC139 | | | | AF180 | AF188 | | | | |
| OC139 | | | | SFT259 | | | | | |
| OC140 | G | N | MU,PH,V,PE,RA | AC127 | ASY29 | 2N1090 | 2N1306 | 2SC90 | |
| OC140 | | | | ASY74 | SFT260 | | | | |
| OC141 | G | N | MU,PH,V,PE,RA | AC127 | ASY75 | 2N1090 | 2N1308 | 2SC91 | |
| OC141 | | | | SFT261 | | | | | |
| OC169 | G | P | V | AF126 | AF127 | | | | |
| OC169 | | | | AF185 | AF137 | | | | |
| OC170 | G | P | MU | AF126 | AF136 | 2N370 | 2N1110 | | |
| OC170 | | | | AF185 | AF124 | | | | |
| OC170 | | | | AF125 | AF133 | | | | |
| OC171 | G | P | MU | AF124 | AF125 | 2N2495 | | | |
| OC171 * | | | | AF134 | AF136 | | | | |
| OC171 | | | | AF178 | | | | | |
| OC171M | G | P | | AF124 | AF125 | 2N299 | | | |
| OC171M | | | | AF134 | AF131 | | | | |
| OC171M | | | | AF135 | | | | | |
| OC171V | G | P | | AF124 | AF134 | 2N346 | 2N384 | 2SA235 | |
| OC171V | | | | AF114 | AF130 | | | | |
| OC171V | | | | AF135 | | | | | |
| OC200 | S | P | MU,PH,PE | (BC178A) | BC177V | MPS6517 | 2N328 | 2SA565 | |
| OC200 | | | | BC308VI | BC261 | | | | |
| OC200 | | | | BCZ12 | BC204 | | | | |
| OC200 | | | | BC210 | | | | | |
| OC201 | S | P | MU,PH,PE | (BC178A) | BC177V | MPS6517 | | 2SA565 | |
| OC201 | | | | BC308VI | BC261 | | | | |
| OC201 | | | | BC213 | BC205 | | | | |
| OC201 | | | | BC162 | | | | | |
| OC202 | S | P | MU,PH,PE | (BC178A) | BS211 | | | | |
| OC203 | S | P | MU,PH,PE | (BCY77VII) | BCZ12 | | | | |
| OC204 | S | P | MU,PH,PE | (BCY79VII) | BSY10 | | | | |
| OC205 | S | P | MU,PH,PE | (BCY77VII) | BCY11 | | | | |

| TYPE | M/S | POL | MANUFAC | EUROPEAN | | AMERICAN | | JAPANESE | USE |
|---|---|---|---|---|---|---|---|---|---|
| OC205 | | | | BCY12 | | | | | |
| OC206 | S | P | MU, PH, PE | (BCY79VII) | BCY12 | | | | |
| OC207 | S | P | MU, PH | (BCY79VII) | | | | | |
| OC300 | G | P | | AC128 | AC153 | | | | |
| OC302 | G | P | | AC126 | AC128 | 2N2429 | | | |
| OC302 | | | | AC153 | | | | | |
| OC303 | G | P | IN | AC151IV | AC125 | 2N266 | | 2SB75 | |
| OC303 | | | | AC122 | AC163 | | | | |
| OC303 | | | | AC132 | | | | | |
| OC304 | G | P | IN | AC151 | AC132 | | | 2SB219 | |
| OC304 | | | | OC72 | OC604 | | | | |
| OC304/1 | G | P | IN | AC151IV | AC122 | 2N220 | | 2SB77 | |
| OC304/1 | | | | AC125 | AC132 | | | 2S39 | |
| OC304/1 | | | | AC163 | | | | | |
| OC304/2 | G | P | IN | AC151V | AC125 | 2N238 | | 2SB77A | |
| OC304/2 | | | | AC123 | AC163 | | | 2SB101 | |
| OC304/3 | G | P | IN | AC151V | AC151VI | 2N266 | | 2SB77B | |
| OC304/3 | | | | AC125 | AC128 | | | 2SB219 | |
| OC304/3 | | | | AC163 | | | | | |
| OC305 | G | P | IN | AC151 | GFT22/15 | | | | |
| OC305 | | | | SFT353BA | | | | | |
| OC305N | G | P | | AC125 | | | | | |
| OC305/1 | G | P | IN | AC151VII | AC126 | | | 2SB77 | |
| OC305/1 | | | | AC122 | AC128 | | | | |
| OC305/1 | | | | AC151VI | | | | | |
| OC305/2 | G | P | IN | AC151VII | AC125R | | | 2SB77A | |
| OC305/2 | | | | AC126 | | | | | |
| OC306 | G | P | IN | AC151r | AC125 | | | | |
| OC306 | | | | AC150 | AC151 | | | | |
| OC306/1 | G | P | IN | AC151rIV | AC150 | 2N191 | | 2S873 | |
| OC306/1 | | | | AC125R | AC162 | | | | |
| OC306/2 | G | P | IN | AC151rv | AC151rVI | 2N191 | | 2SB73A | |
| OC306/2 | | | | AC125R | AC151 | | | 2SB220 | |
| OC306/2 | | | | AC162 | | | | | |
| OC306/3 | G | P | | AC151rV | AC151VI | 2N191 | | 2S873B | |
| OC306/3 | | | | AC125R | AC128 | | | 2SB220 | |
| OC306/3 | | | | AC150 | | | | | |
| OC307 | G | P | IN | AC152 | ASY76 | 2N44 | | 2S837 | |
| OC307 | | | | AC131 | AC151IV | | | | |
| OC307/1 | G | P | IN | AC152IV | ASY76 | | | | |
| OC307/1 | | | | AC132 | | | | | |
| OC307/2 | G | P | IN | AC152IV | ASY76 | | | | |
| OC307/2 | | | | AC132 | | | | | |
| OC307/3 | G | P | IN | AC152V | ASY80 | | | | |
| OC307/3 | | | | AC132 | SFT323 | | | | |
| OC308 | G | P | | AC151V | AC131 | 2N280 | | 2SB156A | |
| OC308 | | | | ASY76 | AC132 | | | 2SB33 | |
| OC308 | | | | AC152 | AC153 | | | | |
| OC309 | G | P | IN | ASY48 | ASY48IV | | | | |
| OC309 | | | | ASY24 | ASY77 | | | | |
| OC309 | | | | ASZ10 | | | | | |
| OC309/1 | G | P | IN | ASY48IV | ASY77 | 2N1924 | | | |
| OC309/1 | | | | AC128 | ACY24K | | | | |
| OC309/2 | G | P | IN | ASY48IV | ASY77 | 2N1925 | | | |
| OC309/2 | | | | AC128 | ACY24K | | | | |
| OC309/3 | G | P | IN | ASY48V | ASY80 | 2N1926 | | | |
| OC309/3 | | | | AC128 | | | | | |
| OC318 | G | P | | AC128 | AC121IV | 2N2431 | 2N227 | 2SB226 | |
| OC318 | | | | AC121V | AC120 | | | | |
| OC320 | G | P | NU | (AC151) | OC58 | | | | |
| OC320 | | | | OC57 | OC66 | | | | |
| OC330 | G | P | NU | (AC151IV) | OC58 | | | | |
| OC330 | | | | OC65 | OC622 | | | | |
| OC330 | G | P | IN | (AC151IV) | OC58 | | | | |
| OC330 | | | | OC65 | OC622 | | | | |
| OC331 | G | P | IN | (AC151IV) | OC58 | | | | |
| OC331 | | | | AC129r | OC57 | | | | |
| OC340 | G | P | IN | (AC151V) | OC58 | | | | |
| OC340 | | | | OC57 | OC624 | | | | |
| OC341 | G | P | IN | (AC151V) | OC57 | | | | |
| OC341 | | | | OC58 | AC129ye | | | | |
| OC342 | G | P | IN | (AC151VI) | OC58 | | | | |
| OC342 | | | | OC59 | OC624ye | | | | |
| OC343 | G | P | IN | (AC151VII) | OC59 | | | | |
| OC343 | | | | OC60 | AC129b | | | | |

| TYPE | M/S | POL | MANUFAC | EUROPEAN | | AMERICAN | | JAPANESE | USE |
|------|-----|-----|---------|----------|--|----------|--|----------|-----|
| OC350 | G | P | IN | (AC151VII) | OC59 | | | | |
| OC350 | | | | OO60 | AC126 | | | | |
| OC350 | | | | OC75 | | | | | |
| OC351 | G | P | IN | (AC151VII) | OC59 | | | | |
| OC351 | | | | OO60 | | | | | |
| | | | | | | | | | |
| OC360 | G | P | IN | (AC151V) | OC58 | | | | |
| OC360 | | | | OC65 | OC623 | | | | |
| OC361 | G | P | IN | (AC151V) | OC58 | | | | |
| OC362 | G | P | IN | (AC151VI) | OC58 | | | | |
| OC362 | | | | OC59 | | | | | |
| | | | | | | | | | |
| OC363 | G | P | IN | (AC151VI) | OC58 | | | | |
| OC363 | | | | OO60 | | | | | |
| OC364 | G | P | IN | (AC151V) | AC150 | | | | |
| OC364 | | | | AC162 | | | | | |
| OC390 | G | P | IN | (AC151V) | AF185 | 2N409 | | 2SA31 | |
| | | | | | | | | | |
| OC390 | | | | AF116 | AF127 | | | | |
| OC400 | G | P | IN | (AC151VII) | AF185 | 2N139 | | | |
| OC400 | | | | AF127 | ASY32 | | | | |
| OC410 | G | P | IN | (AC151VII) | AF185 | 2N411 | | 2SA35 | |
| OC410 | | | | AF126 | ASY27 | | | | |
| | | | | | | | | | |
| OC430 | S | P | IN | (BC178A) | BC178IV | | | | |
| OC430 | | | | BSY40 | BC231B | | | | |
| OC430 | | | | BCY33 | BCY34 | | | | |
| OC430 | | | | BCZ11 | | | | | |
| OC430K | S | P | IN | (BC178A) | BC178VI | | | | |
| | | | | | | | | | |
| OC430K | | | | BCZ11 | | | | | |
| OC440 | S | P | IN | (BC178A) | BCY33 | MPS6518 | | 2SA565 | |
| OC440 | | | | BC177 | BC262 | | | | |
| OC440 | | | | BC213 | BC205 | | | | |
| OC440 | | | | BCY34 | | | | | |
| | | | | | | | | | |
| OC440K | S | P | IN | (BC177A) | BC177VI | | | | |
| OC443 | S | P | IN | (BC178A) | BC178VI | MPS6518 | | 2SA565 | |
| OC443 | | | | BC262 | BC213 | | | | |
| OC443 | | | | BC205 | BCY29 | | | | |
| OC443 | | | | BCY33 | | | | | |
| | | | | | | | | | |
| OC443K | S | P | IN | (BC177A) | BC177VI | | | | |
| OC443K | | | | BCY27 | BCY29 | | | | |
| OC443K | | | | BCZ10 | | | | | |
| OC445 | S | P | IN | (BC177A) | BC177VI | MPS6518 | | 2SA565 | |
| OC445 | | | | BC262 | BC213 | | | | |
| | | | | | | | | | |
| OC445 | | | | BC205 | BCY19 | | | | |
| OC445 | | | | BCY30 | | | | | |
| OC445K | S | P | IN | (BC177A) | BC177VI | | | | |
| OC445K | | | | BCY19 | BCZ12 | | | | |
| OC449 | S | P | IN | (BC177A) | BC177VI | MPS6518 | | 2SA565 | |
| | | | | | | | | | |
| OC449 | | | | BC262 | BC213 | | | | |
| OC449 | | | | BCY29 | BCZ12 | | | | |
| OC449 | | | | BC205 | | | | | |
| OC449K | S | P | IN | (BC178A) | BC178VI | | | | |
| OC449K | | | | BCZ12 | BCY29 | | | | |
| | | | | | | | | | |
| OC450 | S | P | IN | (BCY77VII) | BSV68 | MPS6518 | | 2SA565 | |
| OC450 | | | | BC262 | BC213 | | | | |
| OC450 | | | | BC205 | BCZ12 | | | | |
| OC450K | S | P | IN | (BCY77VII) | BCZ12 | | | | |
| OC460 | S | P | IN | (BC178A) | BC178VI | | | | |
| | | | | | | | | | |
| OC460 | | | | BC262 | BC213 | | | | |
| OC460 | | | | BC205 | BCY28 | | | | |
| OC460 | | | | BCY34 | | | | | |
| OC460K | S | P | IN | (BC178A) | BC178VI | MPS6518 | | 2SA565 | |
| OC460K | | | | BCY28 | BCZ11 | | | | |
| | | | | | | | | | |
| OC463 | S | P | IN | (BC178A) | BC178VI | MPS6518 | | 2SA565 | |
| OC463 | | | | BC262 | BC213 | | | | |
| OC463 | | | | BC205 | BCZ11 | | | | |
| OC463K | | | IN | (BC178A) | BC178VI | | | | |
| OC463K | | | | BCY28 | BCZ11 | | | | |
| | | | | | | | | | |
| OC465 | S | P | IN | (BC178A) | BC178VI | MPS6518 | | 2SA565 | |
| OC465 | | | | BC262 | BC213 | | | | |
| OC465 | | | | BCZ11 | | | | | |
| OC465K | | | IN | (BC178A) | BC178VI | | | | |
| OC465K | | | | BCY28 | BCZ11 | | | | |
| | | | | | | | | | |
| OC466 | S | P | IN | (BC178A) | BC178VI | MPS6518 | | 2SA565 | |
| OC466 | | | | BC262 | BC213 | | | | |
| OC466 | | | | BC205 | BCY28 | | | | |
| OC466 | | | | BCZ11 | | | | | |
| OC466K | S | P | IN | (BC178A) | BC178VI | | | | |

| TYPE | M/S | POL | MANUFAC | EUROPEAN | | AMERICAN | | JAPANESE | USE |
|------|-----|-----|---------|----------|----|----------|----|----------|-----|
| OC466K | | | | BCY28 | BCZ11 | | | | |
| OC467 | S | P | IN | (BC178A) | BC178VI | MPS6518 | | 2SA565 | |
| OC467 | | | | BC262 | BC213 | | | | |
| OC467 | | | | BC205 | BCY28 | | | | |
| OC467K | S | P | IN | (BC178A) | BC178VI | | | | |
| | | | | | | | | | |
| OC467K | | | | BCY28 | BCZ11 | | | | |
| OC468 | S | P | IN | (BC178A) | BC178VI | MPS6518 | | 2SA565 | |
| OC468 | | | | BC262 | BC213 | | | | |
| OC468 | | | | BC205 | BCY18 | | | | |
| OC468K | S | P | IN | (BC178A) | BC178VI | | | | |
| | | | | | | | | | |
| OC468K | | | | BCY18 | BCZ11 | | | | |
| OC469 | S | P | IN | (BC177A) | BC177VI | MPS6518 | | 2SA565 | |
| OC469 | | | | BC262 | BC231B | | | | |
| OC469 | | | | BC205 | BCY18 | | | | |
| OC469K | S | P | IN | (BC177A) | BC178 | | | | |
| | | | | | | | | | |
| OC469K | | | | BCZ12 | | | | | |
| OC470 | S | P | IN | (BC177A) | BC307 | MPS6518 | | 2SA565 | |
| OC470 | | | | BC178VI | BC262 | | | | |
| OC470 | | | | BC205 | BCY17 | | | | |
| OC470K | S | P | IN | (BC177A) | BCY17 | | | | |
| | | | | | | | | | |
| OC470K | | | | BCZ10 | BCZ11 | | | | |
| OC480 | S | P | | BCY20 | | | | | |
| OC480K | S | P | | BCY20 | | | | | |
| OC601 | G | P | TF | (ASY48IV) | AC125 | 2N2429 | | | |
| OC601 | | | | AC126 | OC70 | | | | |
| | | | | | | | | | |
| OC602 | | | | AC122 | AC126 | 2N238 | 2N2429 | 2SB459 | |
| OC602 | | | | AC151IV | SFT351 | 2N37 | | | |
| OC602 | | | | AC152 | AC162 | | | | |
| OC602S | G | P | | AC151VI | AC131 | 2N44 | | 2SB220 | |
| OC602S | | | | AC125 | AC132 | | | | |
| | | | | | | | | | |
| OC602S | | | | AC152 | ACY76 | | | | |
| OC602SP | G | P | | AC152VI | AC128 | | | | |
| OC602SP | | | | AC131 | | | | | |
| OC603 | G | P | | AC151I-IV | AC125 | 2N238 | 2N2078 | 2SB451 | |
| OC603 | | | | AC162 | | 2N2429 | | 2SB32 | |
| | | | | | | | | | |
| OC604 | G | P | | AC126 | AC151IV | 2N2429 | 2N238 | 2SB451 | |
| OC604 | | | | AC151IV | AC122 | 2N34 | | HJ15 | |
| OC604 | | | | AC125 | | | | | |
| OC604S | G | P | | AC131 | AC152 | 2N43 | | HJ15D | |
| OC604S | | | | AC153 | | | | | |
| | | | | | | | | | |
| OC604SP | G | P | | AC126 | AC128 | 2N610 | | 2SB32 | |
| OC604SP | | | | AC151V | AC152VI | | | | |
| OC604SP | | | | AC131 | | | | | |
| OC610 | G | P | | AF126 | | | | | |
| OC612 | G | P | | AF185 | AF127 | 2N642 | 2N111 | 2SA240 | |
| | | | | | | | | | |
| OC612 | | | | AFY15 | AF137 | | | HJ22D | |
| OC613 | G | P | | AF185 | AF126 | 2N641 | 2N113 | 2SA240 | |
| OC613 | | | | AFY15 | AF137 | | | | |
| OC613 | | | | SFT316 | | | | | |
| OC614 | G | P | | AF185 | AF125 | 2N1110 | 2N370 | 2SA156 | |
| | | | | | | | | | |
| OC614 | | | | AF136 | AF135 | | | HJ32 | |
| OC615 | G | P | TF | AF124 | AF168 | 2N2495 | 2N299 | | |
| OC615 | | | | AF130 | AF134 | | | | |
| OC615 | | | | AF178 | | | | | |
| OC615V | G | P | | AF125 | AF178 | 2N2495 | 2N1110 | 2SA76 | |
| | | | | | | | | | |
| OC615V | | | | AF132 | AF124 | | | | |
| OC615V | | | | AF135 | | | | | |
| OC615M | G | P | | AF124 | AF125 | 2N346 | | 2SA76 | |
| OC615M | | | | AF132 | OC615 | | | | |
| OC615M | | | | AF134 | | | | | |
| | | | | | | | | | |
| OC622 | G | P | TF | (AC151IV) | OC58 | | | | |
| OC622 | | | | ASZ23 | OC65 | | | | |
| OC622 | | | | OC331 | | | | | |
| OC623 | G | P | TF | (AC151V) | OC58 | | | | |
| OC623 | | | | OC59 | OC65 | | | | |
| | | | | | | | | | |
| OC623 | | | | OC341 | | | | | |
| OC624 | G | P | TF | (AC151VI) | OC60 | | | | |
| OC624 | | | | OC58 | OC66 | | | | |
| OC700 | S | P | IN | (BC178A) | | | | | |
| OC700A | S | P | IN | (BC178A) | | | | | |
| | | | | | | | | | |
| OC700B | S | P | IN | (BC178A) | | | | | |
| OC701 | S | P | IN | (BCY77VII) | | | | | |
| OC702 | S | P | IN | (BC178A) | | | | | |
| OC702A | S | P | IN | (BC178A) | | | | | |
| OC702B | S | P | IN | (BC178A) | | | | | |

| TYPE | M/S | POL | MANUFAC | EUROPEAN | | AMERICAN | | JAPANESE | USE |
|------|-----|-----|---------|----------|---|----------|---|----------|-----|
| OC704 | S | P | IN | (BC178A) | | | | | |
| OC810 | G | P | | AC125 | AC126 | 2N2429 | | | |
| OC811 | G | P | | AC125 | AC126 | 2N2429 | | | |
| OC6015 | G | P | | AF178 | AC125 | 2N2495 | | | |
| OC6015 | | | | AF114 | | | | | |
| | | | | | | | | | |
| OD603 | G | P | | AD149 | AD131IV | 2N2836 | 2N2066 | 2S886 | |
| OD603 | | | | AD138/50 | TI3029 | 2N68 | | | |
| OD603 | | | | OD30 | | | | | |
| OD603/50 | G | P | | AD149 | AD131 | 2N2836 | | 2SB471 | |
| OD603/50 | | | | AD138/50 | TI3029 | | | | |
| | | | | | | | | | |
| OD603/50 | | | | OC26 | | | | | |
| OD604 | G | P | | AD149 | OC30 | 2N2836 | | | |
| OD605 | G | P | | AD149 | OC26 | 2N2837 | 2N2836 | | |
| OD650 | G | P | | AD133 | AD138 | | | | |
| OD650 | | | | ADZ11 | | | | | |
| | | | | | | | | | |
| OD651 | G | P | | AD133 | AD138 | | | | |
| OD651 | | | | ADZ11 | | | | | |
| OD651A | G | P | | AD133 | AD138 | | | | |
| OD651A | | | | ADZ11 | | | | | |
| OP400 | | P | | | | LS400 | | | |
| | | | | | | | | | |
| OP420 | P | | | | | LS400 | | | |
| OP563 | P | | | | | TIL63 | | | |
| OP564 | P | | | | | TIL64 | | | |
| OP565 | P | | | | | TIL65 | | | |
| OP566 | P | | | | | TIL66 | | | |
| | | | | | | | | | |
| OP567 | P | | | | | TIL67 | | | |
| OP568 | P | | | | | TIL63 | | | |
| OP569 | P | | | | | TIL64 | | | |
| OP570 | P | | | | | TIL65 | | | |
| OP571 | P | | | | | TIL66 | | | |
| | | | | | | | | | |
| OP572 | P | | | | | TIL67 | | | |
| OP600 | P | | | | | LS600 | | | |
| OP601 | P | | | | | TIL601 | | | |
| OP602 | P | | | | | TIL602 | | | |
| OP603 | P | | | | | TIL603 | | | |
| | | | | | | | | | |
| OP604 | P | | | | | TIL604 | | | |
| OP605 | P | | | | | TIL604 | | | |
| OP606 | P | | | | | TIL603 | | | |
| OP607 | P | | | | | TIL601 | | | |
| OP608 | P | | | | | TIL602 | | | |
| | | | | | | | | | |
| OP611 | P | | | | | TIL601 | | | |
| OP612 | P | | | | | TIL602 | | | |
| OP613 | P | | | | | TIL603 | | | |
| OP614 | P | | | | | TIL604 | | | |
| OP620 | P | | | | | TIL601 | | | |
| | | | | | | | | | |
| OP621 | P | | | | | TIL601 | | | |
| OP622 | P | | | | | TIL602 | | | |
| OP623 | P | | | | | TIL603 | | | |
| OP624 | P | | | | | TIL604 | | | |
| OP630 | P | | | | | LS600* | | | |
| | | | | | | | | | |
| OP631 | P | | | | | LS600* | | | |
| OP632 | P | | | | | LS600* | | | |
| OP633 | P | | | | | LS600* | | | |
| OP634 | P | | | | | LS600* | | | |
| OP700 | P | | | | | TIL612 | | | |
| | | | | | | | | | |
| OX3003 | G | P | | AC126 | | 2N2429 | | | |
| OX3004 | G | P | | AC128 | | 2N2431 | | | |
| OX4001 | G | P | | AF185 | | | | | |
| P1003 | J | P | | | | 2N5265 | 2N5266 | | |
| P1004 | J | P | | | | 2N5267 | | | |
| | | | | | | | | | |
| P1005 | J | P | | | | 2N5269 | 2N5270 | | |
| P1027 | J | P | TI | | | 2N5266 | 2N3329 | | |
| P1028 | J | P | TI | | | 2N5268 | 2N3331 | | |
| P1029 | J | P | TI | | | 2N5270 | 2N3331 | | |
| P1069E | J | P | TI | | | MPF970 | P1117E | | |
| | | | | | | | | | |
| P1086E | J | P | IL, NS, TI | | | MPF970 | 2N5018 | | |
| P1087E | J | P | IL, NS, TI | | | MPF970 | 2N5019 | | |
| P1117E | J | P | | | | MPF970 | P1069E | | |
| P1118E | J | P | | | | MPF971 | 2N2609 | | |
| P1119E | J | P | | | | MPF971 | 2N5033 | | |
| | | | | | | | | | |
| PADT23 | G | P | | AF185 | | | | | |
| PADT24 | G | P | | AF178 | | 2N2495 | | | |
| PADT25 | G | P | | AF178 | | 2N2495 | | | |
| PADT28 | G | P | | AF178 | | 2N2495 | | | |
| PADT30 | G | P | | AF178 | | 2N2495 | | | |

| TYPE | M/S | POL | MANUFAC | EUROPEAN | AMERICAN | | JAPANESE | USE |
|------|-----|-----|---------|----------|----------|---|----------|-----|
| PADT31 | G | P | | AF178 | 2N2495 | | | |
| PBC107 | S | N | Ss, ML | BC237 | | | | |
| PBC108 | S | N | Ss, ML | BC238 | | | | |
| PBC109 | S | N | Ss, ML | BC239 | | | | |
| PE3100 | S | N | F | | PE5031 | | | |
| PE4001-18 | S | N | F | | SE4001 | | | |
| PE4002-18 | S | N | F | | SE4002 | | | |
| PE4010-18 | S | N | F | | SE4010 | | | |
| PE4030B | S | N | F | | MPS6539 | SE5032 | | |
| PE5010 | S | N | F | | MPSH32 | | | |
| PE5013 | S | N | F | (BF198) | 2N3688 | | | |
| PE5015 | S | N | F | (BF198) | SE5006 | | | |
| PE5025 | S | N | F | (BF241) | SE5035 | | | |
| PE5029 | S | N | F | (BF198) | 2N3688 | | | |
| PE5030B | S | N | F | (BF198) | MPS6540 | SE5030B | | |
| PE5031 | S | N | F | | MPS6542 | MPS6567 | | |
| PE6020 | S | N | F | (BF198) | SE5035 | | | |
| PE6020-5 | S | N | F | (BSX46-16) | SE6020 | | | |
| PE6021 | S | N | F | (BSX47-10) | | | | |
| PE6021-5 | S | N | F | | SE6021 | | | |
| PET1001 | S | N | | | MPS3693 | MPS3694 | | |
| | | | | | SE1001 | | | |
| PET1002 | S | N | | | MPS6393 | MPS3694 | | |
| PET1002 | | | | | SE1002 | | | |
| PET1075 | S | N | | | 2N5830 | | | |
| PET1075A | S | N | | | 2N5831 | | | |
| PET2001 | S | N | | | MPS3693 | MPS3694 | | |
| PET2001 | | | | | SE2001 | | | |
| PET2002 | S | N | | | MPS3693 | MPS3694 | | |
| PET2002 | | | | | SE2002 | | | |
| PET3001 | S | N | | | 2N5770 | SE3001 | | |
| PET3002 | S | N | | | 2N5770 | SE3002 | | |
| PET3702 | S | P | | | MPS3638A | 2N3638A | | |
| PET3703 | S | P | | | MPS3638 | 2N3638 | | |
| PET3704 | S | N | | | 2N4401 | 2N3566 | | |
| PET3705 | S | N | | | 2N4400 | SE6001 | | |
| PET3706 | S | N | | | 2N4401 | 2N3566 | | |
| PET3903 | S | N | | | 2N3903 | EN3903 | | |
| PET3904 | S | N | | | 2N3904 | EN3904 | | |
| PET3905 | S | P | | | 2N3905 | EN3905 | | |
| PET3906 | S | P | | | 2N3906 | EN3906 | | |
| PET4001 | S | N | | | 2N5961 | SE4001 | | |
| PET4002 | S | N | | | 2N5961 | SE4002 | | |
| PET4003 | S | N | | | 2N5961 | SE4002 | | |
| PET4058 | S | P | | | 2N5086 | 2N4248 | | |
| PET4058 | | | | | 2N5087 | 2N4250 | | |
| PET4059 | S | P | PC | | 2N5086 | 2N4248 | | |
| PET4059 | | | | | 2N5087 | 2N4250 | | |
| PET4060 | S | P | PC | | 2N5086 | 2N4248 | | |
| PET4061 | S | P | PC | | 2N5086 | 2N4248 | | |
| PET4062 | S | P | PC | | 2N5086 | 2N4248 | | |
| PET4062 | | | | | 2N5087 | 2N4250 | | |
| PET4123 | S | N | PC | | 2N4123 | EN4123 | | |
| PET4124 | S | N | PC | | 2N4124 | EN4124 | | |
| PET4125 | S | P | PC | | 2N4125 | EN4125 | | |
| PET4126 | S | P | PC | | 2N4126 | EN4126 | | |
| PET6001 | S | N | PC | | 2N4400 | SE6001 | | |
| PET6002 | S | N | PC | | 2N4401 | SE6002 | | |
| PET8000 | S | N | PC | | 2N5961 | SE4001 | | |
| PET8001 | S | N | PC | | 2N5961 | 2N3565 | | |
| PET8002 | S | N | PC | | 2N5961 | 2N3565 | | |
| PET8003 | S | N | PC | | 2N5961 | SE4010 | | |
| PET8004 | S | N | PC | | 2N5961 | SE4010 | | |
| PET8005 | S | N | PC | | 2N3903 | 2N3691 | | |
| PET8005A | S | N | PC | | 2N3903 | 2N3691 | | |
| PET8006 | S | N | PC | | 2N3903 | 2N3691 | | |
| PET8006 | | | | | 2N3904 | 2N3692 | | |
| PET8006A | S | N | PC | | 2N3903 | 2N3691 | | |
| PET8006A | | | | | 2N3904 | 2N3692 | | |
| PET8007 | S+ | N | PC | | 2N3904 | 2N3692 | | |
| PET8007A | S | N | PC | | 2N3903 | 2N3691 | | |
| PET8101 | S | N | PC | | 2N5770 | 2N3563 | | |
| PET8200 | S | N | PC | | 2N4123 | EN4123 | | |
| PET8201 | S | N | PC | | 2N4123 | EN4123 | | |

| TYPE | M/S | POL | MANUFAC | EUROPEAN | | AMERICAN | | JAPANESE | USE |
|------|-----|-----|---------|----------|--|----------|--|----------|-----|
| PET8202 | S | N | PC | | | 2N4124 | EN4124 | | |
| PET8203 | S | N | PC | | | 2N4124 | EN4124 | | |
| PET8204 | S | N | PC | | | 2N4124 | EN4124 | | |
| PET8250 | S | N | A | | | 2N4400 | SE6001 | | |
| PET8251 | S | N | PC | | | 2N4401 | SE6002 | | |
| PET8300 | S | P | PC | | | 2N5086 | 2N4248 | | |
| PET8301 | S | P | PC | | | 2N5086 | 2N4248 | | |
| PET8302 | S | P | PC | | | 2N5087 | 2N4250 | | |
| PET8303 | S | P | PC | | | 2N5771 | 2N4258 | | |
| PET8304 | S | P | PC | | | 2N5086 | 2N4248 | | |
| PET8350 | S | P | PC | | | MPS3638 | 2N3638 | | |
| PET8351 | S | P | PC | | | MPS3638A | 2N3638A | | |
| PET8352 | S | P | PC | | | MPS3638 | 2N3638 | | |
| PET8353 | S | P | PC | | | MPS3638A | 2N3638A | | |
| PET9001 | S | N | PC | | | 2N5772 | 2N4275 | | |
| PET9001A | S | N | PC | | | 2N5772 | 2N4275 | | |
| PET9002 | S | N | PC | | | 2N5772 | 2N4274 | | |
| PET9002A | S | N | PC | | | 2N5772 | 2N4274 | | |
| PET9021 | S | N | PC | | | 2N5772 | 2N4275 | | |
| PET9022 | S | N | PC | | | 2N5772 | 2N4272 | | |
| PF510 | J | P | | | | 2N5018 | | | |
| PF511 | J | P | | | | 2N5018 | | | |
| PN918-18 | S | N | NS | | | SE3002 | | | |
| PN1613 | S | N | F | (BSX45-6) | | | | | |
| PN1711 | S | N | F | (BSX45-16) | | | | | |
| PN1893 | S | N | F | (BSX47-6) | | | | | |
| PN2218 | S | N | F | BCX73-16 | | | | | |
| PN2218A | S | N | F | BCX74-16 | | | | | |
| PN2219 | S | N | F | BCX73-16 | | | | | |
| PN2219A | S | N | F | BCX74-16 | | | | | |
| PN2221 | S | N | F | BCX73-16 | | | | | |
| PN2222 | S | N | F | BCX73-16 | | | | | |
| PN2222A | S | N | F | BCX74-16 | | | | | |
| PN2484 | S | N | F | (BC414B) | | | | | |
| PN2484-18 | S | N | F | | | EN2484 | | | |
| PN2904 | S | P | F | BCX76-16 | | | | | |
| PN2904A | S | P | F | (BCX76-16) | | | | | |
| PN2905 | S | P | F | BCX76-16 | | | | | |
| PN2905A | S | P | F | (BCX76-16) | | | | | |
| PN2906 | S | P | F | BCX76-16 | | | | | |
| PN2906A | S | P | F | (BCX76-16) | | | | | |
| PN2907 | S | P | F | BCX76-16 | | | | | |
| PN2907A | S | P | F | (BCX76-16) | | | | | |
| PN3250 | S | P | F | BCX79VII | | | | | |
| PN3250A | S | P | F | (BCY79VII) | | | | | |
| PN3251 | S | P | F | BCX79VII | | | | | |
| PN3251A | S | P | F | BCX79VII | | | | | |
| PN3563-18 | S | N | F | | | 2N3563 | | | |
| PN3565 | S | N | F | (BC413B) | | | | | |
| PN3565-18 | S | N | F | | | 2N3565 | | | |
| PN3566 | S | N | F | (BC237B) | | | | | |
| PN3566-5 | S | N | F | | | 2N3566 | | | |
| PN3567 | S | N | F | (BSX45-6) | | | | | |
| PN3567-5 | S | N | F | | | 2N3567 | | | |
| PN3568 | S | N | F | (BSX46-6) | | | | | |
| PN3568-5 | S | N | F | | | 2N3568 | | | |
| PN3569 | S | N | F | (BSX45-10) | | | | | |
| PN3569-5 | S | N | F | | | 2N3569 | | | |
| PN3639-18 | S | P | F | | | 2N3639 | | | |
| PN3640-18 | S | P | F | | | 2N3640 | | | |
| PN3641 | S | N | F | (BCX73-16) | | | | | |
| PN3641-5 | S | N | F | | | 2N3641 | | | |
| PN3642 | S | N | F | (BCX74-16) | | | | | |
| PN3642-5 | S | N | F | | | 2N3642 | | | |
| PN3643 | S | N | F | (BCX73-16) | | | | | |
| PN3643-5 | S | N | F | | | 2N3643 | | | |
| PN3644 | S | P | F | (BCX76-16) | | | | | |
| PN3644-5 | S | P | F | | | 2N3644 | | | |
| PN3645 | S | P | F | (BCX76-16) | | | | | |
| PN3645-5 | S | P | F | | | 2N3645 | | | |
| PN3688 | S | N | F | (BF241) | | | | | |
| PN3689 | S | N | F | (BF241) | | | | | |
| PN3690 | S | N | F | (BF241) | | | | | |
| PN3692-18 | S | N | F | | | EN3692 | | | |
| PN4248 | S | P | F | BC416C | | | | | |

| TYPE | M/S | POL | MANUFAC | EUROPEAN | AMERICAN | JAPANESE | USE |
|---|---|---|---|---|---|---|---|
| PN4248-18 | S | P | F | | 2N4248 | | |
| PN4249 | S | F | F | (BC416B) | | | |
| PN4249-18 | S | P | F | | 2N4249 | | |
| PN4250 | S | P | F | BC416C | | | |
| PN4250A | S | P | F | (BC416C) | | | |
| PN4250-18 | S | P | F | | 2N4250 | | |
| PN4250A-18 | S | P | F | | 2N4250A | | |
| PN4258-18 | S | P | F | | 2N4257 | 2N4258 | |
| PN4258A-18 | S | P | F | | 2N4258A | | |
| PN4274-18 | S | N | F | | 2N4274 | | |
| PN4275-18 | S | N | F | | 2N4275 | | |
| PN4355-5 | S | P | F | | 2N4355 | | |
| PN4356-5 | S | P | F | | 2N4356 | | |
| PN4916 | S | P | F | (BC415A) | | | |
| PN4917 | S | P | F | (BC415B) | | | |
| PN5126 | S | N | F | (BF198) | | | |
| PN5128 | S | N | F | (BSX48) | | | |
| PN5128-18 | S | N | F | | 2N5128 | | |
| PN5129 | S | N | F | (BSX48) | | | |
| PN5130 | S | N | F | (BFX89) | | | |
| PN5130-18 | S | N | F | | 2N5130 | | |
| FN5131 | S | N | F | (BC413B) | | | |
| PN5132 | S | N | F | (BC413B) | | | |
| PN5133 | S | N | F | (BC413C) | | | |
| PN5133-18 | S | N | F | | 2N5133 | | |
| PN5134 | S | N | F | (BSY17) | | | |
| PN5134-18 | S | N | F | | 2N5134 | | |
| PN5135 | S | N | F | BC337-25 | | | |
| PN5135-5 | S | N | F | | 2N5135 | | |
| PN5136 | S | N | F | BC338-16 | | | |
| PN5136-5 | S | N | F | | 2N5136 | | |
| PN5137 | S | N | F | BC338-16 | | | |
| PN5138 | S | N | F | (BC413C) | | | |
| PN5138-18 | S | P | F | | 2N5138 | | |
| PN5139 | S | P | F | | | | |
| PN5142 | S | P | F | (BCX75-16) | | | |
| PN5142-5 | S | P | F | | 2N5142 | | |
| PN5143 | S | P | F | (BCX75-16) | | | |
| PN5855 | S | P | F | (8SV16-16) | | | |
| PN5856 | S | N | F | (BSX46-16) | | | |
| PN5857 | S | P | F | (BSV17-10) | | | |
| PN5858 | S | N | F | (BSX47-10) | | | |
| PN5910-18 | S | P | F | | 2N5910 | | |
| PN5964 | S | N | F | (BF457) | | | |
| PN5965 | S | N | F | (BF458) | | | |
| PT200 | M | N | | | MFE3004 | | |
| PT201 | M | N | | | MFE3004 | | |
| PT320 | M | P | | | MFE3003 | | |
| PT904L | P | | | | TIL65* | | |
| PT4416 | G | P | | OC16 | | | |
| Q6 | G | P | | AC128 | 2N2431 | | |
| Q7 | G | P | | AC128 | 2N2431 | | |
| Q8 | G | P | | AC128 | 2N2431 | | |
| QS100 | P | | | | TIL63* | | |
| QS101 | P | | | | TIL64* | | |
| QS102 | P | | | | TIL65* | | |
| QS103 | P | | | | TIL66* | | |
| QS104 | P | | | | TIL67* | | |
| QS105 | P | | | | TIL64* | | |
| QS106 | P | | | | TIL67* | | |
| QS107 | P | | | | TIL65* | | |
| QS200 | P | | | | TIL614* | | |
| QS201 | P | | | | TIL615* | | |
| QS202 | P | | | | TIL613* | | |
| QS203 | P | | | | TIL615* | | |
| QS204 | P | | | | TIL614 | | |
| QS205 | P | | | | TIL615 | | |
| QS230 | P | | | | TIL614 | | |
| QS400 | P | | | | LS400 | | |
| QS401 | P | | | | LS400* | | |
| QS402 | P | | | | LS400* | | |
| QS403 | P | | | | LS400* | | |
| QS404 | P | | | | LS400* | | |
| QS600 | P | | | | LS600 | | |
| QS601 | P | | | | TIL601 | | |

| TYPE | M/S | POL | MANUFAC | EUROPEAN | | AMERICAN | JAPANESE | USE |
|---|---|---|---|---|---|---|---|---|
| QS602 | P | | | | | TIL602 | | |
| QS603 | P | | | | | TIL603 | | |
| QS604 | P | | | | | TIL604 | | |
| QS605 | P | | | | | TIL604* | | |
| RCA1A01 | S | N | RC | | | 2N5320 | | 06 |
| RCA1A02 | S | P | RC | | | 2N5322 | | 06 |
| RCA1A03 | S | P | RC | | | 2N5338 | | 06 |
| RCA1A05 | S | P | RC | | | 2N5322 | | 06 |
| RCA1A06 | S | N | RC | | | 2N5320 | | 06 |
| RCA1A07 | S | N | RC | | | 2N5321 | | 06 |
| RCA1A08 | S | P | RC | | | 2N5323 | | 06 |
| RCA1A09 | S | N | RC | | | 2N3439 | | 06 |
| RCA1A10 | S | N | RC | | | FT5416 | | 06 |
| RCA1A11 | S | N | RC | | | 2N3439 | | 06 |
| RCA1A15 | S | N | RC | | | 2N3440 | | 06 |
| RCA1A16 | S | P | RC | | | FT5416 | | 06 |
| RCA1A17 | S | N | RC | | | | | 06 |
| RCA1A18 | S | N | RC | | | | | 06 |
| RCA1A19 | S | P | RC | | | 2N5322 | | 06 |
| RCA1B01 | S | N | RC | | | 2N5629 | | 06 |
| RCA1B04 | S | N | | | | FT410 | | 06 |
| RCA1B05 | S | N | RC | | | 2N6250 | | 06 |
| RCA1B06 | S | N | RC | | | FT410 | | 06 |
| RCA1B07 | S | N | RC | | | SE9305 | | |
| RCA1C05 | S | N | RC | | | | | 06 |
| RCA1C06 | S | P | RC | | | | | |
| RCA1C07 | S | N | RC | | | 2N6131 | | 06 |
| RCA1C08 | S | P | RC | | | 2N6134 | | 06 |
| RCA1C09 | S | N | RC | | | FT3055 | | 06 |
| RCA1C10 | S | N | RC | | | 2N6129 | | 06 |
| RCA1C11 | S | N | RC | | | 2N6132 | | 06 |
| RCA1C14 | S | N | RC | | | 2N6130 | | 06 |
| RCA29 | S | N | RC | | | TIP29 | | 06 |
| RCA29A | S | N | RC | | | TIP29A | | 06 |
| RCA29B | S | N | RC | | | TIP29B | | 06 |
| RCA29C | S | N | RC | | | TIP29C | | 06 |
| RCA30 | S | P | RC | | | TIP30 | | 06 |
| RCA30A | S | P | RC | | | TIP30A | | 06 |
| RCA30B | S | P | RC | | | TIP30B | | 06 |
| RCA30C | S | P | RC | | | TIP30C | | 06 |
| RCA31 | S | N | RC | | | TIP31 | | 06 |
| RCA31A | S | N | RC | | | TIP31A | | 06 |
| RCA31B | S | N | RC | | | TIP31B | | 06 |
| RCA31C | S | N | RC | | | TIP31C | | 06 |
| RCA32 | S | P | RC | | | TIP32 | | 06 |
| RCA32A | S | P | RC | | | TIP32A | | 06 |
| RCA32B | S | P | RC | | | TIP32B | | 06 |
| RCA32C | S | P | RC | | | TIP32C | | 06 |
| RCA41 | S | N | RC | | | TIP41 | | 06 |
| RCA41A | S | N | RC | | | TIP41A | | 06 |
| RCA41B | S | N | RC | | | TIP41B | | 06 |
| RCA41C | S | N | RC | | | TIP41C | | 06 |
| RCA42 | S | P | RC | | | TIP42 | | 06 |
| RCA42A | S | P | RC | | | TIP42A | | 06 |
| RCA42B | S | P | RC | | | TIP42B | | 06 |
| RCA42C | S | P | RC | | | TIP42C | | 06 |
| RCA120 | SD | N | RC | | | TIP120 | | 06 |
| RCA121 | SD | N | RC | | | TIP121 | | 06 |
| RCA125 | SD | P | RC | | | | | 06 |
| RCA126 | SD | P | RC | | | TIP126 | | 06 |
| RCA410 | S | N | RC | | | FT410 | | 06 |
| RCA411 | S | N | RC | | | FT411 | | 06 |
| RCA413 | S | N | RC | | | FT413 | | 06 |
| RCA423 | S | N | RC | | | FT423 | | 06 |
| RCA431 | S | N | RC | | | FT431 | | 06 |
| RCA1000 | SD | N | RC | | | SE9303 | | 06 |
| RCA1001 | SD | N | RC | | | SE9304 | | 06 |
| RCA3054 | S | N | RC | | | | | 06 |
| RCA3055 | A | N | RC | | | FT3055 | | 06 |
| RCA8203A | SD | P | RC | | | SE9400 | | 06 |
| RCA8203B | SD | P | RC | | | SE9401 | | 06 |
| RF1 | G | N | | AF185 | | | | |
| RR34Z | G | P | | OC58 | | | | |
| RR83 | G | P | | AC126 | | | | |
| RR87 | G | P | | AC126 | | 2N2429 | | |

| TYPE | M/S | POL | MANUFAC | EUROPEAN | AMERICAN | JAPANESE | USE |
|------|-----|-----|---------|----------|----------|----------|-----|
| RR117 | G | P | | AC126 | 2N2429 | | |
| RR160 | G | P | | AF185 | | | |
| RR161 | G | P | | AF185 | | | |
| RR162 | G | P | | AF185 | | | |
| RRJ14 | G | P | | AC126 | 2N2429 | | |
| RRJ20 | G | P | | AC126 | 2N2429 | | |
| RRJ34 | G | P | | AC126 | 2N2429 | | |
| RRJZ14 | G | P | | OC58 | | | |
| RRJZ20 | G | P | | OC58 | | | |
| RRJZ34 | G | P | | OC58 | | | |
| RRJZ38 | G | P | | OC58 | | | |
| S40251 | S | N | | | 40251 | | |
| S40309 | S | N | | | 40309 | | |
| S40310 | S | N | | | 40310 | | |
| S40311 | S | N | | | 40311 | | |
| S40312 | S | N | | | 40312 | | |
| S40314 | S | N | | | 40314 | | |
| S40315 | S | N | | | 40315 | | |
| S40316 | S | N | | | 40316 | | |
| S40317 | S | N | | | 40317 | | |
| S40319 | S | P | | | 40319 | | |
| S40320 | S | N | | | 40320 | | |
| S40321 | S | N | | | 40321 | | |
| S40323 | S | N | | | 40323 | | |
| S40324 | S | N | | | 40324 | | |
| S40325 | S | N | | | 40325 | | |
| S40326 | S | N | | | 40326 | | |
| S40327 | S | N | | | 40327 | | |
| S40360 | S | N | | | 40360 | | |
| S40361 | S | N | | | 40361 | | |
| S40362 | S | P | | | 40362 | | |
| S40363 | S | N | | | 40363 | | |
| S40364 | S | N | | | 40364 | | |
| S40406 | S | P | | | 40406 | | |
| S40407 | S | N | | | 40407 | | |
| S40408 | S | N | | | 40408 | | |
| S40411 | S | N | | | 40411 | | |
| S40537 | S | P | | | 40537 | | |
| S40538 | S | P | | | 40538 | | |
| S40539 | S | N | | | 40539 | | |
| S40544 | S | N | | | 40544 | | |
| S40594 | S | N | | | 40594 | | |
| S40595 | S | P | | | 40595 | | |
| S40611 | S | N | | | 40611 | | |
| S40616 | S | N | | | 40616 | | |
| S40634 | S | P | | | 40634 | | |
| S40635 | S | N | | | 40635 | | |
| SB100 | G | P | | AF185 | | | |
| SC12 | G | P | | AC126 | 2N2429 | | |
| SC1611 | M | P | | | 2N4352 | | |
| SC1612 | M | P | | | 2N4352 | | |
| SC1613 | M | P | | | 2N4352 | | |
| SC1614 | M | P | | | 2N4352 | | |
| SCC321 | S | N | F | | TIP35A | | |
| SCC421 | S | P | F | | TIP36A | | |
| SCD321 | S | N | F | | TIP33B | | |
| SCD421 | S | P | F | | TIP36A | | |
| SCE321 | S | N | F | | TIP33C | | |
| SCE421 | S | P | F | | TIP36C | | |
| SD345 | S | N | | | 2N2593 | TIP29A | |
| SD345 | | | | | 2N5294 | 2N6123 | |
| SD445 | S | P | | | TIP30A | | |
| SD1440/1 | P | | | | TIL610* | | |
| SD1440/2 | P | | | | TIL611* | | |
| SD1440/3 | P | | | | TIL612* | | |
| SD1440/4 | P | | | | TIL612* | | |
| SD1441/1 | P | | | | TIL609* | | |
| SD1441/2 | P | | | | TIL610* | | |
| SD1441/3 | P | | | | TIL611* | | |
| SD2440/1 | P | | | | TIL601 | | |
| SD2440/2 | P | | | | TIL602 | | |
| SD2440/3 | P | | | | TIL603 | | |
| SD2440/4 | P | | | | TIL604 | | |
| SD2441/1 | P | | | | TIL603* | | |
| SD2441/2 | P | | | | TIL604* | | |

| TYPE | M/S | POL | MANUFAC | EUROPEAN | AMERICAN | | JAPANESE | USE |
|---|---|---|---|---|---|---|---|---|
| SD2441/3 | P | | | | | TIL604* | | |
| SD3440/1 | P | | | | | TIL81* | | |
| SD3440/2 | P | | | | | TIL81* | | |
| SD3440/3 | P | | | | | TIL81* | | |
| SD3442/1 | P | | | | | TIL81* | | |
| SD3442/2 | P | | | | | TIL81* | | |
| SD3442/3 | P | | | | | TIL81* | | |
| SD5440/1 | P | | | | | TIL81* | | |
| SD5440/2 | P | | | | | TIL81* | | |
| SD5440/3 | P | | | | | TIL81* | | |
| SD5440/4 | P | | | | | TIL81 | | |
| SD5442/1 | P | | | | | TIL81* | | |
| SD5442/2 | P | | | | | TIL81* | | |
| SD5442/3 | P | | | | | TIL81* | | |
| SDA345 | S | N | | | 2N6121 | 2N5295 | | |
| SDA345 | | | | | 2N6122 | MJE520 | | |
| SDA345 | | | | | TIP31 | | | |
| SDA445 | S | P | | | 2N6124 | MJE370 | | |
| SDA445 | | | | | 2N6125 | MJE371 | | |
| SDA445 | | | | | TIP30 | | | |
| SDB345 | S | N | | | 2N6122 | 2N5297 | | |
| SDB345 | | | | | 2N6123 | 2N5298 | | |
| SDB345 | | | | | TIP31A | | | |
| SDB445 | S | P | | | TIP32A | 2N6125 | | |
| SDB445 | | | | | 2N6126 | | | |
| SDC345 | S | N | | | 2N4921 | | | |
| SDC445 | S | P | | | 2N4918 | | | |
| SDD345 | S | N | | | 2N4922 | | | |
| SDD445 | S | P | | | 2N4919 | | | |
| SDE345 | S | N | | | 2N4923 | | | |
| SDE445 | S | P | | | 2N4920 | | | |
| SDF345 | S | N | | | 2N5190 | | | |
| SDF445 | S | P | | | 2N5193 | | | |
| SDG345 | S | N | | | 2N5191 | | | |
| SDG445 | S | P | | | 2N5194 | | | |
| SDH345 | S | N | | | 2N5192 | | | |
| SDH445 | S | P | | | 2N5195 | | | |
| SDI345 | S | N | F | | 2N6121 | 40622 | | |
| SDI345 | | | | | 2N6290 | 40618 | | |
| SDI345 | | | | | TIP41 | 40621 | | |
| SDI445 | S | P | F | | 2N6124 | TIP42 | | |
| SDI445 | | | | | 2N6109 | | | |
| SDJ345 | S | N | F | | 2N6290 | TIP41 | | |
| SDJ445 | S | P | F | | 2N6109 | TIP42 | | |
| SDK345 | S | N | F | | 40624 | 40627 | | |
| SDK345 | | | | | 2N6121 | TIP41 | | |
| SDK345 | | | | | 2N6290 | | | |
| SDK445 | S | P | F | | 2N6124 | TIP42 | | |
| SDK445 | | | | | 2N6109 | | | |
| SDL345 | S | N | F | | 2N6122 | TIP41A | | |
| SDL345 | | | | | 2N6292 | | | |
| SDL445 | S | P | F | | 2N6125 | TIP42A | | |
| SDL445 | | | | | 2N6107 | | | |
| SDM345 | S | N | F | | 2N6121 | TIP41 | | |
| SDM445 | S | P | F | | 2N6124 | TIP42 | | |
| SDN345 | S | N | F | | 2N6122 | TIP41A | | |
| SDN445 | S | P | F | | 2N6125 | TIP42A | | |
| SDO345 | S | N | F | | 2N6123 | TIP41B | | |
| SDO445 | S | P | F | | 2N6126 | TIP42B | | |
| SDP345 | S | N | F | | TIP41C | | | |
| SDP445 | S | P | F | | TIP42C | | | |
| SDT402 | S | N | SD | | TIP54 | | | |
| SDT410 | S | N | SD | | RCA410 | TIP51 | | |
| SDT411 | S | N | SD | | RCA411 | TIP52 | | |
| SDT413 | S | N | SD | | RCA413 | | | |
| SDT423 | S | N | SD | | RCA423 | TIP54 | | |
| SDT431 | S | N | SD | | RCA431 | | | |
| SDT1050 | S | N | SD | | FT410 | | | |
| SDT1051 | S | N | SD | | FT413 | | | |
| SDT1055 | S | N | SD | | 2N5838 | | | |
| SDT1056 | S | N | SD | | FT423 | | | |
| SDT1060 | S | N | SD | | 2N5838 | | | |
| SDT1061 | S | N | SD | | FT431 | | | |
| SDT3509 | S | P | PI,SD | | TIP32 | | | |
| SDT3510 | S | P | PI,SD | | TIP32A | | | |

| TYPE | M/S | POL | MANUFAC | EUROPEAN | AMERICAN | | JAPANESE | USE |
|------|-----|-----|---------|----------|----------|---|----------|-----|
| SDT3511 | S | P | PI,SD | | TIP35B | | | |
| SDT3512 | S | P | PI,SD | | TIP32C | | | |
| SDT3513 | S | P | PI,SD | | TIP32 | | | |
| SDT3514 | S | P | PI,SD | | TIP32A | | | |
| SDT3515 | S | P | PI,SD | | TIP32B | | | |
| | | | | | | | | |
| SDT3516 | S | P | PI,SD | | TIP32C | | | |
| SDT3550 | S | P | SD | | 2N4235 | 2N5781 | | |
| SDT3551 | S | P | SD | | 2N4236 | | | |
| SDT3552 | S | P | SD | | 2N4234 | 2N5783 | | |
| SDT3553 | S | P | SD | | 2N4235 | 2N5781 | | |
| | | | | | | | | |
| SDT3554 | S | P | SD | | 2N4236 | | | |
| SDT3575 | S | P | SD | | 2N5956 | TIP30 | | |
| SDT3576 | S | P | SD | | 2N4899 | 2N5955 | | |
| SDT3576 | | | | | TIP30A | | | |
| SDT3577 | S | P | SD | | 2N4900 | 2N5954 | | |
| | | | | | | | | |
| SDT3577 | | | | | TIP30B | | | |
| SDT3578 | S | P | SD | | 2N4898 | TIP30 | | |
| SDT3579 | S | P | SD | | 2N4899 | TIP30A | | |
| SDT3701 | S | P | SD | | 2N5956 | TIP42 | | |
| SDT3702 | S | P | SD | | 2N5955 | TIP55A | | |
| | | | | | | | | |
| SDT3703 | S | P | SD | | 2N5956 | TIP42 | | |
| SDT3704 | S | P | SD | | 2N5955 | TIP42A | | |
| SDT3705 | S | P | SD | | 2N5954 | TIP42B | | |
| SDT3706 | S | P | SD | | 2N5956 | TIP42 | | |
| SDT3707 | S | P | SD | | 2N5955 | TIP42 | | |
| | | | | | | | | |
| SDT3708 | S | P | SD | | 2N5955 | TIP42A | | |
| SDT3709 | S | P | SD | | 2N5956 | TIP42 | | |
| SDT3710 | S | P | SD | | 2N5955 | TIP42 | | |
| SDT3711 | S | P | SD | | 2N5955 | TIP42A | | |
| SDT3712 | S | P | SD | | 2N5956 | TIP42 | | |
| | | | | | | | | |
| SDT3713 | S | P | SD | | 2N5955 | TIP42A | | |
| SDT3714 | S | P | SD | | 2N5954 | TIP42A | | |
| SDT3715 | S | P | SD | | 2N5956 | TIP42 | | |
| SDT3716 | S | P | SD | | 2N5956 | TIP42 | | |
| SDT3717 | S | P | SD | | 2N5955 | TIP42A | | |
| | | | | | | | | |
| SDT3718 | S | P | SD | | 2N5954 | TIP42B | | |
| SDT3719 | S | P | SD | | TIP42C | | | |
| SDT3720 | S | P | SD | | 2N5956 | TIP42 | | |
| SDT3721 | S | P | SD | | 2N5956 | TIP42 | | |
| SDT3722 | S | P | SD | | 2N5955 | TIP42A | | |
| | | | | | | | | |
| SDT3723 | S | P | SD | | 2N5954 | TIP42B | | |
| SDT3724 | S | P | SD | | TIP42C | | | |
| SDT3725 | S | P | SD | | 2N5956 | TIP42 | | |
| SDT3726 | S | P | SD | | 2N5956 | TIP42 | | |
| SDT3727 | S | P | SD | | 2N5955 | TIP42A | | |
| | | | | | | | | |
| SDT3728 | S | P | SD | | 2N5954 | TIP42B | | |
| SDT3729 | S | P | SD | | 2N5956 | TIP42 | | |
| SDT3730 | S | P | SD | | 2N5955 | TIP42A | | |
| SDT3731 | S | P | SD | | 2N5954 | TIP42A | | |
| SDT3732 | S | P | SD | | TIP42C | | | |
| | | | | | | | | |
| SDT3733 | S | P | SD | | 2N5956 | TIP42 | | |
| SDT3750 | S | P | SD | | 2N4904 | 2N6246 | | |
| SDT3750 | | | | | TIP34 | | | |
| SDT3751 | S | P | SD | | 2N4905 | 2N6246 | | |
| SDT3751 | | | | | TIP34A | | | |
| | | | | | | | | |
| SDT3752 | S | P | SD | | 2N4901 | 2N6246 | | |
| SDT3752 | | | | | TIP34 | | | |
| SDT3753 | S | P | SD | | 2N4902 | 2N6246 | | |
| SDT3753 | | | | | TIP34A | | | |
| SDT3754 | S | P | SD | | 2N4903 | 2N6247 | | |
| | | | | | | | | |
| SDT3754 | | | | | TIP34B | | | |
| SDT3755 | S | P | SD | | 2N6248 | TIP34C | | |
| SDT3756 | S | P | SD | | 2N4904 | 2N6246 | | |
| SDT3756 | | | | | TIP34 | | | |
| SDT3757 | S | P | SD | | 2N4904 | 2N6246 | | |
| | | | | | | | | |
| SDT3757 | | | | | TIP34 | | | |
| SDT3758 | S | P | SD | | 2N4905 | 2N6246 | | |
| SDT3758 | | | | | TIP34A | | | |
| SDT3759 | S | P | SD | | 2N4906 | 2N6247 | | |
| SDT3759 | | | | | TIP34B | | | |
| | | | | | | | | |
| SDT3760 | S | P | SD | | 2N6248 | TIP34C | | |
| SDT3761 | S | P | SD | | 2N4904 | 2N6246 | | |
| SDT3761 | | | | | TIP34 | | | |
| SDT3762 | S | P | SD | | 2N4904 | 2N6246 | | |
| SDT3762 | | | | | TIP34 | | | |

| TYPE | M/S | POL | MANUFAC | EUROPEAN | | AMERICAN | | JAPANESE | USE |
|------|-----|-----|---------|----------|--|----------|--|----------|-----|
| SDT3763 | S | P | SD | | | 2N4905 | 2N6246 | | |
| SDT3763 | | | | | | TIP34A | | | |
| SDT3764 | S | P | SD | | | 2N4906 | 2N6247 | | |
| SDT3764 | | | | | | TIP34B | | | |
| SDT3765 | S | P | SD | | | 2N6248 | TIP34C | | |
| SDT3766 | S | P | SD | | | 2N4904 | 2N6246 | | |
| SDT3766 | | | | | | TIP34 | | | |
| SDT3825 | S | P | SD | | | 2N6246 | TIP34 | | |
| SDT3826 | S | P | SD | | | 2N5880 | 2N6247 | | |
| SDT3826 | | | | | | TIP34B | | | |
| SDT3827 | S | P | SD | | | 2N6246 | TIP34 | | |
| SDT3875 | S | P | SD | | | 2N4398 | TIP36 | | |
| SDT3876 | S | P | SD | | | 2N5884 | TIP36A | | |
| SDT3877 | S | P | SD | | | 2N4398 | TIP36 | | |
| SDT4301 | S | N | PI,SD | | | 2N4237 | | | |
| SDT4302 | S | N | PI,SD | | | 2N4238 | | | |
| SDT4303 | S | N | PI,SD | | | 2N4239 | | | |
| SDT4304 | S | N | PI,SD | | | 2N5321 | | | |
| SDT4305 | S | N | PI,SD | | | 2N5334 | | | |
| SDT4306 | S | N | PI,SD | | | 2N5335 | | | |
| SDT4307 | S | N | PI,SD | | | 2N5321 | | | |
| SDT4308 | S | N | PI,SD | | | 2N5334 | | | |
| SDT4309 | S | N | PI,SD | | | 2N5335 | | | |
| SDT4311 | S | N | PI,SD | | | 2N5334 | | | |
| SDT4312 | S | N | PI,SD | | | 2N5335 | | | |
| SDT4901 | S | N | KE,SD | | | 2N6078 | | | |
| SDT4902 | S | N | KE,SD | | | 2N6078 | | | |
| SDT4903 | S | N | KE,SD | | | 2N6077 | | | |
| SDT4904 | S | N | KE,SD | | | 2N6077 | | | |
| SDT4905 | S | N | KE,SD | | | 2N6078 | | | |
| SDT5901 | S | N | SD,KE,PI | | | TIP41 | | | |
| SDT5902 | S | N | KE,SD | | | TIP41A | | | |
| SDT5903 | S | N | KE,PI,SD | | | TIP41B | | | |
| SDT5904 | S | N | KE,SD,PI | | | TIP41C | | | |
| SDT6901 | S | N | KE,SD | | | 2N6078 | | | |
| SDT6902 | S | N | KE,SD | | | 2N6078 | | | |
| SDT6903 | S | N | KE,SD | | | 2N6078 | | | |
| SDT6904 | S | N | KE,SD | | | 2N6078 | | | |
| SDT6905 | S | N | KE,SD | | | 2N6078 | | | |
| SDT6906 | S | N | KE,SD | | | 2N6078 | | | |
| SDT6907 | S | N | KE,SD | | | 2N6078 | | | |
| SDT6908 | S | N | KE,SD | | | 2N6078 | | | |
| SDT7601 | S | N | KE,SD,PI | | | 2N5039 | TIP33 | | |
| SDT7602 | S | N | KE,SD,PI | | | 2N5039 | TIP33A | | |
| SDT7603 | S | N | KE,SD,PI | | | 2N5038 | TIP33B | | |
| SDT7604 | S | N | KE,SD,PI | | | 2N6249 | | | |
| SDT7605 | S | N | KE,SD,PI | | | 2N6249 | | | |
| SDT7607 | S | N | KE,SD,PI | | | 2N5039 | TIP33 | | |
| SDT7608 | S | N | KE,SD,PI | | | 2N5039 | TIP33A | | |
| SDT7609 | S | N | KE,SD,PI | | | 2N5038 | TIP33B | | |
| SDT7610 | S | N | KE,SD,PI | | | 2N6249 | | | |
| SDT7611 | S | N | KE,SD,PI | | | 2N6249 | | | |
| SDT7612 | S | N | KE,SD,PI | | | 2N6249 | | | |
| SDT7731 | S | N | SD | | | 2N6254 | 2N5301 | | |
| SDT7732 | S | N | SD | | | 2N5881 | 2N6254 | | |
| SDT7732 | | | | | | 2N5301 | | | |
| SDT7733 | S | N | SD | | | 2N5882 | 2N6254 | | |
| SDT7733 | | | | | | 2N5301 | | | |
| SDT7734 | S | N | SD | | | 2N5629 | 2N3773 | | |
| SDT7734 | | | | | | 2N5301 | | | |
| SDT7735 | S | N | SD | | | 2N3773 | | | |
| SDT7736 | S | N | SD | | | 2N6259 | | | |
| SDT8002 | S | N | KE,SD,PI | | | 2N3266 | | | |
| SDT8003 | S | N | KE,SD,PI | | | 2N3265 | | | |
| SDT8012 | S | N | KE,SD,PI | | | 2N3266 | | | |
| SDT8013 | S | N | KE,SD,PI | | | 2N3265 | | | |
| SDT8015 | S | N | KE,SD,PI | | | 2N3266 | | | |
| SDT8016 | S | N | KE,SD,PI | | | 2N3265 | | | |
| SDT8105 | S | N | SD | | | 2N3264 | | | |
| SDT8106 | S | N | SD | | | 2N3263 | | | |
| SDT8112 | S | N | SD | | | 2N3264 | | | |
| SDT8113 | S | N | SD | | | 2N3263 | | | |
| SDT8301 | S | N | KE,SD,PI | | | 2N3266 | | | |
| SDT8302 | S | N | KE,SD,PI | | | 2N3265 | | | |
| SDT8303 | S | N | KE,SD,PI | | | 2N3266 | | | |

| TYPE | M/S | POL | MANUFAC | EUROPEAN | | AMERICAN | | JAPANESE | USE |
|---|---|---|---|---|---|---|---|---|---|
| SDT8304 | S | N | KE,SD,PI | | | 2N3265 | | | |
| SDT9201 | S | N | PI,SD | | | 2N6569 | 2N3055 | | |
| SDT9201 | | | | | | TIP35 | | | |
| SDT9202 | S | N | PI,SD | | | 2N5882 | 2N6254 | | |
| SDT9202 | | | | | | TIP35B | | | |
| SDT9203 | S | N | PI,SD | | | 2N5629 | 2N4348 | | |
| SDT9203 | | | | | | TIP35C | | | |
| SDT9204 | S | N | PI,SD | | | 2N5630 | 2N4348 | | |
| SDT9204 | | | | | | 2N5301 | | | |
| SDT9205 | S | N | PI,SD | | | 2N6569 | 2N3055 | | |
| SDT9205 | | | | | | TIP35 | | | |
| SDT9206 | S | N | PI,SD | | | 2N3055 | TIP35A | | |
| SDT9207 | S | N | PI,SD | | | 2N5882 | 2N6254 | | |
| SDT9207 | | | | | | TIP35B | | | |
| SDT9208 | S | N | PI,SD | | | 2N5629 | 2N4348 | | |
| SDT9208 | | | | | | TIP35C | | | |
| SDT9209 | S | N | PI,SD | | | 2N5630 | 2N4348 | | |
| SDT9209 | | | | | | 2N5301 | | | |
| SDT9210 | S | N | PI,SD | | | 2N6253 | TIP35 | | |
| SDT9701 | S | N | PI,SD | | | 2N5303 | 2N6258 | | |
| SDT9702 | S | N | PI,SD | | | 2N5629 | 2N3773 | | |
| SDT9703 | S | N | PI,SD | | | 2N5630 | 2N3773 | | |
| SDT9704 | S | N | PI,SD | | | 2N5886 | 2N6254 | | |
| SDT9705 | S | N | PI,SD | | | 2N5629 | 2N3773 | | |
| SDT9706 | S | N | PI,SD | | | 2N5630 | 2N3773 | | |
| SDT9707 | S | N | PI,SD | | | 2N3055 | | | |
| SDT9801 | S | N | | | | 2N6569 | 2N6254 | | |
| SDT9801 | | | | | | TIP35 | | | |
| SDT9802 | S | N | | | | 2N3055 | 2N6254 | | |
| SDT9802 | | | | | | TIP35A | | | |
| SDT9803 | S | N | | | | 2N5878 | 2N6254 | | |
| SDT9803 | | | | | | TIP35B | | | |
| SDT9804 | S | N | | | | 2N3773 | TIP35C | | |
| SDT9901 | S | N | | | | 2N6569 | 2N4301 | | |
| SDT9902 | S | N | | | | 2N3055 | 2N4301 | | |
| SDT9903 | S | N | | | | 2N5878 | 2N4301 | | |
| SDT9903 | | | | | | 2N4301 | | | |
| SE1001 | S | N | F,CA,NU,NS | (BF241) | BF173 | MPS3693 | MPS3694 | | |
| SE1001 | | | | BF194 | BC118 | | | | |
| SE1002 | S | N | F,CA,NU,NS | (BF240) | BF194 | MPS3693 | MPS3694 | | |
| SE1002 | | | | BF237 | | | | | |
| SE1010 | S | N | F,NU | BC239B | BF189 | | | | |
| SE1010 | | | | BF184 | BF194 | | | | |
| SE1010 | | | | BF237 | | | | | |
| SE2001 | S | N | F,NS | (BC413B) | | MPS3693 | MPS3694 | | |
| SE2001 | | | | | | TIS98 | | | |
| SE2002 | S | N | F | (BC413A) | | 2N3692 | | | |
| SE3001 | S | N | F,CA,NS | (BFX89) | BF195 | 2N5770 | 2N3015 | | |
| SE3001 | | | | BFY19 | BF194 | TIS62 | | | |
| SE3001 | | | | BFY88 | | | | | |
| SE3002 | S | N | F,CA,NS | (BFX89) | | PN918-18 | 2N5770 | | |
| SE3005 | S | N | F | (BFY90) | | 2N2857 | | | |
| SE3646 | S | N | F | | | 2N3646 | 2N3009 | | |
| SE3646 | | | | | | 2N3013 | | | |
| SE4001 | S | N | F,CA,NU,NS | BC182 | BC413B | PE4001-18 | 2N5961 | 2SC458 | |
| SE4001 | | | | BC107 | BC237A | TIS94 | 2N2921 | | |
| SE4002 | S | N | F,CA,NU,NS | BC413C | | PE4002-18 | 2N5961 | | |
| SE4002 | | | | | | TIS97 | | | |
| SE4010 | S | N | F,CA,NU,NS | BC413C | | PE4010-18 | 2N5961 | | |
| SE4010 | | | | | | TIS97 | 2N2511 | | |
| SE4020 | S | N | F | (BC414C) | | 2N5961-18 | 2N4961 | | |
| SE4020 | | | | | | 2N5088 | 2N2586 | | |
| SE4020 | | | | | | 2N3117 | | | |
| SE4021 | S | N | F | BC414C | | 2N5962-18 | FT107B | | |
| SE4022 | S | N | F | (BC413C) | | FT107A | | | |
| SE5001 | S | N | F | (BF241) | BF173 | | | 2SC464 | |
| SE5001 | | | | BF237 | | | | | |
| SE5002 | S | N | F,NS | (BF241) | BF162 | 2N3337 | | | |
| SE5003 | S | N | F | (BF241) | BF162 | 2N3339 | | | |
| SE5006 | S | N | F | (BF241) | BF162 | 2N3339 | | | |
| SE5020 | S | N | F,NS | (BF198) | | TIS84 | | | |
| SE5021 | S | N | F,NS | (BF198) | | TIS108 | | | |
| SE5022 | S | N | F,NS | (BF198) | | TIS108 | | | |
| SE5023 | S | N | F,NS | (BF198) | | TIS108 | | | |
| SE5024 | S | N | F,NS | (BF198) | | TIS108 | | | |

| TYPE | M/S | POL | MANUFAC | EUROPEAN | | AMERICAN | | JAPANESE | USE |
|------|-----|-----|---------|----------|--|----------|--|----------|-----|
| SE5025 | S | N | F | (BF198) | | 2N3337 | | | |
| SE5030B | S | | F | | | PE5030B | | | |
| SE5050 | S | N | F,NS | (BF199) | | 2N3137 | SE5015 | | |
| SE5051 | S | N | F,NS | (BF199) | | 2N5126 | | | |
| SE5052 | S | | F,NS | | | FPS6568 | | | |
| | | | | | | | | | |
| SE5055 | S | N | F,NS | (BF198) | BF167 | | | | |
| SE6001 | S | N | F,NS | BSX45-10 | BC107A | 2N4400 | 2N4401 | | |
| SE6001 | | | | BC237A | | 2N2921 | | 2SC458 | |
| SE6002 | S | N | F,NS | BSX45-10 | | 2N5961 | 2N3565 | | |
| SE6002 | | | | | | MPS3392 | MPS3393 | | |
| | | | | | | | | | |
| SE6020 | S | N | F | BSX46-10 | | PE6020-5 | MPSA05 | | |
| SE6020 | | | | | | MPSA06 | 2N4960 | | |
| SE6020A | S | N | F | BSX46-10 | | SE6021A | | | |
| SE6021 | S | N | F | BSX47-10 | | PE6021-5 | 2N4961 | | |
| SE6021 | | | | | | 2N3109 | 2N3110 | | |
| | | | | | | | | | |
| SE6021A | | | | | | 2N3665 | | | |
| SE6021A | S | N | F | BSX47-10 | | | | | |
| SE6022 | S | N | F | (BSX46-10) | | 2N4962 | | | |
| SE6023 | S | N | F | (BSX47-10) | | 2N3057A | | | |
| SE6063 | S | N | | | | SE6062 | | | |
| | | | | | | | | | |
| SE7001 | S | N | F | (BF457) | | 2N5182 | TIS100 | | |
| SE7002 | S | N | F | (BF457) | | 2N5182 | TIS100 | | |
| SE7010 | S | N | | | | 2N5182 | | | |
| SE7015 | S | N | F | (BF457) | | 2N3923 | SE7016 | | |
| SE7016 | S | N | F | (BF457) | | SE7017 | | | |
| | | | | | | | | | |
| SE7017 | S | N | F | (BF458) | | | | | |
| SE7055 | S | N | F,NS | (BF458) | | | | | |
| SE7056 | S | N | F,NS | (BF458) | | | | | |
| SE7057 | S | N | | (BF459) | | | | | |
| SE7066 | S | N | | | | 2N3742 | | | |
| | | | | | | | | | |
| SE8001 | S | N | F | BSX45-6 | BSY34 | 2N4945 | 2N2218A | 2SC479 | |
| SE8002 | S | N | F | BSX45-6 | | 2N4945 | | | |
| SE8010 | S | N | F | BSX46-10 | | SE8012 | | | |
| SE8012 | S | N | F | BSX46-10 | | SE8010 | | | |
| SE8040 | S | N | F | BSX45-10 | | SE8041 | SE8042 | | |
| | | | | | | | | | |
| SE8041 | S | N | F | BSX45-10 | | SE8040 | SE8042 | | |
| SE8042 | S | N | F | BSX45-10 | | SE8040 | SE8041 | | |
| SE8520 | S | P | F | | | SE8510 | | | |
| SE8521 | S | P | F | | | 2N4355 | | | |
| SE8540 | S | P | F | BSV15-10 | | SE8541 | SE8542 | | |
| | | | | | | | | | |
| SE8541 | S | P | F | BSV15-10 | | SE8540 | SE8542 | | |
| SE8542 | S | P | F | BSV15-10 | | SE8541 | SE8540 | | |
| SE9051 | S | N | F | (BUY75) | | | | | |
| SE9052 | S | N | F | (BUY76) | | | | | |
| SE9300 | S | N | F | | | MJE800 | MJE802 | | |
| | | | | | | | | | |
| SE9300 | | | | | | MJE1100 | MJE1101 | | |
| SE9300 | | | | | | 2N6386 | 2N6387 | | |
| SE9300 | | | | | | MJE110 | TIP120 | | |
| SE9301 | S | N | F | | | MJE801 | MJE803 | | |
| SE9301 | | | | | | MJE1102 | MJE1103 | | |
| | | | | | | | | | |
| SE9301 | | | | | | 2N6388 | TIP111 | | |
| SE9301 | | | | | | TIP121 | | | |
| SE9302 | S | N | F | | | TIP112 | TIP122 | | |
| SE9303 | S | N | F | | | MJE1000 | MJE3000 | | |
| SE9303 | | | | | | MJE4000 | 2N6383 | | |
| | | | | | | | | | |
| SE9303 | | | | | | 2N6384 | 2N6055 | | |
| SE9303 | | | | | | RCA1000 | TIP640 | | |
| SE9303 | | | | | | TIP140 | | | |
| SE9304 | S | N | F | | | MJE1001 | MJE3001 | | |
| SE9304 | | | | | | MJE4001 | 2N6385 | | |
| | | | | | | | | | |
| SE9304 | | | | | | 2N6056 | RCA1001 | | |
| SE9304 | | | | | | TIP641 | TIP141 | | |
| SE9305 | S | N | F | | | TIP642 | TIP142 | | |
| SES3705 | S | N | | BC337 | | | | | |
| SFB1087 | J | N | | | | 2N5485 | | | |
| | | | | | | | | | |
| SFB1091 | J | N | | | | 3N126 | | | |
| SFB1092 | J | N | | | | 2N5484 | | | |
| SFT101 | G | P | | AC126 | AC125 | 2N2429 | | | |
| SFT102 | G | P | SE | AC126 | AC125 | 2N2429 | | | |
| SFT103 | G | P | SE | AC126 | | 2N2429 | | | |
| | | | | | | | | | |
| SFT105 | G | P | SE | AC126 | | 2N2429 | | | |
| SFT106 | G | P | SE | (AC121IV) | AF185 | | | | |
| SFT106 | | | | AF116 | AF126 | | | | |
| SFT107 | G | P | SE | (AC121IV) | AF185 | | | | |
| SFT107 | | | | AF116 | AF128 | | | | |

| TYPE | M/S | POL | MANUFAC | EUROPEAN | | AMERICAN | | JAPANESE | USE |
|------|-----|-----|---------|----------|---|----------|---|----------|-----|
| SFT108 | | | | (AC121V) | AF185 | | | | |
| SFT108 | G | P | SE | AF115 | AF125 | | | | |
| SFT109 | G | P | SE | AC126 | AC125 | 2N2429 | | | |
| SFT111 | G | P | SE | AC125 | | | | | |
| SFT112 | G | P | SE | AC132 | | | | | |
| SFT113 | | | | (AD130IV) | AD149 | 2N2836 | | | |
| SFT113 | G | P | SE | OC26 | | | | | |
| SFT114 | | | | (AD131IV) | ASZ15 | | | | |
| SFT114 | G | P | SE | ASZ17 | | | | | |
| SFT115 | G | P | SE | (AF127) | AF185 | | | | |
| SFT115 | | | | AF116 | AF126 | | | | |
| SFT116 | G | P | SE | AF185 | AF115 | | | | |
| SFT116 | | | | AF125 | | | | | |
| SFT117 | G | P | SE | AF178 | AF114 | 2N2495 | | | |
| SFT117 | | | | AF124 | | | | | |
| SFT118 | G | P | SE | AF178 | AF114 | 2N2495 | | | |
| SFT118 | | | | AF124 | | | | | |
| SFT119 | G | P | SE | AF185 | AF116 | | | | |
| SFT119 | | | | AF126 | | | | | |
| SFT120 | G | P | SE | AF185 | AF115 | | | | |
| SFT120 | | | | AF125 | | | | | |
| SFT121 | G | P | SE | (AC152IV) | AC128 | 2N2431 | | | |
| SFT121 | | | | AC132 | | | | | |
| SFT122 | G | P | SE | (AC152IV) | AC128 | 2N2431 | | | |
| SFT122 | | | | AC132 | | | | | |
| SFT123 | G | P | SE | (AC152IV) | AC128 | 2N2431 | | | |
| SFT123 | | | | AC132 | | | | | |
| SFT124 | G | P | NU,SE | AC128 | AC153IV | 2N2431 | 2N4106 | 2SB370A | |
| SFT124 | | | | AC117 | AC131 | 2N249 | | 2SB226 | |
| SFT124 | | | | AC152 | | | | | |
| SFT125 | G | P | NU,SE | AC128 | AC153VI | 2N2431 | 2N4106 | 2SB370A | |
| SFT125 | | | | AC117 | AC126 | 2N223 | | 2SB222 | |
| SFT125 | | | | AC131 | | | | | |
| SFT126 | G | P | SE | (AC152IV) | ASY26 | | | | |
| SFT126 | | | | 2G139 | 2G138 | | | | |
| SFT127 | G | P | SE | (AC152IV) | ASY26 | | | | |
| SFT127 | | | | 2G138 | 2G139 | | | | |
| SFT128 | G | P | SE | (AC152V) | ASY27 | | | | |
| SFT128 | | | | 2G140 | 2G141 | | | | |
| SFT130 | G | P | NU,SE | AC128 | AC151VI | 2N2431 | 2N386 | ST172 | |
| SFT130 | | | | AC128K | AC117 | | | | |
| SFT131 | G | P | NU,SE | AC128 | AC128K | 2N2431 | 2N223 | 2SB415 | |
| SFT131 | | | | AC153VI | AC131 | | | | |
| SFT135 | G | P | SE | (AC152IV) | | | | | |
| SFT136 | G | P | SE | (AC152IV) | | | | | |
| SFT141 | G | P | SE | (ASY48IV) | | | | | |
| SFT142 | G | P | SE | (ASY48IV) | AC128 | | | | |
| SFT143 | G | P | NU,SE | AC128 | | | | | |
| SFT144 | G | P | NU,SE | AC128 | AC153 | 2N226 | | 2SB222 | |
| SFT145 | G | P | NU,SE | | | | | | |
| SFT146 | G | P | NU,SE | AC127 | AC128 | | | | |
| SFT150 | G | P | SE | (AD132III) | ASZ15 | | | | |
| SFT150 | | | | ASZ16 | | | | | |
| SFT151 | G | P | SE | AC126 | AC125 | 2N2429 | | | |
| SFT152 | G | P | SE | (AC151VI) | AC126 | 2N2429 | | | |
| SFT152 | | | | AC125 | | | | | |
| SFT153 | G | P | SE | (AC151VI) | AC126 | | | | |
| SFT155 | G | P | SE | (AF127) | | | | | |
| SFT162 | G | P | NU,SE | AF118 | | 2N2207 | | 2SA76 | |
| SFT163 | G | P | NU,SE | AF121 | AF212 | | | | |
| SFT163 | | | | AF200 | | | | | |
| SFT170 | G | P | SE | AF109R | AF180 | 2N3588 | | | |
| SFT171 | G | P | SE,NU | AF106 | AF102 | | | 2SA230 | |
| SFT172 | G | P | NU,SE | AF106 | AF102 | | | 2SA230 | |
| SFT173 | G | P | NU,SE | (AF201U) | AF201 | | | 2SA239 | |
| SFT173 | | | | AF121 | AF102 | | | | |
| SFT174 | G | P | NU,SE | (AF202S) | AF202 | | | 2SA239 | |
| SFT174 | | | | AF121S | AF121 | | | | |
| SFT174 | | | | AF102 | | | | | |
| SFT184 | G | N | NU,SE | AC127 | AC179 | 2N2430 | 2N1304 | 2SD96 | |
| SFT186 | S | N | NU,SE | (BF457) | BF140 | | | | |
| SFT186 | | | | AF178 | BF117 | | | | |
| SFT186N | S | N | SE | BF110 | BF178 | | | 2SC856 | |
| SFT186N | | | | BF258 | | | | | |
| SFT185P | S | N | SE | (BF457) | BF110 | | | | |

| TYPE | M/S | POL | MANUFAC | EUROPEAN | | AMERICAN | | JAPANESE | USE |
|------|-----|-----|---------|----------|--|----------|--|----------|-----|
| SFT187 | S | N | SE,ML,Ss | (BF457) | BF114 | | | | |
| SFT187 | | | | BF110 | BF178 | | | | |
| SFT187N | S | N | SE | BF178 | BF117 | | | 2SC856 | |
| SFT190 | G | P | SE | AD132III | AD132 | 2N2065 | | 2SB472 | |
| SFT190 | | | | AD138/50 | ADZ12 | | | | |
| SFT190 | | | | AD149 | | | | | |
| SFT191 | G | P | SE | (AD131III) | AD131 | TI3029 | | 2SB471 | |
| SFT191 | | | | ADZ11 | AD149 | | | | |
| SFT191 | | | | ASZ18 | | | | | |
| SFT192 | G | P | SE | AD131IV | | | | | |
| SFT206 | G | P | SE | ASY26 | ASY14 | | | | |
| SFT207 | G | P | SE | ASY26 | ASY14 | | | | |
| SFT207 | | | | ASY12 | | | | | |
| SFT208 | G | P | SE | ASY27 | ASY14 | 2N2447 | | | |
| SFT208 | | | | ASY13 | | | | 2S13 | |
| SFT211 | G | P | SE | (AUY22IV) | ASZ18 | | | | |
| SFT212 | G | P | NU,SE | AD130III | AD138 | TI3028 | 2N83A | 2SB242 | |
| SFT212 | | | | AD149 | AD153 | | | | |
| SFT212 | | | | ASZ15 | | | | | |
| SFT213 | G | P | SE | AD131III | AUY28 | TI3029 | 2N176 | 2SB242 | |
| SFT213 | | | | AD153 | AD148 | 2N257 | | | |
| SFT213 | | | | ASZ16 | AD149 | | | | |
| SFT214 | G | P | SE,NU | AD131III | AD138/50 | TI3029 | | | |
| SFT214 | | | | ASZ17 | AUY28 | | | | |
| SFT221 | G | P | NU,SE | (AC152IV) | ACY23V | 2N1303 | 2N1307 | 2SB37 | |
| SFT221 | | | | AC131 | AC128 | | | | |
| SFT221 | | | | AC153 | ASY26 | | | | |
| SFT221 | | | | ACY14 | | | | | |
| SFT222 | G | P | NU,SE | (AC152V) | ACY23V | 2N526 | 2N1303 | 2SB219 | |
| SFT222 | | | | AC131 | ASY14 | 2N1307 | | | |
| SFT222 | | | | AC153 | ASY26 | | | | |
| SFT223 | G | P | NU,ML,Ss,SE | AC152VI | ASY26 | 2N215 | | HJ15 | |
| SFT223 | | | | AC131 | ASY14 | | | | |
| SFT223 | | | | AC117 | AC153 | | | | |
| SFT226 | G | P | NU,SE | (ASY48IV) | AF101 | 2N269 | 2N1305 | 2S40 | |
| SFT226 | | | | GFT45 | OC612 | | | | |
| SFT226 | | | | ASZ10 | | | | | |
| SFT227 | G | P | Ss,ML,NU,SE | ASY26 | ASY14 | 2N1307 | | | |
| SFT227 | | | | ASY30 | ASZ10 | | | | |
| SFT228 | G | P | Ss,ML,NU,SE | ASY27 | ASY14 | 2N3486A | 2N1309 | | |
| SFT228 | | | | ASY30 | ASZ10 | | | | |
| SFT229 | G | P | NU,ML,Ss,SE | (ASY70VI) | ASY27 | 2N1309 | | | |
| SFT229 | | | | ASY13 | | | | | |
| SFT232 | G | P | SE | AC124 | AC128 | 2N176 | | 2SB41 | |
| SFT232 | | | | AC173 | CTP1104 | | | | |
| SFT232 | | | | OC30 | | | | | |
| SFT234 | G | P | Ss,ML,NU,SE | ACY24 | ASY48 | | | | |
| SFT237 | G | P | NU,SE | (AC162) | ACY32V | | | | |
| SFT237 | | | | AC160 | AC160B | | | | |
| SFT237 | | | | ACY32 | | | | | |
| SFT238 | G | P | NU,SE | AUY21III | AD138 | TI3029 | 2N101 | 2SB242 | |
| SFT238 | | | | ASZ16 | ASZ17 | | | | |
| SFT238 | | | | AUY29 | | | | | |
| SFT239 | G | P | NU,SE | AUY21III | AD138/50 | TI3029 | | | |
| SFT239 | | | | ASZ16 | AUY28 | | | | |
| SFT239g | G | P | SE | ASZ16 | ASZ18 | | | | |
| SFT239g | | | | CDT1311 | | | | | |
| SFT239go | G | P | SE | AD149 | ASZ17 | 2N352 | | 2SB86 | |
| SFT239go | | | | CDT1311 | | | | | |
| SFT240 | G | P | NU,SE | (AUY22III) | AUY22 | TI3029 | | | |
| SFT240 | | | | AUY28 | ASZ18 | | | | |
| SFT240go | G | P | SE | AD131 | ASZ15 | 2N157A | | 2SB87 | |
| SFT240go | | | | ASZ18 | | | | | |
| SFT240o | G | P | SE | AD105 | GFT3408 | 2N268 | | 2SB87 | |
| SFT240o | | | | ASZ18 | | | | | |
| SFT241 | G | P | NU,SE | AC152IV | AC131/30 | 2N44 | | 2SB224 | |
| SFT241 | | | | AC128 | AC131 | | | | |
| SFT241 | | | | ASY48 | | | | | |
| SFT242 | G | P | NU,SE | (ASY48V) | AC152IV | 2N284 | | 2SB89 | |
| SFT242 | | | | AC131/30 | AC161 | | | | |
| SFT242 | | | | AC128 | ASY48 | | | | |
| SFT243 | G | P | NU,SE | (ASY48V) | ASY48IV | 2N241 | 2N24A | 2SB89 | |
| SFT243 | | | | ACY24 | AC128 | | | | |
| SFT243 | | | | ACZ10 | | | | | |
| SFT250 | G | P | NU | AD132III | AUY28 | TI3029 | 2N268 | 2SB340 | |

| TYPE | M/S | POL | MANUFAC | EUROPEAN | | AMERICAN | | JAPANESE | USE |
|------|-----|-----|---------|----------|---|----------|---|----------|-----|
| SFT250 | | | | AUY31 | ASY41 | 2N301 | | 2SB249 | |
| SFT250 | | | | ASZ18 | | | | | |
| SFT251 | G | P | NU,SE | (AC151IV) | AC125 | | | | |
| SFT251 | | | | ASY26 | | | | | |
| SFT252 | G | P | NU,SE | (AC151V) | ASY26 | | | | |
| | | | | | | | | | |
| SFT253 | G | P | NU,ML,Ss,SE | (AC151VI) | | | | | |
| SFT259 | G | N | SE | (AC127) | | | | | |
| SFT260 | G | N | SE | (AC127) | ASY74 | 2N1090 | | 2SC90 | |
| SFT260 | | | | OC140 | | | | | |
| SFT261 | G | N | SE | (AC127) | ASY75 | 2N1091 | | 2SC91 | |
| | | | | | | | | | |
| SFT264 | G | P | NU | AD132IV | ADZ11 | TI3030 | | | |
| SFT264 | | | | AUY28 | | | | | |
| SFT265 | G | P | NU | AD132III | AD103 | 2N1146 | | | |
| SFT265 | | | | AD133 | ADZ11 | | | | |
| SFT266 | G | P | NU | AD132III | AD104 | 2N1146A | | | |
| | | | | | | | | | |
| SFT266 | | | | ADZ12 | AUY21 | | | | |
| SFT267 | G | P | NU | AD105 | ADZ12 | 2N1146B | | | |
| SFT267 | | | | ADZ11 | | | | | |
| SFT268 | G | P | SE | | | 2N1100 | | | |
| SFT288 | G | P | NU,ML,Ss,SE | (AC152VI) | ASY27 | TI3030 | 2N1309 | | |
| | | | | | | | | | |
| SFT298 | G | P | NU,ML,Ss,SE | (AC152VI) | ASY27 | | | | |
| SFT306 | G | P | NU | AF185 | AC163 | 2N506 | 2N218 | 2SB459 | |
| SFT306 | | | | AFY15 | AF101 | | | 2SA12 | |
| SFT306 | | | | AC126 | | | | | |
| SFT307 | G | P | NU | AF185 | AC121IV | 2N409 | | 2SA12 | |
| | | | | | | | | | |
| SFT307 | | | | AFY15 | AF187 | | | | |
| SFT307 | | | | GFT45 | | | | | |
| SFT308 | G | P | NU | AF185 | AC151 | 2N112 | | 2SA12 | |
| SFT308 | | | | AFY15 | AF190 | | | | |
| SFT308 | | | | OC613 | AF101 | | | | |
| | | | | | | | | | |
| SFT315 | G | P | NU | AF118 | ASZ20 | 2N2207 | | | |
| SFT316 | G | P | NU,ML,Ss,SE | AF185 | AF132 | 2N247 | | 2SA215 | |
| SFT316 | | | | AF137 | (AF127) | | | | |
| SFT316bl | G | P | SE | AF126 | AF138 | | | | |
| SFT316v | G | P | SE | AF126 | AF138 | | | | |
| | | | | | | | | | |
| SFT317 | G | P | NU,ML,Ss,SE | (AF125) | AF185 | 2N1178 | 2N372 | 2SA81 | |
| SFT317 | | | | AF125 | AF137 | | | | |
| SFT317 | | | | AF135 | AF136 | | | | |
| SFT319 | G | P | NU,ML,Ss,SE | (AF126) | AF185 | 2N373 | | 2SA82 | |
| SFT319 | | | | AF133 | AF136 | | | | |
| | | | | | | | | | |
| SFT319bl | G | P | SE | AF126 | AF137 | | | | |
| SFT319gn | G | P | SE | AF126 | AF137 | | | | |
| SFT320 | G | P | NU,ML,Ss,SE | (AF127) | AF185 | 2N374 | | 2SA83 | |
| SFT320 | | | | AF200 | AF137 | | | | |
| SFT320 | | | | AF131 | AF135 | | | | |
| | | | | | | | | | |
| SFT320 | | | | AF126 | | | | | |
| SFT321 | G | P | NU,ML,Ss,SE | AC152IV | AC126 | 2N464 | 2N1305 | 2SB76 | |
| SFT321 | | | | AC128 | AC125 | | | | |
| SFT321 | | | | AC152III | AC131 | | | | |
| SFT322 | G | P | Ss,ML,NU | AC126 | AC128 | 2N464 | | 2SB76 | |
| | | | | | | | | | |
| SFT322 | | | | AC131 | AC152IV | | | | |
| SFT322 | | | | AC125 | | | | | |
| SFT323 | G | P | NU,ML,Ss,SE | AC152VI | AC126 | 2N408 | | 2SB78 | |
| SFT323 | | | | AC128 | AC152IV | | | | |
| SFT323 | | | | AC131 | AC125 | | | | |
| | | | | | | | | | |
| SFT323 | | | | AC132 | | | | | |
| SFT325 | G | P | NU,SE | AC152VII | AC128 | | | | |
| SFT325 | | | | AC131 | | | | | |
| SFT335 | G | P | SE | AC125 | | | | | |
| SFT337 | G | P | NU,SE | AC151V | AC126 | | | | |
| | | | | | | | | | |
| SFT337 | | | | AC151÷V | AC151VI | | | | |
| SFT337 | | | | AC150 | AC160 | | | | |
| SFT351 | G | P | NU | AC126 | AC151IV | 2N2429 | 2N63 | 2SB75 | |
| SFT351 | | | | AC125 | AC122r | | | | |
| SFT351 | | | | AC131 | | | | | |
| | | | | | | | | | |
| SFT352 | G | P | NU,ML,Ss,SE | AC151IV | AC126 | 2N2429 | 2N591 | 2SB120 | |
| SFT352 | | | | AC162 | AC122r | | | | |
| SFT352 | | | | AC125 | AC131 | | | | |
| SFT352FB | G | P | SE | AC107 | AC150 | | | | |
| SFT352FB | | | | OC603 | | | | | |
| | | | | | | | | | |
| SFT353 | G | P | NU,ML,Ss,SE | AC151V | AC126 | 2N2429 | | | |
| SFT353 | | | | AC163 | AC122vc | | | | |
| SFT353 | | | | AC151 | AC125 | | | | |
| SFT353/1 | G | P | SE | AC151VI | AC151V | | | | |
| SFT353/2 | G | P | SE | AC151VII | AC151 | | | | |

| TYPE | M/S | POL | MANUFAC | EUROPEAN | | AMERICAN | | JAPANESE | USE |
|---|---|---|---|---|---|---|---|---|---|
| SFT353FB | G | P | SE | AC107 | AC150 | | | | |
| SFT353FB | | | | OC603 | | | | | |
| SFT354 | G | P | Ss, ML, NU | AF185 | AF125 | 2N1110 | | 2SA156 | |
| SFT354 | | | | AF136 | AC132 | | | | |
| SFT357 | G | P | Ss, ML, NU | AF178 | AF125 | 2N2495 | 2N1178 | 2SA156 | |
| SFT357 | | | | AF135 | AF133 | 2N299 | | 2SA105 | |
| SFT357P | G | P | NU | AF118 | AF125 | 2N2207 | | | |
| SFT357P | | | | AF135 | | | | | |
| SFT358 | G | P | Ss, ML, NU | AF178 | AC125 | 2N2495 | 2N1110 | 2SA156 | |
| SFT358 | | | | AF134 | AF135 | 2N299 | | 2SA105 | |
| SFT367 | G | P | NU, SE | AC153VII | AC153 | 2N1924 | | 2SB370B | |
| SFT367 | | | | AC131 | | | | | |
| SFT377 | G | N | NU, SE | AC176 | AC186 | | | | |
| SFT377 | | | | AC127 | | | | | |
| SFT443 | S | N | SE | (BSX47-6) | | | | | |
| SFT522 | G | N | SE | AC127 | | | | | |
| SFT522 | G | P | SE | AC128 | AC132 | 2N2431 | | | |
| SFT714 | S | N | SE | BC237A | | | | | |
| SFT714A | S | N | SE | BC237A | | | | | |
| SFT715 | S | N | SE | BC237B | | | | | |
| SFT715A | S | N | SE | BC237B | | | | | |
| SK3003 | G | P | RC | AC126 | AC128 | 2N2429 | 2N2431 | | |
| SK3004 | G | P | RC | AC126 | AC128 | 2N2429 | 2N2431 | | |
| SK3005 | G | P | RC | AF185 | | | | | |
| SK3006 | G | P | RC | AF178 | | 2N2495 | | | |
| SK3007 | G | P | RC | AF178 | | 2N2495 | | | |
| SK3008 | G | P | RC | AF185 | | | | | |
| SK3009 | G | P | RC | AD149 | | 2N2836 | | | |
| SK3010 | G | N | RC | AC127 | | 2N2430 | | | |
| SK3012 | G | P | RC | AD149 | | 2N2836 | | | |
| SK3013 | G | P | RC | AD149 | | | | | |
| SK3014 | G | P | RC | AD149 | | 2N2836 | | | |
| SK3015 | G | P | RC | AD149 | | | | | |
| SO88 | G | P | | AC128 | | 2N2431 | | | |
| SP8A | G | P | | AC126 | | 2N2429 | | | |
| SP8B | G | P | | AC126 | | 2N2429 | | | |
| SP8C | G | P | | AC126 | | 2N2429 | | | |
| SP8400 | S | N | SG | BSX47-10 | | | | | |
| SP8401 | S | N | SG | BSX46-10 | | | | | |
| SP8402 | S | N | SG | BSX46-6 | | | | | |
| SPC410 | S | N | SU | | | RCA410 | | | |
| SPC411 | S | N | SU | | | RCA411 | | | |
| SPC413 | S | N | SU | | | RCA413 | | | |
| SPC423 | S | N | SU | | | RCA423 | | | |
| SPC431 | S | N | SU | | | RCA431 | | | |
| ST5 | G | P | | AD149 | AD148 | 2N2836 | 2N376 | | |
| ST5 | | | | OC30 | | | | | |
| ST28C | G | P | | AF185 | AF117 | 2N309 | | | |
| ST28C | | | | AF127 | | | | | |
| ST36 | G | P | | AD149 | AD131 | 2N2836 | 2N301 | | |
| ST36 | | | | OC28 | | | | | |
| ST37D | G | P | | AF185 | AF117 | 2N252 | | | |
| ST37D | | | | AF126 | | | | | |
| ST121 | G | P | | AC126 | AC125 | 2N2429 | 2N47 | | |
| ST121 | | | | AC163 | | | | | |
| ST122 | G | P | | AC128 | AC117 | 2N2431 | 2N43 | | |
| ST122 | | | | AC153 | | | | | |
| ST123 | G | P | | AC126 | AC122 | 2N2429 | 2N65 | | |
| ST123 | | | | AC163 | | | | | |
| ST124 | G | P | | AC126 | AC125 | 2N2429 | | | |
| ST125 | G | P | | AC126 | | 2N2429 | | | |
| ST162 | G | P | | AF101 | AF116 | | | | |
| ST162 | | | | OC612 | | | | | |
| OC163 | G | P | | AF101 | AF117 | | | | |
| ST163 | | | | OC410 | | | | | |
| ST171 | G | P | | AF185 | AF117 | 2N308 | | | |
| ST172 | G | P | | AF185 | AC117 | 2N386 | | | |
| ST172 | | | | AF126 | | | | | |
| ST173 | G | P | | AF101 | AF117 | | | | |
| ST173 | | | | OC613 | | | | | |
| ST301 | G | P | | AC126 | AC122 | 2N2429 | 2N34 | | |
| ST301 | | | | AC163 | | | | | |
| ST302 | G | P | | AC126 | AC122 | 2N2429 | 2N77 | | |
| ST302 | | | | AC163 | | | | | |
| ST303 | G | P | | AC126 | AC125 | 2N2429 | 2N81 | | |

| TYPE | M/S | POL | MANUFAC | EUROPEAN | | AMERICAN | | JAPANESE | USE |
|---|---|---|---|---|---|---|---|---|---|
| ST303 | S | N | | AC163 | | | | | |
| ST722 | S | N | | ZT22 | | | | | |
| ST723 | S | N | | ZT22 | | | | | |
| ST724 | S | N | | ZT23 | | | | | |
| STC1015 | S | N | | BLY17 | | | | | |
| STC1016 | S | N | | BLY17 | | | | | |
| STC1024 | S. | N | | BLY17 | | | | | |
| STC1400 | S | N | | BLY17 | | | | | |
| STPT40 | P | | | | | LS400 | | | |
| STPT60 | P | | | | | LS600 | | | |
| STPT300 | P | | | | | TIL81* | | | |
| STPT310 | P | | | | | TIL81* | | | |
| STS410 | S | N | | | | RCA410 | | | |
| STS411 | S | N | | | | RCAA411 | | | |
| STS413 | S | N | | | | RCAA413 | | | |
| STS423 | S | N | | | | RCA423 | | | |
| STS431 | S | N | | | | RCA431 | | | |
| SU2028 | J | N | IL | | | 2N3934 | | | |
| SU2029 | J | N | IL | | | 2N5197 | | | |
| SU2030 | J | N | IL | | | 2N3935 | | | |
| SU2031 | J | N | IL | | | 2N5198 | | | |
| SU2032 | J | N | IL | | | 2N5545 | 2N5197 | | |
| SU2033 | J | N | IL | | | 2N5545 | | | |
| SU2034 | J | N | IL | | | 2N5547 | | | |
| SU2035 | J | N | IL | | | 2N5547 | | | |
| SU2074 | J | N | TI | | | 2N5545 | | | |
| SU2075 | J | N | TI | | | 2N5545 | | | |
| SU2076 | J | N | TI | | | 2N5545 | | | |
| SU2077 | J | N | TI | | | 2N5547 | | | |
| SU2078 | J | N | TI | | | 2N5547 | 2N4083 | | |
| SU2079 | J | N | TI | | | 2N5547 | 2N4083 | | |
| SU2080 | J | N | TI | | | 2N5547 | 2N4085 | | |
| SU2081 | J | N | TI | | | 2N5547 | 2N4085 | | |
| SU2098 | J | N | TI, IL | | | 2N5545 | | | |
| SU2098A | J | N | TI, IL | | | 2N5545 | | | |
| SU2098B | J | N | TI, IL | | | 2N5196 | | | |
| SU2099 | J | N | TI, IL | | | 2N5547 | 2N3955 | | |
| SU2099A | J | N | TI, IL | | | 2N5547 | 2N5198 | | |
| SU2365 | J | N | TI | | | 2N3954 | | | |
| SU2365A | J | N | TI | | | 2N5197 | | | |
| SU2366 | J | N | TI | | | 2N3454 | | | |
| SU2366A | J | N | TI | | | 2N5197 | | | |
| SU2367 | J | N | TI | | | 2N5198 | | | |
| SU2367A | J | N | TI | | | 2N5198 | | | |
| SU2368 | J | N | TI | | | 2N3955 | | | |
| SU2368A | J | N | TI | | | 2N5198 | | | |
| SU2369 | J | N | TI | | | 2N5199 | | | |
| SU2369A | J | N | TI | | | 2N5199 | | | |
| SU2410 | J | N | TI | | | TD5907 | | | |
| SU2411 | J | N | TI | | | TD5908 | | | |
| SU2412 | J | N | TI | | | TD5909 | | | |
| T34A | G | P | | OC65 | | | | | |
| T34B | G | P | | OC65 | | | | | |
| T34C | G | P | | OC65 | | | | | |
| T34D | G | P | | AC128 | AC132 | 2N2431 | 2N281 | | |
| T34D | | | | OC72 | | | | | |
| T34E | G | P | | AC128 | AC132 | 2N2431 | 2N281 | | |
| T34E | | | | OC72 | | | | | |
| T34F | G | P | | AC128 | AC132 | 2N2431 | 2N281 | | |
| T34F | | | | OC72 | | | | | |
| T65 | G | P | | AC126 | | 2N2429 | | | |
| T1040 | G | P | | AD149 | OC26 | 2N2836 | | | |
| T1041 | G | P | | AD149 | OC26 | 2N2836 | | | |
| T1159 | G | P | | AC128 | AC132 | 2N2431 | | | |
| T1360 | G | P | | AF185 | AF126 | | | | |
| T1361 | G | P | | AF185 | AF125 | | | | |
| T1369 | G | P | | AD149 | | 2N2836 | | | |
| T1375 | G | P | | AF185 | AF125 | | | | |
| T1376 | G | P | | AC128 | | 2N2431 | | | |
| T1377 | G | P | | AC128 | | 2N2431 | | | |
| T1390 | G | P | | AF185 | AF126 | | | | |
| T1482 | S | N | TX | | | 40311 | | | |
| T1484 | S | N | TX | | | 2N697 | | | |
| T1492 | S | N | TX | | | 40407 | | | |
| T1493 | S | N | TX | | | 2N1613 | | | |

| TYPE | M/S | POL | MANUFAC | EUROPEAN | | AMERICAN | | JAPANESE | USE |
|------|-----|-----|---------|----------|---|----------|---|----------|-----|
| T1494 | S | N | TX | | | 40320 | | | |
| T1675 | G | P | | AF185 | AF125 | | | | |
| T1690 | G | P | | AF185 | AF125 | | | | |
| T1691 | G | P | | AF178 | AF124 | 2N2495 | | | |
| T1692 | G | P | | AF185 | AF126 | | | | |
| T1693 | G | P | | AFZ12 | | | | | |
| T1694 | G | P | | AFZ12 | | | | | |
| T1695 | G | P | | AF178 | AFZ12 | 2N2495 | | | |
| T1696 | G | P | | AFZ12 | | | | | |
| T1727 | G | P | | AF185 | AF126 | | | | |
| T1737 | G | P | | AF185 | AF125 | | | | |
| T1814 | G | P | | AF185 | AF125 | | | | |
| T1832 | G | P | | AC126 | | | | | |
| T1833 | G | P | | AC126 | | | | | |
| T2024 | G | P | | AC126 | | | | | |
| T2028 | G | P | | AC126 | | | | | |
| T2030 | G | P | | AC126 | | | | | |
| T2079 | G | P | | AF178 | | 2N2495 | | | |
| T2384 | G | P | | AF185 | AF178 | 2N2495 | | | |
| T2399 | G | P | | AF178 | | 2N2495 | | | |
| T2400 | G | P | | AF185 | | | | | |
| T2478 | S | N | | | | 2N706A | | | |
| TD5902 | J | N | TI | | | U248 | | | |
| TD5902A | J | N | TI | | | U248 | | | |
| TD5903 | J | N | TI | | | U249 | | | |
| TD5903A | J | N | TI | | | U249 | | | |
| TD5904 | J | N | TI | | | U250 | | | |
| TD5904A | J | N | TI | | | U250 | | | |
| TD5905 | J | N | TI | | | U251 | | | |
| TD5905A | J | N | TI | | | U251 | | | |
| TD5906 | J | N | TI | | | U248A | | | |
| TD5906A | J | N | TI | | | U248A | | | |
| TD5907 | J | N | TI | | | U249A | | | |
| TD5907A | J | N | TI | | | U249A | | | |
| TD5908 | J | N | TI | | | U250A | | | |
| TD5908A | J | N | TI | | | U250A | | | |
| TD5909 | J | N | TI | | | U251A | | | |
| TD5909A | J | N | TI | | | U251A | | | |
| TD5911 | J | N | TI | | | U252 | | | |
| TD5911A | J | N | TI | | | U252 | | | |
| TD5912 | J | N | TI | | | U253 | | | |
| TD5912A | J | N | TI | | | U253 | | | |
| TF49 | G | P | S | ASY27 | AF101 | 2N218 | 2N1307 | 2SA12 | |
| TF49 | | | | ASY26 | | | | | |
| TF65 | G | P | S | AC126 | AC125 | 2N2429 | | | |
| TF65 | | | | AC151r | | | | | |
| TF65bl | G | P | S | AC151V | AC122ye | | | | |
| TF65bl | | | | AC125 | | | | | |
| TF65br | G | P | S | AC151VII | AC122w | | | | |
| TF65br | | | | AC122v | | | | | |
| TF65gn | G | P | S | AC151V | AC122ye | | | | |
| TF65gn | | | | AC125 | AC122 | | | | |
| TF65gn | | | | OC71 | OC604 | | | | |
| TF65gr | G | P | S | AC151VI | AC122ye | | | | |
| TF65gr | | | | AC126 | AC125 | | | | |
| TF65or | G | P | S | AC151IV | AC122r | 2N1190 | 2N238 | 2SB459 | |
| TF65or | | | | AC125 | | | | | |
| TF65r | G | P | S | AC151IV | AC122r | 2N1190 | 2N238 | 2SB459 | |
| TF65r | | | | AC125 | AC125 | 2N63 | | 2SB220 | |
| TF65v | G | P | S | AC151VI | AC122ye | 2N266 | | 2SB219 | |
| TF65v | | | | AC126 | AC122 | | | | |
| TF65ye | G | P | S | AC151IV | AC122r | 2N1190 | 2N238 | 2SB450 | |
| TF65ye | | | | AC125 | AC122 | 2N190 | | 2SB101 | |
| TF65/30 | G | P | S | AC126 | AC151 | 2N2429 | | | |
| TF65/30 | | | | OC71 | OC604 | | | | |
| TF65/30gn | G | P | | AC122 | GFT25 | 2N36 | | 2SB101 | |
| TF65/30gn | | | | OC71 | | | | | |
| TF65/30gr | G | P | S | AC122 | OC304/I | 2N89 | | 2SB101 | |
| TF65/30gr | | | | OC602ye | | | | | |
| TF65/30r | G | P | S | AC122 | AC125 | 2N63 | | 2SB220 | |
| TF65/30r | | | | OC602r | | | | | |
| TF65/30v | G | P | S | AC122 | OC304/III | 2N266 | | 2SB219 | |
| TF65/30v | | | | OC604v | | | | | |
| TF65/60 | G | P | S | ASY23 | ASY77 | | | | |
| TF65/60 | | | | OC77 | | | | | |

| TYPE | M/S | POL | MANUFAC | EUROPEAN | | AMERICAN | | | JAPANESE | USE |
|---|---|---|---|---|---|---|---|---|---|---|
| TF65M | G | P | S | AC125 | OC71 | | | | | |
| TF65/30M | G | P | S | OC71 | | | | | | |
| TF65/60M | G | P | S | OC77 | | | | | | |
| TF66 | G | P | S | AC131 | AC152 | 2N44 | 2N1303 | 2SB220 | | |
| TF66 | | | | ASY70 | | | | | | |
| TF66I | G | P | S | AC128 | AC152IV | 2N2431 | 2N4106 | | | |
| TF66I | | | | AC131r | | | | | | |
| TF66II | G | P | S | AC128 | AC152V | 2N2431 | 2N4106 | | | |
| TF66II | | | | AC131ye | | | | | | |
| TF66III | G | P | S | AC128 | AC152VI | 2N2431 | 2N610 | | | |
| TF66III | | | | AC131gr | | | | | | |
| TF66/30 | G | P | S | AC128 | AC152 | 2N2431 | 2N1924 | 2SB156 | | |
| TF66/30 | | | | AC131/30 | AC117 | 2N238 | 2N59 | 2SB222 | | |
| TF66/60 | G | P | S | ASY48IV | ACY24 | 2N241 | 2N24A | 2SB89 | | |
| TF66/60 | | | | ASY81 | AC128 | | | | | |
| TF66/60 | | | | ASY77 | ASZ10 | | | | | |
| TF68 | G | P | S | AF185 | AF126 | | | | | |
| TF68 | | | | OC44 | | | | | | |
| TF69/30 | G | P | S | AC128 | | 2N2431 | | | | |
| TF70 | G | N | S | ASY73 | OC139 | | | | | |
| TF71 | G | N | S | ASY70 | OC140 | | | | | |
| TF72 | G | N | S | ASY74 | OC140 | | | | | |
| TF75 | G | P | S | AC128 | OC72 | 2N2431 | | | | |
| TF77 | G | P | S | AC128 | AC126 | 2N2431 | | | | |
| TF77 | | | | OC74 | | | | | | |
| TF77/30 | G | P | S | AC128 | OC74 | 2N2431 | | | | |
| TF77/30 | | | | OD603 | | | | | | |
| TF77/70 | G | P | S. | ASZ15 | OC28 | | | | | |
| TF78 | G | P | S | AD149 | OC80 | 2N2836 | | 2SB86 | | |
| TF | | | | OD603 | | | | | | |
| TF78/30 | G | P | S | AC152 | AD169 | | | 2SB86 | | |
| TF78/30 | | | | AC128 | AD149 | | | | | |
| TF78/30 | | | | ASZ18 | OD603 | | | | | |
| TF78/60 | G | P | S | AD131 | ASZ15 | | | | | |
| TF78/60 | | | | OD603/50 | | | | | | |
| TF80 | G | P | | AD149 | OC26 | 2N2836 | | | | |
| TF80 | | | | OC30 | | | | | | |
| TF80/30 | G | P | S | AD149 | AD130 | 2N2836 | TI3029 | 2SB337 | | |
| TF80/30 | | | | AD150 | AD153 | 2N1195 | | 2SB83 | | |
| TF80/60 | G | P | | AD131 | AD138/50 | TI3039 | 2N268 | 2SB471 | | |
| TF80/60 | | | | AD149 | ASZ16 | | | 2SB86 | | |
| TF80/80 | G | P | S | AD132 | AUY28 | 2N2065 | | 2SB472 | | |
| TF80/80 | | | | AD149 | ASZ15 | | | | | |
| TF81/30 | G | P | S | AD149 | | 2N2836 | | | | |
| TF85 | G | P | S | AD149 | OC26 | 2N2836 | | | | |
| TF90 | G | P | S | AD149 | AD133 | 2N2836 | | | | |
| TF90 | | | | AD137 | OC26 | | | | | |
| TF90/30 | G | P | S | AD149 | AD133 | 2N2836 | | | | |
| TF90/30 | | | | AUY21 | AD153 | | | | | |
| TF90/30 | | | | ADZ11 | | | | | | |
| TF90/60 | G | P | | AUY22 | AD149 | | | | | |
| TF90/60 | | | | ADZ12 | OC26 | | | | | |
| TF260 | S | N | S | BC107 | BC197 | 2N3568 | 2N2921 | 2SC453 | | |
| TF260 | | | | BC182A | | | | | | |
| THP44 | G | P | | AC128 | AC132 | 2N2431 | | | | |
| THP45 | G | P | | AD149 | | 2N2836 | | | | |
| THP46 | G | P | | AD149 | | 2N2836 | | | | |
| THP47 | G | P | | ASZ17 | | | | | | |
| THP50 | G | P | | AD149 | | 2N2836 | | | | |
| THP51 | G | P | | AD149 | | 2N2836 | | | | |
| THP52 | G | P | | AD149 | | 2N2836 | | | | |
| TI3027 | G | P | TX | ASZ16 | AUY22IV | TI3028 | | 2SB339 | | |
| TI3027 | | | | AD138/50 | | | | | | |
| TI3028 | G | P | TX | ASZ15 | AUY22III | TI3029 | | 2SB341 | | |
| TI3028 | | | | AUY28 | | | | | | |
| TI3029 | G | P | TX | ASZ15 | AUY22III | TI3030 | | | | |
| TI3029 | | | | AUY28 | | | | | | |
| TI3030 | G | P | TX | ASZ15 | AUY22III | TI3031 | | | | |
| TI3030 | | | | AUY28 | | | | | | |
| TI3031 | G | P | TX | ASZ15 | AUY22III | | | 2SB341 | | |
| TI3031 | | | | AUY28 | | | | | | |
| TIP29 | S | N | TX, F | BD239 | BD437 | SDA345 | 2N6121 | | | |
| TIP29 | | | | BD131 | | RCA29 | | | | |
| TIP29A | S | N | TX, F | BD439 | BD239A | SDA345 | 2N6122 | | | |
| TIP29A | | | | BD137 | | | RCA29A | | | |

| TYPE | M/S | POL | MANUFAC | EUROPEAN | | AMERICAN | | JAPANESE | USE |
|------|-----|-----|---------|----------|---|----------|---|----------|-----|
| TIP29B | S | N | TX, F | BD441 | BD239B | 2N6123 | RCA29B | | |
| TIP29C | S | N | TX, F | (BD441) | BD239C | 2N6123 | RCA29C | | |
| TIP30 | S | P | TX, F | BD438 | BD240 | SDA445 | RCA30 | | |
| TIP30 | | | | BD132 | | | | | |
| TIP30A | S | P | TX, F | BD440 | BD240A | SDA445 | RCA30A | | |
| | | | | | | | | | |
| TIP30A | | | | BD138 | | | | | |
| TIP30B | S | P | TX, F | BD442 | BD240B | RCA30B | | | |
| TIP30C | S | P | TX, F | (BD442) | BD240C | RCA30C | | | |
| TIP31 | S | N | TX, F | BD437 | BD241 | SDA345 | | 2N6121 | |
| TIP31 | | | | BD131 | | RCA31 | | | |
| TIP31A | S | N | TX, F | BD439 | BD241A | SDB345 | | 2N6122 | |
| TIP31A | | | | | | RCA31A | | | |
| TIP31B | S | N | TX, F | BD441 | BD241B | 2N6123 | RCA31B | | |
| TIP31C | S | N | TX, F | (BD441) | BD241C | 2N6123 | RCA31C | | |
| TIP32 | S | P | TX, F | BD242 | BD438 | SDA445 | | 2N6124 | |
| | | | | | | | | | |
| TIP32 | | | | BD132 | | RCA32 | | | |
| TIP32A | S | P | TX, F | BD440 | BD242A | SDB445 | | 2N6125 | |
| TIP32A | | | | | | RCA32A | | | |
| TIP32B | S | P | TX, F | BD442 | BD242B | 2N6125 | RCA32B | | |
| TIP32B | | | | | | 2N2126 | | | |
| | | | | | | | | | |
| TIP32C | S | P | TX, F | (BD442) | BD242C | 2N6126 | RCA32C | | |
| TIP33 | S | N | TX | BD245 | BDY38 | 2N6486 | 2N6129 | | |
| TIP33A | S | N | TX | BD245A | AM291 | 2N3715 | 2N648] | | |
| TIP33A | | | | BDX10 | | 2N3055 | 2N613C | | |
| TIP33B | S | N | TX | BD245B | | 2N3716 | 2N6488 | | |
| | | | | | | | | | |
| TIP33B | | | | | | 2N6131 | | | |
| TIP33C | S | N | TX | BD245C | | 2N5629 | 2N6131 | | |
| TIP34 | S | P | TX | BD246 | | 2N6489 | 2N6132 | | |
| TIP34A | S | P | TX | BD246A | | 2N3791 | 2N6490 | | |
| TIP34A | | | | | | 2N6133 | | | |
| | | | | | | | | | |
| TIP34B | S | P | TX | BD246B | | 2N3792 | 2N6491 | | |
| TIP34B | | | | | | 2N6134 | | | |
| TIP34C | S | P | TX | BD246C | | 2N6020 | 2N6134 | | |
| TIP35 | S | N | TX | BD249 | | 2N5301 | | | |
| TIP35A | S | N | TX | BD249A | | 2N5302 | | | |
| | | | | | | | | | |
| TIP35B | S | N | TX | BD249B | | 2N5303 | | | |
| TIP35C | S | N | TX | BD249C | | | | | |
| TIP36 | S | P | TX | BD250 | | 2N4398 | | | |
| TIP36A | S | P | TX | BD250A | | 2N4399 | | | |
| TIP36B | S | P | TX | BD250B | | MS4502 | | | |
| | | | | | | | | | |
| TIP36C | S | P | TX | BD250C | | | | | |
| TIP41 | S | N | TX, F | (BD437) | BD243 | 2N6129 | 2N6121 | | |
| TIP41 | | | | | | RCA41 | | | |
| TIP41A | S | N | TX, F | (BD439) | BD243A | 2N6130 | 2N6122 | | |
| TIP41A | | | | | | RCA41A | | | |
| | | | | | | | | | |
| TIP41B | S | N | TX, F | (BD441) | BD243B | 2N6131 | 2N6123 | | |
| TIP41B | | | | | | RCA41B | | | |
| TIP41C | S | N | TX, F | (BD441) | BD243C | 2N6123 | 2N6131 | | |
| TIP41C | | | | | | RCA41C | | | |
| TIP42 | S | P | TX, F | (BD438) | BD244 | 2N6132 | 2N6124 | | |
| | | | | | | | | | |
| TIP42 | | | | | | RCA42 | | | |
| TIP42A | S | P | TX, F | (BD440) | BD244A | 2N6125 | 2N6133 | | |
| TIP42A | | | | | | RCA42A | | | |
| TIP42B | S | P | TX, F | (BD442) | BD244B | 2N6134 | 2N6126 | | |
| TIP42B | | | | | | RCA42B | | | |
| | | | | | | | | | |
| TIP42C | S | P | TX, F | (BD442) | BD244C | 2N6126 | 2N6134 | | |
| TIP42C | | | | | | RCA42C | | | |
| TIP47 | S | N | TX | | | FT47 | TA8863C | | |
| TIP48 | S | N | TX | | | FT48 | TA8863B | | |
| TIP49 | S | N | TX | | | FT49 | TA8863A | | |
| | | | | | | | | | |
| TIP50 | S | N | TX | | | FT50 | TA8863A | | |
| TIP51 | S | N | TX | (BUY77) | | 2N5838 | | | |
| TIP52 | S | N | TX | (BUY78) | | FT401 | | | |
| TIP53 | S | N | TX | (BUY79) | | 2N5840 | | | |
| TIP54 | S | N | TX | (BUY79) | | | | | |
| | | | | | | | | | |
| TIP110 | S | N | TX, F | BDX33A | BD677 | SE9300 | | | |
| TIP111 | S | N | TX, F | BDX33B | BD679 | SE9301 | | | |
| TIP112 | S | N | TX, F | BDX33C | (BD679) | SE9302 | | | |
| TIP115 | S | P | TX, F | BDX34A | BD678 | | | | |
| TIP116 | S | P | TX, F | BDX34B | BD680 | | | | |
| | | | | | | | | | |
| TIP117 | S | P | TX, F | BDX34C | (BD680) | | | | |
| TIP120 | S | N | TX, F | BDX33A | BD645 | SE9300 | TIP121 | | |
| TIP121 | S | N | TX, F | BDX33B | BD647 | SE9301 | TIP122 | | |
| TIP122 | S | N | TX, F | BDX33C | BD649 | SE9302 | | | |
| TIP125 | S | P | TX, F | BDX34A | BD646 | TIP126 | | | |

| TYPE | M/S | POL | MANUFAC | EUROPEAN | | AMERICAN | | JAPANESE | USE |
|------|-----|-----|---------|----------|--|----------|--|----------|-----|
| TIP126 | S | P | TX,F | BDX34B | BD648 | TIP127 | | | |
| TIP127 | S | P | TX,F | BDX34C | BD650 | | | | |
| TIP140 | S | N | TX | | | SE9300 | SE9303 | | |
| TIP141 | S | N | TX | | | SE9301 | SE9304 | | |
| TIP142 | S | N | TX | | | SE9302 | SE9305 | | |
| | | | | | | | | | |
| TIP145 | S | P | TX | | | SE9400 | | | |
| TIP146 | S | P | TX | | | SE9401 | | | |
| TIP147 | S | P | TX | | | SE9402 | | | |
| TIP501 | S | N | TX | | | 2N5321 | | | |
| TIP502 | S | N | TX | | | 2N5320 | | | |
| | | | | | | | | | |
| TIP503 | S | N | TX | | | 2N3441 | | | |
| TIP504 | S | N | TX | | | 2N3441 | | | |
| TIP509 | S | N | TX | BUY55 | | | | | |
| TIP510 | S | N | TX | BUY56 | | | | | |
| TIP515 | S | N | TX | (BUY57) | | | | | |
| | | | | | | | | | |
| TIP516 | S | N | TX | (BUY58) | | | | | |
| TIP525 | S | N | TX | BUX27A | BUY72 | | | | |
| TIP530 | S | N | TX | (BUY78) | | SE9052 | | | |
| TIP531 | S | N | TX | (BUY75) | | 2N6250 | | | |
| TIP532 | S | N | TX | (BUY76) | | | | | |
| | | | | | | | | | |
| TIP535 | S | N | TX | BUX17A | BUY74 | | | | |
| TIP536 | S | N | TX | BUY75 | | | | | |
| TIP537 | S | N | TX | BUY76 | | | | | |
| TIP538 | S | N | TX | (BUY74) | | 2N6250 | | | |
| TIP539 | S | N | TX | (BUY75) | | 2N6250 | | | |
| | | | | | | | | | |
| TIP540 | S | N | TX | (BUY76) | | | | | |
| TIP544 | S | P | TX | | | 2N6248 | | | |
| TIP546 | S | P | TX | | | 2N6469 | | | |
| TIP640 | S | N | TX | | | SE9303 | | | |
| TIP641 | S | N | TX | | | SE9304 | | | |
| | | | | | | | | | |
| TIP642 | S | N | TX | | | SE9305 | | | |
| TIP2955 | S | P | TX | | | FT2955 | 40878 | | |
| TIP3054 | S | N | TX | | | RCA3054 | | | |
| TIP3055 | S | N | TX | AM1291 | BDX10 | FT3055 | RCA3055 | | |
| TIP3055 | | | | | | 2N3055 | 2N6131 | | |
| | | | | | | | | | |
| TIP3055 | | | | | | 2N6099 | | | |
| TIP5530 | S | P | TX | | | TIP2955 | | | |
| TIS05 | S | P | TX | | | 2N5462 | 2N5465 | | |
| TIS14 | J | N | TX | | | 2N4220A | 2N4222A | | |
| TIS14 | | | | | | 2N4224 | | | |
| | | | | | | | | | |
| TIS25 | J | N | TX | | | 2N5045 | 2N5197 | | |
| TIS26 | J | N | TX | | | 2N5046 | 2N5198 | | |
| TIS27 | J | N | TX | | | 2N5047 | 2N5199 | | |
| TIS34 | J | N | NS,TX | BF256 | | 2N5486 | 2N5248 | | |
| TIS34 | | | | | | 2N3823 | | | |
| | | | | | | | | | |
| TIS37 | S | P | TX | BC308V1 | | EN3905 | 2N3905 | | |
| TIS38 | S | P | TX | BC308V1 | | EN3905 | 2N3905 | | |
| TIS39 | S | N | TX | | | 2N4874 | | | |
| TIS41 | J | N | IL,TX | | | MFE2009 | 2N4859 | | |
| TIS42 | J | N | TX | | | 2N4092 | 2N4093 | | |
| | | | | | | | | | |
| TIS42 | | | | | | | | | |
| TIS43 | U | P | N TX, | | | U1898E | | | |
| TIS56 | S | N | TX | | | TIS57 | | | |
| TIS57 | S | N | TX | | | TIS56 | | | |
| TIS58 | J | N | NS,TX | | | 2N5458 | 2N4302 | | |
| | | | | | | | | | |
| TIS59 | J | N | TX | | | 2N5670 | U1837E | | |
| TIS62 | S | P | TX | | | 2N3563 | 2N5770 | | |
| TIS63 | S | N | TX | | | 2N5770 | 2N3563 | | |
| TIS64 | S | N | TX | | | 2N3563 | 2N5770 | | |
| TIS69 | J | N | TX | | | | | | |
| | | | | | | | | | |
| TIS70 | J | N | TX | | | | | | |
| TIS73 | J | N | IL,NS,TX | | | 2N5638 | U1897E | | |
| TIS74 | J | N | IL,NS,TX | | | 2N5639 | U1898E | | |
| TIS75 | J | N | IL,NS,TX | | | 2N5640 | U1898E | | |
| TIS78 | J | N | TX | | | 2N5543 | | | |
| | | | | | | | | | |
| TIS79 | J | N | TX | | | 2N5544 | | | |
| TIS84 | S | N | TX | | | | | | |
| TIS85 | S | N | TX | | | | | | |
| TIS86 | S | N | TX | | | SE5030A | SE5030B | | |
| TIS86 | | | | | | PE5030B | | | |
| | | | | | | | | | |
| TIS87 | S | N | TX | | | SE5030A | SE5030B | | |
| TIS87 | | | | | | PE3050B | | | |
| TIS88 | J | N | TX | | | 2N5486 | | | |
| TIS90 | S | N | TX | | | 2N4946 | 2N4401 | | |
| TIS90M | S | N | TX | | | SE8040 | | | |

| TYPE | M/S | POL | MANUFAC | EUROPEAN | | AMERICAN | | JAPANESE | USE |
|------|-----|-----|---------|----------|--|----------|--|----------|-----|
| TIS91 | S | P | TX | | | 2N3644 | 2N4403 | | |
| TIS91M | S | P | TX | | | SE8540 | | | |
| TIS92 | S | N | TX | | | 2N4946 | 2N4401 | | |
| TIS92M | S | N | TX | | | SE8040 | | | |
| TIS93 | S | P | TX | | | 2N3644 | 2N4403 | | |
| | | | | | | | | | |
| TIS93M | S | P | TX | | | SE8540 | | | |
| TIXS11 | M | P | TX | | | 2N4352 | | | |
| TIXS33 | J | N | TX | | | MFE2009 | 2N4860 | | |
| TIXS35 | J | N | TX | | | TIX36 | | | |
| TIXS36 | J | N | TX | | | | | | |
| | | | | | | | | | |
| TIXS39 | S | N | TX | BFV17 | BFY39 | 2N918 | | | |
| TIXS39 | | | | BFW17 | | | | | |
| TIXS41 | J | N | TX | | | MFE2009 | 2N4391 | | |
| TIXS42 | J | N | TX | | | MFE2004 | 2N4092 | | |
| TIXS67 | M | P | TX | | | 2N4352 | | | |
| | | | | | | | | | |
| TIXS78 | J | N | TX | | | 3N126 | | | |
| TIXS79 | J | N | TX | | | 3N126 | | | |
| TIXS80 | J | N | TX | | | | | | |
| TIXS81 | J | N | TX | | | TIXS80 | | | |
| TJ320 | G | P | | AC126 | | 2N2429 | | | |
| | | | | | | | | | |
| TJ363 | G | P | | AF185 | | | | | |
| TJ364 | G | P | | AF185 | | | | | |
| TJ385 | G | P | | AF185 | | | | | |
| TJ386 | G | P | | AF185 | | | | | |
| TJ387 | G | P | | AF185 | | | | | |
| | | | | | | | | | |
| TJ388 | G | P | | AF185 | | | | | |
| TJ389 | G | P | | AF185 | | | | | |
| TJ397 | G | P | | AF185 | | | | | |
| TJ398 | G | P | | AF185 | | | | | |
| TJ399 | G | P | | AF185 | | | | | |
| | | | | | | | | | |
| TJN1 | G | P | | AC126 | | 2N2429 | | | |
| TJN1B | G | P | | AC126 | | 2N2429 | | | |
| TJN2F | G | P | | AC126 | | 2N2429 | | | |
| TJN2F8 | G | P | | AC126 | | 2N2429 | | | |
| TJN2G | G | P | | AC126 | | 2N2429 | | | |
| | | | | | | | | | |
| TJN2GB | G | P | | AC126 | | 2N2429 | | | |
| TJN3 | G | P | | AC126 | | 2N2429 | | | |
| TJN4 | G | P | | AC126 | | 2N2429 | | | |
| TJN300/2 | G | P | | AD149 | | 2N2836 | | | |
| TJN300/2A | G | P | | AD149 | | 2N2836 | | | |
| | | | | | | | | | |
| TK20B | G | P | | V6/4R2 | | | | | |
| TK21B | G | P | | V6/2R3 | | | | | |
| TK23 | G | P | | ACY31 | | | | | |
| TK23A | G | P | | GET104 | NKT217 | | | | |
| TK23A | | | | NKT227 | | | | | |
| | | | | | | | | | |
| TK23C | G | P | | NKT217 | NKT227 | | | | |
| TK24 | G | P | | V6/2R4 | | | | | |
| TK24B | G | P | | ASY64 | | | | | |
| TK25 | G | P | | ASY60 | | | | | |
| TK25B | G | P | | V6/8R | | | | | |
| | | | | | | | | | |
| TK26B | G | P | | V6/2R3 | | | | | |
| TK27B | G | P | | V6/2R4 | | | | | |
| TK28 | G | P | | ASY63 | | | | | |
| TK28B | G | P | | V6/2R4 | | | | | |
| TK30C | G | P | | NKT126 | | 2G301 | | | |
| | | | | | | | | | |
| TK30D | G | P | | NKT126 | | | | | |
| TK31 | G | P | | ASY55 | | | | | |
| TK31C | G | P | | NKT125 | | 2G302 | | | |
| TK31D | G | P | | NKT125 | | | | | |
| TK35 | G | P | | ASY56 | | | | | |
| | | | | | | | | | |
| TK36 | G | P | | ASY57 | | | | | |
| TK37 | G | P | | ASY58 | | | | | |
| TK38 | G | P | | ASY59 | | | | | |
| TK40 | G | P | | AC126 | ACY30 | | | | |
| TK40A | G | P | | GET102 | NKT213 | | | | |
| | | | | | | | | | |
| TK40A | | | | NKT223 | | | | | |
| TK40C | G | P | | AC156 | NKT213 | | | | |
| TK40C | | | | NKT223 | | | | | |
| TK41 | G | P | | AC128 | ACY27 | | | | |
| TK41C | G | P | | NKT214 | NKT224 | | | | |
| | | | | | | | | | |
| TK42 | G | P | | ACY28 | | | | | |
| TK42C | G | P | | AC156 | NKT213 | | | | |
| TK42C | | | | NKT223 | | | | | |
| TK45 | G | P | | ACY29 | NKT216 | | | | |
| TK45 | | | | NKT226 | | | | | |

| TYPE | M/S | POL | MANUFAC | EUROPEAN | | AMERICAN | | JAPANESE | USE |
|------|-----|-----|---------|----------|--|----------|--|----------|-----|
| TK46 | G | P | | ASY50 | | | | | |
| TK46C | G | P | | NKT215 | NKT225 | | | | |
| TK47C | G | P | | NKT215 | NKT225 | | | | |
| TK48C | G | P | | NKT217 | NKT227 | | | | |
| TK49 | G | N | | ASY53 | | | | | |
| | | | | | | | | | |
| TK49C | G | N | | NKT713 | | | | | |
| TK400A | G | P | | NKT404 | | | | | |
| TK401A | G | P | | NKT401 | | | | | |
| TK402A | G | P | | NKT402 | | | | | |
| TN4117 | J | N | | | | MFE2093 | 2N5647 | | |
| | | | | | | | | | |
| TN4117A | J | N | SP,TI | | | MFE2093 | U1714 | | |
| TN4118 | J | N | SP,TI | | | MFE2094 | 2N5649 | | |
| TN4118A | J | N | SP,TI | | | MFE2094 | U1714 | | |
| TN4119 | J | N | TI | | | 2N5649 | | | |
| TN4119A | J | N | SP,TI | | | MFE2095 | U1714 | | |
| | | | | | | | | | |
| TN4338 | J | N | | | | 2N4220A | | | |
| TN4339 | J | N | | | | 2N4220A | | | |
| TN4340 | J | N | | | | 2N4220A | | | |
| TN4341 | J | N | | | | 2N4221A | | | |
| TP5114 | J | P | SP | | | 2N3993 | 2N5018 | | |
| | | | | | | | | | |
| TP5115 | J | P | SP | | | 2N3993 | 2N5018 | | |
| TP5116 | J | P | SP | | | 2N3993 | 2N5019 | | |
| TR722 | G | P | IC,St | OC58 | | | | | |
| TR760 | G | P | St | AF185 | | 2N520 | | | |
| TR761 | G | P | St | AF185 | | 2N521 | | | |
| | | | | | | | | | |
| TR802 | G | P | St | AF127 | | | | | |
| TRC44 | G | P | St | AF185 | AF126 | | | | |
| TRC45 | G | P | St | AF185 | AF127 | | | | |
| TRC65 | G | P | St | AC125 | | | | | |
| TRC66 | G | P | St | AC126 | | | | | |
| | | | | | | | | | |
| TRC70 | G | P | St | AC126 | AC125 | 2N2429 | | | |
| TRC71 | G | P | St | AC126 | AC125 | 2N2429 | | | |
| TRC72 | G | P | St | AC128 | AC132 | 2N2431 | | | |
| TRC76 | G | P | St | ASY76 | OC76 | | | | |
| TRC77 | G | P | St | ASY77 | OC77 | | | | |
| | | | | | | | | | |
| TRC360 | G | P | St | OC58 | OC65 | | | | |
| TRC601 | G | P | St | AC126 | AC125 | 2N2429 | | | |
| TRC601 | | | | OC70 | | | | | |
| TRC602 | G | P | St | AC126 | AC125 | 2N2429 | | | |
| TRC602 | | | | OC71 | | | | | |
| | | | | | | | | | |
| TS1 | G | P | | AF185 | | | | | |
| TS2 | G | P | | AF185 | | | | | |
| TS3 | G | P | | AF185 | | | | | |
| TS7 | G | P | | AF185 | | | | | |
| TS8 | G | P | | AF185 | | | | | |
| | | | | | | | | | |
| TS9 | G | P | | AC128 | | 2N2431 | | | |
| TS13 | G | P | | AC126 | | 2N2429 | | | |
| TS14 | G | P | | AC126 | | 2N2429 | | | |
| TS161 | G | P | | 2-AC128 | 2-AC132 | | | | |
| TS161 | | | | 2-OC72 | | | | | |
| | | | | | | | | | |
| TS162 | G | P | | AC126 | AC125 | 2N2429 | | | |
| TS162 | | | | OC71 | | | | | |
| TS163 | G | P | | AC126 | AC125 | 2N2429 | | | |
| TS163 | | | | OC71 | | | | | |
| TS164 | G | P | | AC126 | AC125 | 2N2429 | | | |
| | | | | | | | | | |
| TS164 | | | | OC71 | | | | | |
| TS165 | G | P | | AC126 | OC72 | 2N2429 | 2N281 | | |
| TS166 | G | P | | AC126 | AC125 | 2N2429 | | | |
| TS176 | G | P | | AD149 | OC70 | 2N2836 | 2N2429 | | |
| TS306 | G | P | | AC128 | | 2N2431 | 2N2836 | | |
| | | | | | | | | | |
| TS620 | G | P | | OC58 | OC65 | 2N2431 | | | |
| TS620 | | | | OC66 | | | | | |
| TS621 | G | P | | OC58 | OC65 | | | | |
| TS621 | | | | OC70 | | | | | |
| TS739 | G | P | | AC126 | | 2N2429 | | | |
| | | | | | | | | | |
| TS739B | G | P | | AF185 | | | | | |
| TS740 | G | P | | AC128 | | | | | |
| TS2218 | S | N | TX,IT | | | 2N1613 | | | |
| TS2219 | S | N | TX,IT | | | 2N1711 | | | |
| TS2904 | S | P | TX,IT | | | 40406 | | | |
| | | | | | | | | | |
| U110 | J | P | IL,SX,TI | | | 2N5474 | | | |
| U112 | J | P | IL,SX,NS,TI | | | 2N5476 | | | |
| U133 | J | P | IL,SX | | | 2N5475 | | | |
| U146 | J | P | IL,SX,TI | | | 2N3909 | | | |
| U147 | J | P | IL,SX,TI | | | 2N3909 | | | |

| TYPE | M/S | POL | MANUFAC | EUROPEAN | AMERICAN | | JAPANESE | USE |
|------|-----|-----|---------|----------|----------|---|----------|-----|
| U148 | J | P | IL,SX,11 | | 2N3909 | | | |
| U149 | J | P | IL,SX,NS,TI | | 2N3330 | | | |
| U168 | J | P | IL | | 2N2608 | 2N3330 | | |
| U182 | J | N | SX | | 2N4092 | 2N4860 | | |
| U182 | | | | | 2N3970 | | | |
| U183 | J | N | IL,SX | | MFE3001 | 2N3458 | | |
| U183 | | | | | 2N3823 | | | |
| U184 | J | N | IL,SX | | MFE2001 | 2N4416 | | |
| U184 | | | | | 2N3823 | | | |
| U197 | J | N | | | 2N3460 | TN4328 | | |
| U198 | J | N | IL,SX | | 2N3437 | 2N3459 | | |
| U198 | | | | | TN4340 | | | |
| U199 | J | N | IL,SX | | 2N3436 | 2N3458 | | |
| U199 | | | | | TN4341 | | | |
| U200 | J | N | IL,SX | | MFE2004 | 2N5549 | | |
| U200 | | | | | 2N4092 | | | |
| U201 | J | N | IL,SX | | MFE2005 | 2N4861 | | |
| U201 | | | | | 2N4091 | | | |
| U202 | J | N | IL,SX | | MFE2006 | 2N4860 | | |
| U202 | | | | | 2N4092 | | | |
| U205 | | | SX | | MMF1 | MMF2 | | |
| U206 | | | SX | | MMF3 | MMF4 | | |
| U207 | | | SX | | MMF5 | MMF6 | | |
| U221 | J | N | SX | | 2N4092 | | | |
| U222 | J | N | SX | | 2N4856 | | | |
| U231 | J | N | IL,SX | | 2N5545 | 2N3954 | | |
| U232 | J | N | IL,SX | | 2N5546 | 2N3955 | | |
| U233 | J | N | IL,SX | | 2N5547 | 2N3956 | | |
| U234 | J | N | IL,SX | | 2N5547 | 2N3957 | | |
| U235 | J | N | IL,SX | | 2N5045 | 2N3958 | | |
| U240 | J | N | IL,SX | | MFE2012 | SFC1783 | | |
| U240 | | | | | 2N4445 | | | |
| U241 | J | N | IL,SX | | MFE2012 | SFC1785 | | |
| U241 | | | | | 2N4446 | | | |
| U242 | J | N | IL,SX | | MFE2012 | SFC1783 | | |
| U242 | | | | | 2N4447 | | | |
| U243 | J | N | IL,SX | | MFE2011 | SFC1785 | | |
| U243 | | | | | 2N4448 | | | |
| U244 | J | N | SX | | MFE2012 | | | |
| U254 | J | N | | | 2N4859 | | | |
| U255 | J | N | | | 2N4860 | | | |
| U256 | J | N | | | 2N4861 | | | |
| U257 | J | N | IL,SX | | 2N5047 | TD5912 | | |
| U266 | J | N | SX | | MFE2012 | | | |
| U273A | J | N | SX | | 2N4220 | | | |
| U274A | J | N | SX | | 2N4220 | | | |
| U275 | J | N | SX | | 2N4220 | | | |
| U275A | J | N | SX | | 2N4220 | | | |
| U290 | J | N | SX | | MFE2012 | | | |
| U291 | J | N | SX | | MFE2012 | | | |
| U300 | J | P | SX | | 2N3993 | | | |
| U301 | J | P | SX | | 2N3993 | | | |
| U304 | J | P | SX | | 2N3993 | | | |
| U305 | J | P | SX | | 2N3993 | | | |
| U306 | J | P | SX | | 2N3993 | | | |
| U308 | J | P | SX | | 2N4416 | | | |
| U309 | J | N | SX | | 2N4416 | | | |
| U311 | J | N | SX | | 2N4416 | | | |
| U312 | J | N | SX | | 2N4416 | | | |
| U314 | J | N | SX | | 2N5484 | | | |
| U315 | J | N | SX | | 2N5486 | | | |
| U320 | J | N | SX | | 2N4391 | | | |
| U321 | J | N | SX | | 2N4391 | | | |
| U322 | J | N | SX | | 2N4391 | | | |
| U1177 | J | N | SX | | 2N4220A | MFE2095 | | |
| U1178 | J | N | SX | | MFE2093 | MFE2094 | | |
| U1179 | J | N | SX | | MFE2093 | | | |
| U1180 | J | N | SX | | 2N4221A | | | |
| U1181 | J | N | SX | | 2N4220A | | | |
| U1182 | J | N | SX | | MFE2093 | | | |
| U1277 | J | N | IL,TI | | MFE2095 | 2N5361 | | |
| U1277 | | | | | 2N3822 | | | |
| U1278 | J | N | | | 2N5359 | 2N3821 | | |
| U1279 | J | N | IL,TI | | MFE2093 | 2N5362 | | |
| U1279 | | | | | 2N3821 | | | |

| TYPE | M/S | POL | MANUFAC | EUROPEAN | | AMERICAN | | JAPANESE | USE |
|---|---|---|---|---|---|---|---|---|---|
| U1280 | J | N | IL,TI | | | MFE2093 | MFE2095 | | |
| U1280 | | | | | | 2N5359 | 2N4224 | | |
| U1281 | J | N | IL,TI | | | 2N5549 | 2N3822 | | |
| U1282 | J | N | IL,TI | | | 2N3822 | 2N3458 | | |
| U1282 | | | | | | TN4341 | | | |
| U1283 | J | N | IL,TI | | | 2N3822 | 2N3459 | | |
| U1283 | | | | | | TN4340 | | | |
| U1284 | J | N | IL,TI | | | 2N3821 | 2N3822 | | |
| U1284 | | | | | | 2N3458 | 2N3069 | | |
| U1285 | J | N | IL,TI | | | MFE2093 | 2N3453 | | |
| U1286 | J | N | IL,TI | | | 2N3821 | 2N3459 | | |
| U1286 | | | | | | 2N3069 | | | |
| U1287 | J | N | IL | | | 2N4860 | 2N4092 | | |
| U1321 | J | N | | | | 2N3966 | 2N4221 | | |
| U1322 | J | N | SX | | | 2N4222A | 2N3459 | | |
| U1322 | | | | | | 2N4221A | | | |
| U1323 | J | N | | | | 2N3459 | 2N4221A | | |
| U1324 | J | N | | | | 2N5362 | 2N4220A | | |
| U1325 | J | N | IL,TI | | | 2N4220A | | | |
| U1714 | J | N | IL,TI | | | 2N4220A | 2N3459 | | |
| U1714 | | | | | | TN4340 | | | |
| U1715 | J | N | TI | | | 2N5803 | 2N5278 | | |
| U1837E | J | N | IL,NS,TI | | | 2N5486 | 2N5245 | | |
| U1837E | | | | | | 2N5163 | | | |
| U1897E | J | N | IL,NS,TI | | | 2N5638 | TIS73 | | |
| U1897E | | | | | | KE4091 | | | |
| U1898E | J | N | IL,NS,TI | | | 2N5639 | TIS74 | | |
| U1898E | | | | | | KE4092 | | | |
| U1899 | J | N | SX | | | 2N5640 | | | |
| U1899E | J | N | NS,IL,TI | | | TIS75 | KE4093 | | |
| U1994 | J | N | SX | | | 2N5486 | | | |
| U1994E | J | N | IL,NS,TI | | | 2N5245 | KE4416 | | |
| U2047E | J | N | TI | | | 2N5247 | KE4416 | | |
| U3000 | J | N | | | | 2N3459 | 2N3069 | | |
| U3001 | J | N | SX | | | 2N3365 | 2N3459 | | |
| U3001 | | | | | | 2N3070 | 2N3071 | | |
| U3002 | | | SX | | | 2N3366 | | | |
| U3003 | J | N | SX | | | 2N3367 | | | |
| U3010 | J | N | SX | | | 2N3365 | 2N3458 | | |
| U3010 | | | | | | 2N4222 | | | |
| U3011 | J | N | SX | | | 2N3366 | 2N3459 | | |
| U3011 | | | | | | 2N4221 | | | |
| U3012 | J | N | SX | | | 2N3367 | 2N3460 | | |
| U3012 | | | | | | 2N4220 | | | |
| UC20 | J | N | IL | | | 2N5486 | 2N5358 | | |
| UC20 | | | | | | 2N5849 | | | |
| UC21 | J | N | IL | | | 2N5486 | | | |
| UC23 | J | N | | | | 2N5486 | | | |
| UC100 | J | N | IL | | | 2N4221A | 2N5361 | | |
| UC100 | | | | | | 2N3822 | | | |
| UC105 | J | N | | | | TN4341 | | | |
| UC110 | J | N | IL | | | 2N4220A | 2N5360 | | |
| UC110 | | | | | | 2N3821 | | | |
| UC115 | J | N | IL | | | 2N3459 | TN4340 | | |
| UC120 | J | N | | | | 2N4220A | | | |
| UC130 | J | N | IL | | | 2N4220A | | | |
| UC150 | J | N | | | | 2N4416 | | | |
| UC150w | J | N | | | | 2N4416 | | | |
| UC155 | J | N | IL,SD | | | 2N3972 | 2N5364 | | |
| UC155 | | | | | | 2N4416 | | | |
| UC155w | J | N | SD | | | 2N5640 | | | |
| UC200 | J | N | IL,SD | | | 2N4393 | | | |
| UC201 | J | N | IL,SD | | | 2N4093 | 2N5364 | | |
| UC201 | | | | | | 2N4416 | | | |
| UC210 | J | N | IL,SD | | | MFE2000 | 2N5362 | | |
| UC210 | | | | | | 2N3822 | | | |
| UC220 | J | N | IL,SD | | | 2N4221 | 2N5360 | | |
| UC220 | | | | | | 2N3968 | | | |
| UC240 | J | N | IL | | | 2N4221A | 2N3459 | | |
| UC240 | | | | | | 2N5396 | | | |
| UC241 | J | N | IL,SD | | | 2N5361 | 2N3822 | | |
| UC250 | J | N | IL,NS,SD | | | 2N4091 | 2N4391 | | |
| UC250 | | | | | | 2N3970 | | | |
| UC251 | J | N | IL,NS,SD | | | 2N4093 | 2N4392 | | |

| TYPE | M/S | POL | MANUFAC | EUROPEAN | | AMERICAN | | JAPANESE | USE |
|---|---|---|---|---|---|---|---|---|---|
| UC251 | | P | | | | 2N3971 | | | |
| UC300 | J | P | | | | 2N5267 | | | |
| UC310 | J | P | | | | 2N5265 | | | |
| UC320 | J | P | | | | 2N5265 | | | |
| UC330 | J | P | | | | 2N5473 | | | |
| | | | | | | | | | |
| UC340 | J | P | | | | 2N5265 | | | |
| UC400 | J | P | IL,SD | | | MFE4012 | 2N3331 | | |
| UC400 | | | | | | 2N2609 | | | |
| UC401 | J | P | IL,SD | | | 2N3993 | 2N3994 | | |
| UC401 | | | | | | 2N5019 | | | |
| | | | | | | | | | |
| UC410 | J | P | IL,SD | | | MFE4009 | 2N3330 | | |
| UC410 | | | | | | 2N2609 | | | |
| UC420 | J | P | IL,SD | | | MFE4001 | 2N3329 | | |
| UC420 | | | | | | 2N5021 | | | |
| UC450 | J | P | | | | 2N3993 | | | |
| | | | | | | | | | |
| UC451 | J | P | | | | 2N3994 | | | |
| UC701 | J | N | | | | 2N4220 | | | |
| UC703 | J | N | IL,SD | | | 2N4220 | 2N5362 | | |
| UC703 | | | | | | 2N3822 | | | |
| UC704 | J | N | IL | | | 2N4221A | 2N5364 | | |
| | | | | | | | | | |
| UC704 | | | | | | 2N3822 | | | |
| UC705 | J | N | IL,SD | | | 2N4221A | 2N5364 | | |
| UC705 | | | | | | 2N3824 | | | |
| UC707 | J | N | IL,SD | | | MFE2000 | 2N4861 | | |
| UC707 | | | | | | 2N4091 | | | |
| | | | | | | | | | |
| UC714 | J | N | IL,NS,SD | | | 2N3437 | 2N3823 | | |
| UC714A | J | N | | | | 2N5484 | | | |
| UC714E | J | N | | | | 2N5950 | U1837E | | |
| UC734 | J | N | IL,NS,SD | | | 2N4224 | 2N4416 | | |
| UC734E | J | N | IL,NS,SD | | | 2N5486 | 2N5245 | | |
| | | | | | | | | | |
| UC734E | | | | | | U1994E | | | |
| UC750 | J | N | | | | TN4338 | | | |
| UC751 | J | N | | | | 2N4091 | 2N3458 | | |
| UC751 | | | | | | TN4340 | | | |
| UC752 | J | N | IL | | | 2N4091 | | | |
| | | | | | | | | | |
| UC753 | J | N | IL | | | 2N4091 | 2N3458 | | |
| UC753 | | | | | | 2N4092 | | | |
| UC754 | J | N | IL | | | 2N4091 | 2N3458 | | |
| UC754 | | | | | | TN4340 | | | |
| UC755 | J | N | IL,SD | | | 2N4091 | 2N3458 | | |
| | | | | | | | | | |
| UC755 | | | | | | TN4341 | | | |
| UC756 | J | N | IL,SD | | | 2N4091 | 2N3458 | | |
| UC756 | | | | | | 2N4224 | | | |
| UC805 | J | P | SD | | | 2N3330 | 2N3331 | | |
| UC807 | J | N | SD | | | 2N3972 | 2N4861 | | |
| | | | | | | | | | |
| UC814 | J | P | IL,SD | | | 2N5265 | 2N3331 | | |
| UC851 | J | P | IL,SD | | | 2N5265 | 2N2608 | | |
| UC853 | J | P | IL | | | 2N5265 | 2N2607 | | |
| UC854 | J | P | IL,SD | | | 2N5265 | 2N2608 | | |
| UC855 | J | P | IL,SD | | | 2N5265 | 2N2609 | | |
| | | | | | | | | | |
| UC1700 | J | P | IL,SD | | | 3N155A | | | |
| UC1764 | J | P | IL,SD | | | 3N163 | | | |
| UC2130 | J | N | IL | | | 2N5545 | 2N3954 | | |
| UC2132 | J | N | IL | | | 2N3955 | | | |
| UC2134 | J | N | IL | | | 2N3956 | | | |
| | | | | | | | | | |
| UC2136 | J | N | IL | | | 2N3958 | | | |
| UC2138 | J | N | IL | | | 2N3958 | | | |
| UC2139 | J | N | IL,SD | | | 2N3958 | | | |
| UC2147 | J | N | IL,SD | | | 2N3958 | | | |
| UC2148 | J | N | IL,SD | | | 2N3958 | | | |
| | | | | | | | | | |
| UC2149 | J | N | IL,SD | | | 2N3958 | | | |
| V6/1R | G | P | | NKT164 | | | | | |
| V6/2R | G | P | | NKT143 | NKT164 | | | | |
| V6/2RC | G | P | | NKT164 | | | | | |
| V6/2RM | G | P | | NKT164 | | | | | |
| | | | | | | | | | |
| V6/3R | G | P | | NKT164 | | | | | |
| V6/3RM | G | P | | NKT164 | | | | | |
| V6/4R | G | P | | NKT163 | NKT143 | | | | |
| V6/4RC | G | P | | NKT163 | | | | | |
| V6/4RM | G | P | | NKT162 | | | | | |
| | | | | | | | | | |
| V6/6R | G | P | | NKT163 | | | | | |
| V6/6RM | G | P | | NKT162 | | | | | |
| V6/8R | G | P | | NKT162 | NKT142 | | | | |
| V6/8RC | G | P | | NKT162 | | | | | |
| V6/8RM | G | P | | NKT162 | | | | | |

| TYPE | M/S | POL | MANUFAC | EUROPEAN | | AMERICAN | | JAPANESE | USE |
|------|-----|-----|---------|----------|--|----------|--|----------|-----|
| V6/R2 | G | P | | NKT164 | NKT143 | | | | |
| V6/R4 | G | P | | NKT163 | NKT143 | | | | |
| V6/R4 | | | | GET873 | | | | | |
| V6/R8 | G | P | | NKT162 | NKT142 | | | | |
| V6/R8 | | | | GET874 | | | | | |
| V10/15 | G | P | | AC126 | | 2N2429 | | | |
| V10/30 | G | P | | AC126 | | 2N2429 | | | |
| V10/50 | G | P | | AC126 | | 2N2429 | | | |
| V30/20P | G | P | | AD149 | OC26 | 2N2836 | | | |
| V30/30P | G | P | | AD149 | OC27 | 2N2836 | | | |
| V60/10P | G | P | | NKT403 | | | | | |
| V60/10PD | G | P | | NKT403 | | | | | |
| V60/20IP | G | P | | NKT301 | | | | | |
| V60/20P | G | P | | NKT403 | | | | | |
| V60/20PD | G | P | | NKT403 | | | | | |
| V60/30P | G | P | | NKT403 | | | | | |
| V60/30NP | G | P | | GET573 | | | | | |
| V208 | G | P | | AD149 | OC26 | 2N2836 | | | |
| V308 | G | P | | AD149 | OC26 | 2N2836 | | | |
| VB701 | G | P | | V10/50A2 | | | | | |
| VB704 | G | P | | V10/30A2 | | | | | |
| VB705 | G | P | | V10/30A | | | | | |
| VB706 | G | P | | V10/50A | | | | | |
| VB707 | G | P | | V6/4R | | | | | |
| VB708 | G | P | | V6/8R | | | | | |
| VB709 | G | P | | V10/50A2 | | | | | |
| VB710 | G | P | | V10/50A | | | | | |
| VCR2N | J | N | | | | 2N4857 | | | |
| VCR3P | J | P | | | | TP5115 | | | |
| VCR4N | J | N | | | | 2N5278 | | | |
| VCR5P | J | P | | | | 2N3331 | | | |
| VCR6P | J | P | | | | 2N3330 | | | |
| VCR7N | J | N | | | | 2N4885 | | | |
| VCR10N | J | N | | | | 2N4224 | | | |
| VCR11N | J | N | | | | TD5921A | | | |
| VCR20N | J. | N | | | | U1715 | | | |
| WK5457 | J | N | WA | | | 2N5457 | | | |
| WK5458 | J | N | WA | | | 2N5458 | | | |
| WK5459 | J | N | WA | | | 2N5459 | | | |
| X137 | G | P | | | | 2N677B | | | |
| XA101 | G | P | | AF185 | OC45 | | | | |
| XA102 | G | P | | AF185 | OC44 | | | | |
| XA111 | G | P | | AF185 | | | | | |
| XA112 | G | P | | AF185 | | | | | |
| XA131 | G | P | | AF178 | | 2N2495 | | | |
| XA141 | G | P | | AF178 | | 2N2495 | | | |
| XA142 | G | P | | AF178 | | 2N2495 | | | |
| XA143 | G | P | | AF178 | | 2N2495 | | | |
| XA161 | G | P | | AF178 | | 2N2495 | | | |
| XB102 | G | P | | AC126 | | 2N2429 | | | |
| XB103 | G | P | | OC58 | OC66 | | | | |
| XB103 | | | | OC71 | | | | | |
| XB104 | G | P | | AC126 | | 2N2429 | | | |
| XB112 | G | P | | AC126 | | 2N2429 | | | |
| XB113 | G | P | | AC126 | | 2N2429 | | | |
| XC101 | G | P | | AC128 | OC72 | 2N2431 | | | |
| XC131 | G | P | | AC128 | | 2N2431 | | | |
| XC171 | G | P | | AC128 | | 2N2431 | | | |
| XFT2 | G | P | | V10/50A | | | | | |
| XS101 | G | P | | OC139 | V10/2S | | | | |
| XS111 | G | P | | V6/2R | | | | | |
| Y203A | G | P | | XS101 | | | | | |
| Y203A2 | G | P | | XS104 | | | | | |
| Y203HB | G | P | | XS121 | | | | | |
| Y214N2 | G | P | | XC142 | | | | | |
| Y214N5 | G | P | | XC155 | | | | | |
| Y214N6 | G | P | | XC156 | | | | | |
| Y215J1 | G | P | | XA151 | | | | | |
| Y215J2 | G | P | | XA152 | | | | | |
| Y217HA1 | G | P | | XA141 | | | | | |
| Y217HA2 | G | P | | XA142 | | | | | |
| Y217HA3 | G | P | | XA143 | | | | | |
| Y221HB1 | G | P | | XA161 | | | | | |
| Y221HB2 | G | P | | XA162 | | | | | |
| Y222HB | G | P | | XB121 | | | | | |

| TYPE | M/S | POL | MANUFAC | EUROPEAN | | AMERICAN | | JAPANESE | USE |
|------|-----|-----|---------|----------|--|----------|--|----------|-----|
| Y363 | G | P | | AC126 | | 2N2429 | | | |
| Y482 | G | P | | AF185 | | | | | |
| Y483 | G | P | | AF185 | | | | | |
| Y485 | G | P | | AF185 | | | | | |
| Y633 | G | P | | AC128 | | 2N2431 | | | |
| ZJ13 | G | P | | AC128 | | 2N2431 | | | |
| ZS4 | G | P | | AF185 | | | | | |
| ZS5 | G | P | | AF185 | | | | | |
| ZS8 | G | P | | AF185 | | | | | |
| ZS12 | G | P | | AC128 | | 2N2431 | | | |
| ZS15 | G | P | | AC128 | | 2N2431 | | | |
| ZS30 | G | P | | AF185 | | | | | |
| ZS31 | G | P | | AF185 | | | | | |
| ZS34 | G | P | | AC128 | | 2N2431 | | | |
| ZS35 | G | P | | AF185 | | | | | |
| ZS36 | G | P | | AF185 | | | | | |
| ZS38 | G | P | | AC128 | | 2N2431 | | | |
| ZS41 | G | P | | AF185 | | | | | |
| ZS43 | G | P | | AF185 | | | | | |
| ZS45 | G | P | | AF185 | | | | | |
| ZS52 | G | P | | AF185 | | | | | |
| ZS56 | G | P | | AC128 | | 2N2431 | | | |
| ZS91 | G | P | | AC128 | | 2N2431 | | | |
| ZS109 | G | P | | AF185 | | | | | |
| ZS110 | G | P | | AF185 | | | | | |
| ZS112 | G | P | | AF185 | | | | | |
| ZS141 | G | P | | AF185 | | | | | |
| ZS142 | G | P | | AF185 | | | | | |
| ZT20 | S | N | FE | BC108A | | | | | |
| ZT21 | S | N | FE | BC108A | | | | | |
| ZT22 | S | N | FE | BC107A | | | | | |
| ZT23 | S | N | FE | BC107A | | | | | |
| ZT24 | S | N | FE | BC107A | | | | | |
| ZT40 | S | N | FE | BC108A | | | | | |
| ZT41 | S | N | FE | BC108A | | | | | |
| ZT42 | S | N | FE | BC107A | | | | | |
| ZT43 | S | N | FE | BC107A | | | | | |
| ZT44 | S | N | FE | BC107A | | | | | |
| ZT60 | S | N | FE | BSX45-6 | | | | | |
| ZT61 | S | N | FE | BSX45-6 | | | | | |
| ZT62 | S | N | FE | BSX46-6 | | | | | |
| ZT63 | S | N | FE | BSX46-6 | | | | | |
| ZT64 | S | N | FE | BSX47-6 | | | | | |
| ZT80 | S | N | FE | BC338-16 | | | | | |
| ZT81 | S | N | FE | BC337-16 | | | | | |
| ZT82 | S | N | FE | BC337-16 | | | | | |
| ZT83 | S | N | FE | BC337-16 | | | | | |
| ZT84 | S | N | FE | BC337-16 | | | | | |
| ZT86 | S | N | FE | (BSX47-6) | | | | | |
| ZT87 | S | N | FE | BC338-16 | | | | | |
| ZT88 | S | N | FE | (BSX47-10) | | | | | |
| ZT89 | S | N | FE | (BSX47-10) | | | | | |
| ZT90 | S | N | FE | BSX46-10 | | | | | |
| ZT91 | S | N | FE | BSX47-6 | | | | | |
| ZT92 | S | N | FE | BSX47-10 | | | | | |
| ZT93 | S | N | FE | BSX47-6 | | | | | |
| ZT94 | S | N | FE | BSX45-6 | | | | | |
| ZT95 | S | N | FE | BSX45-10 | | | | | |
| ZT110 | S | N | FE | BC338-16 | | | | | |
| ZT111 | S | N | FE | BC337-16 | | | | | |
| ZT112 | S | N | FE | BC337-16 | | | | | |
| ZT113 | S | N | FE | BC337-16 | | | | | |
| ZT114 | S | N | FE | BC337-16 | | | | | |
| ZT116 | S | N | FE | (BSX47-6) | | | | | |
| ZT117 | S | N | FE | BC338-16 | | | | | |
| ZT118 | S | N | FE | (BSX47-10) | | | | | |
| ZT119 | S | N | FE | (BSX47-10) | | | | | |
| ZT180 | S | P | FE | BC328-16 | | | | | |
| ZT181 | S | P | FE | BC327-16 | | | | | |
| ZT182 | S | P | FE | BC327-16 | | | | | |
| ZT183 | S | P | FE | BC327-16 | | | | | |
| ZT184 | S | P | FE | BC327-16 | | | | | |
| ZT187 | S | P | FE | BC328-16 | | | | | |
| ZT189 | S | P | FE | (BC327-16) | | | | | |
| ZT202 | S | N | FE | BC108A | | | | | |

| TYPE | M/S | POL | MANUFAC | EUROPEAN | | AMERICAN | | JAPANESE | USE |
|------|-----|-----|---------|----------|--|----------|--|----------|-----|
| ZT203 | S | P | FE | BC108A | | | | | |
| ZT204 | S | N | FE | BC108A | BSY10 | | | | |
| ZT210 | S | P | FE | BSV16-6 | | | | | |
| ZT211 | S | P | FE | BSV17-6 | | | | | |
| ZT280 | S | P | FE | BC328-16 | | | | | |
| ZT281 | S | P | FE | BC327-16 | | | | | |
| ZT282 | S | P | FE | BC327-16 | | | | | |
| ZT283 | S | P | FE | BC327-16 | | | | | |
| ZT284 | S | P | FE | BC327-16 | | | | | |
| ZT287 | S | P | FE | BC328-16 | | | | | |
| ZT402 | S | N | FE | BC108A | | | | 2S731 | |
| ZT403 | S | N | FE | BC108A | | | | | |
| ZT404 | S | N | FE | BC108A | | | | | |
| ZT706 | S | N | FE | BCY34 | | 2N706 | | | |
| ZT708 | S | N | FE | | | 2N708 | 2N2413 | | |
| ZT709 | S | N | FE | | | 2N709 | | | |
| ZT1420 | S | N | FE | | | 2N1420 | | | |
| ZT1479 | S | N | FE | BSX45-6 | | | | | |
| ZT1480 | S | N | FE | BSX46-6 | | | | | |
| ZT1481 | S | N | FE | BSX45-6 | | | | | |
| ZT1482 | S | N | FE | BSX46-6 | | | | | |
| ZT1483 | S | N | FE | BSX62-6 | | | | | |
| ZT1484 | S | N | FE | (BSX63-6) | | | | | |
| ZT1485 | S | N | FE | BSX62-10 | | | | | |
| ZT1486 | S | N | FE | (BSX63-10) | | | | | |
| ZT1487 | S | N | FE | | | 2N3055 | | | |
| ZT1488 | S | N | FE | DT4111 | DT4112 | 2N3055 | 2N1488 | | |
| ZT1489 | S | N | FE | | | 2N3055 | | | |
| ZT1490 | S | N | FE | DT4121 | | 2N3055 | 2N1490 | | |
| ZT1700 | S | N | FE | BSX45-6 | | | | | |
| ZT1702 | S | N | FE | | | 2N3055 | | | |
| ZT1708 | S | N | FE | BFY44 | | 2N1708 | | | |
| ZT2205 | S | N | FE | BFY26 | | 2N2205 | | 2S131 | |
| ZT2206 | S | N | FE | BFY27 | | 2N2206 | | | |
| ZT2270 | S | N | FE | BFY15 | BFY16 | 2N2270 | | 2SO19 | |
| ZT2270 | S | N | FE | DT1521 | | | | | |
| ZTX107 | S | N | FE | BC237 | BC107 | | | | |
| ZTX107A | S | N | FE | BC237A | | | | | |
| ZTX107B | S | N | FE | BC237B | | | | | |
| ZTX108 | S | N | FE | BC238 | BC108 | | | | |
| ZTX108A | S | N | FE | BC238A | | | | | |
| ZTX108B | S | N | FE | BC238B | | | | | |
| ZTX108C | S | N | FE | BC238C | | | | | |
| ZTX109 | S | N | FE | BC239 | BC109 | | | | |
| ZTX109B | S | N | FE | BC239B | | | | | |
| ZTX109C | S | N | FE | BC239C | | | | | |
| ZTX114 | S | N | FE | BC413B | | | | | |
| ZTX300 | S | N | FE | BC338-16 | BCW10 | | | | |
| ZTX301 | S | N | FE | BC337-16 | BCW12 | | | | |
| ZTX302 | S | N | FE | BC337-16 | BCW14 | | | | |
| ZTX303 | S | N | FE | BC337-16 | BCW16 | | | | |
| ZTX304 | S | N | FE | (BC337-16) | BCW18 | | | | |
| ZTX310 | S | N | FE | BSY63 | BSV23 | 2N706 | | | |
| ZTX311 | S | N | FE | BSY63 | BSV24 | | | | |
| ZTX311 | S | N | FE | BSY95A | | | | | |
| ZTX312 | S | N | FE | (BSY63) | BSV25 | 2N706A | | | |
| ZTX313 | S | N | FE | (BSY63) | BSV26 | 2N2369 | | | |
| ZTX314 | S | N | FE | (BSY63) | BSV27 | 2N2369A | | | |
| ZTX320 | S | N | FE | (BFY90) | BSW97 | 2N918 | | | |
| ZTX321 | S | N | FE | (BFY90) | | | | | |
| ZTX325 | S | N | FE | (BFY90) | | | | | |
| ZTX326 | S | N | FE | (BFY90) | | | | | |
| ZTX330 | S | N | FE | BC337-25 | BCW20 | 2N3707 | | | |
| ZTX331 | S | N | FE | BC337-16 | BCW22 | 2N929 | | | |
| ZTX341 | S | N | FE | (BF457) | BSV28 | | | | |
| ZTX342 | S | N | FE | (BF457) | BSV29 | | | | |
| ZTX360 | S | N | FE | (BSX49) | | | | | |
| ZTX382 | S | N | FE | BC414B | | | | | |
| ZTX383 | S | N | FE | BC413B | | | | | |
| ZTX384 | S | N | FE | BC413B | | | | | |
| ZTX500 | S | P | FE | BC328-16 | BCW11 | | | | |
| ZTX501 | S | P | FE | BC327-16 | BCW13 | | | | |
| ZTX502 | S | P | FE | BC327-16 | BCW15 | | | | |
| ZTX503 | S | P | FE | BC327-16 | BCW17 | | | | |
| ZTX504 | S | P | FE | (BC327-16) | BCW19 | | | | |

| TYPE | M/S | POL | MANUFAC | EUROPEAN | | AMERICAN | | JAPANESE | USE |
|------|-----|-----|---------|----------|--|----------|--|----------|-----|
| ZTX530 | S | P | FE | BC327-25 | | | | | |
| ZTX531 | S | P | FE | BC327-16 | | | | | |
| 2CY17 | G | P | | ACY17 | | | | | |
| 2CY18 | G | P | | ACY18 | | | | | |
| 2CY19 | G | P | | ACY19 | | | | | |
| 2CY20 | G | P | | ACY20 | | | | | |
| 2CY21 | G | P | | ACY21 | | | | | |
| 2CY22 | G | P | | ACY22 | | | | | |
| 2G101 | G | P | TX | ACZ21 | AC163 | 2N506 | 2N2273 | 2SB459 | |
| 2G101 | | | | AC126 | AC128 | | | | |
| 2G101 | | | | AF139 | AC171 | | | | |
| 2G102 | G | P | TX | AC171 | AC126 | 2N506 | 2N2273 | 2SB459 | |
| 2G102 | | | | ACZ21 | AC173 | | | | |
| 2G102 | | | | AC128 | AF139 | | | | |
| 2G103 | G | P | TX | ACZ21 | | 2N2273 | | | |
| 2G104 | G | P | TX | ACZ21 | | 2N2273 | | | |
| 2G106 | G | P | TX | AF124 | | 2N990 | | | |
| 2G108 | G | P | TX | AC126 | AC163 | 2N2429 | | 2SB459 | |
| 2G108 | | | | AC171 | AC173 | | | | |
| 2G109 | G | P | TX | AC126 | AC163 | 2N2429 | | 2SB459 | |
| 2G109 | | | | AC171 | AC173 | | | | |
| 2G110 | G | P | TX | ASZ21 | | 2N2273 | | | |
| 2G138 | G | P | TX | AF185 | | | | | |
| 2G139 | G | P | TX | AF106 | AF185 | | | | |
| 2G140 | G | P | TX | AU105 | AU103 | | | 2SB468 | |
| 2G140 | | | | AF185 | | | | | |
| 2G141 | G | P | TX | AF106 | AF185 | | | | |
| 2G201 | G | P | TX | AC117R | AC128 | 2N2431 | 2N4106 | 2SB370 | |
| 2G202 | G | P | TX | AC128 | AC117R | 2N2431 | 2N4106 | 2SB370 | |
| 2G202 | | | | AC153 | | | | | |
| 2G210 | G | P | TX | ASZ15 | | 2N1533 | | | |
| 2G220 | G | P | TX | ACZ16 | ASZ16 | 2N1536 | | | |
| 2G220 | | | | 2G221 | | | | | |
| 2G221 | G | P | TX | ASZ15 | 2G222 | 2N1533 | 2N1533 | | |
| 2G222 | G | P | TX | ASZ15 | | 2N1046B | | | |
| 2G223 | G | P | TX | AUY29 | | 2N1167 | | | |
| 2G224 | G | P | TX | AUY29/5 | | 2N1167 | | | |
| 2G225 | G | P | TX | AUY29/5 | | 2N1167 | | | |
| 2G226 | G | P | TX | AUY29/5 | | 2N1167 | | | |
| 2G227 | G | P | TX | AUY29/5 | | 2N1167 | | | |
| 2G228 | G | P | TX | AUY29/5 | | 2N1167 | | | |
| 2G229 | G | P | TX | AUY29/5 | | 2N1167 | | | |
| 2G230 | G | P | TX | AUY29/5 | | 2N1167 | | | |
| 2G231 | G | P | TX | AUY29/5 | | 2N1167 | | | |
| 2G240 | G | P | TX | AU103 | AU105 | 2N2147 | | 2SB468 | |
| 2G240 | | | | AL103 | | | | | |
| 2G270 | G | P | TX | AC114 | AC128 | 2N2431 | 2N4106 | 2SB222 | |
| 2G270 | | | | AC153 | AC132 | | | | |
| 2G271 | G | P | TX | AC114 | AC128 | 2N2431 | 2N4106 | 2SB222 | |
| 2G271 | | | | AC132 | AC153 | | | | |
| 2G301 | G | P | TX | AC114 | AC128 | 2N2431 | 2N2614 | 2SB222 | |
| 2G301 | | | | AC153 | AF185 | 2N4106 | | | |
| 2G301 | | | | OC44N | | | | | |
| 2G302 | G | P | TX | AF185 | AU105 | 2N2614 | | | |
| 2G302 | | | | AW103 | | | | | |
| 2G304 | G | P | TX | OC44N | | 2N2614 | | | |
| 2G306 | G | P | TX | OC44N | | 2N2614 | | | |
| 2G308 | G | P | TX | OC44N | | 2N2614 | | | |
| 2G309 | G | P | TX | OC44N | | 2N2614 | | | |
| 2G319 | G | P | TX | AC126 | AC128 | 2N1176 | 2N1190 | 2SB383 | |
| 2G319 | | | | AC163 | AC171 | 2N2429 | | | |
| 2G319 | | | | ACY17 | | | | | |
| 2G320 | G | P | TX | AC126 | AC128 | 2N1176 | 2N1190 | 2SB383 | |
| 2G320 | | | | AC163 | AC171 | 2N2429 | | | |
| 2G320 | | | | ACY17 | | | | | |
| 2G321 | G | P | TX | ACY17 | | 2N1176 | | | |
| 2G322 | G | P | TX | ACY17 | | 2N1176 | | | |
| 2G323 | G | P | TX | ACY17 | | 2N1176 | | | |
| 2G324 | G | P | TX | ACY17 | | 2N1176 | | | |
| 2G339 | G | N | TX | AC127 | | 2N2430 | | 2SD96 | |
| 2G344 | G | P | TX | OC44N | | 2N2431 | | | |
| 2G345 | G | P | TX | OC44N | | 2N2614 | | | |

| TYPE | M/S | POL | MANUFAC | EUROPEAN | | AMERICAN | | JAPANESE | USE |
|------|-----|-----|---------|----------|--|----------|--|----------|-----|
| 2G371 | G | P | TX | AC126 | AC128 | 2N2431 | 2N610 | 2S32 | |
| 2G371 | | | | AC152V | AC117K | | | | |
| 2G374 | G | P | TX | AC128 | AC153III | | | 2SB415 | |
| 2G376 | G | P | TX | AC126 | | 2N2431 | | | |
| 2G377 | G | P | TX | AC126 | | 2N2431 | | | |
| | | | | | | | | | |
| 2G381 | G | P | TX | AC117K | AC128 | 2N467 | 2N2706 | 2SB222 | |
| 2G381 | | | | AC153 | | | | | |
| 2G382 | G | P | TX | AC117K | AC128 | 2N4106 | 2N1373 | 2SB370 | |
| 2G382 | | | | AC153 | | | | | |
| 2G383 | G | P | TX | ACY17 | | 2N1176 | | | |
| | | | | | | | | | |
| 2G384 | G | P | TX | ACY17 | | 2N1176 | | | |
| 2G385 | G | P | TX | ACY17 | | 2N1176 | | | |
| 2G386 | G | P | TX | ACY17 | | 2N1176 | | | |
| 2G387 | G | P | TX | ACY17 | | 2N1176 | | | |
| 2G395 | G | P | TX | ASY27 | | 2N1305 | | | |
| | | | | | | | | | |
| 2G396 | G | P | TX | ASY27 | | 2N1305 | | | |
| 2G397 | G | P | TX | ASY27 | | 2N1305 | | | |
| 2G398 | G | P | TX | ACY17 | | 2N1176 | | | |
| 2G401 | G | P | TX | AF106 | AF124 | 2N990 | | 2SA230 | |
| 2G401 | | | | AF185 | AF190 | | | | |
| | | | | | | | | | |
| 2G402 | G | P | TX | AF106 | AF185 | 2N990 | | 2SA230 | |
| 2G402 | | | | AF190 | | | | | |
| 2G403 | G | P | TX | AF124 | | 2N990 | | | |
| 2G524 | G | P | TX | ACY17 | | 2N1176 | | | |
| 2G525 | G | P | TX | ACY17 | | 2N1176 | | | |
| | | | | | | | | | |
| 2G526 | G | P | TX | ASY17 | ASY24K | 2N527 | 2N1176 | 2SB89 | |
| 2G526 | | | | ASY48 | ASY80 | | | | |
| 2G526 | | | | ASY81 | | | | | |
| 2G527 | G | P | TX | ACY17 | | 2N1176 | | | |
| 2G577 | G | P | TX | ACY17 | ACY24K | | | | |
| | | | | | | | | | |
| 2G577 | | | | ASY48 | ASY77 | | | | |
| 2G577 | | | | ACY81 | | | | | |
| 2G605 | G | P | TX | ASY27 | | 2N1305 | | | |
| 2G1024 | G | P | TX | ACY17 | ACY24K | 2N241 | 2N1176 | 2SB89 | |
| 2G1024 | | | | ASY48 | ASY77 | | | | |
| | | | | | | | | | |
| 2G1024 | | | | ASY81 | | | | | |
| 2G1025 | G | P | TX | ASY48 | ASY77 | 2N241 | 2N1176 | 2SB89 | |
| 2G1025 | | | | ASY81 | ACY17 | | | | |
| 2G1026 | G | P | TX | ASY48 | ACY24K | 2N241 | 2N1176 | 2SB89 | |
| 2G1026 | | | | ASY77 | ASY81 | | | | |
| | | | | | | | | | |
| 2G1026 | | | | ACY17 | | | | | |
| 2G1027 | G | P | TX | ACY17 | | 2N1176 | | | |
| 2N2X | S | N | TX | | | | | | |
| 2N24 | G | P | WE | | | | | | 01 |
| 2N24A | G | P | WE | ASY48 | ACY24K | | | 2SB89 | 01 |
| | | | | | | | | | |
| 2N24A | | | | ASY77 | ACZ10 | | | | 01 |
| 2N24A | | | | OC77 | | | | | 01 |
| 2N27 | G | N | WE | ASY29 | | 2N1304 | | | 01 |
| 2N28 | G | N | WE | ASY29 | | 2N1304 | | | 01 |
| 2N29 | G | N | WE | ASY29 | | 2N1304 | | | 01 |
| | | | | | | | | | |
| 2N34 | G | P | ET, NP, SR, St, UP | AC125 | AC126 | 2N406 | 2N1191 | 2SB101 | 01 |
| 2N34 | | | | AC122 | AC124 | 2N2429 | 2N2431 | | 01 |
| 2N34 | | | | AC151 | | | | | 01 |
| 2N34A | G | P | ET, NP, St, UP, CI | AC125 | AC126 | 2N406 | 2N2429 | | 01 |
| 2N34A | | | | AC132 | AC163 | 2N2431 | | | 01 |
| | | | | | | | | | |
| 2N34A | | | | AC132 | | | | | 01 |
| 2N35 | G | N | ET, NP, SR, St, CI | AC127 | AC176 | 2N2430 | | 2SD11 | 01 |
| 2N35 | | | | AC179 | | | | | 01 |
| 2N35A | G | N | | AC127 | AC130 | 2N2430 | | 2SD11 | 01 |
| 2N36 | G | P | ET, NP, St, UP, CI | AC126 | AC128 | 2N2429 | 2N2431 | 2SB101 | 01 |
| | | | | | | | | | |
| 2N36 | | | | AC151 | ACY17 | 2N1191 | 2N1176 | | 01 |
| 2N36 | | | | AC122 | AC125 | | | | 01 |
| 2N36 | | | | AC124 | | | | | 01 |
| 2N37 | G | P | ET, NP, St, UP | AC122 | AC125 | 2N406 | 2N1191 | 2SB220 | 01 |
| 2N37 | | | | AC126 | AC128 | 2N2429 | 2N2431 | | 01 |
| | | | | | | | | | |
| 2N37 | | | | AC132 | AC151IV | | | | 01 |
| 2N38 | G | P | ET, NP, St, UP | AC122 | AC124 | 2N406 | 2N1191 | 2SB220 | 01 |
| 2N38 | | | | AC125 | AC126 | 2N2429 | 2N2431 | | 01 |
| 2N38 | | | | AC128 | AC151 | | | | 01 |
| 2N38A | G | P | CB | AC122 | AC124 | 2N406 | 2N1191 | 2SB220 | 01 |
| | | | | | | | | | |
| 2N38A | | | | AC125 | AC126 | 2N2429 | 2N2431 | | 01 |
| 2N38A | | | | AC128 | AC151IV | | | | 01 |
| 2N39 | G | N | CB | AC125 | AC126 | 2N406 | | | |
| 2N40 | G | P | CB | AC125 | AC151 | 2N406 | 2N1191 | 2SB220 | |
| 2N40 | | | | AC162 | AC170 | | | | |

| TYPE | M/S | POL | MANUFAC | EUROPEAN | | AMERICAN | | JAPANESE | USE |
|------|-----|-----|---------|----------|--|----------|--|----------|-----|
| 2N41 | G | P | | AC122 | AC125 | 2N404 | 2N406 | 2SB219 | 01 |
| 2N41 | | | | AC151 | AC163 | 2N1190 | 2N2447 | 2SB459 | 01 |
| 2N41 | | | | OC58 | | | | | 01 |
| 2N42 | G | P | CB | AC122 | AC125 | 2N404 | 2N1190 | 2SB220 | |
| 2N42 | | | | AC151 | AC163 | 2N2447 | | 2SB459 | |
| 2N42 | | | | OC70 | | | | | |
| 2N43 | G | P | ES, ET, NP, SR, St | AC125 | AC128 | 2N525 | 2N2706 | 2SB225 | 01 |
| 2N43 | | | | AC131/20 | AC152 | | | | 01 |
| 2N43A | G | P | ES, ET, NP, SR, St | AC117 | AC128 | 2N525 | 2N2706 | 2SB225 | 01 |
| 2N43A | | | | AC131/30 | AC152 | | | | 01 |
| 2N43A | | | | AC153 | | | | | 01 |
| 2N44 | G | P | ET, NP, SS, St, UP | AC124 | AC125 | 2N524 | 2N2431 | 2SB224 | 01 |
| 2N44 | | | | AC128 | AC131/30 | 2N2706 | | | 01 |
| 2N44 | | | | AC152 | | | | | 01 |
| 2N44A | G | P | ET, NP, SR, St, UP | ACY117 | AC117 | 2N1176 | | 2SB33 | 01 |
| 2N44A | | | | AC124 | AC128 | | | | 01 |
| 2N45 | G | P | ET, NP, St, UP | AC125 | AC126 | 2N406 | 2N404 | 2SB224 | 01 |
| 2N45 | | | | AC128 | AC131/30 | 2N524 | | | 01 |
| 2N45 | | | | AC151 | | | | | 01 |
| 2N45A | G | P | ET, NP, St, UP | | | | | | 01 |
| 2N46 | G | P | | AC123 | AC125 | 2N406 | | 2SB101 | 01 |
| 2N46 | | | | AC151 | OC58 | | | | 01 |
| 2N47 | G | P | PC | AC122 | AC123 | 2N404 | 2N406 | 2SB32 | 01 |
| 2N47 | | | | AC125 | AC151IV | 2N1191 | | | 01 |
| 2N47 | | | | OC58 | | | | | 01 |
| 2N48 | G | P | PC | AC122 | AC123 | 2N404 | 2N406 | 2SB32 | 01 |
| 2N48 | | | | AC125 | AC126 | 2N1191 | 2N2431 | | 01 |
| 2N48 | | | | AC151 | | | | | 01 |
| 2N49 | G | P | PC | AC122 | AC123 | 2N404 | 2N406 | 2SB32 | 01 |
| 2N49 | | | | AC126 | AC151IV | 2N1191 | 2N2431 | | 01 |
| 2N50 | G | P | CV | AC122 | AC125 | 2N1191 | 2N404 | | 10 |
| 2N50 | | | | AC151 | | | | | 10 |
| 2N51 | G | P | CV | AC117 | AC122 | 2N404 | 2N1191 | 2SB222 | 10 |
| 2N51 | | | | AC125 | AC128 | | | | 10 |
| 2N51 | | | | AC151 | AC153 | | | | 10 |
| 2N52 | G | P | CV | AC122 | AC151 | 2N404 | 2N1191 | 2SB222 | 10 |
| 2N53 | G | P | CV | AC151 | | 2N404 | 2N1191 | | 10 |
| 2N54 | G | P | W | AC122 | AC124 | 2N1176 | 2N1191 | 2SB224 | 01 |
| 2N54 | | | | AC126 | AC128 | 2N2429 | 2N2431 | | 01 |
| 2N54 | | | | AC131 | AC151 | | | | 01 |
| 2N54 | | | | ACY17 | | | | | 01 |
| 2N55 | G | P | W | AC122 | AC125 | 2N404 | 2N1176 | 2SB224 | 01 |
| 2N55 | | | | AC124 | AC128 | 2N1191 | | | 01 |
| 2N55 | | | | AC131 | AC151IV | | | | 01 |
| 2N55 | | | | ACY17 | | | | | 01 |
| 2N56 | G | P | W | AC122 | AC125 | 2N404 | 2N1176 | 2SB224 | 01 |
| 2N56 | | | | AC128 | AC131 | 2N1191 | | | 01 |
| 2N59 | G | P | ET, NP, St, UP | (ASY48VI) | AC128 | 2N404 | 2N1176 | 2SB222 | 01 |
| 2N59 | | | | AC122 | AC124 | | | | 01 |
| 2N59 | | | | AC151IV | AC152 | | | | 01 |
| 2N59A | G | P | ET, NP, St, UP | (ASY48VI) | AC128 | 2N1176 | 2N2431 | | 01 |
| 2N59A | | | | ACY17 | | | | | 01 |
| 2N59B | G | P | ET, NP, St, UP | (ASY48VI) | ACY17 | 2N1176 | 2N2431 | | 01 |
| 2N59B | | | | AC128 | | | | | 01 |
| 2N59C | G | P | ET, NP, St, UP | (ASY48VI) | AC122/30 | 2N1193 | 2N2431 | 2SB32 | 01 |
| 2N59C | | | | AC125 | AC151IV | 2N1176 | | | 01 |
| 2N59C | | | | AC126 | AC122 | | | | 01 |
| 2N59C | | | | AC163 | | | | | 01 |
| 2N60 | G | P | ET, NP, St, UP | (ASY48V) | AC128 | 2N404 | 2N1176 | 2SB222 | 01 |
| 2N60 | | | | AC153 | ACY17 | 2N1193 | 2N2431 | | 01 |
| 2N60A | G | P | ET, NP, St, UP | (ASY48V) | AC122 | 2N61A | 2N1176 | 2SA219 | 01 |
| 2N60A | | | | AC126 | AC128 | 2N1193 | | 2SB222 | 01 |
| 2N60A | | | | AC151IV | AC153 | | | | 01 |
| 2N60A | | | | ACY17 | ACY33 | | | | 01 |
| 2N60B | G | P | ET, NP, St, UP | (ASY48V) | AC122 | 2N1176 | 2N1193 | 2SA219 | 01 |
| 2N60B | | | | AC122/30 | AC126 | | | | 01 |
| 2N60B | | | | AC151IV | ACY17 | | | | 01 |
| 2N60C | G | P | ET, NP, St, UP | (ASY48V) | ACY17 | 2N59C | 2N1176 | | 01 |
| 2N61 | G | P | ET, NP, St, UP | (ASY48IV) | AC126 | 2N1192 | 2N1176 | | 01 |
| 2N61 | | | | AC128 | AC131 | 2N2431 | | | 01 |
| 2N61 | | | | AC122 | AC151IV | | | | 01 |
| 2N61 | | | | ACY17 | | | | | 01 |
| 2N61A | G | P | ET, NP, St, UP | (ASY48IV) | AC126 | 2N60 | 2N1192 | 2SB224 | 01 |
| 2N61A | | | | AC131/30 | AC151IV | 2N524 | 2N1176 | | 01 |
| 2N61A | | | | ACY17 | AC122 | | | | 01 |

| TYPE | M/S | POL | MANUFAC | EUROPEAN | | AMERICAN | | JAPANESE | USE |
|---|---|---|---|---|---|---|---|---|---|
| 2N61A | G | P | ET, NP, St, UP | AC152 | ACY33 | | | | 01 |
| 2N61B | | | | (ASY48IV) | AC122 | 2N60 | 2N61 | 2SB220 | 01 |
| 2N61B | | | | AC125 | AC151IV | 2N1176 | 2N1192 | | 01 |
| 2N61B | | | | AC131/30 | AC163 | | | | 01 |
| 2N61B | | | | ACY17 | ACY33 | | | | 01 |
| | | | | | | | | | |
| 2N61C | G | P | ET, NP, St, UP | (ASY48IV) | AC122 | 2N60 | 2N61 | 2SB220 | 01 |
| 2N61C | | | | AC125 | AC131/30 | 2N1176 | 2N1192 | | 01 |
| 2N61C | | | | AC151IV | ACY17 | | | | 01 |
| 2N61C | | | | AC163 | ACY32 | | | | 01 |
| 2N62 | G | P | PC | AC124 | AC125 | 2N109 | 2N403 | 2SB224 | 01 |
| | | | | | | | | | |
| 2N62 | | | | AC128 | AC131/30 | 2N406 | 2N1191 | | 01 |
| 2N62 | | | | AC151IV | | 2N2431 | | | 01 |
| 2N63 | G | P | ET, NP, St, UP | AC122 | AC125 | 2N406 | 2N1191 | 2SB220 | 01 |
| 2N63 | | | | AC126 | AC128 | 2N2429 | | | 01 |
| 2N63 | | | | AC132 | AC151IV | | | | 01 |
| | | | | | | | | | |
| 2N64 | G | P | ET, NP, St, UP | AC122 | AC124 | 2N406 | 2N1191 | HJ15 | 01 |
| 2N64 | | | | AC125 | AC125 | 2N2429 | | | 01 |
| 2N64 | | | | AC128 | AC151IV | | | | 01 |
| 2N65 | G | P | ET, NP, St, UP | AC122 | AC125 | 2N406 | 2N1193 | HJ15 | 01 |
| 2N65 | | | | AC126 | AC128 | 2N2429 | | | 01 |
| | | | | | | | | | |
| 2N65 | | | | AC151IV | AV163 | | | | 01 |
| 2N66 | G | P | | AD139 | AD148 | 2N643 | 2N2835 | | 06 |
| 2N66 | | | | AD155 | AD162 | T13027 | | | 06 |
| 2N67 | G | P | | AD162 | | 2N2835 | | | 10 |
| 2N68 | G | P | St, CI, SY | AC128 | AD139 | 2N156 | 2N2706 | 2SB240 | 06 |
| | | | | | | | | | |
| 2N68 | | | | AD155 | AD162 | T13027 | | | 06 |
| 2N68 | | | | OD603 | | | | | 06 |
| 2N68/13 | G | P | St, CI, GP, SZ | | | TI156L | | | 06 |
| 2N69 | G | P | | AC122 | AC125 | 2N1190 | | | |
| 2N69 | | | | AC151 | ACY23 | | | | |
| | | | | | | | | | |
| 2N69 | | | | ACZ10 | | | | | |
| 2N71 | G | P | | AC122 | AC125 | 2N2835 | 2N404 | 2SB240 | 06 |
| 2N71 | | | | AC151 | ACY23 | 2N1190 | | | 06 |
| 2N71 | | | | ACZ10 | AD162 | | | | 06 |
| 2N72 | G | P | | AC123 | AC125 | 2N404 | 2N1190 | 2SB240 | 10 |
| | | | | | | | | | |
| 2N72 | | | | AC151 | ACY23 | | | | 10 |
| 2N72 | | | | ACZ10 | | | | | 10 |
| 2N73 | G | P | | AC122 | AC125 | 2N406 | 2N1190 | | 12 |
| 2N73 | | | | AC151 | ACY23 | 2N1614 | | | 12 |
| 2N73 | | | | ACZ10 | | | | | 12 |
| | | | | | | | | | |
| 2N74 | G | P | | AC122 | AC125 | 2N406 | 2N1190 | | 10 |
| 2N74 | | | | AC151 | ACY23 | 2N1614 | | | 10 |
| 2N74 | | | | ACZ10 | | | | | 10 |
| 2N75 | G | P | | AC125 | AC151 | 2N406 | 2N1190 | | 10 |
| 2N75 | | | | ACY24K | ACZ10 | 2N1614 | | | 10 |
| | | | | | | | | | |
| 2N76 | G | P | GE | AC125 | AC126 | 2N322 | 2N406 | 2SB220 | 01 |
| 2N76 | | | | AC151 | AC163 | 2N319 | 2N1191 | | 01 |
| 2N76 | | | | AC170 | | 2N2429 | | | 01 |
| 2N77 | G | P | ET, NP, St, UP, CI | AC122 | AC126 | 2N465 | 2N565 | 2SB101 | 01 |
| 2N77 | | | | AC163 | ACY29 | 2N1191 | 2N2431 | | 01 |
| | | | | | | | | | |
| 2N77 | | | | OC58 | | | | | 01 |
| 2N78 | G | N | ET, NP, UP, CI | ASY29 | ASY75 | 2N445 | 2N1302 | | 01 |
| 2N78 | | | | | | 2N1304 | | | 01 |
| 2N78A | G | N | ET, UP, CI | ASY29 | | 2N1304 | | | 01 |
| 2N79 | G | P | RC | AC125 | AC126 | 2N406 | 2N1191 | HJ15 | 01 |
| | | | | | | | | | |
| 2N79 | | | | AC128 | AC163 | 2N2429 | | | 01 |
| 2N79 | | | | AC173 | AC171 | | | | 01 |
| 2N80 | G | P | CB | AC122 | AC125 | 2N406 | 2N508 | HJ15 | 01 |
| 2N80 | | | | AC126 | AC128 | 2N2429 | | | 01 |
| 2N80 | | | | AC163 | AC171 | | | | 01 |
| | | | | | | | | | |
| 2N80 | | | | AC173 | | | | | 01 |
| 2N81 | G | P | GE | AC122 | AC125 | 2N406 | 2N1191 | 2SB220 | 01 |
| 2N81 | | | | AC126 | AC128 | 2N2429 | | | 01 |
| 2N81 | | | | AC163 | AC171 | | | | 01 |
| 2N81 | | | | AC173 | | | | | 01 |
| | | | | | | | | | |
| 2N82 | G | P | CB | AC122 | AC125 | 2N406 | 2N1191 | 2SB220 | 01 |
| 2N82 | | | | AC126 | AC128 | 2N2429 | | | 01 |
| 2N82 | | | | AC163 | AC171 | | | | 01 |
| 2N82 | | | | AC173 | | | | | 01 |
| 2N83 | G | P | TR | AD148V | A5Z15 | LT5036 | 2N1533 | 2SB240 | |
| | | | | | | | | | |
| 2N83 | | | | OC30 | OD603 | | | | |
| 2N83 | | | | CTP1104 | | | | | |
| 2N83A | G | P | TR | AD148V | ASZ15 | 2N1533 | | 2SB240 | |
| 2N83A | | | | OC30 | OD603 | | | | |
| 2N84 | G | P | TR | AC124 | AC128K | 2N109 | 2N1533 | 2SB240 | |

| TYPE | M/S | POL | MANUFAC | EUROPEAN | | AMERICAN | | JAPANESE | USE |
|------|-----|-----|---------|----------|---|----------|---|----------|-----|
| 2N84 | | | | AC153 | ASZ16 | 2N4106 | | | |
| 2N84 | | | | OC30 | OD603 | | | | |
| 2N85 | G | P | TR | AC124 | AC126 | 2N109 | 2N403 | | |
| 2N85 | | | | AC128 | AC131/30 | 2N1924 | 2N2429 | | |
| 2N85 | | | | AC132 | AC152 | | | | |
| 2N86 | G | P | TR | AC124R | AC126 | 2N403 | 2N2429 | | |
| 2N86 | | | | AC128 | AC132 | 2N4106 | | | |
| 2N86 | | | | AC152 | AC153 | | | | |
| 2N87 | G | P | TR | AC124R | AC128 | 2N403 | 2N2431 | | |
| 2N87 | | | | AC132 | AC152 | 2N4106 | | | |
| 2N87 | | | | AC153 | | | | | |
| 2N88 | G | P | | AC129v | OC58 | 2N109 | 2N402 | | |
| 2N88 | | | | AFY69 | OC56 | | | | |
| 2N89 | G | P | | AC129v | OC58 | 2N217 | 2N402 | | |
| 2N89 | | | | OC89 | | | | | |
| 2N90 | G | P | | OC66 | | 2N217 | 2N402 | | |
| 2N93 | G | P | | AC162 | AC170 | | | 2SA219 | |
| 2N93 | | | | AC125 | AC173 | | | | |
| 2N93 | | | | AC151 | AC153 | | | | |
| 2N94 | G | P | ET, NP, UP | OC140 | ASY74 | 2N1304 | | | 02 |
| 2N94A | G | N | ET, NP | ASY29 | | 2N1304 | | | 02 |
| 2N94A | | | | ASY74 | ASY29 | | | | 02 |
| 2N94A | | | | OC140 | | | | | 02 |
| 2N95 | G | P | NP, UP | AC176 | AC178 | LT5210 | 2N2430 | 2SB240 | 06 |
| 2N96 | G | P | RC | AC163 | AC171 | 2N331 | 2N403 | 2SB220 | 01 |
| 2N96 | | | | AC128 | AC173 | 2N406 | | | 01 |
| 2N96 | | | | AC125 | AC151 | | | | 01 |
| 2N97 | G | N | ET, NP, UP, II | (AC127) | ASY28 | 2N144 | 2N1302 | | 01 |
| 2N97 | | | | ASY29 | | 2N1304 | | | 01 |
| 2N97A | G | N | BG | AC127 | AC179 | 2N2430 | 2N169A | | 01 |
| 2N97A | | | | ASY29 | | 2N438 | 2N1304 | | 01 |
| 2N98 | G | N | ET, NP, UP | (AC127) | ASY73 | 2N1304 | | 2SA155 | 01 |
| 2N98 | | | | ASY29 | | | | | 01 |
| 2N98A | G | N | BG | ASY73 | ASY29 | 2N169A | 2N444 | | 01 |
| 2N98A | | | | | | 2N1304 | | | 01 |
| 2N99 | G | N | ET, NP | ASY73 | ASY29 | 2N169A | 2N1306 | | 01 |
| 2N99 | | | | | | 2N1304 | | | 01 |
| 2N100 | G | N | BG | ASY75 | ASY73 | 2N446 | 2N1306 | | 01 |
| 2N100 | | | | ACY29 | | 2N1304 | | | 01 |
| 2N101 | G | P | SY | AD155 | AD139 | 2N68 | 2N307 | 2SB240 | 06 |
| 2N101 | | | | OC30 | OD603 | | | | 06 |
| 2N101 | | | | AC188K | | | | | 06 |
| 2N101/13 | G | P | St, GP, SZ | | | | | | |
| 2N102 | G | N | SY | ASY28 | AC187K | 2N1302 | LT5210 | | 06 |
| 2N102/13 | G | N | St, GP, SZ | | | | | | |
| 2N103 | G | N | ET, NP, UP | (AC127) | ASY28 | 2N1302 | 2N1304 | | 01 |
| 2N103 | | | | ASY29 | GT35 | | | | 01 |
| 2N104 | G | P | ET, NP, UP | (AC151IV) | AC126 | 2N650 | 2N2429 | 2S32 | 01 |
| 2N104 | | | | AC153 | AC124R | 2N4106 | 2N612 | | 01 |
| 2N104 | | | | AC128 | AC122 | 2N406 | | | 01 |
| 2N104 | | | | AC125 | | | | | 01 |
| 2N105 | G | P | ET, NP, St, UP | (AC151IV) | OC58 | 2N2429 | 2N1191 | 2SB220 | 01 |
| 2N105 | | | | AC126 | AC162 | 2N321 | 2N402 | | 01 |
| 2N105 | | | | AC107N | AC122 | | | | 01 |
| 2N105 | | | | AC125 | AC163 | | | | 01 |
| 2N106 | G | P | ET, NP, St, UP | (AC151IV) | AC126 | 2N2429 | 2N406 | 2S32 | 01 |
| 2N106 | | | | AC128 | AC153 | 2N1191 | 2N4106 | | 01 |
| 2N106 | | | | AC124R | AC125 | | | | 01 |
| 2N106 | | | | OC72 | | | | | 01 |
| 2N107 | G | P | ET, NP, SR, SS, St | (AC151IV) | AC126 | 2N2429 | 2N2431 | 2SB170 | 01 |
| 2N107 | | | | AC128 | AC162 | 2N406 | 2N464 | | 01 |
| 2N107 | | | | AC170 | AC122 | 2N402 | | | 01 |
| 2N107 | | | | AC125 | | | | | 01 |
| 2N108 | G | P | ET, NP, St, UP | (AC151IV) | AC126 | 2N2429 | 2N2431 | 2SB170 | 01 |
| 2N108 | | | | AC128 | AC162 | 2N322 | 2N406 | | 01 |
| 2N108 | | | | AC170 | AC125 | | | | 01 |
| 2N108 | | | | AC122 | | | | | 01 |
| 2N109 | G | P | ET, NP, St, UP, SR | (ACY151VI) | AC128 | 2N2431 | 2N1192 | 2B37 | 01 |
| 2N109 | | | | AC151VI | AC153K | 2N185 | 2N187A | | 01 |
| 2N109 | | | | AC117K | AC132 | 2N2706 | | | 01 |
| 2N110 | G | P | WE | AC163 | AC171 | 2N2429 | | 2SB383 | 10 |
| 2N110 | | | | AC126 | | | | | 10 |
| 2N111 | G | P | ET, NP, St, UP | AF185 | AF106 | 2N271 | 2N614 | HJ23D | 02 |
| 2N111 | | | | AF101 | OC45 | 2N1305 | | 2SA206 | 02 |
| 2N111 | | | | OC612 | ACY27 | | | | 02 |

| TYPE | M/S | POL | MANUFAC | EUROPEAN | | AMERICAN | | JAPANESE | USE |
|---|---|---|---|---|---|---|---|---|---|
| 2N111A | G | P | ET, NP, UP | AF185 | ASY26 | 2N218 | 2N1305 | | 02 |
| 2N111A | | | | ASY27 | | | | | 02 |
| 2N112 | G | P | ET, NP, UP | AF185 | AF126 | 2N450 | 2N579 | 2SA206 | 02 |
| 2N112 | | | | AF137 | ASY26 | 2N1305 | | | 02 |
| 2N112 | | | | OC45 | ASY27 | | | | 02 |
| 2N112A | G | P | ET, NP, UP | AF185 | ASY26 | 2N218 | 2N1305 | | 02 |
| 2N112A | | | | ASY27 | | | | | 02 |
| 2N113 | G | P | ET, NP, UP | AF185 | AF127 | 2N1305 | | HJ23D | 02 |
| 2N113 | | | | AF115 | ASY27 | | | | 02 |
| 2N113 | | | | AF106 | AF190 | | | | 02 |
| 2N113 | | | | A101 | | | | | 02 |
| 2N114 | G | P | ET, NP, UP | AF185 | AF126 | 2N140 | 2N1309 | | 02 |
| 2N114 | | | | AF137 | OC44 | 2N1305 | | | 02 |
| 2N114 | | | | ASY27 | | | | | 02 |
| 2N115 | G | P | AM | AD149 | AD130III | TI3029 | 2N175 | 2SB221 | 16 |
| 2N115 | | | | AD130IV | OC26 | 2N270 | | | 16 |
| 2N115 | | | | AD179 | AD140 | | | | 16 |
| 2N116 | G | P | | AC129v | OC57 | 2N133A | 2N175 | 2SB39 | |
| 2N116 | | | | OC622 | | | | | |
| 2N117 | S | N | TX, ET, NP, SQ, UP | BC107 | | 2N332 | A157 | | 13 |
| 2N118 | S | N | TX, ET, NP, SQ, UP | BD130 | AM291 | 2N3055 | 2N118A | | 13 |
| 2N118 | | | | BDX10 | BDY10 | 2N119 | A157 | | 13 |
| 2N118 | | | | BC107 | | | | | 13 |
| 2N118A | S | N | TX, ET, NP, SQ | BD130 | AM291 | 2N3055 | A157 | | 13 |
| 2N118A | | | | BDX10 | BDY10 | | | | 13 |
| 2N118A | | | | BC107 | | | | | 13 |
| 2N119 | S | N | TX, ET, NP, SQ | BD130 | AM291 | 2N3055 | 2N118 | | 13 |
| 2N119 | | | | BDX10 | BDY10 | A157 | | | 13 |
| 2N119 | | | | BC107 | | | | | 13 |
| 2N120 | S | N | TX, ET, NP, SQ | BDY10 | BD130 | 2N3055 | 2N118 | | 13 |
| 2N120 | | | | AM291 | BDX10 | A157 | | | 02 |
| 2N120 | | | | BC107 | | | | | 02 |
| 2N122 | S | N | NP, SQ, UP | BSW66 | | 2N1893 | | | 06 |
| 2N123 | G | P | ET, ID, NP, St, UP | AF127 | AF106 | 2N426 | 2N1303 | HJ23D | 13 |
| 2N123 | | | | AF101 | ASY27 | 2N1305 | | | 13 |
| 2N123 | | | | OC44 | | | | | 13 |
| 2N124 | G | N | ET, NP, UP | (AC127) | ASY73 | 2N445 | 2N1302 | | 10 |
| 2N124 | | | | ASY29 | | 2N1304 | | | 10 |
| 2N125 | G | N | ET, NP, UP | (AC127) | ASY74 | 2N585 | 2N1304 | | 10 |
| 2N125 | | | | ASY29 | | | | | 10 |
| 2N126 | G | N | ET, NP, UP | (AC127) | ASY74 | 2N439 | 2N585 | | 10 |
| 2N126 | | | | ASY29 | | 2N1304 | | | 10 |
| 2N127 | G | N | TX | ASY28 | | 2N440 | 2N1304 | | 10 |
| 2N128 | G | P | SM, SP, SQ | AF125 | AF126 | 2N274 | 2N604 | | 02 |
| 2N128 | | | | AF135 | AF124 | 2N990 | | | 02 |
| 2N129 | G | P | PC | AF125 | AF135 | 2N373 | 2N603 | | 02 |
| 2N129 | | | | AF124 | | 2N990 | | | 02 |
| 2N130 | G | P | ET, NP, UP | AC162 | AC131 | 2N1191 | 2N1924 | 2SB224 | 01 |
| 2N130 | | | | AC128 | AC125 | 2N406 | 2N613 | | 01 |
| 2N130 | | | | AC152 | | 2N1056 | | | 01 |
| 2N130A | G | P | ET, NP, UP | AC162 | AC131 | 2N650 | 2N1924 | 2SB224 | 01 |
| 2N130A | | | | AC128 | AC125 | 2N406 | 2N402 | | 01 |
| 2N130A | | | | AC152 | | 2N1413 | | | 01 |
| 2N131 | G | P | ET, NP, UP | AC153 | AC122 | 2N1192 | 2N568 | 2SB103 | 01 |
| 2N131 | | | | AC125 | AC117 | 2N569 | 2N406 | | 01 |
| 2N131 | | | | | | 2N569 | 2N406 | | 01 |
| 2N131A | G | P | ET, NP, UP | AC153 | AC122 | 2N651 | 2N568 | 2SB103 | 01 |
| 2N131A | | | | AC125 | | 2N406 | | | 01 |
| 2N132 | G | P | ET, NP, UP | AC126 | AC151 | 2N2429 | 2N1192 | 2SB103 | 01 |
| 2N132 | | | | AC123 | AC125 | 2N406 | 2N1190 | | 01 |
| 2N132 | | | | AC124 | AC128 | 2N466 | | | 01 |
| 2N132 | | | | AC152 | | | | | 01 |
| 2N132A | G | P | ET, NP, UP | AC128 | AC151 | 2N2431 | 2N651 | 2SB32 | 01 |
| 2N132A | | | | AC122 | AC163 | 2N1190 | 2N641 | | 01 |
| 2N132A | | | | AC125 | | 2N406 | | | 01 |
| 2N133 | G | P | ET, NP, UP | AC151 | AC122 | 2N1192 | 2N1190 | | 01 |
| 2N133 | | | | AC117 | AC128 | 2N175 | 2N406 | | 01 |
| 2N133 | | | | AC153 | AC125 | | | | 01 |
| 2N133A | G | P | ET, NP, UP | AC128 | OC57 | 2N651 | 2N175 | | 01 |
| 2N133A | | | | OC622 | AC125 | 2N406 | | | 01 |
| 2N135 | G | P | ET, NP, UP | AF185 | AF126 | 2N139 | 2N1305 | | 02 |
| 2N135 | | | | AFY15 | ASY27 | | | | 02 |
| 2N135 | | | | OC390 | | | | | 02 |
| 2N136 | G | P | ET, NP, UP | AF127 | AF101 | 2N1305 | | | 02 |
| 2N136 | | | | AF106 | AF190 | | | | 02 |

| TYPE | M/S | POL | MANUFAC | EUROPEAN | | AMERICAN | | JAPANESE | USE |
|------|-----|-----|---------|----------|--|----------|--|----------|-----|
| 2N136 | | | | OC45 | ASY27 | | | | 02 |
| 2N137 | G | P | ET, NP, UP | AF185 | AF127 | 2N1305 | | | 02 |
| 2N137 | | | | AF101 | AF106 | | | | 02 |
| 2N137 | | | | AF190 | ASY27 | | | | 02 |
| 2N138 | G | P | ET, NP, UP | AC126 | AC153 | 2N2429 | 2N4106 | | 01 |
| 2N138 | | | | AC117 | AC128 | 2N406 | 2N2706 | | 01 |
| 2N138A | G | P | RY | AC128 | AC153 | 2N2431 | 2N4106 | 2SB222 | 01 |
| 2N138A | | | | AC124 | AC152 | 2N1008 | 2N1128 | | 01 |
| 2N138A | | | | AC125 | | 2N406 | | | 01 |
| 2N138B | G | P | RY | AC128 | AC153 | 2N2431 | 2N4106 | 2SA219 | 01 |
| 2N138B | | | | AC117 | OC318 | 2N270 | 2N406 | | 01 |
| 2N138B | | | | AC125 | | | | | 01 |
| 2N139 | G | P | ET, NP, UP | AF185 | AF127 | 2N2614 | | 2S36 | 01 |
| 2N139 | | | | AF106 | OC44N | | | | 01 |
| 2N139 | | | | AFY15 | AF190 | | | | 01 |
| 2N139 | | | | AF101 | | | | | 01 |
| 2N140 | G | P | ET, NP | AF185 | AF127 | 2N2614 | | 2SA35 | 01 |
| 2N140 | | | | AFY15 | OC44N | | | | 01 |
| 2N140 | | | | AF117 | SFT354 | | | | 01 |
| 2N141 | G | P | SY | AD148V | AD139 | 2N1038 | 2N1172 | 2SB240 | 06 |
| 2N141 | | | | OC30 | OD603 | | | | 06 |
| 2N141/13 | G | P | St | AD162 | | 2N2835 | | | 06 |
| 2N142 | G | N | SY | | | 2N144 | | | 06 |
| 2N142/13 | G | N | St | AD161 | | 2N4077 | | | 06 |
| 2N143 | G | P | SY | OC30 | OD603 | 2N141 | 2N1038 | 2SB240 | 06 |
| 2N143 | | | | AD162 | | | | | 06 |
| 2N143/13 | G | P | St | | | | | | 06 |
| 2N144 | G | N | SY | | | | | | 06 |
| 2N144/13 | G | N | St | | | | | | 06 |
| 2N145 | G | N | ET, NP, UP | (AC127) | ASY73 | 2N1302 | 2N1304 | | 02 |
| 2N145 | | | | ASY29 | | | | | 02 |
| 2N146 | G | N | ET, NP | (AC127) | AUY19 | 2N1302 | 2N1304 | | 02 |
| 2N146 | | | | ASY74 | ASY29 | | | | 02 |
| 2N147 | G | N | ET, ME, NP | (AC127) | AUY19 | 2N1302 | 2N1304 | | 02 |
| 2N147 | | | | ASY29 | | | | | 02 |
| 2N148 | G | N | St, TX | ASY29 | | 2N1302 | 2N1304 | | 02 |
| 2N148A | G | N | TX | ASY29 | | 2N1304 | | | 02 |
| 2N155 | G | P | SD, ST, ET, ES, NP | AD130III | AD148 | 2N176 | 2N301 | 2SB107 | 06 |
| 2N155 | | | | AD149 | OC26 | TI3027 | 2N1536 | | 06 |
| 2N155 | | | | OC30 | ASZ16 | | | | 06 |
| 2N156 | G | P | ST, SQ | (AD131III) | AD149 | 2N2836 | 2N176 | 2SB107 | 06 |
| 2N156 | | | | OC26 | OC30 | TI3027 | 2N1536 | | 06 |
| 2N156 | | | | ASZ16 | | | | | 06 |
| 2N157 | G | P | GB | AD150IV | AD138 | 2N1531 | 2N1022A | 2SB107 | 06 |
| 2N157 | | | | OC26 | OC30 | 2N1038 | 2N1536 | | 06 |
| 2N157A | G | P | CB | OD603 | ASZ16 | 2N1532 | 2N1014 | | 06 |
| 2N157A | | | | OC26 | OC30 | 2N1533 | | | 06 |
| 2N157A | | | | OD603 | ASZ15 | | | | 06 |
| 2N158 | G | P | ST, SQ, St | (AD132III) | AD166 | 2N2139 | TI156 | | 06 |
| 2N158 | | | | AD149 | OC26 | TI3017 | 2N1536 | | 06 |
| 2N158 | | | | OC30 | ASZ15 | | | | 06 |
| 2N158A | G | P | ES, St | ASZ16 | ASZ15 | 2N2141 | TI3027 | | 06 |
| 2N158A | | | | | | 2N1533 | | | 06 |
| 2N160 | S | N | ET, NP, SM, SQ, UP | (BC107A) | BC107 | 2N160A | A157 | | |
| 2N160A | S | N | ET, NP, SM, SQ | (BC107A) | BC107 | 2N161A | A157 | | 01 |
| 2N161 | S | N | ET, NP, SM, SQ | (BC107A) | BC107 | 2N161A | A157 | | 01 |
| 2N161A | S | N | ET, NP, SM, SQ | (BC107A) | BC107 | 2N163A | A157 | | 01 |
| 2N162 | S | N | ET, NP, UP | (BC107A) | BC107 | 2N162A | A157 | | 01 |
| 2N162A | S | N | ET, NP, UP | (BC107A) | BC107 | 2N163A | A157 | | 01 |
| 2N163 | S | N | ET, NP, SM, UP | (BC107A) | BC107 | 2N163A | A157 | | 01 |
| 2N163A | S | N | ET, NP, SM | (BC107A) | BC107 | 2N162A | A157 | | 01 |
| 2N164 | G | N | ET | (AC127) | | 2N165 | | | |
| 2N164A | G | N | ET | (AC127) | ASY29 | 2N1304 | | | |
| 2N165 | G | N | ET | (AC127) | ASY73 | 2N1304 | | | |
| 2N165 | | | | ASY29 | ASY74 | | | | |
| 2N166 | G | N | ET | (AC127) | | | | | 02 |
| 2N167 | G | N | ET | (AC127) | ASY29 | 2N1090 | 2N1306 | | 02 |
| 2N167 | | | | | | 2N1304 | | | 02 |
| 2N167A | G | N | ET | (AC127) | ASY29 | 2N1304 | | | 13 |
| 2N168 | G | N | ET | (AC127) | ASY73 | 2N1306 | 2N1304 | HJ23D | 02 |
| 2N168 | | | | ASY29 | | | | | 02 |
| 2N168A | G | N | ET | (AC127) | ASY75 | 2N1304 | | | 02 |
| 2N168A | | | | ASY28 | | | | | 02 |
| 2N169 | G | N | ET, SR | AC127 | ASY29 | 2N1308 | 2N1304 | 2S36 | 02 |
| 2N169 | | | | ASY75 | | | | | 02 |

| TYPE | M/S | POL | MANUFAC | EUROPEAN | | AMERICAN | | JAPANESE | USE |
|---|---|---|---|---|---|---|---|---|---|
| 2N169A | G | N | ET, SR | (AC127) | ASY75 | 2N1304 | | 2S36 | 01 |
| 2N169A | | | | ASY29 | | | | | 01 |
| 2N170 | G | N | ET, SA | (AC127) | ASY74 | 2N1308 | 2N1304 | 2SA206 | 02 |
| 2N170 | | | | ASY29 | | | | | 02 |
| 2N172 | G | N | ET | (AC127) | ASY74 | 2N1308 | 2N1304 | 2SA206 | 02 |
| 2N172 | | | | ASY29 | | | | | 02 |
| 2N173 | G | P | DD, MO | AUY21IV | AD138/50 | TI3027 | 2N1100 | | 06 |
| 2N173 | | | | ADZ11 | ASZ16 | | | | 06 |
| 2N173 | | | | ADZ12 | | | | | 06 |
| 2N174 | G | P | DD, MO | ADZ12 | | TI3027 | 2N1100 | | 16 |
| 2N174A | G | P | DD | ADZ12 | | TI3027 | 2N1100 | | 16 |
| 2N175 | G | P | ET | AC163 | AC122g | 2N1192 | 2N406 | 2SB221 | |
| 2N175 | | | | AC122 | OC16 | | | | |
| 2N175 | | | | AC125 | | | | | |
| 2N176 | G | P | MO, SR, ET | (AD131IV) | AD149 | 2N2836 | TI3027 | 2SB107 | 02 |
| 2N176 | | | | AC166 | OC30 | 2N1536 | | | 02 |
| 2N176 | | | | OD603 | ASZ16 | | | | 02 |
| 2N178 | G | P | MO, ET | (AD149IV) | AD166 | TI3027 | 2N1536 | 2SB107 | 01 |
| 2N178 | | | | AD149 | ADZ16 | | | | 01 |
| 2N179 | G | P | MO | | | 2N176 | | | 01 |
| 2N180 | G | P | ET | AC128 | AC153 | 2N2431 | 2N1192 | 2S32 | 01 |
| 2N180 | | | | AC117 | AC132 | 2N217 | 2N406 | | 01 |
| 2N181 | G | P | ET | AC128 | AC162 | 2N2431 | 2N1192 | 2SB222 | 01 |
| 2N181 | | | | AC131 | AC132 | 2N270 | 2N406 | | 01 |
| 2N181 | | | | AC152 | | | | | 01 |
| 2N182 | G | N | ET | ASY74 | ASY73 | 2N1302 | 2N1304 | | 10 |
| 2N182 | | | | ASY29 | | | | | 10 |
| 2N183 | G | N | ET | ASY74 | ASY29 | 2N1302 | 2N1304 | | 10 |
| 2N184 | G | N | ET | ASY75 | ASY29 | 2N1306 | 2N1304 | | 10 |
| 2N184 | | | | | | 2N2706 | | | 10 |
| 2N185 | G | P | ET | AC128 | AC153 | 2N2431 | 2N650 | 2SB221 | 01 |
| 2N185 | | | | AC124 | AC122 | 2N2430 | 2N362 | | 01 |
| 2N185 | | | | AC132 | | | | | 01 |
| 2N186 | G | P | ET | AC128 | AC153 | 2N2431 | 2N1191 | | 01 |
| 2N186 | | | | AC123 | AC132 | 2N2706 | 2N4106 | | 01 |
| 2N186 | | | | AC152 | | 2N217 | | | 01 |
| 2N186A | G | P | ET | AC128 | | 2N2431 | 2N1191 | | 01 |
| 2N186A | | | | | | 2N270 | 2N2706 | | 01 |
| 2N187 | G | P | ET, NP, UP | AC128 | AC153 | 2N2431 | 2N1191 | 2SB220 | 01 |
| 2N187 | | | | AC122 | OC72 | 2N2706 | 2N4106 | | 01 |
| 2N187 | | | | | | 2N633 | | | 01 |
| 2N187A | G | P | ET, NP, SR, UP | AC128 | AC117 | 2N2431 | 2N1191 | 2S37 | 01 |
| 2N187A | | | | AC153 | | 2N270 | 2N2706 | | 01 |
| 2N188 | G | P | ET, NP, St, UP | AC128 | AC153 | 2N2431 | 2N1191 | 2SB220 | 01 |
| 2N188 | | | | AC122 | AC117 | 2N2706 | 2N2430 | | 01 |
| 2N188 | | | | | | 2N109 | | | 01 |
| 2N188A | G | P | ET, NP, SR, St, UP | AC128 | AC162 | 2N2431 | 2N1191 | 2SB222 | 01 |
| 2N188A | | | | AC131 | AC125 | 2N270 | 2N2706 | | 01 |
| 2N188A | | | | AC153 | | | | | 01 |
| 2N189 | G | P | ET, NP, SR, St, UP | AC126 | AC162 | 2N2429 | 2N1191 | 2SB222 | 01 |
| 2N189 | | | | AC131 | AC128 | 2N2706 | 2N270 | | 01 |
| 2N189 | | | | AC122 | AC125 | 2N465 | | | 01 |
| 2N190 | G | P | ET, NP, SR, St, UP | AC126 | AC151 | 2N2429 | 2N1191 | 2SB219 | 01 |
| 2N190 | | | | AC125 | AC128 | 2N2706 | 2N408 | | 01 |
| 2N190 | | | | AC122 | | | | | 01 |
| 2N191 | G | P | ET, NP, St, UP | AC128 | AC153 | 2N2431 | 2N1192 | 2SB220 | 01 |
| 2N191 | | | | AC131 | AC125 | 2N2706 | 2N1190 | | 01 |
| 2N191 | | | | AC126 | | 2N270 | | | 01 |
| 2N192 | G | P | ET, NP, SR, St, UP | AC128 | AC163 | 2N2431 | 2N1193 | 2SB221 | 01 |
| 2N192 | | | | AC131 | AC126 | 2N1191 | 2N270 | | 01 |
| 2N192 | | | | AC122 | | | | | 01 |
| 2N193 | G | N | ET, NP, St, UP | ASY28 | ASY29 | 2N313 | 2N1302 | 2SA31 | 02 |
| 2N193 | | | | | | 2N1304 | | | 02 |
| 2N194 | G | N | ET, NP, St, UP | ASY73 | ASY29 | 2N313 | 2N1302 | 2SA31 | 02 |
| 2N194 | | | | | | 2N1304 | | | 02 |
| 2N194A | G | N | ET, NP, St, UP | ASY73 | ASY29 | 2N1304 | | | 02 |
| 2N195 | G | P | TR | AC128 | AC131 | 2N2432 | 2N217 | | |
| 2N195 | | | | AC132 | AC125 | 2N403 | 2N406 | | |
| 2N196 | G | P | TR | AC128 | AC163 | 2N2432 | 2N4106 | 2SB221 | |
| 2N196 | | | | AC131 | AC132 | 2N406 | 2N265 | | |
| 2N196 | | | | AC125 | | 2N403 | | | |
| 2N197 | G | P | TR | AC128 | AC163 | 2N2431 | 2N4106 | 2SB221 | |
| 2N197 | | | | AC131 | AC132 | 2N265 | 2N403 | | |
| 2N197 | | | | AC125 | | | | | |
| 2N198 | G | P | TR | AC128 | AC163 | 2N2431 | 2N4106 | 2SB170 | |

| TYPE | M/S | POL | MANUFAC | EUROPEAN | | AMERICAN | | JAPANESE | USE |
|------|-----|-----|---------|----------|---|----------|---|----------|-----|
| 2N198 | | | | AC131 | AC132 | 2N406 | 2N217 | | |
| 2N198 | | | | AC162 | AC125 | 2N403 | | | |
| 2N199 | G | P | TR | AC128 | AC163 | 2N2431 | 2N4106 | 2SB170 | |
| 2N199 | | | | AC131 | AC132 | 2N406 | 2N198 | | |
| 2N199 | | | | AC162 | AC125 | 2N403 | | | |
| 2N200 | G | P | TR | AC126 | AC153 | 2N2429 | 2N331 | | |
| 2N200 | | | | AC131 | AC125 | 2N406 | | | |
| 2N200 | | | | OC71 | | | | | |
| 2N204 | G | P | TR | AC151V | AC131 | 2N1373 | 2N1377 | | |
| 2N204 | | | | AC138 | AC128 | 2N406 | | | |
| 2N204 | | | | AC125 | OC71 | | | | |
| 2N205 | G | P | TR | AC151V | AC131 | 2N1372 | 2N1377 | | |
| 2N205 | | | | AC138 | AC128 | 2N406 | | | |
| 2N205 | | | | AC125 | OC71 | | | | |
| 2N206 | G | P | ET, NP, UP | AC126 | AC128 | 2N2429 | 2N2431 | 2S39 | 01 |
| 2N206 | | | | AC153 | AC125 | 2N2706 | 2N1191 | | 01 |
| 2N206 | | | | AC122 | OC71 | 2N1193 | | | 01 |
| 2N206 | | | | AC163 | | | | | 01 |
| 2N207 | G | P | ET, NP, UP | AC122 | AC163 | 2N1193 | 2N1372 | 2SB221 | 01 |
| 2N207 | | | | OC71 | AC125 | 2N1377 | 2N406 | | 01 |
| 2N207A | G | P | ET, NP, UP | AC151 | AC122 | 2N1190 | 2N1193 | 2SB221 | 01 |
| 2N207A | | | | AC125 | AC107 | 2N406 | 2N1372 | 2SB32 | 01 |
| 2N207A | | | | AC150 | AC162 | 2N536 | | | 01 |
| 2N207B | G | P | ET, NP, UP | AC163 | AC150 | 2N1193 | 2N535 | 2SB32 | 01 |
| 2N207B | | | | AC125 | AC122 | 2N536 | 2N406 | | 01 |
| 2N207B | | | | AC107 | AC162 | | | | 01 |
| 2N211 | G | N | ET, NP, UP | (AC127) | ASY28 | 2N1302 | 2N1304 | | 02 |
| 2N211 | | | | AF190 | ASY29 | | | | 02 |
| 2N212 | G | N | ET, NP, UP | (AC127) | ASY28 | 2N1059 | 2N1302 | | 02 |
| 2N212 | | | | ASY29 | | 2N1304 | | | 02 |
| 2N213 | G | N | ET, NP, UP | AC127 | ASY28 | 2N2430 | 2N1304 | | 01 |
| 2N213 | | | | ASY29 | | | | | 01 |
| 2N213A | G | N | ET, NP, St | AC127 | AC176 | 2N2430 | | | 01 |
| 2N214 | G | N | ET, NP, SR, UP | AC127 | AC176 | 2N2430 | 2N1192 | | 01 |
| 2N214 | | | | | | 2N1304 | | | 01 |
| 2N214A | G | N | ET, NP, St | (AC127) | AC176 | 2N2430 | | | 01 |
| 2N215 | G | P | ET, NP, SR | (AC151V) | AC126 | 2N2429 | 2N1189 | HJ15 | 01 |
| 2N215 | | | | AC122 | AC125 | 2N406 | 2N237 | | 01 |
| 2N215 | | | | AC128 | AC117 | 2N404 | | | 01 |
| 2N215 | | | | AC153 | | | | | 01 |
| 2N216 | G | N | ET, NP, UP | AC127 | AC130 | 2N1302 | 2N1304 | | 02 |
| 2N216 | | | | ASY28 | OC139 | | | | 02 |
| 2N216 | | | | ASY29 | | | | | 02 |
| 2N217 | G | P | ET, NP, NU, SR, UP | AC128 | AC151V | 2N2431 | 2N1192 | HJ17D | 01 |
| 2N217 | | | | AC131/30 | AC106 | 2N2706 | 2N4106 | | 01 |
| 2N217 | | | | AC132 | | 2N404 | | | 01 |
| 2N218 | G | P | ET, NP, SS, UP | (AC121V) | AF185 | 2N404 | 2N2614 | HJ22D | 01 |
| 2N218 | | | | AC121IV | AFY15 | | | | 01 |
| 2N218 | | | | OC44N | AF101 | | | | 01 |
| 2N218 | | | | AF181 | OC45 | | | | 01 |
| 2N219 | G | P | ET, NP, UP | (AC121V) | AF185 | 2N404 | 2N2614 | HJ23D | 01 |
| 2N219 | | | | AC121IV | AC131V | 2N406 | | | 01 |
| 2N219 | | | | OC44N | AFY15 | | | | 01 |
| 2N219 | | | | AF101 | ASZ20 | | | | 01 |
| 2N220 | G | P | ET, NP, SR, St | (AC121V) | AC126 | 2N2429 | 2N1189 | | 01 |
| 2N220 | | | | AC125 | | | | | 01 |
| 2N221A | S | N | | BCY86 | | | | | |
| 2N222 | G | P | | AC126 | | 2N2429 | 2N2439 | | |
| 2N223 | G | P | ET, NP, St, UP | AC128 | AC153 | 2N2431 | 2N1193 | 2SB222 | 01 |
| 2N223 | | | | AC117 | | 2N2706 | 2N4106 | | 01 |
| 2N224 | G | P | ET, NP, St, UP | AC153 | AC117 | 2N1192 | 2N4106 | 2SB222 | 01 |
| 2N224 | | | | AC128 | | 2N406 | 2N2706 | | 01 |
| 2N225 | G | P | ET, NP, St, UP | AC128 | AC153 | 2N2431 | 2N1193 | 2SB226 | 01 |
| 2N225 | | | | AC131 | AC106 | 2N224X2 | 2N4106 | | 01 |
| 2N225 | | | | AC117 | | 2N404 | | | 01 |
| 2N226 | G | P | ET, NP, St, UP | AC128 | AC153 | 2N2431 | 2N1192 | 2SB226 | 01 |
| 2N226 | | | | AC117 | OC308 | 2N2706 | 2N1406 | | 01 |
| 2N226 | | | | | | 2N404 | | | 01 |
| 2N227 | G | P | ET, NP, UP | AC128 | AC153 | 2N2431 | 2N1406 | 2SB226 | 01 |
| 2N227 | | | | AC117 | OC308 | 2N226X2 | 2N270 | | 01 |
| 2N227 | | | | | | 2N404 | | | 01 |
| 2N228 | G | N | ET, NP, UP | AC127 | AC176 | 2N2430 | | | 01 |
| 2N229 | G | N | ET, NP, UP | AC127 | AC130 | 2N2430 | 2N1302 | | 01 |
| 2N230 | G | P | MR | AD149 | OC30 | 2N2836 | 2N325 | 2SB107 | 06 |
| 2N230 | | | | OC26 | | | | | 06 |

| TYPE | M/S | POL | MANUFAC | EUROPEAN | | AMERICAN | | JAPANESE | USE |
|------|-----|-----|---------|----------|--|----------|--|----------|-----|
| 2N231 | G | P | NP, SP | AF126 | AF137 | 2N404 | 2N218 | | 02 |
| 2N231 | | | | AF136 | OC45 | | | | 02 |
| 2N231 | | | | AF124 | | | | | 02 |
| 2N232 | G | P | St | AF126 | AF137 | 2N404 | 2N218 | | 02 |
| 2N232 | | | | AF136 | OC45 | 2N990 | | | 02 |
| 2N232 | | | | AF124 | | | | | 02 |
| 2N233 | G | N | ET, NP, UP | AC127 | AC130 | 2N1306 | 2N1304 | | 02 |
| 2N233 | | | | ASY29 | | | | | 02 |
| 2N233A | G | N | ET, NP, UP | AC130 | | | | | 02 |
| 2N234 | G | P | SD | AD131IV | AD149 | 2N2836 | 2N554 | 2SB107 | 06 |
| 2N234 | | | | OC30 | OC26 | 2N1536 | TI156 | | 06 |
| 2N234 | | | | ASZ16 | | 2N301 | | | 06 |
| 2N234A | G | P | ET, SD, ST NP, SR | AD130IV | AD149 | 2N2836 | 2N555 | 2SB107 | 06 |
| 2N234A | | | | AD150 | ASZ16 | 2N1536 | | | 06 |
| 2N235 | G | P | SD | AD131IV | AD149 | 2N2836 | 2N350A | 2SB222 | 06 |
| 2N235 | | | | AD131 | OC26 | 2N1536 | 2N301 | | 06 |
| 2N235 | | | | AC128 | ASZ16 | TI3027 | | | 06 |
| 2N235A | G | P | ET, SD, ST | AD131IV | AD149 | 2N2836 | 2N3611 | | 06 |
| 2N235A | | | | AD131 | AUY19 | 2N1536 | 2N301 | | 06 |
| 2N235A | | | | OC26 | ASZ16 | TI3027 | | | 06 |
| 2N235B | G | P | ET, SD, ST | AD131IV | AD149 | 2N2836 | 2N3616 | | 06 |
| 2N235B | | | | AD131 | OC26 | TI3027 | 2N1536 | | 06 |
| 2N235B | | | | ASZ16 | | | | | 06 |
| 2N236 | G | P | SD | AD132IV | AD149 | 2N2836 | 2N350A | 2SB250A | 06 |
| 2N236 | | | | AD131 | AC128 | 2N1536 | 2N235 | | 06 |
| 2N236 | | | | AC117 | ASZ16 | TI3027 | | | 06 |
| 2N236A | G | P | ET, SD, ST | AD132IV | AD131 | 2N351A | 2N301 | | 06 |
| 2N236A | | | | AUY19 | AD149 | TI3027 | 2N1536 | | 06 |
| 2N236A | | | | OC26 | ASZ16 | | | | 06 |
| 2N236B | G | P | ET, SD, ST | AD132IV | AD131 | 2N376A | 2N1078 | 2SB107A | 06 |
| 2N236B | | | | AD149 | OC26 | TI3027 | 2N1536 | | 06 |
| 2N236B | | | | OC30 | ASZ16 | | | | 06 |
| 2N237 | G | P | ET, NP, UP | AD131 | AC128 | 2N220 | 2N404 | HJ15 | 01 |
| 2N237 | | | | AC117 | AC153 | | | | 01 |
| 2N237 | | | | OC72 | AC125 | | | | 01 |
| 2N238 | G | P | ET, NP, St, UP | AC126 | AC128 | 2N2429 | 2N2431 | 2SB101 | 01 |
| 2N238 | | | | AC153 | AC122R | 2N2706 | 2N1192 | | 01 |
| 2N238 | | | | AC132 | OC72 | 2N4106 | | | 01 |
| 2N239 | G | P | | AC153 | AC122R | 2N4106 | | 2SB226 | |
| 2N239 | | | | AC128 | AC117 | | | | |
| 2N240 | G | P | NP, SM, SP, SQ, St | AC163 | AC122R | 2N404 | 2N582 | 2SB32 | 10 |
| 2N240 | | | | AC125 | AF124 | 2N990 | | | 10 |
| 2N241 | G | P | ET, NP, St, UP | AC163 | AC131 | 2N321 | 2N4106 | 2SB221 | 01 |
| 2N241 | | | | AC128 | AC117 | 2N2706 | 2N281 | | 01 |
| 2N241 | | | | AC153 | | 2N404 | | | 01 |
| 2N241A | G | P | ET, NP, SR | AC128 | AC117 | 2N2431 | 2N321 | 2SB226 | 01 |
| 2N241A | | | | AC153 | | 2N270 | 2N2706 | | 01 |
| 2N241A | | | | | | 2N1536 | | | 01 |
| 2N242 | G | P | MO, ET, NP, SR, UP | (AUY21IV) | AC128 | 2N2431 | 2N4106 | 2SB221 | 01 |
| 2N242 | | | | AC163 | AC131 | 2N282 | 2N1501 | 2SB248A | 01 |
| 2N242 | | | | ASZ16 | AC117 | | | | 01 |
| 2N242 | | | | AC153 | AD149 | | | | 01 |
| 2N243 | S | N | TX, ET, NP, SQ | BSX45 | BFY10 | 2N2297 | | | 01 |
| 2N243 | | | | BFY50 | | | | | 01 |
| 2N244 | S | N | TX, ET, NP, SQ | BFY10 | BFY50 | 2N2297 | | | 01 |
| 2N245 | S | N | | BFY50 | | 2N2297 | | | |
| 2N246 | S | N | | BFY50 | | 2N2297 | | | |
| 2N247 | G | P | RC, SY | AF185 | AF126 | 2N2188 | 2N990 | 2S43 | 02 |
| 2N247 | | | | AF136 | AF116 | | | | 02 |
| 2N247 | | | | AF125 | AF124 | | | | 02 |
| 2N248 | G | P | ET, TX | AF185 | AF126 | 2N2188 | 2N267 | 2SA215 | 01 |
| 2N248 | | | | AF136 | AF116 | 2N990 | | | 01 |
| 2N248 | | | | AF125 | AF124 | | | | 01 |
| 2N249 | G | P | ET, NP, UP | AC128 | AC153 | 2N2431 | 2N270 | 2SB226 | 01 |
| 2N249 | | | | AC117 | ACY17 | 2N1176 | | | 01 |
| 2N250 | G | P | ET, ST, NP, SR, SS | AD130IV | AD149 | 2N2836 | 2N3611 | 2SB226 | 06 |
| 2N250 | | | | AD130V | AD138 | 2N250 | 2N456A | | 06 |
| 2N250 | | | | AC128 | AC153 | | | | 06 |
| 2N250 | | | | ASZ16 | | | | | 06 |
| 2N250A | G | P | ET, ST, NP, SR, UP | ASZ16 | | 2N2836 | 2N3611 | | 06 |
| 2N250A | | | | | | 2N1536 | | | 06 |
| 2N251 | G | P | ET, ST, NP, SR, SS | AD131IV | AUY22III | 2N1530 | 2N301A | 2SB201 | 06 |
| 2N251 | | | | OC30 | ASZ15 | 2N456A | 2N1536 | 2SB107 | 06 |
| 2N251 | | | | OD603 | ASZ16 | | | | 06 |
| 2N251A | G | P | ET, ST, SR, NP, UP | (AUY22IV) | ASZ16 | 2N3616 | 2N251 | | 06 |

| TYPE | M/S | POL | MANUFAC | EUROPEAN | | AMERICAN | | JAPANESE | USE |
|---|---|---|---|---|---|---|---|---|---|
| 2N251A | | | | | | 2N456A | 2N1536 | | 06 |
| 2N252 | G | P | ET, NP, UP | AF185 | AF127 | 2N374 | 2N2188 | ST37D | 02 |
| 2N252 | | | | AF106 | AF101 | 2N990 | | | 02 |
| 2N252 | | | | OC613 | AF124 | | | | 02 |
| 2N253 | G | N | ET, NP, UP | ASY73 | ASY29 | 2N1302 | 2N1304 | | 02 |
| 2N254 | G | N | ET, NP, UP | ASY73 | ASY29 | 2N1302 | 2N1304 | | 02 |
| 2N255 | G | P | ST, ES, ET, NP, UP | (AD130III) | AD149 | 2N1302 | 2N554 | 2SB107 | 06 |
| 2N255 | | | | AD148 | OC26 | 2N1536 | | | 06 |
| 2N255 | | | | ASZ16 | | | | | 06 |
| 2N255A | G | P | ST, ET, NP, SS, UP | (AD130III) | AD149 | 2N2836 | 2N1536 | | 06 |
| 2N255A | | | | ASZ16 | | | | | 06 |
| 2N256 | G | P | ST, ES, ET, NP, UP | (AD130III) | AD149 | 2N2836 | 2N555 | 2SB107 | 06 |
| 2N256 | | | | AD148 | OC26 | 2N1636 | 2N301 | | 06 |
| 2N256 | | | | OC30 | ASZ16 | TI3027 | | | 06 |
| 2N256A | G | P | ST, ET, NP, SR, UP | (AD130III) | AD149 | 2N2836 | TI3027 | | 06 |
| 2N256A | | | | AD148 | ASZ16 | 2N1536 | | | 06 |
| 2N257 | G | P | ST, ET, NP, SR, UP | (AUY21III) | AD149 | 2N2836 | 2N3611 | 2SB107A | 06 |
| 2N257 | | | | AD150IV | AD138 | 2N301 | TI3027 | | 06 |
| 2N257 | | | | OC26 | ASZ16 | 2N1536 | | | 06 |
| 2N257A | G | P | | AD149 | | 2N2836 | | | 06 |
| 2N257B | G | P | ST, ET, NP, UP | (AUY21III) | ASZ16 | 2N257W | 2N1536 | | |
| 2N257G | G | P | ST, ET, NP, UP | (AUY21III) | AD149 | 2N2836 | 2N2578 | | |
| 2N257G | | | | ASZ16 | | 2N2836 | 2N1536 | | |
| 2N257W | G | P | ST, ET, NP, UP | (AUY21IV) | AD149 | 2N257W | 2N1536 | | |
| 2N257W | | | | ASZ16 | | 2N2836 | | | |
| 2N260 | S | P | CV | BC177 | | 2N3965 | | | 01 |
| 2N260A | S | P | CV | BC177 | | 2N3965 | | | 01 |
| 2N261 | S | P | CV | BC177 | | 2N3965 | | | 01 |
| 2N262 | S | P | CV | BC177 | | 2N3965 | | | 01 |
| 2N262A | S | P | CV | BC177 | | 2N3965 | | | 01 |
| 2N263 | S | N | TX, NP, SM, SQ | BC107 | | A157 | | | 01 |
| 2N264 | S | N | TX, NP, SM, SQ | BC107 | | 2N337 | A157 | | 01 |
| 2N265 | G | P | ET, NP, UP | AC128 | AC151 | 2N2431 | 2N1175 | 2SB221 | 01 |
| 2N265 | | | | AC122 | AC132 | 2N408 | 2N406 | | 01 |
| 2N265 | | | | AC163 | AC125 | | | | 01 |
| 2N266 | G | P | GE | AC128 | AC151 | 2N2431 | 2N408 | 2SB219 | 01 |
| 2N266 | | | | AC122 | AC132 | 2N381 | | | 01 |
| 2N266 | | | | AC163 | | | | | 01 |
| 2N267 | G | P | St, RC | AF185 | AF126 | 2N247 | 2N2188 | 2SA215 | 02 |
| 2N267 | | | | AF136 | AF124 | 2N390 | | | 02 |
| 2N267 | | | | | | | | | |
| 2N268 | G | P | ST, ET, NP, SR, UP | AF116 | AF125 | | | | 02 |
| 2N268 | | | | (AUY22IV) | AD132II | 2N1530 | 2N301 | 2SB249 | 06 |
| 2N268 | | | | ASZ15 | OC36 | TI3027 | 2N1533 | | 06 |
| 2N268A | G | P | ST, ET, NP, SR, UP | (AUY22IV) | ASZ15 | 2N1536 | TI3027 | | 16 |
| 2N268A | | | | | | 2N1533 | | | 16 |
| 2N269 | G | P | ET, NP, St, UP | ASZ15 | ASY26 | TI3027 | 2N1303 | | 10 |
| 2N269 | | | | ASY27 | | 2N1305 | | | 10 |
| 2N270 | G | P | ET, NP, UP | AC128 | AC153 | 2N2431 | 2N1193 | HJ34 | 01 |
| 2N270 | | | | AC151 | AC106 | 2N2706 | 2N4106 | | 01 |
| 2N270 | | | | | | 2N404 | | | 01 |
| 2N271 | G | P | ET, NP, UP | AF185 | ASY27 | 2N2905 | 2N404 | | 02 |
| 2N271 | | | | OC44 | | 2N1305 | 2N1707 | | 02 |
| 2N271 | | | | | | 2N1307 | | | 02 |
| 2N271A | G | P | ET, NP | AF185 | OC44 | 2N404 | 2N1307 | | 02 |
| 2N271A | | | | ASY27 | | 2N1305 | | | 02 |
| 2N272 | G | P | ET, NP, UP | AC126 | AC128 | 2N2429 | 2N2431 | 2SB33 | 01 |
| 2N272 | | | | AC153 | AC125 | 2N406 | 2N4106 | | 01 |
| 2N272 | | | | AC117R | GFT32 | 2N273 | | | 01 |
| 2N272 | | | | OC72 | | | | | 01 |
| 2N273 | G | P | ET, NP, UP | AC128 | AC153 | 2N2431 | 2N4106 | 2SB33 | 01 |
| 2N273 | | | | AC117 | AC132 | 2N109 | 2N2706 | | 01 |
| 2N274 | G | P | St | AF126 | AF124 | 2N2188 | 2N990 | | 02 |
| 2N277 | G | P | DD, MO, NP, PH, UP | ADZ11 | AD211 | 2N1100 | | | 06 |
| 2N277 | | | | ADZ12 | | | | | 06 |
| 2N277A | G | P | | AC176 | | 2N2480 | | | 06 |
| 2N278 | G | P | DD, MO, NP, SS, UP | ADZ11 | ADZ12 | 2N1100 | | | 06 |
| 2N279 | G | P | ET, NP, UP | AC128 | AC151IV | 2N2431 | 2N650 | 2SB37 | 01 |
| 2N279 | | | | AC122/30 | AC125 | 2N406 | 2N4106 | | 01 |
| 2N279 | | | | AC131 | AC152 | 2N119 | | | 01 |
| 2N280 | G | P | ET, PH, NP, UP | AC151IV | AC126 | 2N2429 | 2N2480 | 2SB33 | 01 |
| 2N280 | | | | AC151V | OC71 | 2N650 | 2N4106 | | 01 |
| 2N280 | | | | AC122/30 | AC125 | 2N406 | | | 01 |
| 2N280 | | | | AC117 | | | | | 01 |
| 2N281 | G | P | ET, PH, NP, UP | AC151IV | AC153 | 2N2431 | 2N651 | 2SB221 | 01 |
| 2N281 | | | | AC128 | AC122/30 | 2N2706 | 2N4106 | | 01 |

| TYPE | M/S | POL | MANUFAC | EUROPEAN | | AMERICAN | | JAPANESE | USE |
|---|---|---|---|---|---|---|---|---|---|
| 2N281 | | | | AC125 | AC117 | 2N2907 | | | 01 |
| 2N281 | | | | AC132 | | | | | 01 |
| 2N282 | G | P | ET, PH, NP, UP | AC151IV | AC128 | 2N4106 | 2N281X2 | 2SB225 | 01 |
| 2N282 | | | | AC153 | AC122/30 | | | | 01 |
| 2N282 | | | | AC125 | AC117 | | | | 01 |
| | | | | | | | | | |
| 2N282 | | | | AC132 | | | | | 01 |
| 2N283 | G | P | ET, NP, UP | AC151IV | AC151 | 2N650 | 2N4106 | 2SB225 | 10 |
| 2N283 | | | | AC122 | AC125 | 2N403 | | 2SB220 | 10 |
| 2N283 | | | | AC126 | AC131 | | | | 10 |
| 2N283 | | | | AC152 | | | | | 10 |
| | | | | | | | | | |
| 2N284 | G | P | ET, PH, NP, UP | ASY48IV | AC151 | 2N464 | 2N563 | 2SB219 | 10 |
| 2N284 | | | | AC122/30 | AC122 | 2N406 | | | 10 |
| 2N284 | | | | AC125 | AC131 | | | | 10 |
| 2N284 | | | | AC152 | ASY76 | | | | 10 |
| 2N284A | G | P | ET, NP, UP | ASY48IV | AC125 | 2N2706 | | | 10 |
| | | | | | | | | | |
| 2N285 | G | P | SD | AD149 | AUY22III | 2N2836 | 2N3617 | | 06 |
| 2N285 | | | | AUY28 | ASZ15 | 2N1536 | | | 06 |
| 2N285 | | | | ASZ16 | | | | | 06 |
| 2N285A | G | P | ET, NP, SR | AD149 | ASZ16 | 2N2836 | 2N3617 | | 06 |
| 2N285A | | | | | | 2N1536 | | | 06 |
| | | | | | | | | | |
| 2N285B | G | P | ET, NP, SR | AD149 | ASZ16 | 2N2836 | 2N1536 | | 06 |
| 2N290 | G | P | DD | AD149 | ADZ12 | 2N2836 | 2N1100 | | 06 |
| 2N291 | G | P | ET, NP, UP | AC128 | AC153 | 2N2431 | 2N1191 | 2SA219 | 01 |
| 2N291 | | | | AC131 | AC152 | 2N4106 | 2N2706 | | 01 |
| 2N292 | G | N | ET, NP, SR, UP | ASY74 | ASY26 | 2N1302 | 2N1304 | | 02 |
| | | | | | | | | | |
| 2N292 | | | | ASY29 | | | | | 02 |
| 2N292A | G | N | ET, NP, UP | ASY29 | | 2N164A | 2N1304 | | |
| 2N293 | G | N | ET, NP, SR, UP | ASY29 | | 2N1304 | | HJ23D | 02 |
| 2N296 | G | P | ET, NP, SR, St, UP | AD149 | OC30 | 2N1531 | 2N456A | 2SB107 | 01 |
| 2N296 | | | | OD603 | ASZ15 | 2N3146 | 2N1533 | | 01 |
| | | | | | | | | | |
| 2N297 | G | P | MO, ET, NP, SR, UP | (AUY22III) | AD131IV | 2N297A | TI3027 | 2SB252 | 06 |
| 2N297 | | | | AD138 | OC30 | TI3028 | 2N1536 | | 06 |
| 2N297 | | | | ASZ15 | OD603 | | | | 06 |
| 2N297 | | | | ASZ16 | | | | | 06 |
| 2N297A | G | P | MO, ET, NP, SR, UP | (AUY22III) | ASZ15 | 2N457 | 2N2188 | | 06 |
| | | | | | | | | | |
| 2N297A | | | | AD131IV | ASZ16 | 2N1536 | | | 06 |
| 2N299 | G | P | St, PH | AF124 | AF135 | 2N623 | 2N2188 | 2SA116 | 02 |
| 2N299 | | | | AF194 | AF114 | 2N990 | | | 02 |
| 2N299 | | | | AF130 | | | | | 02 |
| 2N300 | G | P | PH | AF178 | AF124 | 2N2495 | 2N2188 | 2SA116 | 02 |
| | | | | | | | | | |
| 2N300 | | | | AF135 | AF194 | 2N990 | | | 02 |
| 2N300 | | | | AF114 | | | | | 02 |
| 2N301 | G | P | ET, MO, SD | AD131IV | AD149 | 2N2836 | 2N3611 | HJ35 | 06 |
| 2N301 | | | | AD131 | OC16 | 2N257 | 2N1536 | | 06 |
| 2N301 | | | | AD148 | ASZ16 | | | | 06 |
| | | | | | | | | | |
| 2N301A | G | P | ET, MO, SD | AD132IV | ASZ15 | 2N3612 | 2N1536 | 2SB42 | 06 |
| 2N301A | | | | OC22 | ASZ16 | | | | 06 |
| 2N302 | G | P | ET, NP, UP | AC128 | AC153 | 2N4106 | 2N4106 | 2SB34 | 02 |
| 2N302 | | | | AC131 | AC117 | 2N1431 | 2N1305 | | 02 |
| 2N302 | | | | ASY27 | | | | | 02 |
| | | | | | | | | | |
| 2N303 | G | P | ET, NP, UP | AC128 | AC117 | 2N2431 | 2N269 | 2SB34 | 02 |
| 2N303 | | | | AC153 | ASY27 | 2N305 | | | 02 |
| 2N306 | G | N | ET, NP, UP | ASY28 | | 2N406 | | 2SB32 | 01 |
| 2N306A | G | N | ET, NP, SR | AC127 | | 2N2430 | | | |
| 2N307 | G | P | MO, ET, NP, SR, UP | (AUY21IV) | AC162 | 2N4106 | 2N301 | 2SB240 | 06 |
| | | | | | | | | | |
| 2N307 | | | | AC122 | OC30 | 2N1536 | | | 06 |
| 2N307 | | | | ASZ16 | AC128 | | | | 06 |
| 2N307 | | | | AC125 | OC26 | | | | 06 |
| 2N307A | G | P | MO, ET, SR, UP, UT | (AUY21IV) | AD149 | 2N236 | 2N353 | 2SB41 | 06 |
| 2N307A | | | | OC26 | OC30 | 2N1536 | | | 06 |
| | | | | | | | | | |
| 2N307A | | | | OD603 | ASZ16 | | | | 06 |
| 2N307B | G | P | | ADZ16 | | 2N1536 | | | 06 |
| 2N308 | G | P | ET, NP, UP | AF185 | AF127 | 2N373 | 2N799 | 2SA155 | 02 |
| 2N308 | | | | AF101 | AF117 | 2N909 | | | 02 |
| 2N308 | | | | AF124 | | | | | 02 |
| | | | | | | | | | |
| 2N309 | G | P | ET, NP, UP | AF185 | AF126 | 2N373 | 2N990 | 2SA156 | 02 |
| 2N309 | | | | AF137 | OC45 | | | | 02 |
| 2N309 | | | | AF131 | AF124 | | | | 02 |
| 2N310 | G | P | ET, NP, UP | AF185 | AF126 | 2N1111 | 2N1112 | 2SA156 | 02 |
| 2N310 | | | | AF136 | AF116 | 2N990 | | | 02 |
| | | | | | | | | | |
| 2N310 | | | | AF127 | | | | | 02 |
| 2N311 | G | P | ET, NP, St, UP | AC153 | AC131 | 2N4106 | 2N404 | 2SA156 | 16 |
| 2N311 | | | | AC128 | AC117 | 2N461 | 2N406 | 2SB220 | 16 |
| 2N311 | | | | AC126 | AC125 | | | | 16 |
| 2N312 | G | N | ET, NP, St, UP | | | 2N585 | 2N1304 | 2SD11 | 16 |

| TYPE | M/S | POL | MANUFAC | EUROPEAN | | AMERICAN | | JAPANESE | USE |
|------|-----|-----|---------|----------|---|----------|---|----------|-----|
| 2N313 | G | N | GE | ASY29 | | 2N292 | 2N1304 | | |
| 2N314 | G | N | GE | ASY29 | | 2N293 | 2N1304 | | |
| 2N315 | G | P | ET, NP, St, UP | ASY27 | | 2N578 | 2N1305 | | 10 |
| 2N315A | G | P | ET, NP, SS, St, UP | ASY27 | | 2N1305 | | | 10 |
| 2N315B | G | P | St | ASY27 | | 2N1305 | | | 10 |
| 2N316 | G | P | ET, NP, St, UP | ASY27 | | 2N579 | 2N1305 | | 10 |
| 2N316A | G | P | ET, NP, St, UP | ASY27 | | 2N1305 | | | 10 |
| 2N317 | G | P | ET, NP, St, UP | ASY27 | | 2N592 | 2N582 | | 10 |
| 2N317 | | | | | | 2N1305 | | | 10 |
| 2N317A | G | P | ET, NP, St, TX, UP | ASY27 | | 2N1305 | | | 10 |
| 3N318 | P | P | | | | | | | 04 |
| 2N319 | G | P | MO, GE, ET, NP, UP | (AC152IV) | AC128 | 2N2431 | 2N270 | 2SB219 | 01 |
| 2N319 | | | | AC151 | AC117 | 2N2706 | | | 01 |
| 2N319 | | | | AC122 | AC126 | | | | 01 |
| 2N320 | G | P | MO, GS, ET, NP, UP | (AC152IV) | AC126 | 2N2429 | 2N319 | 2SB220 | 01 |
| 2N320 | | | | AC151 | AC117 | 2N270 | 2N2706 | | 01 |
| 2N320 | | | | AC128 | AC190 | | | | 01 |
| 2N330 | | | | AC153 | | | | | 01 |
| 2N321 | G | P | MO, GS, ET, NP, UP | (AC152V) | AC128 | 2N2429 | 2N319 | 2SB226 | 01 |
| 2N321 | | | | AC151V | AC117 | 2N270 | 2N1176 | | 01 |
| 2N321 | | | | ACY17 | AC128 | | | | 01 |
| 2N321 | | | | AC190 | AC153 | | | | 01 |
| 2N322 | G | P | MO, GS, ET, NP, UP | (AC152IV) | AC128 | 2N2431 | 2N319 | 2SB221 | 01 |
| 2N322 | | | | ASY26 | AC117 | 2N1130 | 2N1176 | | 01 |
| 2N322 | | | | AC153 | ACY17 | | | | 01 |
| 2N323 | G | P | MO, GS, ET, NP, UP | (AC152V) | AC128 | 2N2431 | 2N319 | | 01 |
| 2N323 | | | | ASY26 | AC132 | 2N270 | 2N1305 | | 01 |
| 2N323 | | | | AC153 | ACY17 | | | | 01 |
| 2N324 | G | P | MO, GS, ET, NP, UP | (AC152VI) | AC128 | 2N2431 | 2N319 | 2SB222 | 01 |
| 2N324 | | | | AC153 | AC117 | 2N4106 | 2N407 | | 01 |
| 2N324 | | | | AC118 | ASY17 | 2N1305 | | | 01 |
| 2N325 | G | P | SY | AD149 | OC30 | 2N236 | 2N3611 | 2SB107 | 01 |
| 2N325 | | | | OD603 | ACY17 | 2N1536 | | | 01 |
| 2N326 | G | N | NP, St | AD161 | | 2N4077 | | 2SB41 | 01 |
| 2N327 | S | P | St | BCY27 | BC177 | 2N1479 | | 2SB34 | 01 |
| 2N327 | | | | BC210 | BCY32 | | | | 01 |
| 2N327 | | | | BC261 | BC212 | | | | 01 |
| 2N327A | S | P | ET, NP, SR, St, UP | BC204 | | | | | 01 |
| 2N327B | S | P | SR, SS, St, TD | BCY32 | | 2N1475 | | | 05 |
| | | | | BCY32 | | 2N1475 | | | 05 |
| 2N318 | S | P | St | BC210 | GFT31/15 | 2N1475 | | 2SB34 | 01 |
| 2N318 | | | | SFT124 | BCY32 | | | | 01 |
| 2N328A | S | P | ET, NP, SR, St, TD | BCY32 | | 2N1475 | | | 05 |
| 2N328B | S | P | SR, St, TD, SQ | BFS95 | | 2N4036 | | | 05 |
| 2N329 | S | P | St | GFT31/15 | SFT124 | 2N1475 | | 2SB34 | 01 |
| 2N329 | | | | BCY32 | | | | | 01 |
| 2N329A | S | P | ET, NP, SR, SQ, UP | BCY29 | BCY32 | 2N1475 | | | 05 |
| 2N329B | S | P | SR, SQ, TD | BFS95 | | 2N4036 | | | 05 |
| 2N330 | S | P | RY | GFT31/15 | SFT124 | 2N1475 | | 2SB34 | 01 |
| 2N330 | | | | BCY32 | | | | | 01 |
| 2N330A | S | P | SM, SQ, SS | BCY32 | | 2N1475 | | | 05 |
| 2N331 | G | P | ET, MO, NP | ASY26 | AC117 | 2N4106 | 2N1291 | 2SB225 | 01 |
| 2N331 | | | | AC128 | AC153 | 2N1502 | 2N1176 | | 01 |
| 2N331 | | | | ACY17 | | | | | 01 |
| 2N332 | S | N | ET, TX, NP, St, UP | (BC107A) | BC140-6 | 2N2297 | | | 02 |
| 2N332 | | | | BFY50 | | | | | 02 |
| 2N332A | S | N | ET, NP, SQ, St, UP | (BC107A) | BC140-6 | 2N2297 | | | 01 |
| 2N332A | | | | BFY10 | BFY50 | | | | 02 |
| 2N333 | S | N | ET, TX, NP, St, UP | (BC107A) | BC140-6 | 2N2297 | | | 02 |
| 2N333 | | | | BSY44 | BFY11 | | | | 02 |
| 2N333 | | | | BFY50 | | | | | 02 |
| 2N333A | S | N | ET, NP, SS, St, UP | (BC107A) | BFY50 | 2N2297 | | | 01 |
| 2N334 | S | N | ET, TX, NP, St, UP | (BC107A) | BC140-6 | 2N2297 | | | 02 |
| 2N334 | | | | BSY44 | BSY11 | | | | 02 |
| 2N334 | | | | BFY50 | | | | | 02 |
| 2N334A | S | N | ET, SR, SQ, St, TR | (BC107A) | BFY50 | 2N2297 | | | 01 |
| 2N334B | S | N | | BFY50 | | 2N2297 | | | 01 |
| 2N335 | S | N | ET, TX, NP, TR, UP | (BC107A) | BC140-6 | 2N2297 | | | 02 |
| 2N335 | | | | BSY44 | BSY11 | | | | 02 |
| 2N335 | | | | BFY50 | | | | | 02 |
| 2N335A | S | N | ET, ST, TR, UP | (BC107A) | BFY50 | 2N2297 | | | 01 |
| 2N335B | S | N | ET, NP, ST, St, UP | (BC107A) | BFY50 | 2N2297 | | | 01 |
| 2N336 | S | S | ET, TX, St, TR, UP | (BC107A) | BC140-10 | 2N2297 | | | 02 |
| 2N336 | | | | BFY11 | BFY50 | | | | 02 |
| 2N336A | S | N | ET, NP, SR, St, UP | (BC107A) | BC140-16 | 2N2297 | | | 01 |

| TYPE | M/S | POL | MANUFAC | EUROPEAN | | AMERICAN | | JAPANESE | USE |
|------|-----|-----|---------|----------|---|----------|---|----------|-----|
| 2N336A | | | | BSY44 | BSY11 | | | | 01 |
| 2N336A | | | | BFY50 | | | | | 01 |
| 2N337 | S | N | ET, TX, PH, St, UP | (BC107A) | BSY11 | 2N2297 | | | 10 |
| 2N337 | | | | BFY50 | | | | | 10 |
| 2N337A | S | N | ET, NP, St, TR, UP | (BC107A) | BFY50 | 2N2297 | | | 01 |
| | | | | | | | | | |
| 2N338 | S | N | ET, TX, NP, PH, UP | (BC107A) | BFY11 | 2N2297 | | | 10 |
| 2N338 | | | | BFY50 | | | | | 10 |
| 2N338A | S | N | ET, NP, St, TR, UP | BC107A | BSY11 | 2N2297 | | | 01 |
| 2N338A | | | | BFY50 | | | | | 01 |
| 2N339 | S | N | ET, TX, NP, St, UP | BCY65EVII | BSY10 | 2N2297 | | | 01 |
| | | | | | | | | | |
| 2N339 | | | | BFY50 | | | | | 01 |
| 2N339A | S | N | ET, NP, SQ, UP | BCY65EVII | BFY50 | 2N2297 | | | 02 |
| 2N340 | S | N | ET, TX, NP, SQ, UP | (BCY65EVII) | BSW66 | 2N1893 | | | 01 |
| 2N340A | S | N | ET, NP, SQ, St, UP | (BCY65EVII) | BSX46 | 2N1893 | | | 02 |
| 2N340A | | | | BSW66 | | | | | 02 |
| 2N341 | S | N | ET, TX, NP, St, UP | (BF457) | BF178 | 2N1893 | | | 01 |
| 2N341 | | | | BF114 | BF109 | | | | 01 |
| 2N341 | | | | BFY43 | BSW66 | | | | 01 |
| 2N341A | S | N | ET, NP, SR, St, UP | (BF457) | BSW66 | 2N1893 | | | 02 |
| 2N342 | S | N | ET, TX, NP, SQ, UP | BCY65EVII | BSY10 | 2N1893 | | | 01 |
| | | | | | | | | | |
| 2N342 | | | | BFY50 | | | | | 01 |
| 2N342A | S | N | ET, NP, SQ, St, UP | (BCY65EVII) | BSW66 | 2N1893 | | | 01 |
| 2N342B | S | N | ET, SQ, St | (BCY65EVII) | BSW66 | 2N1893 | | | 01 |
| 2N343 | S | N | ET, TX, NP, SR, UP | BCY65EVII | BCY59 | 2N1893 | | | 01 |
| 2N343 | | | | BSY10 | BSW66 | | | | 01 |
| | | | | | | | | | |
| 2N343A | S | N | ET, NP, St, UP | BCY65EVII | BFY50 | 2N2297 | | | 01 |
| 2N343B | S | N | ET, NP, UP, SQ | BCY65EVII | BFY50 | 2N2297 | | | 01 |
| 2N344 | G | P | NP, SP, SQ | AC126 | AF137 | 2N274 | 2N345 | HJ74 | 02 |
| 2N344 | | | | AF126 | AF153 | 2N404 | 2N990 | HJ75 | 02 |
| 2N344 | | | | AF116 | AF124 | | | | 02 |
| 2N345 | G | P | NP, SP, SQ | AC126 | AF137 | 2N274 | 2N404 | HJ75 | 02 |
| 2N345 | | | | AF126 | AF153 | 2N990 | | | 02 |
| 2N345 | | | | AF116 | AF124 | | | | 02 |
| 2N346 | G | P | NP, SM, SR, SP, SQ | AF114 | AF124 | 2N404 | 2N990 | 2SA235 | 02 |
| 2N346 | | | | AF135 | | 2N504 | | | 02 |
| | | | | | | | | | |
| 2N347 | S | N | BG | BFY50 | | 2N2297 | | | 01 |
| 2N348 | S | N | BG | BSW66 | | 2N1893 | | | 02 |
| 2N349 | S | N | BG | BSW66 | | 2N1893 | | | 10 |
| 2N350 | G | P | MO, ET, NP, SR, UP | (AUY21IV) | AD149 | 2N2836 | 2N301 | 2SB248 | 06 |
| 2N350 | | | | AD138 | OC26 | TI3027 | 2N1536 | | 06 |
| | | | | | | | | | |
| 2N350 | | | | OC30 | ASZ16 | | | | 06 |
| 2N350A | G | P | MO, ET, NP, SR, UP | (AUY21IV) | AD149 | 2N2836 | 2N1536 | | 02 |
| 2N350A | | | | ASZ16 | | | | | 02 |
| 2N351 | G | P | MO, ET, NP, SR, UP | (AUY21IV) | AD149 | 2N2836 | TI3027 | | 06 |
| 2N351 | | | | OC30 | ASZ16 | 2N1536 | | | 06 |
| | | | | | | | | | |
| 2N351A | G | P | MO, ET, NP, SR, UP | (AUY21IV) | AD149 | 2N2836 | 2N1536 | | 06 |
| 2N351A | | | | | | | | | 06 |
| 2N352 | G | P | PC | AD149 | OC30 | 2N2836 | 2N1536 | 2SB41 | 06 |
| 2N352 | | | | ASZ16 | | | | | 06 |
| 2N353 | G | P | PC | AD149 | OC30 | 2N2836 | 2N1536 | 2SB41 | 06 |
| | | | | | | | | | |
| 2N353 | | | | ASZ16 | | | | | 06 |
| 2N354 | S | P | PC | BC211 | BC177 | 2N3965 | | | 02 |
| 2N355 | S | P | PC | BC177 | | 2N3965 | | | 10 |
| 2N356 | G | N | ET, NP, St, SS, UP | ASY73 | ASY29 | 2N1302 | 2N1304 | | 10 |
| 2N356A | G | N | ET, SS, St | ASY29 | | 2N1304 | | | 10 |
| | | | | | | | | | |
| 2N357 | G | N | ET, NP, SS, St, UP | ASY75 | ASY29 | 2N1302 | 2N1304 | | 10 |
| 2N357A | G | N | ET, NP, SS, St, UP | ASY29 | | 2N1304 | | | 10 |
| 2N358 | G | N | ET, NP, SS, St, UP | ASY28 | ASY75 | 2N1304 | | | 10 |
| 2N358 | | | | ASY29 | | | | | 10 |
| 2N358A | G | N | ET, NP, SS, St, UP | ASY29 | | 2N1304 | | | 10 |
| | | | | | | | | | |
| 2N359 | G | P | ET, NP, St, UP | AC153 | AC117R | 2N652 | 2N369 | HJ17D | 01 |
| 2N359 | | | | AC128 | OC72 | 2N1305 | | | 01 |
| 2N359 | | | | ASY27 | | | | | 01 |
| 2N360 | G | P | ET, NP, St, UP | AC153 | AC117 | 2N1192 | 2N369 | HJ17D | 01 |
| 2N360 | | | | AC128 | ASY27 | 2N1305 | | | 01 |
| | | | | | | | | | |
| 2N361 | G | P | ET, NP, St, UP | AC153 | AC131 | 2N1191 | 2N363 | 2SB226 | 01 |
| 2N361 | | | | AC128 | AC117 | 2N1305 | | | 01 |
| 2N361 | | | | ASY27 | | | | | 01 |
| 2N362 | G | P | ET, NP, St, UP | AC126 | AC153 | 2N2429 | 2N1192 | 2SB227 | 01 |
| 2N362 | | | | AC131 | AC128 | 2N1305 | | | 01 |
| | | | | | | | | | |
| 2N362 | | | | AC125 | ASY27 | | | | 01 |
| 2N363 | G | P | ET, NP, St, UP | AC126 | AC153 | 2N2429 | 2N1192 | 2SB227 | 01 |
| 2N363 | | | | AC131 | AC128 | 2N1176 | | 2SB226 | 01 |
| 2N363 | | | | AC125 | ACY17 | | | | 01 |
| 2N364 | G | N | ET, NP, UP | AC127 | ASY29 | 2N2430 | 2N1304 | | 10 |

| TYPE | M/S | POL | MANUFAC | EUROPEAN | | AMERICAN | | JAPANESE | USE |
|------|-----|-----|---------|----------|---|----------|---|----------|-----|
| 2N365 | G | N | ET, NP, UP | AC127 | ASY29 | 2N2430 | 2N1304 | 2T66 | 10 |
| 2N366 | G | N | ET, NP, UP | AC127 | ASY29 | 2N2430 | 2N1304 | | 10 |
| 2N367 | G | P | ET, NP, St, UP | AC126 | AC153 | 2N2429 | 2N1191 | 2SB101 | 10 |
| 2N367 | | | | AC131 | AC128 | 2N1176 | | | 10 |
| 2N367 | | | | AC125 | ACY17 | | | | 10 |
| | | | | | | | | | |
| 2N368 | G | P | ET, NP, St, UP | AC126 | AC153 | 2N2429 | 2N1191 | 2SB101 | 10 |
| 2N368 | | | | AC122 | AC125 | 2N406 | | | 10 |
| 2N368 | | | | AC128 | AC131 | | | | 10 |
| 2N368 | | | | AC132 | | | | | 10 |
| 2N369 | G | P | ET, NP, St, UP | AC153 | AC117 | 2N1191 | 2N406 | HJ17D | 10 |
| | | | | | | | | | |
| 2N369 | | | | AC128 | AC125 | 2N4106 | 2N2429 | | 10 |
| 2N370 | G | P | NP | AF185 | AF125 | 2N3324 | 2N990 | HJ32 | 02 |
| 2N370 | | | | AF135 | AF115 | | | | 02 |
| 2N370 | | | | AF124 | OC614 | | | | 02 |
| 2N371 | G | P | RC | AF185 | AF126 | 2N3324 | 2N426 | HJ37 | 02 |
| | | | | | | | | | |
| 2N371 | | | | AF136 | AF116 | 2N990 | | | 02 |
| 2N371 | | | | AF124 | | | | | 02 |
| 2N371/33 | G | P | SY | AF124 | | 2N990 | | | |
| 2N372 | G | P | NP, St | AF185 | AF126 | 2N3324 | 2N990 | HJ72 | 02 |
| 2N372 | | | | AF136 | AF116 | | | | 02 |
| | | | | | | | | | |
| 2N372 | | | | AF124 | | | | | 02 |
| 2N373 | G | P | RC, SY | AF185 | AF126 | 2N2188 | 2N990 | HJ73 | 02 |
| 2N373 | | | | AF136 | AF124 | | | | 02 |
| 2N373 | | | | AF131 | AF116 | | | | 02 |
| 2N373 | | | | AF117 | | | | | 02 |
| | | | | | | | | | |
| 2N374 | G | P | RC, SY | AF185 | AF125 | 2N3325 | 2N384 | HJ74 | 02 |
| 2N374 | | | | AF135 | AF115 | 2N990 | | | 02 |
| 2N374 | | | | AF117 | AF124 | | | | 02 |
| 2N375 | G | P | MO, ET, NP, SR, UP | (AD132IV) | AC153 | 2N4106 | 2N1324 | 2SB249 | 06 |
| 2N375 | | | | AC117 | AC128 | 2N1437 | 2N1533 | | 06 |
| | | | | | | | | | |
| 2N375 | | | | AC105 | ASZ15 | | | | 06 |
| 2N376 | G | P | MO, ET, NP, SR, UP | (AUY21IV) | AD149 | 2N2836 | 2N1536 | 2SB107A | 06 |
| 2N376 | | | | OC30 | OC26 | | | | 06 |
| 2N376 | | | | ASZ16 | | | | | 06 |
| 2N376A | G | P | MO, ET, NP, SR, UP | (AUY21IV) | ASZ16 | 2N1536 | | | 06 |
| | | | | | | | | | |
| 2N377 | G | N | ET, NP, TX, St, UP | ASY75 | ASY29 | 2N357 | 2N1301 | 2SD11 | 10 |
| 2N377 | | | | | | 2N1304 | | | 10 |
| 2N377A | G | N | ET, NP, St, UP | ASY29 | | 2N1304 | | | 10 |
| 2N378 | G | P | MO, ET, NP, SR, UP | (AUY21IV) | AC153 | 2N106 | 2N561 | 2SB246 | 16 |
| 2N378 | | | | AC117 | AC128 | 2N1536 | TI3027 | | 16 |
| | | | | | | | | | |
| 2N378 | | | | ASZ16 | | | | | 16 |
| 2N379 | G | P | MO, DD, ET, NP, UP | (AUY21IV) | ADZ11 | 2N1538 | TI3027 | | 16 |
| 2N379 | | | | ASZ15 | | TI3029 | | | 16 |
| 2N380 | G | P | MO, DD, ET, NP, UP | (AUY21IV) | AD149 | TI3027 | TI3030 | | 16 |
| 2N380 | | | | ASZ15 | ASZ16 | 2N1536 | | | 16 |
| | | | | | | | | | |
| 2N381 | G | P | MO, ET, NP, St, SR | (ASY48IV) | AC153 | 2N4106 | 2N270 | 2SB219 | 01 |
| 2N381 | | | | AC117A | AC128 | 2N1305 | 2N1176 | | 01 |
| 2N381 | | | | AC162 | ASY26 | | | | 01 |
| 2N381 | | | | ACY17 | | | | | 01 |
| 2N382 | G | P | MO, ET, NP, SR, UP | (ASY48V) | AC153 | 2N270 | 2N1176 | 2SB220 | 01 |
| | | | | | | | | | |
| 2N382 | | | | AC117 | AC125 | | | | 01 |
| 2N382 | | | | AC128 | ACY17 | | | | 01 |
| 2N383 | G | P | MO, ET, NP, SR, UP | (ASY48VI) | AC153 | 2N4106 | 2N270 | 2SB221 | 01 |
| 2N383 | | | | AC131 | AC128 | 2N1176 | | | 01 |
| 2N383 | | | | ACY17 | AC125 | | | | 01 |
| | | | | | | | | | |
| 2N383 | | | | AC106 | AC117 | | | | 01 |
| 2N384 | G | P | NP, St | AF118 | AF137 | 2N3325 | 2N4033 | HJ74 | 02 |
| 2N384 | | | | AF124 | AF135 | 2N2189 | 2N990 | | 02 |
| 2N384 | | | | AF136 | AF124 | | | | 02 |
| 2N384/33 | G | P | SY | AF124 | | 2N990 | | | |
| | | | | | | | | | |
| 2N385 | G | N | ET, NP, UP | ASY75 | OC141 | 2N357 | 2N1304 | 2SD11 | 10 |
| 2N385A | G | N | ET, NP, UP | ASY29 | | 2N1304 | | | 10 |
| 2N385A | | | | ASY29 | | 2N1304 | | | 10 |
| 2N386 | G | P | PC | AC153 | AC117 | 2N1531 | 2N651A | 2SB247 | 06 |
| 2N386 | | | | AC125 | AC128 | 2N1533 | MP689 | | 06 |
| | | | | | | | | | |
| 2N386 | | | | ASZ15 | | | | | 06 |
| 2N387 | G | P | AC | AC153 | AC117 | 2N1531 | 2N1358 | 2SB247 | 06 |
| 2N387 | | | | AC125 | AC128 | 2N1433 | 2N1533 | 2SB252 | 06 |
| 2N387 | | | | ASZ15 | | | | | 06 |
| 2N388 | G | N | ET, NP, NU, PH, TX | AC127 | ASY29 | 2N1308 | 2N1304 | | 10 |
| | | | | | | | | | |
| 2N388A | G | N | ET, NP, TX, SR, TX, UP | (AC127) | ASY29 | 2N1304 | | | 10 |
| 2N389 | S | N | TX, ET, SR, TR, UP | BDY39 | AM291 | 2N3445 | 2N3055 | | 06 |
| 2N389 | | | | BDY11 | BLY17 | 2N5068 | | | 06 |
| 2N389 | | | | BDY20 | | | | | 06 |
| 2N389A | S | N | ET, NP, TX, St, UP | BDY20 | | 2N5068 | | | 06 |

| TYPE | M/S | POL | MANUFAC | EUROPEAN | | AMERICAN | | JAPANESE | USE |
|---|---|---|---|---|---|---|---|---|---|
| 2N389/1 | S | N | SU | BDY20 | | 2N3055 | | | |
| 2N391 | G | P | | AC153 | AC117 | 2N651A | | | |
| 2N391 | | | | AC125 | AC128 | | | | |
| 2N392 | G | P | DD, EL, NP, SS, UP | AUY21IV | AD138/50 | 2N1550 | TI3027 | | 06 |
| 2N392 | | | | ASZ16 | | 2N1536 | | | 06 |
| 2N393 | G | P | ES, SP, SQ | ASZ20 | AF124 | 2N967 | 2N990 | | 10 |
| 2N393A | G | P | | ACY27 | | | | | |
| 2N394 | G | P | ET, NP, UP | AC152V | OC80 | 2N404 | 2N1305 | | 13 |
| 2N394 | | | | OC76 | | | | | 13 |
| 2N394A | G | P | ET, SR, NP | ASY27 | | 2N1305 | | | 13 |
| 2N395 | G | P | SR, ET, NP, TX, UP | AF126 | AF137 | 2N581 | 2N1305 | 2SA205 | 13 |
| 2N395 | | | | ASY26 | ASY27 | 2N1308 | | | 13 |
| 2N396 | G | P | ET, TX, ML, NP, UP | (AC151IV) | ASY26 | 2N393 | 2N404 | 2SA206 | 13 |
| 2N396 | | | | AF127 | AF137 | 2N1305 | | | 13 |
| 2N396 | | | | OC45 | ASY27 | | | | 13 |
| 2N396A | G | P | ET, NP, PH, SR | (AC151IV) | ASY27 | 2N1305 | | | 13 |
| 2N397 | G | P | ET, TX, NP, PH, UP | (AC151IV) | ASY26 | 2N582 | 2N1307 | | 13 |
| 2N397 | | | | 2G397 | ASY27 | 2N1305 | | | 13 |
| 2N398 | G | P | ET, MO, NP, St, TX | ASY77 | | | | | 16 |
| 2N398A | G | P | MO, ET, NP, St, TX | | | 2N2043 | | | 01 |
| 2N398B | G | P | NP, St, TX | | | 2N2043 | | | 16 |
| 2N399 | G | P | ET, SD, ST, NP, UP | AD131IV | AD149 | 2N2836 | 2N351A | 2SB107A | 02 |
| 2N399 | | | | OC30 | OC26 | 2N1536 | TI3027 | | 02 |
| 2N399 | | | | ASZ16 | | | | | 02 |
| 2N400 | G | P | ET, ST, NP, SR, UP | AD131IV | AD149 | 2N2836 | 2N350A | 2SB107A | 06 |
| 2N400 | | | | AD131 | OC30 | 2N1536 | TI3027 | | 06 |
| 2N400 | | | | OC26 | ASZ16 | | | | 06 |
| 2N401 | G | P | ET, ST, NP, SR, UP | AD131IV | AD149 | 2N2836 | 2N3611 | 2SB107A | 06 |
| 2N401 | | | | AD131 | AUY19 | 2N1536 | | | 06 |
| 2N401 | | | | OC30 | SFT232 | | | | 06 |
| 2N401 | | | | ASZ16 | | | | | 06 |
| 2N402 | G | P | ET, NP, UP | AC153 | AC131 | 2N1191 | 2N1924 | 2SB219 | 01 |
| 2N402 | | | | AC128 | AC132 | 2N406 | 2N1176 | | 01 |
| 2N402 | | | | AC152 | ACY17 | | | | 01 |
| 2N403 | G | P | ET, NP, UP | AC153 | AC117 | 2N1191 | 2N215 | 2SB220 | 01 |
| 2N403 | | | | AC128 | AC131 | 2N1176 | | | 01 |
| 2N403 | | | | AC152 | ACY17 | | | | 01 |
| 2N404 | G | P | GE, MO, ET, ML, NP | (ASY48IV) | ASY27 | 2N1305 | | | 10 |
| 2N404 | | | | ASY26 | | | | | 10 |
| 2N404A | G | P | GE, MO, ET, NP, TX | (ASY48IV) | ASY27 | 2N1305 | | | 10 |
| 2N405 | G | P | ET, NP, St | AC126 | AC153 | 2N2429 | 2N322 | 2SB32 | 01 |
| 2N405 | | | | AC117 | AC125 | 2N4106 | 2N406 | | 01 |
| 2N405 | | | | AC128 | AC132 | | | | 01 |
| 2N406 | G | P | ET, NP, SR, St | AC126 | AC151 | 2N2429 | 2N322 | 2S44 | 01 |
| 2N406 | | | | AC125 | AC122 | 2N323 | | | 01 |
| 2N406 | | | | AC132 | AC128 | | | | 01 |
| 2N407 | G | P | ET, NP, SR, St | AC128 | AC153 | 2N2431 | 2N324 | 2S33 | 01 |
| 2N407 | | | | AC117R | AC132 | 2N2706 | | | 01 |
| 2N408 | G | P | ET, NP, SR, St | AC128 | AC132 | 2N2431 | 2N324 | HJ51 | 01 |
| 2N408 | | | | AC153 | | 2N2706 | | | 01 |
| 2N409 | G | P | ET, NP, SR, St | AF185 | AF127 | 2N2614 | | 2S31 | 02 |
| 2N409 | | | | AF136 | OC44N | | | | 02 |
| 2N409 | | | | AF190 | AF117 | | | | 02 |
| 2N409 | | | | AF126 | | | | | 02 |
| 2N410 | G | P | ET, NP, SR, St | AF185 | AF126 | 2N2614 | | HJ56 | 02 |
| 2N410 | | | | AF127 | AF181 | | | | 02 |
| 2N410 | | | | OC44N | | | | | 02 |
| 2N411 | G | P | ET, NP, St | AF185 | AF117 | 2N2614 | | 2S30 | 02 |
| 2N411 | | | | AF126 | | | | | 02 |
| 2N411 | | | | OC44N | | | | | 02 |
| 2N412 | G | P | ET, NP, St | AF185 | AF117 | 2N2614 | | HJ57 | 02 |
| 2N412 | | | | AF126 | AF127 | | | | 02 |
| 2N412 | | | | OC44N | | | | | 02 |
| 2N413 | G | P | ET, NP, SR, St, UP | (AC151IV) | AF126 | 2N218 | 2N1305 | HJ56 | 02 |
| 2N413 | | | | AF137 | SET316 | | | | 02 |
| 2N413 | | | | AF190 | ASY26 | | | | 02 |
| 2N413 | | | | ACY27 | | | | | 02 |
| 2N413A | G | P | ET, NP, St, UP | (AC151IV) | ASY26 | 2N218 | 2N1305 | | 02 |
| 2N413A | | | | ASY27 | | | | | 02 |
| 2N414 | G | P | ET, NP, SR, St, UP | (AC151V) | AF126 | 2N218 | 2N1305 | | 02 |
| 2N414 | | | | AF137 | SET316 | | | | 02 |
| 2N414 | | | | AF188 | ASY27 | | | | 02 |
| 2N414A | G | P | ET, NP, St, UP | (AC151V) | AF126 | 2N218 | 2N1305 | | 02 |
| 2N414A | | | | AF188 | ASY27 | | | | 02 |
| 2N414B | G | P | ET, NP, St | ASY27 | | 2N1307 | 2N1305 | | 02 |

| TYPE | M/S | POL | MANUFAC | EUROPEAN | | AMERICAN | | JAPANESE | USE |
|------|-----|-----|---------|----------|---|----------|---|----------|-----|
| 2N414C | G | P | ET, St, NP | ASY27 | | 2N1305 | | | 02 |
| 2N415 | G | P | ET, NP, St | (AC151VI) | AF126 | 2N274 | 2N271 | | 02 |
| 2N415 | | | | AF137 | SET316 | 2N374 | 2N1305 | | 02 |
| 2N415 | | | | AF127 | AF187 | | | | 02 |
| 2N415 | | | | ASY27 | | | | | 02 |
| 2N415A | G | P | ET, NP, St, UP | (AC151VI) | ASY27 | 2N374 | | 2N1307 | 02 |
| 2N415A | | | | | | 2N1305 | | | 02 |
| 2N416 | G | P | ET, NP, St, UP | (AC151VI) | AF126 | 2N247 | 2N1309 | | 02 |
| 2N416 | | | | AF137 | SET316 | 2N1305 | | | 02 |
| 2N416 | | | | AF188 | ASY27 | | | | 02 |
| 2N417 | G | P | ET, NP, St, UP | AC162 | AF126 | 2N247 | 2N1309 | | 02 |
| 2N417 | | | | AF137 | SET316 | 2N1305 | | | 02 |
| 2N417 | | | | AF188 | ASY27 | | | | 02 |
| 2N418 | G | P | ET, NP, SR | ASZ15 | | 2N1537 | 2N1100 | | 16 |
| 2N418 | | | | | | 2N1533 | | | 16 |
| 2N419 | G | P | ET, NP, SR | AC153 | AC117 | 2N561 | 2N1536 | 2SB248A | 06 |
| 2N419 | | | | AC125 | AC128 | | | | 06 |
| 2N419 | | | | AD149 | ASZ16 | | | | 06 |
| 2N420 | G | P | ET, NP, SR | AUY21II | AUY28 | 2N1535 | 2N1533 | | 16 |
| 2N420 | | | | ASZ18 | ASZ16 | | | | 16 |
| 2N420A | G | P | ET, NP, SR | ASZ18 | ASZ15 | 2N1537 | 2N1533 | | 16 |
| 2N422 | G | P | ET, NP, St | AC126 | AC153 | 2N2429 | 2N651 | 2SB220 | 01 |
| 2N422 | | | | AC117 | ACY17 | 2N1176 | | | 01 |
| 2N422 | | | | AC125 | AC128 | | | | 01 |
| 2N424 | S | N | ET, NP, SR, St, TX | BLY17 | BDY20 | 2N3446 | 2N5069 | | 06 |
| 2N424 | | | | | | 2N3055 | | | 06 |
| 2N424A | S | N | ET, NP, SR, St, TX | BDY20 | | 2N3446 | 2N3055 | | 06 |
| 2N424/1 | S | N | SQ | BDX11 | | 2N3442 | | | |
| 2N425 | G | P | ET, NP, St, UP | (AC152IV) | ASY27 | 2N1305 | | | 10 |
| 2N425 | | | | ASY22 | | | | | 10 |
| 2N426 | G | P | ET, NP, SR, St, TX | (AC152IV) | AF126 | 2N578 | 2N1305 | HJ37 | 10 |
| 2N426 | | | | AF136 | AF116 | | | | 10 |
| 2N426 | | | | AF137 | ASY27 | | | | 10 |
| 2N427 | G | P | ET, NP, SR, TX, UP | (AC152V) | AF127 | 2N579 | 2N1307 | 2SA206 | 10 |
| 2N427 | | | | AFY15 | OC45 | 2N1305 | | | 10 |
| 2N427 | | | | AF101 | ASY27 | | | | 10 |
| 2N428 | G | P | ET, TX, NP, St, TX | (AC152IV) | ASY27 | 2N1307 | 2N1309 | 2SA206 | 10 |
| 2N428 | | | | AF127 | AFY15 | 2N1305 | | | 10 |
| 2N428 | | | | OC45 | AF101 | | | | 10 |
| 2N428A | G | P | ET, NP, St, UP | (AC152VI) | ASY27 | 2N1305 | | | 10 |
| 2N432 | S | N | | BFY50 | | 2N2297 | | | |
| 2N433 | S | N | | BFY50 | | 2N2297 | | | |
| 2N438 | G | N | ET, NP, St, TX, UP | ASY29 | | 2N1304 | | | 10 |
| 2N438A | G | N | ET, NP, St, TX, UP | ASY29 | | 2N1302 | 2N1304 | | 10 |
| 2N439 | G | N | ET, NP, St, TX | ASY29 | | 2N1304 | | | 10 |
| 2N439A | G | N | ET, NP, St | ASY29 | | 2N357 | 2N1306 | | 10 |
| 2N439A | | | | | | 2N1304 | | | 10 |
| 2N440 | G | N | ET, NP, St, TX, UP | ASY29 | | 2N1304 | | | 10 |
| 2N440A | G | N | ET, NP, St | ASY29 | | 2N358 | 2N1306 | | 10 |
| 2N440A | | | | | | 2N1304 | | | 10 |
| 2N441 | G | P | DD, MO, NP, UT | ADZ11 | ADZ12 | 2N1100 | | | 06 |
| 2N442 | G | P | DD, MO, NP, SR, UT | ADZ11 | ADZ12 | 2N1100 | | | 06 |
| 2N443 | G | P | DD, MO, NP, SR, UT | ADZ12 | ASZ16 | 2N1100 | 2N1304 | | 06 |
| 2N444 | G | N | ET, NP, St | AC176 | | 2N1012 | 2N1059 | 2SD11 | 01 |
| 2N444 | | | | | | 2N2430 | | | 01 |
| 2N444A | G | N | ET, NP, St | AC176 | | 2N2430 | | | 01 |
| 2N445 | G | N | ET, NP, St | ASY29 | | 2N356 | 2N1304 | | 01 |
| 2N445A | G | N | ET, NP, SR | ASY29 | | 2N1304 | | | 01 |
| 2N446 | G | N | ET, NP, St | ASY29 | | 2N357 | 2N1304 | | 10 |
| 2N446A | G | N | ET, NP, St | ASY29 | | 2N1304 | | | 10 |
| 2N447 | G | N | ET, NP, St | ASY29 | | 2N358 | 2N1304 | | 10 |
| 2N447A | G | N | ET, NP, St | ASY29 | | 2N1304 | | | 10 |
| 2N447B | G | N | ET | ASY29 | | 2N1304 | | | 10 |
| 2N448 | G | N | ET, NP, St | ASY29 | | 2N1304 | | | 02 |
| 2N449 | G | N | ET, NP | ASY29 | | 2N1304 | | | 02 |
| 2N450 | G | P | ET, NP, St | AF127 | AFY15 | 2N1308 | 2N1305 | 2SA206 | 13 |
| 2N450 | | | | OC45 | AF101 | | | | 13 |
| 2N450 | | | | ASY27 | | | | | 13 |
| 2N451 | S | N | St | BDY20 | | | | | |
| 2N452 | S | N | GE | BDY20 | | 2N3055 | | | |
| 2N453 | S | N | GE | BDY20 | | 2N3055 | | | |
| 2N454 | S | N | GE | BDY20 | | 2N3055 | | | |
| 2N456 | G | P | MO, TX, ET, NP, St | (AUY21IV) | ASZ16 | 2N456A | 2N1536 | | 06 |
| 2N456 | | | | ASZ17 | | | | | 06 |
| 2N456A | G | P | MO, TX, DD, ET, St | (AUY21IV) | ASZ16 | 2N1536 | | | 06 |

| TYPE | M/S | POL | MANUFAC | EUROPEAN | | AMERICAN | | JAPANESE | USE |
|------|-----|-----|---------|----------|---|----------|---|----------|-----|
| 2N456B | G | P | TX, DD, ET, SR | (AUY21IV) | ASZ16 | 2N1553 | 2N1536 | | 06 |
| 2N457 | G | P | MO, TX, ET, SR, SS | AUY21IV | AD131 | MP251 | 2N1536 | | 06 |
| 2N457 | | | | ASZ17 | ASZ16 | | | | 06 |
| 2N457A | G | P | MO, TX, DD, ET, St | (AUY21IV) | ASZ16 | 2N1536 | | | 06 |
| 2N457B | G | P | TX, DD, ET, NP, SS | (AUY21IV) | ASZ16 | 2N1553 | 2N1536 | | 06 |
| 2N458 | G | P | MO, TX, ET, NP, SS | (AUY21IV) | AUY22II | 2N458A | 2N561 | | 06 |
| 2N458 | | | | AUY28 | AUY21II | | | | 06 |
| 2N458A | G | P | MO, TX, DD, ET, NP | (AUY22IV) | ASZ16 | 2N1536 | | | 06 |
| 2N458B | G | P | TX, DD, ET, NP, SS | (AUY22IV) | ASZ16 | 2N1555 | 2N1536 | | 06 |
| 2N459 | G | P | ET, MO, NP, SS, UT | ASZ15 | | 2N378 | 2N1533 | | 16 |
| 2N459A | G | P | ET, MO, NP, SR, SS | ASZ15 | | 2N1533 | | | 16 |
| 2N460 | G | P | MO, ET, NP, SR, St | (ASY48IV) | AC128 | 2N2431 | 2N4106 | 2SB224 | 01 |
| 2N460 | | | | AC153 | AC131 | 2N1303 | 2N1176 | | 01 |
| 2N460 | | | | AC105 | AC117 | | | | 01 |
| 2N460 | | | | ACY17 | | | | | 01 |
| 2N461 | G | P | MO, ET, NP, SR, St | (ASY48IV) | AC128 | 2N2431 | 2N331 | 2SB220 | 01 |
| 2N461 | | | | AC153 | AC117 | 2N1176 | | | 01 |
| 2N461 | | | | ACY17 | | | | | 01 |
| 2N462 | G | P | ET, PC | AC153 | AC117 | 2N331 | 2N2706 | 2SB220 | 10 |
| 2N462 | | | | OC73 | AC128 | | | | 10 |
| 2N462 | | | | OC72 | | | | | 10 |
| 2N463 | G | P | WE | AD156 | OC30 | 2N1555 | 2N1551 | 2SB107A | 06 |
| 2N463 | | | | AD148 | ASZ16 | 2N1536 | | | 06 |
| 2N464 | G | P | MO, ET, NP, SR, St | (AC152IV) | AC128 | 2N2431 | 2N4270 | 2SB219 | 01 |
| 2N464 | | | | AC162 | AC122 | 2N270 | 2N1176 | | 01 |
| 2N464 | | | | ACY17 | AC125 | | | | 01 |
| 2N464 | | | | AC131 | | | | | 01 |
| 2N465 | G | P | MO, ET, NP, SR, St | (AC152IV) | AC128 | 2N2431 | 2N270 | 2SB220 | 01 |
| 2N465 | | | | AC153 | AC117 | 2N1176 | | | 01 |
| 2N465 | | | | ASY17 | ASY77 | | | | 01 |
| 2N466 | G | P | MO, ET, NP, SR, St | (AC152V) | AC128 | 2N2431 | 2N270 | 2SB220 | 01 |
| 2N466 | | | | AC151VI | AC117 | 2N1274 | 2N1176 | 2SB222 | 01 |
| 2N466 | | | | AC126 | AC153 | | | | 01 |
| 2N466 | | | | ACY17 | | | | | 01 |
| 2N467 | G | P | MO, ET, NP, SR, St | (AC152VI) | AC128 | 2N2431 | 2N585 | 2SB227 | 01 |
| 2N467 | | | | AC153 | AC171 | 2N1176 | | | 01 |
| 2N467 | | | | AC126 | ASY80 | | | | 01 |
| 2N467 | | | | ACY17 | | | | | 01 |
| 2N468 | G | N | St | AD161 | | 2N4077 | | | |
| 2N469 | P | P | | | | | | | 04 |
| 2N470 | S | N | TR, ET, NP, SQ, St | BSX45/6 | BFY10 | 2N2297 | | | 02 |
| 2N470 | | | | BFY49 | BFY50 | | | | 02 |
| 2N471 | S | N | ET, NP, SQ, St | BSX45/6 | BFY10 | 2N706 | 2N2297 | | 01 |
| 2N471 | | | | BFY49 | BFY50 | | | | 01 |
| 2N471A | S | N | TR, ET, NP, SQ, St | BFY10 | BFY49 | 2N706 | 2N2297 | | 01 |
| 2N471A | | | | BFY50 | | | | | 01 |
| 2N472 | S | N | TR, ET, NP, SQ, St | BSX45/6 | BFY10 | 2N706 | 2N2297 | | 02 |
| 2N472 | | | | BFY49 | BFY50 | | | | 02 |
| 2N472A | S | N | TR, ET, NP, SQ, St | BFY10 | BFY50 | 2N2297 | | | 02 |
| 2N473 | S | N | TR, ET, NP, SQ, St | BSX45/6 | BFY11 | 2N706 | 2N2297 | | 01 |
| 2N473 | | | | BFY49 | BFY50 | | | | 01 |
| 2N474 | S | N | TR, ET, NP, SQ, St | BFY11 | BFY69 | 2N706 | 2N2297 | | 01 |
| 2N474 | | | | BFY50 | | | | | 01 |
| 2N474A | S | N | TR, ET, NP, SQ, St | BFY10 | BFY69 | 2N706 | 2N2297 | | 01 |
| 2N474A | | | | BFY50 | | | | | 01 |
| 2N475 | S | N | TR, ET, NP, SQ, St | BSX45/6 | BFY11 | 2N706 | 2N2297 | | 01 |
| 2N475 | | | | BFY50 | | | | | 01 |
| 2N475A | S | N | TR, ET, NP, SQ, St | BFY50 | | 2N2297 | | | 01 |
| 2N476 | S | N | TR, ET, NP, SQ, St | BCY65 | BSY11 | 2N706 | 2N2297 | | 01 |
| 2N476 | | | | BFY50 | | | | | 01 |
| 2N477 | S | N | TR, ET, NP, SR, St | BCY65 | BSY11 | 2N706 | 2N2297 | | 01 |
| 2N477 | | | | BFY50 | | | | | 01 |
| 2N478 | S | N | TR, ET, NP, SR, St | BCY65 | BSY11 | 2N706 | 2N2297 | | 02 |
| 2N478 | | | | BFY60 | | | | | 02 |
| 2N479 | S | N | TR, ET, NP, SQ, St | BCY65 | BSY11 | 2N706 | 2N2297 | | 02 |
| 2N479 | | | | BFY50 | | | | | 02 |
| 2N479A | S | N | TR, ET, SR, SQ, St | BFY50 | | 2N2297 | | | 01 |
| 2N480 | S | N | TR, ET, NP, SR, TX | BCY65 | BSY11 | 2N706 | 2N2297 | | 02 |
| 2N480 | | | | BFY50 | | | | | 02 |
| 2N480A | S | N | TR, ET, NP, SQ, St | BFY50 | | 2N2297 | | | 01 |
| 2N481 | G | P | ET, NP, SR, St, UP | AF185 | AF126 | 2N371 | 2N1305 | | 02 |
| 2N481 | | | | AFY15 | AF190 | | | | 02 |
| 2N481 | | | | ASY27 | | | | | 02 |
| 2N482 | G | P | ET, NP, St, UP | AF185 | AF126 | 2N373 | 2N2189 | | 02 |
| 2N482 | | | | AFY15 | AF190 | 2N1305 | | | 02 |

| TYPE | M/S | POL | MANUFAC | EUROPEAN | | AMERICAN | | JAPANESE | USE |
|------|-----|-----|---------|----------|---|----------|---|----------|-----|
| 2N482 | | | | ASY27 | AF126 | 2N373 | 2N2189 | | 02 |
| 2N483 | G | P | ET, NP, St, UP | AF185 | AF126 | 2N373 | 2N2189 | | 02 |
| 2N483 | | | | AFY15 | AF190 | 2N1305 | | | 02 |
| 2N483 | | | | ASY27 | | | | | 02 |
| 2N484 | G | P | ET, NP, St, UP | AF185 | AF126 | 2N373 | 2N2190 | | 02 |
| | | | | | | | | | |
| 2N484 | | | | AFY15 | ASY27 | 2N1305 | | | 02 |
| 2N485 | G | P | ET, NP, St, UP | AF185 | AF126 | 2N374 | 2N2190 | | 02 |
| 2N485 | | | | AFY15 | AF190 | 2N1305 | | | 02 |
| 2N485 | | | | ASY27 | | | | | 02 |
| 2N486 | G | P | ET, NP, St, UP | AF185 | ASY27 | 2N1305 | | | 02 |
| | | | | | | | | | |
| 2N487 | G | P | NP | | | | | 2SA32 | 01 |
| 2N489 | U | | PN,GE, SM, TX | | | | | | |
| 2N489A | U | | PN,GE, SM, TX | | | | | | |
| 2N489B | U | | PN,GE, SM, TX | | | | | | |
| 2N490 | U | | PN,GE, SM, TX | | | | | | |
| | | | | | | | | | |
| 2N490A | U | | PN,GE, SM, TX | | | | | | |
| 2N490B | U | | PN,GE, SM, TX | | | | | | |
| 2N490C | U | | PN,GE, SM, TX | | | | | | |
| 2N491 | U | | PN,GE, SM, TX | | | | | | |
| 2N491A | U | | PN,GE, SM, TX | | | | | | |
| | | | | | | | | | |
| 2N491B | U | | PN,GE, SM, TX | | | | | | |
| 2N492 | U | | PN,GE, SM, TX | | | | | | |
| 2N492A | U | | PN,GE, SM, TX | | | | | | |
| 2N492B | U | | PN,GE, SM, TX | | | | | | |
| 2N492C | U | | PN,GE, SM, TX | | | | | | |
| | | | | | | | | | |
| 2N493 | U | | PN,GE, SM, TX | | | | | | |
| 2N493A | U | | PN,GE, SM, TX | | | | | | |
| 2N493B | U | | PN,GE, SM, TX | | | | | | |
| 2N494 | U | | PN,GE, SM, TX | | | | | | |
| 2N494A | U | | PN,GE, SM, TX | | | | | | |
| | | | | | | | | | |
| 2N494B | U | | PN,GE, SM, TX | | | | | | |
| 2N494C | U | | PN,GE, SM, TX | | | | | | |
| 2N495 | S | P | SQ | BCY28 | BC177 | 2N354 | 2N2945 | | 02 |
| 2N495 | | | | BC211 | | 2N3965 | | | 02 |
| 2N495/18 | S | P | SP | BC177 | | 2N3965 | | | |
| | | | | | | | | | |
| 2N496 | S | P | ID, SM, SQ | BC177 | | 2N3965 | | | 10 |
| 2N496/18 | S | P | SP | BC177 | | 2N3965 | | | |
| 2N497 | S | N | ET, F, TX, NP, PH | BSX46-6 | BFY50 | 2N3498 | 2N2297 | | 01 |
| 2N497A | S | N | ET, TX, NP, SS, St | BSX46-6 | BFY50 | 2N2297 | 2N5681 | | 01 |
| 2N498 | S | N | ET, F, TX | (BSX47-6) | BSW66 | 2N3498 | | | 01 |
| | | | | | | | | | |
| 2N498 | | | | | | 2N1613 | | | 01 |
| 2N498A | S | N | ET, TX | (BSX47-6) | BSW66 | 2N5681 | 2N1893 | | 01 |
| 2N499 | G | P | ET, MO | (AF127) | AF106 | 2N3326 | 2N371 | | 02 |
| 2N499 | | | | AF137 | AF102 | 2N2188 | 2N990 | | 02 |
| 2N499 | | | | AF124 | | | | | 02 |
| | | | | | | | | | |
| 2N499A | G | P | ET, MO | (AF127) | AF124 | 2N3323 | 2N990 | | 02 |
| 2N500 | G | P | SR | AF124 | | 2N3323 | 2N2189 | | 02 |
| 2N500 | | | | | | 2N990 | | | 02 |
| 2N501 | G | P | ET, MO | (AF126) | AF106 | 2N960 | 2N2189 | | 13 |
| 2N501 | | | | AF137 | AF102 | | | | 13 |
| | | | | | | | | | |
| 2N501 | | | | AF124 | | | | | 13 |
| 2N501A | G | P | ET, MO | (AF127) | AF124 | 2N960 | 2N990 | | 13 |
| 2N501/18 | G | P | SY | AF124 | | 2N990 | | | |
| 2N502 | G | P | ET, MO | (AF127) | ASZ21 | 2N3283 | 2N2169 | | 02 |
| 2N502 | | | | AF124 | | 2N990 | | | 02 |
| | | | | | | | | | |
| 2N502A | G | P | ET, MO | (AF127) | AF124 | 2N3284 | 2N990 | | 02 |
| 2N502B | G | P | ET, MO | (AF127) | AF124 | 2N990 | | | 02 |
| 2N503 | G | P | ET, NP, SQ | ASZ21 | AF106 | 2N3284 | 2N2189 | | 02 |
| 2N504 | G | P | ET, NP, SP | AF185 | AF124 | 2N3323 | 2N373 | 2SA235 | 02 |
| 2N504 | | | | AF134 | AF114 | 2N2189 | 2N990 | | 02 |
| | | | | | | | | | |
| 2N504 | | | | AF135 | | | | | 02 |
| 2N505 | G | P | ET, NP | ASY27 | | 2N1305 | | | 01 |
| 2N506 | G | P | ET, NP | AC151 | AC125 | 2N406 | | | 01 |
| 2N506 | | | | AC122 | AC163 | | | | 01 |
| 2N506 | | | | OC71 | | | | | 01 |
| | | | | | | | | | |
| 2N507 | G | N | ET, NP | AC127 | AC176 | 2N2430 | | | 01 |
| 2N508 | G | P | GE, MO, ET, St, UP | (AC152VI) | AC126 | 2N2429 | 2N1176 | | 01 |
| 2N508 | | | | 2G508 | ACY17 | | | | 01 |
| 2N508A | G | P | GE, MO, ET, NP, St | (ASY70VI) | AC126 | 2N2429 | 2N1189 | | 01 |
| 2N508A | | | | ACY17 | | | | | 01 |
| | | | | | | | | | |
| 2N509 | G | P | WE | ACY17 | | 2N1195 | 2N1176 | | 02 |
| 2N511 | G | P | ET, SR, SS | ADY26 | | 2N1554 | 2N456A | | 06 |
| 2N511 | | | | | | 2N1100 | | | 06 |
| 2N511A | G | P | ET, SS | | | 2N1555 | | | 06 |
| 2N511B | G | P | ET, NP, SR, SS | | | 2N1556 | | | 16 |

| TYPE | M/S | POL | MANUFAC | EUROPEAN | | AMERICAN | | JAPANESE | USE |
|---|---|---|---|---|---|---|---|---|---|
| 2N512 | G | P | ET, NP, TX | | | 2N1558 | 2N456A | | 06 |
| 2N512A | G | P | ET, NP, SR, SS, TX | | | 2N1559 | | | 06 |
| 2N512B | G | P | ET, NP, SR, SS, TX | | | 2N1560 | | | 16 |
| 2N513 | G | P | ET, NP, SR | | | 2N1163 | 2N456A | | 06 |
| 2N513A | G | P | ET, NP, SR | | | 2N1165 | | | 06 |
| | | | | | | | | | |
| 2N513B | G | P | ET, NP, SR | | | 2N1167 | | | 16 |
| 2N514 | G | P | ET, NP, SR | ADY26 | | 2N1163 | 2N1100 | | 16 |
| 2N514A | G | P | ET, NP, SR | | | 2N1165 | | | 16 |
| 2N514B | G | P | ET, NP, SR | | | 2N1167 | | | 16 |
| 2N515 | G | N | ET, NP | ASY26 | ASY73 | 2N1304 | | | 02 |
| | | | | | | | | | |
| 2N515 | | | | ASY29 | | | | | 02 |
| 2N516 | G | N | CI, ET | ASY26 | ASY29 | 2N1304 | | | 02 |
| 2N516 | | | | ASY73 | | | | | 02 |
| 2N517 | G | N | ET, CI | ASY26 | ASY73 | 2N1306 | 2N1304 | | 02 |
| 2N517 | | | | ASY29 | | | | | 02 |
| | | | | | | | | | |
| 2N518 | G | P | ET, CI | ASY27 | | 2N404 | 2N1305 | | 10 |
| 2N519 | G | P | ET, CI, II | AC153 | AC117R | 2N404 | 2N578 | | 10 |
| 2N519 | | | | AC128 | ASY27 | 2N1305 | | | 10 |
| 2N519A | G | P | CI, II, ET | ASY17 | | 2N1176 | | | 10 |
| 2N520 | G | P | CI, ET, II | ASY26 | ASY27 | 2N404 | 2N578 | | 10 |
| | | | | | | | | | |
| 2N520 | | | | | | 2N1305 | | | 10 |
| 2N520A | G | P | CI, ET, II | ASY27 | | 2N1305 | | | 10 |
| 2N521 | G | P | CI, ET, II | ASY27 | | 2N579 | 2N1377 | | 10 |
| 2N521 | | | | | | 2N1305 | | | 10 |
| 2N521A | G | P | CI, ET, II | ASY27 | | 2N1305 | | | 10 |
| | | | | | | | | | |
| 2N522 | G | P | CI, ET, II | ASY27 | | 2N522A | 2N1309 | | 10 |
| 2N522 | | | | | | 2N1305 | | | 10 |
| 2N522A | G | P | CI, ET, II | ASY27 | | 2N1305 | | | 10 |
| 2N523 | G | P | CI, ET, II | ASY27 | | 2N1305 | 2N1377 | | 10 |
| 2N523A | G | P | CI, ET, II | ASY27 | | 2N1305 | | | 10 |
| | | | | | | | | | |
| 2N524 | G | P | MO, GE, TX | ASY48IV | AC152 | 2N1305 | 2N1176 | 2SB224 | 01 |
| 2N524 | | | | AC131/50 | AC128 | | | | 01 |
| 2N524 | | | | OC76 | ACY17 | | | | 01 |
| 2N524A | G | P | MO, CI, ET, II | (ASY48IV) | ACY17 | 2N1176 | | | 01 |
| 2N525 | G | P | GE, MO, TX | ASY48IV | AC152 | 2N1373 | 2N1191 | 2SB225 | 01 |
| | | | | | | | | | |
| 2N525 | | | | ASY26 | OC80 | 2N1176 | | | 01 |
| 2N525 | | | | AC153 | OC72 | | | | 01 |
| 2N525 | | | | ACY17 | | | | | 01 |
| 2N525A | G | P | MO, CI, ET, II | (ASY48IV) | ACY17 | 2N1176 | | | 01 |
| 2N526 | G | P | GE, MO, TX | (ASY48V) | ASY48VI | 2N586 | 2N1307 | 2SB226 | 01 |
| | | | | | | | | | |
| 2N526 | | | | ASY80 | ASY26 | 2N1176 | | | 01 |
| 2N526 | | | | AC117 | AC128 | | | | 01 |
| 2N526 | | | | AC153 | ACY17 | | | | 01 |
| 2N526A | G | P | MO, CI, ET, II | (ASY48VI) | ACY17 | | | | 01 |
| 2N527 | G | P | GE, MO, TX | ASY48VI | AC152 | 2N1307 | 2N1176 | 2SB227 | 01 |
| | | | | | | | | | |
| 2N527 | | | | ASY80 | AC131/50 | | | | 01 |
| 2N527 | | | | AC117 | AC128 | | | | 01 |
| 2N527 | | | | ACY17 | | | | | 01 |
| 2N527A | G | P | MO, CI, ET, II | (ASY48VII) | ACY17 | 2N1307 | 2N1176 | | 01 |
| 2N528 | G | P | WE | | ACY17 | 2N1176 | | | 01 |
| | | | | | | | | | |
| 2N529 | G | P | ET, CI | ASY27 | | 2N1303 | 2N1305 | | |
| 2N530 | G | P | ET, CI | ASY48IV | AC122gn | 2N404 | 2N1303 | 2SB264 | |
| 2N530 | | | | AC126 | ASY27 | 2N1305 | | | |
| 2N531 | G | P | ET, CI | ASY27 | | 2N1305 | | | |
| 2N532 | G | P | CI, ET | ASY27 | | 2N1305 | | | |
| | | | | | | | | | |
| 2N533 | G | P | ET, FR, UP | ASY27 | | 2N1305 | | | |
| 2N534 | G | P | ET, NS, PH | AC125 | | 2N1189 | 2N406 | | |
| 2N535 | G | P | CN, ET, FR | AC126 | AC117 | 2N2429 | 2N1192 | 2SB264 | 01 |
| 2N535 | | | | AC153 | AF181 | 2N404 | 2N406 | | 01 |
| 2N535 | | | | AC125 | | | | | 01 |
| | | | | | | | | | |
| 2N535A | G | P | ET | AC126 | ACY17 | 2N2429 | 2N1192 | | 01 |
| 2N535A | | | | | | 2N1176 | | | 01 |
| 2N535B | G | P | ET | ACY17 | | 2N1176 | | | 01 |
| 2N536 | G | P | ET | AF181 | ASY27 | 2N1193 | 2N404 | | 10 |
| 2N536 | | | | | | 2N1305 | | | 10 |
| | | | | | | | | | |
| 2N537 | G | P | WE | AF139 | AF186 | | | | 02 |
| 2N537 | | | | AF238S | | | | | 02 |
| 2N538 | G | P | SR, SS | AUY21II | AUY28 | 2N2140 | TI3027 | | 16 |
| 2N538 | | | | ASZ18 | OC26 | 2N1533 | | | 16 |
| 2N538 | | | | ASZ15 | | | | | 16 |
| | | | | | | | | | |
| 2N538A | G | P | SR, SS | ASZ15 | | 2N2140 | 2N1533 | | 16 |
| 2N539 | G | P | SR, SS, UP | ADY26 | ASZ15 | 2N2145 | TI3027 | | 16 |
| 2N539 | | | | ASZ18 | | 2N1533 | | | 16 |
| 2N539A | G | P | SR, UP | ASZ15 | | 2N2145 | 2N1533 | | 16 |
| 2N540 | G | P | SR, SS | AD138/50 | ASZ18 | 2N1551 | TI3027 | | 16 |

| TYPE | M/S | POL | MANUFAC | EUROPEAN | | AMERICAN | | JAPANESE | USE |
|------|-----|-----|---------|----------|--|----------|--|----------|-----|
| 2N540 | | | | OC26 | | 2N1533 | | | 16 |
| 2N540A | G | P | SR, SS | ASZ15 | | 2N1551 | 2N1533 | | 16 |
| 2N541 | S | N | TR, ET, TX, NP, SM | BCY59 | BSY44 | 2N2297 | | | 02 |
| 2N541 | | | | BSY11 | BFY50 | | | | 02 |
| 2N542 | S | N | TR, ET, NP, TX, SR | BFY50 | | 2N2297 | | | 02 |
| | | | | | | | | | |
| 2N542A | S | N | TR, ET, NP, SR, St | BFY50 | | 2N2297 | | | 01 |
| 2N543 | S | N | TR, ET, NP, TX, SR | BFY50 | | 2N2297 | | | 02 |
| 2N543A | S | N | TR, ET, SR, SQ, St | BFY50 | | 2N2297 | | | 01 |
| 2N544 | G | P | RC, SY | AF185 | AF126 | 2N990 | | HJ75 | 02 |
| 2N544 | | | | AF138 | AF116 | | | | 02 |
| | | | | | | | | | |
| 2N544/33 | G | P | SY | AF124 | | 2N990 | | | |
| 2N545 | S | N | TR, ET, GS, NP, UN | BSW66 | | 2N4238 | 2N1893 | | 02 |
| 2N546 | S | N | TR, ET, GS, NP, UN | BFY50 | | 2N4237 | 2N2297 | | 02 |
| 2N547 | S | N | TR, ET, UN, NP, SQ | BSW66 | | 2N3766 | 2N4238 | | 02 |
| 2N547 | | | | | | 2N1893 | | | 02 |
| | | | | | | | | | |
| 2N548 | S | N | TR, ET, NP, St, UN | BFY50 | | MJ3101 | 2N4237 | | 02 |
| 2N548 | | | | | | 2N2297 | | | 02 |
| 2N549 | S | N | TR, ET, NP, St, UN | BSW66 | | 2N1893 | 2N2243A | | 02 |
| 2N549 | | | | | | 2N4238 | | | 02 |
| 2N550 | S | N | TR, ET, NP, St, SQ | BFY50 | | 2N1893 | 2N2243A | | 02 |
| | | | | | | | | | |
| 2N550 | | | | | | 2N4237 | 2N2297 | | 02 |
| 2N551 | S | N | TR, ET, NP, SQ, St | BSW66 | | 2N1893 | 2N2243A | | 02 |
| 2N552 | S | N | TR, ET, NP, SQ, St | BFY50 | | 2N1893 | 2N2243A | | 02 |
| 2N552 | | | | | | 2N2297 | | | 02 |
| 2N553 | G | P | ET, NP, SR, SS, St | ASZ15 | ASZ16 | 2N2144 | 2N1536 | | 16 |
| | | | | | | | | | |
| 2N554 | G | P | MO, DD, ET, SR, St | AD149IV | ASZ16 | TI301 | 2N301 | | 06 |
| 2N554 | | | | | | TI3027 | 2N1536 | | 06 |
| 2N555 | G | P | MO, RC, NP, SR, St | AD149IV | ASZ16 | TI3027 | 2N1536 | | 06 |
| 2N556 | G | N | ET, NP | ASY75 | ASY29 | 2N1551 | 2N1302 | | 10 |
| 2N556 | | | | | | 2N1304 | | | 10 |
| | | | | | | | | | |
| 2N556A | G | N | | | | | | | |
| 2N557 | G | N | ET, NP | ASY75 | ASY29 | 2N1304 | | | 10 |
| 2N557A | G | N | | | | 2N5681 | | | |
| 2N558 | G | N | NP | ASY75 | ASY29 | 2N1306 | 2N1304 | | 10 |
| 2N558A | G | N | | ASY29 | | 2N1304 | | | |
| | | | | | | | | | |
| 2N559 | P | | TX, WE | AF106 | | 2N645 | | | 10 |
| 2N560 | S | N | NP, SM, SR, SQ, TD | BSX33 | | 2N731 | | | 10 |
| 2N561 | G | P | ET, NP, SR | AD131 | AD149 | 2N456A | 2N618 | 2SB249 | 01 |
| 2N561 | | | | ASZ15 | ASZ18 | 2N1533 | | | 01 |
| 2N561 | | | | | | | | | 01 |
| | | | | | | | | | |
| 2N563 | G | P | ET, NP | AC128 | AC153 | 2N2431 | 2N650 | 2SB219 | 10 |
| 2N563 | | | | AC131 | AC152 | 2N1924 | 2N1176 | | 10 |
| 2N563 | | | | OC76 | ACY17 | | | | 10 |
| 2N564 | G | P | ET, NP, St | AC128 | AC152 | 2N2431 | 2N650 | 2SB224 | 10 |
| 2N564 | | | | AC131 | OC76 | 2N1176 | | | 10 |
| | | | | | | | | | |
| 2N564 | | | | ACY17 | | | | | 10 |
| 2N565 | G | P | ET, NP, St | AC128 | AC153 | 2N2431 | 2N651 | 2SB101 | 10 |
| 2N565 | | | | AC117 | OC72 | 2N1176 | | | 10 |
| 2N565 | | | | ACY17 | | | | | 10 |
| 2N566 | G | P | ET, NP, St | AC128 | AC153 | 2N2431 | 2N651 | 2SB101 | 10 |
| | | | | | | | | | |
| 2N566 | | | | AC117 | OC72 | 2N1176 | | | 10 |
| 2N566 | | | | ACY17 | | | | | 10 |
| 2N567 | G | P | ET, NP, St | AC128 | AC157 | 2N2431 | 2N651 | 2SB103 | 10 |
| 2N567 | | | | AC131 | AC152 | 2N1176 | | | 10 |
| 2N567 | | | | OC76 | ACY17 | | | | 10 |
| | | | | | | | | | |
| 2N568 | G | P | ET, NP, St | AC128 | AC153 | 2N2431 | 2N651 | 2SB103 | 10 |
| 2N568 | | | | AC117 | OC72 | 2N1176 | | | 10 |
| 2N568 | | | | ACY17 | | | | | 10 |
| 2N569 | G | P | ET, NP, St | AC128 | AC153 | 2N2431 | 2N1193 | 2SB103 | 10 |
| 2N569 | | | | AC117 | OC72 | 2N1176 | | | 10 |
| | | | | | | | | | |
| 2N569 | | | | ACY17 | | | | | 10 |
| 2N570 | G | P | ET, NP, St, UP | AC128 | AV153 | 2N2431 | 2N1192 | | 10 |
| 2N570 | | | | AC117R | ACY17 | 2N1176 | | | 10 |
| 2N571 | G | P | ET, NP, St | AC126 | AC153 | 2N2431 | 2N1193 | | 10 |
| 2N571 | | | | AC117R | ACY17 | 2N1176 | | | 10 |
| | | | | | | | | | |
| 2N572 | G | P | ET, NP, St | AC128 | AC153 | 2N2431 | 2N1193 | | 10 |
| 2N572 | | | | AC117R | ACY17 | 2N1176 | | | 10 |
| 2N573 | G | P | ET, NP | ACY17 | | 2N1176 | | | 01 |
| 2N574 | G | P | SQ, SS | AUY20VI | ADZ12 | 2N1550 | 2N456A | | 16 |
| 2N574 | | | | AUY22 | ASZ16 | 2N1022A | 2N1536 | | 16 |
| | | | | | | | | | |
| 2N574A | G | P | SQ, SS | ASZ15 | | 2N1551 | 2N1533 | | 16 |
| 2N575 | G | P | SQ, SS | AUY20VI | ADY36 | 2N1554 | | | 16 |
| 2N575 | | | | ADY26 | AUY22 | | | | 16 |
| 2N575A | G | P | SQ, SS | | | 2N1555 | | | 16 |
| 2N576 | G | N | ET, NP | ASY26 | ASY73 | 2N1304 | 2N1306 | | 10 |

| TYPE | M/S | POL | MANUFAC | EUROPEAN | | AMERICAN | | JAPANESE | USE |
|------|-----|-----|---------|----------|---|----------|---|----------|-----|
| 2N576 | | | | ASY29 | | | | | 10 |
| 2N576A | G | N | ES, ET, NP | ASY29 | | 2N1304 | | | 10 |
| 2N578 | G | P | ET, NP, St, UP | ASY27 | | 2N404 | 2N1305 | | 10 |
| 2N579 | G | P | ET, NP, St, UP | AF127 | AF101 | 2N404 | 2N1305 | | 10 |
| 2N579 | | | | OC45 | ASY27 | | | | 10 |
| 2N580 | G | P | ET, NP, St, UP | ASY27 | | 2N1307 | 2N1309 | | 10 |
| 2N580 | | | | | | 2N1305 | | | 10 |
| 2N581 | G | P | ET, NP, SS, St, TX | ASY27 | | 2N1305 | | | 10 |
| 2N582 | G | P | ET, NP, SR, St, TX | ASY27 | | 2N1305 | | | 10 |
| 2N583 | G | P | ET, NP | AFY12 | ASY27 | 2N1305 | | | 10 |
| 2N584 | G | P | ET, NP | ASY27 | | 2N1305 | | | 10 |
| 2N585 | G | P | ET, NP, SR | AC117 | AC153 | | | 2SB225 | 10 |
| 2N585 | | | | ASY25 | ASY29 | | | 2SB225 | 10 |
| 2N586 | G | P | ET, NP | AC153 | | 2N1191 | 2N2706 | 2SB225 | 10 |
| 2N586 | | | | AC128 | AC117 | | | | 10 |
| 2N586 | | | | AC132 | | | | | 10 |
| 2N587 | G | N | ET, NP, SS, St, TX | AC176 | | 2N2430 | | 2ST11 | 10 |
| 2N588 | G | P | ET, NP, SP | ASZ21 | AF124 | 2N3324 | 2N990 | | 02 |
| 2N588A | G | P | St | AF124 | | 2N990 | | | 02 |
| 2N589 | G | P | ET, NP | ASZ21 | ASZ21 | 2N3324 | 2N1532 | | 06 |
| 2N589 | | | | | | 2N1533 | | | 06 |
| 2N591 | G | P | ET, NP, SS | AC126 | AC153VI | 2N2429 | 2N406 | 2SB100 | 01 |
| 2N591 | | | | AC122/30 | AC122 | | | | 01 |
| 2N591 | | | | AC128 | AC125 | | | | 01 |
| 2N591/5 | G | P | SY | AC126 | | 2N2429 | 2N406 | | |
| 2N592 | G | P | St | AC153 | AC131 | 2N607 | 2N608 | 2SB65 | 10 |
| 2N592 | | | | OC76 | AC152 | 2N406 | | | 10 |
| 2N592 | | | | AC125 | | | | | 10 |
| 2N593 | G | P | St | AC153 | AC131 | 2N604 | 2N608 | 2SB65 | 10 |
| 2N593 | | | | OC76 | AC152 | 2N406 | | | 10 |
| 2N593 | | | | AC125 | | | | | 10 |
| 2N594 | G | N | SS, St, TX | ASY29 | | 2N1304 | | | 10 |
| 2N595 | G | N | SS, St, TX | ASY29 | | 2N1304 | | | 10 |
| 2N596 | G | N | ID, SS, TX | ASY29 | | 2N1304 | | | 10 |
| 2N597 | G | P | ET, NP, St | AC153 | AC131 | 2N3427 | 2N1305 | 2SB225 | 10 |
| 2N597 | | | | AC128 | AC117 | 2N1176 | | | 10 |
| 2N597 | | | | OC72 | ACY17 | | | | 10 |
| 2N598 | G | P | ES, ET, NP, St | ACY17 | | 2N3427 | 2N1997 | | 10 |
| 2N598 | | | | | | 2N1998 | 2N1176 | | 10 |
| 2N599 | G | P | ET, NP, SQ, St | ASY27 | | 2N3428 | 2N1997 | | 10 |
| 2N599 | | | | | | 2N1999 | 2N1305 | | 10 |
| 2N600 | G | P | SQ | | | 2N3427 | 2N1997 | | 16 |
| 2N600 | | | | | | 2N1998 | | | 16 |
| 2N601 | G | P | SQ, ID | | | 2N3428 | 2N1997 | | 16 |
| 2N601 | | | | | | 2N1999 | | | 16 |
| 2N602 | G | P | SM, SQ | AC152 | ASY24 | 2N643 | 2N2635 | 2SB65 | 13 |
| 2N602 | | | | AC128 | AC131 | 2N990 | | | 13 |
| 2N602 | | | | AF124 | | | | | 13 |
| 2N602A | G | P | SM, SQ | AF124 | | 2N990 | | | |
| 2N603 | G | P | SM, SQ | AC152 | ASY24 | 2N644 | 2N2635 | 2SB65 | 13 |
| 2N603 | | | | AC128 | AC131 | 2N990 | | | |
| 2N603 | | | | AF124 | | | | | 13 |
| 2N603A | G | P | SM, SQ | AF124 | | 2N990 | | | |
| 2N604 | G | P | SM, SQ | AC152 | ASY24 | 2N645 | 2N2635 | 2SB65 | 13 |
| 2N604 | | | | AC128 | AC131 | 2N990 | | | 13 |
| 2N604 | | | | OC76 | AF124 | | | | |
| 2N604A | G | P | SM, SQ | AF124 | | 2N990 | | | 13 |
| 2N605 | G | P | St | AC152 | ASY24 | 2N608 | 2N2635 | 2SB65 | 02 |
| 2N605 | | | | AC128 | AC131 | 2N406 | | | 02 |
| 2N605 | | | | OC307 | AC125 | | | | 02 |
| 2N606 | G | P | St | AC152 | ASY24 | 2N603 | 2N2635 | 2SB65 | 02 |
| 2N606 | | | | AC128 | AC131 | 2N406 | | | 02 |
| 2N606 | | | | OC76 | AC125 | | | | 02 |
| 2N607 | G | P | St | AC152 | ASY24 | 2N605 | 2N2635 | 2SB65 | 02 |
| 2N607 | | | | AC128 | AC131 | 2N406 | | | 02 |
| 2N607 | | | | OC76 | AC125 | | | | 02 |
| 2N608 | G | P | St | AC152 | ASY24 | 2N605 | 2N2635 | 2SB65 | 02 |
| 2N608 | | | | AC128 | AC131 | 2N406 | | | 02 |
| 2N608 | | | | OC72 | AC125 | | | | 02 |
| 2N609 | G | P | ET, NP | AC128 | AC153 | 2N2431 | 2N1193 | | 01 |
| 2N609 | | | | AC117R | ACY17 | 2N217 | 2N404 | | 01 |
| 2N609 | | | | | | 2N1176 | | | 01 |
| 2N610 | G | P | ET, NP, UP | AC128 | AC153 | 2N2431 | 2N1193 | 2SB222 | 01 |
| 2N610 | | | | AC117 | OC72 | 2N217 | 2N404 | | 01 |
| 2N610 | | | | ACY17 | | 2N1176 | | | 01 |

| TYPE | M/S | POL | MANUFAC | EUROPEAN | | AMERICAN | | JAPANESE | USE |
|---|---|---|---|---|---|---|---|---|---|
| 2N611 | G | P | ET, NP, UP | AC128 | AC153 | 2N2431 | 2N1192 | 2SB222 | 01 |
| 2N611 | | | | AC117 | OC72 | 2N217 | 2N1309 | | 01 |
| 2N611 | | | | ACY17 | | 2N1176 | | | 01 |
| 2N612 | G | P | ET, NP | AC128 | AC152 | 2N2431 | 2N1191 | 2SB224 | 01 |
| 2N612 | | | | AC122 | AC131 | 2N217 | 2N406 | | 01 |
| 2N612 | | | | ASY26 | AC125 | | | | 01 |
| 2N613 | G | P | ET, NP, UP | AC128 | AC152 | 2N2431 | 2N1191 | 2SB224 | 01 |
| 2N613 | | | | AC122 | AC131 | 2N217 | 2N270 | | 01 |
| 2N613 | | | | ASY26 | AC125 | 2N406 | | | 01 |
| 2N614 | G | P | ET, NP | AF185 | AF124 | 2N373 | 2N2614 | | 02 |
| 2N614 | | | | AF137 | OC44N | | | | 02 |
| 2N615 | G | P | ET, NP | AF185 | AF127 | 2N373 | 2N2614 | | 02 |
| 2N615 | | | | AF137 | OC44N | | | | 02 |
| 2N616 | G | P | ET, NP | AF185 | OC44N | 2N2614 | | | 02 |
| 2N617 | G | P | ET, NP, UP | AF185 | AF106 | 2N374 | 2N2614 | | 02 |
| 2N617 | | | | AFY15 | OC44N | | | | 02 |
| 2N618 | G | P | ET, MO, SR, NP, SS | AD131 | AD138/50 | 2N561 | 2N1533 | 2SB249 | 06 |
| 2N618 | | | | OC2B | ADZ12 | | | | 06 |
| 2N618 | | | | ASZ15 | (AD132V) | | | | 06 |
| 2N619 | S | N | SM | BC107 | | A157 | | | 01 |
| 2N620 | S | N | SM | BFY11 | BC107 | A157 | | | 01 |
| 2N621 | S | N | SM | BC107 | | A157 | | | 01 |
| 2N622 | S | N | SM | BFY50 | | 2N2297 | | | 05 |
| 2N623 | G | P | St | AF124 | AF134 | 2N645 | 2N990 | 2SA116 | |
| 2N623 | | | | AF130 | AF135 | | | | |
| 2N624 | G | P | SY | AC153 | AF134 | 2N188 | 2N2188 | | 02 |
| 2N624 | | | | AC128 | AF124 | 2N990 | | | 02 |
| 2N625 | G | N | SY | AD161 | | 2N4077 | | | 10 |
| 2N627 | G | P | MO, ET, SR, NP | ASZ16 | | 2N1536 | | | 06 |
| 2N628 | G | P | MO, ET, NP, SR | ASZ16 | | 2N561 | TI3027 | | 06 |
| 2N628 | | | | | | 2N1536 | | | 06 |
| 2N629 | G | P | MO, ET, NP, SR | ADZ12 | ASZ15 | 2N561 | TI3027 | | 06 |
| 2N629 | | | | | | 2N1533 | | | 06 |
| 2N630 | G | P | MO, ET, NP, SR | | | 2N1014 | TI3027 | | 06 |
| 2N630 | | | | | | 2N1533 | | | 06 |
| 2N631 | G | P | ET, NP, SQ, St, UP | AC128 | AC153 | 2N2431 | 2N1194 | 2SB33 | 01 |
| 2N631 | | | | AC124 | OC72 | 2N404 | 2N1305 | | 01 |
| 2N631 | | | | ASY26 | ASY27 | | | | 01 |
| 2N632 | G | P | ET, NP, St, UP | AC128 | AC131 | 2N2431 | 2N1193 | 2SB37 | 01 |
| 2N632 | | | | AC152 | OC76 | 2N404 | 2N1305 | | 01 |
| 2N632 | | | | ASY27 | | | | | 01 |
| 2N633 | G | P | ET, NP, St, UP | AC128 | AC153 | 2N2431 | 2N1192 | 2SB37 | 01 |
| 2N633 | | | | AC131 | OC76 | 2N404 | 2N1176 | 2SB220 | 01 |
| 2N633 | | | | AC117 | OC72 | | | | 01 |
| 2N633 | | | | ACY17 | | | | | 01 |
| 2N634 | G | N | ET, NP | ASY29 | | 2N1304 | | | 13 |
| 2N634A | G | N | ET, NP, SS, TX | ASY29 | | 2N1304 | 2N1306 | | 10 |
| 2N635 | G | N | ET, NP | ASY29 | | 2N1091 | 2N1304 | | 13 |
| 2N635A | G | N | ET, NP, SS, TX | ASY29 | | 2N1304 | | | 10 |
| 2N636 | G | N | ET, NP | ASY29 | | 2N1091 | 2N1304 | | 13 |
| 2N636A | G | N | ET, NP, SS, TX | ASY29 | | 2N1304 | | | 10 |
| 2N637 | G | P | ET, NP, SR | AD131 | OC28 | 2N1535 | 2N561 | 2SB248A | 16 |
| 2N637 | | | | OD605 | ASZ16 | 2N638 | 2N1536 | | 16 |
| 2N637A | G | P | ET, NP, SR | ASZ16 | | 2N1537 | 2N561 | | 16 |
| 2N637A | | | | | | 2N1536 | | | 16 |
| 2N637B | G | P | ET, NP, SR | ASZ15 | | 2N1538 | 2N1533 | | 16 |
| 2N638 | G | P | SD, ET, NP, SR | AC153 | AC131 | 2N1530 | 2N561 | 2SB248A | 16 |
| 2N638 | | | | OC76 | OC28 | 2N637 | 2N1536 | | 16 |
| 2N638 | | | | ASZ16 | | | | | 16 |
| 2N638A | G | P | SD, ET, NP, SR | ASZ15 | | 2N1532 | 2N561 | | 16 |
| 2N638A | | | | | | 2N1533 | | | 16 |
| 2N638B | G | P | SD, ET, NP, SR | ASZ16 | | 2N1533 | 2N561 | | 16 |
| 2N638B | | | | | | 2N1536 | | | 16 |
| 2N639 | G | P | ET, NP, SR | ASZ16 | | 2N1530 | 2N561 | | 16 |
| 2N639 | | | | | | 2N1536 | | | 16 |
| 2N639A | G | P | ET, NP, SR | ASZ15 | | 2N1532 | 2N456A | | 16 |
| 2N639A | | | | | | 2N561 | 2N1533 | | 16 |
| 2N639B | G | P | ET, NP, SR | ASZ15 | | 2N1533 | | | 16 |
| 2N640 | G | P | RC | AF185 | AF125 | 2N642 | 2N2188 | 2SA114 | 01 |
| 2N640 | | | | AF136 | AF115 | 2N990 | | | 01 |
| 2N640 | | | | AF116 | AF126 | | | | 01 |
| 2N640 | | | | AF127 | | | | | 01 |
| 2N641 | G | P | RC | AF185 | AF125 | 2N990 | | 2SA114 | 01 |
| 2N641 | | | | AF136 | AF126 | | | | 01 |
| 2N641 | | | | AF132 | AF124 | | | | 01 |

| TYPE | M/S | POL | MANUFAC | EUROPEAN | | AMERICAN | | JAPANESE | USE |
|---|---|---|---|---|---|---|---|---|---|
| 2N642 | G | P | RC | AF185 | AF126 | 2N990 | | 2SA114 | 01 |
| 2N642 | | | | AF136 | AF132 | | | | 01 |
| 2N642 | | | | AF137 | AF124 | | | | 01 |
| 7N643 | G | P | RC | AF124 | | 2N2955 | 2N1309 | | 10 |
| 2N643 | | | | | | 2N2635 | 2N990 | | 10 |
| | | | | | | | | | |
| 2N644 | G | P | RC | AF124 | | 2N2955 | 2N1309 | | 10 |
| 2N644 | | | | | | 2N2635 | 2N990 | | 10 |
| 2N645 | G | P | RC, St | AF124 | | 2N2955 | 2N1309 | | 10 |
| 2N646 | G | N | St | AC176 | | 2N2635 | | | 01 |
| 2N647 | G | N | ET, NP | AC126 | ASY29 | 2N2430 | 2N1306 | | 01 |
| | | | | | | | | | |
| 2N647 | | | | AC176 | | | | | 01 |
| 2N647/22 | G | N | SY | AC176 | | 2N2430 | | | |
| 2N649 | G | N | ET, NP | AC127 | AC176 | 2N2430 | 2N1308 | | 01 |
| 2N649/22 | G | N | SY | AC176 | | 2N2430 | | | |
| 2N650 | G | P | ET, MO, ES, NP, SR | (ASY48IV) | AC153 | 2N1997 | 2N1176 | 2SB247 | 01 |
| | | | | | | | | | |
| 2N650 | | | | AC117 | AC128 | | | | 01 |
| 2N650 | | | | OC318 | ACY17 | | | | 01 |
| 2N650A | G | P | ET, MO, ES, NP, SR | (ASY48IV) | ACY17 | 2N1176 | | | 01 |
| 2N651 | G | P | ET, MO, NP, SR, WA | (ASY48V) | AC153 | 2N1997 | 2N1176 | 2SB247 | 01 |
| 2N651 | | | | AC117 | AC128 | | | | 01 |
| | | | | | | | | | |
| 2N651 | | | | ACY17 | | | | | 01 |
| 2N651A | G | P | ET, MO, ES, NP, SR | ASY48V | AC117 | 2N1997 | 2N1176 | 2SB247 | 01 |
| 2N651A | | | | AC128 | AC153 | | | | 01 |
| 2N651A | | | | ACY17 | | | | | 01 |
| 2N652 | G | P | ET, MO, SR, SS, WA | (ASY48VI) | AC153 | 2N1997 | 2N1176 | 2SB247 | 01 |
| | | | | | | | | | |
| 2N652 | | | | ASY26 | AC128 | | | 2SB222 | 01 |
| 2N652 | | | | AC117 | ACY17 | | | | 01 |
| 2N652A | G | P | ET, MO, NP, SR, St | (ASY48VII) | ACY17 | 2N1997 | 2N1176 | 2SB222 | 01 |
| 2N652A | | | | AC128 | AC153 | | | | 01 |
| 2N652A | | | | ACY17 | | | | | 01 |
| | | | | | | | | | |
| 2N653 | G | P | ET, MO, NP, SR, St | (AC151V) | ACY17 | 2N1997 | 2N1176 | | 01 |
| 2N654 | G | P | ET, MO, NP, SR, St | (AC151VI) | ACY17 | 2N1997 | 2N1176 | | 01 |
| 2N655 | G | P | ET, MO, NP, SR, UP | (AC151VIII) | ACY17 | 2N1997 | 2N1176 | | 01 |
| 2N656 | S | N | PH, ET, F, MO, TX | BSX46/6 | BSX45 | 2N2102 | 2N3498 | | 01 |
| 2N656 | | | | BSX22 | BFY50 | 2N4331 | 2N2297 | | 01 |
| | | | | | | | | | |
| 2N656A | S | N | ET, MP, SM, TD, TX | BFY50 | | 2N2297 | | | 01 |
| 2N657 | S | N | F, MO, TX, SR, ET | (BSX47·6) | BSW66 | 2N3498 | 2N1893 | | 01 |
| 2N657A | S | N | ET, TX, NP, SM, St | (BSX47·6) | BSW66 | 2N1893 | | | 01 |
| 2N658 | G | P | ET, NP, SS, St, TX | AC153 | AC117 | 2N2000 | 2N1305 | | 10 |
| 2N658 | | | | AC128 | AD162 | | | | 10 |
| | | | | | | | | | |
| 2N658 | | | | ASY27 | | | | | 10 |
| 2N659 | G | P | ET, NP, SQ, St, TX | AC153 | AC117 | 2N2000 | 2N578 | | 10 |
| 2N659 | | | | AC128 | AD162 | 2N1305 | | | 10 |
| 2N659 | | | | ASY27 | | | | | 10 |
| 2N660 | G | P | ET, NP, SR, St, TX | AC153 | AC117 | 2N643 | 2N2000 | | 10 |
| | | | | | | | | | |
| 2N660 | | | | AC128 | AD162 | 2N1305 | | | 10 |
| 2N660 | | | | ASY27 | | | | | 10 |
| 2N661 | G | P | ET, NP, SR, St, TX | AD162 | ASY29 | 2N643 | 2N2000 | | 10 |
| 2N661 | | | | | | 2N1305 | | | 10 |
| 2N662 | G | P | ET, NP, SR, St, TX | AC153 | AC117 | 2N579 | 2N2000 | | 10 |
| | | | | | | | | | |
| 2N662 | | | | OC76 | AC128 | 2N1305 | | | 10 |
| 2N662 | | | | AD162 | ASY27 | | | | 10 |
| 2N663 | G | P | ET, NP | ASZ16 | | 2N2143 | 2N1536 | | 16 |
| 2N665 | G | P | ET, MO, ES, NP, SR | (AUY22IV) | ADY26 | T13027 | 2N1536 | | 16 |
| 2N665 | | | | ASZ16 | | | | | 16 |
| | | | | | | | | | |
| 2N669 | G | P | ET, MO, SR, NP, SS | (AD131V) | | T13027 | 2N1536 | | 06 |
| 2N670 | G | P | SQ | AC117 | AC128 | 2N3428 | 2N1038 | 2SB222 | 01 |
| 2N670 | | | | AC153 | ACY17 | 2N1176 | | | 01 |
| 2N671 | G | P | SS, PH | ACY17 | | 2N3428 | 2N1038 | | 01 |
| 2N671 | | | | | | 2N1176 | | | 01 |
| | | | | | | | | | |
| 2N672 | G | P | ET, NP, SQ | ACY17 | | 2N3428 | 2N1038 | | 01 |
| 2N672 | | | | | | 2N1176 | | | 01 |
| 2N673 | G | P | SQ | ACY17 | | 2N3428 | 2N1038 | | 01 |
| 2N673 | | | | | | 2N1176 | | | 01 |
| 2N674 | G | P | SQ | ACY17 | | 2N3428 | | | 01 |
| | | | | | | | | | |
| 2N674 | | | | | | 2N1176 | | | 01 |
| 2N675 | G | P | SQ | ACY17 | | 2N3428 | 2N1176 | | 01 |
| 2N677 | G | P | ET, SD, ST, SR, NP | (AUY29IV) | ASZ16 | 2N1553 | 2N456A | | 06 |
| 2N677 | | | | | | 2N1536 | | | 06 |
| 2N677A | G | P | ET, SD, ST, SR, NP | (AUY29IV) | ASZ16 | 2N1554 | 2N1536 | | 06 |
| | | | | | | | | | |
| 2N677B | G | P | ET, NP, SR | ASZ15 | | 2N1555 | 2N1533 | | 06 |
| 2N677C | G | P | SR | ASZ15 | | 2N1556 | 2N1533 | | 06 |
| 2N678 | G | P | ET, SD, ST, SR, NP | (AUY29V) | AD133 | 2N1557 | 2N456A | | 06 |
| 2N678 | | | | ADZ11 | ASZ16 | 2N1536 | | | 06 |
| 2N678A | G | P | ET, SD, ST, SR, NP | (AUY29V) | ASZ16 | 2N1558 | 2N1536 | | 06 |

| TYPE | M/S | POL | MANUFAC | EUROPEAN | | AMERICAN | | JAPANESE | USE |
|---|---|---|---|---|---|---|---|---|---|
| 2N678B | G | P | SD, NP, SR | ASZ15 | | 2N1559 | 2N1533 | | 06 |
| 2N678C | G | P | SD, NP, SR | ASZ15 | | 2N1560 | 2N1533 | | 06 |
| 2N679 | G | N | ET, NP | ASY79 | | 2N1304 | | | |
| 2N680 | G | P | ET, NP | AC153 | AC117 | 2N1191 | 2N404 | | 01 |
| 2N680 | | | | AC128 | ACY17 | 2N1309 | 2N1176 | 2SD11 | 01 |
| 2N694 | S | N | WE | AF124 | | 2N990 | | | 02 |
| 2N695 | G | P | MO | ASZ21 | AF106 | 2N2635 | | | 13 |
| 2N696 | S | N | F, MO, TX, ST, FE | BFY56 | BSX45-6 | 2N596 | 2N3567 | | 10 |
| 2N696 | | | | BSY44 | BFY50 | 2N2218A | 2N2218 | | 10 |
| 2N696 | | | | | | 2N697 | 2N2297 | | 10 |
| 2N696A | S | N | ET, SM, St | BSX45-6 | BFY50 | 2N2218 | 2N2297 | | 10 |
| 2N697 | S | N | F MO, TX, FE, IT | BSX45-6 | BFY56 | EN697 | 2N2218A | | 10 |
| 2N697 | | | | BSX45-10 | BSY44 | 2N2218 | 2N2297 | | 10 |
| 2N697 | | | | BSY51 | BFY50 | | | | 10 |
| 2N697A | S | N | ET, NP, St, TD | BSX45-6 | BFY50 | 2N2218 | 2N2297 | | 10 |
| 2N698 | S | N | F, IC, RA, RY, TR | BSX47-6 | BSW66 | 2N3498 | 2N2243A | | 10 |
| 2N698 | | | | BSX46-10 | BF178 | 2N2297 | | | 10 |
| 2N698 | | | | BFY50 | | | | | 10 |
| 2N699 | S | N | F, IC, MO, RY, RC | BSX47-6 | BSX47-10 | 2N3498 | 2N2243A | | 10 |
| 2N699 | | | | BSW67 | BF178 | 2N1893 | | | 10 |
| 2N699 | | | | BSW66 | | | | | 10 |
| 2N699A | S | N | ET, F, RC, CN, CA | BSX47-6 | BSW66 | 2N1893 | | | 10 |
| 2N699B | S | N | F, RY, CN, CA, ET | BSX47-6 | BSW66 | 2N3498 | 2N1893 | | 10 |
| 2N700 | G | P | MO, CN, ID, SR | (AF126) | AF139 | 2N2415 | 2N5043 | | 02 |
| 2N700 | | | | AF186 | AF239S | | | | 02 |
| 2N700A | G | P | MO, CN, SQ | (AF127) | AF239S | | | | 02 |
| 2N700A/.18 | G | P | SY | AF239S | | | | | |
| 2N700/18 | G | P | SY | AF239S | | | | | |
| 2N702 | S | N | ET, MO, CN, SM, SQ | (BCY58VII) | BSX20 | 2N835 | 2N2369 | | 13 |
| 2N703 | S | N | ET, F, MO, CN, TR | BCY58VII | BFY74 | 2N3691 | 2N835 | | 13 |
| 2N703 | | | | BSX20 | | 2N2369 | | | 13 |
| 2N705 | G | P | TX, MO, SR, PH, ES | AFY11 | AF106 | 2N964 | | | 13 |
| 2N705 | | | | AFY19 | ASZ21 | | | | 13 |
| 2N705A | G | P | CN, SR | AF106 | | 2N964 | | | 13 |
| 2N706 | S | N | F, MO, TX, CN, ET | BSY62A | BSX87 | EN914 | 2N706A | | 13 |
| 2N706 | | | | BSY62 | BSX19 | 2N964 | 2N2369 | | 13 |
| 2N706 | | | | BSY38 | BSY20 | | | | 13 |
| 2N706 | | | | BSY70 | | | | | 13 |
| 2N706A | S | N | BL, ET, FE, MO, PH | BSY62A | BSX19 | EN706 | 2N2369 | | 13 |
| 2N706A | | | | BSY38 | | | | | 13 |
| 2N706A/46 | S | N | SM | BSX20 | | 2N2369 | | | |
| 2N706A/51 | S | N | SY | BSX20 | | 2N2369 | | | |
| 2N706B | S | N | F, MO, TX, GI, IT | BSY62A | BSX20 | EN706 | 2N2369 | | 13 |
| 2N706B/46 | S | N | SM | BSX20 | | 2N2369 | | | |
| 2N706B/51 | S | N | SY | BSX20 | | 2N2369 | | | |
| 2N706C | S | N | ET, CN, CA, FR, RY | BSY62A | | | | | 13 |
| 2N760C/46 | S | N | SY | BSX20 | | 2N2369 | | | |
| 2N706C/51 | S | N | SY | BSX20 | | 2N2369 | | | |
| 2N706C/46 | S | N | SY | BSX20 | | 2N2369 | | | |
| 2N706/51 | S | N | SY | BSX20 | | 2N2369 | | | |
| 2N707 | S | N | ET, MO, CN, EM, SM | BSX26 | BSW64 | EN3014 | 2N2483 | | 03 |
| 2N707 | | | | | | 2N2484 | 2N2222A | | 03 |
| 2N707A | S | N | ET, MO, EM, FR, SM | BSW64 | | 2N2483 | 2N2222A | | 02 |
| 2N708 | S | N | F, BL, ET, FE, IT | BSX88 | BSY63 | EN914 | 2N2369 | | 13 |
| 2N708 | | | | BSX19 | BSX20 | | | | 13 |
| 2N708 | | | | BSY19 | | | | | 13 |
| 2N708A | S | N | F, FR, ID | BSY63 | | 2N834 | 2N2222A | | 13 |
| 2N708/46S | S | N | SY | BSX20 | | 2N2369 | | | |
| 2N708/51 | S | N | SY | BSX20 | | 2N2369 | | | |
| 2N709 | S | N | F, ET, CN, NT, RC | BSX27 | BSY18 | 2N2369A | 2N2369 | | 13 |
| 2N709 | | | | BSX19 | BSX44 | | | | 13 |
| 2N709 | | | | BSX20 | | | | | 13 |
| 2N709A | S | N | F, MU, CN | (BSY18) | BSX27 | 2N2369 | | | 13 |
| 2N709A | | | | BSX20 | | | | | 13 |
| 2N709A/46 | S | N | SM | BSX20 | | 2N2369 | | | |
| 2N709A/51 | S | N | TR, SY | BSX20 | | 2N2369 | | | |
| 2N709/46 | S | N | SM | BSX20 | | 2N2369 | | | |
| 2N720 | G | P | TX, MO, SR | ASZ21 | | 2N964 | 2N838 | | 13 |
| 2N710A | G | P | SR | ASZ21 | | 2N964 | | | 13 |
| 2N711 | G | P | TX, MO, SR, PH, MU | AFY11 | AC125 | 2N964 | 2N838 | | 13 |
| 2N711 | | | | ASZ21 | AF106 | | | | 13 |
| 2N711A | G | P | MO, TX, ES, FR, NU | (AFY11) | ASZ21 | | | | 13 |
| 2N711B | G | P | MO, TX, FR, SR | (AFY11) | ASZ21 | | | | 13 |
| 2N715 | S | N | ET, SM, SQ, St | BSW64 | | 2N2221 | 2N4875 | | 02 |
| 2N715 | | | | | | 2N2222A | | | 02 |

| TYPE | M/S | POL | MANUFAC | EUROPEAN | | AMERICAN | | JAPANESE | USE |
|------|-----|-----|---------|----------|--|----------|--|----------|-----|
| 2N716 | S | N | ET, SM, SQ | BSW64 | | 2N2221 | 2N4875 | | 02 |
| 2N716 | | | | | | 2N2222A | | | 02 |
| 2N717 | S | N | F, ET, RY, TR, TI | BFX69 | BSX45-6 | 2N4436 | 2N2222 | | 02 |
| 2N717 | | | | BSX33 | | 2N2221 | 2N731 | | 02 |
| 2N717A | S | N | EM | BSX73 | | 2N731 | | | |
| | | | | | | | | | |
| 2N718 | S | N | F, MO, TX, ET, IC | (BSX45-6) | | | | | 02 |
| 2N718A | S | N | F, MO, TX, ET, RY | (BSX45-6) | | | | | 02 |
| 2N719 | S | N | F, ET, IC, RY, TX | BSX47-6 | | 2N3498 | 2N2222 | | 02 |
| 2N719 | | | | | | 2N3700 | | | 02 |
| 2N719A | S | N | F, ET, TX, CN, EM | BSX47-6 | | 2N3498 | 2N3700 | | 02 |
| | | | | | | | | | |
| 2N720 | S | N | F, ET, RY, TX, CN | BSX47-6 | BSX47-10 | 2N3498 | 2N2222 | | 02 |
| 2N720 | | | | | | 2N3700 | | | 02 |
| 2N720A | S | N | F, ET, MO, TX, TI | BSX47-6 | BSX47-10 | 2N3498 | 2N3700 | | 10 |
| 2N721 | S | P | F, MO, TX, RY, TT | (BSV16-6) | BSX36 | EN722 | 2N2837 | | 02 |
| 2N721 | | | | BSW24 | | 2N2907 | 2N2907A | | 02 |
| | | | | | | | | | |
| 2N721A | S | P | F, FR, RY, SQ, TD | (BSV16-6) | BSW24 | 2N2907A | | | 02 |
| 2N722 | P | | F, MO, TX, RY, NU | BSV16-6 | BSX36 | EN722 | 2N2907 | | 02 |
| 2N722 | | | | BSW24 | | 2N2907A | | | 02 |
| 2N722A | S | P | F, RY, TR, SM, FR | BSV16-6 | BSW24 | 2N2837 | 2N2907A | | 02 |
| 2N725 | S | P | SY | AF201U | AF201 | 2N2635 | | | 13 |
| | | | | | | | | | |
| 2N725 | | | | AF202 | AF121 | | | | 13 |
| 2N725 | | | | AF106 | | | | | 13 |
| 2N726 | S | P | ET, MO, EM, ET, TX | BC177A | BC178VI | 2N3250 | 2N3965 | | 01 |
| 2N726 | | | | BC177 | | | | | 01 |
| 2N727 | S | P | ET, MO, FE, FR, TX | BC177A | BC178VI | 2N3250 | 2N3965 | | 01 |
| | | | | | | | | | |
| 2N727 | | | | BC177 | | | | | 01 |
| 2N728 | S | N | SS, TR | BSY62 | BSY63 | 2N2539 | 2N2222A | | 13 |
| 2N728 | | | | BSW64 | | | | | 13 |
| 2N729 | S | N | SS, TR | BSW64 | | 2N2539 | 2N2222A | | 13 |
| 2N730 | S | N | TX, ET, TR, CN, RY | BSX45-6 | BSX33 | 2N2218 | 2N731 | | 01 |
| | | | | | | | | | |
| 2N730A | S | N | TX | BSX45-6 | BSX45-10 | | | | 01 |
| 2N731 | S | N | MO, TX, ET, TR, RY | BSX45-6 | BSX33 | 2N2221A | | | 01 |
| 2N733 | S | N | | | | 2N2221A | | | |
| 2N734 | S | N | ET, TX, CN, TT, RA | BSX46-6 | BSX46 | 2N2221A | 2N2222A | | 01 |
| 2N734 | | | | BFY80 | BSW64 | | | | 01 |
| | | | | | | | | | |
| 2N734A | | N | ET, SS | BSW64 | | 2N2222A | | | 01 |
| 2N735 | S | N | ET, MO, TR, SD, CN | BSX46-6 | BSX46 | 2N2221 | 2N1091 | | 01 |
| 2N735 | | | | BFY80 | BSW64 | | | | 01 |
| 2N735A | S | N | ET, SD, CN, SQ, TD | BSX46-6 | BSW64 | 2N2222A | | | 01 |
| 2N736 | S | N | MO, ET, TR, LI, TD | BSX46-10 | BSX46 | 2N2222A | 2N1091 | | 01 |
| | | | | | | | | | |
| 2N736 | | | | BSY80 | BFY44 | | | | 01 |
| 2N736 | | | | BSW64 | | | | | 01 |
| 2N736A | S | N | ET, CN, SD, TD, TX | BSX46-10 | BSW64 | 2N2222 | 2N2222A | | 01 |
| 2N736B | S | N | ET, SD, CN, SQ | BSX46-10 | BSW64 | 2N2222A | | | 01 |
| 2N738 | S | N | ET, CN, TR, SM, SQ | BSX47-6 | BSW64 | 2N2222A | | | 01 |
| | | | | | | | | | |
| 2N738A | S | N | ET, SS | BSW64 | | 2N2222A | | | 01 |
| 2N739 | S | N | ET, MO, TR, CN, SM | BSX47-6 | BSW64 | 2N2221A | 2N2222A | | 01 |
| 2N739A | S | N | ET, SD, CN, SQ | BSX47-6 | BSW64 | 2N2222A | | | 01 |
| 2N740 | S | N | ET, MO, TR, TX, SD | BSX47-10 | BC141 | 2N2222A | | | 01 |
| 2N740 | | | | BSW64 | | | | | 01 |
| | | | | | | | | | |
| 2N740A | S | N | ET, SD, CN, SM, SQ | BSX47-10 | BFY45 | 2N2222A | | | 01 |
| 2N740A | | | | BSW64 | | | | | 01 |
| 2N741 | G | P | MO, SQ | AF202 | AF202S | 2N2996 | 2N5043 | | 02 |
| 2N741 | | | | AF121S | AF106 | | | | 02 |
| 2N741A | G | P | MO, SM | AF202 | AF106 | | | | 02 |
| | | | | | | | | | |
| 2N742 | S | N | ET, SM, SQ, TD | BCY65EVII | BSW64 | 2N2218 | 2N2217 | | 10 |
| 2N742 | | | | | | 2N2219 | 2N2222A | | 10 |
| 2N742A | S | N | ET, CN, SM, SQ, TD | BCY65EVII | BSW64 | 2N2218 | 2N2222A | | 10 |
| 2N743 | S | N | BL, F, MO, PH, GI | BSX90 | BSY17 | 2N835 | 2N2369 | | 13 |
| 2N743 | | | | BSX19 | BSY21 | | | | 13 |
| | | | | | | | | | |
| 2N743 | | | | BF168 | BSX20 | | | | 13 |
| 2N743A | S | N | CA, RY, SM, SQ, TI | BSX20 | | 2N2369 | | | 13 |
| 2N743/46 | S | N | SY | BSX20 | | 2N2369 | | | |
| 2N743/51 | S | N | SY | BSX20 | | 2N2369 | | | |
| 2N744 | S | N | BL, F, IT, RY, V | BSX91 | BSY18 | EN744 | 2N2369 | | 13 |
| | | | | | | | | | |
| 2N744 | | | | BSX20 | BSY21 | | | | 13 |
| 2N744 | | | | BF168 | | | | | 13 |
| 2N744A | S | N | CA, RY, SM, SQ | BSX20 | | 2N2369 | | | 13 |
| 2N744/46 | S | N | SY | BSX20 | | 2N2369 | | | |
| 2N744/51 | S | N | SY | BSX20 | | 2N2369 | | | |
| | | | | | | | | | |
| 2N749 | S | N | RY | BCY59 | BSY44 | 2N697 | 2N2222A | | 02 |
| 2N749 | | | | BSY11 | BSW66 | | | | 02 |
| 2N750 | S | N | RY | BCY59 | BSY44 | | | | |
| 2N750 | | | | BSY11 | | | | | |
| 2N751 | S | N | RY | BSW66 | | 2N697 | 2N2222A | | 02 |

| TYPE | M/S | POL | MANUFAC | EUROPEAN | | AMERICAN | | JAPANESE | USE |
|---|---|---|---|---|---|---|---|---|---|
| 2N752 | S | N | CN, ET, SM, SQ | BFY44 | BSW66 | 2N2221 | 2N736 | | 02 |
| 2N752 | | | | | | 2N2222A | | | 02 |
| 2N753 | S | N | F, MO, PH, TX, BL | BSY62B | BSY62 | 2N4275 | 2N2369 | | 13 |
| 2N753 | | | | BSX20 | BSY39 | | | | 13 |
| 2N753 | | | | BSY70 | | 2N2369 | | | 13 |
| 2N753/46 | S | N | SM | BSX20 | | 2N2369 | | | |
| 2N753/51 | S | N | SY | BSX20 | | 2N2369 | | | |
| 2N754 | S | N | TR, CN, ET, SM, SR | BSY10 | BSW66 | 2N2218 | 2N1893 | | 02 |
| 2N754 | | | | | | 2N2243A | 2N2222A | | 02 |
| 2N755 | S | N | TR, CN, ET, SM, SQ | | | 2N2218 | 2N1893 | | 02 |
| 2N755 | | | | | | 2N2243A | 2N3019 | | 02 |
| 2N756 | S | N | ET, CN, TR, SM, SQ | BCY59VII | BSY10 | 2N734 | 2N2222A | | 01 |
| 2N756 | | | | BSW66 | | | | | 01 |
| 2N756A | S | N | ET, CN, SM, SQ | BCY65EVII | BSW66 | 2N2222A | | | 01 |
| 2N757 | S | N | ET, CN, IC, SM, TR | BCY59VII | BSY10 | 2N734 | 2N2222A | | 01 |
| 2N757A | | | | BSW66 | | | | | 01 |
| 2N757A | S | N | ET, CN, SM, SQ | BCY65EVII | BSW66 | 2N2222A | | | 01 |
| 2N758 | S | N | ET, TR, CN, IC, SM | BSY59VII | BSY11 | 2N734 | 2N2222A | | 01 |
| 2N758 | | | | BSW66 | | | | | 01 |
| 2N758A | S | N | ET, CN, SM, TR, SD | BCY65EVII | BSW66 | 2N2222A | | | 01 |
| 2N758B | S | N | ET, SD, CN, SM, SQ | BCY65EVII | BSW66 | 2N2222A | | | 01 |
| 2N759 | S | N | ET, TR, TD, SM, SD | BCY59VII | BSW66 | 2N2222A | | | 01 |
| 2N759A | S | N | ET, TR, SM, SD, TO | BCY65EVII | BSW66 | 2N2222A | | | 01 |
| 2N759B | S | N | ET, SD, SM, RY | BCY65EVII | BSW66 | 2N2222A | | | 01 |
| 2N760 | S | N | ET, NS, RY, TI, CN | BCY59VII | BFY76 | 2N2222A | | | 01 |
| 2N760 | | | | BCY59IX | BSW66 | | | | 01 |
| 2N760A | S | N | ET, NS, RY, TR, TI | BCY65EVII | BCY65EVIII | 2N2483 | 2N2222A | | 01 |
| 2N760A | | | | BSW66 | | | | | 01 |
| 2N760B | S | N | ET, SD, SM, SQ | BCY65EVII | BSW66 | 2N2222A | | | 01 |
| 2N761 | S | N | ET, CN, IC, SZ, SQ | BC107A | BSW66 | 2N2222A | | | 01 |
| 2N762 | S | N | ET, MO, TD, SQ, St | BC107A | BSW66 | 2N2222A | | | 01 |
| 2N768 | G | P | FR, ID, SP | AF124 | | 2N961 | 2N990 | | 13 |
| 2N769 | G | P | F, ID, SP | AF124 | | 2N961 | 2N990 | | 13 |
| 2N770 | S | N | PH | | | 2N3014 | | | 13 |
| 2N771 | S | N | PH | | | 2N3014 | | | 13 |
| 2N772 | S | N | PH | | | 2N3014 | | | 13 |
| 2N773 | S | N | PH | | | 2N3014 | | | 02 |
| 2N774 | S | N | PH | | | 2N3014 | | | 02 |
| 2N775 | S | N | PH | | | 2N3014 | | | 02 |
| 2N776 | S | N | PH | | | 2N3014 | | | 02 |
| 2N777 | S | N | PH | | | 2N3014 | 2N734 | | 02 |
| 2N778 | S | N | PH | | | 2N734 | 2N3014 | | 02 |
| 2N779 | G | P | SQ | AF106 | | 2N964 | | | 13 |
| 2N779A | G | P | FR, MO, SP, SQ, ID | AF106 | | 2N964 | | | 13 |
| 2N779B | G | P | PH | AF106 | | 2N964 | | | 13 |
| 2N780 | S | N | ET, CN | BCY59VII | BF115 | 2N2220 | A157 | | 01 |
| 2N780 | | | | BC107A | BC107 | | | | 01 |
| 2N781 | G | P | SY | | | 2N2635 | | | 13 |
| 2N782 | G | P | SR | | | 2N2635 | | | 13 |
| 2N783 | S | N | F, ET, FR, RY, CA | (BSY63) | BSX28 | 2N4274 | 2N834 | | 13 |
| 2N783 | | | | BSX20 | | 2N2369A | 2N2369 | | 13 |
| 2N784 | S | N | CN, ET, IT, RY, FR | BSX28 | BSX20 | 2N4274 | 2N834 | | 13 |
| 2N784 | | | | | | 2N2369A | 2N2369 | | 13 |
| 2N784A | S | N | CA, ET, MN, RY | BSX20 | | 2N834 | 2N2369 | | 13 |
| 2N784/46 | S | N | | BSX20 | | 2N2369 | | | |
| 2N784A/51 | S | N | | BSX20 | | 2N2369 | | | |
| 2N785 | G | P | | AF124 | | 2N990 | | | |
| 2N789 | S | N | SQ | BCY32 | | 2N332 | 2N1475 | | 01 |
| 2N790 | S | N | RY | BCY32 | | 2N333 | 2N1475 | | 01 |
| 2N791 | S | N | RY | BCY32 | | 2N334 | 2N1475 | | 01 |
| 2N792 | S | N | RY | BCY32 | | 2N335 | 2N1475 | | 01 |
| 2N793 | S | N | RY | BCY32 | | 2N336 | 2N1475 | | 01 |
| 2N794 | G | P | SM, SP, SQ | AF124 | | 2N2635 | 2N990 | | 13 |
| 2N795 | G | P | FR, SP, SM, SQ, ID | AF124 | | 2N2635 | 2N990 | | 13 |
| 2N796 | G | P | FR, ID, SM, SP, SQ | AF124 | | 2N2635 | 2N990 | | 13 |
| 2N797 | G | N | TX, SQ | | | 2N2369 | | | 13 |
| 2N799 | G | P | RY | AF101 | AF117 | 2N1305 | | 2SA155 | 10 |
| 2N799 | | | | AF127 | ASY27 | | | | 10 |
| 2N800 | G | P | RY | ASY27 | | 2N404 | 2N1305 | | 10 |
| 2N801 | G | P | RY | ASY27 | | 2N404 | 2N1305 | | 10 |
| 2N802 | G | P | RY | ASY27 | | 2N404 | 2N1305 | | 10 |
| 2N803 | G | P | RY | ASY27 | | 2N404 | 2N1305 | | 10 |
| 2N804 | G | P | RY | ASY27 | | 2N404 | 2N1305 | | 10 |
| 2N805 | G | P | RY | ASY27 | | 2N404 | 2N1305 | | 10 |
| 2N806 | G | P | RY | ASY27 | | 2N404 | 2N1305 | | 10 |

| TYPE | M/S | POL | MANUFAC | EUROPEAN | | AMERICAN | | JAPANESE | USE |
|---|---|---|---|---|---|---|---|---|---|
| 2N807 | G | P | RY | ASY27 | | 2N404 | 2N1305 | | 10 |
| 2N808 | G | P | RY | ASY27 | | 2N404 | 2N1305 | | 10 |
| 2N809 | G | P | RY | ASY27 | | 2N404 | 2N1305 | | 02 |
| 2N810 | G | P | RY | ASY27 | | 2N404 | 2N1305 | | 02 |
| 2N811 | G | P | RY | ASY27 | | | 2N1305 | | 02 |
| 2N812 | G | P | RY | ASY27 | | 2N404 | 2N1305 | | 02 |
| 2N813 | G | P | RY | ASY27 | | 2N404 | 2N1305 | | 02 |
| 2N814 | G | P | RY | ASY27 | | 2N404 | 2N1305 | | 02 |
| 2N815 | G | N | RY | ASY29 | | 2N1304 | | | 10 |
| 2N816 | G | N | RY | ASY29 | | 2N1304 | | | 10 |
| 2N817 | G | N | RY | ASY29 | | 2N1304 | | | 10 |
| 2N818 | G | N | RY | ASY29 | | 2N1304 | | | 10 |
| 2N819 | G | N | RY | ASY29 | | 2N1304 | | | 10 |
| 2N820 | G | N | RY | ASY29 | | 2N1304 | | | 10 |
| 2N821 | G | N | GI, RY | ASY29 | | 2N1304 | | | 10 |
| 2N822 | G | N | RY | ASY29 | | 2N1304 | | | 10 |
| 2N823 | G | N | RY | ASY29 | | 2N1304 | | | 10 |
| 2N824 | G | P | RY | ASY27 | | 2N1305 | | | 02 |
| 2N825 | G | P | RY | ASY27 | | 2N404 | 2N1305 | | 10 |
| 2N826 | G | P | RY | ASY27 | | 2N404 | 2N1305 | | 10 |
| 2N827 | G | P | MO, SQ | | | | | | 13 |
| 2N828 | G | P | MO, SR, SQ | | | | | | 13 |
| 2N828A | G | P | MO, SQ | | | | | | 13 |
| 2N829 | G | P | MO, SQ | | | | | | 13 |
| 2N834 | S | N | MO, F, IT, TI, GI | BSX28 | BSY63 | 2N4274 | 2N3014 | | 13 |
| 2N834 | | | | BCY56 | BSY23 | 2N2369 | | | 13 |
| 2N834 | | | | BSX20 | | | | | 13 |
| 2N834A | S | N | CN, CA, RY, IT, SG | BSX28 | BSY63 | 2N4274 | 2N2369 | | 13 |
| 2N834A | | | | BFY66 | BSX20 | | | | 13 |
| 2N834/46 | S | N | SM | BSX20 | | 2N2369 | | | |
| 2N834/51 | S | N | TR | BSX20 | | 2N2369 | | | |
| 2N835 | S | N | F, MO, IT, TR, GI | BSY63 | BSX28 | 2N4274 | 2N3014 | | 13 |
| 2N835 | | | | BSY62 | BSX20 | 2N2369 | | | 13 |
| 2N835/46 | S | N | SM | BSX20 | | 2N2369 | | | |
| 2N835/51 | S | N | TR | BSX20 | | 2N2369 | | | |
| 2N837 | G | P | SR | | | 2N838 | | | 13 |
| 2B838 | G | P | MO | | | 2N2635 | | | 13 |
| 2N839 | S | N | ET, TR, TI, SM, SQ | BCY59VII | BSY44 | 2N2222 | 2N992 | | 02 |
| 2N839 | | | | BF177 | BSY11 | 2N930 | A157 | | 02 |
| 2N838 | | | | BC107 | | | | | 02 |
| 2N840 | S | N | ET, MO, TR, SM, TI | BCY59VII | BC107 | 2N2221 | 2N929 | | 02 |
| 2N840 | | | | | | 2N930 | A157 | | 02 |
| 2N841 | S | N | ET, MO, TR, TI, SM | BCY59VII | BC107 | 2N2222 | 2N929 | | 02 |
| 2N841 | | | | | | 2N930 | A157 | | 02 |
| 2N841/46 | S | N | SM | BC107 | | | | | |
| 2N841/51 | S | N | TR | BC107 | | A157 | | | |
| 2N842 | S | N | ET, TR, SM, SQ, TI | BCY59VII | BC107 | 2N2221 | 2N4252 | | 02 |
| 2N842 | | | | | | 2N4253 | A157 | | 02 |
| 2N843 | S | N | ET, TR, SM, SQ, TI | BCY59VII | BC107 | 2N2222 | 2N4252 | | 02 |
| 2N843 | | | | | | 2N4253 | A157 | | 02 |
| 2N844 | S | N | TR, SM, SQ, TI | BC107 | | 2N1893 | 2N2243A | | 02 |
| 2N844 | | | | | | A157 | | | 02 |
| 2N845 | S | N | TR, SM, SQ, TI | BSX21 | | 2N1893 | 2N2243A | | 02 |
| 2N845 | | | | | | 2N2896 | | | 02 |
| 2N846 | G | P | SP, PH | | | 2N960 | 2N964 | | 13 |
| 2N846A | G | P | FR, ID, SP | | | 2N960 | 2N964 | | 13 |
| 2N846B | G | P | PH | | | 2N960 | 2N964 | | 13 |
| 2N847 | S | N | RY | BSX20 | | 2N2369 | | | 10 |
| 2N848 | S | N | RY | BSX20 | | 2N2369 | | | 10 |
| 2N849 | S | N | TX, SM, SQ | BSX48 | BSX19 | 2N835 | 2N2369 | | 13 |
| 2N849 | | | | BSX20 | | | | | 13 |
| 2N850 | S | N | TX, SM | BSX18 | BSX20 | 2N834 | 2N2369 | | 13 |
| 2N851 | S | N | TX, SM, SQ | BSX18 | BSX19 | 2N835 | 2N2369 | | 13 |
| 2N851 | | | | BSX20 | | | | | 13 |
| 2N852 | S | N | TX, SM, SQ | BSX20 | | 2N834 | 2N2369 | | 13 |
| 2N858 | S | P | CR, SM, ID, SP, SQ | BSW24 | | 2N2945 | 2N2907A | | 10 |
| 2N859 | S | P | CR, ID, SM, SP, SQ | BSW24 | | 2N2945 | 2N1907A | | 10 |
| 2N860 | S | P | CN, SP, CR, SM, SQ | BSW24 | | 2N2945 | 2N2907A | | 10 |
| 2N861 | S | P | CN, CR, SP, SM, SQ | BSW24 | | 2N2944 | 2N2945 | | 10 |
| 2N861 | | | | | | 2N2907A | | | 10 |
| 2N862 | S | P | CR, SP, FR, SM, ID | BSW24 | | 2N2944 | 2N2945 | | 10 |
| 2N862 | | | | | | 2N2907A | | | 10 |
| 2N863 | S | P | CN, CR, SP, FR, SM | BSW24 | | 2N2944 | 2N2945 | | 10 |
| 2N863 | | | | | | 2N2907A | | | 10 |
| 2N864 | S | P | CR, SP, FR, SM, ID | BSW24 | | 2N2904 | 2N2905 | | 10 |

| TYPE | M/S | POL | MANUFAC | EUROPEAN | | AMERICAN | | JAPANESE | USE |
|------|-----|-----|---------|----------|---|----------|---|----------|-----|
| 2N864 | | | | | | 2N2907A | | | 10 |
| 2N864A | S | P | CR, FR, ID | BSW24 | | 2N2904 | 2N2905 | | 10 |
| 2N864A | | | | | | 2N2907A | | | 10 |
| 2N865 | S | P | CR, SP, SM, FR, ID | BSW24 | | 2N2904 | 2N2905 | | 10 |
| 2N865 | | | | | | 2N2907A | | | 10 |
| | | | | | | | | | |
| 2N865A | S | P | CR, FR | BSW24 | | 2N2904 | 2N2905 | | 10 |
| 2N865A | | | | | | 2N2907A | | | 10 |
| 2N866 | S | N | St | BSW54 | | 2N2219A | | | 10 |
| 2N867 | S | N | St | BSW54 | | 2N2219A | | | 10 |
| 2N869 | S | P | F, MO, TI, CN, EM | BCY78VII | BSX29 | 2N4389 | 2N2904 | | 02 |
| | | | | | | | | | |
| 2N869 | | | | BSW24 | | 2N2905 | 2N2907A | | 02 |
| 2N869A | S | P | F, MO, ES, IT, NS | BCY78VII | BSW25 | 2N4313 | 2N3250 | | 10 |
| 2N869A | | | | | | 2N2894 | 2N3576 | | 10 |
| 2N869A | | | | | | 2N3546 | | | 10 |
| 2N870 | S | N | F, CN, RY, TD, TX | BSX46-6 | BSX46-10 | 2N2222 | 2N1990R | | 02 |
| | | | | | | | | | |
| 2N870 | | | | BSX21 | | | | | 02 |
| 2N871 | S | N | F, RY, ET, TX, TI | BSX46-10 | BSX21 | 2N2222 | 2N1990R | | 02 |
| 2N902 | S | N | RY | BSW64 | | 2N332 | 2N2222A | | 01 |
| 2N903 | S | N | RY | BSW64 | | 2N333 | 2N2222A | | 01 |
| 2N904 | S | N | RY | BSW64 | | 2N334 | 2N2222A | | 01 |
| | | | | | | | | | |
| 2N905 | S | N | RY | BSW64 | | 2N335 | 2N2222A | | 01 |
| 2N906 | S | N | RY | BSW64 | | 2N336 | 2N2222A | | 01 |
| 2N907 | S | N | RY | BSW64 | | 2N337 | 2N3015 | | 01 |
| 2N907 | | | | | | 2N2222A | | | 01 |
| 2N908 | S | N | RY | BSW64 | | 2N338 | 2N3015 | | 01 |
| | | | | | | | | | |
| 2N908 | | | | | | 2N2222A | | | 01 |
| 2N909 | S | N | CN, FR, ET, SM, SR | BSX33 | | 2N2222 | 2N2192 | | 01 |
| 2N909 | | | | | | 2N2243A | 2N701 | | 01 |
| 2N910 | S | N | F, MO, TX, ET, TX | BSX46-6 | BSX46-10 | 2N2222 | 2N1990R | | 01 |
| 2N910 | | | | BFY65 | BSX21 | | | | 01 |
| | | | | | | | | | |
| 2N911 | S | N | F, ET, MO, TX, RY | BSX46-10 | BSX21 | 2N2222 | 2N1990R | | 01 |
| 2N912 | S | N | F, ET, RY, TI, TX | BSX46-6 | BSX21 | 2N2222 | 2N1990R | | 01 |
| 2N913 | S | N | EM, SM, SQ | BC107 | | A157 | | | |
| 2N914 | S | N | F, BL, MO, NU, PH | BSX87 | BSX87A | EN914 | 2N708 | | 13 |
| 2N914 | | | | BSY63 | BSX20 | 2N2369 | | | 13 |
| | | | | | | | | | |
| 2N914 | | | | BCY59 | BSY21 | | | | 13 |
| 2N914A | S | N | F | BSX20 | | 2N2369 | | | 13 |
| 2N914B | S | N | F | BCY86 | | | | | |
| 2N914/46 | S | N | SM | BSX20 | | 2N2364 | | | |
| 2N914/51 | S | N | SM | BSX20 | | 2N2369 | | | |
| | | | | | | | | | |
| 2N915 | S | N | F, MO, RY, ET, ME | (BSX49) | BFY75 | EN915 | 2N2221A | | 02 |
| 2N915 | | | | BF115 | BF225 | 2N2222A | | | 02 |
| 2N915 | | | | BF194 | BFY27 | | | | 02 |
| 2N915 | | | | BSY22 | BCY86 | | | | 02 |
| 2N915 | | | | BSW64 | | | | | 02 |
| | | | | | | | | | |
| 2N915A | S | N | TI, SM, SQ, TD | BSW64 | | 2N2222A | | | 03 |
| 2N916 | S | N | F, MO, ET, ME, RY | (BCX48) | BFY74 | 2N3691 | 2N2222A | | 02 |
| 2N916 | | | | BSY63 | BCY56 | | | | 02 |
| 2N916 | | | | BFY27 | BSW64 | | | | 02 |
| 2N916A | S | N | TI, RY, SM, SQ, TD | BSW64 | | 2N2222A | | | 02 |
| | | | | | | | | | |
| 2N916B | S | N | TI, SM, SQ, TD | BSW64 | | 2N2222A | | | 03 |
| 2N917 | S | N | RY, TX, NS, TI, CA | BFX73 | | 2N3563 | 2N918 | | 02 |
| 2N917A | S | N | CA, RY, SM, SQ | BFX73 | | 2N918 | | | 02 |
| 2N917/46 | S | N | SM | BFX73 | | 2N918 | | | |
| 2N917/51 | S | N | SM, SY, TR | BFX73 | | 2N918 | | | |
| | | | | | | | | | |
| 2N918 | S | N | F, MO, PH, TX, FR | (BFX89) | BFX73 | EN918 | | | 02 |
| 2N918 | | | | BSX19 | BFY20 | | | | 02 |
| 2N918 | | | | BFX62 | BFY66 | | | | 02 |
| 2N918/46 | S | N | TR, SY | BFX73 | | 2N918 | | | |
| 2N918/51 | S | N | SY, TR | BFX73 | | 2N918 | | | |
| | | | | | | | | | |
| 2N919 | S | N | CN, ET, MU | BSX64 | | 2N834 | 2N2222A | | 13 |
| 2N920 | S | N | CN, ET, MU | BSW64 | | 2N834 | 2N2222A | | 13 |
| 2N921 | S | N | CN, ET | BSW64 | | 2N834 | 2N2222A | | 13 |
| 2N922 | S | N | CN, ET | BSW64 | | 2N834 | 2N2222A | | 13 |
| 2N923 | S | P | CR, SM, SQ, RY, SD | BC177 | | 2N3965 | | | 01 |
| | | | | | | | | | |
| 2N924 | S | P | CN, RY, SD, SQ, SM | BC177 | | 2N3965 | | | 01 |
| 2N925 | S | P | CR, SM, SQ, RY, SD | BC177 | | 2N3965 | | | 01 |
| 2N926 | S | P | CN, RY, SD, SQ, SM | BC177 | | 2N3965 | | | 01 |
| 2N927 | S | P | CR, SD, SQ, SM | BSX21 | BC177 | 2N2604 | 2N2605 | | 01 |
| 2N927 | | | | | | 2N3965 | | | 01 |
| | | | | | | | | | |
| 2N928 | S | P | SR, SD, SQ, SM | BC177 | | 2N2604 | 2N2605 | | 01 |
| 2N928 | | | | | | 2N3965 | | | 01 |
| 2N929 | S | N | F, MO, PH, TX, FR | BC414B | BFX92 | 2N3565 | 2N930 | | 01 |
| 2N929 | | | | BFX92A | BC107A | | | | 01 |
| 2N929 | | | | BC107 | BSY11 | | | | 01 |

| TYPE | M/S | POL | MANUFAC | EUROPEAN | | AMERICAN | | JAPANESE | USE |
|---|---|---|---|---|---|---|---|---|---|
| 2N929 | | | | BC109 | | | | | 01 |
| 2N929A | S | N | MO, TX, ME, RY, TI | (BC414B) | BC109 | 2N930 | | | 01 |
| 2N929/51 | S | | TR, SY | BC109 | | 2N930 | | | |
| 2N930 | S | N | F, MO, PH, TX, NS | BC414B | BFX93 | EN920 | | | 01 |
| 2N930 | | | | BFX93A | BC107B | | | | 01 |
| 2N930 | | | | BC107 | BCY59 | | | | 01 |
| 2N930 | | | | BC109 | | | | | 01 |
| 2N930A | S | N | MO, TX, ME, RY, SD | (BC414B) | BC109 | 2N930 | | | 01 |
| 2N930A/46 | S | N | SM | BC109 | | 2N930 | | | |
| 2N930A/51 | S | N | TR | BC109 | | 2N930 | | | |
| 2N930B | S | N | CA, RY, TI | BC109 | | 2N930 | | | 01 |
| 2N930/46 | S | N | SM | BC109 | | 2N930 | | | |
| 2N930/51 | S | N | TR, SY | BC109 | | 2N930 | | | |
| 2N934 | G | P | RC | | | 2N965 | 2N2635 | | 13 |
| 2N934 | | | | | | 2N2907A | | | 13 |
| 2N935 | S | P | SD, CR, CN, RY, SM | BSW24 | | 2N327A | 2N2945 | | 01 |
| 2N935 | | | | | | 2N3546 | | | 01 |
| 2N936 | S | P | SD, CR, CN, RY, SM | BSW24 | | 2N328A | 2N2945 | | 01 |
| 2N936 | | | | | | 2N2907A | | | 01 |
| 2N937 | S | P | SD, CR, RY, SQ, SM | BSW24 | | 2N329A | 2N2945 | | 01 |
| 2N937 | | | | | | 2N2907A | | | 01 |
| 2N938 | S | P | SD, CR, RY, SQ, TR | BSW24 | | 2N2945 | 2N2907A | | 01 |
| 2N939 | S | P | SD, CR, CN, RY, SQ | BSW24 | | 2N2945 | 2N2907A | | 01 |
| 2N940 | S | P | SD, CR, RY, SM, TD | BSW24 | | 2N2945 | 2N2907A | | 01 |
| 2N941 | S | P | SD, CR, RY, SM, SQ | BSW24 | | 2N2945 | 2N2907A | | 12 |
| 2N942 | S | P | SD, CR, RY, SQ, TD | BSW24 | | 2N2945 | 2N2907A | | 12 |
| 2N943 | S | P | SD, CR, CN, RY, SM | BSW24 | | 2N2945 | 2N2907A | | 12 |
| 2N944 | S | P | SD, CR, RY, SM, SQ | BSW24 | | 2N2945 | 2N2907A | | 12 |
| 2N945 | S | P | SD, CR, RY, SM, SQ | BSW24 | | 2N2945 | 2N2907A | | 12 |
| 2N946 | S | P | SD, CR, CN, SM, TD | BSW24 | | 2N2945 | 2N2907A | | 12 |
| 2N947 | S | N | CN, SM, SG, SQ | BSX87 | BSY62 | EN914 | 2N834 | | 10 |
| 2N947 | | | | BSY63 | BSX20 | 2N706 | 2N2329 | | 10 |
| 2N955 | G | N | RC, MO | | | 2N797 | | | 13 |
| 2N955A | G | N | RC | | | | | | 13 |
| 2N956 | S | N | F, MO, TX, ET, RY | BSX45-16 | BSX33 | EN956 | 2N2222A | | 02 |
| 2N956 | | | | BC141-10 | BSY83 | 2N2222 | 2N731 | | 02 |
| 2N956 | | | | BC140C | | | | | 02 |
| 2N957 | S | N | CN, CA, EM, ET, FR | BFY74 | BSY10 | 2N3691 | 2N2501 | | 02 |
| 2N957 | | | | BSY11 | BSX20 | 2N2484 | 2N2369 | | 02 |
| 2N958 | S | N | TW | BSX20 | | 2N706 | 2N2369 | | 13 |
| 2N959 | S | N | TW | BSX20 | | 2N706 | 2N2369 | | 13 |
| 2N960 | G | P | MO, TX, SR | ACY26 | | 2N964 | | | 13 |
| 2N960/46 | G | P | SY | | | | | | |
| 2N961 | G | P | MO, SR, TX, SS, SQ | (ACY26) | | 2N964 | | | 13 |
| 2N961/46 | G | P | SY | | | | | | |
| 2N962 | G | P | MO, SR, SQ, SS, TX | (ASY26) | | 2N964 | | | 13 |
| 2N962/46 | G | P | SY | | | | | | |
| 2N963 | G | P | MO, SR, SS, TX | (ASY26) | | 2N964 | | | 13 |
| 2N964 | G | P | MO, SR, TX | ASY26 | ASY27 | | | | 13 |
| 2N964A | G | P | MO, ES, SR | ASY26 | | 2N964 | | | 13 |
| 2N964/46 | G | P | SY | | | | | | |
| 2N965 | G | P | MO, SR, ES, SS, TX | ASY26 | | 2N964 | | | 13 |
| 2N966 | G | P | MO, SR, SS, TX | (ASY26) | | 2N964 | | | 13 |
| 2N967 | G | P | MO, SR, SS, TX | (ASY27) | | 2N964 | | | 13 |
| 2N968 | G | P | MO, SR, SQ, TX | (ASY26) | | 2N964 | | | 13 |
| 2N969 | G | P | MO, SR, SQ, TX | ASY26 | | 2N964 | | | 13 |
| 2N970 | G | P | MO, SR, SQ, TX | (ASY26) | | 2N964 | | | 13 |
| 2N971 | G | P | MO, SR, SQ, TX | (ASY26) | | 2N964 | | | 13 |
| 2N972 | G | P | MO, SR, SQ, TX | (ASY27) | | 2N964 | | | 13 |
| 2N973 | G | P | MO, SR, SQ, TX | (ASY27) | | 2N964 | | | 13 |
| 2N974 | G | P | MO, SR, SQ, TX | (ASY27) | | 2N964 | | | 13 |
| 2N975 | G | P | MO, SR, SQ, TX | (ASY27) | | 2N964 | | | 13 |
| 2N976 | G | P | SQ | | | 2N964 | 2N961 | | 13 |
| 2N977 | G | P | PH | | | 2N964 | 2N985 | | 13 |
| 2N978 | S | P | F, MO, TR, SM, CN | BC108A | BSX36 | 2N5142 | 2N2837 | | 02 |
| 2N978 | | | | BSW24 | | 2N721 | 2N2907 | | 02 |
| 2N978 | | | | | | 2N2907A | | | 02 |
| 2N979 | G | P | SP, FR, ID | | | 2N2635 | | | 13 |
| 2N980 | G | P | SP, FR, ID, SM, SQ | | | 2N2635 | | | 13 |
| 2N981 | S | N | FR, NS, SM, SQ | BC107 | | A157 | | | 01 |
| 2N982 | G | P | SP, FR, ID, SQ | | | 2N964 | | | 13 |
| 2N983 | G | P | SP, FR, ID, SQ | | | 2N964 | | | 13 |
| 2N984 | G | P | SP, FR, ID, SQ | | | 2N964 | 2N985 | | 13 |
| 2N985 | G | P | TX, MO, SR, SQ | | | 2N964 | | | 13 |
| 2N986 | P | N | F, SG | BPY65 | | LS600 | | | 04 |

| TYPE | M/S | POL | MANUFAC | EUROPEAN | | AMERICAN | | JAPANESE | USE |
|------|-----|-----|---------|----------|---|----------|---|----------|-----|
| 2N987 | G | P | AM, MU, PE | AF106 | AF124 | 2N2635 | 2N990 | | 02 |
| 2N988 | S | N | SM, SQ, TI | BSW64 | | 2N2221 | 2N706 | | 02 |
| 2N988 | | | | | | 2N2222A | | | 02 |
| 2N989 | S | N | SM, TI, SQ | BSW64 | | 2N2221 | 2N706 | | 02 |
| 2N989 | | | | | | 2N2222A | | | 02 |
| | | | | | | | | | |
| 2N990 | G | P | AN, PE | AF185 | AF124 | | | | 02 |
| 2N990 | | | | AF134 | | | | | 02 |
| 2N991 | G | P | PE | AF185 | AF125 | 2N2635 | 2N990 | | 02 |
| 2N991 | | | | AF135 | AF124 | | | | 02 |
| 2N992 | G | P | PE | AF185 | AF126 | 2N2635 | 2N990 | | 02 |
| | | | | | | | | | |
| 2N992 | | | | AF136 | AF124 | | | | |
| 2N993 | G | P | AM, PE | AF185 | AF127 | 2N2635 | 2N990 | | 02 |
| 2N993 | | | | AF137 | AF124 | | | | 02 |
| 2N994 | G | P | SR | | | | | | 13 |
| 2N995 | S | P | F, MO, TI, CN, NS | BC178A | BC179VI | 2N4389 | 2N2907A | | 02 |
| | | | | | | | | | |
| 2N995 | | | | BSW19 | BC179 | | | | 02 |
| 2N995 | | | | BC206 | BSW24 | | | | 02 |
| 2N995A | S | P | F, MO, IT, SG | BC178A | BSW24 | 2N4313 | 2N3250 | | 02 |
| 2N995A | | | | | | 2N2907A | | | 02 |
| 2N996 | S | P | F, MO, SM, SQ, TD | BC178A | BSX29 | 2N3248 | 2N2906 | | 02 |
| | | | | | | | | | |
| 2N996 | | | | BSW24 | | 2N2907 | 2N2907A | | 02 |
| 2N997 | S | N | TX, F, RY, GE, SG | BFX67 | | | | | 01 |
| 2N998 | S | N | F, GE, RY, TI, MO | BFX66 | | 2N997 | | | 04 |
| 2N999 | S | N | F, GE, RY, MO, CN | BFX67 | | 2N997 | | | 04 |
| 2N1000 | G | N | CN, ET, GI | ASY29 | | 2N1304 | | | 10 |
| | | | | | | | | | |
| 2N1003 | G | P | MO | ASY27 | | 2N1305 | | | 02 |
| 2N1004 | G | P | MO | ASY27 | | 2N1305 | | | 02 |
| 2N1005 | S | N | TX, St | BC107 | | A157 | | | 01 |
| 2N1006 | S | N | TX, St | BC107 | | A157 | | | 01 |
| 2N1007 | G | P | ET, CN, KS | AD131IV | ADY27 | 2N1536 | | | 06 |
| | | | | | | | | | |
| 2N1007 | | | | AD149 | ASZ16 | | | | 06 |
| 2N1008 | G | P | ET, MO, SR, CN, FR | (ASY70VI) | AC117 | 2N1176 | | 2SB222 | 01 |
| 2N1008 | | | | AC128 | AC153 | | | | 01 |
| 2N1008 | | | | ACY17 | | | | | 01 |
| 2N1008A | G | P | ET, MO, CN, FR, IC | ASY48VI | ACY17 | 2N1176 | | | 01 |
| | | | | | | | | | |
| 2N1008B | G | P | ET, MO, ES, SR, FR | (ASY48VI) | ACY17 | 2N1176 | | | 01 |
| 2N1009 | G | P | SD | AC153 | AC117 | 2N1176 | | 2SA219 | 01 |
| 2N1009 | | | | AC128 | ACY17 | | | | 01 |
| 2N1010 | G | N | CN, ET | AC127 | ASY29 | 2N1302 | 2N2430 | | 01 |
| 2N1010 | | | | | | 2N1304 | | | 01 |
| | | | | | | | | | |
| 2N1011 | G | P | ET, MO, SD, PP, CN | (AUY22IV) | AUY21II | TI3027 | 2N1536 | | 06 |
| 2N1011 | | | | ASZ18 | ADY26 | | | | 06 |
| 2N1012 | G | N | GI, ET, CN | ASY73 | ASY29 | 2N388A | 2N1306 | 2SD11 | 10 |
| 2N1012 | | | | | | 2N1304 | 2N1304 | | 10 |
| 2N1014 | G | P | RC | AC153 | AS117 | 2N1552 | 2N456A | 2SB248A | 06 |
| | | | | | | | | | |
| 2N1014 | | | | AC128 | ASZ18 | 2N1021 | 2N1533 | | 06 |
| 2N1014 | | | | ASZ15 | | | | | 06 |
| 2N1015 | S | N | W, ET, SZ, CN, FR | BLY17 | BDY20 | 2N3713 | 2N3055 | | 16 |
| 2N1015A | S | N | W, ET, SZ, CN, FR | BDY20 | | 2N3055 | | | 16 |
| 2N1015B | S | N | W, ET, SZ, CN, FR | BDX50 | | 2N3773 | | | 16 |
| | | | | | | | | | |
| 2N1015C | S | N | W, ET, SZ, CN, FR | BDX50 | | 2N3773 | | | 16 |
| 2N1015D | S | N | W, ET, SZ, SN, FR | BU120 | | | | | 16 |
| 2N1015E | S | N | W, SZ, FR, SF, SU | BU120 | | | | | 16 |
| 2N1015F | S | N | FR, SU, SQ, SF | BU120 | | | | | 16 |
| 2N1016 | S | N | W, SZ, ET, FR, SF | BDY20 | | 2N3713 | 2N3055 | | 16 |
| | | | | | | | | | |
| 2N1016A | S | N | W, ET, SZ, CN, FR | BDY20 | | 2N3055 | | | 16 |
| 2N1016B | S | N | W, SZ, ET, CN, SF | BDX50 | | 2N3773 | | | 16 |
| 2N1016C | S | N | W, ET, SZ, FR, SF | BDX50 | | 2N3773 | | | 16 |
| 2N1016D | S | N | W, SZ, ET, FR, SF | BU120 | | | | | 16 |
| 2N1016E | S | N | W, FR, SU, SZ, SQ | BU120 | | | | | 16 |
| | | | | | | | | | |
| 2N1016F | S | N | FR, SQ, SU | BU120 | | | | | 16 |
| 2N1017 | G | P | IC, CN, FR, SZ, UP | ASY27 | | 2N404 | 2N582 | | 10 |
| 2N1017 | | | | | | 2N1305 | | | 10 |
| 2N1018 | G | P | CN, FR, UP, ET, IC | ASY27 | | 2N404 | 2N582 | | 10 |
| 2N1018 | | | | | | 2N1305 | | | 10 |
| | | | | | | | | | |
| 2N1021 | G | P | ET, MO, TX, SD, CN | AUY22IV | ASZ15 | 2N456A | 2N1014 | | 06 |
| 2N1021 | | | | | | 2N1533 | | | 06 |
| 2N1021A | G | P | ET, TX, SD, CN, KS | (AUY22IV) | ASZ15 | 2N1021 | 2N1533 | | 06 |
| 2N1022 | G | P | ET, MO, TX, SD, CM | (AUY22IV) | ASZ15 | 2N456A | 2N1100 | | 06 |
| 2N1022 | | | | | | 2N1533 | | | 06 |
| | | | | | | | | | |
| 2N1022A | G | P | ET, TX, SD, KS, PP | (AUY22IV) | ASZ15 | 2N1022 | 2N990 | | 06 |
| 2N1023 | G | P | RC | AF106 | AFZ12 | 2N3323 | 2N2635 | | 01 |
| 2N1023 | | | | AF124 | | 2N990 | | | 01 |
| 2N1024 | S | P | SD, CR, RY, ET, CN | BC160 | BCY12 | 2N1132 | 2N2944 | | 01 |
| 2N1024 | | | | BCY32 | | 2N2945 | 2N1475 | | 01 |

| TYPE | M/S | POL | MANUFAC | EUROPEAN | | AMERICAN | | JAPANESE | USE |
|---|---|---|---|---|---|---|---|---|---|
| 2N1025 | S | P | SD, CR, ET, RY, CN | BC160 | BCY11 | 2N32 | 2N2944 | | 01 |
| 2N1025 | | | | BCY32 | | 2N2945 | 2N1475 | | 01 |
| 2N1026 | S | P | SD, ET, CR, RY, SQ | BC160 | BCY11 | 2N1132 | 2N2944 | | 01 |
| 2N1026 | | | | BCY12 | BCY32 | 2N2945 | 2N1475 | | 01 |
| 2N1026A | S | P | CR, ET | BCY32 | | 2N1475 | | | 01 |
| 2N1027 | S | P | ET, SD, CR, RY, CN | (BC178A) | BC178VI | 2N2944 | 2N2945 | | 01 |
| 2N1027 | | | | BC178 | BC205 | 2N1475 | | | 01 |
| 2N1027 | | | | BCY23 | | | | | 01 |
| 2N1028 | S | P | ET, SD, CR, RY, SM | (BC178A) | BCY32 | 2N2944 | 2N1475 | | 01 |
| 2N1029 | G | P | ET, CI, SR | ASZ16 | | 2N1553 | TI3027 | | 06 |
| 2N1029 | | | | | | 2N1536 | | | 06 |
| 2N1029A | G | P | KS | ASZ16 | | 2N1554 | TI3027 | | 06 |
| 2N1029A | | | | | | 2N1536 | | | 06 |
| 2N1029B | G | P | KS | ASZ16 | | 2N1555 | TI3027 | | 06 |
| 2N1029B | | | | | | TI3031 | 2N1533 | | 06 |
| 2N1029C | G | P | KS | ASZ16 | | 2N1556 | 2N456A | | 06 |
| 2N1029C | | | | | | 2N3146 | 2N1533 | | 06 |
| 2N1030 | G | P | ET, CI, SR | | | 2N1557 | 2N456A | | 06 |
| 2N1030 | | | | | | 2N514A | | | 06 |
| 2N1030A | G | P | ET, CI, SR | | | 2N1558 | 2N456A | | 06 |
| 2N1030A | | | | | | 2N514 | | | 06 |
| 2N1030B | G | P | ET, CI, SR | | | 2N1559 | | | 06 |
| 2N1030C | G | P | ET, CI, SR | | | 2N1560 | | | 06 |
| 2N1031 | G | P | ET, SD, PP | (AUY29V) | AD133 | 2N1553 | TI3027 | | 06 |
| 2N1031 | | | | ADZ11 | | | | | 06 |
| 2N1031A | G | P | ET, SD, CN, PP | (AUY29V) | | 2N1554 | TI3027 | | 06 |
| 2N1031B | G | P | SD, ET, PP, CN | | | 2N1555 | TI3027 | | 06 |
| 2N1031B | | | | | | TI3031 | | | 06 |
| 2N1031C | G | P | SD | | | 2N1556 | 2N456A | | 06 |
| 2N1031C | | | | | | 2N3146 | | | 06 |
| 2N1032 | G | P | ET, SD | (AUY29V) | | 2N1557 | 2N456A | | 06 |
| 2N1032 | | | | | | 2N514A | | | 06 |
| 2N1032A | G | P | ET, SD, CN | (AUY29V) | | 2N456A | 2N514B | | 06 |
| 2N1034 | S | P | RY, SD, CN, ET, St | BCY32 | | 2N2944 | 2N2945 | | 01 |
| 2N1034 | | | | | | 2N1475 | | | 01 |
| 2N1035 | S | P | RY, CR, SD, SN, ET | BCY32 | | 2N2944 | 2N2945 | | 01 |
| 2N1035 | | | | | | 2N1475 | | | 01 |
| 2N1036 | S | P | RY, CR, SD, SM, TD | BCY32 | | 2N2944 | 2N2945 | | 01 |
| 2N1036 | | | | | | 2N1475 | | | 01 |
| 2N1037 | S | P | RY, CR, SD, SM, TD | BCY32 | | 2N2944 | 2N2945 | | 01 |
| 2N1037 | | | | | | 2N1475 | | | 01 |
| 2N1038 | G | P | TX, KS, MO, NU, ES | AD149 | AD149IV | 2N2138 | 2N2836 | 2SB240 | 06 |
| 2N1038 | | | | OC30 | OD603 | 2N586 | 2N2552 | | 06 |
| 2N1038 | | | | AD162 | | | | | 06 |
| 2N1038/1 | G | P | KS | AD162 | | 2N2835 | | | |
| 2N1038/2 | G | P | KS | AD162 | | 2N2835 | | | |
| 2N1039 | G | P | TX, KS, MO, CN, ES | AD138/50 | ASZ17 | 2N2139 | 2N1038 | 2SB181 | 06 |
| 2N1039 | | | | OC26 | OC30 | 2N1041 | 2N2835 | | 06 |
| 2N1039/1 | G | P | KS | AD162 | | 2N2835 | | | 06 |
| 2N1039/1 | | | | AD162 | | | | | |
| 2N1039/2 | G | P | KS | AD162 | | 2N235 | | | |
| 2N1040 | G | P | TX, NU, KS, MO, Ss | AD162 | AD149 | 2N2140 | 2N1038 | 2SB181 | 06 |
| 2N1040 | | | | OC26 | OC30 | 2N1041 | 2N2835 | | 06 |
| 2N1040 | | | | OD603 | | | | | 06 |
| 2N1040/1 | G | P | KS | AD162 | | 2N2835 | | | |
| 2N1040/2 | G | P | KS | AD162 | | 2N2835 | | | |
| 2N1041 | G | P | TX, KS, MO, CN, ID | AUY21IV | AD138/50 | 2N2141 | 2N1038 | 2SB181 | 06 |
| 2N1041 | | | | ASZ15 | OC26 | 2N1040 | 2N1533 | | 06 |
| 2N1041 | | | | OC30 | | | | | 06 |
| 2N1041/1 | G | P | KS | ASZ15 | | 2N1533 | | | |
| 2N1041/2 | G | P | KS | ASZ15 | | 2N1533 | | | |
| 2N1042 | G | P | TX, KS, MO, CN, TR | ASZ16 | | 2N2143 | 2N1536 | | 06 |
| 2N1042/1 | G | P | KS | ASZ16 | | 2N1536 | | | |
| 2N1042/2 | G | P | KS | ASZ16 | | 2N1536 | | | |
| 2N1043 | G | P | TX, MO, TR, KS | AD131 | AD138/50 | 2N2144 | 2N1038 | 2SB181 | 06 |
| 2N1043 | | | | OC28 | ASZ16 | 2N1536 | | 2SB151 | 06 |
| 2N1043/1 | G | P | KS | ASZ16 | | 2N1536 | | | |
| 2N1043/2 | G | P | KS | ASZ16 | | 2N1536 | | | |
| 2N1044 | G | P | TX, MO, KS, TR | AD131 | AD138/50 | 2N2145 | 2N1038 | 2SB181 | 06 |
| 2N1044 | | | | OC28 | OD605 | 2N1043 | 2N1533 | 2SB151 | 06 |
| 2N1044 | | | | ASZ15 | | | | | 06 |
| 2N1044/1 | G | P | KS | ASZ16 | | 2N1533 | | | |
| 2N1044/2 | G | P | KS | ASZ16 | | 2N1533 | | | |
| 2N1045 | G | P | TX, TR, KS | ASZ15 | | 2N2146 | 2N1014 | | 06 |
| 2N1045 | | | | | | 2N1038 | 2N1533 | | 06 |

| TYPE | M/S | POL | MANUFAC | EUROPEAN | | AMERICAN | | JAPANESE | USE |
|------|-----|-----|---------|----------|--|----------|--|----------|-----|
| 2N1045/1 | G | P | KS | ASZ15 | | 2N1038 | 2N2563 | | |
| 2N1045/1 | | | | | | 2N1533 | | | |
| 2N1045/2 | G | P | KS | ASZ15 | | 2N1038 | 2N2567 | | |
| 2N1045/2 | | | | | | 2N1533 | | | |
| 2N1046 | G | P | TX, ET, SQ, UP, CN | AUY29/5 | | 2N2832 | 2N1907 | | 03 |
| 2N1046 | | | | | | 2N1167 | | | 03 |
| 2N1046A | G | P | ET, SQ, UP, FR, TX | AL100 | | 2N2832 | 2N1907 | | 03 |
| 2N1046A | | | | | | 2N2147 | | | 03 |
| 2N1046B | G | P | ET, SQ, UP, FR, TX | AL100 | | 2N2833 | 2N1907 | | 03 |
| 2N1046B | | | | | | 2N2147 | | | 03 |
| 2N1047 | S | N | TX, ET, SF, SZ, CN | BDY79 | | 2N4912 | 2N5050 | | 06 |
| 2N1047A | S | N | TX, ET, SF, SZ, SQ | BDY79 | | 2N4912 | 2N5050 | | 06 |
| 2N1047B | S | N | TX, ET, SZ, SQ, FR | BDY79 | | 2N4912 | 2N5050 | | 06 |
| 2N1047C | S | N | | | | 2N4912 | | | 06 |
| 2N1048 | S | N | TX, ET, SF, SZ, CN | BDY79 | | 2N5050 | | | 06 |
| 2N1048A | S | N | TX, ET, SF, SZ, CN | BDY79 | | 2N5050 | | | 06 |
| 2N1048B | S | N | TX, ET, SZ, SQ, FR | BDY79 | | 2N5050 | | | 06 |
| 2N1049 | S | N | TX, ET, SF, SZ, CN | BDY79 | | 2N4912 | 2N5050 | | 06 |
| 2N1049A | S | N | TX, ET, SF, SZ, SQ | BDY79 | | 2N4912 | 2N5050 | | 06 |
| 2N1049B | S | N | TX, ET, SF, SZ, CN | BDY79 | | 2N4912 | 2N5050 | | 06 |
| 2N1049C | S | N | | BDY79 | | 2N4912 | 2N5050 | | 06 |
| 2N1050 | S | N | TX, ET, SF, SZ, FR | BDY79 | | 2N5050 | | | 06 |
| 2N1050A | S | N | TX, ET, SF, SZ, ES | BDY79 | | 2N5050 | | | 06 |
| 2N1050B | S | N | TX, ET, SZ, SQ, FR | BDY79 | | 2N5050 | | | 06 |
| 2N1050C | S | N | TX | BDY79 | | 2N5050 | | | 06 |
| 2N1051 | S | N | ID, SQ | | | 2N2217 | 2N2219 | | 02 |
| 2N1051 | | | | | | 2N2219A | | | 02 |
| 2N1052 | S | N | TR, SQ, SM | BSW66 | | 2N5058 | 2N1893 | | 01 |
| 2N1053 | S | N | SM, TR, SQ | BSW66 | | 2N1893 | | | 01 |
| 2N1054 | S | N | TX, ET, UN, CN, SM | BSW66 | | 2N5059 | 2N1893 | | 01 |
| 2N1055 | S | N | TR, SM, St, UN, CN | BSW66 | | 2N1893 | | | 01 |
| 2N1056 | G | P | TX | AC153 | ACY24 | 2N2043 | 2N1176 | 2SB224 | 01 |
| 2N1056 | | | | AC128 | AC131 | | | | 01 |
| 2N1056 | | | | AC152 | ACY17 | | | | 01 |
| 2N1057 | G | P | ET, SR | AC153 | AC131/30 | 2N1924 | 2N1176 | 2SB225 | 01 |
| 2N1057 | | | | OC72 | AC128 | | | | 01 |
| 2N1057 | | | | AC117 | ACY17 | | | | 01 |
| 2N1058 | G | N | ET, NP | ADY26 | ASY74 | 2N1304 | | | |
| 2N1058 | | | | ASY29 | | | | | |
| 2N1059 | G | N | NP, ET | AC127 | ASY29 | 2N2430 | 2N1304 | 2SD11 | 01 |
| 2N1060 | S | N | DD, CI, SR | BSW64 | | 2N2501 | 2N2217 | | 13 |
| 2N1060 | | | | | | 2N2219 | 2N2222A | | 13 |
| 2N1065 | G | P | MO | AF124 | | 2N2188 | 2N990 | | 01 |
| 2N1066 | G | P | RC, PE, MO | AF118 | AFZ12 | 2N3323 | 2N990 | | 02 |
| 2N1066 | | | | AF124 | | | | | 02 |
| 2N1067 | S | N | SF, SU, SQ, SZ | ZT1486 | | 2N3766 | 2N4237 | | 16 |
| 2N1067 | | | | | | 2N1486 | | | 16 |
| 2N1068 | S | N | SF, SU, SQ, SZ | ZT1486 | | 2N3766 | 2N4237 | | 16 |
| 2N1068 | | | | | | 2N1486 | | | 16 |
| 2N1069 | S | N | ET, SD, SZ, SF, SQ | BDY20 | | 2N3766 | 2N4913 | | 16 |
| 2N1069 | | | | | | 2N5067 | 2N3055 | | 16 |
| 2N1070 | S | N | ET, SD, SZ, SF, SQ | BDY20 | | 2N3766 | 2N4913 | | 16 |
| 2N1070 | | | | | | 2N5067 | 2N3055 | | 16 |
| 2N1072 | S | N | GP, SZ | BDY78 | | 2N3766 | | | 16 |
| 2N1073 | G | P | MO, SD, ET, DD, KS | (AUY21III) | AU103 | 2N2147 | | | 06 |
| 2N1073 | | | | AL100 | | | | | 06 |
| 2N1073A | G | P | MO, SD, DD, KS, ET | (AUY22III) | AL100 | 2N2147 | | | 06 |
| 2N1073B | G | P | MO, SD, KS, DD | (AUY22III) | AL100 | 2N2147 | | | 06 |
| 2N1074 | S | N | WE | | | 2N328A | | | 01 |
| 2N1075 | S | N | MO | | | 2N3288 | | | 01 |
| 2N1076 | S | N | ET | | | 2N328A | | | 01 |
| 2N1078 | G | P | KS | CTP1104 | SFT232 | 2N2835 | | 2SB107A | 06 |
| 2N1078 | | | | TF78/30 | AD162 | | | | 06 |
| 2N1079 | S | N | TR, ET, SQ | BDY23 | | 2N5068 | 2N3445 | | 03 |
| 2N1080 | S | N | TR, ET, SQ | BDY23 | | 2N4914 | 2N3445 | | 03 |
| 2N1081 | S | N | | BFY50 | | 2N3724 | 2N3725 | | 10 |
| 2N1081 | | | | | | 2N2297 | | | 10 |
| 2N1082 | G | N | GP | BFY50 | | 2N2217 | 2N2219 | | 02 |
| 2N1082 | | | | | | 2N2297 | | | 02 |
| 2N1084 | S | P | SM, TR, SQ | BFS95 | | 2N4036 | | | |
| 2N1085 | S | N | SM, TR, SQ | BFY50 | | 2N2297 | | | |
| 2N1086 | G | N | CN, SR, ET | ASY29 | | 2N1308 | 2N1304 | | 02 |
| 2N1086A | G | N | ET, SR | ASY29 | | 2N1308 | 2N1304 | | 02 |
| 2N1087 | G | N | CN, SR, ET | ASY29 | | 2N1308 | 2N1304 | | 02 |
| 2N1090 | G | N | CN, GI, SZ, ET | ASY29 | | 2N1304 | 2N1605 | | 10 |

| TYPE | M/S | POL | MANUFAC | EUROPEAN | | AMERICAN | | JAPANESE | USE |
|---|---|---|---|---|---|---|---|---|---|
| 2N1091 | G | N | CN, GI, SZ, ET | ASY29 | | 2N1304 | 2N1605 | | 10 |
| 2N1092 | S | N | CN, SQ, ET | BFY50 | | 2N4237 | 2N2297 | | 16 |
| 2N1093 | G | P | CN, SZ, ET | AF106 | AF178 | 2N1305 | | 2SA206 | 01 |
| 2N1093 | | | | AF190 | AF101 | | | | 01 |
| 2N1093 | | | | AF126 | AF127 | | | | 01 |
| 2N1093 | | | | ASY27 | | | | | 01 |
| 2N1094 | G | P | WE | AF106 | | 2N1308 | | | 02 |
| 2N1097 | G | P | ET, SR, CN, FR, SZ | AC128 | AC153 | 2N1414 | 2N2431 | 2SB219 | 01 |
| 2N1097 | | | | AC131 | AC105 | 2N1098 | 2N406 | | 01 |
| 2N1097 | | | | AC117 | AC125 | | | | 01 |
| 2N1098 | G | P | ET, SR, CN, FR, SZ | AC128 | AC153 | 2N1414 | 2N2431 | 2SB219 | 01 |
| 2N1098 | | | | AC117 | AC125 | 2N404 | | | 01 |
| 2N1099 | G | P | DD, ET, MO, SD, CN | ADZ12 | ADY26 | 2N1100 | | | 06 |
| 2N1100 | G | P | DD, ET, MO, MU, PH | AD132V | ADZ12 | | | | 06 |
| 2N1101 | G | P | CN, NP, ET | AC127 | AC179 | 2N2430 | 2N647 | | 01 |
| 2N1101 | | | | AC176 | | 2N1302 | | | 01 |
| 2N1102 | G | N | NP, ET, CN | AC127 | AC179 | 2N2430 | 2N612 | | 01 |
| 2N1102 | | | | AC176 | | | | | 01 |
| 2N1103 | S | N | TX | BFY50 | | 2N2297 | | | 01 |
| 2N1104 | S | N | SM | BFY50 | | 2N2297 | 2N1306 | | 01 |
| 2N1106 | S | N | TX | | | 2N5681 | | | 01 |
| 2N1107 | G | P | CN, ET | AF185 | AF124 | 2N990 | | | 02 |
| 2N1108 | G | P | CN, ET | AF185 | AF125 | 2N1110 | 2N2188 | 2SA159 | 02 |
| 2N1108 | | | | AF137 | AF124 | 2N990 | | | 02 |
| 2N1108 | | | | AF181 | AF115 | | | | 02 |
| 2N1108 | | | | AF131 | | | | | 02 |
| 2N1109 | G | P | CN, ET | AF185 | AF116 | 2N2188 | 2N990 | 2SA154 | 02 |
| 2N1109 | | | | AF126 | AF132 | | | | 02 |
| 2N1109 | | | | AF124 | | | | | 02 |
| 2N1110 | G | P | CN, ET | AF185 | AF125 | 2N2188 | 2N1108 | 2SA156 | 02 |
| 2N1110 | | | | AF125 | AF124 | 2N990 | | | 02 |
| 2N1110 | | | | AF181 | AF131 | | | | 02 |
| 2N1110 | | | | AF136 | | | | | 02 |
| 2N1111 | G | P | CN, ET | AF185 | AF126 | 2N2188 | 2N990 | 2SA155 | 02 |
| 2N1111 | | | | AF126 | | | | | 02 |
| 2N1111A | G | P | ET | AF124 | | 2N990 | | | |
| 2N1111B | G | P | ET | AF124 | | 2N991 | | | |
| 2N1114 | G | N | CN, ET, SZ | ASY29 | | 2N1304 | | | 10 |
| 2N1115 | G | P | ET | ASY27 | | 2N1305 | | | 10 |
| 2N1115A | G | P | GE | ASY27 | AF132 | 2N1305 | | | 10 |
| 2N1115A | | | | AF181 | AF124 | | | | 10 |
| 2N1116 | S | N | ET, ST, TR, UN, SQ | BSX46-6 | BFY34 | 2N4231 | 2N3252 | | 02 |
| 2N1116 | | | | BSX45 | BSX22 | 2N2243A | 2N2297 | | 02 |
| 2N1116 | | | | BFY50 | | | | | 02 |
| 2N1117 | S | N | TX, TR, UN, SZ, ET | BFY50 | | 2N2193 | 2N2243A | | 02 |
| 2N1117 | | | | | | 2N2297 | | | 02 |
| 2N1118 | S | P | SP, CR, ID, SM, SQ | BFX29 | | 2N2604 | 2N2605 | | 02 |
| 2N1118 | | | | | | 2N2905A | | | 02 |
| 2N1118A | S | P | CR, RY, SP, FR, ES | BFX29 | | 2N2604 | 2N2605 | | 02 |
| 2N1118A | | | | | | 2N2905A | | | 02 |
| 2N1119 | S | P | CR, SP, FR, RY, SM | BFX29 | | 2N2604 | 2N2605 | | 10 |
| 2N1119 | | | | | | 2N2905A | | | 10 |
| 2N1120 | G | P | MO, SD, ET | (AD133IV) | AD133 | TI3027 | TI3031 | | 06 |
| 2N1120 | | | | ASZ15 | | 2N1533 | | | 06 |
| 2N1121 | G | N | ET | ASY29 | | 2N1306 | 2N1304 | | 02 |
| 2N1122 | G | P | FR, SM, SQ, ID, SP | AF126 | AF137 | 2N961 | 2N964 | 2SA155 | 13 |
| 2N1122 | | | | AF132 | AF124 | 2N990 | | | 13 |
| 2N1122A | G | P | FR, SM, SQ, ID, SP | AF126 | AF132 | 2N960 | 2N964 | 2SA155 | 13 |
| 2N1122A | | | | AF137 | AF124 | 2N990 | | | 13 |
| 2N1123 | G | P | GI, SQ | | | 2N3427 | 2N1997 | | 13 |
| 2N1124 | G | P | CN, ET, ES | ACY17 | | 2N651 | 2N1377 | | 01 |
| 2N1124 | | | | | | 2N1176 | | | 01 |
| 2N1125 | G | P | CN, ET | ACY17 | | 2N651 | 2N2000 | | 13 |
| 2N1125 | | | | | | 2N1176 | | | 13 |
| 2N1126 | G | P | PH | ACY17 | | 2N651 | 2N1176 | | 10 |
| 2N1127 | G | P | PH | ACY17 | | 2N3428 | 2N1176 | | 10 |
| 2N1128 | G | P | CN, ET | AC128 | AC153 | 2N1192 | 2N2431 | 2SB222 | 01 |
| 2N1128 | | | | AC117 | ACY17 | 2N1377 | 2N1176 | | 01 |
| 2N1129 | G | P | CN, ET | AC153 | AC117 | 2N3427 | 2N1377 | 2SB222 | 01 |
| 2N1129 | | | | AC128 | ACY17 | 2N1379 | 2N1176 | 2SB223 | 01 |
| 2N1130 | G | P | CN, ET | AC153 | AC117 | 2N1193 | 2N1377 | 2SB222 | 01 |
| 2N1130 | | | | AC128 | ACY17 | 2N1176 | | 2SB221 | 01 |
| 2N1131 | S | P | F, MO, PH, TX, RY | BSV16-6 | BFX74 | EN1132 | 2N2904 | | 10 |
| 2N1131 | | | | BCZ12 | | 2N1132 | 2N2905 | | 10 |
| 2N1131 | | | | BFX30 | | 2N2905A | | | 10 |

| TYPE | M/S | POL | MANUFAC | EUROPEAN | | AMERICAN | | JAPANESE | USE |
|------|-----|-----|---------|----------|--|----------|--|----------|-----|
| 2N1131A | S | P | F, MO, FR, SQ, TR | BSV16-6 | BFX30 | 2N2800 | 2N2905A | | 10 |
| 2N1131A/51 | S | P | SY | BFX30 | | 2N2905A | | | |
| 2N1131/51 | S | P | SY | BFX30 | | 2N2905A | | | |
| 2N1132 | S | P | IT, TX, MO, PH, SE | BSV16-6 | BFX74 | 2N4037 | EN1132 | | 10 |
| 2N1132 | | | | BFX74A | BSV16-6 | 2N2904 | 2N2905 | | 10 |
| 2N1132 | | | | BFS95 | BCY18 | 2N4036 | | | 10 |
| 2N1132 | | | | BCZ11 | BCZ12 | | | | 10 |
| 2N1132A | S | P | IT, MO, SG, F, SM | BSV16-6 | BFX74A | 2N4037 | EN1132 | | 10 |
| 2N1132A | | | | BFS95 | | 2N4036 | | | 10 |
| 2N1132A/46 | S | P | SM | BSW24 | | 2N2907A | | | |
| 2N1132A/51 | S | P | SY | BSW24 | | 2N2907A | | | |
| 2N1132B | S | P | RY, SQ, TD, SM, EM | BFX29 | | 2N2905A | | | 10 |
| 2N1132B/46 | S | P | SM | BSW24 | | 2N2907A | | | |
| 2N1132B/51 | S | P | SY | BSW24 | | 2N2907A | | | |
| 2N1132/46 | S | P | SM | BSW24 | | 2N2907A | | | |
| 2N1132/51 | S | P | SY | BSW24 | | 2N2907A | | | |
| 2N1135 | S | P | PH | BSW25 | | 2N3446 | | | 10 |
| 2N1135A | S | P | PH | BSW25 | | 2N3546 | | | 10 |
| 2N1136 | G | P | ET, ST, SD, PP, CN | (AUY21IV) | AUY21 | 2N1540 | MP249 | 2SB248 | 06 |
| 2N1136 | | | | AD138 | ASZ18 | TI3027 | 2N1536 | | 06 |
| 2N1136 | | | | AC117 | AC153 | | | | 06 |
| 2N1136 | | | | ASZ16 | | | | | 06 |
| 2N1136A | G | P | ET, ST, SD, CN, KS | (AUY22IV) | ASZ15 | 2N1542 | 2N1533 | | 06 |
| 2N1136B | G | P | ST, SD, ET, PP, CN | (AUY22IV) | AUY21 | 2N1543 | 2N1533 | | 06 |
| 2N1136B | | | | ASZ15 | | | | | 06 |
| 2N1137 | G | P | ET, ST, SD, KS, PP | (AUY21IV) | AUY21 | 2N1544 | MP438 | 2SB248 | 06 |
| 2N1137 | | | | AD138 | ASZ18 | 2N456A | 2N1533 | | 06 |
| 2N1137 | | | | AC117 | AC153 | | | | 06 |
| 2N1137 | | | | ASZ16 | | | | | 06 |
| 2N1137A | G | P | ET, ST, SD, KS, CN | (AUY22IV) | ASZ15 | 2N1547 | MP438A | | 06 |
| 2N1137B | G | P | ST, SD, PP, KS | (AUY22IV) | ASZ15 | 2N1546 | MP438B | | 06 |
| 2N1137B | | | | | | 2N1533 | | | 06 |
| 2N1138 | G | P | ET, ST, SD, PP, CN | (AUY21IV) | ASZ17 | MP280 | 2N1545 | | 06 |
| 2N1138A | G | P | ET, ST, SD, PP, CN | (AUY22IV) | ASZ15 | 2N1547 | MP281 | | 06 |
| 2N1138A | | | | | | 2N1533 | | | 06 |
| 2N1138B | G | P | ET, SD, PP, KS | (AUY22IV) | ASZ15 | 2N1548 | MP282 | | 06 |
| 2N1138B | | | | | | 2N1533 | | | 06 |
| 2N1139 | S | N | TR, ET, CN | BSW54 | | 2N835 | 2N2219A | | 13 |
| 2N1141 | G | P | MO, TX | (AFY18D) | AF178 | 2N2495 | | | 02 |
| 2N1141 | | | | AF106 | | | | | 02 |
| 2N1141A | G | P | MO, TX | (AFY18D) | AFY18 | | | | 02 |
| 2N1141A | | | | AF106 | | | | | 02 |
| 2N1142 | G | P | MO, TX | (AFY18D) | AF178 | 2N2405 | | | 02 |
| 2N1142 | | | | AFY12 | AFZ12 | | | | 02 |
| 2N1142 | | | | AF106 | | | | | 02 |
| 2N1142A | G | P | MO, TX | (AFY18D) | AFY18 | | | | 02 |
| 2N1142A | | | | AF106 | | | | | 02 |
| 2N1143 | G | P | MO, TX | (AFY18D) | AF178 | 2N2495 | | | 02 |
| 2N1143 | | | | ASY76 | AFY12 | | | | 02 |
| 2N1143 | | | | AF212 | AF106 | | | | 02 |
| 2N1143A | G | P | MO, TX, ES | (AFY18D) | AFY18 | | | | 02 |
| 2N1143A | | | | AF106 | | | | | 02 |
| 2N1144 | G | P | SN, ET | AC128 | AC153 | 2N231 | 2N2431 | 2SB37 | 02 |
| 2N1144 | | | | AC131 | AC152 | 2N1303 | 2N1176 | | 02 |
| 2N1144 | | | | OC76 | ACY17 | | | | 02 |
| 2N1145 | G | P | CN, ET | AC128 | AC153 | 2N1414 | 2N2431 | 2SB37 | 01 |
| 2N1145 | | | | AC131 | AC152 | 2N1303 | 2N1176 | | 01 |
| 2N1145 | | | | OC76 | ACY17 | | | | 01 |
| 2N1146 | G | P | MO, ST, CN, ET, SD | (AUY29V) | AD133 | 2N456A | 2N1536 | | 16 |
| 2N1146 | | | | AD138 | ADZ11 | | | | 16 |
| 2N1146 | | | | ADZ12 | ASZ16 | | | | 16 |
| 2N1146A | G | P | MO, ST, ET, CN, KS | (AUY29V) | AUY21IV | 2N456A | 2N1536 | | 16 |
| 2N1146A | | | | ADZ11 | ADZ12 | | | | 16 |
| 2N1146A | | | | ASZ16 | | | | | 16 |
| 2N1146B | G | P | ET, MO, SD, KS, PP | AUY22IV | ASZ16 | 2N1536 | | | 16 |
| 2N1146C | G | P | ET, SD, MO, KS, PP | ADZ12 | ASZ16 | 2N456A | 2N1533 | | 16 |
| 2N1147 | G | P | MO, ST, ET, CN, KS | (AUY29V) | ASZ16 | 2N1536 | | | 16 |
| 2N1147A | G | P | MO, ST, SD, ET, KS | (AUY29V) | ASZ16 | 2N1536 | | | 16 |
| 2N1147B | G | P | ET, SD, MO, CN, KS | ASZ16 | | 2N1536 | | | 16 |
| 2N1147C | G | P | ET, SD, MO, KS, PP | ASZ15 | | 2N1533 | | | 16 |
| 2N1149 | S | N | TX, ET, SQ, CN, SM | BSW54 | | 2N2219A | | | 01 |
| 2N1150 | S | N | TX, ET, SQ, CN, SM | BSW54 | | 2N2219A | | | 01 |
| 2N1151 | S | N | TX, ET, SQ, CN, SM | BSW54 | | 2N2219A | | | 01 |
| 2N1151 | S | N | TX, ET, SQ, CN, SM | BSW54 | | 2N2219A | | | 01 |
| 2N1153 | S | N | TX, ET, SQ, CN, SM | BSW54 | | 2N2210A | | | 01 |

| TYPE | M/S | POL | MANUFAC | EUROPEAN | | AMERICAN | | JAPANESE | USE |
|------|-----|-----|---------|----------|---|----------|---|----------|-----|
| 2N1154 | S | N | TX, ET, SQ, CN, SM | BC107 | | A157 | | | 01 |
| 2N1155 | S | N | TX, ET, SQ, CN, SM | BC107 | | A157 | | | 01 |
| 2N1156 | S | N | TX, ET, SQ, CN, SM | BC107 | | A157 | | | 01 |
| 2N1157 | G | P | SD, CD | | | MP501 | | | 16 |
| 2N1157A | | P | SD, CN | | | MP502 | | | 16 |
| | | | | | | | | | |
| 2N1158 | G | P | CN, ET | AF239S | | 2N1143 | | | 02 |
| 2N1158A | G | P | CN, ET | AF239S | | 2N1142 | | | 02 |
| 2N1159 | G | P | DD, ET, PP, SD, CN | AUY22III | AUY28 | 2N3616 | 2N456A | | 16 |
| 2N1159 | | | | ASZ25 | ADY26 | 2N3146 | 2N1533 | | 16 |
| 2N1159 | | | | ASZ15 | | | | | 16 |
| | | | | | | | | | |
| 2N1160 | G | P | ET, DE, DD, PP, SD | (AUY22IV) | AUY22 | 2N3616 | 2N456A | | 16 |
| 2N1160 | | | | ASZ16 | ASZ18 | 2N3146 | 2N1533 | | 16 |
| 2N1160 | | | | ASZ15 | | | | | 16 |
| 2N1162A | G | P | MO, ET, SD, CN, KS | | | 2N1162 | | | 16 |
| 2N1163 | G | P | MO, ET, SD, CN, KS | | | 2N1162 | | | 16 |
| | | | | | | | | | |
| 2N1163A | G | P | MO, ET, SD, KS | | | 2N1162 | | | 16 |
| 2N1164 | G | P | MO, ET, SD, CN, KS | | | 2N1166 | | | 16 |
| 2N1164A | G | P | MO, ET, SD, CN, KS | | | 2N1166 | | | 16 |
| 2N1165 | G | P | MO, ET, SD, CN, KS | | | 2N1166 | | | 16 |
| 2N1165A | G | P | MO, ET, SD, CN, KS | | | 2N1166 | | | 16 |
| | | | | | | | | | |
| 2N1166A | G | P | MO, KS, SD, ET | | | 2N1166 | | | 16 |
| 2N1167 | G | P | MO, ET, SD, CN, KS | | | 2N1166 | | | 16 |
| 2N1167A | G | P | MO, ET, SD, CN, KS | | | 2N1166 | | | 16 |
| 2N1168 | G | P | DD, ET, SD, CN, KS | AUY19III | ASZ18 | 2N3614 | TI3027 | | 06 |
| 2N1168 | | | | ASZ16 | AUY21 | 2N1536 | | | 06 |
| | | | | | | | | | |
| 2N1169 | G | N | CN, SS, SZ | ASY29 | | 2N1304 | | | 10 |
| 2N1170 | G | N | CN, SZ | ASY29 | | 2N1304 | | | 10 |
| 2N1171 | G | P | CN, ET, IC, UP | | | 2N1305 | | | 10 |
| 2N1172 | G | P | KS | AD156 | AD139 | 2N2137 | TI3027 | 2SB240 | 16 |
| 2N1172 | | | | AD148 | OC22 | TI3028 | 2N2197 | | 16 |
| | | | | | | | | | |
| 2N1172 | | | | OC30 | | | | | 16 |
| 2N1173 | G | N | WE | ASY29 | | 2N1304 | | | 10 |
| 2N1174 | G | P | WE | ASY27 | | 2N404 | 2N1305 | | 10 |
| 2N1175 | G | P | MO, GE, ET, SR, UP | (AC152VI) | ACY17 | 2N1176 | | | 01 |
| 2N1175A | G | P | ET, GE, SR, FR, SZ | ASY17 | | 2N1176 | | | 01 |
| | | | | | | | | | |
| 2N1176 | G | P | CN, GI, ET | ACY17 | | 2N1189 | 2N1038 | | 01 |
| 2N1176 | | | | | | 2N1176B | | | 01 |
| 2N1176A | G | P | CN, ET | ACY17 | | 2N1176B | | | 01 |
| 2N1176B | G | P | ET | OC77N | | | | | 01 |
| 2N1177 | G | P | RC, AT | AF178 | AF118 | 2N2957 | 2N2495 | 2SA118 | 02 |
| | | | | | | | | | |
| 2N1177 | | | | AF125 | AF115 | 2N990 | 2N1180 | | 02 |
| 2N1177 | | | | AF136 | AF124 | 2N2188 | | | 02 |
| 2N1178 | G | P | RC, AT | AF178 | AF118 | 2N2953 | 2N2495 | 2SA118 | 02 |
| 2N1178 | | | | AF125 | AF115 | 2N2188 | 2N990 | | 02 |
| 2N1178 | | | | AF136 | AF124 | | | | 02 |
| | | | | | | | | | |
| 2N1179 | G | P | RC, AT | AF178 | AF118 | 2N2956 | 2N2495 | 2SA118 | 02 |
| 2N1179 | | | | AF125 | AF115 | 2N2188 | 2N990 | | 02 |
| 2N1179 | | | | AF136 | AF124 | | | | 02 |
| 2N1180 | G | P | RC, AT | AF185 | AF118 | 2N2956 | 2N2188 | 2SA118 | 02 |
| 2N1180 | | | | AF178 | AF125 | 2N990 | | | 02 |
| | | | | | | | | | |
| 2N1180 | | | | AF115 | AF136 | | | | 02 |
| 2N1180 | | | | AF124 | | | | | 02 |
| 2N1182 | G | P | GP | ASZ15 | | 2N2140 | 2N1533 | | 16 |
| 2N1183 | G | P | ST, RC, KS | AD136V | AD136 | 2N2139 | 2N1038 | 2SB242 | 16 |
| 2N1183 | | | | AUY18 | AD160 | 2N2140 | 2N1184B | | 16 |
| | | | | | | | | | |
| 2N1183 | | | | AC136 | OC30 | | | | 16 |
| 2N1183 | | | | OD603 | | | | | 16 |
| 2N1183A | G | P | ST, RC, KS | (AUY18V) | AUY18 | 2N2140 | 2N1038 | | 16 |
| 2N1183A | | | | AD136 | | 2N11848 | | | 16 |
| 2N1183B | G | P | ST, RC, KS | (AUY18V) | AD136 | 2N2141 | 2N1038 | | 16 |
| | | | | | | | | | |
| 2N1183B | | | | | | 2N11848 | | | 16 |
| 2N1184 | G | P | ST, RC, KS | AD136VI | AD136 | 2N2144 | 2N1038 | | 16 |
| 2N1184 | | | | | | 2N2564 | 2N1184B | | 16 |
| 2N1184A | G | P | ST KS, RC | AUY18V | AD136 | 2N2145 | 2N1038 | | 16 |
| 2N1184A | | | | | | 2N2564 | 2N1184B | | 16 |
| | | | | | | | | | |
| 2N1184B | G | P | ST, RC, KS | (AUY18V) | AD136 | 2N2146 | 2N1038 | | 16 |
| 2N1184B | | | | | | 2N2565 | | | 16 |
| 2N1185 | G | P | MO, ET, SR, CN, IC | (ASY48VI) | ACY17 | 2N1375 | 2N1377 | | 01 |
| 2N1185 | | | | | | 2N1188 | | | 01 |
| 2N1186 | G | P | MO, IC, SR, CN | (ASY48IV) | ACY17 | 2N1375 | 2N1377 | | 01 |
| | | | | | | | | | |
| 2N1186 | | | | | | 2N1188 | | | 01 |
| 2N1187 | G | P | MO, IC, SR, CN | (ASY48V) | ACY17 | 2N1376 | 2N1377 | | 01 |
| 2N1187 | | | | | | 2N1188 | | | 01 |
| 2N1188 | G | P | MO, IC, SR, CN | (ASY48VI) | ACY17 | 2N1376 | 2N1377 | | 01 |
| 2N1189 | G | P | MO, ET, SR, CN, IC | (ASY48V) | ACY17 | 2N1377 | | | 01 |

| TYPE | M/S | POL | MANUFAC | EUROPEAN | | AMERICAN | | JAPANESE | USE |
|------|-----|-----|---------|----------|-----|----------|-----|----------|-----|
| 2N1190 | G | P | MO, ET, SR, CN | (ASY48VI) | ACY17 | 2N1377 | 2N1188 | | 01 |
| 2N1191 | G | P | MO, ET, SR | (ASY48IV) | AC153 | 2N404 | 2N1305 | 2SB225 | 01 |
| 2N1191 | | | | AC117 | AC128 | 2N1188 | | | 01 |
| 2N1191 | | | | OC72 | ACY17 | | | | 01 |
| 2N1192 | G | P | MO, ET, SR, CN, GI | (ASY48V) | AC153 | 2N404 | 2N1188 | 2SB226 | 01 |
| 2N1192 | | | | AC117 | AC128 | | | | 01 |
| 2N1192 | | | | ACY17 | | | | | 01 |
| 2N1193 | G | P | MO, ET, SR, IC, SZ | (ASY48VI) | AC153 | 2N404 | 2N1188 | 2SB227 | 01 |
| 2N1193 | | | | AC117 | AC128 | | | | 01 |
| 2N1194 | G | P | MO, ET, SR, St, CN | (ASY48VI) | ACY17 | 2N1188 | | | 01 |
| 2N1194 | G | P | MO | OC318 | ACY17 | | | | 01 |
| 2N1195 | G | P | MO, ES, TX | (AFY18D) | AF178 | 2N2495 | 2N404 | | 02 |
| 2N1195 | | | | AF106 | AF102 | | | | 02 |
| 2N1195 | | | | AFY12 | | | | | 02 |
| 2N1196 | S | P | EM, SQ, SM | BC177 | | 2N3965 | | | 02 |
| 2N1197 | S | P | EM, SQ, SM | BC177 | | 2N3965 | | | 02 |
| 2N1198 | G | N | CN, ET | ASY29 | | 2N1304 | | | 16 |
| 2N1199 | S | N | ET | BFX73 | | 2N835 | 2N918 | | 16 |
| 2N1199A | S | N | PH | BFX73 | | 2N835 | 2N918 | | 16 |
| 2N1200 | S | N | PH | BFX73 | | 2N4252 | 2N918 | | 02 |
| 2N1201 | S | N | PH | BFX73 | | 2N4252 | 2N918 | | 02 |
| 2N1202 | S | N | SD, KS | ASZ15 | | 2N2145 | 2N456A | | 16 |
| 2N1202 | | | | | | 2N3146 | 2N1533 | | 16 |
| 2N1203 | G | P | SD, KS | ASZ15 | | 2N2146 | 2N456A | | 16 |
| 2N1203 | | | | | | 2N3146 | 2N1533 | | 16 |
| 2N1204 | G | P | MO | (ASY26) | | | | | 13 |
| 2N1205 | S | N | ET, TR | BSW38 | | 2N2219A | | | |
| 2N1206 | S | N | CN, ET | BSW54 | | 2N5059 | 2N2219A | | 02 |
| 2N1207 | S | N | CN, ET | BSW54 | | 2N5059 | 2N2219A | | 02 |
| 2N1208 | S | N | TR, ET, SZ, CN, ML | BDY11 | BUY38 | 2N3445 | 2N3487 | | 06 |
| 2N1208 | | | | | | 2N3054 | | | 06 |
| 2N1208/1 | S | N | SQ | BUY38 | | 2N3054 | | | |
| 2N1209 | S | N | TR, SZ, ML, SM | BUY38 | | 2N3445 | 2N1724 | | 03 |
| 2N1209 | | | | | | 2N3054 | | | 03 |
| 2N1209/1 | S | N | SQ | BUY38 | | 2N3054 | | | |
| 2N1210 | S | N | TR, ET, SD, SZ, CN | BUY38 | | 2N3713 | 2N1722 | | 03 |
| 2N1210 | | | | | | 2N4232 | 2N3054 | | 03 |
| 2N1210/1 | S | N | SQ | BUY38 | | 2N3054 | | | |
| 2N1211 | S | N | TR, ET, SD, SZ, CN | BUY38 | | 2N3445 | 2N1722 | | 03 |
| 2N1211 | | | | | | 2N4132 | 2N3054 | | 03 |
| 2N1211/1 | S | N | SQ | BUY38 | | 2N3054 | | | |
| 2N1212 | S | N | TR, ET, SZ, CN, FR | BUY38 | | 2N3445 | 2N1724 | | 03 |
| 2N1212 | | | | | | 2N3054 | | | 03 |
| 2N1212/1 | S | N | SQ | BUY38 | | 2N3054 | | | |
| 2N1217 | S | N | CN, ET | ASY29 | | 2N1308 | 2N1304 | | 13 |
| 2N1218 | G | N | CN, KS | AD162 | | 2N4077 | | | 06 |
| 2N1219 | S | P | SD, CR, RY, SQ, CN | BC160 | BCY12 | 2N1132 | 2N4036 | | 01 |
| 2N1219 | | | | BSF95 | | | | | 01 |
| 2N1220 | S | P | SD, CR, RY, SQ, CN | BC160 | BCY12 | 2N1132 | 2N1214 | | 01 |
| 2N1220 | | | | BSF96 | | 2N4036 | 2N2904 | | 01 |
| 2N1220 | | | | | | 2N2905 | | | 01 |
| 2N1221 | S | P | SD, CR, RY, SQ, CN | BFS95 | | 2N2904 | 2N2905 | | 01 |
| 2N1221 | | | | | | 2N4036 | | | 01 |
| 2N1222 | S | P | SD, CR, RY, SQ, CN | BSF95 | | 2N2904 | 2N2905 | | 01 |
| 2N1222 | | | | | | 2N4036 | | | 01 |
| 2N1223 | S | P | SD, CR, RY, SQ, CN | BSF95 | | 2N2404 | 2N2905 | | 01 |
| 2N1223 | | | | | | 2N4036 | | | 01 |
| 2N1224 | G | P | AM, RC, PE | (AF125) | AF126 | 2N990 | | | 13 |
| 2N1224 | | | | AF137 | AF116 | | | | 13 |
| 2N1224 | | | | ASZ20 | AF124 | | | | 13 |
| 2N1225 | G | P | AM, RC, NU, PE | AF125 | AF135 | 2N990 | | | 02 |
| 2N1225 | | | | AF115 | AF118 | | | | 02 |
| 2N1225 | | | | AF124 | | | | | 02 |
| 2N1226 | G | P | RC, PE, AM | AF124 | AF137 | 2N2635 | 2N90 | | 02 |
| 2N1226 | | | | AF114 | AF118 | | | | 02 |
| 2N1227 | G | P | ET, ST, SD, PP, CN | (AD130V) | AD149 | 2N3611 | TI3027 | | 06 |
| 2N1227 | | | | ASZ16 | | 2N1536 | | | 06 |
| 2N1228 | S | P | ET, ST, CR, RY, SD | (BC178A) | BCY32 | 2N1475 | | | 10 |
| 2N1229 | S | P | ET, ST, CR, RY, SD | (BC178A) | BCY32 | 2N1475 | | | 10 |
| 2N1230 | S | P | ET, ST, CR, RY, SD | (BC177A) | BCY32 | 2N1475 | | | 10 |
| 2N1231 | S | P | ET, ST, CR, RY, SD | (BC177A) | BCY32 | 2N1475 | | | 10 |
| 2N1232 | S | P | ET, ST, CR, SM, SQ | (BCY65EVII) | BCY32 | 2N1475 | | | 10 |
| 2N1233 | S | P | ET, ST, RY, CR, SM | (BCY65EVII) | BCY32 | 2N1475 | | | 10 |
| 2N1234 | S | P | CR, ET, SQ, St, ES | BCY32 | | 2N1475 | | | 10 |
| 2N1238 | S | P | HU | BCY32 | | 2N1475 | | | 10 |

| TYPE | M/S | POL | MANUFAC | EUROPEAN | | AMERICAN | | JAPANESE | USE |
|---|---|---|---|---|---|---|---|---|---|
| 2N1239 | S | P | HU | BCY32 | | 2N1475 | | | 10 |
| 2N1240 | S | P | HU, St | BCY32 | | 2N1475 | | | 10 |
| 2N1241 | S | P | HU, St | BCY32 | | 2N1475 | | | 10 |
| 2N1242 | S | P | HU, St | BCY32 | | 2N1475 | | | 10 |
| 2N1243 | S | P | HU, St | BCY32 | | 2N1475 | | | 10 |
| 2N1244 | S | P | HU, St | BCY32 | | 2N1475 | | | 10 |
| 2N1245 | G | P | CB | AD162 | OC30 | 2N404 | | 2SB250 | 06 |
| 2N1246 | | | | OD603 | SFT232 | | | | 06 |
| 2N1246 | G | P | CB | AC153 | AC117 | 2N404 | 2N1263 | 2SB253 | 06 |
| 2N1246 | | | | AC128 | | | | | 06 |
| 2N1247 | S | N | TR, ET, SQ, CN | BC107 | | 2N930 | | | 01 |
| 2N1248 | S | N | CN, SQ, TR, ET | BC109 | | 2N930 | | | 01 |
| 2N1249 | S | N | TR, ET, SQ, CN | BC109 | | 2N930 | | | 01 |
| 2N1250 | S | N | TR, SZ, ET, SU, SQ | BDY20 | | 2N3713 | 2N4914 | | 06 |
| 2N1250 | | | | | | 2N3055 | | | 06 |
| 2N1251 | G | N | CN, ET, NP | AC127 | | 2N2430 | 2N1304 | | 01 |
| 2N1251/1 | S | N | SQ | BDY20 | | 2N3055 | | | |
| 2N1252 | S | N | F, GI, TR, ET, IC | (BSY58) | BSX30 | 2N2537 | 2N2218 | | 10 |
| 2N1252 | | | | BSX45 | | | | | 10 |
| 2N1252A | S | N | RY | BFY50 | | 2N2537 | 2N2297 | | 10 |
| 2N1253 | S | N | F, TR, GI, ET, IC | (BSY58) | BSX30 | 2N2537 | 2N2218 | | 10 |
| 2N1253 | | | | BSX45 | | 2N2297 | | | 10 |
| 2N1253A | S | N | RY | BFY50 | | 2N2537 | | | 10 |
| 2N1254 | S | P | CN, SM, TR, EM, SQ | | | 2N722 | 2N2907 | | 13 |
| 2N1255 | S | P | CN, SM, TR, EM, SQ | | | 2N722 | 2N2907 | | 13 |
| 2N1256 | S | P | CN, SM, EM, TR, SQ | | | 2N722 | 2N2907 | | 13 |
| 2N1257 | S | P | CN, SM, TR, EM, SQ | BFX29 | | 2N722 | 2N2907 | | 13 |
| 2N1257 | | | | | | 2N2905A | | | 13 |
| 2N1258 | S | P | CN, SM, TR, EM, SQ | | | 2N722 | 2N2907 | | 13 |
| 2N1259 | S | P | CN, SM, EM, SQ | | | 2N722 | 2N2907 | | 13 |
| 2N1261 | G | P | SD, KS, CN | AC153 | AC117 | 2N1531 | 2N1262 | 2SB252 | 16 |
| 2N1261 | | | | AC128 | AC105 | 2N1536 | | | 16 |
| 2N1261 | | | | ASZ16 | | | | | 16 |
| 2N1262 | G | P | SD, KS, CN | AC153 | AC131 | 2N1531 | 2N1261 | 2SB252 | 16 |
| 2N1262 | | | | AC128 | AC105 | 2N1536 | | | 16 |
| 2N1262 | | | | AC117 | ASZ16 | | | | 16 |
| 2N1263 | G | P | SD, KS, CN | AC153 | AUY28 | 2N3617 | 2N1536 | 2SB253 | 16 |
| 2N1263 | | | | AC128 | AC117 | | | | 16 |
| 2N1263 | | | | ASZ16 | | | | | 16 |
| 2N1264 | G | P | SY | AF178 | AF127 | 2N1191 | 2N2495 | | 02 |
| 2N1265 | | | | AF137 | | | | | 02 |
| 2N1265 | G | P | CN, ET, UP | | | 2N1192 | 2N404 | | 02 |
| 2N1266 | G | P | CN, ET | AF185 | AF127 | 2N1191 | 2N404 | | 02 |
| 2N1266 | | | | AF122 | AC128 | 2N1188 | | | 02 |
| 2N1266 | | | | ACY17 | | | | | 02 |
| 2N1267 | S | N | CN, ET | | | 2N4252 | 2N4253 | | 02 |
| 2N1268 | S | N | ET | | | 2N4252 | 2N4253 | | 02 |
| 2N1269 | S | N | ET | | | 2N4252 | 2N4253 | | 02 |
| 2N1270 | S | N | ET | | | 2N4252 | 2N4253 | | 02 |
| 2N1271 | S | N | ET | | | 2N4252 | 2N4253 | | 02 |
| 2N1272 | S | N | ET | | | 2N4252 | 2N4253 | | 02 |
| 2N1273 | G | P | TX, SR, ET, MO | AC128 | AC153 | 2N1191 | 2N2431 | 2SB222 | 01 |
| 2N1273 | | | | AC117 | OC72 | 2N404 | 2N1188 | | 01 |
| 2N1273 | | | | ACY17 | | | | | 01 |
| 2N1274 | G | P | TX, GI, SR, ET, MO | AC128 | ASY26 | 2N1191 | 2N2431 | 2SB222 | 01 |
| 2N1274 | | | | AC153 | ACY17 | 2N404 | 2N1188 | | 01 |
| 2N1274 | | | | AC117 | AC122/30 | | | | 01 |
| 2N1274 | | | | OC72 | | | | | 01 |
| 2N1275 | S | P | CR, SD, SQ, ET | | | 2N2501 | | | 05 |
| 2N1278 | S | N | ET, TX, TR | | | | | | 01 |
| 2N1279 | N | | ET, TR, TX | | | 2N2501 | | | 01 |
| 2N1280 | G | P | TI, ET, UP | | | 2N1305 | | | 10 |
| 2N1281 | G | P | IC, ET | | | 2N1307 | | | 10 |
| 2N1282 | G | P | IC, ET | | | 2N1307 | | | 10 |
| 2N1284 | G | P | IC, ET, UP | | | 2N1305 | | | 10 |
| 2N1285 | G | P | SY | | | 2N2188 | | | 02 |
| 2N1287 | G | P | SD | AC128 | AC153 | 2N651 | 2N2431 | 2SB225 | 01 |
| 2N1287 | | | | AC137 | OC318 | 2N1303 | | | 01 |
| 2N1287A | G | P | SD | | | 2N652 | | | 01 |
| 2N1291 | G | P | ST, CN, KS, ET | AD130IV | AC153 | 2N1529 | TI3027 | 2SB248 | 06 |
| 2N1291 | | | | AC117 | AC128 | | | | 06 |
| 2N1291 | | | | OC318 | | | | | 06 |
| 2N1292 | G | P | SZ, GP, CI | | | | | | 06 |
| 2N1293 | G | P | ST, ET, KS | AD132IV | AC153 | 2N1531 | TI3027 | 2SB248A | 06 |
| 2N1293 | | | | AC117 | AC128 | | | | 06 |

| TYPE | M/S | POL | MANUFAC | EUROPEAN | | AMERICAN | | JAPANESE | USE |
|------|-----|-----|---------|----------|---|----------|---|----------|-----|
| 2N1293 | | | | OC74 | | | | | 06 |
| 2N1295 | G | P | ST, ET, KS | AD133IV | AC153 | 2N1532 | 2N456 | 2SB249 | 06 |
| 2N1295 | | | | AC117 | AC128 | | | | 06 |
| 2N1295 | | | | OC74 | | | | | 06 |
| 2N1296 | G | N | SZ, GP, CI | | | | | | |
| 2N1297 | G | P | ST, CN, KS, ET | AD163IV | | 2N1533 | 2N456A | | 06 |
| 2N1297 | | | | | | 2N3146 | | | 06 |
| 2N1298 | G | N | KS | | | 2N1302 | | | 06 |
| 2N1299 | G | N | CN, ET | | | 2N1306 | | | 10 |
| 2N1300 | G | P | SR, II | ASY27 | ASZ20 | 2N2535 | 2N990 | | 13 |
| 2N1300 | | | | AF124 | | | | | 13 |
| 2N1301 | G | P | CN, FR, SQ, ES | ASY27 | ASZ20 | 2N2635 | 2N990 | | 13 |
| 2N1301 | | | | AF124 | | | | | 13 |
| 2N1302 | G | N | PH, TX, NL, SR, ET | (AC127) | ASY28 | 2N1304 | | | 10 |
| 2N1302 | | | | ASY73 | ASY29 | | | | 10 |
| 2N1303 | G | P | GE, PH, TX, GI, NT | (AC152) | ASY26 | 2N1192 | 2N1305 | | 10 |
| 2N1303 | | | | ASY27 | | | | | 10 |
| 2N1304 | G | N | PH, TX, ET, GI, NU | (AC127) | ASY28 | | | | 10 |
| 2N1304 | | | | ASY29 | | | | | 10 |
| 2N1305 | G | P | PH, TX, ET, GE, NT | (AC152) | ASY26 | | | | 10 |
| 2N1305 | | | | ASY27 | | | | | 10 |
| 2N1306 | G | N | PH, TX, ET, GI, NU | (AC127) | ASY29 | 2N1304 | | | 10 |
| 2N1307 | G | P | PH, TX, ET, GE, NT | (AC152) | ASY27 | 2N1305 | | | 10 |
| 2N1307 | | | | ASY26 | | | | | 10 |
| 2N1308 | G | N | PH, TX, ET, GI, NU | (AC127) | ASY29 | 2N1304 | | | 10 |
| 2N1309 | G | P | PH, TX, ET, NT, RC | (AC152) | ASY27 | 2N1305 | | | 10 |
| 2N1309 | | | | ASY26 | | | | | 10 |
| 2N1310 | G | N | CN, SR, ES | | | MP2373-1 | | | 04 |
| 2N1311 | G | N | CN, SR | | | | | | 06 |
| 2N1313 | G | P | ET, IC, SZ, GI | | | | | | 10 |
| 2N1314 | G | P | AM, ST, ET, PE | AD149IV | AD149 | 2N3611 | | | 06 |
| 2N1314 | | | | AD150 | | | | | 06 |
| 2N1315 | G | P | AM | ASZ17 | | 2N3611 | | | 06 |
| 2N1320 | G | P | KS | AC153 | AC117 | | | 2SB248 | 06 |
| 2N1320 | | | | AC128 | | | | | 06 |
| 2N1321 | G | N | KS, SZ, GP | | | | | | |
| 2N1322 | G | P | KS | AC153 | AC117 | | | 2SB248A | 06 |
| 2N1322 | | | | AC128 | | | | | 06 |
| 2N1323 | G | N | KS | | | | | | |
| 2N1324 | G | P | KS | AC153 | AC117 | | | 2SB249 | 06 |
| 2N1325 | G | N | KS | AC128 | | | | | 06 |
| 2N1326 | G | P | KS | | | 2N1038 | | | 06 |
| 2N1327 | G | N | KS | | | | | | |
| 2N1328 | G | P | KS | AC153 | AC117 | 2N1038 | | 2SB248 | 06 |
| 2N1328 | | | | AC128 | | | | | 06 |
| 2N1329 | G | N | KS | | | | | | 06 |
| 2N1331 | G | P | KS | AC153 | AC117 | 2N1038 | | 2SB249 | 06 |
| 2N1331 | | | | OC74 | AC128 | | | | 06 |
| 2N1333 | G | P | KS | ASZ15 | | 2N1533 | | | 06 |
| 2N1335 | S | N | SM, SQ | BSX47-6 | | | | | 03 |
| 2N1336 | S | N | SM, SQ | BSX47-6 | | | | | 03 |
| 2N1337 | S | N | SM, SQ | BSX47-6 | | | | | 03 |
| 2N1338 | S | N | NU, SM, SQ | BSX46-6 | BSX46 | 2N2219A | | | 03 |
| 2N1338 | | | | BSY46 | BFY13 | | | | 03 |
| 2N1338 | | | | BSW54 | | | | | 03 |
| 2N1339 | S | N | SM, SQ | BSX47-6 | | | | | 03 |
| 2N1340 | S | N | SM, NU, SQ | BSX47-7 | BFY45 | 2N2219A | | | 03 |
| 2N1340 | | | | BF178 | BSW66 | | | | 03 |
| 2N1340 | | | | BSY45 | BSW54 | | | | 03 |
| 2N1341 | S | N | SM, SQ | BSX47-6 | BFY45 | 2N1341 | 2N2219A | | 03 |
| 2N1342 | S | N | NU, SM, SQ | (BSX47-6) | BSW66 | | | | 03 |
| 2N1342 | | | | BF178 | BSW54 | | | | 03 |
| 2N1342 | | | | BSY45 | | | | | 03 |
| 2N1343 | G | P | IC, ET, UP, CN, FR | | | 2N404 | | | 10 |
| 2N1344 | G | P | IC, ET, UP, CN, FR | | | 2N404 | | | 10 |
| 2N1345 | G | P | IC, ET, UP, CN, FR | | | 2N404 | | | 10 |
| 2N1346 | G | P | IC, ET, UP, CN, FR | | | 2N404 | | | 10 |
| 2N1347 | G | P | IC, ET, UP, CN, FR | | | 2N404 | | | 10 |
| 2N1348 | G | P | CN, IC, ET | | | 2N404 | | | 10 |
| 2N1349 | G | P | CN, IC, ET | | | 2N404 | | | |
| 2N1350 | G | P | CN, IC, ET | | | 2N404 | | | |
| 2N1351 | G | P | CN, IC, ET | | | 2N404 | | | |
| 2N1352 | G | P | IC, ET, UP, CN, GI | | | 2N651 | | | 01 |
| 2N1353 | G | P | IC, ET, UP, CN | | | 2N404 | | | 10 |

| TYPE | M/S | POL | MANUFAC | EUROPEAN | | AMERICAN | | JAPANESE | USE |
|---|---|---|---|---|---|---|---|---|---|
| 2N1354 | G | P | IC, ET, CN | | | 2N404 | | | 10 |
| 2N1355 | G | P | IC, ET, CN | | | 2N404 | | | 10 |
| 2N1356 | G | P | IC, ET, CN | | | 2N404 | | | 10 |
| 2N1357 | G | P | IC, ET, CN | | | 2N404 | | | 10 |
| 2N1358 | G | P | DD, ET, NU, MO, NP | AUY29 | AD138/50 | 2N2929 | 2N1100 | 2SB242 | 16 |
| 2N1358 | | | | ASZ16 | | | | | 16 |
| 2N1358A | G | P | DD, MO, NU, KS | ADZ12 | AC128 | 2N1100 | | | 16 |
| 2N1358A | | | | AC153 | AD212 | | | | 16 |
| 2N1359 | G | P | MO, ET, PP, SD, CN | (AD131IV) | AD149 | 2N1536 | | 2SB249 | 06 |
| 2N1359 | | | | OC74 | OC318 | | | | 06 |
| 2N1359 | | | | ADZ16 | | | | | 06 |
| 2N1360 | G | P | MO, ET, PP, SD, CN | (AD131IV) | ASZ16 | T13027 | 2N1536 | | 06 |
| 2N1362 | G | P | MO, ET, PP, SD, CN | (AD163IV) | AUY34 | 2N456 | 2N3146 | | 06 |
| 2N1362 | | | | ASZ15 | | 2N1533 | | | 06 |
| 2N1363 | G | P | MO, ET, PP, SD, CN | (AD163IV) | ASZ15 | 2N456A | 2N1346 | | 06 |
| 2N1363 | | | | | | 2N1533 | | | 06 |
| 2N1364 | G | P | MO, KS, SD, CN | (AD163IV) | ASZ15 | 2N456A | 2N3146 | | 06 |
| 2N1364 | | | | | | 2N1533 | | | 06 |
| 2N1365 | G | P | MO, KS, SD, CN | (AD163IV) | ASZ15 | 2N456A | 2N3146 | | 06 |
| 2N1365 | | | | | | 2N1533 | | | 06 |
| 2N1366 | G | N | CN, KS | | | 2N1302 | | | 01 |
| 2N1367 | G | N | CN, KS | | | 2N1304 | | | 01 |
| 2N1370 | G | P | TX, ET, GI, MO, St | ASY26 | ACY17 | 2N1192 | 2N1377 | | 01 |
| 2N1370 | | | | | | 2N1188 | | | 01 |
| 2N1371 | G | P | TX, ET, GI, MO, St | ACY17 | | 2N1192 | 2N1377 | | 01 |
| 2N1371 | | | | | | 2N1188 | | | 01 |
| 2N1372 | G | P | TX, ET, GE, SR, SS | ACY17 | | 2N1191 | 2N1377 | | 01 |
| 2N1372 | | | | | | 2N1188 | | | 01 |
| 2N1373 | G | P | TX, ET, SR, GE, IC | AC153 | AC117 | 2N1191 | 2N1377 | 2SB225 | 01 |
| 2N1373 | | | | AC128 | AC127 | 2N1188 | | | 01 |
| 2N1373 | | | | ACY17 | | | | | 01 |
| 2N1374 | G | P | TX, ET, SR, GE, IC | ACY17 | | 2N1192 | 2N1377 | | 01 |
| 2N1374 | | | | | | 2N1188 | | | 01 |
| 2N1375 | G | P | TX, ET, SR, GE, IC | AC153 | AC117 | 2N1192 | 2N1377 | 2SB226 | 01 |
| 2N1375 | | | | AC128 | ACY17 | 2N1188 | | | 01 |
| 2N1376 | G | P | TX, ET, SR, GE, IC | ACY17 | | 2N1192 | 2N1377 | | 01 |
| 2N1376 | | | | | | 2N1188 | | | 01 |
| 2N1377 | G | P | TX, ET, SR, GE, IC | AC153 | AC117 | 2N651 | 2N1188 | 2SB227 | 01 |
| 2N1377 | | | | AC128 | ACY17 | | | | 01 |
| 2N1378 | G | P | TX, ET, SR, GE, IC | ACY17 | | 2N1193 | 2N1377 | | 01 |
| 2N1378 | | | | | | 2N1188 | | | 01 |
| 2N1379 | G | P | TX, ET, SR, GE, IC | ASY26 | ACY17 | 2N1193 | 2N1377 | | 01 |
| 2N1379 | | | | | | 2N1188 | | | 01 |
| 2N1380 | G | P | TX, ET, GE, IC, SR | ASY26 | ACY17 | 2N1192 | 2N1377 | | 01 |
| 2N1380 | | | | | | 2N1188 | | | 01 |
| 2N1381 | G | P | TX, ET, GE, IC, SR | ACY17 | | 2N1192 | 2N1377 | | 01 |
| 2N1381 | | | | | | 2N1188 | | | 01 |
| 2N1382 | G | P | TX, ET, ES, FR, IC | | | 2N1192 | 2N1374 | | 01 |
| 2N1383 | G | P | TX, ET, FR, MO, SZ | | | 2N1192 | 2N1377 | | 01 |
| 2N1384 | G | P | IC | | | 2N2635 | | | 13 |
| 2N1385 | G | P | TX | AF139 | AF186 | | | | 16 |
| 2N1385 | | | | ASZ21 | | | | | 16 |
| 2N1386 | S | N | CN, SM, ET | | | 2N2218 | | | 10 |
| 2N1387 | S | N | CN, SM, ET | | | 2N2218 | | | 10 |
| 2N1388 | S | N | CN, ET, SM | | | 2N2218 | | | 02 |
| 2N1389 | S | N | CN, SM, ET, SR | | | 2N2218 | | | 02 |
| 2N1390 | S | N | CN, SM, ET | | | 2N2218 | | | 02 |
| 2N1392 | G | P | | AC151 | AC125 | 2N1394 | | 2SB111 | 04 |
| 2N1392 | | | | OC70 | AC122 | | | | 04 |
| 2N1392 | | | | AC162 | | | | | 04 |
| 2N1394 | G | P | | AC151 | AC125 | 2N1392 | | 2SB111 | 04 |
| 2N1394 | | | | OC70 | AC122 | | | | 04 |
| 2N1394 | | | | AC162 | | | | | 04 |
| 2N1395 | G | P | AM, PE, RC, CN | AF124 | | 2N2955 | 2N2188 | | 02 |
| 2N1395 | | | | | | 2N990 | | | 02 |
| 2N1396 | G | P | RC, CN, PE, AM | AF118 | ASZ20 | 2N3323 | 2N2191 | | 02 |
| 2N1396 | | | | AF124 | | 2N990 | | | 02 |
| 2N1397 | G | P | RC, PE, CN | AF118 | ASZ20 | 2N3323 | 2N2191 | | 02 |
| 2N1397 | | | | AF124 | | 2N990 | | | 02 |
| 2N1398 | G | P | TX | | | 2N2996 | | | 02 |
| 2N1399 | G | P | TX | AF106 | AFZ12 | 2N2996 | | | 02 |
| 2N1400 | G | P | TX | AF124 | AF134 | 2N2996 | | | 02 |
| 2N1400 | | | | AF131 | | | | | 02 |
| 2N1401 | G | P | TX | AF124 | AF134 | 2N2996 | | | 02 |
| 2N1402 | G | P | TX | AF124 | AF134 | 2N2996 | | | 02 |

| TYPE | M/S | POL | MANUFAC | EUROPEAN | | AMERICAN | | JAPANESE | USE |
|---|---|---|---|---|---|---|---|---|---|
| 2N1403 | G | P | TX | | | 2N2996 | | | 02 |
| 2N1404 | G | P | TX, ET, GI, SR, UP | AF124 | AF134 | 2N1303 | 2N1307 | | 10 |
| 2N1404 | | | | ACY27 | | 2N1305 | | | 10 |
| 2N1404A | G | P | TX | | | 2N1303 | | | 10 |
| 2N1405 | G | P | TX | | | 2N2996 | | | 02 |
| 2N1406 | G | P | TX | AF178 | | 2N2495 | 2N2996 | | 02 |
| 2N1407 | G | P | TX | AF178 | (ASY48IV) | 2N2495 | 2N2996 | | 02 |
| 2N1408 | G | P | ET, MO, GI, SR, CN | (ASY48IV) | ACY17 | 2N2000 | 2N1188 | | 10 |
| 2N1409 | S | N | ET, CN, SM, SQ, ET | BSZ45-6 | | | | | 13 |
| 2N1409A | S | N | ET, CN, SM, SQ | BCW77 16 | | | | | 13 |
| 2N1410 | S | N | ET, CN, SM, SQ | BSX45-16 | | | | | 13 |
| 2N1410A | S | N | ET, SQ, SM | BCW77-16 | BSX46 | | | | 13 |
| 2N1411 | G | P | CN, ID, SP, FR, SM | AF124 | AF134 | | | | 10 |
| 2N1412 | G | P | DD, KS, NP, SD, MO | | | 2N962 | 2N2188 | | 16 |
| 2N1413 | G | P | MO, GE, ET, SQ, CN | AC152IV | | 2N1100 | | | 10 |
| 2N1414 | G | P | MO, GE, ET, IC, SR | (AC152IV) | | | | | 10 |
| 2N1415 | G | P | MO, GE, ET, SQ, UP | (AC152V) | | | | | 10 |
| 2N1416 | G | P | MO, CN, ET | (AC152V) | AC153 | 2N1193 | | | 01 |
| 2N1416 | | | | AC117 | AC128 | | | | 01 |
| 2N1419 | G | P | IN | | | 2N1164 | | | 16 |
| 2N1420 | S | N | IT, SG, PH, SE, F | BSX45-6 | BFY56 | 2N1711 | 2N3643 | | 02 |
| 2N1420 | | | | BFY67 | BSX46-6 | 2N2222 | 2N2243A | | 02 |
| 2N1420 | | | | BSY10 | | | | | 02 |
| 2N1420A | S | N | F, TI, SM, SQ, SG | BSX45-6 | BSX46-10 | 2N3643 | 2N2219 | | 02 |
| 2N1420A | | | | | | 2N2243A | | | 02 |
| 2N1425 | G | P | RC | AF185 | AF124 | 2N2188 | | | 01 |
| 2N1425 | | | | AF134 | AF126 | | | | 01 |
| 2N1425 | | | | AF137 | | | | | 01 |
| 2N1426 | G | P | RC | AF185 | AF124 | 2N2188 | | | 01 |
| 2N1426 | | | | AF134 | AF126 | | | | 01 |
| 2N1426 | | | | AF136 | | | | | 01 |
| 2N1427 | G | P | ID, SP, SQ, SM | AF124 | AF134 | 2N962 | 2N2635 | | 13 |
| 2N1428 | S | P | PH | | | 2N1132 | 2N2905 | | 10 |
| 2N1429 | S | P | SP, CR, SQ, ID | (BC178A) | BC202R | 2N1132 | 2N2905 | | 10 |
| 2N1429 | | | | BC238 | BC239 | | | | 10 |
| 2N1429 | | | | BC173 | | | | | 10 |
| 2N1431 | G | N | ET, NP | AC127 | | 2N2430 | 2N1302 | | 01 |
| 2N1432 | G | P | SY | | | 2N2189 | | | 01 |
| 2N1433 | G | P | CB | AC153 | AC117 | | | 2SB252 | 06 |
| 2N1433 | | | | AC128 | | | | | 06 |
| 2N1434 | G | P | CB | AD148 | AD139 | 2N1435 | | 2SB259 | 06 |
| 2N1434 | | | | OC30 | OD603 | | | | 06 |
| 2N1435 | G | P | CB | AD148 | AD139 | 2N1434 | | 2SB259 | 06 |
| 2N1435 | | | | OC30 | OD603 | | | | 06 |
| 2N1437 | G | P | KS, SZ | AC153 | AC117 | 2N456A | 2N3146 | 2SB249 | 06 |
| 2N1437 | | | | AC128 | OC74 | | | | 06 |
| 2N1438 | G | P | KS, SZ | AC153 | AC117 | 2N456A | 2N3146 | 2SB252A | 06 |
| 2N1438 | | | | AC128 | | | | | 06 |
| 2N1439 | S | P | CN, RY, CR, SD, SQ | | | 2N2945 | 2N2946 | | 01 |
| 2N1440 | S | P | CN, ET, SD, SQ, CR | | | 2N2945 | 2N2946 | | 01 |
| 2N1441 | S | P | CN, ET, SM, SQ, CR | | | 2N2945 | 2N2946 | | 01 |
| 2N1442 | S | P | CN, ET, SM, CR, RY | | | 2N2945 | 2N2946 | | 01 |
| 2N1443 | S | P | CN, RY, CR, SM, SD | | | 2N2945 | 2N2946 | | 01 |
| 2N1444 | S | N | WE | | | 2N3252 | | | 13 |
| 2N1445 | S | N | CN, SQ, TR | | | 2N5682 | | | 06 |
| 2N1446 | G | P | IC, ET, CN | | | 2N1191 | 2N1373 | | 01 |
| 2N1446 | | | | | | 2N1377 | | | 01 |
| 2N1447 | G | P | IC, ET, CN | | | 2N1191 | 2N1373 | | 01 |
| 2N1448 | G | P | IC, ET, CN | | | 2N1377 | | | 01 |
| 2N1448 | | | | | | 2N1192 | 2N1373 | | 01 |
| 2N1449 | G | P | IC, ET, CN | | | 2N1377 | | | 01 |
| 2N1450 | G | P | CN, ET | | | 2N1189 | 2N1375 | | 01 |
| 2N1451 | G | P | IC, ET, CN | | | 2N1377 | 2N1143 | | 10 |
| 2N1451 | | | | | | 2N464 | 2N1375 | | 01 |
| 2N1452 | G | P | IC, ET, CN | | | 2N1377 | | | 01 |
| 2N1452 | | | | | | 2N1191 | 2N1375 | | 01 |
| 2N1465 | G | P | CN, ks | | | 2N1377 | | | 01 |
| 2N1466 | G | P | CN, KS | | | 2N456A | 2N3146 | | 06 |
| 2N1466 | | | | | | 2N456A | 2N3146 | | 06 |
| 2N1469 | S | P | SD, CR, RY, ET, SM | | | 2N2944 | 2N2945 | | 01 |
| 2N1470 | G | N | CN, SF | | | 2N5068 | | | 06 |
| 2N1471 | G | P | IC, ET, CN | | | 2N1309 | | | 10 |
| 2N1472 | G | N | CN, ET | | | 2N2537 | 2N3015 | | 13 |
| 2N1473 | G | N | CN, ET | | | 2N2000 | | | 10 |

| TYPE | M/S | POL | MANUFAC | EUROPEAN | | AMERICAN | | JAPANESE | USE |
|---|---|---|---|---|---|---|---|---|---|
| 2N1474 | S | P | SD, ET, SM, CR | BSY16 | BCY11 | 2N2944 | 2N2945 | | 01 |
| 2N1474A | S | P | SD, CR, SM, CN, ET | BCY11 | BCY12 | 2N2944 | 2N2945 | | 01 |
| 2N1475 | S | P | SD, CR, SM, CN, ET | BCY11 | | 2N2944 | 2N2945 | | 01 |
| 2N1476 | S | P | 2D, CR, SM, CN | | | 2N2944 | 2N2945 | | 01 |
| 2N1477 | S | P | SD, CR, SM, CN | | | 2N2944 | 2N2945 | | 01 |
| 2N1478 | S | P | CN, GI, IC, ET | | | 2N3427 | 2N1307 | | 10 |
| 2N1479 | S | N | RC, SZ, LU, SQ, TR | BSX45-6 | BFX34 | 2N2987 | 2N4237 | | 16 |
| 2N1480 | S | N | RC, SZ, ET, LU, SQ | BSX46-6 | BFX34 | 2N2988 | 2N4238 | | 16 |
| 2N1481 | S | N | RC, SZ, ES, ID, LU | (BSX45-6) | BFX34 | 2N2989 | 2N4239 | | 16 |
| 2N1481 | | | | | | 2N4237 | | | 16 |
| 2N1482 | S | N | RC, SZ, ET, IC, PI | BSX46-6 | BFX34 | 2N2990 | 2N4238 | | 16 |
| 2N1483 | S | N | RC, SZ, ES, PI, UP | BSX62-6 | | 2N3766 | 2N4231 | | 16 |
| 2N1484 | S | N | RC, SZ, ID, SF, SU | (BSX63-6) | | 2N3766 | 2N4232 | | 16 |
| 2N1485 | S | N | RC, SZ, ES, PI, UP | BSX62-10 | | 2N3766 | 2N4231 | | 16 |
| 2N1486 | S | N | RC, SZ, ES, PI, UP | (BSX63-10) | | 2N3766 | 2N4232 | | 16 |
| 2N1487 | S | N | RC, SZ, ET, SD, SM | BDY38 | BD130 | 2N3713 | 2N3055 | | 16 |
| 2N1487 | | | | AM291 | | 2N4913 | | | 16 |
| 2N1488 | S | N | RC, ET, SD, SZ, PP | BDY20 | BD130 | 2N3714 | 2N3055 | | 16 |
| 2N1488 | | | | AM291 | | 2N4914 | | | 16 |
| 2N1489 | S | N | RC, ET, SD, SZ, PP | BDY38 | BD130 | 2N3713 | 2N3055 | | 16 |
| 2N1489 | | | | AM291 | | 2N4913 | | | 16 |
| 2N1490 | S | N | RC, ET, SZ, SD, PI | BDY20 | BD130 | 2N3714 | 2N3055 | | 16 |
| 2N1490 | | | | AM291 | | 2N4914 | | | 16 |
| 2N1491 | S | N | RC, SM, SQ, CN | (BCY65EVII) | | | | | 02 |
| 2N1492 | S | N | RC, SQ, SM | (BCY58VII) | | | | | 02 |
| 2N1493 | S | N | RC, SQ, TD, SM | (BCY65EVII) | | | | | 02 |
| 2N1494 | G | P | MO | (ASY26) | | | | | 13 |
| 2N1494A | G | P | MO | (ASY26) | | | | | 13 |
| 2N1495 | G | P | MO | (ASY26) | | | | | 13 |
| 2N1496 | G | P | MO | ASY26 | | | | | 13 |
| 2N1499 | G | P | CN, FR, SM, ET, MO | | | 2N960 | 2N964 | | 13 |
| 2N1499A | G | P | ET, SP, MO, ID, SM | AF106 | AF190 | 2N960 | 2N964 | | 13 |
| 2N1499B | G | P | SP, ET, MO, FR, CN | | | | | | 13 |
| 2N1500 | G | P | ET, ID, SP, FR, MO | | | 2N962 | 2N964 | | 13 |
| 2N1501 | G | P | SD, KS | AC153 | AC117 | 2N2144 | | 2SB24BB | 13 |
| 2N1501 | | | | AC128 | ASZ16 | | | | 13 |
| 2N1502 | G | P | SD, KS | AC153 | AC117 | 2N2143 | TI3027 | 2SB248 | 13 |
| 2N1502 | | | | AC128 | | | | | 13 |
| 2N1504 | G | P | SZ | | | 2N456A | 2N3146 | | 06 |
| 2N1505 | S | N | NU, TW, SM, SQ | BSX45-6 | BSX46-6 | 2N2218 | 2N2217 | | 03 |
| 2N1505 | | | | BFY12 | | 2N2219 | | | 03 |
| 2N1506 | S | N | NU, TW, SD, SQ, CN | BSX45-6 | BSX46-6 | 2N2218 | 2N2217 | | 03 |
| 2N1506 | | | | BFY12 | | 2N2219 | | | 03 |
| 2N1506A | S | N | NU, TW, ID, SD, SQ | BSX46-6 | | | | | 03 |
| 2N1507 | S | N | TI, TX, RY, ET, CA | BSX45-16 | BSX45-10 | 2N1711 | 2N2219 | | 10 |
| 2N1507 | | | | | | 2N2243A | | | 10 |
| 2N1511 | S | N | SZ, SQ | | | 2N3713 | 2N4913 | | 16 |
| 2N1512 | S | N | SZ, SQ | | | 2N4914 | | | 16 |
| 2N1513 | S | N | SZ, SQ | | | 2N4913 | | | 16 |
| 2N1514 | S | N | SZ, SQ | | | 2N4914 | | | 16 |
| 2N1515 | G | P | AM | AF185 | AF126 | | | | |
| 2N1515 | | | | AF137 | AF127 | | | | |
| 2N1516 | G | P | AM | AF185 | AF125 | | | | 02 |
| 2N1516 | | | | AF135 | AF126 | | | | 02 |
| 2N1517 | G | P | AM | AF178 | AF124 | 2N2495 | | | |
| 2N1517 | | | | AF134 | AF185 | | | | |
| 2N1518 | G | P | DD, ET, NP, CN | | | 2N2153 | MP943 | | 16 |
| 2N1519 | G | P | DD, NP, CN | | | 2N2154 | MP943A | | 16 |
| 2N1520 | G | P | DD, ET, NP, CN | | | 2N2153 | MP944 | | 16 |
| 2N1521 | G | P | DD, NP, CN | | | 2N2154 | MP944A | | 16 |
| 2N1622 | G | P | DD, ET, NP, CN | | | 2N2153 | | | 16 |
| 2N1523 | G | P | DD, NP | | | 2N2154 | | | 02 |
| 2N1524 | G | P | SR, RC | AF185 | | 2N3325 | | | 16 |
| 2N1525 | G | P | SR, RC | AF185 | AF200 | 2N3325 | TIS37 | | 02 |
| 2N1525 | | | | AF181 | AF127 | | | | 02 |
| 2N1526 | G | P | RC, SR | AF185 | | 2N3325 | TIS37 | | 02 |
| 2N1527 | G | P | RC, SR | AF185 | | 2N3325 | TIS37 | | 02 |
| 2N1528 | S | N | RC, SR | BSY34 | BSW51 | 2N2218 | | | 02 |
| 2N1529 | G | P | MO, ET, TX, CN, KS | AUY19III | | | | | 06 |
| 2N1529A | G | P | MO, ET, SD, CN, KS | AUY19III | | | | | 06 |
| 2N1530 | G | P | MO, ET, TX, UP, CN | AUY19III | | | | | 06 |
| 2N1530A | G | P | MO, KS, SD, ET, PP | AUY19III | | | | | 06 |
| 2N1531 | G | P | MO, ET, TX, UP, CN | AUY20III | | | | | 06 |
| 2N1531A | G | P | MO, ET, PP, SD, CN | AUY20III | | | | | 06 |
| 2N1532 | G | P | MO, ET, PP, TX, UP | AUY34III | | | | | 06 |

| TYPE | M/S | POL | MANUFAC | EUROPEAN | | AMERICAN | | JAPANESE | USE |
|------|-----|-----|---------|----------|---|----------|---|----------|-----|
| 2N1532A | G | P | MO, KS, SD, ET, PP | (AUY34III) | AUY23III | | | | 06 |
| 2N1533 | G | P | MO, ET, TX, UP, CN | AUY34III | | | | | 06 |
| 2N1534 | G | P | MO, DD, KS, ET, SD | AUY19IV | | | | | 06 |
| 2N1534A | G | P | MO, ET, PP, SD, CN | AUY19IV | | | | | 06 |
| 2N1535 | G | P | MO, DD, ET, TX, KS | AUY19IV | AD133 | | | | 06 |
| 2N1535 | | | | ADZ11 | | | | | 06 |
| 2N1535A | G | P | MO, KS, SD, ET, PP | AUY19IV | | | | | 06 |
| 2N1536 | G | P | MO, DD, ET, TX, KS | AUY20IV | ASZ18 | | | | 06 |
| 2N1536A | G | P | MO, ET, PP, SD, CN | AUY20IV | | | | | 06 |
| 2N1537 | G | P | MO, ET, TX, UP, CN | AUY34IV | | | | | 06 |
| 2N1537A | G | P | MO, ET, PP, SD, CN | AUY34IV | | | | | 06 |
| 2N1538 | G | P | MO, ET, SD, TX, CN | AUY34IV | | | | | 06 |
| 2N1539 | G | P | MO, DD, ET, TX, SD | AUY19V | | | | | 06 |
| 2N1539A | G | P | MO, KS, SD, ET, PP | AUY19V | | | | | 06 |
| 2N1540 | G | P | MO, DD, TX, ET, CN | AUY19V | ASZ16 | | | | 06 |
| 2N1540A | G | P | MO, ET, PP, SD, CN | AUY19V | | | | | 06 |
| 2N1541 | G | P | MO, ET, TX, KS, SD | AUY20V | | | | | 06 |
| 2N1541A | G | P | MO, KS, SD, ET, PP | AUY20V | | | | | 06 |
| 2N1542 | G | P | MO, DD, TX, UP, CN | AUY34V | | | | | 06 |
| 2N1542A | G | P | MO, KS, SD, CN, PP | AUY34V | | | | | 06 |
| 2N1543 | G | P | MO, KS, TX, UP, CN | AUY34V | | | | | 06 |
| 2N1544 | G | P | MO, DD, TX, ET, KS | AUY19V | ASZ16 | | | | 06 |
| 2N1544A | G | P | MO, ET, PP, SD, CN | AUY19V | | | | | 06 |
| 2N1545 | G | P | MO, ET, TX, KS, UP | AUY19V | ASZ18 | | | | 06 |
| 2N1545A | G | P | MO, KS, SD, ET, PP | AUY19V | | | | | 06 |
| 2N1546 | G | P | MO, DD, KS, ET, TX | AUY20V | ASZ15 | | | | 06 |
| 2N1546A | G | P | MO, ET, PP, SD, CN | AUY20V | | | | | 06 |
| 2N1547 | G | P | MO, KS, SD, TX, CN | AUY34V | | | | | 06 |
| 2N1547A | G | P | MO, KS, SD, CN, PP | AUY34V | | | | | 06 |
| 2N1548 | G | P | MO, KS, TX, UP, CN | AUY34V | | | | | 06 |
| 2N1549 | G | P | MO, ET, PP, UP, CN | AUY29IV | | TI3027 | | | 06 |
| 2N1549A | G | P | MO, ET, PP, SD, CN | AUY29III | | | | | 06 |
| 2N1550 | G | P | MO, ET, PP, UP, CN | AUY29III | | TI3028 | | | 06 |
| 2N1550A | G | P | MO, ET, PP, SD, CN | AUY29III | | | | | 06 |
| 2N1551 | G | P | MO, ET, PP, UP, CN | ADZ12 | | | | | 06 |
| 2N1552 | G | P | MO, ET, PP, UP, CN | | | 2N1021A | | | 06 |
| 2N1552A | G | P | MO, ET, PP, SD, CN | | | 2N1021A | | | 06 |
| 2N1553 | G | P | MO, ET, PP, UP, CN | AUY29IV | | TI3027 | | | 06 |
| 2N1553A | G | P | MO, ET, PP, SD, CN | AUY29IV | | TI3027 | | | 06 |
| 2N1554 | G | P | MO, ET, PP, UP, CN | AUY29IV | | TI3028 | | | 06 |
| 2N1554A | G | P | MO, ET, PP, SD, CN | AUY29IV | | | | | 06 |
| 2N1555 | G | P | MO, ET, PP, UP, CN | ADY26 | ADZ12 | | | | 06 |
| 2N1556 | G | P | MO, ET, PP, UP, CN | | | 2N1021A | 2N1100 | | 06 |
| 2N1556A | G | P | MO, ET, SD, CN, KS | | | 2N1021A | | | 06 |
| 2N1557 | G | P | MO, ET, SD, CN, KS | AUY29V | | 2N456A | 2N514 | | 06 |
| 2N1557A | G | P | CN, KS, SD, MO, ET | AUY29V | | 2N456A | 2N514 | | 06 |
| 2N1558 | G | P | MO, ET, SD, CN, KS | AUY29V | | 2N514A | | | 06 |
| 2N1558A | G | P | MO, KS, SD, ET | AUY29V | | 2N514A | | | 06 |
| 2N1559 | | | MO, ET, SD, CN, KS | | | 2N514B | | | 06 |
| 2N1564 | S | N | NU, PH, TX, ET, SQ | (BSX46-6) | BSX46 | 2N2218 | | 2SC154 | 01 |
| 2N1564 | | | | BFY80 | | | | | 01 |
| 2N1565 | S | N | TX, PH, SE, NU, ET | (BSX46-6) | BSX46 | 40360 | 2N2218 | 2SC154 | 01 |
| 2N1565A | S | N | TX | BFY80 | BSW51 | 40360 | | | 01 |
| 2N1566 | S | N | NU, PH, TX, ET, BT | (BSX46-16) | BSX46 | 2N2219 | 2N2218 | 2SC154 | 01 |
| 2N1566 | | | | BFY80 | BSW52 | | | | 01 |
| 2N1566A | S | N | ET, TX, CN, ML, TD | (BSX46-10) | BC141-10 | 2N2219 | | | 01 |
| 2N1572 | S | N | CN, NU, SQ, TX, ET | BF177 | BSX47-6 | | | 2SC857 | 01 |
| 2N1572 | | | | BFY14B | | | | | 01 |
| 2N1573 | S | N | TX, PH, NU, ET, SM | BF178 | BSX47-6 | 40409 | | 2SC857 | 01 |
| 2N1573 | | | | BFY14B | BFY14C | | | | 01 |
| 2N1574 | S | N | TX, PH, ET, SM, CN | BSX47-10 | BFY14C | 40409 | 2N1893 | 2SC857 | 01 |
| 2N1574 | | | | BFY14D | | | | | 01 |
| 2N1605 | G | N | CN, TX, ET, RC, GI | | | 2N1304 | | | 10 |
| 2N1605A | G | N | CN, ET, RC, ES, GI | | | 2N1305 | 2N1605 | | 10 |
| 2N1609 | G | P | DD | | | 2N2140 | | | 06 |
| 2N1610 | G | P | DD | | | 2N2145 | | | 06 |
| 2N1611 | G | P | DD | | | 2N2138 | | | 06 |
| 2N1612 | G | P | DD | | | 2N2143 | | | 06 |
| 2N1613 | S | N | RY, F, MO, NU, RA | BSX46-6 | BFX69 | 2N3567 | | | 10 |
| 2N1613 | | | | BFX69A | BFY67 | | | | 10 |
| 2N1613 | | | | BFY34 | BSX45-6 | | | | 10 |
| 2N1613 | | | | BFY33 | | | | | 10 |
| 2N1613A | S | N | CA, SM, St, TD, RY | BFX69A | | 2N2218 | 2N1613 | | 10 |
| 2N1613B | S | N | CA, SM, St, RY, SQ | BSX47-6 | | | | | 10 |

| TYPE | M/S | POL | MANUFAC | EUROPEAN | | AMERICAN | | JAPANESE | USE |
|---|---|---|---|---|---|---|---|---|---|
| 2N1613S | S | N | MO | | | 2N1613 | | | 10 |
| 2N1614 | G | P | GE, CN, UP, SR | (ASY48IV) | ASY48 | 2N1924 | 2N2000 | | 10 |
| 2N1614 | | | | ACY24 | | | | | 10 |
| 2N1615 | S | N | ET, TR, UP, CN, SM | (BSX47-6) | | | | | 02 |
| 2N1616 | R | N | TR, SZ, ET, SD, EM | AM291 | BDY11 | 2N3487 | 2N3055 | | 03 |
| 2N1616 | | | | | | 2N1210 | 2N1724 | | 03 |
| 2N1616A | S | N | SZ, TR, ET, SM, SD | | | 2N3487 | | | 06 |
| 2N1617 | S | N | TR, SZ, ET, SD, SM | BDY91 | BCY28 | 2N3487 | 2N1211 | | 03 |
| 2N1617 | | | | BFC38 | BDY17 | 2N1724 | | | 03 |
| 2N1617A | S | N | SZ, TR, ET, SM, SD | | | 2N3487 | | | 06 |
| 2N1618 | S | N | TR, SZ, ET, SD, ML | BDY90 | BFY34 | 2N3488 | 2N1724 | | 03 |
| 2N1618 | | | | BDY11 | | | | | 03 |
| 2N1618A | S | N | SZ, TR, ET, SM, SD | | | 2N3488 | | | 06 |
| 2N1620 | S | N | TR, ET, SD, SZ, SQ | | | 2N3446 | 2N1724 | | 03 |
| 2N1624 | G | N | CN, GI, ET | | | 2N1308 | | | 10 |
| 2N1631 | G | P | St, RC | AF185 | | 2N3325 | 2N2635 | | 02 |
| 2N1632 | G | P | St, RC | AF185 | | 2N3325 | 2N2635 | | 02 |
| 2N1633 | G | P | St, RC | AF185 | AF106 | 2N2635 | | 2SA230 | 02 |
| 2N1633 | | | | AF136 | | | | | 02 |
| 2N1634 | G | P | St, RC | AF185 | AF106 | 2N2635 | | 2SA230 | 02 |
| 2N1634 | | | | AF135 | | | | | 02 |
| 2N1635 | G | P | St, RC | AF185 | AF106 | 2N2635 | | 2SA230 | 02 |
| 2N1635 | | | | AF135 | | | | | 02 |
| 2N1636 | G | P | St, RC | AF185 | AF106 | 2N2635 | | 2SA230 | 02 |
| 2N1636 | | | | AF135 | | | | | 02 |
| 2N1637 | G | P | St | AF185 | AF124 | 2N3325 | 2N2635 | 2SA235 | 02 |
| 2N1637 | | | | AF135 | | | | | 02 |
| 2N1638 | G | P | St | AF185 | AF124 | 2N3325 | 2N2635 | 2SA235 | 02 |
| 2N1638 | | | | AF136 | AF134 | | | | 02 |
| 2N1639 | G | P | St | AF185 | AF124 | 2N3325 | 2N2635 | 2SA235 | 02 |
| 2N1639 | | | | AF135 | AF134 | | | | 02 |
| 2N1640 | S | P | CR, SM, SQ, RY | | | 2N2945 | 2N2946 | | 12 |
| 2N1641 | S | P | CR, SM, SQ, RY | | | 2N2945 | 2N2946 | | 12 |
| 2N1642 | S | P | CR, SM, SQ, RY | | | 2N2945 | 2N2946 | | 12 |
| 2N1643 | S | P | CR, SD, SQ, RY | | | 2N2945 | 2N2944 | | 01 |
| 2N1644 | S | N | SM, TI, SQ | | | 2N2218 | 2N1893 | | 10 |
| 2N1644 | | | | | | 2N2243A | | | 10 |
| 2N1646 | G | P | SY | (AF201U) | AF201 | | | 2SA230 | 13 |
| 2N1646 | | | | AF202 | AF106 | | | | 13 |
| 2N1647 | S | N | TR, SZ, SQ, UN, CN | | | 2N2150 | | | 03 |
| 2N1648 | S | N | TR, SZ, SQ, UN, CN | | | 2N2151 | | | 03 |
| 2N1649 | S | N | TR, SZ, SQ, UN, CN | | | 2N2150 | | | 03 |
| 2N1650 | S | N | TR, SZ, SQ, UN, CN | | | 2N2151 | | | 03 |
| 2N1651 | G | P | SD, ET, MO, SQ, CN | | | 2N2832 | | | 06 |
| 2N1652 | G | P | SD, KS, SQ, MO, CN | | | 2N2833 | | | 06 |
| 2N1653 | G | P | SD, KS, SQ, MO, CN | | | 2N2834 | | | 06 |
| 2N1654 | S | P | CN, ET, SQ, CR, SD | | | 2N2944 | 2N2945 | | 06 |
| 2N1655 | S | P | CN, ET, SQ, CR, SD | | | 2N2944 | 2N2945 | | 06 |
| 2N1656 | S | P | CN, ET, SQ, CR, SD | | | 2N2944 | 2N2945 | | 06 |
| 2N1657 | S | N | TX | | | 2N5320 | | | 06 |
| 2N1660 | S | N | TX | | | 2N1722 | | | 06 |
| 2N1661 | S | N | TX | | | 2N1722 | | | 06 |
| 2N1662 | S | N | TX | | | 2N1722 | | | 06 |
| 2N1663 | S | N | PH, TX | | | 2N2369A | 2N3011 | | 13 |
| 2N1666 | S | P | PE, PH, GP | AUY22II | AUY22III | 2N3616 | TI3027 | 2SB341 | 16 |
| 2N1666 | | | | ASZ15 | | | | | 16 |
| 2N1667 | G | P | PE, AM | AUY21III | AUY21IV | 2N3618 | TI3027 | 2SB341 | 16 |
| 2N1667 | | | | AUY23III | AUY28 | | | | 16 |
| 2N1667 | | | | ASZ16 | | | | | 16 |
| 2N1668 | G | P | PH, PE | AUY21III | AUYIV | 2N3616 | TI3027 | 2SB341 | 16 |
| 2N1668 | | | | AD138 | ASZ16 | | | | 16 |
| 2N1668 | | | | ASZ17 | | | | | 16 |
| 2N1669 | G | P | PH, PE | AUY22IV | AUY22III | 2N3616 | TI3027 | 2SB341 | 16 |
| 2N1669 | | | | ASZ18 | ASZ16 | | | | 16 |
| 2N1670 | G | P | SM, SQ | | | 2N398 | | | 10 |
| 2N1671 | U | PN | GE, SM, TX, UP, CN | | | | | | |
| 2N1671A | U | PN | GE, TX, ES, SB, UP | BC160 | | 2N1671 | 2N1132 | | |
| 2N1672 | G | N | GI, ET, UP, CN | | | 2N1302 | | | 04 |
| 2N1673 | G | P | SY | AF200 | AF181 | 2N404 | | | 02 |
| 2N1676 | S | P | ID, SP, SQ, SM | | | 2N2944 | 2N2945 | | 12 |
| 2N1677 | S | P | ID, SP, SQ, SM | | | 2N2944 | 2N2945 | | 12 |
| 2N1678 | G | P | SM, SQ | | | 2N2191 | | | 10 |
| 2N1679 | S | N | TX | | | 2N5335 | | | 10 |
| 2N1680 | S | N | TX | | | 2N5334 | | | 10 |
| 2N1682 | S | N | SM, SQ | | | EN914 | 2N2217 | | 10 |

| TYPE | M/S | POL | MANUFAC | EUROPEAN | | AMERICAN | | JAPANESE | USE |
|------|-----|-----|---------|----------|---|----------|---|----------|-----|
| 2N1682 | G | P | RC, UP | | | 2N2219 | | | 10 |
| 2N1683 | S | N | TX, SU, SQ, ET, SZ | | | 2N2635 | | | 13 |
| 2N1690 | S | N | TX, SU, SQ, ET, SZ | | | 2N4912 | | | 06 |
| 2N1694 | G | N | ET | | | 2N1302 | | | 10 |
| 2N1700 | S | N | RC, ET, SZ, F, SM | BFY50 | | 2N2218 | | | 10 |
| 2N1701 | S | N | RC, SZ, FE, SF, SU | | | 2N2218 | | | 10 |
| 2N1702 | S | N | RC, ET, SZ, FE, SM | | | 2N2218 | 2N4913 | | 10 |
| 2N1703 | S | S | CN, SM, SQ, FE, SZ | | | 2N2218 | | | 10 |
| 2N1704 | S | N | CN, ET | | | 2N2218 | 2N1893 | | 10 |
| 2N1704 | | | | | | 2N2243A | | | 10 |
| 2N1705 | G | P | MO, ET, CN, GI, SR | (AC152VI) | | | | | 01 |
| 2N1706 | G | P | MO, ET, CN, GI, St | (AC152VI) | | | | | 01 |
| 2N1707 | G | P | MO, ET, CN, GI, St | (AC152VI) | | | | | 01 |
| 2N1708 | S | N | F, MO, FE, CN, SM | BSY62 | BSX87 | EN914 | 2N473 | | 13 |
| 2N1708A | S | N | CN, SQ | BSX87 | | 2N743 | | | 13 |
| 2N1708B | S | N | | | | 2N743 | | | |
| 2N1711 | S | N | F, MO, TX, V, AT | BSX45-16 | BFX68 | EN1711 | 2N2219A | | 10 |
| 2N1711 | | | | BFX68A | BFY68 | 2N2219 | | | 10 |
| 2N1711 | | | | BFY46 | BSX45-10 | | | | 10 |
| 2N1711A | S | N | RY, TX, CN, FR, SM | BSX46-16 | BFX68A | 2N1711 | 2N3643 | | 02 |
| 2N1711A | | | | | | 2N2219A | | | 02 |
| 2N1711B | S | N | RY, CA, SQ, St, FR | (BSX47-6) | | 2N2219A | | | 02 |
| 2N1711S | S | N | TX | | | 2N1711 | | | |
| 2N1714 | S | S | TX, UN, ET, SM, SQ | BSX46-6 | | 2N1480 | 2N4237 | | 06 |
| 2N1715 | S | S | TX, UN, ET, SM, TR | BSX46-6 | | 2N5681 | | | 06 |
| 2N1716 | S | N | TX, ET, SM, UN, TR | (BSX47-6) | | 2N1482 | 2N4237 | | 06 |
| 2N1717 | S | N | TX, UN, ET, SM, TR | (BSX47-6) | | 2N5681 | | | 06 |
| 2N1718 | S | N | TX, UN, FR, SD, TR | | | 2N3766 | | | 06 |
| 2N1719 | S | N | TX, UN, FR, SQ, CN | | | 2N3766 | 2N3767 | | 06 |
| 2N1720 | S | N | TX, UN, FR, SD, TR | | | 2N3766 | | | 06 |
| 2N1721 | S | N | TX, UN, FR, SQ, CN | | | 2N3767 | | | 06 |
| 2N1722 | S | S | TX, ET, SZ, SD, TR | | | 2N3446 | | | 06 |
| 2N1723 | S | S | TX, SZ, SD, TR, SQ | BLY17 | | 2N3448 | | | 06 |
| 2N1724 | S | S | TX, ET, MO, SD, F | BLY17 | | 2N4347 | | | 06 |
| 2N1724A | S | N | TX, SZ, TR, St, ML | | | 2N4347 | | | 06 |
| 2N1725 | S | N | TX, SD, UN, MO, SZ | AM291 | BDX10 | 2N3055 | | | 06 |
| 2N1726 | S | P | ET, SM, SP, FR | | | 2N3323 | | | 02 |
| 2N1727 | G | P | ET, SM, SP, FR | AF124 | AF134 | 2N3324 | 2N2996 | 2SA235 | 02 |
| 2N1728 | G | P | ET, ID, SP, FR, SM | | | 2N3324 | 2N2996 | | 02 |
| 2N1729 | G | P | ET, UP | | | 2N1303 | | | 10 |
| 2N1730 | G | N | ET | | | 2N1302 | | | 10 |
| 2N1731 | G | P | ET | | | 2N1303 | | | 01 |
| 2N1732 | G | N | ET | | | 2N1302 | | | 01 |
| 2N1742 | G | P | ET, SP, MO, ID, SM | AF127 | AF137 | 2N3288 | 2N2996 | | 02 |
| 2N1742 | | | | AF124 | | | | | 02 |
| 2N1743 | G | P | ET, ID, SP, FR | | | 2N3284 | 2N2996 | | 02 |
| 2N1744 | G | P | ET, ID, SP, FR | | | 2N3284 | 2N2996 | | 02 |
| 2N1745 | G | P | ET, ID, SP, FR | AF126 | AF137 | 2N3285 | 2N2996 | | 02 |
| 2N1745 | | | | AF136 | | | | | 02 |
| 2N1746 | G | P | ET, ID, SP, FR, SM | | | 2N3323 | 2N2996 | | 02 |
| 2N1747 | G | P | ET, ID, SP, FR, SM | | | 2N3324 | 2N2996 | | 02 |
| 2N1748 | G | P | ET, ID, SP, FR, SM | | | 2N3324 | 2N2996 | | 02 |
| 2N1748A | G | P | ET, ID, SP, FR, SM | | | 2N3323 | 2N2996 | | 02 |
| 2N1749 | G | P | ET, ID, SP, FR, SM | | | 2N3323 | 2N2996 | | 02 |
| 2N1750 | G | P | PH | | | 2N2996 | | | 01 |
| 2N1751 | G | P | SD, MO, TR, KS | | | 2N2832 | 2N2996 | | 06 |
| 2N1752 | G | P | ET, ID, SP, FR | | | 2N3325 | 2N2996 | | 01 |
| 2N1754 | G | P | ET, ID, SP, MO, FR | | | 2N964 | 2N2996 | | 13 |
| 2N1755 | G | P | ST, ET, KS | AUY19IV | | 2N2137 | 2N1308 | | 16 |
| 2N1756 | G | P | ST, ET, KS | (AUY19IV) | | 2N2138 | 2N1038 | | 16 |
| 2N1756 | | | | | | 2N2554 | | | 16 |
| 2N1757 | G | P | ST, ET, KS | (AUY20IV) | | 2N2139 | 2N1038 | | 16 |
| 2N1757 | | | | | | 2N2552 | 2N2554 | | 16 |
| 2N1758 | G | P | ST, KS | (AUY34IV) | | 2N2140 | 2N1038 | | 16 |
| 2N1758 | | | | | | 2N2555 | | | 16 |
| 2N1759 | G | P | ST, ET, KS | (AUY19V) | | 2N2142 | 2N1038 | | 16 |
| 2N1759 | | | | | | 2N2564 | | | 16 |
| 2N1760 | G | P | ST, ET, KS, ID | (AUY19V) | AUY21III | 2N2143 | | 2SA341 | 16 |
| 2N1760 | | | | AD138 | ASZ15 | | | | 16 |
| 2N1761 | G | P | ST, ET, KS | (AUY20V) | AUY21III | 2N2144 | | 2SA341 | 16 |
| 2N1761 | | | | AUY28 | ASZ18 | | | | 16 |
| 2N1762 | G | P | ST, KS | (AUY34IV) | | 2N2145 | 2N2567 | | 16 |
| 2N1763 | S | N | RY | | | 2N3014 | | | 10 |
| 2N1764 | S | N | RY | | | 2N2369A | 2N3011 | | 10 |
| 2N1768 | S | N | CN, SZ, SF, SM, SQ | | | 2N3713 | 2N1058 | | 10 |

| TYPE | M/S | POL | MANUFAC | EUROPEAN | | AMERICAN | | JAPANESE | USE |
|---|---|---|---|---|---|---|---|---|---|
| 2N1768 | | | | | | 2N3445 | 2N4231 | | 10 |
| 2N1769 | S | N | SF, SZ, CN, SM, SQ | | | 2N3713 | 2N1050 | | 10 |
| 2N1769 | | | | | | 2N3445 | 2N4232 | | 10 |
| 2N1785 | G | P | CN, SP, ET, ID, SQ | | | 2N3324 | 2N2996 | | 02 |
| 2N1786 | G | P | ET, SP, CN, FR, SM | | | 2N3323 | 2N1996 | | 02 |
| 2N1787 | G | P | ET, SP, CN, FR, SM | | | 2N3324 | 2N2996 | | 02 |
| 2N1788 | G | P | ET, SP, CN, FR, SM | | | 2N3324 | 2N2996 | | 02 |
| 2N1789 | G | P | ET, SP, CN, FR, SM | | | 2N3325 | 2N2996 | | 02 |
| 2N1790 | G | P | ET, SP, CN, FR, SM | | | 2N3323 | 2N2996 | | 02 |
| 2N1808 | G | N | TX, GI, ET | | | 2N1302 | | | 10 |
| 2N1837 | S | N | CN, SM, TI, ET, SQ | BF194 | BF115 | 2N2218 | | 2SC260 | 13 |
| 2N1837A | S | N | ET, SQ, TI, SM | | | 2N2218 | | | 13 |
| 2N1837B | S | N | GE | | | | | | 13 |
| 2N1838 | S | N | ET, YI, CN, SM, SQ | BF194 | BF115 | 2N2218 | | 2SC260 | 13 |
| 2N1839 | S | N | CN, SM, TI, ET, SQ | BF194 | BF115 | 2N2218 | | 2SC260 | 13 |
| 2N1840 | S | N | CN, SM, TI, ET, SQ | BF194 | BF115 | 2N2218 | | 2SC260 | 13 |
| 2N1841 | S | N | NS | | | 2N5320 | | | 03 |
| 2N1853 | G | P | FR, UP, SQ | | | 2N2635 | | | 13 |
| 2N1854 | G | P | FR, UP, SQ | | | 2N2635 | | | 13 |
| 2N1864 | G | P | ET, SP, CN, FR, SM | | | 2N3324 | 2N2997 | | 02 |
| 2N1865 | G | P | CN, FR, SM, SP, ET | | | 2N3325 | 2N2997 | | 02 |
| 2N1866 | G | P | ET, SP, CN, FR, SM | | | 2N3323 | 2N2997 | | 02 |
| 2N1867 | G | P | ET, SP, CN, FR, SM | | | 2N3324 | 2N2997 | | 02 |
| 2N1868 | G | P | ET, SP, CN, FR, SM | | | 2N3325 | 2N2997 | | 02 |
| 2N1886 | S | N | TR, SZ, SM, SU, UN | BLY17 | | 2N4914 | 2N4911 | | 03 |
| 2N1889 | S | N | TX, SG, SE, F, ET | BSW65 | BSX46-6 | 2N3498 | 2N699 | | 02 |
| 2N1889 | | | | BSX46-10 | BC141-10 | | | | 02 |
| 2N1889 | | | | BSY87 | BF109 | | | | 02 |
| 2N1890 | S | N | F, ET, RY, TX, TI | BSW66 | BSX46-16 | 2N3499 | | | 02 |
| 2N1890 | | | | BSX46 | BSY88 | | | | 02 |
| 2N1890 | | | | BF109 | | | | | 02 |
| 2N1891 | G | N | TX, St | | | 2N1304 | 2N1306 | | 13 |
| 2N1892 | G | P | TX, ET, SQ, CN | | | 2N1333 | | | 10 |
| 2N1893 | S | N | MO, TX, V, F, RC | BFW33 | BSX47-10 | 2N3498 | | 2SC708 | 02 |
| 2N1893 | | | | BSY45 | BF109 | | | | 02 |
| 2N1893 | | | | BFY14 | BSX47-6 | | | | 02 |
| 2N1893A | S | N | CA, SM, SQ, RY, SZ | | | 2N3498 | | | 03 |
| 2N1893S | S | N | MO | | | 2N1893 | | | |
| 2N1895 | S | N | RY | | | 2N4239 | | | 06 |
| 2N1896 | S | N | RY | | | 2N5336 | | | 06 |
| 2N1897 | S | N | RY | | | 2N5336 | | | 06 |
| 2N1898 | S | N | RY | | | 2N5338 | | | 06 |
| 2N1899 | S | N | TW, PH, SQ, SM, LI | | | 2N4002 | | | 14 |
| 2N1901 | S | N | TW, SQ, SM | | | 2N4002 | | | 14 |
| 2N1905 | G | P | RC, SG, SQ, ID | (AD163IV) | | 2N2832 | 2N1046 | | 06 |
| 2N1906 | G | P | RC, SQ, AT | (AD163IV) | AL100 | 2N2832 | 2N1907 | | 06 |
| 2N1907 | G | P | TX, UP, SQ | | | 2N2832 | MP1907 | | 03 |
| 2N1907A | G | P | TX | | | 2N1907 | | | 03 |
| 2N1908 | G | P | TX, SQ, UP, ID | | | 2N2833 | MP1910 | | 03 |
| 2N1908A | G | P | TX | | | 2N1907 | 2N1908 | | 03 |
| 2N1917 | S | P | SD, CR, SM, UP, CN | BC160 | BCY12 | 2N1132 | | | 12 |
| 2N1918 | S | P | SD, CR, SM, UP, CN | BC160 | BCY12 | 2N1132 | 2N2944 | | 12 |
| 2N1918 | | | | | | 2N2945 | | | 12 |
| 2N1919 | S | P | SD, CR, RY, SQ, SM | BCY29 | BCZ12 | 2N2944 | 2N2945 | | 12 |
| 2N1919 | | | | BCZ12 | | | | | 12 |
| 2N1920 | S | P | SD, CR, SM, UP, CN | BCY29 | BCZ12 | 2N2944 | 2N2945 | | 12 |
| 2N1921 | S | P | SD, CR, SM, UP, CN | BCZ12 | | 2N2944 | 2N2945 | | 12 |
| 2N1922 | S | P | SD, CR, SQ, UP, CN | BCZ12 | | 2N2944 | 2N2945 | | 12 |
| 2N1924 | G | P | GE, MO, ET, NU, Ss | ASY77 | ASY48IV | 2N1305 | 2N1307 | | 01 |
| 2N1924 | | | | AC131-30 | | | | | 01 |
| 2N1925 | G | P | GE, NU, ET, MO, Ss | ASY77 | ASY48IV | 2N1307 | | | 01 |
| 2N1925 | | | | ASY48V | AC131-30 | | | | 01 |
| 2N1926 | G | P | GE, MO, TX, PH, SS | (ASY48VI) | ASY77 | | | | 01 |
| 2N1936 | S | N | ET, SZ, Ss, ML, TR | | | 2N3846 | | | 06 |
| 2N1937 | S | N | Ss, ML, SZ, TR, TX | | | 2N3846 | | | 06 |
| 2N1940 | G | P | | | | TI3027 | | | 03 |
| 2N1943 | S | N | SM, SQ | | | 2N1893 | 2N2243A | | 01 |
| 2N1944 | S | N | IC, SZ, Ss, SM, SQ | | | 2N1893 | 2N2243A | | 10 |
| 2N1945 | S | N | IC, SZ, Ss, SM, SQ | | | 2N1893 | 2N2243A | | 10 |
| 2N1946 | S | N | IC, SZ, Ss, SM, SQ | | | 2N1893 | 2N2243A | | 10 |
| 2N1954 | G | P | CN, GI, ET | | | 2N651 | 2N2000 | | 10 |
| 2N1955 | G | P | CN, ET | | | 2N1190 | 2N2000 | | 10 |
| 2N1956 | G | P | CN, ET | | | 2N651 | 2N2000 | | 10 |
| 2N1957 | G | P | CN, ET | | | 2N1187 | 2N2000 | | 10 |
| 2N1958 | S | N | CN, ET, SZ, St, TR | | | 2N2537 | | | 13 |

| TYPE | M/S | POL | MANUFAC | EUROPEAN | | AMERICAN | | JAPANESE | USE |
|------|-----|-----|---------|----------|---|----------|---|----------|-----|
| 2N1958A | S | N | CN, SQ, TR, ET, St | | | 2N2537 | | | 13 |
| 2N1959 | S | N | MO, ET, SQ, CN, HS | BSY34 | | 2N2537 | | | 13 |
| 2N1959A | S | N | CN, ET, SQ, SM, St | | | 2N2537 | | | 13 |
| 2N1960 | G | P | SY | | | 2N964 | | | 13 |
| 2N1961 | G | P | SY | | | 2N964 | | | 13 |
| 2N1962 | S | N | SY | | | 2N834 | 2N2369A | | 13 |
| 2N1962 | | | | | | 2N3011 | | | 13 |
| 2N1963 | S | N | SY | | | 2N834 | 2N2369A | | 13 |
| 2N1963 | | | | | | 2N3011 | | | 13 |
| 2N1964 | S | N | SY | | | 2N2539 | 2N2537 | | 13 |
| 2N1964 | | | | | | 2N3015 | | | 13 |
| 2N1965 | S | N | SY | | | 2N2539 | 2N2537 | | 13 |
| 2N1965 | | | | | | 2N3015 | | | 13 |
| 2N1968 | G | P | TG | | | 2N2997 | | | 04 |
| 2N1969 | G | P | CN, ET, UP | | | 2N2996 | | | 10 |
| 2N1970 | G | P | DD, MO, ET, SD, CN | | | 2N1100 | | | 06 |
| 2N1971 | G | P | CN, SQ, SD | | | 2N2140 | | | 06 |
| 2N1972 | S | N | TI, CN, ET, IC, SR | BFX68 | | 2N3643 | 2N2219 | | 02 |
| 2N1973 | S | N | F, TX, ET, RY, TI | BSX46-16 | BSX46-10 | 2N2219 | | | 01 |
| 2N1973 | | | | BC141-10 | BSX46 | | | | 01 |
| 2N1973 | | | | BF109 | | | | | 01 |
| 2N1974 | S | N | TX, F, RY, TO, ET | BSX46-10 | BSX46-6 | 40360 | 2N3498 | | 01 |
| 2N1974 | | | | BC141-6 | BSX46 | | | | 01 |
| 2N1974 | | | | BF109 | | | | | 01 |
| 2N1975 | S | N | TX, F, ET, RY, TI | BSX46-6 | BC141-6 | 40360 | 2N3498 | | 01 |
| 2N1975 | | | | BSX46 | BSX21 | | | | 01 |
| 2N1983 | S | N | F, MO, TX, RY, TI | BSX45-16 | BCY65 | 2N2218 | | | 01 |
| 2N1983 | | | | BSY92 | BF177 | | | | 01 |
| 2N1983 | | | | BSY10 | | | | | 01 |
| 2N1984 | S | N | SG, F, MO, ET, RY | BSX45-10 | BFY33 | 40360 | 2N2218 | | 01 |
| 2N1984 | | | | BSY91 | BSX95 ● | | | | 01 |
| 2N1984 | | | | BSY10 | | | | | 01 |
| 2N1985 | S | N | SG, F, ET, RY, TI | BSX45-6 | BFY33 | 40360 | 2N3642 | | 01 |
| 2N1985 | | | | BSY91 | BSX95 | 2N2218 | 2N1893 | | 01 |
| 2N1986 | S | N | SG, F, ET, IC, RY | BSX45-16 | BFX68 | 2N3053 | 2N3641 | | 02 |
| 2N1986 | | | | BSX45 | BFY65 | 2N2218 | | | 02 |
| 2N1986 | | | | BSY10 | | | | | 02 |
| 2N1987 | S | N | SG, F, ET, RY, TI | BSX45-6 | BFX69 | 2N697 | 2N3643 | | 02 |
| 2N1987 | | | | BSX45 | BFY65 | 2N2218 | 2N1986 | | 02 |
| 2N1988 | S | N | F, ET, GI, RY, TI | BSX46-6 | | 2N2218A | 2N1893 | | 02 |
| 2N1988 | | | | | | 2N2243A | | | 02 |
| 2N1989 | S | N | F, ET, GI, RY, TI | BSX46-6 | | 2N2218A | 2N1893 | | 02 |
| 2N1989 | | | | | | 2N2243A | | | 02 |
| 2N1990 | S | N | TX, SE, MO, F, ET | BF257 | BSX46-6 | 2N697 | 2N696 | | 16 |
| 2N1990 | | | | BSX21 | BFY45 | | | | 16 |
| 2N1990 | | | | BFY65 | | | | | 16 |
| 2N1990N | S | N | SE | BFY45 | | | | | |
| 2N1990R | S | N | SE, TX, Ss, NU, ML | (BSX47-6) | BFY45 | | | | |
| 2N1990S | S | N | MO, SE, TX, NU, SQ | BF257 | BSX47-6 | | | | |
| 2N1990S | | | | BFY45 | | | | | |
| 2N1991 | S | P | F, MO, TR, EM, HS | BSY58 | BFY64 | 2N5143 | 2N1132 | | 02 |
| 2N1991 | | | | | | 2N2905 | | | 02 |
| 2N1992 | S | N | NS | | | 2N2369A | 2N3011 | | 13 |
| 2N1993 | G | N | CN, GI, TX, ET | | | 2N1302 | 2N1306 | | 10 |
| 2N1994 | G | N | TX, CN | | | 2N1306 | 2N1308 | | 10 |
| 2N1995 | G | N | TX, SZ, CN, St | | | 2N1306 | 2N1308 | | 10 |
| 2N1997 | G | P | TX, ET, IC, St, CN | | | 2N1307 | | | 10 |
| 2N1998 | G | P | TX, ET, IC, St, CN | | | 2N1307 | | | 10 |
| 2N1999 | G | P | TX, ET, IC, CN, GI | | | 2N1997 | | | 10 |
| 2N2000 | G | P | TX, IC, CN, SR | ASY48 | ACY24 | | | | 10 |
| 2N2000 | | | | OC123 | | | | | 10 |
| 2N2001 | G | P | TX, ET, SR, CN, St | | | | | | 10 |
| 2N2002 | S | P | CN, SD, SQ, CR | | | 2N2944 | 2N2945 | | 12 |
| 2N2003 | S | P | CN, RY, SQ, CR, SD | | | 2N2944 | 2N2945 | | 12 |
| 2N2004 | S | P | CN, RY, SQ, CR, SD | | | 2N2944 | 2N2945 | | 12 |
| 2N2005 | S | P | CN, RY, SQ, CR, SD | | | 2N2944 | 2N2945 | | 12 |
| 2N2006 | S | P | CN, SD, SQ, CR | | | 2N2944 | 2N2945 | | 12 |
| 2-I2007 | S | P | CN, SD, SQ, CR | | | 2N2944 | 2N2945 | | 12 |
| 2N2008 | S | N | F, RY, SG, SQ, CN | (BF457) | | 2N3500 | 2N2990 | | 01 |
| 2N2015 | S | N | RC, SZ, SQ, FE | | | 2N3715 | 2N5881 | | 01 |
| 2N2016 | S | N | RC, SZ, SQ, FE | | | 2N3715 | 2N5882 | | 01 |
| 2N2017 | S | N | GE, CN, TR, NS, SQ | | | | | | 01 |
| 2N2018 | S | N | TR, GS, SQ, CN | | | 2N3738 | 2N3996 | | 03 |
| 2N2019 | S | N | TR, GS, SQ, CN | | | 2N3788 | 2N3996 | | 03 |
| 2N2020 | S | N | TR, SQ, CN | | | 2N3738 | | | 03 |

| TYPE | M/S | POL | MANUFAC | EUROPEAN | | AMERICAN | | JAPANESE | USE |
|------|-----|-----|---------|----------|---|----------|---|----------|-----|
| 2N2021 | S | N | TR, SQ | | | 2N3738 | | | 03 |
| 2N2032 | S | N | TR, CN, SZ, SU, SQ | | | 2N3713 | 2N1209 | | 03 |
| 2N2032 | | | | | | 2N4914 | 2N4032 | | 03 |
| 2N2033 | S | N | SZ, ET, SM, SU, SQ | | | 2N3420 | | | 16 |
| 2N2034 | S | N | TX, SZ, PI, SD, SQ | | | 2N5784 | 2N2341 | | 16 |
| | | | | | | | | | |
| 2N2034 | | | | | | 2N4238 | | | 16 |
| 2N2035 | S | N | SZ, PI, SM, SU, SQ | | | 2N4911 | 2N4232 | | 16 |
| 2N2036 | S | N | SZ, SQ, SU | | | 2N4911 | 2N4232 | | 16 |
| 2N2048 | G | P | CN, IC, SP, ET, MO | BSX46-16 | BFX69 | 2N2955 | 2N2635 | | 13 |
| 2N2049 | S | N | SG, F, RY, TI, SR | BSX46-16 | BFX68 | 2N1711 | 2N2219A | | 13 |
| | | | | | | | | | |
| 2N2049 | | | | BFY46 | BF114 | | | | 13 |
| 2N2049 | | | | BF109 | | | | | 13 |
| 2N2060 | S | N | F, GE, ME, MO, RY | BFX70 | | | | | 05 |
| 2N2060A | S | N | F, ME, MO, TI, ML | BFY83 | | 2N2060 | | | 05 |
| 2N2060B | S | N | F, SG, St, TI, ME | BFX99 | | 2N2060 | | | |
| | | | | | | | | | |
| 2N2061 | G | P | ET | AD130IV | AF149 | 2N3611 | 2N2836 | | 10 |
| 2N2061 | | | | | | 2N3643 | | | 10 |
| 2N2061A | G | P | ET, KS | (AUY21IV) | AD150IV | 2N2836 | TI3027 | | 16 |
| 2N2061A | | | | AD149 | | | | | 16 |
| 2N2062 | G | P | ET, CN, MO | AD130V | AF149 | 2N3611 | 2N2836 | | 10 |
| | | | | | | | | | |
| 2N2062A | G | P | ET, CN, KS | (AUY21IV) | AD131IV | 2N2836 | TI3027 | | 16 |
| 2N2062A | | | | AD149IV | AF149 | | | | 16 |
| 2N2063 | G | P | ET, CN, MO | AD130V | AD130III | 2N3611 | 2N2836 | | 10 |
| 2N?063 | | | | AD131III | AF149 | | | | 10 |
| 2N2063 | | | | AD131V | | | | | 10 |
| | | | | | | | | | |
| 2N2063A | G | P | ET, KS | (AUY21IV) | AD131IV | TI3027 | | | 16 |
| 2N2063A | | | | AD138 | AF149 | | | | 16 |
| 2N2064 | G | P | ET, CN, MO | AD130V | AD130IV | 2N3611 | 2N2836 | | 10 |
| 2N2064 | | | | AD149 | OC26 | | | | 10 |
| 2N2064A | G | P | ET, CN, KS | (AUY21IV) | AD132III | | | 2SB472 | 16 |
| | | | | | | | | | |
| 2N2065 | G | P | ET, CN, MO | AD132V | AD131V | 2N3615 | | | 10 |
| 2N2065 | | | | AD132II | AD132IV | | | | 10 |
| 2N2065 | | | | OD603/50 | | | | | 10 |
| 2N2065A | G | P | ET, CN, KS | (AUY22IV) | AD132III | TI3027 | TI3030 | 2SB472 | 16 |
| 2N2066 | G | P | ET, CN | AD132V | AD131IV | 2N3615 | | | 10 |
| | | | | | | | | | |
| 2N2066 | | | | GFT4012 | SFT250 | | | | 10 |
| 2N2036A | G | P | ET, CN, KS | AUY22IV | AD132III | 2N1532 | TI3027 | 2SB472 | 16 |
| 2N2066A | | | | AD138/50 | | TI3030 | | | 16 |
| 2N2067 | G | P | ST, ET, KS | (AUY19III) | | 2N1536 | 2N2553 | | 10 |
| 2N2067-0 | G | P | ST, ET, KS | (AUY19III) | | | | | |
| | | | | | | | | | |
| 2N2067B | G | P | ST, ET, KS | (AUY19III) | | | | | |
| 2N2067G | G | P | ST, ET, KS | (AUY19III) | | | | | |
| 2N2067W | G | P | ST, ET, KS | (AUY19III) | | | | | |
| 2N2068 | G | P | ST, ET, KS | (AUY20III) | | 2N1531 | 2N2555 | | 10 |
| 2N2068-0 | G | P | ST, ET, KS | (AUY20IV) | | | | | |
| | | | | | | | | | |
| 2N2068G | G | P | ST, ET, KS | (AUY20IV) | | | | | |
| 2N2069 | G | P | IN | (AUY21IV) | | 2N1539 | | | 10 |
| 2N2070 | G | P | IN | (AUY21IV) | | 2N1541 | | | 10 |
| 2N2071 | G | P | IN | (AUY21IV) | | MPS1539 | | | 10 |
| 2N2072 | G | P | IN | (AUY22IV) | | MPS1541 | | | 10 |
| | | | | | | | | | |
| 2N2084 | G | P | AM, PE | AFY11 | ASZ21 | 2N2189 | | | 02 |
| 2N2085 | G | N | CN, ET | | | 2N1304 | | | 01 |
| 2N2086 | S | N | CN, SM, ET | | | 2N2243A | | | 13 |
| 2N2087 | S | N | CN, ET, SM | | | 2N2243A | | | 13 |
| 2N2089 | G | P | AM, PE | AF124 | AF134 | 2N2188 | 2N2495 | | 02 |
| | | | | | | | | | |
| 2N2089 | | | | AF178 | AF114 | | | | 02 |
| 2N2090 | G | P | PE | AF125 | AF135 | 2N2190 | 2N2188 | 2SA156 | 02 |
| 2N2090 | | | | AF178 | AF115 | 2N2495 | | | 02 |
| 2N2091 | G | P | PE | AF126 | AF137 | 2N2190 | 2N2188 | 2SA240 | 02 |
| 2N2091 | | | | AF125 | AF136 | | | | 02 |
| | | | | | | | | | |
| 2N2091 | | | | AF185 | AF116 | | | | 02 |
| 2N2092 | G | P | AM, PE | AF127 | AF137 | 2N2192 | 2N2189 | 2SA240 | 02 |
| 2N2092 | | | | AF185 | AF117 | | | | 02 |
| 2N2093 | G | P | AM | AF127 | AF127C | 2N2189 | 2N2193 | 2SA240 | 02 |
| 2N2093 | | | | AF137 | AF185 | | | | 02 |
| | | | | | | | | | |
| 2N2093 | | | | AC117C | | | | | 02 |
| 2N2095 | G | P | ID, SQ | | | 2N2999 | | | 03 |
| 2N2096 | G | P | MO, SQ | (ASY26) | | 2N2997 | | | 13 |
| 2N2097 | G | P | MO, SQ | (ASY26) | | 2N2997 | | | 13 |
| 2N2098 | G | P | MO | (ASY26) | | 2N2999 | | | 02 |
| | | | | | | | | | |
| 2N2099 | G | P | MO, SQ | (ASY26) | | 2N2997 | | | 13 |
| 2N2100 | G | P | MO | (ASY26) | | 2N2997 | | | 13 |
| 2N2101 | S | N | ET, SD, CN, PP, SQ | | | 2N3487 | | | 06 |
| 2N2102 | S | N | ET, SD, CN, TX, TI, V | BSX47-6 | BSX45VI | 2N2270 | | | 13 |
| 2N2102 | | | | BSX47VI | BFR22 | | | | 13 |

| TYPE | M/S | POL | MANUFAC | EUROPEAN | | AMERICAN | | JAPANESE | USE |
|------|-----|-----|---------|----------|---|----------|---|----------|-----|
| 2N2102 | | | | BFY55 | BSX64 | | | | 13 |
| 2N2102A | S | N | RY, TX, TI, CA, SQ | BSX47-6 | | | | | 13 |
| 2N2102S | | N | MO | | | 2N2102 | | | |
| 2N2104 | S | P | ND | | | 2N2905 | | | 13 |
| 2N2105 | S | P | ND | | | 2N2904A | 2N2905 | | 13 |
| 2N2106 | S | N | GE, SM, TR, CN, SQ | | | 2N2218 | 2N2987 | | 01 |
| 2N2106 | | | | | | 2N4238 | | | 01 |
| 2N2107 | S | N | GE, ET, SQ, TR, CN | | | 2N2218 | 2N2987 | | 01 |
| 2N2107 | | | | | | 2N4238 | | | 01 |
| 2N2108 | S | N | CN, SM, TR, ES, SQ | | | 2N2219 | 2N2989 | | 01 |
| 2N2108 | | | | | | 2N4238 | | | 01 |
| 2N2109 | S | N | W, SZ, SQ, FR, SU | | | 2N3846 | | | 16 |
| 2N2110 | S | N | W, SZ, SQ, PT, SU | | | 2N3846 | | | 16 |
| 2N2111 | S | N | W, SZ, SQ, PT, SU | | | 2N3846 | | | 16 |
| 2N2112 | S | N | W, SU, SQ, SZ | | | 2N3846 | | | 16 |
| 2N2113 | S | N | W, SU, SQ, SZ | | | 2N3846 | | | 16 |
| 2N2114 | S | N | W, SU, SQ, SZ | | | 2N3846 | | | 16 |
| 2N2116 | S | N | W, SU, SQ, SZ | | | 2N3846 | | | |
| 2N2117 | S | N | W, SU, PT, SQ, SZ | | | 2N3846 | | | 16 |
| 2N2118 | S | N | W, SZ, SQ, PT, SU | | | 2N3846 | | | 16 |
| 2N2119 | S | N | W, SU, SQ, SZ | | | 2N3846 | | | 16 |
| 2N2123 | S | N | W, SU, SQ, SZ | | | 2N4002 | | | 16 |
| 2N2124 | S | N | W, SZ, SQ, PT, SU | | | 2N4002 | | | 16 |
| 2N2125 | S | N | W, SZ, SQ, PT, SU | | | 2N4002 | | | 16 |
| 2N2126 | S | N | W, SZ, SQ, PT, SU | | | 2N4002 | | | 16 |
| 2N2130 | S | N | W, SU, SQ, SZ | | | 2N4002 | | | 16 |
| 2N2131 | S | N | W, SU, SQ, SZ | | | 2N4002 | | | 16 |
| 2N2132 | S | N | W, SZ, SQ, PT, SU | | | 2N4002 | | | 16 |
| 2N2133 | S | N | W, SZ, SQ, PT, SU | | | 2N4002 | | | 16 |
| 2N2137 | G | P | MO, SD, ET | AD130IV | AUY19IV | 2N1038 | 2N2552 | | 06 |
| 2N2137A | G | P | MO, ET | AD150III | AD150IV | 2N1038 | | | 06 |
| 2N2137A | | | | AD130IV | AUY19IV | | | | 06 |
| 2N2138 | G | P | MO, ET, SD, CN, KS | (AD131IV) | AD149IV | 2N1038 | 2N2552 | | 06 |
| 2N2138 | | | | AUY19IV | | | | | 06 |
| 2N2138A | G | P | MO, ET, CN | (AD131IV) | AD149 | 2N1038 | 2N2552 | | 06 |
| 2N2138A | | | | AUY19IV | | | | | 06 |
| 2N2139 | G | P | MO, KS, SD, ET | AD131IV | AUY19IV | 2N1038 | 2N2554 | | 06 |
| 2N2139A | G | P | MO, ET | AD131 | AD138/50 | 2N1038 | 2N2554 | | 06 |
| 2N2139A | | | | AD149 | AD131IV | | | | 06 |
| 2N2139A | | | | AUY19IV | | | | | 06 |
| 2N2140 | G | P | MO, ET, SD, CN, KS | AD132IV | AUY20IV | 2N1038 | 2N2555 | | 06 |
| 2N2140A | G | P | MO, ET | AD132IV | AUY20IV | 2N1038 | 2N2555 | | 06 |
| 2N2141 | G | P | MO, ET, SD, CN, KS | AD163IV | AUY34IV | 2N1038 | 2N2555 | | 06 |
| 2N2141A | G | P | MO, ET | AD163IV | AUY34IV | 2N1038 | 2N2555 | | 06 |
| 2N2142 | G | P | MO, ET, SD, CN, KS | AD130V | AUY19V | | | | 06 |
| 2N2142A | G | P | MO, ET, CN | AD130V | AUY19V | | | | 06 |
| 2N2143 | G | P | MO, ET, SD, CN, KS | (AD131V) | AD149V | | | | 06 |
| 2N2143 | | | | AUY19V | | | | | 06 |
| 2N2143A | G | P | MO, CN | (AD131V) | AD149 | | | | 06 |
| 2N2143A | | | | AD149V | AUY19V | | | | 06 |
| 2N2144 | G | P | MO, ET, SD, CN, KS | AD131V | AUY19V | | | | 06 |
| 2N2144A | G | P | MO, ET, CN | AD131 | AD138/50 | | | | 06 |
| 2N2144A | | | | AD149 | AD131IV | | | | 06 |
| 2N2144A | | | | AUY19V | | | | | 06 |
| 2N2145 | G | P | MO, ET, SD, CN, KS | AD132V | AUY20V | | | | 06 |
| 2N2145A | G | P | MO, ET | AD132V | AUY20V | | | | 06 |
| 2N2146 | G | P | MO, KS, SD, CN | (AD163IV) | | | | | 06 |
| 2N2146A | G | P | MO, CN | (AD163IV) | | | | | 06 |
| 2N2147 | G | P | ET, RC, ES, SD, CN | (AUY22IV) | AD167 | 2N1907 | 2N2832 | | 06 |
| 2N2147 | | | | AD149 | | | | | 06 |
| 2N2148 | G | P | ET, RC, SD, ES | (AUY21IV) | AD166 | 2N1908 | 2N2837 | | 06 |
| 2N2148 | | | | AD145 | | 2N2832 | | | 06 |
| 2N2162 | S | P | SP, FR, CR, RY, SQ | | | 2N2945 | 2N2946 | | 12 |
| 2N2163 | S | P | SP, CR, SM, SQ, FR | | | 2N2944 | 2N2945 | | 12 |
| 2N2164 | S | P | SP, CR, FR, RY, SQ | | | 2N2944 | 2N2945 | | 12 |
| 2N2165 | S | P | SP, CR, RY, SQ, SM | | | 2N2945 | 2N2946 | | 12 |
| 2N2166 | S | P | SP, FR, RY, SQ, CR | | | 2N2944 | 2N2945 | | 12 |
| 2N2167 | S | P | SP, CR, FR, SM, SQ | | | 2N2944 | 2N2945 | | 12 |
| 2N2168 | G | P | SP, ET, ID, CN, FR | | | 2N2997 | | | 13 |
| 2N2169 | S | P | SP, ET, ID, CN, FR | | | 2N2996 | | | 13 |
| 2N2170 | G | P | SP, ET, ID, CN, FR | | | 2N2997 | | | 13 |
| 2N2171 | G | P | MO, ET, SR | (ASY48VI) | | 2N1376 | 2N1377 | | 01 |
| 2N2172 | G | P | ET | | | 2N1376 | 2N1377 | | 10 |
| 2N2175 | S | P | SD, RY, SQ, CR, SM | | | 2N2944 | 2N2945 | | 01 |
| 2N2176 | S | P | SD, RY, SQ, CR, SM | | | 2N2944 | 2N2945 | | 01 |

| TYPE | M/S | POL | MANUFAC | EUROPEAN | | AMERICAN | | JAPANESE | USE |
|---|---|---|---|---|---|---|---|---|---|
| 2N2177 | S | P | SD, RY, SQ, CR, SM | | | 2N2944 | 2N2945 | | 01 |
| 2N2178 | S | P | SD, RY, SQ, CR, SM | | | 2N2944 | 2N2945 | | 01 |
| 2N2180 | G | P | PH | | | 2N2635 | | | 13 |
| 2N2181 | S | P | RY | | | 2N2944 | 2N2945 | | 12 |
| 2N2182 | S | P | RY | | | 3N108 | 3N111 | | 12 |
| 2N2183 | S | P | PH | | | 2N2944 | 2N2945 | | 12 |
| 2N2184 | S | P | PH | | | 3N108 | 3N111 | | 12 |
| 2N2185 | S | P | CR, RY, SP, TD, FR | | | 2N2944 | 2N2945 | | 12 |
| 2N2186 | S | P | CR, RY, SP, TD, FR | | | 3N108 | 3N111 | | 12 |
| 2N2187 | S | P | CR, RY, SP, TD, FR | | | 3N108 | 3N111 | | 12 |
| 2N2188 | G | P | TX, SR | | | 2N3323 | | | 02 |
| 2N2189 | G | P | SR, TX | | | 2N3323 | | | 02 |
| 2N2190 | G | P | SR, TX | | | 2N3323 | | | 02 |
| 2N2191 | G | P | SR, TX | | | 2N3323 | | | 02 |
| 2N2192 | S | N | IT, TX, SE, F, MO | BSX45-16 | BFX68A | 2N1711 | 2N2219A | | 13 |
| 2N2192 | | | | BSX45 | BFY70 | 2N2243A | 2N3569 | | 13 |
| 2N2192A | S | N | F, MO, TX, RY, TI | BSX45-16 | BFX68A | 2N2243A | 2N2219A | | 13 |
| 2N2192A | | | | | | 2N3569 | | | 13 |
| 2N2192B | S | N | F, MO, TX, RY, TI | BSX45-10 | BFX68A | 2N2192A | 2N2243A | | 13 |
| 2N2192B | | | | | | 2N3569 | | | 13 |
| 2N2193 | S | N | TF, IT, TX, SG, SE | BSX46-6 | BSX45 | 2N1613 | 2N2218A | 2SC708 | 13 |
| 2N2193 | | | | BFY444 | BSY46 | 2N2243A | 2N3568 | | 13 |
| 2N2193 | | | | BSY85 | | | | | 13 |
| 2N2193A | S | N | F, MO, TX, RY, TI | BSX46-6 | | 2N2243A | 2N2218A | | 13 |
| 2N2193A | | | | | | 2N3568 | | | 13 |
| 2N2193B | S | N | F, MO, TX, RY, TI | BSX46-6 | | 2N3568 | | | 13 |
| 2N2194 | S | N | IT, TX, SE, ML, F | BSX45-6 | BSX45 | 2N699 | 2N2218A | | 13 |
| 2N2194 | | | | BSY71 | BFY70 | 2N3567 | | | 13 |
| 2N2194A | S | N | F, MO, TX, TI, RY | BSX45-6 | | 2N2218A | 2N3567 | | 13 |
| 2N2194B | S | N | F, MO, TX, RY, TI | BSX45-6 | | 2N3567 | | | 13 |
| 2N2195 | S | N | IT, TX, SG, SE, RY | BSX45-6 | BFY70 | 2N697 | 2N2218 | | 13 |
| 2N2195 | | | | | | 2N3641 | | | 13 |
| 2N2195A | S | N | SG, F, MO, TX, TE | BSX45-6 | | 2N697 | 2N2218 | | 13 |
| 2N2195A | | | | | | 2N3641 | | | 13 |
| 2N2195B | S | N | F, MO, TX, TI, RY | BSX45-6 | | 2N2218 | 2N3641 | | 13 |
| 2N2196 | S | N | SE, TR, GE, Ss, SM | (BSX46-6) | | 2N3766 | | | 06 |
| 2N2197 | S | N | SE, TR, CN, ML, SQ | (BSX46-6) | BSX45 | 2N3766 | | | 06 |
| 2N2201 | S | N | GE, SQ, TR, SM | | | 2N3738 | 2N4239 | | 01 |
| 2N2201 | | | | | | 2N5681 | | | 01 |
| 2N2202 | S | N | SM, SQ | | | 2N3738 | 2N4239 | | 01 |
| 2N2202 | | | | | | 2N5681 | | | 01 |
| 2N2203 | S | N | SM, SQ | | | 2N3738 | 2N4239 | | 01 |
| 2N2203 | | | | | | 2N5681 | | | 01 |
| 2N2204 | S | N | SM, SQ | | | 2N3738 | 2N4239 | | 01 |
| 2N2204 | | | | | | 2N5681 | | | 01 |
| 2N2205 | S | N | F, IN, FE, IT, SM | BSY62A | BSX87 | 2N853 | 2N706 | | 13 |
| 2N2205 | | | | | | 2N4274 | | | 13 |
| 2N2206 | S | N | F, IN, MO, FE, SR | BSY62B | BSX87 | 2N835 | 2N2410 | | 13 |
| 2N2206 | | | | | | 2N3015 | 2N3646 | | 13 |
| 2N2207 | G | P | PE | AF118 | | | | | 02 |
| 2N2210 | G | P | MO | | | 2N2075 | | | 06 |
| 2N2214 | S | N | TW | | | 2N706 | | | 13 |
| 2N2216 | S | P | MO | | | 2N3498 | | | 13 |
| 2N2217 | S | N | IT, TX, F, MO, PH | BCW77-16 | BFY72 | 2N697 | 2N2218 | | 13 |
| 2N2217 | | | | BSX45 | BSW77XVI | 2N2219 | | | 13 |
| 2N2217 | | | | BF168 | | | | | 13 |
| 2N2218 | S | N | TF, IT, TX, MO, SG | BCW77-16 | BFX96 | 2N697 | 2N2219 | 2SC479 | 13 |
| 2N2218 | | | | BSX45 | BCW77XVI | 2N3641 | | | 13 |
| 2N2218 | | | | BSX73 | BSY34 | | | | 13 |
| 2N2218 | S | N | SE, F, PH | BCW77-16 | BFX73 | 2N697 | 2N2219 | 2SC479 | 13 |
| 2N2218 | | | | BSX45 | BCW77XVI | 2N3641 | | | 13 |
| 2N2218B | | | | BFX96 | BSY34 | | | | 13 |
| 2N2218A | S | N | F, MO, PH, TX | BCW78-16 | BFY72 | 2N3053 | 2N2219 | | 13 |
| 2N2218A | | | | BCW78XVI | BSW53 | 2N3641 | | | 13 |
| 2N2218B | S | N | | BFY72 | | | | | |
| 2N2219 | S | N | F, MO, PH, TX, GI | BCW77-16 | BFX97 | 2N3641 | | | 13 |
| 2N2219 | | | | BSX45 | BCW77XVI | | | | 13 |
| 2N2219 | | | | BSX74 | BSY34 | | | | 13 |
| 2N2219A | S | N | F, MO, PH, TX, IN | BCW78-16 | BF72 | | | | 13 |
| 2N2219A | | | | BCW78XVI | BSW54 | | | | 13 |
| 2N2220 | S | N | F, MO, PH, TX, RY | BCW73-16 | BFY72 | 2N2222 | 2N2221 | | 13 |
| 2N2220 | | | | | | 2N4436 | | | 13 |
| 2N2221 | S | N | F, MO, PH, TX, V | BCW73-16 | BFX94 | 2N2222 | 2N2220 | | 13 |
| 2N2221 | | | | BSX45 | BCW73XVI | 2N4436 | | | 13 |
| 2N2221 | | | | BF168 | BSX34 | | | | 13 |

| TYPE | M/S | POL | MANUFAC | EUROPEAN | | AMERICAN | | JAPANESE | USE |
|------|-----|-----|---------|----------|--|----------|--|----------|-----|
| 2N2221A | S | N | F, MO, PH, TX, RY | BCW74-16 | BFY72 | 2N4436 | | | 13 |
| 2N2221A | | | | BCW74XVI | BSW63 | | | | 13 |
| 2N2222 | S | N | F, MO, PH, TX, IT | BCN73-16 | BFX95 | 2N2221 | 2N4437 | | 13 |
| 2N2222 | | | | BSX45 | BCW73XVI | | | | 13 |
| 2N2222 | | | | BFY34 | BSW64 | | | | 13 |
| 2N2222 | | | | BSY44 | BC232 | | | | 13 |
| 2N2222A | S | N | F, MO, PH, TX, RY | BCW74-16 | BFY83 | 2N4437 | | | 13 |
| 2N2222A | | | | BSX45A | BCW74XVI | | | | 13 |
| 2N2222A | | | | BSW64 | | | | | 13 |
| 2N2223 | S | N | GI, MO, RY, TI, GE | BFX72 | BFX71 | | | | 05 |
| 2N2224 | S | N | MO, SM, HS | BSY34 | | 2N2218 | 2N2219 | | 13 |
| 2N2225 | G | P | KS | | | 2N1143 | | | 10 |
| 2N2230 | S | N | W, SZ, SQ, SM, SU | BUY12 | BUY56IV | | | | 06 |
| 2N2236 | S | N | RY, CA, SM, SQ | BSX45-6 | BSY34 | 2N2218 | 2N2193 | | 13 |
| 2N2236 | | | | BSX73 | | 2N2243A | | | 13 |
| 2N2237 | S | N | RY, CA, SM, SQ | BSX45-6 | BSY58 | 2N2218 | 2N2152 | | 13 |
| 2N2237 | | | | BSX73 | | 2N2243A | | | 13 |
| 2N2239 | S | N | SZ, SQ | | | 2N3766 | 2N4232 | | 01 |
| 2N2240 | S | N | SM, SQ | | | 2N699 | 2N2243A | | 13 |
| 2N2241 | S | N | SM, SQ | | | 2N1890 | 2N2243A | | 13 |
| 2N2242 | S | N | MO, IT, SM, SG, SR | BSY63 | BSX87 | 2N2501 | 2N2369 | | 13 |
| 2N2242 | | | | | | 2N2369A | EN914 | | 13 |
| 2N2243 | S | N | TX, GI, TI, RY, NS | BSX47-6 | BSW65 | 2N1893 | 2N2219 | | 13 |
| 2N2243A | S | N | TX, GI, TI, RY, NS | BSX47-6 | | 2N1893 | | | 13 |
| 2N2244 | S | N | NS | | | 2N835 | 2N929 | | 01 |
| 2N2244 | | | | | | 2N930 | | | 01 |
| 2N2245 | S | N | NS | | | 2N835 | 2N929 | | 01 |
| 2N2245 | | | | | | 2N930 | | | 01 |
| 2N2246 | S | N | NS | | | 2N835 | 2N929 | | 01 |
| 2N2246 | | | | | | 2N930 | | | 01 |
| 2N2247 | S | N | NS | | | 2N835 | 2N929 | | 01 |
| 2N2247 | | | | | | 2N930 | | | 01 |
| 2N2248 | S | N | NS | | | 2N835 | 2N929 | | 01 |
| 2N2248 | | | | | | 2N930 | | | 01 |
| 2N2249 | S | N | NS | | | 2N834 | 2N929 | | 01 |
| 2N2249 | | | | | | 2N930 | | | 01 |
| 2N2250 | S | N | NS | | | 2N835 | 2N929 | | 01 |
| 2N2250 | | | | | | 2N930 | | | 01 |
| 2N2251 | S | N | NS | | | 2N935 | 2N929 | | 01 |
| 2N2251 | | | | | | 2N930 | | | 01 |
| 2N2252 | S | N | NS | | | 2N834 | 2N929 | | 01 |
| 2N2252 | | | | | | 2N930 | | | 01 |
| 2N2253 | S | N | NS | | | 2N834 | 2N929 | | 01 |
| 2N2253 | | | | | | 2N930 | | | 01 |
| 2N2254 | S | N | NS | | | 2N834 | 2N929 | | 01 |
| 2N2254 | | | | | | 2N930 | | | 01 |
| 2N2255 | S | N | NS | | | 2N834 | 2N929 | | 01 |
| 2N2255 | | | | | | 2N930 | | | 01 |
| 2N2256 | S | N | MO, SM, SQ | (BSY17) | | | | | 13 |
| 2N2257 | S | N | MO, SM, SQ | (BSY18) | | | | | 13 |
| 2N2258 | G | P | MO, SQ | | | 2N964 | 2N972 | | 13 |
| 2N2259 | G | P | MO, SQ | | | 2N964 | 2N972 | | 13 |
| 2N2266 | G | P | SD, KS | | | 2N2145 | | | 16 |
| 2N2267 | G | P | SD, KS | | | 2N2145 | | | 16 |
| 2N2268 | G | P | SD | | | 2N2145 | | | 16 |
| 2N2269 | G | P | SD | | | 2N2145 | | | 16 |
| 2N2270 | S | N | RC, TX, TI, ET, FR | BSX46-10 | | 2N2219 | 2N2102 | | 01 |
| 2N2270 | | | | | | 2N2243A | 2N3053 | | 01 |
| 2N2270A | S | N | MO | | | 2N2270 | | | |
| 2N2270S | G | N | MO | | | 2N2270 | | | |
| 2N2271 | G | P | ET, UP | AC153 | AC117 | 2N404 | | | 01 |
| 2N2271 | | | | AC128 | | | | | 01 |
| 2N2272 | S | N | GE | | | 2N914 | | | 13 |
| 2N2273 | G | P | MO, SQ, SM | AF121 | AFY12 | | | | 02 |
| 2N2273 | | | | AF106 | | | | | 02 |
| 2N2274 | S | P | CR, RY, SP, ID, SM | | | 2N2944 | 2N2945 | | 12 |
| 2N2288 | G | P | MO, SD, ET, SQ, CN | (AUY21IV) | | 2N2526 | 2N1046 | | 06 |
| 2N2288 | | | | | | 2N1907 | | | 06 |
| 2N2289 | G | P | MO, SD, ET, SQ, CN | (AUY22IV) | | 2N2526 | | | 06 |
| 2N2290 | G | P | SD, KS, SQ, CN, MO | | | 2N2526 | | | 06 |
| 2N2291 | G | P | MO, SD, ET, SQ, CN | (AUY21IV) | | 2N1907 | | | 06 |
| 2N2292 | G | P | MO, SD, ET, SQ, CN | (AUY22IV) | | | | | 06 |
| 2N2294 | G | P | SD, ET, SQ, CN, KS | | | 2N1907 | | | 16 |
| 2N2297 | S | N | TX, IT, SG, PH, RT | BSX45-6 | BFY56 | 2N1613 | 2N2243A | 2SC708 | 02 |
| 2N2297 | | | | BFY56A | BSX45 | 2N3252 | 2N3567 | | 02 |

| TYPE | M/S | POL | MANUFAC | EUROPEAN | | AMERICAN | | JAPANESE | USE |
|------|-----|-----|---------|----------|--|----------|--|----------|-----|
| 2N2297 | | | | BSY46 | BFY55 | | | | 02 |
| 2N2297 | | | | BSY40 | | | | | 02 |
| 2N2297S | S | N | MO | | | | | | |
| 2N2303 | S | P | IT, TX, F, MO, TR | BSV16-10 | BFY64 | 2N1613 | | | |
| 2N2303 | | | | | | 40315 | 2N2801 | | |
| 2N2303 | | | | | | 2N3649 | | | 02 |
| 2N2304 | S | N | SM, SZ, SU, SF | | | 2N3766 | 2N4910 | | 06 |
| 2N2305 | S | N | SZ, SD, PP, SU, SQ | | | 2N4913 | 2N5068 | | 06 |
| 2N2308 | S | N | SZ, SF, SQ, SM, SU | | | 2N4912 | | | 06 |
| 2N2309 | S | N | RY, SM, SQ, CA | | | 2N696 | 2N697 | | 01 |
| 2N2310 | S | N | RY, CA, SM, SQ, CN | | | 2N698 | 2N2243A | | 01 |
| 2N2311 | S | N | RY, SM, SQ, CA | | | 2N698 | 2N2243A | | 01 |
| 2N2311 | | | | | | 2N5681 | | | 01 |
| 2N2312 | S | N | RY, CA, SM, SQ, CN | | | 2N699 | 2N2243A | | 01 |
| 2N2313 | S | N | CA, SM, SQ, RY | | | 2N1889 | 2N2243A | | 01 |
| 2N2313 | | | | | | 2N5681 | | | 01 |
| 2N2314 | S | N | RY, CA, SM, SQ, CN | | | 2N698 | 2N43A | | 01 |
| 2N2315 | S | N | RY, CA, SM, SQ, CN | | | 2N699 | 2N2243A | | 01 |
| 2N2315 | | | | | | 2N2222 | | | 01 |
| 2N2316 | S | N | RY, SM, TD, CA, SQ | | | 2N1893 | 2N2243A | | 01 |
| 2N2317 | S | N | RY, CA, SM, TD, CN | | | 2N1613 | | | 01 |
| 2N2318 | S | N | CN, SQ, ET | | | 2N834 | 2N3014 | | 13 |
| 2N2319 | S | N | GI | | | 2N834 | 2N3014 | | 13 |
| 2N2330 | S | N | TX, MO, HS, SM, SQ | | | 40814 | 2N4124 | | 12 |
| 2N2330 | | | | | | 2N834 | 2N3014 | | 12 |
| 2N2330 | | | | | | 2N2432 | | | 12 |
| 2N2331 | S | N | MO, SM, SQ, CN | | | 2N2432 | | | 12 |
| 2N2332 | S | P | CN, RY, SD, SQ, CR | | | 2N2944 | 2N2945 | | 12 |
| 2N2333 | S | P | CN, RY, SD, CR, SQ | | | 2N2944 | 2N2945 | | 12 |
| 2N2334 | S | P | RY, CN, SD, SQ, CR | | | 2N2944 | 2N2945 | | 12 |
| 2N2335 | S | P | CN, RY, SD, SQ, CR | | | 2N2944 | 2N2945 | | 12 |
| 2N2336 | S | P | CN, RY, CR, SD, SQ | | | 2N2944 | 2N2945 | | 12 |
| 2N2337 | S | P | RY, SD, CR, SQ, CN | | | 2N2944 | 2N2945 | | 12 |
| 2N2338 | S | N | RC, SQ | | | 2N3713 | | | 06 |
| 2N2339 | S | N | CN, SF, ET | | | MJ3101 | 2N1049 | | 06 |
| 2N2339 | | | | | | 2N4910 | | | 06 |
| 2N2340 | S | N | DD | | | 2N5320 | | | 03 |
| 2N2341 | S | N | DD | | | 2N5320 | | | 03 |
| 2N2342 | S | N | DD | | | 2N5320 | | | 03 |
| 2N2343 | S | N | DD | | | 2N5320 | | | 03 |
| 2N2350 | S | N | CA, RY, SQ, TI, IT | | | 2N2192 | 2N2243A | | 13 |
| 2N2350A | S | N | CA, RY, SQ, TD, TI | | | 2N2192 | 2N2243A | | 12 |
| 2N2351 | S | N | F, TX, SQ, TI, UP | (BSX46-6) | BSX33 | 2N2193 | 2N2243A | | 12 |
| 2N2351 | | | | | | 2N3668 | | | 12 |
| 2N2351A | S | N | F, TX, RY, SQ, TI | (BSX46-6) | | 2N2193A | 2N2243A | | 12 |
| 2N2351A | | | | | | 2N3568 | | | 12 |
| 2N2352 | S | N | CN, IT, SM, CA, RY | BSX33 | | 2N2194 | 2N2243A | | 12 |
| 2N2352 | | | | | | 2N3567 | | | 12 |
| 2N2352A | S | N | CN, IT, SM, TD, RY | BSX33 | | 2N2194 | 2N2243A | | 12 |
| 2N2352A | | | | | | 2N3567 | | | 12 |
| 2N2353 | S | N | CN, IT, SM, TD, RY | BSX33 | | 2N2243 | 2N2243A | | 12 |
| 2N2353 | | | | | | 2N3643 | | | 12 |
| 2N2353A | S | N | CA, RY, SQ, TI, UP | BSX33 | | 2N2243A | | | 12 |
| 2N2354 | G | N | SQ | | | 2N1302 | | | 01 |
| 2N2356 | S | N | GE, SQ | | | 3N76 | 3N79 | | 12 |
| 2N2356A | S | N | GE, SQ | | | 3N74 | 3N79 | | 12 |
| 2N2360 | G | P | ID, SP | AF139 | | 2N2997 | 2N3283 | | 02 |
| 2N2361 | G | P | ID, SP | | | 2N3284 | 2N2997 | | 02 |
| 2N2362 | G | P | ID, SP | | | 2N3284 | | | 02 |
| 2N2363 | G | P | TX | | | 2N2997 | | | 02 |
| 2N2364 | S | N | CA, SM, TD, TI, RY | | | 2N2243A | | | |
| 2N2368 | S | N | F, EM, ET, Ss, FR | BSX92 | BSY63 | 2N3227 | 2N3641 | 2SC689 | 13 |
| 2N2368 | | | | BSY21 | BSX19 | | | | 13 |
| 2N2368 | | | | BSX20 | | | | | 13 |
| 2N2369 | S | N | F, Ss, FR, IT, MC | BSX93 | BSY19 | 2N3227 | 2N4275 | 2SC689 | 13 |
| 2N2369 | | | | BSY63 | BSS11 | EN2369A | | | 13 |
| 2N2369 | | | | BSX20 | | | | | 13 |
| 2N2369A | S | N | F, BL, FR, MO, NT | BSX28 | BSY63 | 2N3227 | | | 13 |
| 2N2369A | | | | BSX20 | | | | | 13 |
| 2N2370 | S | P | CR, SQ | | | 2N2944 | 2N2945 | | |
| 2N2371 | S | P | CR, SQ | | | 2N2944 | 2N2945 | | |
| 2N2372 | S | P | CR, SQ | | | 2N2944 | 2N2945 | | |
| 2N2373 | S | P | CR, SQ | | | 2N2944 | 2N2945 | | |
| 2N2374 | G | P | ET, IC, SZ, CN, GI | | | 2N3427 | 2N404 | | 01 |
| 2N2375 | G | P | CN, GI, SS, St, ET | | | 2N1193 | 2N404 | | 01 |
| 2N2376 | G | P | CN, GI, St, ET, SQ | | | 2N1193 | 2N404 | | 01 |

| TYPE | M/S | POL | MANUFAC | EUROPEAN | | AMERICAN | | JAPANESE | USE |
|------|-----|-----|---------|----------|---|----------|---|----------|-----|
| 2N2377 | S | P | SP, FR, RY, CR, SS | | | 2N2944 | 2N2245 | | 02 |
| 2N2378 | S | P | SP, FR, SQ, CR, ID | | | 2N2944 | 2N2945 | | 02 |
| 2N2380 | S | N | CA, SM, SQ, RY | | | 2N1893 | 2N2243A | | 13 |
| 2N2380A | S | N | CA, SQ, RY | | | 2N2277 | 2N2219 | | 13 |
| 2N2383 | S | N | SZ, SM, St, ET | | | 2N4914 | | | 06 |
| | | | | | | | | | |
| 2N2384 | S | N | SZ, SQ, SM | | | 2N4914 | | | 06 |
| 2N2386 | J | P | TX, SD, TI, ID | | | 2N3330 | | | |
| 2N2386A | J | P | TX, IL | | | 2N3330 | | | |
| 2N2387 | S | N | TX | BC237A | | | | | 01 |
| 2N2388 | S | N | TX | BC237A | | | | | 01 |
| | | | | | | | | | |
| 2N2389 | S | N | TX, SQ | (BSX46-6) | BSX45VI | | | | 01 |
| 2N2390 | S | N | TX, SQ | (BSX46-10) | | | | | 01 |
| 2N2395 | S | N | TX, SQ | (BSX45-6) | | | | | 01 |
| 2N2396 | S | N | TX, SQ | (BSX45-6) | BC140 | 2N2221A | | | 01 |
| 2N2396 | | | | BSY46 | | | | | 01 |
| | | | | | | | | | |
| 2N2397 | S | N | SY | | | 2N2369A | 2N3011 | | 13 |
| 2N2397 | | | | | | 2N3329 | | | 13 |
| 2N2398 | G | P | FR, SP, ID | | | 2N3284 | 2N2997 | | 02 |
| 2N2399 | G | P | FR, SP, ID | | | 2N3284 | 2N2997 | | 13 |
| 2N2400 | G | P | FR, SP, ID | | | 2N964 | 2N711 | | 13 |
| | | | | | | | | | |
| 2N2401 | G | P | FR, SM, SQ, ID, SP | | | 2N964 | 2N711A | | 13 |
| 2N2402 | G | P | FR, SP, ID | | | 2N956 | 2N964 | | 13 |
| 2N2402 | | | | | | 2N711B | | | 13 |
| 2N2405 | S | N | F, MO, V, RC, RY | BSX47-10 | | 2N3498 | 2N1893 | | 01 |
| 2N2405 | | | | | | 2N2243A | | | 01 |
| | | | | | | | | | |
| 2N2410 | S | N | TX, SG, PH, RT, F | BSY34 | BSX60 | 2N3053 | 2N2218 | 2SC479 | 13 |
| 2N2410 | | | | BSX45/10 | BFY51 | 2N3015 | 2N2537 | | 13 |
| 2N2410 | | | | BSX45 | BSX61 | | | | 13 |
| 2N2411 | S | P | PH, TX, MO, NS, SM | (BSX48) | BCY78VII | 2N3250 | | | 13 |
| 2N2411 | | | | BCY78VI | BSY40 | | | | 13 |
| | | | | | | | | | |
| 2N2412 | S | P | PH, TX, MO, NS, SM | (BSX48) | BCY78 | 2N3250 | | | 13 |
| 2N2412 | | | | BSY41 | BC178VI | | | | 13 |
| 2N2414 | S | N | RY, SQ, SM | | | 2N2060 | | | 04 |
| 2N2415 | G | P | MO, TX | (AF 239S) | AF 186 | | | | 02 |
| 2N2416 | G | P | MO, TX | (AF 239S) | | | | | 02 |
| | | | | | | | | | |
| 2N2417 | U | PN | GE | | | 2N3980 | | | |
| 2N2417A | U | PN | GE | | | 2N3980 | | | |
| 2N2417B | U | PN | GE | | | 2N3980 | | | |
| 2N2418 | U | PN | GE | | | 2N3980 | | | |
| 2N2418A | U | PN | GE | | | 2N3980 | | | |
| | | | | | | | | | |
| 2N2418B | U | PN | GE | | | 2N3980 | | | |
| 2N2419 | U | PN | GE | | | 2N3980 | | | |
| 2N2419A | U | PN | GE | | | 2N3980 | | | |
| 2N2419B | U | PN | GE | | | 2N3980 | | | |
| 2N2420 | U | PN | GE | | | 2N3980 | | | |
| | | | | | | | | | |
| 2N2420A | U | PN | GE | | | 2N3980 | | | |
| 2N2420B | U | PN | GE | | | 2N3980 | | | |
| 2N2421 | U | PN | GE | | | 2N3980 | | | |
| 2N2421A | U | PN | GE | | | 2N3980 | | | |
| 2N2421B | U | PN | GE | | | 2N3980 | | | |
| | | | | | | | | | |
| 2N2422 | U | PN | GE | | | 2N3980 | | | |
| 2N2422A | U | PN | GE | | | 2N3980 | | | |
| 2N2422B | U | PN | GE | | | 2N3980 | | | |
| 2N2423 | G | P | KS, TR, SD | | | 2N3616 | 2N456A | | 16 |
| 2N2423 | | | | | | 2N3146 | | | 16 |
| | | | | | | | | | |
| 2N2424 | S | P | CR, SM | | | 2N2944 | 2N2945 | | 10 |
| 2N2425 | S | P | CR, SQ, SM | | | 2N2945 | 2N2946 | | 01 |
| 2N2426 | G | N | SY | | | | | | 01 |
| 2N2328 | G | P | AM, PH, PE, NU | AC151VII | AC151 | 2N1377 | 2N652 | 2SB459 | 01 |
| 2N2428 | | | | AC122 | AC126 | 2N1381 | 2N2429 | | 01 |
| | | | | | | | | | |
| 2N2429 | G | P | AM, PH, NU | AC151IV | AC171 | 2N1377 | 2N652 | | 01 |
| 2N2429 | | | | AC125 | AC151 | 2N1381 | | | 01 |
| 2N2429 | | | | AC163 | AC126 | | | | 01 |
| 2N2430 | G | N | AM, PH, PE, NU | AC152VI | AC186 | 2N1304 | | | 01 |
| 2N2430 | | | | AC127 | | | | | 01 |
| | | | | | | | | | |
| 2N2431 | G | P | AM, PH, PE, NU | AC153VI | AC153V | 2N1377 | 2N1381 | 2SB770B | 01 |
| 2N2431 | | | | AC128 | AC117 | | | | 01 |
| 2N2431 | | | | AC153 | | | | | 01 |
| 2N2432 | S | N | TX, TR, CN, TD | (BCY58VII) | BCY59 | | | | 12 |
| 2N2432A | S | N | TX, TD, CR, TR | (BCY59VII) | | | | | 12 |
| | | | | | | | | | |
| 2N2436 | S | N | TI, SQ, TR, SM | BC110 | | | | | 13 |
| 2N2437 | S | N | TI, SQ, TR, SM | | | 2N1893 | 2N2243A | | 02 |
| 2N2438 | S | N | TI, SQ, TR, SM | | | 2N1893 | 2N2243A | | 02 |
| 2N2439 | S | N | TI, SQ, TR, SM | | | 2N1893 | 2N2243A | | 02 |
| 2N2443 | S | N | F, SG, TI, TR, SM | BSX47-10 | | 2N1890 | 2N2243A | | 02 |

| TYPE | M/S | POL | MANUFAC | EUROPEAN | | AMERICAN | | JAPANESE | USE |
|---|---|---|---|---|---|---|---|---|---|
| 2N2444 | G | P | KS, SQ, SD | | | 2N456A | 2N3146 | | 06 |
| 2N2445 | G | P | SD, TR | | | 2N456A | 2N3146 | | 06 |
| 2N2447 | G | P | RY | | | 2N1187 | 2N1309 | | 01 |
| 2N2448 | G | P | RY | | | 2N1187 | 2N1309 | | 01 |
| 2N2449 | G | P | RY | AC151 | AC122 | 2N1307 | 2N652 | | 01 |
| 2N2450 | G | P | RY | AC151 | AC122 | 2N1307 | 2N652 | | 01 |
| 2N2450 | | | | AC125 | | | | | 01 |
| 2N2451 | G | P | SP, ID, SM, FR | | | 2N2635 | | | 13 |
| 2N2452 | P | N | F, SG | BFY65 | | | | | 04 |
| 2N2453 | S | N | TI, MO, RY, TX, GE | BFY81 | | 2N3680 | | | 05 |
| 2N2453A | S | N | TI, GE, MO, BT, IL | BFY81 | | 2N3680 | | | 05 |
| 2N2456 | G | P | SY | | | 2N2999 | | | 13 |
| 2N2472 | S | N | SM | | | 2N2432 | | | 06 |
| 2N2473 | S | N | GE | | | 2N2432 | | | 06 |
| 2N2474 | S | P | CR, SM | | | | | | 06 |
| 2N2475 | S | N | F, TX, RC, TR, FR | BSY17 | BSX27 | 2N3013 | | | 13 |
| 2N2475 | | | | BSX44 | | | | | 13 |
| 2N2476 | S | N | F, MO, RC, ET, SP | (BSY34) | BSX30 | 2N3252 | 2N2539 | | 13 |
| 2N2476 | | | | | | 2N3015 | | | 13 |
| 2N2477 | S | N | F, MO, RC, SP, ET | (BSY34) | BSX30 | 2N3252 | 2N2537 | | 13 |
| 2N2477 | | | | | | 2N3015 | | | 13 |
| 2N2478 | S | N | ET | BSW51 | | 2N2218 | 2N2537 | | 13 |
| 2N2478 | | | | | | 2N3015 | | | 13 |
| 2N2479 | S | N | CN, ET, TD, CA, RY | | | 2N2218 | 2N3252 | | 13 |
| 2N2480 | S | N | GE, MO, TI, RY, TD | BFY83 | | 2N2060 | | | 05 |
| 2N2480A | S | N | GE, RY, MO, Ss, ML | BFY83 | | 2N2639 | 2N2640 | | 05 |
| 2N2481 | S | N | NO, TX, HS, RY, TD | BSY63 | BSX28 | 2N4275 | | | 13 |
| 2N2482 | G | N | St | | | 2N797 | | | 02 |
| 2N2483 | S | N | F, MO, TX, SD, TR | (BC414B) | BFX92A | MM2483 | 2N2484 | 2SC648 | 01 |
| 2N2483 | | | | BCY65EVII | BC107B | EN2483 | | | 01 |
| 2N2483 | | | | BCY65 | BFY27 | | | | 01 |
| 2N2484 | S | N | F, MO, TX, ME, NS | (BC414B) | BFX93A | 2N2483 | MM2484 | 2SC648 | 01 |
| 2N2484 | | | | BCY65EIX | BC107B | EN2484 | | | 01 |
| 2N2484 | | | | BCY66 | | | | | 01 |
| 2N2484R | S | N | TX, TI, CA, RY, CN | (BC414B) | | | | | 01 |
| 2N2486 | J | P | NS | | | 2N2497 | | | 03 |
| 2N2486A | J | P | NS | | | 2N2499 | | | |
| 2N2487 | G | P | SP, ID, SQ, FR, SM | | | 2N2966 | | | 13 |
| 2N2488 | G | P | SP, ID, SQ, FR, SM | | | 2N2966 | | | 13 |
| 2N2489 | G | P | SP, ID, SQ, FR, SM | | | 2N2966 | | | 13 |
| 2N2494 | G | P | PE | AF106 | AF190 | 2N2996 | 2N2495 | | 02 |
| 2N2494 | | | | AF102 | AF178 | | | | 02 |
| 2N2495 | G | P | PE | AF106 | AF178 | 2N2996 | | | 02 |
| 2N2496 | G | P | PE, AM | | | 2N2996 | | | 02 |
| 2N2497 | J | P | TX, TI, IL, SD | | | 2N5267 | 2N3329 | | 02 |
| 2N2498 | J | P | TX, TI, SD, IN | | | 2N3330 | | | |
| 2N2499 | J | P | TX, TI, IL, SD | | | 2N3909A | 2N3331 | | |
| 2N2500 | J | P | TX, SD, TI, IL | | | 2N5267 | 2N5268 | | |
| 2N2500 | | | | | | 2N3014 | | | |
| 2N2501 | S | N | MO, SM, TR, TI, HS | (BSY63) | | 2N3014 | | | 13 |
| 2N2509 | S | N | TI, F, IT, GI, RY | BFY77 | | 2N3014 | SE4001 | | 02 |
| 2N2510 | S | N | TI, F, IT, NS, GI | BFY77 | | 2N930 | 2N3565 | | 02 |
| 2N2511 | S | N | TI, F, IT, NS, GI | BFY77 | | 2N3444 | 2N2484 | | 02 |
| 2N2511 | | | | | | 2N2586 | SE4010 | | 02 |
| 2N2512 | G | P | AM | AF118 | | | | | 02 |
| 2N2520 | S | N | SD, SQ, SM | | | 2N929 | 2N930 | | 01 |
| 2N2521 | S | N | SD, SQ, SM | | | 2N929 | 2N930 | | 01 |
| 2N2522 | S | N | SD, SQ, SM | | | 2N929 | 2N930 | | 01 |
| 2N2523 | S | N | SD, SQ, SM | | | 2N929 | 2N930 | | 01 |
| 2N2524 | S | N | SD, SQ, SM | | | 2N930 | | | 01 |
| 2N2526 | G | P | MO | AU103 | AU105 | | | | 14 |
| 2N2527 | G | P | MO | AU103 | AU105 | | | | 14 |
| 2N2528 | G | P | MO | AU103 | AU105 | | | | 14 |
| 2N2535 | G | P | RC | | | 2N1038 | 2N2555 | | 01 |
| 2N2536 | G | P | RC | | | 2N1038 | 2N2565 | | 01 |
| 2N2537 | S | N | MO, RY, TX, ET, SM | BSY34 | BSX73 | 40635 | 2N3015 | | 13 |
| 2N2538 | A | N | MO, ET, TX, RY, CN | BSY34 | BSX73 | 2N1711 | 2N2219 | | 13 |
| 2N2538 | | | | | | 2N3015 | | | 13 |
| 2N2539 | S | N | MO, TX, ET, RY, HS | BSX49 | | 2N2222A | 2N3015 | | 13 |
| 2N2539 | | | | | | 2N2222 | | | 13 |
| 2N2540 | S | N | MO, ET, RY, TX, CN | BSX49 | | 2N2222A | 2N3015 | | 13 |
| 2N2540 | | | | | | 2N2222 | | | 13 |
| 2N2541 | G | P | RY, SQ, St, CN | | | 2N1038 | | | 10 |
| 2N2552 | G | P | TX, KS, CN, MO | | | 2N1038 | | | 06 |
| 2N2553 | G | P | TX, MO, KS, TT | | | 2N1038 | | | 06 |

| TYPE | M/S | POL | MANUFAC | EUROPEAN | | AMERICAN | | JAPANESE | USE |
|---|---|---|---|---|---|---|---|---|---|
| 2N2554 | G | P | TX, KS, TI, CN, MO | | | 2N1038 | | | 06 |
| 2N2555 | G | P | TX, MO, KS, TT | | | 2N1038 | | | 06 |
| 2N2556 | G | P | TX, KS, TT, CN, MO | | | 2N1038 | | | 06 |
| 2N2557 | G | P | TX, KS, TT, CN, MO | | | 2N1038 | | | 06 |
| 2N2558 | G | P | TX, KS, TT, CN, MO | | | 2N1038 | | | 06 |
| 2N2559 | G | P | TX, KS, TT, CN, MO | | | 2N1038 | | | 06 |
| 2N2560 | G | P | TX, KS, TT, CN, MO | | | 2N1038 | | | 06 |
| 2N2561 | G | P | TX, MO, CN, KS, TT | | | 2N1038 | | | 06 |
| 2N2562 | G | P | TX, KS, TT, CN, MO | | | 2N1038 | | | 06 |
| 2N2563 | G | P | TX, KS, TT, CN, MO | | | 2N1038 | | | 06 |
| 2N2564 | G | P | TX, KS, TT, CN, MO | | | 2N1038 | | | 06 |
| 2N2565 | G | P | TX, KS, TT, CN, MO | | | 2N1038 | | | 06 |
| 2N2566 | G | P | TX, KS, TT, CN, MO | | | 2N1038 | | | 06 |
| 2N2567 | G | P | TX, KS, TT, CN, MO | | | 2N1038 | | | 06 |
| 2N2569 | S | N | AM, PE, RA, V, MU | | | 2N2432 | | | 12 |
| 2N2570 | S | N | PH, AM, PE, RA, V | (BCY58VII) | BSY62 | 2N2432 | | | 12 |
| 2N2570 | | | | BSX20 | | | | | 12 |
| 2N2581 | S | N | DD, SD, SU, PT | | | 2N3847 | | | 16 |
| 2N2582 | S | N | DD, SD | | | 2N3847 | | | 16 |
| 2N2583 | S | N | DD, SD, SU, PT | | | 2N3847 | | | 16 |
| 2N2586 | S | N | F, TX, CS, IT, TI | (BC414B) | BFY77 | 2N2484 | SE4020 | | 01 |
| 2N2586 | | | | BCY66 | BC107A | | | | 01 |
| 2N2588 | G | P | TX | | | 2N1038 | 2N2188 | | 02 |
| 2N2590 | S | P | SD, SQ, SM | | | 2N2604 | 2N2605 | | 02 |
| 2N2591 | S | P | SD, SM, SQ, CN | | | 2N2604 | 2N2605 | | 02 |
| 2N2592 | S | P | SD, SM, SQ, CN | | | 2N2604 | 2N2605 | | 02 |
| 2N2593 | S | P | SD, SM, SQ, CN | | | 2N2604 | 2N2605 | | 02 |
| 2N2594 | S | N | CN, TR, TI, SQ | | | 2N5321 | | | 01 |
| 2N2595 | S | P | SD, SM, SQ, CN | | | 2N2604 | | | 02 |
| 2N2596 | S | P | SD, SM, SQ, CN | | | 2N2604 | 2N2605 | | 02 |
| 2N2597 | S | P | SD, SM, SQ, CN | | | 2N736 | | | 02 |
| 2N2598 | S | P | SD, SM, SQ, CN | | | 2N2604 | 2N2605 | | 02 |
| 2N2599 | S | P | SD, SM, SQ, CN | | | 2N2604 | 2N2605 | | 02 |
| 2N2599A | S | P | SD, SM, SQ, CN | | | 2N2604 | 2N2605 | | 02 |
| 2N2600 | S | P | SD, SM, SQ, CN | | | 2N2604 | 2N2605 | | 02 |
| 2N2600A | S | P | SD, SQ, SM | | | 2N2604 | 2N2605 | | 02 |
| 2N2601 | S | P | SD, SM, TI, CN, SQ | | | 2N2604 | 2N2605 | | 02 |
| 2N2602 | S | P | SD, SM, TI, CN, SQ | | | 2N2604 | 2N2605 | | 02 |
| 2N2603 | S | P | SD, SM, TI, CN, SQ | | | 2N2604 | 2N2605 | | 02 |
| 2N2604 | S | P | A, F, TX, SD, NS, MO | BCY77VII | BC177VI | 2N2605 | | | 02 |
| 2N2604 | | | | BCY79 | | | | | 02 |
| 2N2605 | S | P | A, F, TX, SD, TI, NS | (BC416B) | BFX37 | 2N3798 | 2N4248 | | 02 |
| 2N2605A | S | P | SD, SM, TD, TI, F | BC117A | BCY79X | 2N2605 | 2N4250A | | 02 |
| 2N2606 | J | P | SX, IL, TI, ES, TX | | | 2N5474 | SM5536 | | |
| 2N2606 | | | | | | 2N2843 | | | |
| 2N2607 | J | P | SX, SD, TI, IL, TX | | | 2N5475 | 2N5476 | | |
| 2N2607 | | | | | | SF9737 | | | |
| 2N2608 | J | P | SX, SD, TX, TI, IL | | | 2N3330 | 2N3329 | | |
| 2N2609 | J | P | SX, F, SD, IL, TI | | | 2N3330 | | | |
| 2N2610 | S | N | SM, SQ | | | 2N1149 | | | 01 |
| 2N2611 | S | N | SM, SQ | | | 2N3766 | | | 06 |
| 2N2612 | G | P | SD | | | 2N1559 | | | 06 |
| 2N2613 | G | P | NU, ES, NU | (AC162) | AC126 | 2N404 | 2N1193 | | 01 |
| 2N2613 | | | | AC160gn | | 2N2429 | | 2SC459 | 01 |
| 2N2614 | G | P | NU | (AC162) | AC163 | 2N404 | 2N1193 | | 01 |
| 2N2614 | | | | AC160gn | AC126 | | | | 01 |
| 2N2615 | S | N | CN, F, SQ, SM | BFY78 | | | | | 04 |
| 2N2616 | S | N | F, TI, LI, SQ, CN | (BFX89) | BFY28 | 2N917 | 2N918 | | 04 |
| 2N2616 | | | | | | 2N3563 | | | 04 |
| 2N2617 | S | P | PE | BCZ11 | | 2N2944 | 2N2945 | | 01 |
| 2N2632 | S | N | SD, GX, SM, TR, CN | | | 2N3487 | 2N3421 | | 06 |
| 2N2633 | S | N | SD, GX, SM, SQ, TR | | | 2N3488 | 2N3421 | | 06 |
| 2N2634 | S | N | SD, GX, SM, SQ, TR | | | 2N3489 | 2N3421 | | 06 |
| 2N2639 | S | N | TX, MO, RY, TR, TI | BFY81 | | | | | 05 |
| 2N2640 | S | N | TX, Ss, F, SD, GE | BFY81 | | | | | 05 |
| 2N2641 | S | N | TX, F, Ss, SD, NS | BFY81 | | 2N2639 | | | 05 |
| 2N2642 | S | N | TX, Ss, ML, NS, SD | BFY81 | | | | | 05 |
| 2N2643 | S | N | TX, Ss, ML, NS, SD | BFY81 | | 2N2641 | | | 05 |
| 2N2644 | S | N | TX, Ss, F, ML, NS | BFY81 | | 2N2643 | | | 05 |
| 2N2645 | S | N | F, RY, CR, SM, SG | BSX46-16 | BSX33 | 2N1711 | 2N2219 | | 05 |
| 2N2646 | U | PN | GE, MO, NU, SM, SS | | | TIS43 | | | |
| 2N2647 | U | PN | GE, MO, SB, TX, UP | | | 2N3980 | | | |
| 2N2648 | G | P | CN | | | 2N1377 | 2N1379 | | 10 |
| 2N2651 | S | N | CN, F, ET, SG, SQ | BSX39 | | 2N2501 | 2N3554 | | 13 |

| TYPE | M/S | POL | MANUFAC | EUROPEAN | | AMERICAN | | JAPANESE | USE |
|---|---|---|---|---|---|---|---|---|---|
| 2N2651 | | | | | | EN3014 | | | 13 |
| 2N2652 | S | N | GE, MO, SG, RY, TD | BFY83 | | 2N2060 | 2N2639 | | 05 |
| 2N2652A | S | N | GE, MO, RY, SG, TD | BFY83 | | 2N2060 | | | 05 |
| 2N2654 | G | P | PH, TX, AM, PE | (AF201U) | AF201 | 2N654 | | | 02 |
| 2N2654 | | | | AF121 | AF202 | | | | 02 |
| 2N2654 | | | | AF179 | | | | | 02 |
| 2N2655 | S | N | SM | | | 2N5681 | | | 06 |
| 2N2657 | S | N | SD, F, PI, SZ, UN | BFX34 | | 2N2151 | 2N4238 | | 16 |
| 2N2657 | | | | | | 2N5336 | | | 16 |
| 2N2658 | S | N | SD, NS, F, PI, SZ | BFX34 | BLY17 | 2N2151 | 2N4239 | | 16 |
| 2N2658 | | | | | | 2N5336 | | | 16 |
| 2N2659 | G | P | TX, KS | | | 2N1038 | | | 06 |
| 2N2660 | G | P | TX, KS | | | 2N1038 | | | 06 |
| 2N2661 | G | P | TX, KS | | | 2N1038 | | | 06 |
| 2N2662 | G | P | TX, KS | | | 2N1038 | | | 06 |
| 2N2663 | G | P | TX, KS | | | 2N1038 | | | 06 |
| 2N2664 | G | P | TX, KS | | | 2N1038 | | | 06 |
| 2N2665 | G | P | TX, KS | | | 2N1038 | | | 06 |
| 2N2666 | G | P | TX, KS | | | 2N1038 | | | 06 |
| 2N2667 | G | P | TX, KS | | | 2N1038 | | | 06 |
| 2N2668 | G | P | SS, TX, KS | | | 2N1038 | | | 06 |
| 2N2669 | G | P | TX, KS | | | 2N1038 | | | 06 |
| 2N2670 | G | P | TX, KS | | | 2N1038 | | | 06 |
| 2N2671 | G | P | AM | AF178 | | 2N2495 | | | 06 |
| 2N2672 | G | P | AM | AF185 | | | | | 06 |
| 2N2692 | S | N | TX, SM, TD, SQ | BCY59VII | BCY59 | | | | 13 |
| 2N2692 | | | | BCY70 | | | | | 13 |
| 2N2693 | S | N | TX, SM, TD, SQ | BCY59VII | BCY59 | | | | 13 |
| 2N2693 | | | | BCY70 | | | | | 13 |
| 2N2694 | S | N | TX, SM, SQ, TD | BCY59VII | BCY59 | | | | 13 |
| 2N2694 | | | | BC108A | | | | | 13 |
| 2N2695 | S | P | F, MO, TX, CS, TR | BC328-16 | BSX36 | 2N2907 | EN722 | | 10 |
| 2N2695 | | | | BCY78 | BC238 | | | | 10 |
| 2N2696 | S | P | F, MO, TX, SM, SQ | BC328-16 | BSX36 | 2N2906 | 2N2837 | | 10 |
| 2N2696 | | | | BCY78 | | 2N2907 | EN722 | | 10 |
| 2N2697 | S | N | SD, CN | | | 2N3998 | | | 16 |
| 2N2698 | S | N | SD, CN | | | 2N3998 | | | 16 |
| 2N2699 | G | P | PH | | | 2N964 | | | 13 |
| 2N2706 | S | P | PH, AM, PE | AC151VI | AC151 | 2N404 | 2N2431 | | 01 |
| 2N2706 | | | | AC131 | AC126 | | | | 01 |
| 2N2706 | | | | AC128 | AC132 | | | | 01 |
| 2N2706 | | | | AC152 | | | | | 01 |
| 2N2707 | G | P | AM, PE | AC153 | AC124 | 2N2704 | | | 01 |
| 2N2707 | | | | AC128 | | | | | 01 |
| 2N2708 | S | N | AM, TI, MO, ET, RY | | | 2N918 | | | 02 |
| 2N2709 | S | P | RY | | | 2N2800 | 2N2944 | | 01 |
| 2N2709 | | | | | | 2N2945 | | | 01 |
| 2N2710 | S | N | MO, F, SM, SG | (BSY63) | BSX27 | EN3014 | | | 13 |
| 2N2711 | S | N | GE, ID, SP, TT, FR | BC168A | BC238A | MPS2711 | TIS98 | 2SC458 | 01 |
| 2N2711 | | | | | | 2N5135 | 2N3691 | | 01 |
| 2N2712 | S | N | GE, ID, TT, FR, SP | BC168A | BC238A | MPS2712 | TI2712 | 2SC458 | 01 |
| 2N2712 | | | | | | 2N5135 | 2N3692 | | 01 |
| 2N2713 | S | N | GE, FR, SP, ML, TT | BC168A | BC238 | MPS2713 | TIS98 | 2SC458 | 01 |
| 2N2713 | | | | | | 2N5153 | 2N4275 | | 01 |
| 2N2714 | S | N | GE, FR, ML, TT, SP | BC168A | BSX38 | 2N708 | MPS2714 | 2SC458 | 01 |
| 2N2714 | | | | BC238A | | TIS98 | 2N5135 | | 01 |
| 2N2715 | S | N | ID, TT | BC168A | BC238A | MPS2715 | TIS98 | 2SC458 | 01 |
| 2N2716 | S | N | ID, TT | BC168A | BC238A | MPS2716 | | 2SC458 | 01 |
| 2N2717 | G | P | PE | ASZ21 | | 2N2635 | | | 13 |
| 2N2720 | S | N | SD, TI, MO, IL, SQ | | | 2N2060 | 2N2639 | | 05 |
| 2N2721 | S | N | SD, IL, SQ, TI, MO | | | 2N2060 | 2N2639 | | 05 |
| 2N2721 | | | | | | 2N2640 | | | 05 |
| 2N2722 | S | N | SD, TI, MC, TD, F | | | 2N2916 | 2N2639 | | 05 |
| 2N2726 | S | N | GE, SQ, TR, SZ, St | | | 2N3440 | | | 03 |
| 2N2729 | S | N | F, SM, TD, TI, LI | (BFX89) | BFX73 | 2N3563 | | | 02 |
| 2N2730 | G | P | NP, SD | | | MP506 | | | 16 |
| 2N2731 | G | P | NP, SD | | | MP505 | | | 16 |
| 2N2732 | G | P | SD, NP | | | MP504 | | | 16 |
| 2N2733 | G | P | SD | | | MP506 | | | 16 |
| 2N2734 | G | P | SD | | | MP505 | | | 16 |
| 2N2735 | G | P | SD | | | MP504 | | | 16 |
| 2N2736 | G | P | SD | | | MP506 | | | 16 |
| 2N2737 | G | P | SD | | | MP505 | | | 16 |
| 2N2738 | G | P | SD | | | MP504 | | | 16 |
| 2N2784 | S | N | SM, TR, SQ | | | 2N2369A | 2N3010 | | 13 |

| TYPE | M/S | POL | MANUFAC | EUROPEAN | | AMERICAN | | JAPANESE | USE |
|------|-----|-----|---------|----------|--|----------|--|----------|-----|
| 2N2786 | G | P | SM | AFY18 | AF139 | | | | 02 |
| 2N2787 | S | N | GI, SM, SQ, ET | | | 2N2218 | | | 13 |
| 2N2788 | S | N | GI, MO, SQ, ET, SM | | | 2N2218A | | | 13 |
| 2N2789 | S | N | GI, MO, SQ, ET, SM | | | 2N2219A | | | 13 |
| 2N2790 | S | S | GI, SQ, SM | | | 2N2218 | | | 13 |
| 2N2791 | S | N | GI, MO, SQ, ET, SM | | | 2N2221A | | | 13 |
| 2N2792 | S | N | GI, MO, SQ, ET, SM | | | 2N2222A | | | 13 |
| 2N2795 | G | P | SP, ID | | | 2N2635 | | | 13 |
| 2N2796 | G | P | SP, ID | | | 2N2635 | | | 13 |
| 2N2797 | G | P | SP | | | 2N2635 | | | 13 |
| 2N2798 | G | P | SP | | | 2N2635 | | | 13 |
| 2N2799 | G | P | SP | | | 2N2635 | | | 13 |
| 2N2800 | S | P | IT, TX, MO, F, RY | (BCW80-16) | BFY64 | 40406 | 2N1132 | | 13 |
| 2N2800 | | | | BC160VI | | 2N2904 | 2N2905 | | 13 |
| 2N2800 | | | | | | EN1132 | | | 13 |
| 2N2801 | S | P | IT, TX, MO, F, RY | (BCW80-16) | BFY64 | 40815 | 2N1132 | | 13 |
| 2N2801 | | | | BC160VI | | 2N3244 | 2N3644 | | 13 |
| 2N2802 | S | P | TX, MO, SD, TD, GI | | | 2N3350 | | | 05 |
| 2N2803 | S | P | TX, MO, SD, TD, GI | | | 2N3350 | | | 05 |
| 2N2804 | S | P | TX, MO, SD, TD, GI | | | 2N3350 | | | 06 |
| 2N2805 | S | P | TX, MO, SD, TD, DI | | | 2N3350 | | | 05 |
| 2N2806 | S | P | TS, MO, SD, TD, GI | | | 2N3350 | | | 05 |
| 2N2807 | S | P | TX, MO, SD, TD, GI | | | 2N3350 | | | 06 |
| 2N2811 | S | N | F, PI, UN, KE, PP | | | 2N3487 | 2N4301 | | 06 |
| 2N2812 | S | N | SD, E, PI, UN, KE | | | 2N3488 | 2N4301 | | 06 |
| 2N2813 | S | N | SD, F, PI, UN, KE | | | 2N3489 | 2N4301 | | 06 |
| 2N2814 | S | N | SD, F, PI, UN, KE | | | 2N3490 | 2N4301 | | 06 |
| 2N2815 | S | N | SZ, SU, ET, Ss, KE | | | 2N4002 | | | 16 |
| 2N2816 | S | N | SZ, SU, ET, Ss, KE | | | 2N3846 | | | 16 |
| 2N2817 | S | N | SZ, SU, ET, ML, SM | | | 2N3846 | | | 16 |
| 2N2818 | S | N | SZ, ET, SU, ML, SM | | | 2N3846 | | | 16 |
| 2N2819 | S | N | SZ, KE, PT, Sq, Ss | | | 2N3846 | | | 16 |
| 2N2820 | S | N | SZ, KE, PT, SU, SQ | | | 2N3846 | | | 16 |
| 2N2821 | S | N | SZ, KE, PT, SU, SQ | | | 2N3846 | | | 16 |
| 2N2822 | S | N | SZ, KE, PT, SU, SQ | | | 2N3846 | | | 16 |
| 2N2823 | S | N | SZ, KE, PT, SU, SQ | | | 2N3846 | | | 16 |
| 2N2824 | S | N | SZ, KE, PT, SU, SQ | | | 2N3846 | | | 16 |
| 2N2825 | S | N | SZ, KE, PT, SU, SQ | | | 2N3846 | | | 16 |
| 2N2832 | G | P | MO | | | 2N1907 | 2N1908 | | 16 |
| 2N2835 | G | P | PE | AD148 | AD139 | 2N1038 | 2N2654 | | 01 |
| 2N2835 | | | | AD149 | | 2N2836 | | | 01 |
| 2N2836 | G | P | PE | AD149 | AD148 | 2N3612 | | | 01 |
| 2N2837 | S | P | MO, TX, GI, RY, CN | (BCW76-16) | BSX36 | 2N2904 | 2N2905 | | 13 |
| 2N2837 | | | | | | EN722 | | | 13 |
| 2N2838 | S | P | MO, TX, GI, RY, GS | BCW76-16 | BSX36 | 2N2904 | 2N2905 | | 13 |
| 2N2838 | | | | | | EN722 | | | 13 |
| 2N2840 | U | PN | GE | | | 2N489 | 2N491A | | |
| 2N2841 | J | P | SX, TI, IL | | | 2N5471 | 2N5472 | | |
| 2N2842 | J | P | SX, SD, TI, IL | | | 2N5473 | SM5539 | | |
| 2N2843 | J | P | SX, SD, TI, IL | | | 2N5475 | SM8655 | | |
| 2N2843 | | | | | | 2N5020 | | | |
| 2N2844 | J | P | SX, SD, IL | | | MFE4008 | SM8656 | | |
| 2N2844 | | | | | | 2N5021 | | | |
| 2N2845 | S | N | F, MO, TX, ET, SM | (BSX49) | | 2N2539 | 2N2537 | | 10 |
| 2N2845 | | | | | | 2N3015 | | | 10 |
| 2N2846 | S | N | TX, SG, F, MO, SM | (BSY34) | BSX30 | 2N697 | 2N2537 | | 10 |
| 2N2846 | | | | | | 2N3015 | | | 10 |
| 2N2847 | S | N | F, MO, TX, SM, SQ | (BSX49) | | 2N2539 | 2N2537 | | 10 |
| 2N2847 | | | | | | 2N3015 | | | 10 |
| 2N2848 | S | N | TX, SG, F, MO, HS | BSY34 | BSX30 | 2N697 | 2N2538 | | 10 |
| 2N2848 | | | | | | 2N2537 | | | 10 |
| 2N2849 | S | N | UN, SM, TW, GS, SQ | | | 2N2537 | 2N3015 | | 10 |
| 2N2850 | S | N | UN, SM, TW, SQ, GS | | | 2N5337 | | | 13 |
| 2N2851 | S | N | UN, SM, TW, SQ, GS | | | 2N3421 | 2N5336 | | 13 |
| 2N2852 | S | N | UN, SM, TW, GS, SQ | | | 2N3421 | 2N5336 | | 13 |
| 2N2853 | S | N | UN, SM, TW, GS, SQ | | | 2N3419 | 2N5335 | | 13 |
| 2N2854 | S | N | UN, SM, TW, GS, SQ | | | 2N3418 | 2N5336 | | 13 |
| 2N2855 | S | N | UN, SM, TW, SQ, SQ | | | 2N5336 | | | 13 |
| 2N2856 | S | N | UN, SM, TW, GS, SQ | | | 2N3420 | 2N5336 | | 13 |
| 2N2857 | S | N | F, MO, RC, AM, FR | (BFY90) | BFX62 | 2N3418 | 2N5334 | | 13 |
| 2N2857 | | | | | | 2N918 | SE3005 | 2SC463 | 02 |
| 2N2858 | S | N | SZ, SM, SF, SU, TR | | | 2N5335 | | | 16 |
| 2N2859 | S | N | SZ, SM, SF, SU, TR | | | 2N5338 | | | 16 |
| 2N2860 | G | P | SY | | | 2N764 | | | 13 |
| 2N2863 | S | N | TX, SQ, TD, TR | BFY51 | | 2N5321 | | | 02 |
| 2N2864 | S | N | TX, SQ, TR, TD | BFY51 | | 2N3053 | | | 02 |

| TYPE | M/S | POL | MANUFAC | EUROPEAN | | AMERICAN | | JAPANESE | USE |
|------|-----|-----|---------|----------|--|----------|--|----------|-----|
| 2N2865 | S | N | ET, TX, CS, RY, TI | (BFX89) | BSY62 | | | 2SC321 | 02 |
| 2N2865 | | | | BSY70 | BF180 | | | | 02 |
| 2N2868 | S | N | IT, TX, F, CS, RY | BSX45-6 | BFY56 | 2N3053 | 2N4231 | | 13 |
| 2N2868 | | | | BSX45 | BSX22 | 2N2243A | 2N3052 | | 13 |
| 2N2868 | | | | | | 2N3252 | | | 13 |
| 2N2869 | G | P | RC, KS, SD, ET | AUY21IV | AD131III | MP2050 | 2N3614 | 2SB471 | 06 |
| 2N2869 | | | | AD138/50 | AD149 | | | | 06 |
| 2N2869 | | | | AD131 | | | | | 06 |
| 2N2870 | G | P | RC, KS, SD, ET | AUY22IV | AUY21II | MP2016 | 2N3617 | 2SB340 | 06 |
| 2N2870 | | | | AUY28 | ASZ18 | | | | 06 |
| 2N2870 | | | | | | | | | 06 |
| 2N2873 | G | P | RC | AUY22 | | 2N2997 | | | 02 |
| 2N2875 | S | P | TR, SQ | | | 2N3418 | | | 03 |
| 2N2876 | S | N | RC, KE, SD, FR, SM | | | 2N3632 | | | 02 |
| 2N2877 | S | N | SD, GS, PI, SZ, SM | | | 2N3998 | | | 03 |
| 2N2878 | S | N | SD, PI, GS, NS, PP | | | 2N3998 | | | 03 |
| 2N2879 | S | N | SD, PP, SZ, GS, PI | | | 2N3998 | | | 03 |
| 2N2880 | S | N | SD, PI, TX, GS, NS | | | 2N3998 | | | 03 |
| 2N2881 | S | P | SZ, CR, SM, TR, SQ | | | 2N3740 | 2N4235 | | 06 |
| 2N2881 | | | | | | 2N5333 | | | 06 |
| 2N2882 | S | P | SZ, SM, TR, CR, SQ | | | 2N3741 | 2N4236 | | 06 |
| 2N2882 | | | | | | 2N5333 | | | 06 |
| 2N2883 | S | N | SM, TD, SQ | BFW17 | | 2N3309 | 2N3553 | | 03 |
| 2N2884 | S | N | SM, TD, SQ | BFW17 | | 2N2309 | 2N3553 | | 03 |
| 2N2885 | S | N | TR | | | 2N849 | | | 13 |
| 2N2886 | S | N | TW | | | 2N696 | 2N697 | | 01 |
| 2N2890 | S | N | F, NS, UN, GS, SM | (BSX63-6) | BSX47XVI | 2N3421 | 2N3507 | | 06 |
| 2N2890 | | | | BSW66 | BDY12 | 2N5335 | | | 06 |
| 2N2891 | S | N | F, NS, UN, GS, SM | (BSX63-10) | BSX47X | 2N3421 | 2N3507 | | 16 |
| 2N2891 | | | | BD140 | BDY12 | 2N5335 | | | 16 |
| 2N2892 | S | N | F, UN, GS, SM, SQ | | | 2N3998 | | | 16 |
| 2N2894 | S | P | F, IT, MO, PE, TX | BSX29 | BCY78 | 2N3248 | 2N2894A | | 10 |
| 2N2894A | S | P | F, NS, TX, IT, PE | | | 2N2894A | | | 16 |
| 2N2895 | S | N | MO, RC, SM, TR, TI | (BSX47-6) | | | | | 10 |
| 2N2896 | S | N | MO, RC, TI, SM, TR | (BSX47-10) | | | | | 10 |
| 2N2897 | S | N | MO, RC, TI, SM, TR | (BSX45-10) | | | | | 10 |
| 2N2901 | S | N | | | | 3N74 | | | 12 |
| 2N2903 | S | N | TI, MO, RY, FR, F | BFY81 | | 2N2917 | 2N2639 | | 05 |
| 2N2903 | | | | | | 2N2640 | | | 05 |
| 2N2903A | S | N | TI, MO, RY, F, FR | BFY81 | | 2N2915 | 2N2639 | | 05 |
| 2N2904 | S | P | TX, MO, EM, F, V | BSW23 | BCW80/10 | 2N4036 | 2N2905 | | 13 |
| 2N2904 | | | | | | 2N2905 | | | 13 |
| 2N2904A | S | P | MO, EM, F, NS, SP | BFY64 | BC161X | 2N2905 | 2N3645 | | 13 |
| 2N2904A | | | | BCW80/10 | | | | | 13 |
| 2N2905 | S | P | F, MO, TX, V, EM | BCW80-16 | BFY64 | 2N2905 | | | 13 |
| 2N2905 | | | | BCW80XVI | | | | | 13 |
| 2N2905A | S | P | F, MO, TX, EM, V | (BCW80-16) | BFY64 | 2N2905 | 2N3645 | | 13 |
| 2N2905A | | | | BC161V | BCW80XVI | | | | 13 |
| 2N2906 | S | P | F, MO, TX, CS, BT | BCW76-10 | BSW24 | 2N2907 | EN2927 | | 13 |
| 2N2906 | | | | BCW76X | | | | | 13 |
| 2N2906A | S | P | F, MO, TX, EM, TR | (BCW76-10) | BSX36 | 2N2907 | 2N3645 | | 13 |
| 2N2906A | | | | BC161X | BCW76X | | | | 13 |
| 2N2907 | S | P | F, MO, TX, MU, SD | (BCW76-16) | BSX36 | 2N2907 | | | 13 |
| 2N2907 | | | | BCW76XVI | BC231 | | | | 13 |
| 2N2907A | S | P | MO, EM, F, IN, MU | BSX38 | BC161X | 2N2907 | 2N3649 | | 13 |
| 2N2907A | | | | BCW76XVI | BCW85 | | | | 13 |
| 2N2908 | S | N | | | | 2N5069 | | | 06 |
| 2N2909 | S | N | SM, SQ | | | 2N2193A | 2N2243A | | 13 |
| 2N2910 | S | N | GE, TR, FR, SM, SQ | | | 2N3409 | 2N2639 | | 05 |
| 2N2911 | S | N | SZ, SF, PI, SQ, UP | | | 2N3766 | 2N3421 | | 16 |
| 2N2913 | S | N | F, GE, MO, SD, TI | BFY81 | | 2N2643 | | | 05 |
| 2N2914 | S | N | F, MO, TX, TI, ME | BFY81 | | 2N2643 | | | 05 |
| 2N2915 | S | N | F, GE, MO, RY, SD | BFW39 | | 2N2920 | | | 05 |
| 2N2915A | S | N | F, TX, TI, FR, NS | BFY81 | | 2N2920 | | | 01 |
| 2N2916 | S | N | F, MO, SD, RY, TI | BFW40 | | 2N2920 | | | 05 |
| 2N2916A | S | N | F, TX, TI, RY, FR | BFY81 | | 2N2920 | | | 01 |
| 2N2917 | S | N | F, NS, RY, SD, TX | BFY 81 | | 2N2977 | | | 05 |
| 2N2918 | S | N | F, MO, SD, GE, RY | BFY81 | | 2N2977 | | | 05 |
| 2N2919 | S | N | F, GE, MO, ME, NS | BFY81 | | 2N2920 | | | 05 |
| 2N2919A | S | N | F, TX, TI, ES, NS | BFY81 | BFW39A | 2N2920 | | | 01 |
| 2N2920 | S | N | F, ME, NS, RY, SD | BFY81 | | 2N2920 | | | 05 |
| 2N2920A | S | N | F, CN, TI, TX, IL | BFW40A | | | | | 01 |
| 2N2921 | S | N | SE, Ss, NU, UP, ML | BC167A | BC237 | MPS6565 | TIS98 | | 01 |
| 2N2921 | | | | BC182 | BC207 | | | | 01 |
| 2N2921 | | | | BC168A | BC298 | | | | 01 |

| TYPE | M/S | POL | MANUFAC | EUROPEAN | | AMERICAN | | JAPANESE | USE |
|------|-----|-----|---------|----------|--|----------|--|----------|-----|
| 2N2921 | S | N | SE, Ss, NU, ML | BC107B | | | | | 01 |
| 2N2922 | | | | BC167A | BC238 | MPS6512 | TIS98 | | 01 |
| 2N2922 | | | | BC183 | BC209 | | | | 01 |
| 2N2922 | | | | BC168A | BC172 | | | | 01 |
| 2N2923 | S | N | GE, NU, SP, TT, ID | BC167A | BC168A | MPS2923 | TIS98 | | 01 |
| 2N2923 | | | | BC183A | BC172 | 2N5153 | | | 01 |
| 2N2923 | | | | BC183 | BC238 | | | | 01 |
| 2N2924 | S | N | GE, NU, SP, Ss, ID | BC167B | BC168A | MPS2924 | TIS98 | | 01 |
| 2N2924 | | | | BC172 | BC183 | 2N5153 | 2N3566 | | 01 |
| 2N2924 | | | | BC238C | | | | | 01 |
| 2N2925 | S | N | GE, SP, NU, ES, FR | BC167B | BC168B | MPS2925 | TIS98 | | 01 |
| 2N2925 | | | | BC172 | BC183 | 2N5153 | | | 01 |
| 2N2926 | S | N | GE, Ss, SP, ID, TT | BC167A | BC109 | MPS2926 | TIS98 | | 01 |
| 2N2926br | S | N | GE | BC167A | BC168A | | | | |
| 2N2926gn | S | N | GE | BC167B | BC168B | | | | |
| 2N2926or | S | N | GE | BC167A | BC168A | | | | |
| 2N2926r | S | N | GE | BC167A | BC168A | | | | |
| 2N2926ye | S | N | GE | BC167B | BC168A | | | | |
| 2N2927 | S | P | MO, F, SG, TR, ET | (BCW79-16) | BFY64 | 2N3638 | | | 01 |
| 2N2929 | G | P | MO | | | 2N1141 | | | 02 |
| 2N2930 | G | P | ET | | | 2N3427 | | | 01 |
| 2N2937 | S | N | IL, RY | | | 2N2639 | | | 01 |
| 2N2940 | S | N | ET, TR, SQ | BC160 | BCY12 | 2N1132 | MPS2940 | | 03 |
| 2N2942 | G | P | SP | | | 2N2635 | | | 13 |
| 2N2943 | G | P | SP | | | 2N2635 | | | 13 |
| 2N2944 | S | P | CR, MO, TR, RY, SP | BC178Vl | | 2N2945 | | | 12 |
| 2N2944A | S | P | TX, CR, TR, RY, TD | | | 2N2945 | | | 12 |
| 2N2945 | S | P | CR, MO, TR, RY, SP | BC178Vl | | | | | 12 |
| 2N2946 | S | P | CR, MO, TR, RY, SP | | | 2N3964 | | | 12 |
| 2N2947 | S | N | MO, SM, SQ, KE | (BU310) | | | | | 06 |
| 2N2948 | S | N | MO, SM, SQ, KE | (BU310) | | | | | 06 |
| 2N2951 | S | N | MO, TX, ET, HS, SM | (BSY34) | | 41502 | | | 06 |
| 2N2952 | S | N | TX, MO, ET, SM, SQ | (BSX49) | | | | | 06 |
| 2N2953 | G | P | RC | AC153 | AC171R | 2N1194 | 2N2431 | | 01 |
| 2N2953 | | | | AC128 | | | | | 01 |
| 2N2954 | S | N | | | | 2N918 | | | 13 |
| 2N2955 | G | P | MO, SQ | | | 2N2635 | | | 13 |
| 2N2956 | G | P | MO, SQ | ASY48 | | 2N2635 | | | 13 |
| 2N2957 | G | P | MO, SQ | | | 2N2635 | | | 13 |
| 2N2958 | S | N | MO, TX, SP, FR, HS | (BSY34) | | 2N687 | 2N2217 | | 13 |
| 2N2958 | | | | | | 2N2219 | 2N3641 | | 13 |
| 2N2959 | S | N | MO, TX, SP, ET, F | (BSY34) | | 2N1711 | 2N697 | | 13 |
| 2N2959 | | | | | | EN1711 | | | 13 |
| 2N2966 | G | P | | | | 2N3283 | 2N2997 | | 02 |
| 2N2968 | S | P | SP, ID, SQ, FR, SM | | | 2N2944 | 2N2945 | | 10 |
| 2N2969 | S | P | SP, ID, SQ, FR, SM | | | 2N2944 | 2N2945 | | 10 |
| 2N2970 | S | P | SP, ID, SQ, FR, SM | | | 2N2944 | 2N2945 | | 10 |
| 2N2971 | S | P | SP, SM, SQ, ID | | | 2N2944 | 2N2945 | | 10 |
| 2N2972 | S | N | F, MO, RY, TX, TI | BFY61 | | 2N2977 | | | 05 |
| 2N2973 | S | N | F, MO, RY, TX, TI | BFY81 | | 2N2977 | | | 05 |
| 2N2974 | S | N | F, MO, RY, TX, TI | BFW51 | | 2N2973 | | | 05 |
| 2N2975 | S | N | F, MO, RY, TX, TI | BFW52 | | 2N2977 | | | 05 |
| 2N2976 | S | N | F, MO, RY, TX, TI | BFY81 | | 2N2977 | | | 05 |
| 2N2977 | S | N | F, MO, RY, TX, TI | BFY81 | | | | | 05 |
| 2N2978 | S | N | F, ME, MO, RY, TX | BFY81 | | 2N2979 | | | 05 |
| 2N2979 | S | N | F, ME, MO, RY, TX | BFY81 | | | | | 05 |
| 2N2980 | S | N | F, ME, SG, TI, GI | BFY83 | | 2N2060A | | | 05 |
| 2N2981 | S | N | F, ME, SM, SQ, GI | BFY83 | | 2N2223 | | | 05 |
| 2N2982 | S | N | F, ME, SM, SQ, GI | BFY83 | | 2N2223A | | | 05 |
| 2N2983 | S | N | GS, TR, KE, SQ | | | 2N5335 | | | 06 |
| 2N2984 | S | N | GS, SM, TR, KE, SQ | | | 2N5682 | | | 06 |
| 2N2985 | S | N | GS, SM, TR, KE, SQ | | | 2N5638 | | | 06 |
| 2N2986 | S | N | GS, SM, TR, KE, SQ | | | 2N5682 | | | 06 |
| 2N2987 | S | N | TX, PP, SD, TR, UN | BSX47-6 | | 2N5335 | | | 06 |
| 2N2988 | S | N | TX, PP, SQ, UN, GS | | | 2N5681 | | | 06 |
| 2N2989 | S | N | TX, PP, SD, TR, GS | BSX47-6 | | 2N5681 | | | 06 |
| 2N2990 | S | N | TX, PP, SQ, UN, GS | | | 2N5681 | | | 06 |
| 2N2991 | S | N | TX, SQ, UN, SM, TR | (BSX47-6) | | | | | 06 |
| 2N2993 | S | N | TX, SQ, UN, SM, TR | (BSX47-6) | | | | | 06 |
| 2N2996 | G | P | TX, MO | | | 2N3283 | | | 02 |
| 2N2997 | G | P | TX, MO | | | 2N3279 | | | 02 |
| 2N2998 | G | P | MO, TX | | | 2N3284 | | | 02 |
| 2N2999 | G | P | TX | | | 2N3283 | | | 02 |
| 2N3009 | S | N | F, MO, TX, CN, SM | BSY63 | BSX39 | 2N3511 | EN3009 | 2SC32 | 13 |
| 2N3009 | | | | BSY18 | BSY21 | | | | 13 |

| TYPE | M/S | POL | MANUF.AC | EUROPEAN | | AMERICAN | | JAPANESE | USE |
|------|-----|-----|----------|----------|------|----------|------|----------|-----|
| 2N3009 | | | | BSX20 | | | | | 13 |
| 2N3010 | S | N | F, MO, RY, TX, SG | BSX27 | BSY18 | 2N2369A | | | 13 |
| 2N3010 | | | | BSY21 | BSX19 | | | | 13 |
| 2N3011 | S | N | F, MO, TX, ET, RY | (BSY62) | BSX28 | 2N2369 | EN3011 | | 13 |
| 2N3011 | | | | BSY63 | BSY19 | | | | 13 |
| | | | | | | | | | |
| 2N3011 | | | | BSX20 | BSY628 | | | | 13 |
| 2N3011 | | | | BSS12 | | | | | 13 |
| 2N3012 | S | P | F, MO, RY, TX, IT | BSX29 | BC178V1 | 2N4313 | | | |
| 2N3013 | S | N | F, IT, MO, NS, SG | BSX26 | BSX48 | 2N3511 | EN3013 | | 13 |
| 2N3013 | | | | BSX20 | BSX19 | | | | 13 |
| | | | | | | | | | |
| 2N3013 | | | | BSY21 | BSY63 | | | | 13 |
| 2N3014 | S | N | F, MO, TX, IT, UP | (BSY63) | BSX26 | 2N3511 | EN3014 | | 13 |
| 2N3014 | | | | BSX48 | BSX20 | | | | 13 |
| 2N3015 | S | N | F, MO, TX, ET, ID | BSX30 | BSY34 | 2N2218 | 2N2537 | | 13 |
| 2N3016 | S | N | SD, PP, SQ, CN, SM | | | 2N5337 | | | 03 |
| | | | | | | | | | |
| 2N3019 | S | N | F, MO, TX, RY, ET | BSX47-10 | BFY56 | 2N2243A | SE6021 | | 02 |
| 2N3020 | S | N | MO, SG, F, TX, RY | BSX47-6 | BFY56 | 2N1893 | 2N1893 | | 02 |
| 2N3020 | | | | | | 2N2243A | SE6023 | | 02 |
| 2N3021 | S | P | MO, SD, SS, TR, SM | (BDX27-6) | | 2N4901 | 2N5384 | | 14 |
| 2N3022 | S | P | MO, TX, SD, SS, TR | (BDX27-6) | | 2N5384 | | | 14 |
| | | | | | | | | | |
| 2N3023 | S | P | MO, SD, SS, TR, SM | (BDX28-6) | | 2N4902 | 2N5384 | | 14 |
| 2N3024 | S | P | MO, TX, SD, TR, MU | BDX27-10 | | 2N4904 | 2N5384 | | 14 |
| 2N3025 | S | P | MO, TX, SD, SS, TR | (BDX27-10) | | 2N5384 | | | 14 |
| 2N3026 | S | P | MO, TX, SM, SQ, TR | (BDX28-10) | | 2N4905 | 2N5384 | | 14 |
| 2N3033 | S | N | SM | BF177 | | | | | 04 |
| | | | | | | | | | |
| 2N3034 | S | N | SM | BF177 | | | | | 04 |
| 2N3035 | S | N | SM | BC107A | | | | | 04 |
| 2N3036 | S | N | TX, RY, SQ, TR, CA | BSX47-10 | BFY45 | 2N3019 | 2N5320 | | 01 |
| 2N3036 | | | | BFY80 | BSX21 | | | | 01 |
| 2N3037 | S | N | TX | | | 2N1893 | | | 01 |
| | | | | | | | | | |
| 2N3038 | S | N | TX | | | 2N1893 | | | 01 |
| 2N3043 | S | N | TX, F, MO, SG, RY | | | 2N2916 | | | 05 |
| 2N3044 | S | N | TX, MO, F, RY, SG | | | 2N2918 | | | 01 |
| 2N3045 | S | N | TX, MO, SG, F, RY | | | 2N2914 | | | 01 |
| 2N3046 | S | N | TX, MO, SG, F, RY | | | 2N2915 | | | 05 |
| | | | | | | | | | |
| 2N3047 | S | N | F, TX, MO, SG, RY | | | 2N2917 | | | 05 |
| 2N3048 | S | N | TX, MO, SG, RY, F | | | 2N2913 | | | 01 |
| 2N3053 | S | N | F, MO, RC, TX, ET | BSX45-16 | BSX45 | 2N2243A | 2N3498 | | 13 |
| 2N3054 | S | N | F, RC, RA, W, Ss | BD131 | BUY46 | | | | 06 |
| 2N3054 | | | | BDY13 | | | | | 06 |
| | | | | | | | | | |
| 2N3054A | S | N | MO | | | 2N3054 | | | 06 |
| 2N3054S | S | N | S | | | 2N3054 | | | |
| 2N3055 | S | N | F, RC, ET, RA, SR | BDY20 | BDY39 | 2N3713 | | | |
| 2N3055 | | | | BDX10 | | | | | |
| 2N3055U | S | N | AT | | | 2N4347 | | | |
| | | | | | | | | | |
| 2N3055V | S | N | AT | | | (2N3055) | | | |
| 2N3056 | S | N | F, TX, RY, CA, IT | BSX46-6 | BSX33 | 2N2243 | 2N2243A | | 02 |
| 2N3056 | | | | | | EN870 | | | 02 |
| 2N3056A | S | N | F, TX, RY, SM, TD | BSX47-6 | BSX33 | 2N2243A | EN870 | | 02 |
| 2N3057 | S | N | F, TX, RY, CA, IT | BSX46-16 | BSX33 | 2N2243 | 2N2243A | | 02 |
| | | | | | | | | | |
| 2N3057 | | | | | | 2N4946 | | | 02 |
| 2N3057A | S | N | F, TX, RY, SM, TD | BSX47-10 | BSX33 | 2N2243A | SE6023 | | 02 |
| 2N3058 | S | P | RY, CR, SP, FR, ID | | | 2N2944 | 2N2945 | | 01 |
| 2N3059 | S | P | CR, FR, RY, SP, ID | | | 2N2944 | 2N2945 | | 01 |
| 2N3060 | S | P | CR, RY, SP, TD, SD | BSV16 | BCY11 | 2N2944 | 2N2945 | | 01 |
| | | | | | | | | | |
| 2N3061 | S | P | CR, SP, RY, FR, TD | | | 2N2944 | 2N2945 | | 01 |
| 2N3062 | S | P | CR, SQ, TR, RY, TD | | | 2N2944 | 2N2945 | | 01 |
| 2N3063 | S | P | CR, SQ, TR, RY, TD | | | 2N2944 | 2N2945 | | 01 |
| 2N3064 | S | P | CR, SQ, TR, RY, TD | | | 2N2944 | 2N2945 | | 01 |
| 2N3065 | S | P | CR, SQ, TR, RY, TD | | | 2N2944 | 2N2945 | | 01 |
| | | | | | | | | | |
| 2N3066 | J | N | BT, NU, IL, SX, ES | | | 2N3365 | 2N3437 | | |
| 2N3067 | J | N | TI, IL, SX, NU, BT | | | 2N3366 | 2N3438 | | |
| 2N3068 | J | N | TI, NU, SD, IL, SX | | | 2N3367 | 2N3454 | | |
| 2N3068A | J | N | | | | 2N3367 | | | |
| 2N3069 | S | N | TI, SX, NS, SD, TX | | | 2N3822 | 2N3458 | | |
| | | | | | | | | | |
| 2N3069 | | | | | | TN4341 | | | |
| 2N3070 | J | N | TI, SX, NS, SD, IL | | | 2N3821 | 2N3459 | | |
| 2N3070 | | | | | | TN4340 | | | |
| 2N3071 | J | N | TI, SX, SD, IL, TX | | | 2N3438 | 2N3460 | | |
| 2N3071 | | | | | | TN4339 | | | |
| | | | | | | | | | |
| 2N3072 | S | P | F, MO, CA, RY, ET | (BCW80-16) | BFY64 | 2N2904 | 2N2905 | | 10 |
| 2N3072 | | | | | | 2N3645 | | | 10 |
| 2N3073 | S | P | F, MO, IT, CA, RY | (BCW76-16) | BFY64 | 2N2906 | 2N2907 | | 10 |
| 2N3073 | | | | | | 2N3645 | | | 10 |
| 2N3074 | G | P | PE | AF106 | AF109 | | | 2SA230 | 02 |

| TYPE | M/S | POL | MANUFAC | EUROPEAN | | AMERICAN | | JAPANESE | USE |
|---|---|---|---|---|---|---|---|---|---|
| 2N3074 | | | | AF180 | | | | | 02 |
| 2N3075 | G | P | PH, PE | (AF200U) | AF200 | | | 2SA280 | 02 |
| 2N3075 | | | | AF181 | AF121 | | | | 02 |
| 2N3077 | S | N | PE, SQ, TR, SM | | | 2N2484 | | | 01 |
| 2N3079 | S | N | DD, SU | | | 2N3846 | | | 16 |
| | | | | | | | | | |
| 2N3080 | S | N | DD, SU | | | 2N3847 | | | 16 |
| 2N3082 | S | N | | | | 3N76 | 3N73 | | 12 |
| 2N3083 | S | N | GE | | | 3N74 | 3N79 | | 12 |
| 2N3084 | J | N | CR, IL, BT | | | 2N3821 | 2N3459 | | |
| 2N3084 | | | | | | TN4339 | | | |
| | | | | | | | | | |
| 2N3085 | J | N | CR, IL, BT | | | 2N3821 | 2N3459 | | |
| 2N3085 | | | | | | TN4339 | | | |
| 2N3086 | J | N | CR, IL, BT | | | 2N3821 | 2N3459 | | |
| 2N3086 | | | | | | 2N3070 | | | |
| 2N3087 | J | N | CR, IL, BT | | | 2N3821 | 2N3459 | | |
| | | | | | | | | | |
| 2N3087 | | | | | | 2N3070 | | | |
| 2N3088 | J | N | CR, IL, BT | | | 2N3821 | 2N3460 | | |
| 2N3088 | | | | | | 2N3070 | | | |
| 2N3088A | J | N | CR, IL, BT | | | 2N3821 | 2N3460 | | |
| 2N3088A | | | | | | 2N3070 | | | |
| | | | | | | | | | |
| 2N3089 | J | N | CR, IL, SX, BT | | | 2N3365 | 2N3460 | | |
| 2N3089 | | | | | | 2N3070 | | | |
| 2N3089A | J | N | CR, IL, SX, BT | | | 2N3365 | 2N3460 | | |
| 2N3089A | | | | | | 2N3040 | | | |
| 2N3107 | S | N | F, IN, TX, RY, CA | BSX46-16 | | 2N2243 | 2N2243A | | 10 |
| | | | | | | | | | |
| 2N3107 | | | | | | SE6020 | | | 10 |
| 2N3108 | S | N | SG, F, IN, TX, MU | BSX46-6 | BFW24 | 2N2102 | 2N1613 | | 10 |
| 2N3108 | | | | BSX46XVI | BSY46 | 2N3568 | | | 10 |
| 2N3108 | | | | BFY44 | BSX45 | | | | 10 |
| 2N3109 | S | N | SG, F, IN, TX, RY | BSX45-16 | BFW25 | 2N1711 | 2N697 | | 10 |
| | | | | | | | | | |
| 2N3109 | | | | | | SE6021 | | | 10 |
| 2N3110 | S | N | SG, F, IN, TX, IT | BSX45-6 | BFY56 | 2N3053 | 2N2218A | | 10 |
| 2N3110 | | | | BFW26 | BSX45VI | 2N2243A | SE6021 | | 10 |
| 2N3110 | | | | BFY44 | BFX45 | | | | 10 |
| 2N3112 | J | P | SX, ES | | | 2N5471 | 2N5473 | | |
| | | | | | | | | | |
| 2N3112 | | | | | | 2N2841 | | | |
| 2N3113 | J | P | SX | | | 2N5471 | 2N5473 | | |
| 2N3114 | S | N | MO, F, TX, SQ, TR | BF257 | (BF457) | 2N3500 | 2N5183 | | 02 |
| 2N3114 | | | | BFY57 | BD115 | | | | 02 |
| 2N3115 | S | N | MO, TX, CA, RY, SQ | (BSX49) | | 2N2221 | 2N2222 | | 13 |
| | | | | | | | | | |
| 2N3115 | | | | | | 2N4436 | | | 13 |
| 2N3116 | S | N | MO, TX, ET, HS, SM | (BSX49) | | 2N2221 | 2N2222 | | 16 |
| 2N3116 | | | | | | 2N4437 | | | 16 |
| 2N3117 | S | N | F, TX, SD, TI, TR | (BC414C) | BFY77 | 2N2484 | SE4020 | | 01 |
| 2N3117 | | | | BSY63 | BSY19 | | | | 01 |
| | | | | | | | | | |
| 2N3117 | | | | BSX20 | BSY21 | | | | 01 |
| 2N3120 | S | P | F, MO, CA, IT, RY | (BSW80-16) | BFY64 | 2N2800 | EN1132 | | 10 |
| 2N3121 | S | P | F, MO, CA, RY, SG | (BCW76-16) | BSX36 | 2N2837 | 2N2906 | | 10 |
| 2N3121 | | | | | | 2N2907 | EN722 | | 10 |
| 2N3122 | S | N | RY, SQ, CA | | | 2N5321 | | | 01 |
| | | | | | | | | | |
| 2N3125 | G | P | KS | | | 2N456A | 2N3146 | | 06 |
| 2N3126 | G | P | KS | | | 2N456A | 2N3146 | | 06 |
| 2N3132 | G | P | IT | ADY26 | | 2N1100 | T13031 | | 16 |
| 2N3133 | S | P | MO, TX, GI, NS, PH | BCW80-10 | BSY15VI | 40634 | 2N2904 | | 13 |
| 2N3133 | | | | | | 2N2905 | EN1122 | | 13 |
| | | | | | | | | | |
| 2N3134 | S | P | MO, TX, GI, NS, PH | (BCW80-16) | BFY64 | 2N4037 | 2N2905 | | 13 |
| 2N3134 | | | | | | 2N3644 | | | 13 |
| 2N3135 | S | P | MO, TX, GI, NS, ET | (BCW76-10) | BSX36 | EN722 | | | 13 |
| 2N3136 | S | P | MO, TX, NS, ET, GI | (BCW76-16) | | | | | 13 |
| 2N3137 | S | N | F, NU, MO, FR, TI | BSY58 | | 2N2218 | 2N3014 | | 02 |
| | | | | | | | | | |
| 2N3137 | | | | | | 2N3564 | | | 02 |
| 2N3138 | S | N | SM, TR, UT, SQ, TW | | | 2N3766 | | | 03 |
| 2N3146 | G | P | TX | | | 2N3616 | 2N456A | | 06 |
| 2N3147 | G | P | TX | | | 2N3616 | 2N456A | | 06 |
| 2N3153 | S | N | CR | | | 2N2432 | | | 12 |
| | | | | | | | | | |
| 2N3162 | S | N | | | | 2N3411 | | | 05 |
| 2N3167 | S | P | SZ, SQ, SM | | | MJ2267 | | | 03 |
| 2N3168 | S | P | SZ, SQ, SM | | | 2N3789 | | | 03 |
| 2N3169 | S | P | SZ, SQ, SM | | | 2N3790 | | | 03 |
| 2N3170 | S | P | SZ, SQ, SM | | | 2N3790 | | | 03 |
| | | | | | | | | | |
| 2N3171 | S | P | SZ, SM, SQ, MO, SD | | | 2N3789 | 2N6254 | | 03 |
| 2N3171 | | | | | | MJ2264 | 2N6246 | | 03 |
| 2N3171 | | | | | | 2N4901 | | | 03 |
| 2N3172 | S | P | SZ, SM, SQ, MO, SD | | | 2N3789 | 2N6246 | | 03 |
| 2N3172 | | | | | | 2N4902 | | | 03 |

| TYPE | M/S | POL | MANUFAC | EUROPEAN | AMERICAN | | JAPANESE | USE |
|------|-----|-----|---------|----------|----------|---|----------|-----|
| 2N3173 | S | P | SZ, SM, SQ, MO, SD | | 2N3790 | 2N6247 | | U3 |
| 2N3173 | | | | | 2N4903 | | | 03 |
| 2N3174 | S | P | SZ, SD, SQ, SM | | 2N3790 | 2N6248 | | 03 |
| 2N3175 | S | P | SZ, SM, SQ, PP | | MJ2267 | 2N5003 | | 03 |
| 2N3176 | S | P | SZ, SM, SQ, PP | | 2N3789 | | | 03 |
| 2N3177 | S | P | SZ, SM, SQ, PP | | 2N3790 | | | 03 |
| 2N3178 | S | P | SZ, SM, SQ, PP | | 2N3790 | | | 03 |
| 2N3179 | S | P | SZ, SQ, SM | | MJ2267 | | | 03 |
| 2N3180 | S | P | SZ, SQ, SM | | 2N3789 | | | 03 |
| 2N3181 | S | P | SQ, SZ, SM | | 2N3790 | | | 03 |
| 2N3182 | S | P | SZ, SQ, SM | | 2N3790 | | | 03 |
| 2N3183 | S | P | SZ, SM, SQ, MO, SD | | 2N3789 | 2N6246 | | 03 |
| 2N3183 | | | | | 2N4904 | | | 03 |
| 2N3184 | S | P | SZ, SM, SQ, MO, SD | | 2N3789 | 2N6246 | | 03 |
| 2N3184 | | | | | 2N4905 | | | 03 |
| 2N3185 | S | P | SZ, SM, SQ, MO, SD | | 2N3790 | 2N6247 | | 03 |
| 2N3185 | | | | | 2N4906 | | | 03 |
| 2N3186 | S | P | SZ, SD, SQ, SM | | 2N3790 | 2N6248 | | 03 |
| 2N3187 | S | P | SZ, SQ, SM | | MJ2267 | | | 03 |
| 2N3188 | S | P | SZ, SQ, SM | | 2N3789 | | | 03 |
| 2N3189 | S | P | SZ, SQ, SM | | 2N3790 | | | 03 |
| 2N3190 | S | P | SZ, SQ, SM | | 2N3790 | | | 03 |
| 2N3192 | S | P | SZ, SQ, SM | | 2N3789 | | | 03 |
| 2N3193 | S | P | SZ, SQ, SM | | 2N3790 | | | 03 |
| 2N3194 | S | P | SZ, SM, SQ | | 2N3790 | | | 03 |
| 2N3195 | S | P | SZ, SD, SQ, SM | | 2N3789 | 2N6346 | | 03 |
| 2N3195 | | | | | 2N4904 | | | 03 |
| 2N3196 | S | P | SZ, SD, SQ, SM | | 2N3789 | 2N6246 | | 03 |
| 2N3196 | | | | | 2N4905 | | | 03 |
| 2N3197 | S | P | SZ, SD, SQ, SM | | 2N3790 | 2N6247 | | 03 |
| 2N3197 | | | | | 2N4906 | | | 03 |
| 2N3198 | S | P | SZ, SD, SQ, SM | | 2N3790 | 2N6248 | | 03 |
| 2N3200 | S | P | SZ, SQ, CR | | 2N3740 | | | 03 |
| 2N3201 | S | P | SZ, SQ, CR | | 2N3741 | | | 03 |
| 2N3202 | S | P | SZ, SD, TR, CR, SQ | | 2N5333 | 2N5783 | | 03 |
| 2N3202 | | | | | 2N4234 | | | 03 |
| 2N3203 | S | P | SZ, SM, SQ, TR, CR | | 2N3740 | 2N5333 | | 03 |
| 2N3203 | | | | | 2N5781 | 2N4235 | | 03 |
| 2N3204 | S | P | SZ, SM, SQ, TR, CR | | 2N3741 | 2N5333 | | 03 |
| 2N3204 | | | | | 2N4236 | | | 03 |
| 2N3205 | S | P | SZ, SM, SQ, CR | | 2N5333 | | | 03 |
| 2N3206 | S | P | SZ, SM, SQ, CR | | 2N3740 | 2N5333 | | 03 |
| 2N3207 | S | P | SZ, SM, SQ, CR | | 2N3741 | 2N5333 | | 03 |
| 2N3208 | S | P | SZ, SM, TR, CR | | 2N3740 | 2N5783 | | 03 |
| 2N3208 | | | | | 2N4234 | | | 03 |
| 2N3209 | S | P | F, MO, IT, RY, TX | BSX29 | MM2894 | 2N3576 | | 10 |
| 2N3209 | | | | | 2N4313 | | | 10 |
| 2N3211 | S | N | MO, SQ, SM | (BSY63) | | | | 13 |
| 2N3217 | S | P | CR, SP, RY, ID, TD | | 2N2944 | 2N2945 | | 12 |
| 2N3218 | S | P | CR, ID, SP, TD, RY | | 2N2944 | 2N2945 | | 12 |
| 2N3219 | S | P | CR, RY, SP, FR, SQ | | 2N2944 | 2N2945 | | 12 |
| 2N3220 | S | N | SM, TR, SQ | | 2N3767 | | | 03 |
| 2N3221 | S | N | SM, TR, SQ | | 2N3767 | | | 03 |
| 2N3222 | S | N | SM, TR, SQ | | 2N3766 | | | 03 |
| 2N3223 | S | N | SM, TR, SQ | | 2N3766 | | | 03 |
| 2N3224 | S | P | SM, SQ | | 2N3498 | 2N2905 | | 02 |
| 2N3224 | | | | | 2N5415 | | | 02 |
| 2N3225 | S | P | SM, SQ | | 2N3498 | 2N5415 | | 02 |
| 2N3226 | S | N | SZ, PP, SR, SQ, ET | | 2N3717 | 2N4913 | | 06 |
| 2N3226 | | | | | 2N6253 | | | 06 |
| 2N3227 | S | N | MO, TX, ES, RY, CA | (BSY63) | 2N2369A | 2N3011 | | 13 |
| 2N3232 | S | N | MO, SZ, ET, F, PP | | 2N5877 | 2N3055 | | 03 |
| 2N3232 | | | | | 2N3715 | 2N4914 | | 03 |
| 2N3233 | S | N | SZ, ET, W, F, PP | | 2N4347 | 2N3442 | | 03 |
| 2N3234 | S | N | MO, SZ, W, F, SF | | 2N3055 | 2N6262 | | 03 |
| 2N3235 | S | N | MO, SZ, ET, W, SD | | 2N3055 | 2N3715 | | 03 |
| 2N3236 | S | N | SZ, PP, SF, SQ, W | | 2N3716 | 2N6254 | | 03 |
| 2N3237 | S | N | SZ, SF, SQ, W, SM | | 2N5302 | 2N6258 | | 03 |
| 2N3237 | | | | | 2N5882 | | | 03 |
| 2N3238 | S | N | SZ, SF, SQ, W, SM | | 2N3716 | 2N6258 | | 03 |
| 2N3238 | | | | | 2N5882 | | | 03 |
| 2N3239 | S | N | SZ, SF, SQ, SM, SU | | 2N3716 | 2N6258 | | 03 |
| 2N3239 | | | | | 2N5882 | | | 03 |
| 2N3240 | S | N | SZ, SU, TW, W, SF | | 2N5631 | 2N6259 | | 03 |
| 2N3241 | S | N | RC | (BSX45-10) | 2N2222 | | | 01 |

| TYPE | M/S | POL | MANUFAC | EUROPEAN | | AMERICAN | | JAPANESE | USE |
|------|-----|-----|---------|----------|--|----------|--|----------|-----|
| 2N3241A | S | N | RC | (BSX45-16) | BC140XVI | 2N2222 | | | 01 |
| 2N3241A | | | | BC140 | BSX75 | | | | 01 |
| 2N3242 | S | N | RC | (BSX45-16) | BC140X | 2N730 | 2N2222 | | 01 |
| 2N3242A | S | N | RC | (BSX45-16) | | 2N2222 | 2N730 | | 01 |
| 2N3242A | | | | BSX75 | | | | | 01 |
| | | | | | | | | | |
| 2N3244 | S | P | MO, TX, RY, SQ, TR | (BSV15-10) | | 2N5323 | | | 13 |
| 2N3245 | S | P | MO, TX, RY, SQ, TR | (BSV16-6) | | 2N5323 | | | 13 |
| 2N3246 | S | N | SM, TD, SQ | | | 2N2484 | | | 13 |
| 2N3247 | S | N | TD, UP | | | 2N2484 | | | 13 |
| 2N3248 | S | P | MO, RY, ME, SQ, TR | | | 2N2894 | | | 13 |
| | | | | | | | | | |
| 2N3249 | S | P | MO, ME, RY, SQ, TR | | | 2N2894 | | | 13 |
| 2N3250 | S | P | F, MO, TX, RY, IT | BCY79VII | BFX48 | EN3250 | | | 13 |
| 2N3250A | S | A | F, MO, TX, RY, PE | BCY77VII | | 2N4121 | | | 13 |
| 2N3251 | S | P | MO, F, IT, RY, TX | BFX48 | BCY79VII | 2N3250 | 2N4922 | | 13 |
| 2N3251 | | | | BC177 | | | | | 13 |
| | | | | | | | | | |
| 2N3251A | | | F, MO, TX, RY, ES | BCY77VII | | 2N3250 | 2N4922 | | 13 |
| 2N3252 | S | N | F, MO, TX, RY, IT | (BSY34) | BFX17 | 2N2218 | 2N3250 | | 13 |
| 2N3252 | | | | BSY34 | BFY51 | | | | 13 |
| 2N3252 | | | | BFY55 | BSX45 | | | | 13 |
| 2N3253 | S | N | F, MO, TX, IT, RY | (BSY34) | BSX32 | | | | 13 |
| | | | | | | | | | |
| 2N3253 | | | | BSX45 | BSX59 | | | | 13 |
| 2N3261 | S | N | RC, FE, SQ, AT, SM | BSS10 | BSX20 | | | | 13 |
| 2N3263 | S | N | RC, SQ, TX, TW, SM | | | 2N4002 | | | 16 |
| 2N3264 | S | N | RC, SQ, TX, TW, SM | | | 2N4002 | | | 16 |
| 2N3265 | S | N | RC, PI, SM, SQ, TX | | | 2N4002 | | | 16 |
| | | | | | | | | | |
| 2N3266 | S | N | RC, PI, SQ, SM, TX | | | 2N4002 | | | 16 |
| 2N3268 | S | N | SM, TR, TI, SQ | | | 2N337 | | | 01 |
| 2N3277 | J | P | F, IL | | | 2N5474 | SF1680 | | |
| 2N3277 | | | | | | 2N2606 | | | |
| 2N3278 | J | P | F, IL | | | 2N5475 | SM8661 | | |
| | | | | | | | | | |
| 2N3278 | | | | | | 2N2607 | | | |
| 2N3279 | G | P | MO | (AFY16) | | 2N2997 | | | 02 |
| 2N3280 | G | P | MO | (AFY16) | | 2N2997 | | | 02 |
| 2N3281 | G | P | MO | (AFY16) | | 2N2996 | | | 02 |
| 2N3282 | G | P | MO | (AFY16) | | 2N2996 | | | 02 |
| | | | | | | | | | |
| 2N3283 | G | P | MO | (AFY42) | | 2N2996 | | | 02 |
| 2N3284 | G | P | MO | (AFY42) | | 2N2996 | | | 02 |
| 2N3285 | G | P | MO | (AFY42) | | 2N2996 | | | 02 |
| 2N3286 | G | P | MO | (AFY42) | | 2N2996 | | | 02 |
| 2N3287 | S | N | MO, SM, SQ, ET | | | 2N2944 | 2N2945 | | 02 |
| | | | | | | | | | |
| 2N3288 | S | N | MO, SM, SQ, ET | | | 2N2944 | 2N2945 | | 02 |
| 2N3289 | S | N | MO, SM, TI, ET, SQ | | | 2N918 | | | 02 |
| 2N3291 | S | N | MO, SM, TI, ET, SQ | (BF255) | | 2N918 | | | 02 |
| 2N3292 | S | N | MO, SM, TI, ET, SQ | (BF255) | | 2N697 | 2N918 | | 02 |
| 2N3293 | S | N | MO, SM, TI, ET, SQ | (BF255) | | 2N918 | | | 02 |
| | | | | | | | | | |
| 2N3294 | S | N | MO, SM, TI, ET, SQ | (BF255) | | 2N918 | | | 02 |
| 2N3295 | S | N | MO, SM, SQ, KE | (BFX55) | | 2N2217 | 2N2219 | | 03 |
| 2N3299 | S | N | F, MO, TX, ET, RY | (BCW77-16) | BFY72 | 2N2218A | 2N2537 | | 13 |
| 2N3299 | | | | | | 2N3015 | 2N3641 | | 13 |
| 2N3300 | S | N | MO, F, ET, BT, FR | (BSW77-16) | BFY72 | 2N1711 | 2N2219A | | 13 |
| | | | | | | | | | |
| 2N3300 | | | | BSY34 | BSX73 | 2N3643 | | | 13 |
| 2N3301 | S | N | F, MO, F, TX, ET | (BCW73-16) | BFX94 | 2N2221A | 2N4436 | | 13 |
| 2N3302 | S | N | F, MO, TX, ET, RY | (BCW73-16) | BFX95 | 2N2222A | 2N4437 | | 13 |
| 2N3303 | S | N | F, MO, PE, MU, SG | (BSY58) | BSX12 | | | | 13 |
| 2N3304 | S | P | F, MO, RY, NS, SM | BSX20 | | 2N3546 | 2N2894 | | 10 |
| | | | | | | | | | |
| 2N3304 | | | | | | 2N3639 | | | 10 |
| 2N3305 | S | P | SM, SQ | | | 2N2907 | | | 01 |
| 2N3306 | S | P | SM, SQ | | | 2N2907 | | | 01 |
| 2N3309 | S | N | Ss, NU, SQ, ML, SM | | | 2N3309A | 2N3553 | | 03 |
| 2N3309A | S | N | MO | | | 2N3553 | | | 03 |
| | | | | | | | | | |
| 2N3317 | S | P | SP, FR, RY, UP, CR | | | 2N2944 | 2N2945 | | 13 |
| 2N3318 | S | P | SP, FR, UP, CR, ID | | | 2N2944 | 2N2945 | | 12 |
| 2N3319 | S | P | SP, FR, RY, UP, CR | | | 2N2944 | 2N2945 | | 12 |
| 2N3320 | G | P | FR, UP, ID | | | 2N964 | | | 13 |
| 2N3321 | G | P | FR, ID | | | 2N964 | | | 13 |
| | | | | | | | | | |
| 2N3326 | S | N | CA, IT, SM, TX, UP | | | 2N2218A | 2N3567 | | 13 |
| 2N3327 | S | N | SM, SQ | BFY44 | | 2N3250 | | | 03 |
| 2N3328 | J | P | TX, SX, IL | | | 2N5475 | 2N2607 | | |
| 2N3329 | J | P | TX, SX, TI, IL, SD | | | MFE4009 | 2N2497 | | |
| 2N3330 | J | P | TX, SX, MO, SD, TI | | | 2N2498 | | | |
| | | | | | | | | | |
| 2N3330J | J | P | TX | | | JAN2N3330 | | | |
| 2N3331 | J | P | TX, SX, TI, SD, IL | | | MFE4012 | 2N2499 | | |
| 2N3332 | J | P | TX, IL, TI, SD, ES | | | 2N5267 | 2N5268 | | |
| 2N3332 | | | | | | 2N2500 | | | |
| 2N3337 | S | N | F, SM, SQ, ET, SG | (BF241) | BFY79 | 2N3287 | 2N2883 | | 02 |

| TYPE | M/S | POL | MANUFAC | EUROPEAN | | AMERICAN | | JAPANESE | USE |
|---|---|---|---|---|---|---|---|---|---|
| 2N3337 | | | | | | 2N3688 | | | 02 |
| 2N3338 | S | N | F, SM, SQ, ET, SG | (BF241) | BFY79 | 2N3289 | 2N2883 | | 02 |
| 2N3338 | | | | | | 2N3689 | | | 02 |
| 2N3339 | S | N | F, SM, SQ, ET, SG | (BF241) | | 2N3288 | 2N2883 | | 02 |
| 2N3339 | | | | | | 2N3690 | | | 02 |
| | | | | | | | | | |
| 2N3341 | S | P | SD, SQ, SM | | | 2N2604 | 2N2605 | | 10 |
| 2N3342 | S | P | SD, RY, SQ, CR, SM | | | 2N2944 | 2N2943 | | 10 |
| 2N3343 | S | P | SD, RY, SQ, CR | | | 2N2944 | 2N2945 | | 12 |
| 2N3344 | S | P | SD, RY, SQ, CR | | | 2N2944 | 2N2945 | | 12 |
| 2N3345 | S | P | SD, SQ, CR | | | 2N2944 | 2N2945 | | 12 |
| | | | | | | | | | |
| 2N3346 | S | P | SD, RY, SQ, CR | | | 2N2944 | 2N2945 | | 12 |
| 2N3347 | S | P | TX, TI, F, MO, RY | | | 2N3350 | | | 05 |
| ?N3348 | S | P | TX, F, TI, ML, TD | | | 2N3355 | | | 05 |
| !N3349 | S | P | TX, TI, Ss, ML, NS | | | 2N3350 | | | 05 |
| 2N3351 | S | P | TX, F, TI, SQ, BT | | | 2N3350 | | | 05 |
| | | | | | | | | | |
| 2N3352 | S | P | TX, Ss, ML, NS, TI | | | 2N3350 | | | 05 |
| 2N3365 | J | N | TI, SX, SD, TX, BT | | | 2N3459 | 2N3070 | | |
| 2N3366 | J | N | TI, SX, IL, BT, SD | | | 2N3460 | 2N3070 | | |
| 2N3367 | J | N | TI, IL, TX, BT, SX | | | 2N3070 | | | |
| 2N3368 | J | N | TI, IL, SD, TX, BT | | | 2N3436 | 2N3458 | | |
| | | | | | | | | | |
| 2N3368 | | | | | | 2N4221 | | | |
| 2N3369 | J | N | TI, IL, SD, TX, BT | | | 2N3427 | 2N3460 | | |
| 2N3369 | | | | | | 2N4220A | | | |
| 2N3370 | J | N | TI, IL, SD, TX, BT | | | 2N3438 | 2N3460 | | |
| 2N3370 | | | | | | 2N3070 | | | |
| | | | | | | | | | |
| 2N3375 | S | N | F, MO, RC, SV, TI | BLY22 | BCY22 | | | | 03 |
| 2N3375 | | | | BLY59 | | | | | 03 |
| 2N3376 | J | P | SX, IL, TI, ES | | | 2N3330 | 2N3329 | | |
| 2N3377 | J | P | SX | | | 2N3330 | 2N3376 | | |
| 2N3378 | J | P | SX, IL | | | SM8648 | 2N3330 | | |
| | | | | | | | | | |
| 2N3379 | J | P | SX | | | 2N3330 | 2N3378 | | |
| 2N3380 | J | P | SX, SD, IL | | | 2N3909A | 2N3331 | | |
| 2N3381 | J | P | SX | | | 2N3909A | 2N3380 | | |
| 2N3382 | J | P | SX, IL | | | 2N3994 | SM8650 | | |
| 2N3382 | | | | | | 2N2609 | | | |
| | | | | | | | | | |
| 2N3383 | J | P | SX | | | 2N3994 | 2N3382 | | |
| 2N3384 | J | P | SX, IL | | | 2N3993 | SM8651 | | |
| 2N3384 | | | | | | TP5115 | | | |
| 2N3385 | J | P | SX | | | 2N3993 | 2N3384 | | |
| 2N3386 | J | P | SX, IL | | | 2N3993 | SM8652 | | |
| | | | | | | | | | |
| 2N3386 | | | | | | 2N5018 | | | |
| 2N3387 | J | P | SX | | | 2N3993 | | | |
| 2N3390 | S | N | GE, ML, S, Ss | BC168C | BC168 | MPS6521 | TIS98 | | 01 |
| 2N3390 | | | | BC130C | BC108C | 2N5961 | 2N6002 | | 01 |
| 2N3390 | | | | BC173C | BC183C | | | | 01 |
| | | | | | | | | | |
| 2N3391 | S | N | GE, SP, CN, Ss, NS | BC168B | BC173 | MPS6515 | TIS98 | | 01 |
| 2N3391 | | | | BC183 | BC238 | 2N5961 | 2N3565 | | 01 |
| 2N3391 | | | | BC238B | | | | | 01 |
| 2N3391A | S | N | GE, Ss, SP, FR, NS | BC169B | BC148B | MPS6520 | TIS98 | | 01 |
| 2N3391A | | | | BC238B | BC108 | 2N4401 | SE6002 | | 01 |
| | | | | | | | | | |
| 2N3391A | | | | BC173 | BC184 | | | | 01 |
| 2N3392 | S | N | GE, Ss, ID, SP, S | BC168B | BC168A | MPS3392 | TIS98 | | 01 |
| 2N3392 | | | | BC130A | BC238 | SE6002 | | 2SC458 | 01 |
| 2N3392 | | | | BC109 | BC172 | | | | 01 |
| 2N3392 | | | | BC183 | | | | | 01 |
| | | | | | | | | | |
| 2N3393 | S | N | GE, Ss, ID, SP, TR | BC167A | BC130A | MPS3393 | TIS98 | 2SC458 | 01 |
| 2N3393 | | | | BC108 | BC172 | SE6002 | | | 01 |
| 2N3393 | | | | BC183 | BC238 | | | | 01 |
| 2N3394 | S | N | GE, Ss, ID, SP, TR | BC168A | BC130A | MPS3394 | TIS98 | 2SC458 | 01 |
| 2N3394 | | | | BC108 | BC208 | 2N4401 | 2N3566 | | 01 |
| | | | | | | | | | |
| 2N3394 | | | | BC172 | BC238 | | | | 01 |
| 2N3395 | S | N | GE, Ss, ID, SP, NS | BC168A | BC130 | MPS3395 | TIS98 | 2SC458 | 01 |
| 2N3395 | | | | BC108 | BC168B | SE6002 | | | 01 |
| 2N3395 | | | | BC168C | BC172 | | | | 01 |
| 2N3395ye | S | N | GE | BC168B | | | | | 01 |
| | | | | | | | | | |
| 2N3395w | S | N | GE | BC168B | | | | | |
| 2N3396 | S | N | GE, Ss, NS, SP, TR | BC168B | BC168A | MPS3396 | TIS98 | 2SC458 | 01 |
| 2N3396 | | | | BC130 | BC168C | 2N4401 | SE6002 | | 01 |
| 2N3396 | | | | BC108 | BC183 | | | | 01 |
| 2N3396or | S | N | GE | BC168A | | | | | |
| | | | | | | | | | |
| 2N3396ge | S | N | GE | BC168B | | | | | |
| 2N3396w | S | N | GE | BC168B | | | | | |
| 2N3397 | S | N | GE, Ss, ID, SP, S | BC168A | BC130 | MPS3397 | TIS98 | 2SC458 | 01 |
| 2N3397 | | | | BC108 | BC168B | 2N4400 | 2N5153 | | 01 |
| 2N3397 | | | | BC168C | BC183 | | | | 01 |

| TYPE | M/S | POL | MANUFAC | EUROPEAN | | AMERICAN | | | JAPANESE | USE |
|------|-----|-----|---------|----------|---|----------|---|---|----------|-----|
| 2N3397r | S | N | GE | BC168A | | | | | | |
| 2N3397or | S | N | GE | BC168A | | | | | | |
| 2N3397ye | S | N | GE | BC168B | | | | | | |
| 2N3397w | S | N | GE | BC168B | | | | | | |
| 2N3398 | S | N | GE, Ss, ID, NS, SP | BC168A | BC130 | MPS3398 | TIS98 | | 2SC458 | 01 |
| | | | | | | | | | | |
| 2N3398 | | | | BC108 | BC168B | 2N4400 | 2N5135 | | | 01 |
| 2N3398 | | | | BC158C | | | | | | 01 |
| 2N3398r | S | N | GE | BC168A | | | | | | |
| 2N3398or | S | N | GE | BC168A | | | | | | |
| 2N3398ye | S | N | GE | BC168B | | | | | | |
| | | | | | | | | | | |
| 2N3398w | S | N | GE | BC168B | | | | | | |
| 2N3398bl | S | N | GE | BC168C | | | | | | |
| 2N3399 | G | P | AM, PE, NU | AF139 | | 2N2996 | | | | 02 |
| 2N3401 | S | P | CR, SD, RY | | | 2N2944 | 2N2945 | | | 12 |
| 2N3402 | S | N | GE, Ss, NU, SP, CN | (BC337-16) | BC108 | 2N5449 | MPS6513 | | 2SC458 | 01 |
| | | | | | | | | | | |
| 2N3402 | | | | BC338 | BC183 | 2N4401 | SE6002 | | | 01 |
| 2N3403 | S | N | GE, NU, SP, CN, FR | (BC337-25) | BC108 | 2N5449 | MPS6513 | | 2SC458 | 01 |
| 2N3403 | | | | BC338 | BC172 | 2N4401 | SE6002 | | | 01 |
| 2N3403 | | | | BC183 | | | | | | 01 |
| 2N3404 | S | N | GE, Ss, ID, NU, SP | (BC337-16) | BC337 | 2449 | MPSA05 | | | 01 |
| | | | | | | | | | | |
| 2N3404 | | | | | | MPSA06 | | | | 01 |
| 2N3405 | S | N | GE, Ss, ID, NU, SP | (BC337-25) | BC337 | 2N2449 | 2N5856 | | | 01 |
| 2N3405 | | | | | | MPSA05 | MPSA06 | | | 01 |
| 2N3409 | S | N | MO, SG, SQ, GI | | | 2N2639 | | | | 05 |
| 2N3410 | S | N | MO, GI, SQ, F, SG | | | 2N2639 | | | | 05 |
| | | | | | | | | | | |
| 2N3411 | S | N | MO, GI, SQ, F, SG | | | 2N2639 | | | | 05 |
| 2N3412 | G | P | TX, CN, ET | | | 2N5320 | | | | 01 |
| 2N3414 | S | N | GE, FR, NU, SP, NS | (BC337-16) | BC338 | MPS6513 | 2N5449 | | | 01 |
| 2N3414 | | | | | | 2N4401 | 2N3566 | | | 01 |
| 2N3415 | S | N | GE, NS, NU, SP, Ss | (BC337-25) | BC338 | MPS6515 | 2N5449 | | | 01 |
| | | | | | | | | | | |
| 2N3415 | | | | | | 2N4401 | 2N3566 | | | 01 |
| 2N3416 | S | N | GE, Ss, NU, SP, ML | (BC337-16) | BC141 | 2N5449 | MPS6515 | | | 01 |
| 2N3416 | | | | BC107A | BC337 | MPSA05 | SE6020 | | | 01 |
| 2N3416 | | | | BC182 | | | | | | 01 |
| 2N3417 | S | N | GE, Ss, SP, NU, TR | (BC337-25) | BC337 | MPS6515 | 2N5449 | | | 01 |
| | | | | | | | | | | |
| 2N3417 | | | | | | MPSA05 | SE6020 | | | 01 |
| 2N3418 | S | N | TX, FR, SM, SQ, TW | (BSX63-6) | | 2N5320 | 2N5334 | | | 16 |
| 2N3419 | S | N | TX, GS, SD, UN, CN | (BSX63-6) | | 2N5335 | | | | 16 |
| 2N3420 | S | N | TX, ES, SM, SQ, UN | (BSX63-10) | | 2N5336 | | | | 16 |
| 2N3421 | S | N | TX, SM, UN, GS, TW | BSX63-10 | | 2N5336 | | | | 16 |
| | | | | | | | | | | |
| 2N3423 | S | N | F, ME, TI, MO, RY | BFY84 | | 2N2639 | | | | 05 |
| 2N3424 | S | N | F, ME, TI, MO, RY | BFY84 | | 2N2639 | | | | 05 |
| 2N3425 | S | N | F, RY, SG, MO | | | 2N3014 | | | | 03 |
| 2N3426 | S | N | F, PE, SG, SQ, MU | (BSY58) | BSX12 | 2N3303 | 2N3426 | | | 13 |
| 2N3427 | G | P | MO, SR, IC | (ASY48VI) | | 2N1377 | | | | 01 |
| | | | | | | | | | | |
| 2N3428 | G | P | MO, SR, IC | (ASY48VI) | | 2N1377 | | | | 01 |
| 2N3429 | S | N | W, SZ, KE | | | 2N3713 | | | | 16 |
| 2N3430 | S | N | W, SM, SZ, KE | | | 2N3714 | | | | 16 |
| 2N3436 | J | N | TI, SX, SD, BT, NS | | | 2N3458 | 2N4222A | | | |
| 2N3437 | J | N | TI, SX, SD, BT, NS | | | 2N3459 | 2N4220A | | | |
| | | | | | | | | | | |
| 2N3438 | J | N | TI, SX, SD, BT, NS | | | 2N3460 | 2N4220A | | | |
| 2N3439 | S | N | RC, FE, SQ, MO, F | | | MJ3201 | 2N5058 | | | 02 |
| 2N3440 | S | N | RC, FE, SQ, F, MO | | | MJ3202 | | | | 02 |
| 2N3441 | S | N | RC, FE, Ss, F, NU | BUY14 | | 2N3442 | 2N3738 | | | 06 |
| 2N3442 | S | N | AT, MO, RC, S, AM | BUY12 | BDX11 | 2N5631 | MJ3010 | | | 06 |
| | | | | | | | | | | |
| 2N3444 | S | N | TX, IT, MO, SG, SE | BSY34 | BFX17 | 2N5321 | | | | 13 |
| 2N3444 | | | | BSX61 | | | | | | 13 |
| 2N3445 | S | N | MO, SM, SQ, F, SF | BUY57 | | 2N5877 | 2N6471 | | | 06 |
| 2N3445 | | | | | | 2N3715 | | | | 06 |
| 2N3446 | S | N | MO, SM, TR, F, SQ | BUY57 | | 2N5878 | 2N6472 | | | 06 |
| | | | | | | | | | | |
| 2N3446 | | | | | | 2N3716 | | | | 06 |
| 2N3447 | S | N | MO, SM, SQ, F, SF | BUF57 | BDY61 | 2N5877 | 2N6471 | | | 06 |
| 2N3447 | | | | | | 2N3715 | | | | 06 |
| 2N3448 | S | N | MO, SM, SQ, TR, F | BUY57 | | 2N5878 | 2N6472 | | | 06 |
| 2N3448 | | | | | | 2N3716 | | | | 06 |
| | | | | | | | | | | |
| 2N3450 | S | N | RY | BFY50 | | | | | | 13 |
| 2N3452 | J | N | TI, IL, TX, BT, SX | | | MFE2095 | 2N3821 | | | |
| 2N3453 | J | N | TI, IL, BT, SX, TX | | | MFW2094 | TN4119 | | | |
| 2N3454 | J | N | TI, IL, TX, BT, SX | | | MFE2093 | TN4119 | | | |
| 2N3455 | J | N | TX, TI, IL, BT, SX | | | MFE2095 | 2N3821 | | | |
| | | | | | | | | | | |
| 2N3456 | J | N | TI, IL, TX, BT, SX | | | MFE2094 | 2N3821 | | | |
| 2N3457 | J | N | TI, IL, SD, SX, BT | | | MFE2093 | TN4118 | | | |
| 2N3458 | J | N | TI, SX, TX, SD, NS | | | 2N3436 | 2N4222A | | | |
| 2N3459 | J | N | TI, SX, TX, SD, NS | | | 2N3437 | 2N4220A | | | |
| 2N3460 | J | N | TI, SX, TX, SD, BT | | | 2N3438 | 2N4220A | | | |

| TYPE | M/S | POL | MANUFAC | EUROPEAN | | AMERICAN | | JAPANESE | USE |
|------|-----|-----|---------|----------|--|----------|--|----------|-----|
| 2N3464 | S | N | M, SQ, SM, TW | | | 2N3053 | | | 03 |
| 2N3465 | J | N | CR | | | 2N4220A | | | |
| 2N3466 | J | N | CR, ES | | | 2N4220A | | | |
| 2N3467 | S | P | F, MO, TX, TI, ES | (BSV15-10) | | | | | 13 |
| 2N3468 | S | P | F, MO, TX, IT, ES | (BSV16-6) | | | | | 13 |
| 2N3469 | S | N | SD, KE, PP, SQ, TW | | | 2N5337 | | | 03 |
| 2N3478 | S | N | RC, SQ, SM | (BFX89) | | | | | 02 |
| 2N3485 | S | P | F, MO, TX, RY, TI | (BCW76-16) | | | | | 13 |
| 2N3485A | S | P | F, MO, TX, SM, TI | (BCW76-16) | | | | | 13 |
| 2N3486 | S | P | F, MO, TX, TI, RY | BCW76-16 | | | | | 13 |
| 2N3486A | S | P | F, MO, TX, RY, SM | (BCW76-16) | | | | | 13 |
| 2N3494 | S | P | MO, F, RY, TX, TR | | | 2N2605 | | | 02 |
| 2N3495 | S | P | MO, SM, F, TX, HS | | | 2N2605 | | | 02 |
| 2N3496 | S | P | MO, F, TX, RY, ET | | | 2N2605 | | | 02 |
| 2N3497 | S | P | MO, RY, TX, F, SQ | | | 2N2605 | | | 02 |
| 2N3498 | S | N | MO, F, ID, SQ, TR | (BF457) | | 2N697 | 2N698 | | 02 |
| 2N3499 | S | N | MO, SM, SQ, TR, SM | (BF457) | | 2N5058 | | | 02 |
| 2N3500 | S | N | MO, F, SM, TR, ES | (BF457) | | 2N2243A | | | 02 |
| 2N3501 | S | N | MO, F, SM, TR, TI | (BF457) | | 2N2243A | | | 02 |
| 2N3502 | S | P | F, TX, NS, RY, SG | (BCW80-16) | BC161XVI | 2N2905 | EN3502 | | 13 |
| 2N3502 | | | | BC161 | | | | | 13 |
| 2N3503 | S | P | F, TX, NS, SM, SG | (BCW80-16) | BC161XVI | 2N2905A | 2N2905 | | 13 |
| 2N3503 | | | | BC161 | | 2N3695 | | | 13 |
| 2N3504 | S | P | F, TX, NS, IT, SQ | (BCW76-16) | BSX36 | 2N2907 | EN3504 | | 13 |
| 2N3504 | | | | BC161XVI | BC161 | | | | 13 |
| 2N3505 | S | P | F, TX, NS, SM, TR | (BCW76-16) | BSX36 | 2N2907A | 2N2907 | | 13 |
| 2N3505 | | | | BC161XVI | BC161 | EN3504 | | | 13 |
| 2N3506 | S | N | MO, HS, SD, TR, TI | (BSX62-10) | | 2N5337 | 2N2989 | | 13 |
| 2N3507 | S | N | MO, HS, TR, TI, ES | (BSX63-10) | | 2N5336 | 2N2989 | | 13 |
| 2N3508 | S | N | MO, SQ, SM | (BSY63) | | | | | 13 |
| 2N3509 | S | N | MO, SQ, SM | (BSY63) | | | | | 13 |
| 2N3510 | S | N | MO, F, IT, SQ, CN | (BSY63) | BSX26 | EN3009 | | | 13 |
| 2N3511 | S | N | MO, F, IT, SQ, CN | (BSY63) | BSX26 | EN3009 | | | 13 |
| 2N3512 | S | N | RC, ET, MO, FE, SQ | | | 2N2537 | 2N3015 | | 13 |
| 2N3513 | S | N | GE, F | | | 2N2480A | 2N2639 | | 05 |
| 2N3513 | | | | | | 2N2640 | | | 05 |
| 2N3516 | S | N | GE, F | | | 2N2639 | | | 05 |
| 2N3518 | S | N | F, MO | | | 2N3046 | | | 05 |
| 2N3520 | S | N | SG | | | 2N3043 | | | 05 |
| 2N3521 | S | N | GE, SG | | | 2N2643 | 2N3043 | | 05 |
| 2N3522 | S | N | GE | | | 2N2643 | | | 05 |
| 2N3524 | S | N | F, SG | | | 2N2639 | 2N2640 | | 05 |
| 2N3526 | S | N | SM, TT, SG | BFY57 | | 2N5182 | | | 02 |
| 2N3527 | S | P | CR, SM | | | 2N2944 | 2N2945 | | 01 |
| 2N3543 | S | N | KE, SQ, TW, SM | BDY61 | | | | | 03 |
| 2N3544 | S | N | MO, SQ, SM | | | 2N918 | | | 02 |
| 2N3546 | S | P | MO, NS, SM, TD, ID | | | 2N2894 | 2N3576 | | 13 |
| 2N3549 | S | P | NS, SM, TD, ME, SQ | | | 2N2604 | 2N2605 | | 01 |
| 2N3550 | S | P | NS, SQ | | | 2N2944 | 2N2945 | | 01 |
| 2N3553 | S | N | RC, MO, SV, TF, V | BFY99 | BFW47 | | | | 03 |
| 2N3562 | S | N | TX, SM, TR, RY, SQ | BSY34 | BSX60 | | | | 13 |
| 2N3563 | S | N | F, TI, ET, ME, GI | (BFX89) | | PN3563-18 | TIS62 | | 02 |
| 2N3564 | S | N | F, TI, GI, ME, NS | (BFX89) | | | | | 02 |
| 2N3565 | S | N | F, CS, TI, GI, ME | (BC413B) | BC238 | PN35-18 | MPS6514 | 2SC485 | 01 |
| 2N3565 | | | | BC172 | BC208 | TIS98 | | | 01 |
| 2N3565 | | | | BC183 | | | | | 01 |
| 2N3566 | S | N | F, TI, CS, NU, UP | (BC237B) | | PN3566-5 | MPS6514 | | 01 |
| 2N3566 | | | | | | 2N5449 | | | 01 |
| 2N3567 | S | N | F, CS, TI, UP, BT | BSX45-6 | | PN3567-5 | MPS6530 | | 01 |
| 2N3568 | S | N | F, CS, TI, RY, SS | BSX46-6 | BC337 | PN3568-5 | | | 01 |
| 2N3569 | S | N | F, CS, TI, UP, NP | BSX45-16 | | PN3569-5 | MPS6531 | | 01 |
| 2N3570 | S | N | TX, FE, ML, Ss, KM | (BFY90) | BFY89 | | | | 01 |
| 2N3571 | S | N | TX, FE, ML, Ss, KM | (BFY90) | | 2N3570 | | | 02 |
| 2N3572 | S | N | TX, FE, ML, Ss, KM | (BFY90) | BFX89 | 2N3570 | | | 02 |
| 2N3573 | J | P | TX, TI | | | 2N5471 | 2N5472 | | |
| 2N3573 | | | | | | 2N2841 | | | |
| 2N3574 | J | P | TX, TI, IL | | | 2N5472 | 2N5474 | | |
| 2N3574 | | | | | | 2N2842 | | | |
| 2N3575 | J | P | TX, TI, IL | | | 2N5474 | 2N5475 | | |
| 2N3575 | | | | | | 2N2607 | | | |
| 2N3578 | J | P | SX, IL, ES | | | 2N3330 | 2N2608 | | |
| 2N3579 | S | P | SD, SQ, SM | | | 2N2604 | 2N2605 | | |
| 2N3580 | S | P | SD, SQ, SM | | | 2N2605 | | | 02 |
| 2N3581 | S | P | SD, SQ, SM | | | 2N2605 | | | 02 |
| 2N3582 | S | P | SD, SQ, SM | | | 2N2605 | | | 02 |

| TYPE | M/S | POL | MANUFAC | EUROPEAN | | AMERICAN | | JAPANESE | USE |
|------|-----|-----|---------|----------|---|----------|---|----------|-----|
| 2N3583 | S | N | RC, TX, IT, FE | BUY77 | | SE9331 | MJ2251 | | 03 |
| 2N3584 | S | N | RC, TX, IT, UN, FE | (BUY77) | | | | | 16 |
| 2N3585 | S | N | RC, TX, IT, UN, FE | (BUT78) | BDY94 | 2N3767 | | | 16 |
| 2N3588 | G | P | AM, PE | (AF201U) | AF201 | 2N2495 | | 2SA239 | 05 |
| 2N3588 | | | | AF121 | AF178 | | | | 05 |
| 2N3589 | S | N | GE, SQ, TR, SM | | | SE9331 | | | 03 |
| 2N3597 | S | N | SD, PI, F, GX, SQ | | | 2N3767 | 2N4002 | | 14 |
| 2N3597 | | | | | | 2N3266 | | | 14 |
| 2N3598 | S | N | SD, F, PI, KE, SM | | | 2N3446 | 2N4002 | | 14 |
| 2N3598 | | | | | | 2N3266 | | | 14 |
| 2N3599 | S | N | SD, PI, F, GX, SQ | | | 2N3447 | 2N4002 | | 14 |
| 2N3599 | | | | | | 2N3265 | | | 14 |
| 2N3600 | S | N | RC, ET, SM, SQ, AM | (BFY90) | | 2N918 | | | 02 |
| 2N3605 | S | N | GE, ML, Ss | (BSY62B) | BSY62 | MPS3646 | 2N5772 | | 10 |
| 2N3605 | | | | | | 2N4275 | | | 10 |
| 2N3605A | S | N | GE | BSY63 | BSX20 | MPS3646 | 2N5772 | 2SC321 | 10 |
| 2N3605A | | | | | | 2N4275 | | | 10 |
| 2N3606 | S | N | GE, ML, Ss | (BSY62B) | BSY62 | MPS3646 | 2N5772 | | 10 |
| 2N3606 | | | | | | 2N4275 | | | 10 |
| 2N3606A | S | N | GE | BSY63 | BSX20 | MPS3646 | 2N5772 | 2SC321 | 10 |
| 2N3606A | | | | | | 2N4275 | | | 10 |
| 2N3607 | S | N | GE, ML, Ss, MO | (BSY62B) | BSY62 | MPS3646 | 2N5772 | 2SC321 | 10 |
| 2N3607 | | | | BSY70 | BSX20 | 2N4275 | | | 10 |
| 2N3608 | M | P | IL, MO | | | 2N4352 | | | |
| 2N3609 | M | P | MO | | | MFE3020 | MFE3021 | | |
| 2N3610 | M | P | MO | | | 2N4352 | | | |
| 2N3611 | G | P | MO, ET, ES, KS, SD | AUY21IV | | TI3027 | | | 06 |
| 2N3612 | G | P | MO, ET, ES, PP, CN | AUY21IV | | | | | 06 |
| 2N3613 | G | P | MO, ES, KS, SD, ET | (AUY21IV) | AUY21V | TI3027 | | | 06 |
| 2N3614 | G | P | MO, KS, SD, TR, ET | (AUY21IV) | AUY31V | TI3027 | TI3028 | | 06 |
| 2N3615 | G | P | MO, SD, TR, ET, PP | (AUY22IV) | AUY22V | TI3027 | | | 06 |
| 2N3615 | | | | ASZ16 | | | | | 06 |
| 2N3616 | G | P | MO, PP, TR, CN, ET | AUY22IV | ASZ15 | 2N456A | 2N3146 | | 06 |
| 2N3617 | G | P | MO, TR, CN, KS, SD | (AUY22IV) | AUY22V | TI3027 | TI3030 | | 06 |
| 2N3617 | | | | ASZ16 | | | | | 06 |
| 2N3618 | G | P | MO, CN, KS, SD, ES | (AUY22IV) | AUY22V | 2N456A | 2N3146 | | 06 |
| 2N3631 | M | N | SX | | | 2N3797 | | | |
| 2N3632 | S | N | MO, RC, MU, PE, SV | BLY23 | BLY60 | | | | 03 |
| 2N3634 | S | P | MO, ET, SM, TR, ES | | | FT5415 | | | 02 |
| 2N3636 | S | P | MO, F, SQ, TR, SM | | | FT5416 | | | 02 |
| 2N3638 | S | P | F, ME, CA, TI, GI | BC328-16 | BCW52 | MPS3638-5 | 2N5447 | | 13 |
| 2N3638A | S | P | F, CA, CN, ET, ID | BC328-16 | | MPS3638A-5 | 2N5447 | | 13 |
| 2N3639 | S | P | F, ME, RY, UP, BT | | | PN3639-18 | MPS3639 | | 13 |
| 2N3639 | | | | | | TI553 | | | 13 |
| 2N3640 | S | P | F, ME, CN, ES, NS | | | PN3640-18 | 2N4091 | | 13 |
| 2N3640 | S | N | F, CN, TI, ME, NS | | | MPS3640 | TI554 | | 03 |
| 2N3641 | S | N | F, CN, TI, ME, NS | (BCW77-16) | | PN3641-5 | MPS6530 | | 03 |
| 2N3641 | | | | | | 2N5449 | | | 03 |
| 2N3642 | S | N | F, TI, RY, NP, CA | (BCW78-16) | BC337 | PN3642-5 | MPS6530 | | 03 |
| 2N3642 | | | | | | 2N5449 | | | 03 |
| 2N3643 | S | N | F, TI, UP, SG, NS | (BCW77-16) | | PN3643-5 | MPS6531 | | 03 |
| 2N3643 | | | | | | 2N5449 | | | 03 |
| 2N3644 | S | P | F, CN, ID, NP, RY | (BCW80-16) | BC327 | PN3644-5 | 2N5449 | | 13 |
| 2N3645 | S | P | F, TI, SG, NS, ME | (BCW80-16) | | PN3645-5 | 2N4142 | | 13 |
| 2N3646 | S | N | F, TI, CS, SS, NS | (BSY63) | | MPS3646-18 | MPS3646 | | 13 |
| 2N3647 | S | N | F, MO, TX, SG, SQ | (BSY63) | BSX26 | 2N4422 | | | 13 |
| 2N3648 | S | N | F, MO, SM, SG, SG | (BSY63) | BSX26 | 2N3303 | EN3009 | | 13 |
| 2N3659 | S | N | CN, SQ, TR, SM | | | 2N3303 | EN3009 | | 13 |
| 2N3660 | S | P | TR, SD, SQ, SM | | | 2N5058 | | | 02 |
| 2N3660 | | | | | | 2N4234 | 2N3719 | | 03 |
| 2N3661 | S | P | TR, SM, SQ, CN, SD | | | 2N4235 | 2N3720 | | 03 |
| 2N3662 | S | N | GE, ML, Ss | (BF198) | BF173 | 2N5770 | 2N3563 | | 02 |
| 2N3662 | | | | BF200 | | | | | 02 |
| 2N3663 | S | N | GE, ML, Ss | (BF198) | BF173 | 2N5770 | 2N5363 | | 02 |
| 2N3665 | S | N | IT, TX, F, TR, NS | BSX47-6 | BFY56 | 2N1893 | 2N2432 | | 10 |
| 2N3666 | S | N | F, TX, TR, IT, ME | BSX47-10 | BFY56 | SE6021 | | | 10 |
| 2N3667 | S | N | SZ, SU, SQ, PP, SD | | | 2N2432 | SE6021 | | 10 |
| 2N3671 | S | P | F, TX, RY, MD, CA | (BCW80-16) | BFY64 | 2N375 | 2N5881 | | 16 |
| 2N3672 | S | P | IT, RY, F, SM, IT | (BCW76-16) | BSX36 | 2N2905 | 2N3644 | | 16 |
| 2N3672 | | | | | | 2N699 | 2N2905 | | 10 |
| 2N3673 | S | P | F, RY, SM, SQ, CS | (BCW76-16) | BSX36 | 2N3638A | | | 10 |
| 2N3673 | | | | | | 2N2905 | 2N3638A | | 10 |
| 2N3675 | S | N | SZ, SP, TR, SM, SQ | | | 2N2438 | | | |
| 2N3676 | S | N | SZ, SP, SM | | | 2N4239 | | | 16 |
| 2N3677 | S | P | CR, SQ, TR, MO | | | 2N2944 | 2N2845 | | 16 |

| TYPE | M/S | POL | MANUFAC | EUROPEAN | | | AMERICAN | | JAPANESE | USE |
|------|-----|-----|---------|----------|---|---|----------|---|----------|-----|
| 2N3678 | S | N | F, CN, IT, SQ, SM | (BCW78-16) | | | 2N3568 | | | 12 |
| 2N3681 | S | N | RY, SQ, ET | | | | 2N3570 | | | 02 |
| 2N3682 | S | N | SM | | | | 2N918 | | | 02 |
| 2N3683 | S | N | KM | | | | 2N3570 | | | 02 |
| 2N3684 | J | N | SD, IL, NS, TT, NU | | | | 2N3822 | 2N4221A | | |
| 2N3684A | J | N | SD, IL | | | | 2N3822 | 2N4221A | | |
| 2N3685 | J | N | SD, IL, NL, TI, NU | | | | 2N3821 | 2N4220A | | |
| 2N3685A | J | N | SD, IL | | | | 2N3821 | 2N4220A | | |
| 2N3686 | J | N | SX, NU, TI, NS, SD | | | | 2N3821 | TN4339 | | |
| 2N3686A | J | N | SD, IL | | | | 2N3821 | TN4339 | | |
| 2N3687 | J | N | SX, NU, TI, NS, IL | | | | 2N3438 | TN4338 | | |
| 2N3687A | J | N | SD, IL | | | | TN4338 | | | |
| 2N3688 | S | N | F, CS, NU, SG, CN | (BF241) | | | 2N3689 | 2N3690 | | 02 |
| 2N3689 | S | N | F, RY, SG, CS | (BF241) | | | 2N3688 | | | 02 |
| 2N3690 | S | N | F, RY, SG, CS | (BF241) | | | 2N3688 | 2N3689 | | 02 |
| 2N3691 | S | N | F, TI, GI, CS, BT | BC237A | | | MPS6512 | TIS98 | | 01 |
| 2N3692 | S | N | F, TI, GI, NU, SS | BC237A | | | MPS6513 | | | 01 |
| 2N3693 | S | N | F, CS, ME, TI, SG | (BF241) | | | 2N3694 | | | 02 |
| 2N3694 | S | N | F, TI, CS, ME, CN | (BF240) | | | 2N3693 | | | 02 |
| 2N3695 | J | P | BT, TI | | | | MFE4009 | 2N3329 | | |
| 2N3696 | J | P | BT, TI, ES | | | | MFE4009 | 2N3329 | | |
| 2N3697 | J | P | BT, TI | | | | MFE4007 | SFB6361 | | |
| 2N3697 | | | | | | | 2N2607 | | | |
| 2N3698 | J | P | BT, TI, ES | | | | 2N5473 | 2N2606 | | |
| 2N3700 | S | N | F, IN, V, TY, SM | (BSX47-10) | | | SE6021 | | | 02 |
| 2N3701 | S | N | F, IN, V, RY, CN | (BSX47-6) | | | SE6021 | | | 02 |
| 2N3702 | S | P | GE, TF, TX, SR, V | (BC327-16) | BC257A | | | | 2SA565 | 01 |
| 2N3702 | | | | BC177 | BC306VI | | | | | 01 |
| 2N3703 | S | P | GE, TF, TX, SR, S | (BC327-16) | BC257VI | | | | 2SA565 | 01 |
| 2N3703 | | | | BC177 | BC307VI | | | | | 01 |
| 2N3703 | | | | BC147 | | | | | | 01 |
| 2N3704 | S | N | GE, TF, TX, SR, TF | (BC337-16) | BC337XVI | | 2N2222 | MPS3704 | | 01 |
| 2N3704 | | | | BC337 | BC140 | | 2N3566 | | | 01 |
| 2N3705 | S | N | GE, TF, TX, SR, FF | (BC337-16) | BC337XVI | | 2N221 | MPS3705 | | 01 |
| 2N3705 | | | | BC337 | | | 2N3566 | | | 01 |
| 2N3706 | S | N | GE, TF, TX, SR, BT | (BC337-25) | BC337XVI | | 2N2222 | MPS3706 | | 01 |
| 2N3706 | | | | BC337 | BC168 | | 2N3566 | | | 01 |
| 2N3706 | | | | BSX75 | BC338 | | | | | 01 |
| 2N3707 | S | N | TX, SR, S, UP, St | BC167A | BC167B | | MPS6520 | MPS3707 | 2SC458 | 01 |
| 2N3707 | | | | BC237A | BC209 | | SE4010 | EN4124 | | 01 |
| 2N3707 | | | | BC173 | BC149 | | | | | 01 |
| 2N3707 | | | | BC184 | | | | | | 01 |
| 2N3708 | S | N | TX, SR, St, BT, NU | BC167A | BC237A | | MPS3708 | EN4123 | 2SC458 | 01 |
| 2N3708 | | | | BC167B | BC167C | | EN4124 | 2N3565 | | 01 |
| 2N3709 | S | N | SR, BT, NU, St, UP | BC167A | BC237A | | MPS3709 | EN4123 | 2SC458 | 01 |
| 2N3709 | | | | BC170 | | | EN3903 | | | 01 |
| 2N3710 | S | N | TX, NU, S, UP, SR | BC167A | BC237A | | MPS6565 | MPS3710 | 2SC458 | 01 |
| 2N3710 | | | | BC207 | BC171 | | EN4124 | EN3904 | | 01 |
| 2N3710 | | | | BC167B | BC182 | | | | | 01 |
| 2N3711 | S | N | TX, SR, St, BT, NU | BC167B | BC167A | | MPS3711 | EN3904 | 2SC458 | 01 |
| 2N3711 | | | | BC237B | BC107 | | 2N3565 | | | 01 |
| 2N3711 | | | | BC167C | | | | | | 01 |
| 2N3712 | S | N | TX, MO, TR, HS, SM | BF257 | BF457 | | 2N3440 | | | 02 |
| 2N3712 | | | | BD115 | | | | | | 02 |
| 2N3713 | S | N | TX, MO, F, ET, SM | BDY39IV | | | 2N6471 | 2N3055 | | 03 |
| 2N3714 | S | N | TX, MO, ET, SM, St | BDY39IV | | | 2N6472 | 2N4347 | | 03 |
| 2N3714 | | | | | | | 2N6254 | | | 03 |
| 2N3715 | S | N | TX, MO, F, SM, St | BDY39VI | | | 2N6471 | 2N3055 | | 03 |
| 2N3716 | S | N | TX, MO, F, SQ, SM | BDY39IV | | | 2N6472 | 2N4347 | | 03 |
| 2N3716 | | | | | | | 2N6254 | | | 03 |
| 2N3717 | S | N | F, MO, TX | BSY34 | | | | | | 03 |
| 2N3719 | S | P | MO, TX, SD, HS, SQ | BSX61-10 | BSX62VI | | 2N4234 | 2N5323 | | 14 |
| 2N3719 | | | | | | | 2N5333 | 2N5679 | | 14 |
| 2N3720 | S | P | MO, TX, SD, TR, HS | BSX63-10 | BSX63VI | | 2N4235 | 2N5322 | | 14 |
| 2N3720 | | | | | | | 2N5333 | 2N5679 | | 14 |
| 2N3721 | S | N | GE, SP, UP, CN | BC168A | BC168B | | MPS3721 | 2N5135 | | 01 |
| 2N3721 | | | | BC168C | | | | | | 01 |
| 2N3722 | S | N | F, RY, SG, MO, SM | (BSX46 10) | BSX46VI | | 2N3015 | | | 10 |
| 2N3723 | S | N | F, SM, SQ, MO | (BSX47-10) | BSX47VI | | 2N3015 | | | 13 |
| 2N3724 | S | N | F, SP, TX, TI, KE | BSX32 | BSY34 | | 2N3725 | | | 13 |
| 2N3724 | | | | BSX73 | BSX60 | | | | | 13 |
| 2N3724A | | | | BSY58 | | | | | | 13 |
| 2N3724A | S | N | TX, KE, RY, UP, TI | (BSY34) | | | 2N3725 | | | 13 |
| 2N3725 | S | N | F, SP, TX, TI, IT | BSX32 | BSY34 | | | | | 13 |
| 2N3725 | | | | BSX73 | BSX59 | | | | | 13 |

| TYPE | M/S | POL | MANUFAC | EUROPEAN | | AMERICAN | | JAPANESE | USE |
|------|-----|-----|---------|----------|---|----------|---|----------|-----|
| 2N3725A | S | N | TX, ES, NS, SM, UP | (BSY34) | | | | | 13 |
| 2N3726 | S | P | F, MO, ME, RY, SQ | BFX11 | | | | | 05 |
| 2N3727 | S | P | F, MO, SG, UP, BT | BFX11 | | | | | 05 |
| 2N3731 | G | P | RC | AU106 | | | | | 06 |
| 2N3732 | G | P | RC | (AD163IV) | | | | | 06 |
| 2N3733 | S | N | MO, RC, RA, TX, FE | | | (2N3632) | | | 03 |
| 2N3734 | S | N | MO, TX, F, IT, NS | (BSY58) | BFX17 | | | | 13 |
| 2N3735 | S | N | MO, TX, HS, NS, SM | (BSY34) | | | | | 13 |
| 2N3736 | S | N | MO, TX, F, SQ, UP | (BSX48) | BSX31 | | | | 13 |
| 2N3737 | S | N | MO, TX, IT, TI, ES | (BSX49) | | | | | 13 |
| 2N3738 | S | N | MO, SG, F, ML, Ss | (BUY77) | BU126 | 2N5838 | 2N3584 | | 06 |
| 2N3738 | | | | | | 2N3508 | | | 06 |
| 2N3739 | S | N | MO, IT, SQ, F | (BUY78) | | FT402 | 2N3585 | | 06 |
| 2N3740 | S | P | F, MO, Ss, ML, SQ | BDX28-6 | | 2N3740 | 2N5955 | | 06 |
| 2N3740A | S | P | MO, SQ | BSX28-6 | | | | | 06 |
| 2N3741 | S | P | F, MO, Ss, ML, SQ | BDX29-6 | | 2N3741 | 2N5956 | | 06 |
| 2N3741 | | | | | | 2N5954 | | | 06 |
| 2N3741A | S | P | MO, SQ | BDX29-6 | | | | | 06 |
| 2N3742 | S | N | TX, MO, F, SM, SQ | BF259 | (BF459) | 2N5058 | 2N3439 | | 02 |
| 2N3743 | S | P | MO, IT, SZ, St, F | BFT19B | | 2N5416 | | | 02 |
| 2N3744 | S | N | SD, KE, PI, PP, Tw | | | 2N3996 | | | 03 |
| 2N3745 | S | N | SD, KE, PP, PI, SM | | | 2N3996 | | | 03 |
| 2N3746 | S | N | SD, KE, PI, TR, TW | | | 2N3996 | | | 03 |
| 2N3747 | S | N | SD, PP, TW, PI, TR | | | 2N3996 | | | 03 |
| 2N3748 | S | N | SD, PP, SQ, PI, SM | | | 2N3996 | | | 03 |
| 2N3749 | S | N | SD, PP, TW, UN, PI | | | 2N3996 | | | 03 |
| 2N3750 | S | N | SD, KE, SQ, PI, UN | | | 2N3996 | | | 03 |
| 2N3751 | S | N | SD, PI, GS, UN, SM | | | 2N3996 | | | 03 |
| 2N3752 | S | N | SD, KE, PP, SQ, PI | | | 2N3996 | | | 03 |
| 2N3762 | S | P | MO, HS, SQ, TI, ES | (BSV15-10) | | | | | 13 |
| 2N3763 | S | P | MO, HS, SQ, TI, SM | (BSC16-6) | | | | | 13 |
| 2N3764 | S | N | MO, SQ, TI, HS | (BSV15-10) | | 2N2907 | 2N3486 | | 13 |
| 2N3765 | S | N | MO, SQ, TI, HS | (BSV16-6) | | 2N2907 | 2N3486A | | 13 |
| 2N3766 | S | N | MO, F, KE, SM, TI | BDY13-6 | BDY13 | 2N6373 | 2N3897 | | 06 |
| 2N3766 | | | | BD124 | BDY13X | | | | 06 |
| 2N3767 | S | N | MO, F, KE, SM, SS | BDX25-6 | BDY13X | 2N6372 | 2N3879 | | 06 |
| 2N3771 | S | N | AT, RC, F, W | (BUY57) | | 2N5301 | | | 06 |
| 2N3772 | S | N | AT, RC, TX, SP, F | (BUY57) | | 2N3715 | 2N5302 | | 06 |
| 2N3773 | S | N | AT, RC, F, SD, SQ | (BUY58) | BUY12 | 2N5631 | | | 06 |
| 2N3773 | | | | BD124 | BUY56IV | | | | 06 |
| 2N3774 | S | P | SZ, SD, SQ, CR | | | 2N4234 | 2N5783 | | 16 |
| 2N3775 | S | P | SZ, PP, SQ, CR, SD | | | 2N4235 | 2N5781 | | 16 |
| 2N3776 | S | P | SZ, PP, SQ, CR, SD | | | 2N4236 | | | 16 |
| 2N3777 | S | P | SZ, PP, SQ, CR, SD | | | 2N4236 | 2N4033 | | 16 |
| 2N3777 | | | | | | 2N5679 | | | 16 |
| 2N3778 | S | P | SZ, PP, SQ, CR, SD | | | 2N4234 | 2N3783 | | 16 |
| 2N3779 | S | P | SZ, SD, SQ, CR | | | 2N4235 | 2N5781 | | 16 |
| 2N3780 | S | P | SZ, SD, SQ, CR | | | 2N4236 | | | 16 |
| 2N3781 | S | P | SZ, SD, SQ, CR | | | 2N4236 | 2N5679 | | 16 |
| 2N3782 | S | P | SZ, SD, SQ, CR | | | 2N5783 | 2N4234 | | 16 |
| 2N3782 | | | | | | 2N5840 | 2N5783 | | 16 |
| 2N3783 | G | F | MO | (AFY42) | | 2N5043 | TIXM101 | | 02 |
| 2N3784 | G | P | MO | (BFY42) | | 2N5043 | TIXM101 | | 02 |
| 2N3785 | G | P | MO | (AFY42) | | | | | 02 |
| 2N3788 | S | N | SD, SQ | | | 2N5840 | | | 06 |
| 2N3789 | S | P | MO, TX, F, SQ, TR | | | 2N6246 | | | 06 |
| 2N3790 | S | P | MO, SD, TX, F, SQ | | | 2N3789 | 2N6247 | | 06 |
| 2N3791 | S | P | MO, SD, TX, F, SQ | | | 2N3789 | 2N6246 | | 06 |
| 2N3792 | S | P | MO, TX, F, SQ, TR | | | 2N3789 | 2N6247 | | 06 |
| 2N3793 | S | N | NS, SS, UP | (BC337-16) | BC168 | MPS6530 | | | 01 |
| 2N3793 | | | | BC167 | BC207 | | | | 01 |
| 2N3793 | | | | BC171 | BC182 | | | | 01 |
| 2N3793 | | | | BC237 | | | | | 01 |
| 2N3794 | S | N | NS, SS, UP | (BC337-16) | BC167 | MPS6531 | | | 01 |
| 2N3794 | | | | BC168 | BC208 | | | | 01 |
| 2N3794 | | | | BC172 | BC183 | | | | 01 |
| 2N3794 | | | | BC238 | | | | | 01 |
| 2N3795 | S | P | SZ, SQ | | | 2N5415 | | | 16 |
| 2N3798 | S | P | MO, TX, SM, ME, SQ | BCY77VIII | | 2N2605 | | | 01 |
| 2N3798A | S | P | MO | BCY77VIII | | | | | 01 |
| 2N3799 | S | P | MO, TX, SM, TD, ME | BCY77IX | | 2N2605 | | | 01 |
| 2N3799A | S | P | MO | (BCY77IX) | | | | | 01 |
| 2N3800 | S | P | MO, TI, F, SQ, TD | | | 2N3350 | 2N3352 | | 01 |
| 2N3801 | S | P | MO, RY, St, TD, BT | | | 2N3350 | 2N3352 | | 01 |
| 2N3802 | S | P | MO, F, TI, SQ, TD | | | 2N3347 | 2N3350 | | 05 |

| TYPE | M/S | POL | MANUFAC | EUROPEAN | | AMERICAN | | JAPANESE | USE |
|---|---|---|---|---|---|---|---|---|---|
| 2N3803 | S | P | MO, RY, TD, RT, St | | | 2N3350 | 2N3351 | | 05 |
| 2N3804 | S | P | MO, F, TI, St, BT | | | 2N3350 | | | 05 |
| 2N3804A | S | P | MO, SQ, TD, RY | | | 2N3350 | | | 05 |
| 2N3805 | S | P | MO, RY, TD, BT, SQ | | | 2N3350 | | | 05 |
| 2N3805A | S | P | MO, RY, TD, SQ | | | 2N3350 | | | 05 |
| 2N3806 | S | P | MO, TX, TI, F, RY | | | 2N3350 | | | 01 |
| 2N3807 | S | P | MO, CN, RY, TX, TD | | | 2N3350 | | | 01 |
| 2N3808 | S | P | MO, TI, TX, BT, F | | | 2N3350 | | | 05 |
| 2N3809 | S | P | MO, TX, SQ, BT, RY | | | 2N3350 | | | 05 |
| 2N3810 | S | P | MO, TX, TI, RY, St | | | 2N3350 | | | 05 |
| 2N3810A | S | P | MO, RY, TD, NS, SQ | | | 2N3350 | | | 05 |
| 2N3811 | S | P | MO, NS, SQ, TX, BT | | | 2N3350 | | | 05 |
| 2N3811A | S | P | MO, RY, TD, NS, SS | | | 2N3350 | | | 05 |
| 2N3819 | J | N | TX, SL, V, NS | | | MPF108 | MPF112 | | |
| 2N3819 | | | | | | FE3819 | | | |
| 2N3820 | J | P | TX | | | MPF161 | FT3820 | | |
| 2N3821 | J | N | TX, MD, SX, TI, NS | | | TN4340 | | | |
| 2N3822 | J | N | TX, NS, SD, MO, SX | | | TN4340 | | | |
| 2N3823 | J | N | TX, MU, PE, SD, V | | | 2N4416 | | | |
| 2N3824 | J | N | TX, SD, MO, SX, BT | | | 2N5396 | | | |
| 2N3825 | S | N | TX | BC109 | BC173 | MPS3398 | | | 02 |
| 2N3825 | | | | BC209 | BC184 | | | | 02 |
| 2N3826 | S | N | TX | | | 2N4994 | MPS3826 | | 02 |
| 2N3826 | | | | | | 2N3903 | MPS3693 | | 02 |
| 2N3827 | S | N | TX, NS | | | 2N4995 | MPS3827 | | 02 |
| 2N3827 | | | | | | 2N3904 | MPS3694 | | 02 |
| 2N3828 | S | N | TX | BC109 | BC177 | MPS6565 | | | 02 |
| 2N3828 | | | | BC207 | BC171 | | | | 02 |
| 2N3828 | | | | BC107 | BC182 | | | | 02 |
| 2N3829 | S | P | TX, SQ, SM | | | 2N3964 | | | 13 |
| 2N3830 | S | N | KE, RY, SQ, TI, SM | BFX34 | | | | | 13 |
| 2N3831 | S | N | KE, SM, TX, TI, RY | BD131 | | | | | 13 |
| 2N3832 | S | N | ET | BSY19 | | | | | 13 |
| 2N3834 | S | N | TX, CN | BFX62 | | 2N3570 | 2N3571 | | 03 |
| 2N3838 | S | N | F, MO, RC, KM, SQ | (BFY90) | | SE3005 | | | 02 |
| 2N3840 | S | P | SP, ID, TD, CR, RY | | | 2N2945 | 2N2946 | | 12 |
| 2N3841 | S | P | TD | | | 2N2945 | 2N2946 | | 12 |
| 2N3842 | S | P | TD | | | 2N2945 | 2N2946 | | 12 |
| 2N3843 | S | N | GE, SP, ID | BC167A | | MPS6512 | 2N4400 | | 02 |
| 2N3843 | | | | | | SE6001 | 2N5830 | | 02 |
| 2N3843A | S | N | GE, SP, ID | BC167A | | 2N4400 | SE6001 | | 02 |
| 2N3843A | | | | | | MPS6512 | | | 02 |
| 2N3844 | S | N | GE, ID, SP, CN | BC167A | | MPS6512 | 2N4400 | | 02 |
| 2N3844 | | | | | | SE6001 | 2N5830 | | 02 |
| 2N3844A | S | N | GE, SP, ID | BC167A | | MPS6512 | 2N4400 | | 02 |
| 2N3844A | | | | | | SE6001 | 2N5830 | | 02 |
| 2N3845 | S | N | GE, SP, ID | BC167A | BC109 | MPS6512 | MPS6565 | | 02 |
| 2N3845 | | | | BC173 | BC207 | 2N4400 | SE6001 | | 02 |
| 2N3845 | | | | BC171 | BC107 | | | | 02 |
| 2N3845 | | | | BC182 | | | | | 02 |
| 2N3845A | S | N | GE, SP, ID | BC167A | | MPS6513 | 2N4400 | | 02 |
| 2N3845A | | | | | | SE6001 | | | 02 |
| 2N3850 | S | N | UN, KE, SQ, TW, GX | | | 2N3998 | | | 14 |
| 2N3851 | S | N | UN, KE, SQ, TW, GX | | | 2N3998 | | | 14 |
| 2N3852 | S | N | UN, KE, SQ, TW, GX | | | 2N3998 | | | 14 |
| 2N3853 | S | N | GX, SD, TR, UN, KE | | | 2N3998 | | | 14 |
| 2N3854 | S | N | GE, ID, UP, FR, SP | BC168A | | MPS6512 | 2N3903 | | 02 |
| 2N3854 | | | | | | 2N3691 | | | 02 |
| 2N3854A | S | N | GE, ID, UP, FR, SP | BC167A | | MPS6512 | MPS3693 | | 02 |
| 2N3854A | | | | | | 2N3693 | | | 02 |
| 2N3855 | S | N | GE, ID, UP, FR, SP | BC168A | BC238A | MPS6512 | 2N3903 | | 02 |
| 2N3855 | | | | | | 2N3691 | | | 02 |
| 2N3855A | S | N | GE, ID, UP, FR, SP | BC167A | | MPS6512 | MPS3693 | | 02 |
| 2N3855A | | | | | | 2N3693 | | | 02 |
| 2N3856 | S | N | GE, ID, UP, FR, SP | BC168A | BC108B | MPS6513 | 2N3904 | | 02 |
| 2N3856 | | | | | | 2N3692 | | | 02 |
| 2N3856A | S | N | GE, SP, ID, UP, FR | BC168B | BC238B | MPS6513 | MPS3694 | | 02 |
| 2N3856A | | | | BC167A | | 2N3694 | | | 02 |
| 2N3857 | S | P | TD | | | 2N2944 | 2N2945 | | 01 |
| 2N3858 | S | N | GE, ID, UP, FR, SP | BC167A | | MPS6512 | TIS98 | | 02 |
| 2N3858 | | | | | | MPS3693 | 2N3694 | | 02 |
| 2N3858A | S | N | GE, ID, UP, FR, SP | (BC167A) | | MPS6566 | TIS98 | | 02 |
| 2N3858A | | | | | | 2N5830 | 2N3693 | | 02 |
| 2N3859 | S | N | GE, ID, UP, FR, SP | BC167A | | MPS6513 | TIS98 | | 02 |
| 2N3859 | | | | | | 2N3694 | MPS3694 | | 02 |

| TYPE | M/S | POL | MANUFAC | EUROPEAN | | AMERICAN | | JAPANESE | USE |
|------|-----|-----|---------|----------|--|----------|--|----------|-----|
| 2N3859A | S | N | GE, ID, UP, SP, FR | (BC167A) | | MPS6566 | 2N5830 | | 01 |
| 2N3859A | | | | | | 2N3694 | | | 01 |
| 2N3860 | S | N | GE, ID, UP, FR, SP | BC167B | | MPS6514 | TIS98 | | 02 |
| 2N3860 | | | | | | MPS3694 | 2N3694 | | 02 |
| 2N3863 | S | N | SZ, SM, SQ, PP, SD | | | 2N3716 | 2N3715 | | 16 |
| 2N3863 | | | | | | | | | |
| 2N3864 | S | N | SZ, SM, SP, SQ, PP | | | 2N3055 | | | 16 |
| 2N3865 | S | N | SZ, SP, SQ, SM | | | 2N3716 | 2N3442 | | 16 |
| 2N3866 | S | N | RC, F, MO, PE, SV | BFX55 | | 2N6262 | | | 03 |
| 2N3867 | S | P | MO, TR, SQ | | | 2N5333 | | | 13 |
| 2N3868 | S | P | MO, TR, SQ | | | 2N5333 | | | 13 |
| 2N3877 | S | N | GE, SP, UP, ID, TR | (BF457) | BF17B | 2N4410 | TIS98 | | 01 |
| 2N3877 | | | | | | 2N5830 | | | 01 |
| 2N3877A | S | N | GE, SP, UP, ID, TR | (BF457) | | 2N4410 | TIS98 | | 01 |
| 2N3877A | | | | | | 2N5830 | | | 01 |
| 2N3878 | S | N | RC, KE, PP, SQ, TW | BDX25-10 | BDY13C | 2N5873 | | | 03 |
| 2N3878 | | | | BD124 | | | | | 03 |
| 2N3879 | S | N | RC, KE, PP, SQ, TW | BDX25-6 | | 2N5874 | | | 16 |
| 2N3882 | S | P | RY | | | 2N4352 | | | |
| 2N3900 | S | N | GE, ID, SP, FR | BC168B | | MPS6515 | TIS98 | | 01 |
| 2N3900 | | | | | | 2N4401 | SE6002 | | 01 |
| 2N3900A | S | N | GE, ID, SP, FR | BC169B | | MPS6520 | 2N5088 | | 01 |
| 2N3900A | | | | | | TIS98 | 2N4401 | | 01 |
| 2N3901 | S | N | GE, ID, SP, FR | BC169C | | MPS6521 | 2N5088 | | 01 |
| 2N3902 | S | N | MO, TX, DD, SD, SM | BUX18C | (BUY79) | FT402 | 2N5840 | | 16 |
| 2N3903 | S | N | MO, CA, ME, TX, BT | BC167A | BF195 | EN3903 | | | 13 |
| 2N3903 | | | | BC237A | BFY19 | | | | 13 |
| 2N3904 | S | N | F, MO, TX, CN, NS | BC237B | BC167A | EN3904 | | | 13 |
| 2N3904 | | | | BF194 | BC237A | | | | 13 |
| 2N3904 | | | | BC195 | BFY19 | | | | 13 |
| 2N3904 | | | | BSY34 | BC182L | | | | 13 |
| 2N3905 | S | P | MO, TX, CA, ME, RY | BC307A | BC307 | EN3905 | | | 13 |
| 2N3905 | | | | BCY70 | | | | | 13 |
| 2N3906 | S | P | F, MO, TX, CN, NS | BC307B | BC307A | EN3906 | | | 13 |
| 2N3906 | | | | BCY70 | BC212L | | | | 13 |
| 2N3907 | S | N | TR, F, NS, TD, CN | BFY81 | | 2N2915 | | | 05 |
| 2N3908 | S | N | F, NS, TD, IL, SG | BFY81 | | 2N2916 | | | 05 |
| 2N3909 | J | P | TX, SX, MO, SD, ES | | | 2N2609 | | | |
| 2N3909A | J | P | TX, MO, IL | | | 2N2609 | | | |
| 2N3910 | S | P | RY, CR, TD, CN, SQ | | | 2N2944 | | | 12 |
| 2N3911 | S | P | RY, MO, TD, CR, SQ | | | 2N2944 | 2N2945 | | 12 |
| 2N3912 | S | P | RY, MO, TD, CR, SQ | | | 2N2944 | 2N2945 | | 12 |
| 2N3913 | S | P | RY, SQ, TD, CR | | | 2N2944 | 2N2945 | | 12 |
| 2N3914 | S | P | SR, RY, TD, CR | | | 2N2944 | 2N2945 | | 12 |
| 2N3914 | | | | | | 2N2906 | | | 12 |
| 2N3915 | S | P | RY, SR, TD, CR | | | 2N2944 | 2N2945 | | 12 |
| 2N3921 | J | N | TI, IL, SD, BT, SX | | | MMF6 | 2N5545 | | 05 |
| 2N3921 | | | | | | 2N4084 | | | 05 |
| 2N3922 | J | N | TI, IL, SD, BT, SX | | | MMF6 | 2N4085 | | |
| 2N3923 | S | N | F, TX, SM, SQ, TR | (BF457) | BFX98 | SF5777 | | | 02 |
| 2N3924 | S | N | MO, PH, TX, RA, V | BFW46 | BFY99 | 2N3553 | | | 03 |
| 2N3925 | S | N | MO | | | 2N3375 | | | 03 |
| 2N3926 | S | N | MO, MU, PH, V, RA | BLY57 | | | | | 03 |
| 2N3927 | S | N | MO, MU, PH, V, RA | BLY58 | | | | | 03 |
| 2N3928 | S | N | KE | | | 2N5337 | | | 14 |
| 2N3930 | S | P | F, SG, SM | BFX90 | | 2N2605 | 2N3497 | | 01 |
| 2N3930 | | | | | | 2N4889 | | | 01 |
| 2N3931 | S | P | F, SG, SM | BFX91 | | 2N4889 | | | 01 |
| 2N3934 | J | N | TI, BT | | | 2N5542 | TD5903 | | |
| 2N3935 | J | N | TI, BT | | | 2N5546 | TD5904 | | |
| 2N3941 | S | N | SD | | | 2N2920 | | | 05 |
| 2N3942 | S | N | SD | | | 2N2920 | | | 05 |
| 2N3943 | S | N | SD | | | 2N2920 | | | 05 |
| 2N3944 | S | N | SD | | | 2N2920 | | | 05 |
| 2N3945 | S | N | IT, TR, NS, SQ, F | | | 2N2270 | 2N3568 | | 10 |
| 2N3945 | | | | | | 2N2102 | | | 10 |
| 2N3946 | S | N | F, MO, TX, SQ, TI | BCY65EVII | | 2N2217 | 2N2219 | | 13 |
| 2N3947 | S | N | F, MO, TX, SQ, TI | BCY65EVII | | 2N2217 | 2N2219 | | 13 |
| 2N3948 | S | N | MO, SM, TW, TI, KE | (BFX55) | | 2N2217 | | | 03 |
| 2N3954 | J | N | SD, IL, TX, BT | | | MFE3954 | SF9944 | | |
| 2N3954 | | | | | | 2N5197 | | | |
| 2N3954A | J | N | SD, IL, TX, BT | | | MFE3954A | 2N5545 | | |
| 2N3954A | | | | | | 2N5196 | | | |
| 2N3955 | J | N | SD, IL, TX, BT | | | MFE3955 | 2N5546 | | |
| 2N3955 | | | | | | 2N5198 | | | |

| TYPE | M/S | POL | MANUFAC | EUROPEAN | | AMERICAN | | JAPANESE | USE |
|------|-----|-----|---------|----------|--|----------|--|----------|-----|
| 2N3955A | J | N | SD, IL, TX, BT | | | MFE3955A | 2N5546 | | |
| 2N3955A | | | | | | 2N5197 | | | |
| 2N3956 | J | N | SD, IL, TX, BT | | | MFE3956 | 2N5547 | | |
| 2N3956 | | | | | | 2N5199 | | | |
| 2N3957 | J | N | SD, IL, TX, BT | | | MFE3957 | 2N5547 | | |
| 2N3958 | J | N | SD, IL, TX, BT | | | MFE3958 | 2N5547 | | |
| 2N3958 | | | | | | 2N5046 | | | |
| 2N3959 | S | N | MO, HS, SQ, TI, F | | | 2N4313 | | | 13 |
| 2N3960 | S | N | MO, HS, SQ, TI, F | BFX62 | | 2N4313 | | | 13 |
| 2N3962 | S | P | F, TX, IN, IT, NS | (BC416B) | BFW20 | 2N2605 | 2N3963 | | 01 |
| 2N3962 | | | | BFX37 | | 2N4249 | | | 01 |
| 2N3963 | S | P | F, TX, V, IT, NS | (BC416B) | BFW21 | 2N2605 | 2N4249 | | 01 |
| 2N3964 | S | P | F, TX, IT, ME, SM | (BC416C) | BFW22 | 2N2605 | 2N4250 | | 01 |
| 2N3964 | | | | BCY67 | | | | | 01 |
| 2N3965 | S | P | F, TX, ME, SG, TD | (BC416C) | BFW23 | 2N2605 | 2N4250A | | 01 |
| 2N3966 | J | N | TI, MU, TX, SD, PH | | | 2N4416 | 2N4221 | | |
| 2N3967 | J | N | TI, IL, SD, BT | | | 2N4221A | 2N4222A | | |
| 2N3967 | | | | | | SFB2337 | 2N4221 | | |
| 2N3967A | J | N | TI, IL, BT | | | 2N4221A | 2N4222A | | |
| 2N3967A | | | | | | 2N3822 | | | |
| 2N3968 | J | N | TI, SD, BT | | | 2N4221A | SFB2338 | | |
| 2N3968 | | | | | | 2N3821 | | | |
| 2N3968A | J | N | TI, IL, BT | | | 2N4221A | 2N3821 | | |
| 2N3969 | J | N | BT, SD, TI, IL | | | 2N4220A | SFB2339 | | |
| 2N3969 | | | | | | 2N3821 | | | |
| 2N3969A | J | N | TI, IL, BT | | | 2N4220A | 2N3821 | | |
| 2N3970 | J | N | SD, NS, TI, MO, SX | | | 2N4091 | | | |
| 2N3971 | J | N | SD, NS, TI, MO, SX | | | 2N4092 | | | |
| 2N3972 | J | N | SD, MO, SX, TI, NS | | | 2N4093 | | | |
| 2N3993 | J | P | TX, IL, ES, MO | | | 2N5018 | | | |
| 2N3993A | J | P | TX, IL | | | 2N5018 | | | |
| 2N3994 | J | P | TX, MO, IL | | | 2N5019 | | | |
| 2N3994A | J | P | TX, MO, IL | | | 2N5019 | | | |
| 2N3995 | G | P | TX | | | 2N2929 | 2N1195 | | 02 |
| 2N4000 | S | N | TX | (BSX63-6) | | 2N5536 | 2N3019 | | 14 |
| 2N4000 | | | | | | 2N5320 | | | 14 |
| 2N4001 | S | N | TX, KE, SQ, SM, UP | (BSX63-6) | BSW66 | 2N5339 | 2N5681 | | 14 |
| 2N4002 | S | N | TX, KE, SM, F, TW | | | 2N3265 | | | 06 |
| 2N4004 | S | N | TX, SQ, UP, SM, TW | | | 2N3263 | | | 06 |
| 2N4008 | S | P | CR, TD, TR, SQ | | | 2N2944 | 2N2945 | | 10 |
| 2N4013 | S | N | F, MO, TX, SM, SP | BSX49 | BSX32 | | | | 13 |
| 2N4013 | | | | BSX48 | | | | | 13 |
| 2N4014 | S | N | F, TI, IT, SG, TR | BSX32 | BSX49 | 2N2219 | | | 13 |
| 2N4015 | S | P | F, MO, SQ, TD, UP | BFX11 | | 2N3350 | | | 05 |
| 2N4016 | S | P | F, MO, SQ, TD, UP | BFX11 | | 2N3350 | | | 05 |
| 2N4017 | S | P | F, SG, St, TI, UP | BFX36 | | 2N3350 | | | 01 |
| 2N4018 | S | P | F, SG, St, TI, UP | BFX36 | | 2N3350 | | | 01 |
| 2N4019 | S | P | F, SG, TI, UP, BT | BFX36 | | 2N3350 | | | 01 |
| 2N4020 | S | P | F, SG, St, UP, TD | BFX36 | | | | | 05 |
| 2N4021 | S | P | F, SG, St, UP, BT | BFX36 | | 2N3350 | | | 05 |
| 2N4022 | S | P | F, SG, St, UP, BT | BFX36 | | 2N3350 | | | 05 |
| 2N4023 | S | P | F, SQ, TD, UP, SG | BFX36 | | 2N3350 | | | 05 |
| 2N4024 | S | P | F, SQ, TD, SG, St | BFX36 | | 2N3350 | | | 05 |
| 2N4025 | S | P | F, SQ, TD, SG, St | BFX36 | | 2N3350 | | | 05 |
| 2N4026 | S | P | F, TX, SQ, SG, TR | (BSV16-6) | BFX38 | 2N1132 | 2N2906A | | 01 |
| 2N4026 | | | | BC160 | BCW76X | 2B2907 | 2N4354 | | 01 |
| 2N4027 | S | P | F, TX, SQ, SG, TR | (BSV17-6) | BFX40 | 2N2906A | 2N2907 | | 01 |
| 2N4027 | | | | | | 2N4356 | | | 01 |
| 2N4028 | S | P | F, TX, SQ, SG, TR | (BSV16-16) | BFX39 | 2N2907 | 2N4355 | | 01 |
| 2N4029 | S | P | F, TX, SG, TR | (BSC17-10) | BFX40 | 2N2907 | 2N4356 | | 01 |
| 2N4030 | S | P | IT, TX, SG, F, NS | BSV16-6 | BFX38 | 2N4036 | 2N2905 | | 01 |
| 2N4030 | | | | BFX39 | BCW80X | 2N4354 | | | 01 |
| 2N4031 | S | P | F, IN, TX, ME, SM | BSV17-6 | BFX40 | 2N2905 | 2N4356 | | 01 |
| 2N4031 | | | | BFX41 | BC161X | | | | 01 |
| 2N4031 | | | | BCW80X | | | | | 01 |
| 2N4032 | S | P | F, IN, TX, ME, RY, | BSV16-16 | BFX38 | 2N4042 | 2N2905 | | 01 |
| 2N4032 | | | | BC161X | BCW80XVI | 2N4355 | | | 01 |
| 2N4033 | S | P | F, IN, TX, IT, V | BSV17-10 | BFX40 | 2N2905 | 2N4356 | | 01 |
| 2N4033 | | | | BC161XVI | BCW8XVI | | | | 01 |
| 2N4034 | S | P | F, IN, SM, SQ, IT | BCY79VII | BFX48 | 2N3250 | 2N4121 | | 13 |
| 2N4035 | S | P | F, IN, SM, SQ, SG | BCY79VIII | BFX48 | 2N3250 | 2N4922 | | 13 |
| 2N4036 | S | P | RC, TX, FE, MU, PE | BSV17-10 | BFX23 | 2N5322 | 2N2904 | | 10 |
| 2N4036 | | | | | | 2N2905 | | | 10 |
| 2N4037 | S | P | RC, TX, SM, SS, TI | BSV16-16 | BFR24 | 2N5323 | 2N2904 | | 10 |
| 2N4037 | | | | | | 2N2905 | | | 10 |

| TYPE | M/S | POL | MANUFAC | EUROPEAN | | AMERICAN | | JAPANESE | USE |
|------|-----|-----|---------|----------|---|----------|---|----------|-----|
| 2N4038 | M | N | TW, GI | | | 2N3796 | 2N4351 | | |
| 2N4039 | M | N | TW | | | 2N3796 | 2N4351 | | |
| 2N4042 | S | N | SD | | | 2N3680 | | | 05 |
| 2N4043 | S | N | SD | | | 2N3680 | | | 05 |
| 2N4044 | S | N | SD, QD, SG, St, IL, SM | | | 2N3680 | | | 05 |
| 2N4045 | S | N | SD, QD, SG, St, IL | | | 2N3680 | | | 05 |
| 2N4046 | S | N | F, IN, RY, SG, TI | (BSY34) | BFX17 | 2N3252 | 2N2218 | | 13 |
| 2N4046 | | | | BSX32 | | | | | 13 |
| 2N4047 | S | N | F, IN, IT, RY, SG | (BSY34) | BFX17 | | | | 13 |
| 2N4054 | S | N | GE | | | RCP113C | 2N6176 | | 06 |
| 2N4055 | S | N | GE | | | RCP113B | 2N6175 | | 06 |
| 2N4056 | S | N | GE | | | RCP113B | 2N6175 | | 06 |
| 2N4057 | S | N | GE | | | RCP113B | 2N6175 | | 06 |
| 2N4058 | S | P | TX | BC257A | BC258XI | MPS6522 | 2N5086 | 2SA565 | 01 |
| 2N4058 | | | | BC178 | BC206 | 2N4248 | | | 01 |
| 2N4058 | | | | BC253 | BC258A | | | | 01 |
| 2N4058 | | | | BC258B | | | | | 01 |
| 2N4059 | S | P | TX | BC257A | BC258VI | MPS6516 | 2N5086 | | 01 |
| 2N4059 | | | | BC308B | BC204 | 2N5087 | 2N4248 | | 01 |
| 2N4059 | | | | BC250 | BC258A | | | | 01 |
| 2N4059 | | | | BC258B | | | | | 01 |
| 2N4060 | S | P | TX | BC257A | BC258VI | MPS6516 | 2N5086 | | 01 |
| 2N4060 | | | | BC308VI | BC258A | 2N4248 | | | 01 |
| 2N4061 | S | P | TX | BC257A | BC258VI | MPS6517 | 2N5086 | | 01 |
| 2N4061 | | | | BC308A | BC258A | 2N4248 | | | 01 |
| 2N4061 | | | | BC258B | | | | | 01 |
| 2N4062 | S | P | TX | BC257B | BC258A | MPS6518 | 2N5087 | | 01 |
| 2N4062 | | | | BC308B | BC258B | | | | 01 |
| 2N4063 | S | N | RC, SM, SQ, IC, SZ | | | 2N4250 | 2N3439 | | 01 |
| 2N4064 | S | N | RC, SZ, SQ, IC | | | 2N3440 | | | 06 |
| 2N4065 | M | P | GI | | | 2N4352 | 3N174 | | |
| 2N4070 | S | N | GS, PI, SD, TR, TW | | | 2N5631 | 2N3448 | | 06 |
| 2N4070 | | | | | | 2N5038 | | | 06 |
| 2N4071 | S | N | SD, TR, PI, TW, KE | | | 2N5631 | 2N6249 | | 06 |
| 2N4072 | S | N | MO, SQ, TI, SM, TR | | | 2N2863 | | | 03 |
| 2N4073 | S | N | MO, SQ, TI, SM, TR | | | 2N2863 | | | 03 |
| 2N4075 | S | N | F, SQ, TW, UN, SM | | | 2N3764 | 2N3996 | | 06 |
| 2N4076 | S | N | F, SQ, TW, UN, SM | BDY13X | BDY13 | 2N3996 | | 2SC830 | 06 |
| 2N4076 | | | | BD124 | | | | | 06 |
| 2N4077 | G | N | AM, PE, NS | AD161 | | | | | 06 |
| 2N4078 | G | P | AM, PE | AD162 | | | | 2SB367 | 06 |
| 2N4079 | G | N | AM, PE | AD161 | | | | | 06 |
| 2N4081 | S | N | RC | | | 2N4252 | | | 02 |
| 2N4082 | J | N | TI, IL, BT | | | 2N4083 | TD5903 | | |
| 2N4083 | J | N | TI, IL, SD, BT | | | TD5904 | | | |
| 2N4084 | J | N | TI, IL, SD, SX, BT | | | MMF6 | 2N5545 | | |
| 2N4084 | | | | | | 2N5562 | | | |
| 2N4085 | J | N | TI, IL, SD, BT, SX | | | MMF6 | 2N5546 | | |
| 2N4085 | | | | | | 2N5563 | | | |
| 2N4006 | S | N | PH | | | MPS6514 | TIS98 | | 01 |
| 2N4086 | | N | St, GE | | | 2N4400 | 2N5135 | | 01 |
| 2N4087 | S | N | St, GE | | | MPS6515 | TIS97 | | 01 |
| 2N4087 | | | | | | 2N4401 | 2N5135 | | 01 |
| 2N4087A | S | N | St, GE | | | MPS6515 | 2N4401 | | 01 |
| 2N4087A | | | | | | 2N3566 | 2N5135 | | 01 |
| 2N4088 | J | P | TI | | | MPF161 | 2N3331 | | |
| 2N4089 | J | P | TI | | | MPF161 | 2N3330 | | |
| 2N4090 | J | P | TI | | | MPF161 | 2N3329 | | |
| 2N4090A | J | P | TI | | | | | | |
| 2N4091 | J | N | F, MO, TI, NS, SX | | | 2N4391 | | | |
| 2N4091J | J | N | | | | 2N4091 | | | |
| 2N4092 | J | N | TI, MU, SD, TX, F | | | 2N4392 | | | |
| 2N4092A | J | N | TI | | | 2N4092 | EN4392 | | |
| 2N4092J | J | N | | | | 2N4092 | | | |
| 2N4093 | J | N | TI, MU, SD, TX, F | | | 2N4092 | | | |
| 2N4093A | J | N | TI | | | 2N4093 | 2N4392 | | |
| 2N4093J | J | N | | | | 2N4093 | | | |
| 2N4094 | J | N | TI | | | 2N4091 | 2N4856 | | |
| 2N4095 | J | N | TI | | | 2N4092 | 2N4857 | | |
| 2N4099 | S | N | | | | 2N3680 | | | 05 |
| 2N4104 | S | N | TX, SM | BCY65EIX | | 2N2484 | | | 02 |
| 2N4106 | G | P | AM, PE | AC153 | AC131 | MPS2060 | | 2SB370A | 01 |
| 2N4106 | | | | AC128 | AC152 | | | | 01 |
| 2N4111 | S | N | ET, PP, SD, TR, UP | | | 2N3715 | 2N5877 | | 06 |
| 2N4112 | S | N | ET, PP, SD, TR, UP | | | 2N5877 | | | 06 |

| TYPE | M/S | POL | MANUFAC | EUROPEAN | | AMERICAN | | JAPANESE | USE |
|---|---|---|---|---|---|---|---|---|---|
| 2N4113 | S | N | GS, SM, SQ, TW, UP | | | 2N5877 | 2N3716 | | 06 |
| 2N4115 | S | N | F, SQ, TW, UN, SM | | | 2N3996 | | | 06 |
| 2N4116 | S | N | F, SQ, TW, UP, SM | BDY13XVI | BDY13 | 2N3996 | | 2SC830 | 06 |
| 2N4116 | | | | BD124 | | | | | |
| 2N4117 | J | N | SX, IL, BT | | | 2N3367 | 2N4118 | | |
| | | | | | | | | | |
| 2N4117 | | | | | | 2N4119 | TN4117 | | |
| 2N4117A | J | N | SX, IL, BT | | | 2N3367 | TN4117A | | |
| 2N4118 | J | N | SX, IL, BT | | | 2N3367 | 2N4119 | | |
| 2N4118 | | | | | | TN4118 | | | |
| 2N4118A | J | N | SX, IL, BT | | | 2N3367 | TN4118A | | |
| | | | | | | | | | |
| 2N4119 | J | N | SX, IL, BT | | | 2N3366 | 2N4139 | | |
| 2N4119 | | | | | | TN4119 | | | |
| 2N4119A | J | N | SX BT, IL | | | 2N3366 | TN4419A | | |
| 2N4120 | M | | GI | | | 2N4352 | 3N174 | | |
| 2N4121 | S | P | F, ME, RY, SS, TI | (BC416A) | BFX48 | 2N3905 | 2N4423 | | 02 |
| | | | | | | | | | |
| 2N4122 | S | P | F, ID, NS, TI, SG | (BC416B) | BFX48 | 2N3906 | 2N4423 | | 02 |
| 2N4123 | S | P | F, MO, CA, ME, TX | (BC413A) | | TIS99 | EN4123 | | 13 |
| 2N4124 | S | N | F, MO, CA, ME, TX | (BC413B) | | TIS98 | EN4124 | | 13 |
| 2N4125 | S | P | F, MO, TX, CA, NS | (BC415A) | | 2N5447 | 2N4125 | | 13 |
| 2N4126 | S | P | F, MO, CA, NS, TX | (BC415B) | | 2N4061 | EN4126 | | 13 |
| | | | | | | | | | |
| 2N4130 | S | N | MO, KE, SM, SG | | | 2N3055 | | | 06 |
| 2N4134 | S | N | F, SM, SQ, ET, SG | BFX19 | | | | | 02 |
| 2N4135 | S | N | F, SM, SQ, ET, SG | BFX19 | | | | | 02 |
| 2N4137 | S | N | F, RY, SQ, CA, SM | (BSY63) | BSX28 | 2N4275 | | | 16 |
| 2N4137 | | | | BFX34 | | | | | 16 |
| | | | | | | | | | |
| 2N4138 | S | N | TX, SQ, CR, TR | BFX34 | | 2N2432 | | | 12 |
| 2N4139 | J | N | TI, IL, ME, BT | | | 2N3436 | 2N3458 | | |
| 2N4139 | | | | | | 2N4222 | | | |
| 2N4140 | S | N | GI, CN, ET, NY, RY | | | 2N4400 | | | 02 |
| 2N4141 | S | N | GI, CN, ET, RY, TI | | | 2N4401 | | | 02 |
| | | | | | | | | | |
| 2N4142 | S | P | GI, CN, ME, RY, TI | | | 2N4402 | | | 02 |
| 2N4143 | S | P | GI, CN, ME, RY, TI | | | 2N4403 | | | 02 |
| 2N4150 | S | N | CN, UN, PI, SQ, SM | | | 2N3421 | 2N5337 | | 06 |
| 2N4207 | S | P | F, NS, CA | | | 2N4257 | | | 13 |
| 2N4208 | S | P | F, NS, CA | | | 2N4258 | | | 13 |
| | | | | | | | | | |
| 2N4209 | S | P | F, NS, TI, CA | | | 2N4258 | | | 13 |
| 2N4210 | S | N | TR, KE, SQ, TW, GX | | | 2N4002 | 2N3266 | | 06 |
| 2N4211 | S | N | TR, KE, SQ, GX, SM | | | 2N4002 | 2N3265 | | 06 |
| 2N4220 | J | N | MO, F, SX, TX, ML | | | 2N4220A | 2N5359 | | |
| 2N4220A | J | N | MO, F, SX, TX, ML | | | 2N5359 | | | |
| | | | | | | | | | |
| 2N4221 | J | N | MO, F, SX, TX, ML | | | 2N4221A | 2N5362 | | |
| 2N4221A | J | N | MO, F, SX, TX, NS | | | 2N5362 | | | |
| 2N4222 | J | N | MO, F, SX, TX, Ss | BC264 | | 2N4222A | 2N5363 | | |
| 2N4222A | J | N | MO, F, SX, TX, Ss | | | 2N5363 | | | |
| 2N4223 | J | N | MO, NS, TX, SX, TI | | | 2N4224 | 2N3823 | | |
| | | | | | | | | | |
| 2N4224 | J | N | TI, SX, TX, NS, F | | | 2N4223 | 2N3823 | | |
| 2N4226 | S | N | SD, PP, SQ, KE, SM | | | 2N5334 | | | 06 |
| 2N4227 | S | N | GI, ET, NU, TI, BT | | | 2N4400 | | | 10 |
| 2N4231 | S | N | MO, F, SM, TR, TW | | | 2N6374 | 2N3054 | | 06 |
| 2N4231 | | | | | | 2N6260 | | | 06 |
| | | | | | | | | | |
| 2N4232 | S | N | MO, F, SM, TR, TW | | | 2N6373 | 2N3054 | | 06 |
| 2N4233 | S | N | MO, F, SM, TR, TW | | | 2N6372 | (2N3054) | | 06 |
| 2N4233 | | | | | | 2N6261 | | | 06 |
| 2N4234 | S | P | MO, F, SQ, SM, SD | BSV15-10 | | 2N5783 | 2N4235 | | 16 |
| 2N4235 | S | P | MO, F, SM, SQ, ES | BSV16-10 | | 2N5782 | 2N5333 | | 16 |
| | | | | | | | | | |
| 2N4235 | | | | | | 2N5781 | | | 16, |
| 2N4236 | S | P | MO, F, SM, SQ, ES | BSV17-10 | | 2N5781 | 2N5333 | | 16 |
| 2N4237 | S | N | MO, F, SQ, SG, KE | BSX45-10 | BFX34 | 2N5786 | | | 06 |
| 2N4238 | S | N | MO, F, SQ, SG, KE | BSX46-10 | BFX34 | 2N5785 | 2N5784 | | 06 |
| 2N4239 | S | N | MO, F, SM, HS, KE | BSX47-10 | BFX34 | 2N5784 | | | 06 |
| | | | | | | | | | |
| 2N4240 | S | N | RC, TX, TR, UN | (BUY78) | | SE9331 | | | 06 |
| 2N4241 | G | N | AM, SD, MN | (AUY21IV) | AD149 | TI3027 | | 2S8471 | 01 |
| 2N4242 | G | P | SD | | | TI3027 | TI3028 | | 06 |
| 2N4243 | G | P | SD | | | TI3027 | TI3028 | | 06 |
| 2N4244 | G | P | SD | | | TI3027 | TI3028 | | 06 |
| | | | | | | | | | |
| 2N4245 | G | P | SD | | | TI3027 | TI3028 | | 06 |
| 2N4246 | G | P | SD | | | TI3027 | TI3028 | | 06 |
| 2N4247 | G | P | SD | | | TI3027 | TI3028 | | 06 |
| 2N4248 | S | P | F, CA, ME, RY, SS | BC416C | | 2N4058 | 2N5086 | | 01 |
| 2N4248 | | | | | | PN4248 18 | | | 01 |
| | | | | | | | | | |
| 2N4249 | S | P | F, CA, ME, RY, SS | (BC417B) | | 2N4058 | 2N5086 | | 01 |
| 2N4249 | | | | | | PN4249-18 | | | 01 |
| 2N4250 | S | P | F, CA, ME, RY, SS | BC416C | | 2N4059 | 2N5987 | | 01 |
| 2N4250 | | | | | | PN4250-18 | | | 01 |
| 2N4250A | S | N | F, TI | (BC416C) | | PN4250A | | 2SA828 | |

| TYPE | M/S | POL | MANUFAC | EUROPEAN | | AMERICAN | | JAPANESE | USE |
|------|-----|-----|---------|----------|--|----------|--|----------|-----|
| 2N4253 | S | N | TX, SQ, ET | | | 2N4252 | | | 02 |
| 2N4254 | S | N | TX | | | 2N4996 | MPS6547 | | 01 |
| 2N4254 | | | | | | 2N4770 | SE3005 | | 01 |
| 2N4255 | S | N | TX | | | 2N4997 | MPS6547 | | 01 |
| 2N4255 | | | | | | 2N5770 | SE3005 | | 01 |
| 2N4256 | S | N | GE, ID | BC167B | | 2N3904 | 2N5772 | | 01 |
| 2N4256 | | | | | | 2N4274 | | | 01 |
| 2N4257 | S | P | F, NS, RY, CA | | | PN4258-18 | | | 13 |
| 2N4258 | S | P | F, ES, RT, CA, NS | | | PN4258-18 | | | 13 |
| 2N4258A | S | P | F, NS, CA | | | PN4258A-18 | | | 13 |
| 2N4259 | S | N | SM | | | 2N4252 | | | 13 |
| 2N4260 | S | P | MO, HS, TI, F, RY | | | 2N4261 | | | 13 |
| 2N4261 | S | P | MO, HS, TI, F, RY | | | 2N4260 | | | 13 |
| 2N4264 | S | N | F, MO, BT | BSY63 | BC238A | 2N4275 | | | 10 |
| 2N4265 | S | N | F, MO, BT | BSY63 | BC238A | 2N4274 | | | 13 |
| 2N4267 | M | P | IL | | | SFB4669 | 2N4352 | | |
| 2N4268 | M | P | IL | | | SFB4670 | MFE3003 | | |
| 2N4269 | S | N | TR | | | 2N2243A | | | 01 |
| 2N4271 | S | N | TR, SQ | | | 2N5682 | | | 06 |
| 2N4272 | S | N | TR, SQ | | | 2N5682 | | | 06 |
| 2N4274 | S | N | F, Tx, CA, NP, RY | (BSY62) | BSX90 | 2N4419 | PN4274-18 | | 13 |
| 2N4275 | S | N | F, TX, NP, RY, TI | (BSY63) | | 2N4418 | PN4275-18 | | 13 |
| 2N4276 | G | P | MO | | | 2N4277 | | | 06 |
| 2N4277 | G | P | MO | | | 2N4279 | | | 06 |
| 2N4278 | G | P | MO | | | 2N4279 | | | 06 |
| 2N4279 | G | P | MO | | | 2N4281 | | | 06 |
| 2N4280 | G | P | MO | | | 2N4281 | | | 06 |
| 2N4281 | G | P | MO | | | 2N4283 | | | 06 |
| 2N4282 | G | P | MO | | | 2N4283 | | | 06 |
| 2N4283 | G | P | MO | | | 2N4282 | | | 06 |
| 2N4284 | S | P | NS | | | 2N2944 | 2N2945 | | 01 |
| 2N4285 | S | P | NS | | | 2N4060 | | | 01 |
| 2N4286 | S | N | SS, UP, NS | BC167 | BC168 | MPS6515 | TIS98 | 2SC458 | 01 |
| 2N4286 | | | | BC238C | BC207 | | | | 01 |
| 2N4286 | | | | BC171 | BC168A | | | | 01 |
| 2N4287 | S | N | NS, SS, UP | BC167A | BC277 | MPS6566 | TIS98 | 2SC458 | 01 |
| 2N4287 | | | | BC237 | BC207 | | | | 01 |
| 2N4287 | | | | BC171 | | | | | 01 |
| 2N4288 | S | P | NS, SS, UP | BC258A | BC178B | MPS6518 | | 2SC565 | 01 |
| 2N4288 | | | | BC213 | BC205 | | | | 01 |
| 2N4288 | | | | BC262 | | | | | 01 |
| 2N4289 | S | P | NS, SS, UP | BC257A | BC177B | 2N5086 | | 2SA565 | 01 |
| 2N4289 | | | | BC177 | BC307B | | | | 01 |
| 2N4290 | S | P | NS, UP, SS | (BC328-16) | BC124 | 2N5447 | MPS6539 | | 01 |
| 2N4290 | | | | BC206 | | | | | 01 |
| 2N4291 | S | P | NS, SS, UP | (BC327-16) | BC179 | 2N5447 | MPS6534 | | 01 |
| 2N4291 | | | | BC214 | BC206 | | | | 01 |
| 2N4291 | | | | BC263 | | | | | 01 |
| 2N4292 | S | N | NS | (BFX89) | BFX59 | 2N1132 | MPS6518 | | 01 |
| 2N4292 | | | | BC184 | BC209 | TIS62 | | | 01 |
| 2N4292 | | | | BC173 | BFX62 | | | | 01 |
| 2N4292 | | | | BC239 | | | | | 01 |
| 2N4293 | S | N | NS | BFX89 | BC179 | TIS62 | MPS6518 | | 01 |
| 2N4293 | | | | BC184 | BC209 | | | | 01 |
| 2N4293 | | | | BC173 | BC139 | | | | 01 |
| 2N4294 | S | N | BT, UP, SS, NS | | | 2N4264 | | | 13 |
| 2N4295 | S | N | BT, SS, NS | | | 2N4264 | | | 13 |
| 2N4296 | S | N | IT, SQ, SM | | | SE9331 | | | 16 |
| 2N4300 | S | N | TX, SM, SQ, UN, KE | (BSX63-6) | | 2N5336 | | | 06 |
| 2N4302 | J | N | TI, IL, SD, BT, NS | | | 2N5953 | E102 | | |
| 2N4302 | | | | | | 2N5337 | 2N5457 | | |
| 2N4303 | J | N | TI, IL, NS, BT | | | 2N5952 | IT108 | | |
| 2N4303 | | | | | | 2N5457 | | | |
| 2N4304 | J | N | TI, NS, BT | | | 2N5951 | E100 | | |
| 2N4305 | J | N | TW, SM, TR, KE, SQ | | | 2N4895 | | | 06 |
| 2N4307 | S | N | TW, SM, TR, KE, SQ | | | 2N4895 | 2N5357 | | 06 |
| 2N4309 | S | N | TW, SM, TR, KE, SQ | | | 2N4897 | 2N5337 | | 06 |
| 2N4311 | S | N | TW, SM, TR, KE, SQ | | | 2N4897 | 2N5337 | | 06 |
| 2N4313 | S | P | F, MS | | | 2N4423 | | | 12 |
| 2N4314 | S | P | RC, SM, SQ, ES | BSV1710 | | 2N5322 | | | 06 |
| 2N4338 | J | N | SX, NS, TD, TI, IL | | | 2N3460 | TN4398 | | |
| 2N4338 | | | | | | 2N4220A | | | |
| 2N4339 | J | N | SX, NS, TD, IL, SD | | | SFB5481 | TN4339 | | |
| 2N4339 | | | | | | 2N4220A | | | |
| 2N4340 | J | N | SX, IL, NS, TD, BT | | | 2N3459 | TN4340 | | |

| TYPE | M/S | POL | MANUFAC | EUROPEAN | | AMERICAN | | JAPANESE | USE |
|---|---|---|---|---|---|---|---|---|---|
| 2N4340 | | | | | | 2N4220A | 2N4221A | | |
| 2N4341 | J | N | SX, IL, NS, BT, TD | | | 2N3458 | TN4341 | | |
| 2N4342 | J | P | F, MO, SD, IL | | | 2N4343 | 2N3994 | | |
| 2N4342 | | | | | | P1118E | | | |
| 2N4343 | J | P | F, MO, IL | | | 2N4360 | 2N3993 | | |
| 2N4343 | | | | | | P1117E | 2N4342 | | |
| 2N4346 | G | N | RC | (AUY22III) | | | | | 06 |
| 2N4347 | S | N | RC, ML, PH, AM, Es | BDX12 | | | | | 06 |
| 2N4348 | S | N | AT, RC, Ss, ML, PP | (BUY58) | | 2N5630 | | | 06 |
| 2N4350 | S | N | CN, SQ, SM | | | 2N4349 | | | 06 |
| 2N4351 | M | N | MO, IL, CN | | | 2N4416 | 2N4416A | | |
| 2N4351 | | | | | | 2N4381 | | | |
| 2N4353 | M | P | GI, SQ, IL | | | SFB4379 | 2N4360 | | |
| 2N4354 | S | P | F, CA, NS, SS, CN | BFX39 | BSV16-6 | PN4356-5 | | | 01 |
| 2N4355 | S | P | F, CA, NS, SS, CN | BFX38 | BSV16-16 | PN4355-5 | | | 01 |
| 2N4356 | S | P | F, CA, NS, CN, ME | BFX41 | BSV17-6 | PN4356-5 | | | 01 |
| 2N4357 | S | P | CN, SG, F | BFX90 | | 2N2605 | 2N3494 | | 01 |
| 2N4357 | | | | | | 2N4889 | | | 01 |
| 2N4358 | S | P | CN, F, SG | BFX90 | | 2N2605 | 2N3494 | | 01 |
| 2N4358 | | | | | | 2N4889 | | | 01 |
| 2N4359 | S | P | F, MO, SG, SQ, IT | BFX37 | BC416B | 2N4248 | | | 01 |
| 2N4360 | J | P | F, MO, SD, IL | | | 2N4343 | SFB1986 | | |
| 2N4381 | J | P | F, IL | | | SF9130 | 2N2609 | | |
| 2N4381 | | | | | | 2N3330 | | | |
| 2N4382 | J | P | F, IL | | | SF9131 | 2N2609 | | |
| 2N4382 | | | | | | 2N3994 | | | |
| 2N4384 | S | N | TX, SP, ID, TR, FR | BC337-40 | | | | | 02 |
| 2N4386 | S | N | TX, SP, ID, TR, FR | BC337-40 | | | | | 02 |
| 2N4387 | S | P | TR, SQ | | | 2N5956 | 2N4898 | | |
| 2N4388 | S | P | TR, SQ, CN | | | 2N5955 | 2N4899 | | |
| 2N4388 | | | | | | P1069E | | | |
| 2N4390 | S | N | TX, AT, SM | BFR25 | (BF457) | 2N5058 | | | 10 |
| 2N4391 | J | N | SD, F, MU, NS, SX | | | 2N4091 | | | |
| 2N4392 | J | N | V, TX, SX, NS, SD | | | 2N3971 | | | |
| 2N4393 | J | N | SD, MU, NS, SX, TX | BSV68 | | 2N3972 | | | |
| 2N4395 | S | N | CN, SM, SD, TR, TW | | | 2N3715 | 2N5337 | | 06 |
| 2N4396 | S | N | CN, SM, SD, TR, TW | | | 2N3715 | 2N5337 | | 06 |
| 2N4397 | S | N | RC | | | 2N4252 | | | 05 |
| 2N4398 | S | P | MO, F, SQ, TX, CN | | | | | | 06 |
| 2N4399 | S | P | TX, SQ, CN, F, MO | | | 2N4398 | | | 06 |
| 2N4400 | S | N | F, MO, NS, BT | (BCX74-16) | | 2N5449 | 2N3642 | | 13 |
| 2N4401 | S | N | F, MO, BT, NS | (BC74-16) | | 2N5449 | 2N3643 | | 13 |
| 2N4402 | S | P | F, MO, BT, NS | (BCX76-16) | BC307VI | 2N2904 | 2N2905 | | 13 |
| 2N4402 | | | | | | EN2907 | | | 13 |
| 2N4403 | S | P | F, MO, NS | (BCX76-16) | BC307A | 2N2904 | EN2907 | | 13 |
| 2N4404 | S | P | MO, SQ, TI, SM, TR | BSV17-6 | | 2N1893 | | | 01 |
| 2N4405 | S | P | MO, SQ, TI, SM, TR | BSV17-10 | | 2N2405 | | | 01 |
| 2N4406 | S | P | MO, SQ, TI, SM, TR | (BSV17-6) | | | | | 01 |
| 2N4407 | S | P | MO, SQ, TI, SM, TR | (NSV17-10) | | | | | 01 |
| 2N4409 | S | N | F, MO, BT | (BF457) | | 2N5830 | | | 10 |
| 2N4410 | S | N | F, MO, BT | (BF457) | | 2N5830 | | | 10 |
| 2N4416 | J | N | SD, F, NU, SX, TX | | | 2N5398 | | | |
| 2N4416A | J | N | SX, TX, SD, NS, F | | | 2N4416 | 2N5398 | | |
| 2N4417 | J | N | SD | | | 2N4416 | | | |
| 2N4418 | S | N | IT | | | 2N4264 | 2N5772 | | 10 |
| 2N4418 | | | | | | 2N4275 | | | 10 |
| 2N4419 | S | N | IT | | | 2N4264 | 2N5772 | | 10 |
| 2N4419 | | | | | | 2N4274 | | | 10 |
| 2N4420 | S | N | IT | | | MPS3646 | 2N5769 | | 10 |
| 2N4420 | | | | | | 2N3646 | | | 10 |
| 2N4421 | S | N | IT | | | MPS3646 | 2N5769 | | 10 |
| 2N4421 | | | | | | 2N3646 | | | 10 |
| 2N4422 | S | N | IT | | | MPS3646 | | | 10 |
| 2N4423 | S | N | NS | | | 2N4421 | MPS3640 | | 10 |
| 2N4423 | | | | | | 2N5771 | EN2894A | | 10 |
| 2N4424 | S | N | GE, SP, ID, UP, Ss | (BC337-25) | BC337 | MPS3711 | 2N4401 | | 10 |
| 2N4424 | | | | | | 2N4946 | | | 10 |
| 2N4425 | S | N | GE, ID, SP, UP, Ss | (BC337-25) | BC337 | | | | 10 |
| 2N4427 | S | N | MO, PH, TX, RC, FE | (BFX55) | | | | | 06 |
| 2N4428 | S | N | F, MO, TX, SV, TW | (BFW16A) | BFX55 | | | | 06 |
| 2N4432 | S | N | LI, TX | BFW34 | BSX45 | | | | 02 |
| 2N4432 | | | | (BCY59VII) | | | | | 02 |
| 2N4436 | S | N | F, CA, RY, CN, NU | (BCX73-16) | | 2N5449 | | | 03 |
| 2N4437 | S | N | F, CN, RY, CA, NU | (BCX73-16) | | 2N5449 | | | 03 |
| 2N4438 | S | N | ET, SM | | | 2N3439 | | | 01 |

| TYPE | M/S | POL | MANUFAC | EUROPEAN | AMERICAN | | JAPANESE | USE |
|------|-----|-----|---------|----------|----------|---|----------|-----|
| 2N4439 | S | N | SM | | 2N3439 | | | 01 |
| 2N4440 | S | N | RC, TI, SV, RY, KE | (BLY23) | 2N3632 | | | 06 |
| 2N4445 | J | N | CR, TX, IL | | MFE2012 | SFC1783 | | |
| 2N4445 | | | | | 2N5432 | | | |
| 2N4446 | J | M | CR, TX, IL | | MFE2012 | SFC1784 | | |
| 2N4446 | | | | | | | | |
| 2N4447 | J | N | CR, TX, IL | | 2N5433 | | | |
| 2N4447 | | | | | MFE2012 | SFC1785 | | |
| 2N4448 | J | N | CR, TX, IL | | 2N5433 | | | |
| 2N4448 | | | | | MFE2012 | SFC1785 | | |
| | | | | | 2N5433 | | | |
| 2N4449 | S | N | F, SG | | 2N4275 | | | |
| 2N4450 | S | N | F | BFX95 | 2N3568 | | | 13 |
| 2N4451 | S | P | F | | 2N4313 | | | 13 |
| 2N4452 | S | P | F, SM | | 2N3638 | | | 10 |
| 2N4453 | S | P | F | | 2N4313 | | | 10 |
| | | | | | | | | 10 |
| 2N4572 | S | P | | | 2N4258 | | | |
| 2N4573 | S | N | | | 2N4275 | | | |
| 2N4576 | S | N | | | 2N3716 | | | 03 |
| 2N4856 | J | N | TX, F, MO, NS, SX | | 2N4091 | | | |
| 2N4856A | J | N | TX, MO, IL, NS, SD | | 2N4091 | | | |
| 2N4856J | J | N | | | 2N4856 | | | |
| 2N4857 | J | N | TX, F, MO, NS, SX | | 2N4092 | | | |
| 2N4857A | J | N | TX, MO, IL, NS, SD | | 2N4092 | | | |
| 2N4857J | J | N | | | 2N4857 | | | |
| 2N4858 | J | N | TX, F, MO, NS, SX | | 2N4093 | | | |
| 2N4858A | J | N | TX, MO, IL, NS, SD | | 2N4093 | | | |
| 2N4858J | J | N | | | 2N4858 | | | |
| 2N4859 | J | N | TX, IL, MU, F, MO | | 2N4091 | | | |
| 2N4859A | J | N | TX, MO, IL, NS, SD | | 2N4091 | | | |
| 2N4859J | J | N | | | 2N4859 | | | |
| 2N4860 | J | N | TX, MO, NS, SX, MU | | 2N4092 | | | |
| 2N4860A | J | N | TX, MO, IL, NS, SD | | 2N4092 | | | |
| 2N4860J | J | N | | | 2N4860 | | | |
| 2N4861 | J | N | TX, MO, NS, SX, IL | | 2N4093 | | | |
| 2N4861A | J | N | TX, MO, SX, IL, NS | | 2N4093 | | | |
| 2N4861J | J | N | | | 2N4861 | | | |
| 2N4862 | S | N | CN, PI, TR, KE, SD | | 2N5339 | | | |
| 2N4863 | S | N | PI, SD, TR, GX, CN | | 2N5682 | | | 06 |
| 2N4867 | J | N | SX, IL, TI, BT, TX | | 2N4220A | 2N5391 | | 06 |
| 2N4867A | J | N | SX, IL, TX, TI, BT | | 2N4220A | 2N5391 | | |
| 2N4868 | J | N | SX, IL, TI, BT, TX | | 2N4220A | 2N5392 | | |
| 2N4868A | J | N | SX, IL, TX, TI, BT | | 2N4220A | 2N5392 | | |
| 2N4869 | J | N | SX, IL, TI, BT, TX | | 2N4221A | 2N4222A | | |
| 2N4869 | | | | | 2N5395 | | | |
| 2N4869A | J | N | SX, IL, TX, BT, SD | | 2N4221A | 2N4222A | | |
| 2N4869A | | | | | 2N5395 | | | |
| 2N4872 | S | P | F | BFY64 | | | | 13 |
| 2N4873 | S | N | F, TR, SM | | | | 2SC639 | 13 |
| 2N4874 | S | N | TX, SM, RY | | 2N4875 | | | 02 |
| 2N4876 | S | N | TX, SM, RY | | 2N4875 | | | 02 |
| 2N4877 | S | N | MO, SM, F, SQ, TR | | 2N4239 | | | 06 |
| 2N4881 | S | N | TI, TX, BT | | 2N3365 | 2N5543 | | |
| 2N4882 | J | N | TI, TX, BT | | 2N3365 | 2N5543 | | |
| 2N4883 | J | N | TI, TX, BT | | 2N3365 | 2N5544 | | |
| 2N4884 | J | N | TI, TX, BT | | 2N3365 | 2N5544 | | |
| 2N4885 | J | N | TI, TX, BT | | 2N3365 | 2N5544 | | |
| 2N4886 | J | N | TI, TX, BT | | 2N3365 | 2N5544 | | |
| 2N4890 | S | P | TX, MO, SE, ML, TR | BCW80-16 | BSY16XVI | 2N4037 | | 10 |
| 2N4890 | | | | BSV16 | | | | 10 |
| 2N4895 | S | N | F, SM, SD, TW, KE | BFX34 | | 2N5336 | | 16 |
| 2N4896 | S | N | F, KE, SG, SQ, TW | BFX34 | 2N5337 | | | 16 |
| 2N4897 | S | N | F, SM, SD, TW, KE | BFX34 | 2N5338 | | | 16 |
| 2N4898 | S | P | MO, F, SD, SS, TR | BDX27-6 | 2N5954 | 2N5956 | | 06 |
| 2N4899 | S | P | F, MO, SD, SS, TR | BDX28-6 | 2N5955 | | | 06 |
| 2N4900 | S | P | MO, F, SQ, TR, CN | BDX29-6 | 2N5956 | 2N5954 | | 06 |
| 2N4901 | S | P | TX, MO, SE, F, ML | (BDX27-6) | 2N6469 | 2N6246 | | 06 |
| 2N4902 | S | P | F, MO, TX, ML, SQ | (BDX28-6) | 2N6346 | | | 06 |
| 2N4903 | S | P | F, MO, TX, ML, SQ | (BDX29-6) | 2N6247 | | | 06 |
| 2N4904 | S | P | TX, MO, SE, F, ML | (BDX27-6) | 2N6469 | 2N6246 | | 06 |
| 2N4905 | S | P | F, MO, TX, Ss, ML | (BDX28-6) | 2N6246 | | | 06 |
| 2N4906 | S | P | F, MO, TX, ML, Ss | (BDX29-6) | 2N6247 | | | 06 |
| 2N4907 | S | P | F, SQ | | 2N3791 | 2N6246 | | 06 |
| 2N4907 | | | | | 2N4909 | | | 06 |
| 2N4908 | S | P | F, SQ | | 2N3791 | 2N5875 | | 06 |
| 2N4908 | | | | | 2N6246 | | | 06 |

| TYPE | M/S | POL | MANUFAC | EUROPEAN | | AMERICAN | | JAPANESE | USE |
|---|---|---|---|---|---|---|---|---|---|
| 2N4909 | S | P | F, SQ | | | 2N3790 | 2N5876 | | 06 |
| 2N4909 | | | | | | 2N6247 | 2N5745 | | 06 |
| 2N4910 | S | N | MO, F, SM, TR, TW | | | 2N6374 | 2N6470 | | 06 |
| 2N4910 | | | | | | (2N3054) | 2N6250 | | 06 |
| 2N4910 | | | | | | 2N4911 | | | 06 |
| 2N4911 | S | N | MO, F, SM, TR, TW | | | 2N6373 | 2N6471 | | 06 |
| 2N4911 | | | | | | 2N3054 | 2N4912 | | 06 |
| 2N4912 | S | N | MO, F, SM, TR, TW | | | 2N6372 | (2N3054) | | 06 |
| 2N4912 | | | | | | 2N6261 | 2N4911 | | 06 |
| 2N4913 | S | N | TX, MO, F, SM, SQ | (BUY55) | | 2N6470 | 2N6253 | | 06 |
| 2N4914 | S | N | TX, MO, F, SM, PP | (BUY55) | | 2N6472 | 2N3055 | | 06 |
| 2N4915 | S | N | TX, MO, F, PP, SM | (BUY55) | | 2N6472 | 2N6254 | | 06 |
| 2N4916 | S | P | F, NS, SG, CA, RY | (BC415A) | BFX48 | | | | 13 |
| 2N4917 | S | P | F, CA, RY, TI, SG | (BC415B) | BFX48 | | | | 13 |
| 2N4918 | S | P | MO, UP, NP | BD240 | BD438 | TIP30 | 2N6124 | | 06 |
| 2N4918 | | | | BD132 | | SDC445 | | | 06 |
| 2N4919 | S | P | MO, NP, UP | BD240A | BD440 | TIP30A | 2N6125 | | 06 |
| 2N4919 | | | | BD138 | | SDD445 | | | 06 |
| 2N4919 | | | | BD240B | BD442 | TIP308 | TIP30A | | 06 |
| 2N4920 | S | P | MO, UP, NP | BD140 | | 2N6126 | SDE445 | | 06 |
| 2N4920 | | | | | | | | | 06 |
| 2N4921 | S | N | MO, NP, UP | BD239 | BD437 | TIP29 | 2N6121 | | 06 |
| 2N4921 | | | | BD131 | | SOC345 | | | 06 |
| 2N4922 | S | N | MO, UP, NP | BD239A | BD439 | TIP29A | 2N6122 | | 06 |
| 2N4922 | | | | BD137 | | SOD345 | | | 06 |
| 2N4923 | S | N | MO, NP, UP | BD239B | BD441 | TIP29B | TIP29A | | 06 |
| 2N4923 | | | | BD139 | | | | | 06 |
| | | | | | | 2N6123 | SDE345 | | 06 |
| 2N4924 | S | N | MO, SM, TR, UP HS | (BF457) | | | | | 02 |
| 2N4925 | S | N | MO, SQ, UP, HS, TR | (BF457) | | | | | 02 |
| 2N4926 | S | N | MO, F, SZ, TR, TX | BF258 | (BF458) | 2N3440 | | | 02 |
| 2N4927 | S | N | MO, F, SZ, TR, ET | BF258 | (BF458) | 2N3440 | | | 02 |
| 2N4928 | S | P | TX, MO, TR, SM | BFT28 | | 2N5415 | | | 01 |
| 2N4929 | S | P | MO, SQ, TR, SM | BFT28A | | 2N5415 | | | 01 |
| 2N4930 | S | P | MO, IC, SQ, TR, SZ | BFT28B | | 2N5415 | 2N5416 | | 01 |
| 2N4931 | S | P | IC, SM, SQ, TR, MO | BFT28C | | 2N4252 | | | 01 |
| 2N4934 | S | N | NS | | | | | | |
| 2N4935 | S | N | NS | | | 2N4252 | | | 02 |
| 2N4936 | S | N | NS | | | 2N4449 | | | 02 |
| 2N4944 | S | N | F, CA, NP, TI, CN | (BSX45-6) | | 2N4252 | | | 01 |
| 2N4945 | S | N | F, NP, TI, CN, RY | (BSX46-6) | | | | | 01 |
| 2N4946 | S | N | F, ET, RY, TI, CN | (BSX45-6) | | 2N4449 | | | 01 |
| 2N4951 | S | N | SP, GE, ML, TR, CN | BC337 | | 2N3705 | 2N5450 | | 01 |
| 2N4951 | | | | | | 2N4400 | 2N3641 | | 01 |
| 2N4952 | S | N | SP, Ss, CN, GE, ML | BC337 | | 2N3704 | 2N5499 | | 01 |
| 2N4952 | | | | | | 2N4401 | 2N3643 | | 01 |
| 2N4953 | S | N | SP, Ss, GE, ML, TR | BC337 | | 2N4401 | 2N3643 | | 01 |
| 2N4954 | S | N | SP, Ss, GE, ML, TR | BC338 | | 2N4449 | 2N4400 | | 01 |
| 2N4954 | | | | | | 2N4401 | 2N3641 | | 01 |
| 2N4960 | S | N | F, TR, SQ | BSX46-10 | | SE6020 | | | 01 |
| 2N4961 | S | N | F, SQ, TR, CN | BSX47-10 | | SE6021 | | | 01 |
| 2N4962 | S | N | F, SQ, TR, CN | (BSX46-10) | | SE6022 | | | 01 |
| 2N4963 | S | N | F, TR, SQ | (BSX47-10) | | SE6023 | | | 01 |
| 2N4964 | S | P | RY, CN, F, NP, TI | | | 2N4060 | | | 01 |
| 2N4965 | S | P | RY, CN, F, NP, TI | | | 2N4068 | | | 01 |
| 2N4966 | S | N | BT, CN, F, NP, RY | | | TIS99 | | | 01 |
| 2N4967 | S | N | CN, F, BT, RY, NS | | | TIS99 | | | 01 |
| 2N4968 | S | N | BT, CA, CN, F, NP | | | TIS99 | | | 01 |
| 2N4976 | S- | N | TW | | | 2N4875 | TIS39 | | 03 |
| 2N4977 | J | N | TI, TX | | | MFE2009 | SFB4380 | | |
| 2N4977 | | | | | | 2N5433 | | | |
| 2N4978 | J | N | TI, TX | | | MFE2008 | SFB4381 | | |
| 2N4978 | | | | | | 2N5433 | | | |
| 2N4979 | J | N | TI, ES, TX, BT, IL | | | MFE2007 | SFB4382 | | |
| 2N4979 | | | | | | 2N4860 | | | |
| 2N4994 | S | N | GE, TX, GE, CN | (BC237A) | | MPS3693 | 2N3903 | | 02 |
| 2N4994 | | | | | | 2N3693 | EN3903 | | 02 |
| 2N4995 | S | N | GE, TX, CN | (BC237B) | | MPS3694 | 2N3904 | | 02 |
| 2N4995 | | | | | | 2N3694 | EN3904 | | 02 |
| 2N4996 | S | N | TX, CN | | | 2N5770 | SE3002 | | 02 |
| 2N4997 | S | N | TX, CN | | | 2N5770 | SE3002 | | 02 |
| 2N4997 | | | | | | SE3005 | | | 02 |
| 2N5002 | S | N | F, PP, SQ, TX, KE | | | 2N5347 | | | 06 |
| 2N5003 | S | P | F, PP, SQ, TX, KE | | | 2N6186 | | | 06 |
| 2N5004 | S | N | F, PP, SD, TR, TX | | | 2N5348 | | | 06 |
| 2N5005 | S | P | F, PP, SQ, TX, KE | | | 2N6187 | | | |
| 2N5018 | J | P | TI, TX, IL | | | 2N3993 | TP5114 | | |

| TYPE | M/S | POL | MANUFAC | EUROPEAN | | AMERICAN | | JAPANESE | USE |
|------|-----|-----|---------|----------|--|----------|--|----------|-----|
| 2N5019 | J | P | TI, TX, IL | | | 2N3993 | TP5116 | | |
| 2N5020 | J | P | F, SG, IL | | | MFE4007 | SFB7459 | | |
| 2N5020 | | | | | | 2N2843 | | | |
| 2N5021 | J | P | F, IL | | | MFE4009 | SFB7460 | | |
| 2N5021 | | | | | | 2N2608 | | | |
| 2N5022 | S | P | F, RY, St, TI, IT | | | 2N2386 | | | 13 |
| 2N5023 | S | P | F, RY, St, TI, IT | | | 2N2386 | | | 13 |
| 2N5027 | S | N | CN, ID | | | 2N5769 | 2N3646 | | 10 |
| 2N5028 | S | N | CN, ID | | | 2N5769 | 2N3646 | | 10 |
| 2N5029 | S | N | NS | | | 2N5772 | 2N4275 | | |
| 2N5030 | S | N | NS | | | 2N5772 | 2N4274 | | |
| 2N5031 | S | N | MO, KM | (BFR15) | | 2N3683 | 2N5032 | | 02 |
| 2N5032 | S | N | MO, KM | (BFR15) | | 2N3683 | 2N5031 | | 02 |
| 2N5033 | J | P | F, IL, CN | | | 2N5460 | 2N5265 | | |
| 2N5033 | | | | | | 2N5266 | AsT5460 | | |
| 2N5033 | | | | | | P1069E | | | |
| 2N5034 | S | N | RC | | | 2N3055 | TIP33 | | 06 |
| 2N5034 | | | | | | 2N5877 | | | 06 |
| 2N5035 | S | N | RC | | | 2N3055 | TIP33 | | 06 |
| 2N5035 | | | | | | 2N5877 | | | 06 |
| 2N5036 | S | N | RC | | | TIP33 | 2N3055 | | 06 |
| 2N5036 | | | | | | 2N5877 | | | 06 |
| 2N5037 | S | N | RC | BD181 | | TIP33A | 2N5877 | | 06 |
| 2N5038 | S | N | RC, TX, PP, F, W | (BUY57) | | 2N5038 | | | 16 |
| 2N5039 | S | N | RC, TX, PP, F, W | (BUY57) | | 2N5039 | | | 16 |
| 2N5040 | S | P | F, NP, SS, CN | BSV15-6 | | 2N5041 | | | 01 |
| 2N5041 | S | P | F, SS, CN | BSV15-10 | | | | | 01 |
| 2N5042 | S | P | F, SS, CN | BS V15-10 | BFS45 | | | | 01 |
| 2N5043 | G | P | TX | (AFY42) | | | | | 01 |
| 2N5044 | G | P | TX | (AFY42) | | | | | 01 |
| 2N5045 | S | N | TX, IL, TI, BT, SD | | | 2N3956 | | | |
| 2N5046 | J | N | TX, SD, TI, IL | | | 2N3958 | | | |
| 2N5047 | J | N | TX, SD, TI, IL | | | 2N3958 | | | |
| 2N5050 | S | N | MO, TR, SQ | BDX25-6 | | 2N3584 | | | 06 |
| 2N5051 | S | N | MO, TR, SQ | (BDX25-6) | BD400 | 2N3584 | | | 06 |
| 2N5052 | S | N | MO, TR, SQ | (BDX25-6) | BD400 | SE9331 | 2N3584 | | 06 |
| 2N5053 | S | N | AM, PE | | | 2N918 | | | 02 |
| 2N5054 | S | N | AM, SQ, SM | | | 2N918 | | | 02 |
| 2N5055 | S | P | F, NS, CN | | | 2N3829 | 2N4313 | | 13 |
| 2N5056 | S | P | F, IT, NS, CN | | | 2N3829 | 2N4313 | | 13 |
| 2N5057 | S | P | F, IT, NS, CN | | | 2N3829 | EN2894A | | 13 |
| 2N5058 | S | N | F, TX, TR, SQ | BF259 | (BF459) | 2N5058 | 2N3439 | | 01 |
| 2N5059 | S | N | F, TX, SZ, TR, SQ | BF258 | (BF458) | 2N5059 | 2N3440 | | 01 |
| 2N5065 | S | N | F, SG | (BSY62B) | | | | | 13 |
| 2N5066 | S | N | CR | | | 2N2432 | | | 12 |
| 2N5067 | S | N | TX, MO, F, SF, PP | (BUY55) | | 2N6470 | 2N6254 | | 06 |
| 2N5068 | S | N | TX, MO, F, PP, SF | (BUY55) | | 2N6472 | | | 06 |
| 2N5069 | S | N | TX, MO, F, SF, PP | (BUY55) | | 2N6472 | 2N6254 | | 06 |
| 2N5072 | S | N | L, TW, SQ | BLY40 | | | | | 03 |
| 2N5073 | S | N | LI, SQ, TR, SM | BFW36 | BF458 | 2N5682 | | | 02 |
| 2N5078 | S | N | TI, IL, SD, TD, BT | | | SFB4385 | 2N4416 | | |
| 2N5082 | S | N | IC, SM, SD, TD, BT | | | 2N3055 | | | 16 |
| 2N5086 | S | P | F, MO, BT | BC416B | BC257A | 2N4058 | 2N4249 | 2SA565 | 01 |
| 2N5086 | | | | BC177 | BC307A | | | | 01 |
| 2N5087 | S | P | F, MO, BT | BC416C | BC259A | 2N4249 | | | 01 |
| 2N5087 | | | | BC179 | BC259B | | | | 01 |
| 2N5088 | S | N | F, MO, BT | BC413C | BC169C | SE4021 | | | 01 |
| 2N5088 | | | | BC237B | | | | | 01 |
| 2N5089 | S | N | F, MO, CN, BT | BC413C | BC169C | SE4021 | | | 01 |
| 2N5089 | | | | BC239C | | | | | 01 |
| 2N5091 | S | P | IC, SM, SZ, CN | | | 2N5416 | | | 01 |
| 2N5092 | S | N | IC, SM, SQ, CN, SZ | | | 2N3439 | | | 01 |
| 2N5103 | S | N | BT, IL, SD, TI, ES | | | SFB4547 | 2N3823 | | |
| 2N5104 | J | N | BT, NS, TI, IL, SD | | | SFB4548 | 2N3823 | | |
| 2N5105 | J | N | BT, NS, TI, IL, SD | | | SFB4549 | 2N3823 | | |
| 2N5106 | S | N | F, TR | (BSY34) | | 2N5399 | 2N4945 | | 01 |
| 2N5107 | S | N | F, CN, TR | (BSX49) | | 2N5399 | 2N4945 | | 01 |
| 2N5109 | S | N | MO, RC, SV, TD, RY | (BFX55) | | | | | 03 |
| 2N5110 | S | P | SZ, TR, CR | | | 2N5783 | 2N4234 | | 06 |
| 2N5111 | S | S | SZ, TR, CR | | | 2N4236 | | | 06 |
| 2N5112 | S | P | SZ, CR | | | 2N4234 | | | 06 |
| 2N5113 | S | P | SZ, CR | | | 2N4236 | | | 06 |
| 2N5114 | J | N | SD, NS, SX, IL | | | 2N3993 | TP5114 | | |
| 2N5115 | J | P | SD, NS, SX, IL | | | 2N3993 | TP5115 | | |
| 2N5116 | J | P | SD, NS, SX, IL | | | 2N3993 | SFB6046 | | |

236

| TYPE | M/S | POL | MANUFAC | EUROPEAN | | AMERICAN | | JAPANESE | USE |
|------|-----|-----|---------|----------|--|----------|--|----------|-----|
| 2N5116 | S | N | F, CN, ME, SG, St | (BF19B) | | TP5118 | | | 01 |
| 2N5126 | S | N | F, CN, NU, RY, St | (BFX89) | | TIS98 | | | 01 |
| 2N5127 | S | N | F, CN, ME, RY, TI | (BSY5B) | | TIS98 | | | 01 |
| 2N5128 | S | N | F, CN, ME, RY, TI | (BSY5B) | | PN5128-18 | 2N5451 | | 01 |
| 2N5129 | S | N | F, AT, CN, NU, NS | (BSX4B) | | 2N5451 | | | 01 |
| 2N5130 | S | N | F, CN, NU, RY, SS | (BFX89) | | PN5130-18 | 2N5450 | | 01 |
| 2N5131 | S | N | F, CN, BT, CA, St | (BC413B) | | 2N5451 | | | 01 |
| 2N5132 | S | N | F, CN, CA, SG, RY | (BC413B) | | 2N5451 | | | 01 |
| 2N5133 | S | N | F, CA, BT, NU, TI | BC413C | | PN5133-18 | 2N5449 | | 01 |
| 2N5134 | S | N | F, CN, CA, ME, NU | (BSY17) | | PN5134-18 | 2N4422 | | 13 |
| 2N5135 | S | N | F, CA, NP, NS, SG | (BC337-25) | | PN5135-5 | | | 01 |
| 2N5136 | S | N | F, CA, NU, NS, SG | (BC338-16) | | PN5136-5 | | | 01 |
| 2N5137 | S | N | F, CA, ME, NS, SS | BC338-16 | | | | | 01 |
| 2N5138 | S | P | F, CA, ME, SG, St | BC413C | | PN5138-18 | 2N4061 | | 01 |
| 2N5139 | S | P | F, BT, CA, NS, SG | (BC308A) | BC308VI | 2N3250 | | | 13 |
| 2N5140 | S | P | F, NS, St, CN | | | 2N3250 | | | 13 |
| 2N5141 | S | P | F, RY, CN | | | 2N3829 | | | 13 |
| 2N5142 | S | P | F, CN, NS, SG, TI | (BCW79-16) | | PN5142-5 | 2N3829 | | 13 |
| 2N5143 | S | P | F, CN, NU, RY, TI | (BCW75-16) | | 2N3829 | | | 13 |
| 2N5544 | S | N | F, SG | (BSX49) | | | | | 13 |
| 2N5145 | S | N | F, SG | (BSY34) | | | | | 13 |
| 2N5147 | S | P | F, SD, TR, TX, PP | | | 2N4031 | 2N5679 | | 06 |
| 2N5148 | S | P | F, TX, GX, PP, SD | (BSX63-6) | BSX63 | 2N5336 | 2N5681 | | 06 |
| 2N5148 | | | | BSW10 | BSW65 | | | | 06 |
| 2N5149 | S | P | F, PP, SQ, TX, CN | | | 2N4033 | 2N5679 | | 06 |
| 2N5150 | S | P | F, TX, GX, PP, SD | (BSX63-10) | | 2N5336 | 2N3019 | | 06 |
| 2N5150 | | | | | | 2N5681 | | | 06 |
| 2N5151 | | P | F, PP, TR, TX, KE | | | 2N4031 | | | 06 |
| 2N5152 | S | N | F, ES, KE, SM, SQ | BSX63 | BSW10 | 2N5337 | 2N5336 | | 06 |
| 2N5152 | | | | BSW65 | | | | | 06 |
| 2N5153 | S | P | F, PP, TR, TX, KE | | | 2N4033 | | | 06 |
| 2N5154 | S | N | F, ES, KE, TW, TX | | | 2N3019 | 2N5337 | | 06 |
| 2N5157 | S | | MO, TX, DD, SU, CN | (BUY79) | | FT423 | 2N5840 | | 16 |
| 2N5158 | J | N | CR | | | MFE2012 | | | |
| 2N5159 | J | N | CR | | | MFE2012 | | | |
| 2N5163 | J | N | BT, NS, TI, UP, IL | | | MPF102 | 2N5246 | | |
| 2N5163 | | | | | | 2N4300 | | | |
| 2N5172 | S | N | GE, SP, TT, CN | BC167B | BC237A | 2N4400 | 2N5135 | | 01 |
| 2N5174 | S | N | GE, CN | (BF457) | | | | | 01 |
| 2N5175 | S | N | GE, CN | (BF457) | | | | | 01 |
| 2N5176 | S | N | GE | (BF457) | | | | | 01 |
| 2N5179 | S | N | MO, RC, TI, SM | (BFS55) | | | | | 02 |
| 2N5180 | S | N | RC, ES, SM | (BFY90) | | | | | 02 |
| 2N5189 | S | N | RC, TX, NS, AT, SM | BSY34 | BSX45 | 2N3053 | | | 13 |
| 2N5189 | | | | BSS13 | | | | | 13 |
| 2N5190 | S | N | MO, NP | BD221 | BD241 | TIP31 | 2N6121 | | 06 |
| 2N5190 | | | | BD437 | | SDF345 | 45190 | | 06 |
| 2N5191 | S | N | MO, UP, NP | BD241A | BD439 | TIP31A | 2N6122 | | 06 |
| 2N5191 | | | | | | SDG345 | 45191 | | 06 |
| 2N5192 | S | N | MO, UP, NP | BD241B | BD441 | TIP31A | 2N6123 | | 06 |
| 2N5192 | | | | | | SDH345 | 4592 | | 06 |
| 2N5193 | S | P | MO, UP, NP | BD242 | BD438 | TIP32 | 2N6124 | | 06 |
| 2N5193 | | | | | | SDF445 | 45193 | | 06 |
| 2N5194 | S | P | MO, UP, NO | BD242A | BD440 | TIP32A | 2N6125 | | 06 |
| 2N5194 | | | | | | SDG445 | 45194 | | 06 |
| 2N5195 | S | P | MO, UP, NP | BD242B | BD442 | TIP32A | 2N6126 | | 06 |
| 2N5195 | | | | | | SDN445 | 45195 | | 06 |
| 2N5196 | J | N | SX, SD, TI, UP, IL | | | MMF5 | SFB6588 | | |
| 2N5196 | | | | | | S42098B | | | |
| 2N5197 | J | N | SX, SD, TI, IL, TX | | | MMF5 | 2N5545 | | |
| 2N5198 | J | N | SX, SD, TI, IL, TX | | | MMF5 | 2N5546 | | |
| 2N5199 | J | N | SX, SD, TX, TI, IL | | | MMF5 | 2N5547 | | |
| 2N5202 | S | N | CN, RC, SQ, TW, W | BDX75-6 | | 2N5874 | | | 16 |
| 2N5203 | S | N | L | BFW35 | BSX45 | | | | |
| 2N5208 | S | P | MO | | | 2N3905 | 2N3906 | | 02 |
| 2N5208 | | | | | | 2N4916 | | | 02 |
| 2N5209 | S | N | F, MO, BT | BC414B | BC237 | SE4010 | | | 01 |
| 2N5209 | | | | BC237A | BC237B | | | | 01 |
| 2N5209 | | | | BC237C | | | | | 01 |
| 2N5210 | S | N | F, MO | BC414C | BC237C | SE4010 | | | 01 |
| 2N5219 | S | N | F, MO, UP, BT | BC237B | BC237 | EN4124 | | | 01 |
| 2N5219 | | | | BC238B | BC238 | | | | 01 |
| 2N5219 | | | | BC239 | BC238C | | | | 01 |
| 2N5219 | | | | BC386I | | | | | 01 |
| 2N5220 | S | N | F, MO, BT, UP, AT | BC338-16 | BC338 | 2N5131 | | | 01 |

| TYPE | M/S | POL | MANUFAC | EUROPEAN | | AMERICAN | | JAPANESE | USE |
|------|-----|-----|---------|----------|--|----------|--|----------|-----|
| 2N5220 | | | | BC386L | | | | | 01 |
| 2N5221 | S | N | F, MO, UP, BT | BC328-16 | BC338 | 2N5143 | | | 01 |
| 2N5221 | | | | BC224 | | | | | 01 |
| 2N5222 | S | N | MO, UP | BF254 | BF224 | 2N5770 | 2N3563 | | 01 |
| 2N5223 | S | N | F, MO, UP, BT | BC236C | BC239B | EN4124 | | | 01 |
| | | | | | | | | | |
| 2N5224 | S | N | F, MO, UP, BT | BSX48 | | 2N4274 | | | 13 |
| 2N5225 | S | N | F, MO, UB, TU, P | BC338-25 | BC338XVI | 2N3566 | | | 01 |
| 2N5225 | | | | BC338 | BC358L | | | | 01 |
| 2N5226 | S | P | F, MO, UP, BT | BC328-25 | BC181 | 2N3638 | 2N3638A | | 01 |
| 2N5227 | S | P | F, MO, BT, UP | BC415C | BC224 | EN4126 | | | 01 |
| | | | | | | | | | |
| 2N5228 | S | P | F, MO, UP, BT | BSS22 | | 2N3639 | | | 13 |
| 2N5232 | S | N | GE, ID, SP, CN | (BC167B) | | 2N5961 | 2N3565 | | 01 |
| 2N5232A | S | N | GE, ID, SP, CN | (BC414B) | BC167A | | | | |
| 2N5236 | S | N | F, SG, SQ, SM | | | 2N3564 | | | 02 |
| 2N5237 | S | N | SD, GX, PI, SQ, TW | | | 2N5237 | | | 13 |
| | | | | | | | | | |
| 2N5239 | S | N | RC, SF, SU, SM | BUY77 | | 2N6250 | | | 06 |
| 2N5240 | S | N | RC, SU, SF, SM | BUY78 | BDY97 | FT411 | | | 06 |
| 2N5241 | S | N | TX, MO, DD, SD, SU | BUX18C | (BUY79) | 2N5805 | | | 16 |
| 2N5244 | S | P | F, SG, IT | | | 2N4922 | | | 16 |
| 2N5245 | J | N | TX, IL, TI, BT, NS | | | 2N5486 | | | |
| | | | | | | | | | |
| 2N5246 | J | N | TX, IL, BT, NS | | | 2N5484 | | | |
| 2N5247 | J | N | TX, NS, IL | | | 2N5486 | | | |
| 2N5248 | J | N | TX, NS | | | MPF102 | 2N5486 | | |
| 2N5249 | S | N | GE, CN | BC167C | BC167B | 2N5961 | 2N3565 | | 01 |
| 2N5249A | S | N | GE, CN | (BC414C) | | SE4020 | | | 01 |
| | | | | | | | | | |
| 2N5254 | S | P | CN, IL | | | TIS51 | | | 04 |
| 2N5262 | S | N | RC, TX, SM, AT | (BSY34) | BFX34 | 2N5266 | | | 13 |
| 2N5262 | | | | BSS14 | | | | | 13 |
| 2N5264 | S | N | F, SM, TR, SQ | (BUY72) | | 2N5610 | 2N5804 | | 16 |
| 2N5265 | J | P | MO, IL | | | 2N2608 | | | |
| | | | | | | | | | |
| 2N5266 | J | P | MO, IL | | | 2N2608 | | | |
| 2N5267 | J | P | MO, IL | | | 2N2609 | | | |
| 2N5268 | J | P | MO, IL | | | 2N2609 | | | |
| 2N5269 | J | P | MO, IL | | | 2N2609 | | | |
| 2N5270 | J | P | MO, IL | | | 2N2609 | | | |
| | | | | | | | | | |
| 2N5277 | S | N | TI, TX, BT | | | 2N3822 | SFB9221 | | |
| 2N5277 | | | | | | U1715 | | | |
| 2N5278 | J | N | TI, TX, BT | | | 2N5364 | SFB9222 | | |
| 2N5278 | | | | | | U1715 | | | |
| 2N5279 | S | N | IC, SM, SQ, ET, SZ | | | 2N3439 | | | 02 |
| | | | | | | | | | |
| 2N5280 | S | N | IC, SZ, SQ, SM | | | 2N4063 | | | 02 |
| 2N5281 | S | P | IC, SZ, SQ, SM | | | 2N5415 | | | 01 |
| 2N5282 | S | P | IC, SM, SQ, CN, SZ | | | 2N5416 | | | 01 |
| 2N5284 | S | N | F, GX, SM, SQ, TW | BDY90 | | | | | 06 |
| 2N5288 | S | N | F, SM, SQ, TW, KE | BDY90 | | | | | 06 |
| | | | | | | | | | |
| 2N5292 | S | P | F | | | 2N4313 | | | 13 |
| 2N5293 | S | N | RC, SE, NP, SD, F | BD220 | BD441 | TIP31A | 2N6123 | | 06 |
| 2N5293 | | | | | | SD345 | 2N6122 | | 06 |
| 2N5294 | S | N | RC, SE, NP, UP, F | BD220 | BD441 | TIP31A | 2N6123 | | 06 |
| 2N5294 | | | | | | SD345 | 2N6122 | | 06 |
| | | | | | | | | | |
| 2N5295 | S | N | RC, SE, NP, SD, F | BD221 | BD439 | TIP31 | 2N6121 | | 06 |
| 2N5295 | | | | | | SDA345 | 2N6122 | | 06 |
| 2N5296 | S | N | RC, SE, NP, SD, F | BD221 | BD439 | 2N5298 | 2N3054 | | 06 |
| 2N5296 | | | | | | TIP31 | 2N6121 | | 06 |
| 2N5296 | | | | | | SDA345 | 2N6122 | | 06 |
| | | | | | | | | | |
| 2N5297 | S | N | RC, NP, SD, F | BD222 | BD441 | TIP31A | 2N6122 | | 06 |
| 2N5297 | | | | | | SDB345 | 2N6123 | | 06 |
| 2N5298 | S | N | RC, NP, SD, F | BD222 | BD441 | TIP31A | 2N6122 | | 06 |
| 2N5298 | | | | | | SDB345 | 2N6123 | | 06 |
| 2N5301 | S | N | TX, MO, F, SQ, SM | (BUY57) | | 2N3771 | 2N6258 | | 06 |
| | | | | | | | | | |
| 2N5302 | S | N | TX, MO, F, SQ, TF | BDY29 | (BUY57) | 2N6258 | | | 06 |
| 2N5303 | S | N | F, MO, TX, TF, SQ | (BUY57) | | 2N6258 | | | 06 |
| 2N5305 | S | N | TX, GE, ID, CN | BDY29 | | | | | 04 |
| 2N5309 | S | N | GE, CN | BC167A | | 2N5830 | | 2SC458 | 01 |
| 2N5310 | S | N | GE, CN | BC167A | | 2N5961 | 2N5830 | 2SC458 | 01 |
| | | | | | | | | | |
| 2N5311 | S | N | GE, CN | BC167B | | 2N5961 | 2N3635 | 2SC458 | 01 |
| 2N5311 | | | | | | 2N3565 | | | 01 |
| 2N5312 | S | P | SD, PI, SM, TR, CN | | | 2N5386 | | | 01 |
| 2N5313 | S | P | F, SD, PI, SM, TR | | | | | | 06 |
| 2N5314 | S | P | SD, PP, SO, TR, PI | | | 2N5386 | | | 06 |
| | | | | | | | | | |
| 2N5316 | S | P | SD, PI, SM, TR, CN | | | 2N5384 | | | 06 |
| 2N5317 | S | N | SD, F, PI, SM, TR | | | | | | 06 |
| 2N5318 | S | P | SD, PI, SM, TR, CN | | | 2N5384 | | | 06 |
| 2N5320 | S | N | F, RC, CN, SM, TH | (BSV17-10) | BSY94 | | | | 16 |
| 2N5320 | | | | BSS15 | | | | | 16 |

| TYPE | M/S | POL | MANUFAC | EUROPEAN | | AMERICAN | | JAPANESE | USE |
|------|-----|-----|---------|----------|--|----------|--|----------|-----|
| 2N5321 | S | N | F, RC, CN, SM, TR | (BSV17-10) | BSS16 | | | | 16 |
| 2N5321 | | | | BSV93 | | | | | 16 |
| 2N5322 | S | P | F, RC, AT, SQ, TR | (BSV17-10) | | 2N4036 | | | 16 |
| 2N5323 | S | P | F, RC, CN, SM, SQ | (BSV17-10) | BSS18 | 2N4036 | | | 16 |
| 2N5325 | G | P | MO, TR, SQ | | | 2N5324 | | | 16 |
| 2N5331 | S | N | TW, KE, SD, TR, GX | | | 2N3265 | | | 16 |
| 2N5334 | S | N | F, MO, SM, TR, TW | BSX63-10 | | | | | 16 |
| 2N5335 | S | N | F, MO, SM, TR, TW | BSX63-10 | | | | | 16 |
| 2N5344 | S | P | MO, TR, SQ | | | 2N6211 | | | 16 |
| 2N5345 | S | P | MO, TR, SQ | | | 2N6212 | | | 16 |
| 2N5354 | S | P | GE, SE, ML, SP, NU | (BC327-16) | BC328 | MPS3638 | 2N3638 | | 01 |
| 2N5355 | S | P | GE, SE, SP, NU, ML | (BC327-16) | BC328 | MPS3638A | 2N3639A | | 01 |
| 2N5356 | S | P | GE, SE, ML, NU, SP | (BC327-25) | BC328 | MPS3638 | 2N3639 | | 01 |
| 2N5356 | | | | | | 2N4355 | | | 01 |
| 2N5358 | J | N | MO, NS, TX, IL | | | 2N4220A | | | |
| 2N5359 | J | N | MO, NS, TX, IL | | | 2N4220A | | | |
| 2N5360 | J | N | MO, NS, TX, IL | | | 2N4221A | | | |
| 2N5361 | J | N | MO, TX, NS, IL | | | 2N4221A | | | |
| 2N5362 | J | N | MO, NS, TX, IL | | | 2N4221A | | | |
| 2N5363 | J | N | MO, NS, TX, IL | | | 2N4223 | | | |
| 2N5364 | J | N | MO, NS, TS, IL | | | 2N4223 | | | |
| 2N5365 | S | N | GE, FR, SP, Ss, ML | (BC327-16) | BC327 | 2N3644 | | | 01 |
| 2N5366 | S | P | GE, Ss, ML, SP, CN | (BC327-16) | BC337 | 2N4403 | EN2907 | | 01 |
| 2N5366 | | | | BC327 | | 2N3644 | | | 01 |
| 2N5367 | S | P | GE, FR, SP, Ss, ML | (BC327-25) | BC327 | 2N4403 | 2N3644 | | 01 |
| 2N5367 | | | | | | 2N4355 | | | 01 |
| 2N5368 | S | N | GE, SP, ID, FR | BCX73-16 | | | | | 01 |
| 2N5369 | S | N | GE, SP, ID, FR | BCX73-16 | | | | | 01 |
| 2N5370 | S | N | GE, FR, ID, SP | BCX73-40 | | | | | 01 |
| 2N5371 | S | N | GE, SP, ID, FR | BCX73-25 | | | | | 01 |
| 2N5372 | S | P | GE, SP, ID, FR | BCX75-16 | | | | | 01 |
| 2N5373 | S | P | GE, SP, ID, FR | BCX75-16 | | | | | 01 |
| 2N5374 | S | P | GE, SP, ID, FR | BCX75-25 | | | | | 01 |
| 2N5375 | S | P | GE, SP, ID, FR | BCX75-25 | | | | | 01 |
| 2N5386 | S | P | TX, PP, SD, TR, SM | | | 2N5380 | | | 01 |
| 2N5389 | S | N | TX, SQ, KS, TR | | | 2N5388 | | | 01 |
| 2N5391 | J | N | TI | | | 2N5358 | 2N5359 | | |
| 2N5391 | | | | | | 2N4867A | | | |
| 2N5392 | J | N | TI | | | 2N5360 | 2N5361 | | |
| 2N5392 | | | | | | 2N4868A | | | |
| 2N5393 | J | N | TI | | | 2N5360 | 2N5362 | | |
| 2N5393 | | | | | | 2N4868A | | | |
| 2N5394 | J | N | TI | | | 2N5361 | 2N5362 | | |
| 2N5394 | | | | | | 2N4869A | | | |
| 2N5395 | J | N | TI | | | 2N5362 | 2N4869A | | |
| 2N5396 | J | N | TI | | | 2N5362 | 2N5363 | | |
| 2N5396 | | | | | | 2N4869A | | | |
| 2N5397 | J | N | SX, IL, TX, BT | | | MFE2001 | 2N5078 | | |
| 2N5398 | J | N | SX, BT, IL, TX | | | MFE2001 | 2N5078 | | |
| 2N5400 | S | P | MO, F, BT | | | 2N4888 | | | 01 |
| 2N5401 | S | P | MO, BT, F | | | 2N4889 | | | 01 |
| 2N5404 | S | P | SD, SM, TR, PP, SQ | | | 2N5384 | | | 06 |
| 2N5405 | S | P | SD, SM, TR, PP, SQ | | | 2N5384 | | | 06 |
| 2N5406 | S | P | SD, SM, TR, PP, SQ | | | 2N5384 | | | 06 |
| 2N5407 | S | P | SD, SM, TR, PP, SQ | | | 2N5384 | | | 06 |
| 2N5418 | S | N | GE | (BC337-16) | | | | | 01 |
| 2N5419 | S | N | GE | (BC337-25) | | | | | 01 |
| 2N5420 | S | N | GE | (BC337-40) | | | | | 01 |
| 2N5427 | S | N | MO, F, KE, SQ, TW | BDX26-6 | | 2N6372 | | | 16 |
| 2N5429 | S | N | MO, GX, F, KE, SQ | BDX25-10 | | 2N6465 | | | 16 |
| 2N5430 | S | N | MO, GX, SM, TR, F | BDX25-10 | | | | | 16 |
| 2N5432 | J | N | SX, IL, TX, BT, NS | | | MFE2012 | SFC1783 | | |
| 2N5432 | | | | | | 2N4445 | | | |
| 2N5433 | J | N | SX, IL, TX, BT, NS | | | MFE2012 | SFC1784 | | |
| 2N5433 | | | | | | 2N4447 | | | |
| 2N5434 | J | N | SX, IL, TX, BT, NS | | | MFE2012 | SFC1785 | | |
| 2N5434 | | | | | | 2N4446 | | | |
| 2N5447 | S | P | TX, S, GE, TF | BC307 | BC177 | 2N5556 | MPS3638A | | 01 |
| 2N5447 | | | | BC328 | BC307A | 2N3638A | | | 01 |
| 2N5448 | S | P | GE, TX, S, TX, TF | BC307A | BC307 | MPS3638 | 2N3638 | | 01 |
| 2N5448 | | | | BC307VI | | | | | 01 |
| 2N5449 | S | N | GE, TX, TF, S | BC337-25 | | 2N4401 | 2N3566 | | 01 |
| 2N5450 | S | N | GE, TX, S, TF | BC337-16 | | 2N4400 | SE6001 | | 01 |
| 2N5451 | S | N | GE, TX, S | BC337-40 | | 2N4401 | 2N3566 | | 01 |
| 2N5452 | J | N | SD, IL | | | MMF5 | 2N5545 | | |

| TYPE | M/S | POL | MANUFAC | EUROPEAN | | AMERICAN | | JAPANESE | USE |
|---|---|---|---|---|---|---|---|---|---|
| 2N5452 | | | | | | | | | |
| 2N5453 | J | N | SD, IL | | | 2N5561 | | | |
| 2N5453 | | | | | | MMF5 | 2N5545 | | |
| 2N5454 | | | | | | 2N5562 | | | |
| 2N5454 | J | N | SD, IL | | | MMF5 | 2N5546 | | |
| | | | | | | 2N5563 | | | |
| 2N5455 | S | P | F, SD | | | | | | |
| 2N5457 | J | N | MO, NS, IL | | | | | | 13 |
| 2N5458 | J | N | MO, NS, IL | | | 2N5963 | 2N4302 | | |
| 2N5459 | J | N | MO, NS, IL | | | 2N5952 | 2N4303 | | |
| 2N5460 | J | P | MO, TX, IC | | | 2N5951 | 2N4303 | | |
| | | | | | | P1118E | | | |
| 2N5461 | J | P | MO, TX, IL | | | P1117E | | | |
| 2N5462 | J | P | MO, TX, IL | | | 2N4360 | | | |
| 2N5468 | J | N | SD, TR | | | SE9052 | | | |
| 2N5471 | J | P | MO, SQ | | | 2N2841 | | | 06 |
| 2N5472 | J | P | MO, SQ | | | 2N2842 | | | |
| 2N5473 | J | P | MO, SQ | | | 2N2606 | | | |
| 2N5474 | J | P | MO, SQ, IL | | | 2N2607 | | | |
| 2N5475 | J | P | MO, SQ, IL | | | 2N2607 | | | |
| 2N5476 | J | P | MO, SQ, IL | | | 2N2607 | | | |
| 2N5484 | J | N | MO, NS, TF, IL | | | 2N5246 | U1994E | | |
| 2N5485 | J | N | MO, NS, TF, IL | | | 2N5245 | U1994E | | |
| 2N5486 | J | N | MO, NS, TF, IL | | | 2N5247 | U1994E | | |
| 2N5490 | S | N | RC, SD, NP | (BD439) | | 2N6122 | 2N6121 | | 06 |
| 2N5491 | S | N | RC, SD, NP | (BD439) | | 2N6122 | 2N6121 | | 06 |
| 2N5492 | S | N | RC, SD, NP | (BD441) | | 2N6130 | 2N6122 | | 06 |
| 2N5493 | S | N | RC, SD, NP | (BD441) | | 2N6130 | 2N6122 | | 06 |
| 2N5494 | S | N | RC, SD, NP | (BD439) | | 2N6131 | 2N6129 | | 06 |
| 2N5494 | | | | | | 2N6121 | | | 06 |
| 2N5495 | S | N | RC, SD, NP | (BD439) | | 2N6129 | 2N6121 | | 06 |
| 2N5496 | S | N | RC, SD, NP | (BD441) | | 2N6131 | 2N6123 | | 06 |
| 2N5497 | S | N | RC, SD, NP | (BD441) | | 2N6131 | 2N6123 | | 06 |
| 2N5515 | J | N | SX, TX, IL | | | 2N5561 | | | |
| 2N5516 | J | N | SX, TX, IL | | | 2N5545 | 2N5562 | | |
| 2N5517 | J | N | SX, TX, IL | | | 2N5546 | 2N5563 | | |
| 2N5518 | J | N | SX, TX, IL | | | 2N5547 | 2N5563 | | |
| 2N5519 | J | N | SD, SX, TX, IL | | | 2N5045 | SU2369 | | |
| 2N5520 | J | N | SX, TX, IL | | | 2N5561 | | | |
| 2N5521 | J | N | SX, TX, IL | | | 2N5545 | SU2365A | | |
| 2N5522 | J | N | SX, TX, IL | | | 2N5546 | SU2367A | | |
| 2N5523 | J | N | SX, TX, IL | | | 2N5547 | SU2369A | | |
| 2N5524 | J | N | SX, TX, IL | | | 2N5045 | SU2081 | | |
| 2N5539 | S | N | SD, SQ, TW, SM, TR | | | 3N265 | | | 16 |
| 2N5543 | J | N | TX, TR | | | 2N3822 | 2N4882 | | |
| 2N5544 | J | N | TX, TR | | | 2N3822 | 2N4884 | | |
| 2N5545 | J | N | TX, SX, IL | | | MMF5 | 2N3954 | | |
| 2N5546 | J | N | TX, SX, IL | | | MMF5 | 2N3955 | | |
| 2N5547 | J | N | TX, SX, IL | | | MMF5 | 2N3956 | | |
| 2N5548 | J | P | TX | | | MFE3003 | | | |
| 2N5549 | J | N | TX, IL | | | 2N4093 | | | |
| 2N5550 | S | N | F, MO, BT | (BF458) | BF176 | 2N5831 | | | 01 |
| 2N5550 | | | | BF178 | | | | | 01 |
| 2N5551 | S | N | F, MO | (BF458) | BF176 | 2N5833 | | | 01 |
| 2N5551 | | | | BF178 | | | | | 01 |
| 2N5555 | J | N | MO, NS, IL | | | 2N5949 | U2047E | | |
| 2N5556 | J | N | MO, BT, IL | | | 2N3821 | | | |
| 2N5557 | J | N | MO, IL, BT | | | 2N5361 | | | |
| 2N5558 | J | N | MO, IL, BT | | | 2N5362 | | | |
| 2N5560 | S | N | SD, SQ, TW, UN, SM | | | 3N265 | | | 16 |
| 2N5561 | J | N | SD, UN | | | SU2365E | | | |
| 2N5562 | J | N | SD, UN | | | 2N5545 | 2N4085 | | |
| 2N5563 | J | N | SD, UN | | | 2N5547 | 2N4085 | | |
| 2N5564 | J | N | NS, SX, SD, IL | | | | | | 23 |
| 2N5565 | J | N | NS, SX, SD, IL | | | | | | 23 |
| 2N5566 | J | N | NS, SX, SD, IL | | | | | | 23 |
| 2N5581 | S | N | MO, SQ, TI, SM, TR | BCW74-16 | | | | | |
| 2N5582 | S | N | MO, SQ, TI, SM, TR | BCW74-16 | | | | | |
| 2N5592 | J | N | SD | | | | | | |
| 2N5593 | J | N | SD | | | 2N5392 | | | |
| 2N5594 | J | N | SD, MO | | | 2N5392 | | | |
| 2N5597 | S | P | SQ, TR | | | 2N5392 | | | |
| | | | | | | 2N5955 | | | 06 |
| 2N5598 | S | N | GX, SM, TR, KE, SQ | | | 2N5202 | 2N6202 | | 06 |
| 2N5599 | S | P | SQ, TR | | | 2N5954 | | | 06 |
| 2N5600 | S | N | KE, SQ, TW, SM, TR | | | 2N6500 | 2N3879 | | 06 |
| 2N5601 | S | P | SQ, TR | | | 2N5954 | | | 06 |
| 2N5602 | S | N | KE, SM, TR, TW, SQ | | | 2N3879 | | | 06 |

| TYPE | M/S | POL | MANUFAC | EUROPEAN | AMERICAN | | JAPANESE | USE |
|------|-----|-----|---------|----------|----------|---|----------|-----|
| 2N5604 | S | N | KE, SQ, SM, TR, TW | | 2N6500 | | | 06 |
| 2N5606 | S | N | TR, SM, TW, SQ, KE | | 2N3879 | | | 06 |
| 2N5608 | S | N | KE, SQ, TW, SM, TR | | 2N389 | | | 06 |
| 2N5610 | S | N | KE, SQ, TW, SM, TR | | 2N6500 | | | 06 |
| 2N5612 | S | N | KE, SQ, TW, SM, TR | | 2N6500 | | | 06 |
| 2N5613 | S | P | KE, PP, TR, SQ | | 2N6246 | | | 06 |
| 2N5614 | S | N | TR, TW, SM, SQ, KE | | 2N5039 | | | 06 |
| 2N5615 | S | P | TR, PP, KE, SQ | | 2N6247 | | | 06 |
| 2N5616 | S | P | TW, SQ, KE, SM, TR | | 2N5038 | | | 06 |
| 2N5617 | S | P | KE, SQ, TR, PP | | 2N6242 | | | 06 |
| 2N5618 | S | N | KE, SQ, TW, SM, TR | | 2N5038 | | | 06 |
| 2N5619 | S | P | KE, SQ, TR, PP | | 2N6248 | | | 06 |
| 2N5620 | S | N | KE, SQ, TW, SM, TR | | 2N6496 | 2N5038 | | 06 |
| 2N5622 | S | N | KE, SQ, TW, SM, TR | | 2N5881 | 2N5039 | | 06 |
| 2N5623 | S | P | KE, SQ, TR, PP | | 2N5880 | | | 06 |
| 2N5624 | S | N | KE, SQ, TW, SM, TR | | 2N5878 | 2N5038 | | 06 |
| 2N5625 | S | P | KE, SQ, TR, PP | | 2N5880 | | | 06 |
| 2N5626 | S | N | KE, TR, TW, SQ, SM | | 2N5882 | 2N5038 | | 06 |
| 2N5628 | S | N | TR, TW, SM, KE, SQ | | 2N6496 | 2N5038 | | 06 |
| 2N5629 | S | N | MO, SM, TR, TW, KE | | 2N5629 | 2N4346 | | 06 |
| 2N5629 | | | | | (2N4347) | 2N6259 | | 06 |
| 2N5630 | S | N | MO, SM, TR, TW, KE | | 2N4348 | (2N4347) | | 06 |
| 2N5630 | | | | | 2N6259 | | | 06 |
| 2N5631 | S | N | MO, SM, TR, KE, SQ | | 2N3773 | (2N3442) | | 06 |
| 2N5631 | | | | | 2N6259 | | | 06 |
| 2N5632 | S | N | MO, SQ, TW, TR, SM | | 2N4348 | 2N4347 | | 06 |
| 2N5632 | | | | | 2N3773 | | | 06 |
| 2N5633 | S | N | MO, SQ, TW, SM, TR | | 2N5630 | 2N4348 | | 06 |
| 2N5633 | | | | | 2N4347 | 2N3773 | | 06 |
| 2N5634 | S | N | MO, SQ, TR, SM | BDY37 | 2N5631 | 2N3442 | | 06 |
| 2N5634 | | | | | 2N3773 | | | 06 |
| 2N5636 | S | N | MO, SD, SV | | 2N5681 | | | 01 |
| 2N5638 | J | N | MO, NS, IL | | TIS73 | U1897E | | |
| 2N5639 | J | N | MO, IL, NS | | TIS74 | U1899E | | |
| 2N5640 | J | N | MO, NS, IL | | TIS75 | U1899E | | |
| 2N5647 | J | N | SX, IL | | MFE2093 | TN4119 | | |
| 2N5648 | J | N | SX, IL | | MFE2094 | TN4119 | | |
| 2N5649 | J | N | SX, IL | | MFE2094 | TN4119 | | |
| 2N5653 | J | N | MO, NS, IL | | 2N5639 | TIS74 | | |
| 2N5653 | | | | | U1897E | | | |
| 2N5654 | J | N | MO, NS, IL | | 2N5640 | TIS75 | | |
| 2N5654 | | | | | U1897E | | | |
| 2N5655 | S | N | MO | BF338 | FT47 | 2N6175 | | 06 |
| 2N5656 | S | N | MO | | FT48 | 2N6176 | | 06 |
| 2N5657 | S | N | MO | | FT49 | 2N6177 | | 06 |
| 2N5660 | S | N | UN, SM, TR, KE, SQ | | 2N6077 | SE9331 | | 16 |
| 2N5660 | | | | | 2N6078 | 2N6233 | | 16 |
| 2N5661 | S | N | UN, SM, TR, KE, SQ | | SE9331 | 2N6079 | | 16 |
| 2N5661 | | | | | 2N6234 | | | 16 |
| 2N5664 | S | N | UN, SM, TR, KE, SQ | | 2N6077 | 2N6078 | | 16 |
| 2N5664 | | | | | 2N6233 | | | 16 |
| 2N5665 | S | N | UN, SM, TR, KE, SQ | | 2N6079 | 2N6234 | | 16 |
| 2N5668 | J | N | MO, NS, IL | | 2N5953 | 2N4302 | | |
| 2N5669 | J | N | MO, NS, IL | | 2N4303 | | | |
| 2N5670 | J | N | MO, NS, IL | | U1873E | | | |
| 2N5671 | S | N | RC, TX, PI, TR, TW | (BUY57) | MJ802 | | | 16 |
| 2N5672 | S | N | TX, SE, SG, RC, TR | (BUY58) | 2N3265 | | | 16 |
| 2N5675 | S | P | SD, TR, SQ | | 2N5679 | | | 06 |
| 2N5678 | S | P | SD, TR, SQ | | 2N3265 | | | 16 |
| 2N5679 | S | P | F, MO, SM, TR, ES | (BSV1710) | | | | 06 |
| 2N5680 | S | P | F, MO, SQ, TR, ES | (BSV1710) | | | | 06 |
| 2N5681 | S | N | F, MO, SQ, TW, SM | (BSX4710) | | | | 06 |
| 2N5682 | S | N | F, MO, SQ, TR, SM | (BSX4710) | | | | 06 |
| 2N5685 | S | N | MO, TR, SM | | 2N5578 | 2N6032 | | 06 |
| 2N5686 | S | N | MO, TR, SM | | 2N5578 | 2N6032 | | 06 |
| 2N5687 | S | N | TW, TR | | 40412 | | | 06 |
| 2N5716 | J | N | MO | | ITE4118 | | | |
| 2N5717 | J | N | MO | | ITE4119 | | | |
| 2N5718 | J | N | MO | | 2N5953 | 2N4302 | | |
| 2N5729 | S | N | F, PP, SQ, TW, GX | | 2N5336 | | | 16 |
| 2N5732 | S | N | F, KE, SM, TR, TW | | 2N5303 | 2N5671 | | 16 |
| 2N5733 | S | N | F, KE, SM, TR, GX | | 2N3265 | | | 16 |
| 2N5734 | S | N | F, SM, KE, TR, GX | | 2N5886 | 2N5671 | | 16 |
| 2N5737 | S | P | SD, SQ, TR, SM | | 2N5875 | 2N5879 | | 06 |
| 2N5737 | | | | | 2N6246 | 2N3791 | | 06 |

| TYPE | M/S | POL | MANUFAC | EUROPEAN | AMERICAN | | JAPANESE | USE |
|------|-----|-----|---------|----------|----------|---|----------|-----|
| 2N5738 | S | P | SD, SQ, TR, SM | | 2N6248 | 2N3792 | | 06 |
| 2N5741 | S | P | SD, SQ, TR, SM | | 2N5883 | 2N4399 | | 06 |
| 2N5742 | S | P | SD, SQ, TR, SM | | 2N6029 | | | 06 |
| 2N5743 | S | P | SD, SQ, TR, SM | | 2N5883 | | | 06 |
| 2N5744 | S | P | SD, TR, SQ | | 2N5884 | | | 06 |
| | | | | | | | | |
| 2N5745 | S | P | MO, TR | | 2N5884 | | | 06 |
| 2N5758 | S | N | MO, TX, SQ, SM | | 2N3442 | (2N4347) | | 06 |
| 2N5758 | | | | | 2N6262 | | | 06 |
| 2N5759 | S | N | MO, TX, SM, SQ | | 2N3442 | (2N4347) | | 06 |
| 2N5759 | | | | | 2N6262 | | | 06 |
| | | | | | | | | |
| 2N5760 | S | N | MO, TX, SQ, SM | | 2N3442 | 2N6262 | | 06 |
| 2N5769 | S | N | F | (BSY63) | 2N5952 | 2N5027 | | |
| 2N5769 | | | | | 2N5028 | 2N3646 | | |
| 2N5770 | S | N | F | (BFX89) | 2N3662 | 2N3563 | | |
| 2N5771 | S | P | | | EN2894A | | | |
| | | | | | | | | |
| 2N5772 | S | N | F | (BSY63) | 2N3605 | 2N4275 | | |
| 2N5781 | S | P | RC, SM, TR, PI, SQ | | 2N4236 | 2N4235 | | 06 |
| 2N5782 | S | P | RC, SM, TR, PI, SQ | | 2N4235 | | | 06 |
| 2N5783 | S | P | RC, SM, TR, PI, SQ | | 2N4234 | 2N4236 | | 06 |
| 2N5784 | S | N | RC, SM, TR, PI, SQ | (BSX63-10) | 2N4239 | 2N4237 | | 06 |
| | | | | | | | | |
| 2N5785 | S | N | RC, SM, TR, PI, SQ | (BSX63-10) | 2N4238 | | | 06 |
| 2N5786 | S | N | RC, SM, TR, PI, SQ | BSX62-10 | 2N4237 | 2N4239 | | 06 |
| 2N5804 | S | N | RC, TW, TR | BUY75 | FT411 | | | 16 |
| 2N5805 | S | N | RC, TR | BUY75 | FT411 | | | 16 |
| 2N5810 | S | N | GE, SP, FR | BC337-16 | | | | 01 |
| | | | | | | | | |
| 2N5811 | S | N | GE, SP, FR | BC327-16 | | | | 01 |
| 2N5812 | S | N | GE, SP, FR | BC337-25 | | | | 01 |
| 2N5813 | S | P | GE, SP, FR | BC327-25 | | | | 01 |
| 2N5814 | S | N | GE, SP, FR | BC337-16 | | | | 01 |
| 2N5815 | S | P | GE, SP, FR | BC327-16 | | | | 01 |
| | | | | | | | | |
| 2N5816 | S | N | GE, SP, FR | BC337-16 | | | | 01 |
| 2N5817 | S | P | GE, SP, FR | BC327-16 | | | | 01 |
| 2N5818 | S | N | GE, SP, FR | BC337-25 | | | | 01 |
| 2N5819 | S | P | GE, SP, FR | BC327-25 | | | | 01 |
| 2N5820 | S | N | GE | (BC337-16) | | | | 01 |
| | | | | | | | | |
| 2N5821 | S | P | GE | (BC327-16) | | | | 01 |
| 2N5822 | S | N | GE | (BC337-16) | | | | 01 |
| 2N5823 | S | P | GE | (BC327-16) | | | | 01 |
| 2N5824 | S | N | GE, SP, FR | BC237A | 2N3904 | EN3904 | | 01 |
| 2N5825 | S | N | GE, SP, FR | BC237A | 2N3904 | EN3904 | | 01 |
| | | | | | | | | |
| 2N5826 | S | N | GE, SP, FR | BC237B | 2N5961 | 2N3565 | | 01 |
| 2N5827 | S | N | GE | BC237B | 2N5961 | 2N3565 | | |
| 2N5827A | S | N | GE | | 2N5961 | SE4010 | | 01 |
| 2N5828 | S | N | GE | (BC237B) | 2N5961 | SE4002 | | |
| 2N5828A | S | N | GE | (BC237B) | 2N5961 | SE4010 | | 01 |
| | | | | | | | | |
| 2N5830 | S | N | F | (BF457) | | | | 01 |
| 2N5831 | S | N | F | (BF458) | 2N5832 | | | 01 |
| 2N5832 | S | N | F | (BF458) | | | | 01 |
| 2N5833 | S | N | F | (BF458) | | | | 01 |
| 2N5838 | S | N | RC, SF, TR, SM | BUY75 | | | | 16 |
| | | | | | | | | |
| 2N5839 | S | N | RC, SF, TR, SM | BUY76 | | | | 16 |
| 2N5840 | S | N | RC, SF, TR, SM | BUY76 | | | | 16 |
| 2N5841 | S | N | MO | (BFW30) | | | | 16 |
| 2N5842 | S | N | MO | (BFW30) | | | | 16 |
| 2N5845 | S | N | F, MO | (BSX49) | | | | 10 |
| | | | | | | | | |
| 2N5845A | S | N | F, MO | (BSX49) | | | | 10 |
| 2N5851 | S | N | MO | (BFW30) | | | | 10 |
| 2N5852 | S | N | MO | (BFW30) | | | | 10 |
| 2N5855 | S | P | F, RY | BSV16-16 | 2N5857 | | | 01 |
| 2N5856 | S | N | F, RY | BSX46-16 | | | | 01 |
| | | | | | | | | |
| 2N5857 | S | P | F, RY | BSV17-10 | | | | 01 |
| 2N5858 | S | N | F, RY | BSX47-10 | | | | 01 |
| 2N5861 | S | N | MO, RY | | 2N5321 | | | |
| 2N5864 | S | P | MO, SM, TR, SQ | (BSV17-10) | 40634 | | | 01 |
| 2N5865 | S | P | MO, SQ | BSV17-10 | 40634 | | | 10 |
| | | | | | | | | |
| 2N5867 | S | P | TX, MO, TR, SQ | | 2N6246 | 2N4905 | | 06 |
| 2N5867 | | | | | 2N4908 | | | 06 |
| 2N5868 | S | P | MO, TX, TR, SQ | | 2N6247 | 2N4906 | | 06 |
| 2N5868 | | | | | 2N4909 | | | 06 |
| 2N5869 | S | N | MO, TX, SQ, TR, SF | | 2N6471 | 2N4347 | | 06 |
| | | | | | | | | |
| 2N5869 | | | | | 2N3055 | 2N4914 | | 06 |
| 2N5870 | S | N | MO, TX, SF, SQ, TR | | 2N6472 | 2N4347 | | 06 |
| 2N5870 | | | | | 2N6254 | 2N4915 | | 06 |
| 2N5871 | S | N | MO, TX, TR, SQ | | 2N6246 | | | 06 |
| 2N5872 | S | P | MO, TX, TR, SQ | | 2N6247 | | | 06 |

| TYPE | M/S | POL | MANUFAC | EUROPEAN | AMERICAN | | JAPANESE | USE |
|---|---|---|---|---|---|---|---|---|
| 2N5873 | S | N | MO, TX, F, SQ, SF | | 2N6471 | 2N4347 | | 06 |
| 2N5873 | | | | | 2N3055 | | | 06 |
| 2N5874 | S | N | MO, TX, F, SQ, TR | | 2N6472 | 2N4347 | | 06 |
| 2N5874 | | | | | 2N6254 | | | 06 |
| 2N5875 | S | P | MO, TR, SQ | | 2N6246 | | | 06 |
| 2N5876 | S | P | MO, TR, SQ | | 2N6247 | | | 06 |
| 2N5877 | S | N | MO, TX, F, TR, SQ | | 2N6471 | (2N4347) | | 06 |
| 2N5877 | | | | | 2N6254 | | | 06 |
| 2N5878 | S | N | MO, TX, F, TR, SQ | | 2N6472 | (2N4347) | | 06 |
| 2N5878 | | | | | 2N6254 | | | 06 |
| 2N5879 | S | P | TX, MO, TR, SQ | | 2N6472 | 2N6246 | | 06 |
| 2N5880 | S | P | MO, TR, SQ | | 2N6247 | | | 06 |
| 2N5881 | S | N | MO, TX, F, SQ, SM | | 2N6471 | (2N4347) | | 06 |
| 2N5881 | | | | | 2N6254 | | | 06 |
| 2N5882 | S | N | MO, TX, F, TR; SM | | 2N6472 | (2N4347) | | 06 |
| 2N5882 | | | | | 2N6254 | | | 06 |
| 2N5885 | S | N | F, MO, TX, SQ, SM | | (2N4347) | 2N6258 | | 06 |
| 2N5886 | S | N | F, MO, TX, SQ, TW | | (2N4347) | 2N6258 | | 06 |
| 2N5887 | G | P | MO, KS | AUY21II | | | | 06 |
| 2N5888 | G | P | MO, KS | AUY21II | | | | |
| 2N5889 | G | P | MO, KS | AUY21III | | | | 06 |
| 2N5890 | G | P | MO, KS | AUY21III | | | | 06 |
| 2N5891 | G | P | MO, KS | AUY21III | | | | 06 |
| 2N5892 | G | P | MO, KS | AUY22III | | | | 06 |
| 2N5893 | G | P | MO, KS | AUY21IV | | | | 06 |
| 2N5894 | G | P | MO, KS | AUY21IV | | | | 06 |
| 2N5895 | G | P | MO, KS | AUY21IV | | | | 06 |
| 2N5896 | G | P | MO, KS | AUY22IV | | | | 06 |
| 2N5897 | G | P | MO, KS | AUY21IV | | | | 06 |
| 2N5898 | G | P | MO, KS | AUY21IV | | | | |
| 2N5899 | G | P | MO, KS | AUY21IV | | | | 06 |
| 2N5900 | G | P | MO, KS | AUY22IV | | | | 06 |
| 2N5901 | G | P | MO, KS | AUY21IV | | | | 06 |
| 2N5902 | J | N | SX, IL | | TD5902 | | | |
| 2N5903 | J | N | SX, IL | | TD5903 | | | |
| 2N5904 | J | N | SX, IL | | TD5904 | | | |
| 2N5905 | J | N | SX, IL | | TD5905 | | | |
| 2N5906 | J | N | SX, IL | | TD5906 | | | |
| 2N5907 | J | N | SX, IL | | TD5907 | | | |
| 2N5908 | J | N | SX, IL | | TD5908 | | | |
| 2N5909 | J | N | SX, IL | | TD5909 | | | |
| 2N5910 | S | P | F, NS, BT | | PN5910-18 | | | 10 |
| 2N5911 | J | N | SX, IL | | TD5911 | | | |
| 2N5912 | J | N | SX, IL | | TD5912 | | | |
| 2N5929 | S | N | W, SQ, SM | | 2N5671 | | | 16 |
| 2N5930 | S | N | W, SQ, SM | | 2N5671 | | | 16 |
| 2N5932 | S | N | W, SQ, SM | | 2N5671 | | | 16 |
| 2N5933 | S | N | W, SQ, SM | | 2N5672 | | | 16 |
| 2N5935 | S | N | W; SQ, SM | | 2N6032 | | | 16 |
| 2N5936 | S | N | W, SQ, SM | | 2N6033 | | | 16 |
| 2N5943 | S | N | MO, TI, SD | (BFX55) | | | | 01 |
| 2N5949 | J | N | TX | | 2N5638 | U1994E | | |
| 2N5950 | J | N | TX | | 2N5639 | U2047E | | |
| 2N5950 | | | | | 2N5485 | FE5245 | | |
| 2N5951 | J | N | TX | | 2N5640 | 2N5485 | | |
| 2N5951 | | | | | 2N5484 | | | |
| 2N5952 | J | N | TX | | 2N5640 | 2N5485 | | |
| 2N5952 | | | | | FE5246 | | | |
| 2N5953 | J | N | TX | | 2N5640 | 2N5485 | | |
| 2N5953 | | | | | FE5246 | | | |
| 2N5954 | S | P | RC, TR, SQ | BDX28-6 | 2N4900 | | | 06 |
| 2N5955 | S | P | RC, TR, SQ | BDX29-6 | 2N4899 | | | 06 |
| 2N5956 | S | P | RC, TR, SQ | BDX30-6 | 2N4898 | | | 06 |
| 2N5959 | S | N | TR, SM | | 2N5484 | 2N5486 | | 06 |
| 2N5959 | | | | | FE4245 | FE4247 | | 06 |
| 2N5960 | S | P | TR | | 2N5958 | | | 06 |
| 2N5961 | S | N | F, BT | (BC414C) | | | | 02 |
| 2N5961-18 | S | N | | | SE4020 | | | |
| 2N5962 | S | N | F, BT | (BC414C) | | | | 02 |
| 2N5962-18 | S | N | | | SE4021 | | | |
| 2N5963 | S | N | F, BT | (BC413C) | | | | 02 |
| 2N5966 | S | N | TR | | 2N3265 | | | 06 |
| 2N5968 | S | N | TR | | 2N3265 | | | 06 |
| 2N5970 | S | N | SM, SQ | | 2N5302 | 2N6472 | | 16 |
| 2N5970 | | | | | 2N6254 | | | 16 |

| TYPE | M/S | POL | MANUFAC | EUROPEAN | | AMERICAN | | JAPANESE | USE |
|---|---|---|---|---|---|---|---|---|---|
| 2N5971 | S | N | SM, SQ | | | 2N5302 | 2N6472 | | 16 |
| 2N5971 | S | N | SM, SQ | | | 2N6254 | | | 16 |
| 2N5972 | | | SM, SQ | | | 2N5302 | 2N6472 | | 16 |
| 2N5972 | | | SM, SQ | | | 2N6254 | | | 16 |
| 2N5973 | S | N | SM, SQ | | | 2N6254 | 2N3714 | | 16 |
| 2N5974 | S | P | MO | (BD440) | | 2N6489 | TIP32 | | 06 |
| 2N5975 | S | P | MO | (BD442) | | 2N6490 | TIP32A | | 06 |
| 2N5975 | | | MO | | | 2N6132 | | | 06 |
| 2N5976 | S | P | MO | (BD442) | | 2N6491 | TIP32B | | 06 |
| 2N5976 | | | MO | | | 2N6132 | | | 06 |
| 2N5977 | S | N | MO | (BD439) | | 2N6486 | TIP31 | | 06 |
| 2N5977 | | | MO | | | 2N6129 | | | 06 |
| 2N5978 | S | N | MO | (BD441) | | 2N6487 | TIP31A | | 06 |
| 2N5979 | S | N | MO | (BD441) | | 2N6488 | TIP31B | | 06 |
| 2N5979 | | | MO | | | 2N6129 | | | 06 |
| 2N5980 | S | P | MO | | | 2N6489 | 2N6132 | | 06 |
| 2N5981 | S | P | MO | | | 2N6490 | 2N6134 | | 06 |
| 2N5982 | S | P | MO | | | 2N6491 | | | 06 |
| 2N5983 | S | N | MO | | | 2N6486 | 2N6129 | | 06 |
| 2N5984 | S | N | MO | | | 2N6487 | 2N6130 | | 06 |
| 2N5985 | S | N | MO | | | 2N6488 | 2N6131 | | 06 |
| 2N5986 | S | P | MO | | | 2N6489 | FT2955 | | 06 |
| 2N5987 | S | P | MO | | | 2N6490 | FT2955 | | 06 |
| 2N5988 | S | P | MO | | | 2N6491 | | | 06 |
| 2N5989 | S | N | MO | | | 2N6486 | FT3055 | | 06 |
| 2N5990 | S | N | MO | | | 2N6487 | FT3055 | | 06 |
| 2N5991 | S | N | MO | | | 2N6488 | | | 06 |
| 2N5998 | S | N | GE | BC337-25 | | 2N5961 | SE4020 | | |
| 2N5999 | S | P | GE | (BC327-25) | | 2N5086 | 2N4248 | | |
| 2N6000 | S | N | GE | (B337-16) | | 2N3904 | EN3904 | | 01 |
| 2N6001 | S | P | GE | (BC327-16) | | 2N3906 | EN3906 | | 01 |
| 2N6002 | S | N | GE | (BC337-40) | | 2N5088 | SE4020 | | 01 |
| 2N6003 | S | P | GE | (BC327-40) | | 2N5086 | 2N4248 | | 01 |
| 2N6004 | S | N | GE | (BC337-16) | | 2N3904 | EN3904 | | 01 |
| 2N6005 | S | P | GE | (BC327-16) | | 2N3906 | EN3906 | | 01 |
| 2N6006 | S | N | GE | (BC337-40) | | 2N5088 | SE4020 | | 01 |
| 2N6007 | S | P | GE | (BC327-40) | | 2N5086 | 2N4248 | | 01 |
| 2N6008 | S | N | GE | (BC337-40) | | 2N5088 | SE4020 | | |
| 2N6009 | S | P | GE | (BC327-40) | | 2N5086 | 2N4248 | | |
| 2N6010 | S | N | GE | (BC337-16) | | MPSA05 | MPSA06 | | 01 |
| 2N6010 | | | | | | SE6020 | 2N5856 | | 01 |
| 2N6011 | S | P | GE, St | (BC327-16) | | MPSA55 | MPSA56 | | 01 |
| 2N6011 | | | | | | 2N5857 | | | 01 |
| 2N6012 | S | N | GE, St | (BC337-40) | | MPSA05 | MPSA06 | | 01 |
| 2N6012 | | | | | | SE6020 | 2N5856 | | 01 |
| 2N6013 | S | P | GE, St | (BC327-40) | | MPSA55 | MPSA56 | | 01 |
| 2N6013 | | | | | | 2N5757 | | | 01 |
| 2N6014 | S | N | GE, St | (BC337-16) | | MPSA05 | MPSA06 | | 01 |
| 2N6014 | | | | | | SE6020 | 2N5857 | | 01 |
| 2N6015 | S | P | GE, St | (BC327-16) | | MPSA55 | MPSA56 | | 01 |
| 2N6015 | | | | | | 2N5857 | | | 01 |
| 2N6016 | S | N | GE, St | (BC337-40) | | MPSA05 | MPSA06 | | 01 |
| 2N6016 | | | | | | SE6020 | 2N5856 | | 01 |
| 2N6017 | S | P | GE, St | (BC327-40) | | MPSA55 | MPSA56 | | 01 |
| 2N6017 | | | | | | 2N5857 | | | 01 |
| 2N6034 | S | P | MO | BDX34 | | | | | 06 |
| 2N6035 | S | P | MO | BDX34A | | | | | 06 |
| 2N6036 | S | P | MO | BDX34B | | | | | 06 |
| 2N6037 | S | N | MO | BDX33 | | | | | 06 |
| 2N6038 | S | N | MO | BDX33A | | | | | |
| 2N6039 | S | N | MO | | | | | | |
| 2N6040 | S | P | MO | BDX34A | | | | | |
| 2N6041 | S | P | MO | BDX34B | | SE9300 | | | 06 |
| 2N6042 | S | P | MO | BDX34C | | SE9301 | | | 06 |
| 2N6043 | S | N | MO | BDX33A | | SE9302 | | | 06 |
| 2N6043 | | | MO | | | SE9300 | | | 06 |
| 2N6044 | S | N | MO | BDX33B | | SE9301 | | | 06 |
| 2N6045 | S | N | MO | BDX33C | | SE9302 | | | 06 |
| 2N6046 | S | N | W, TW, SM | | | 2N3266 | | | 16 |
| 2N6047 | S | N | W, TW, SM | | | 2N3265 | | | 16 |
| 2N6048 | S | N | W, SM | | | 2N3265 | | | 16 |
| 2N6049 | S | P | MO | (BDX30-6) | | 2N5955 | 2N4899 | | 06 |
| 2N6050 | S | P | MO | | | RCA8350A | | | 06 |
| 2N6051 | S | P | MO | | | RCA8350B | | | 06 |
| 2N6053 | S | P | MO | | | RCA8350A | | | 06 |
| 2N6054 | S | P | MO | | | RCA8350B | | | 06 |

| TYPE | M/S | POL | MANUFAC | EUROPEAN | | AMERICAN | | JAPANESE | USE |
|------|-----|-----|---------|----------|--|----------|--|----------|-----|
| 2N6055 | S | N | MO | | | SE9303 | | | 06 |
| 2N6056 | S | N | MO | | | SE9304 | | | 06 |
| 2N6057 | S | N | MO | | | 2N6384 | SE9303 | | 06 |
| 2N6058 | S | N | MO | | | 2N6385 | SE9304 | | 06 |
| 2N6059 | S | N | | | | SE9305 | | | 06 |
| | | | | | | | | | |
| 2N6062 | S | N | TR, SM | | | 2N3265 | | | 06 |
| 2N6063 | S | N | TR | | | 2N3265 | | | 06 |
| 2N6067 | S | P | MO | | | | | | 10 |
| 2N6076 | S | P | GE | BC307B | | 2N3906 | EN3906 | | 01 |
| 2N6077 | S | N | RC | (BUY78) | | SE9051 | | | 16 |
| | | | | | | | | | |
| 2N6078 | S | N | RC | (BUY77) | | SE9051 | | | 16 |
| 2N6079 | S | N | RC | (BUY79) | | SE9052 | | | 16 |
| 2N6098 | S | N | RC | | | FT3055 | | | 06 |
| 2N6099 | S | N | RC | | | FT3055 | | | 06 |
| 2N6106 | S | P | RC | (BD442) | | 2N6134 | 2N6126 | | 01 |
| | | | | | | | | | |
| 2N6107 | S | P | RC | (BD442) | | 2N6134 | 2N6126 | | 01 |
| 2N6108 | S | P | RC | (BD440) | | 2N6133 | 2N6132 | | 01 |
| 2N6109 | S | P | RC | (BD440) | | 2N6133 | 2N6132 | | 01 |
| 2N6110 | S | P | RC | (BD438) | | 2N6132 | | | 01 |
| 2N6111 | S | P | RC | (BD438) | | 2N6132 | | | 01 |
| | | | | | | | | | |
| 2N6121 | S | N | F | (BD437) | | 2N6920 | 2N6290 | | 06 |
| 2N6121 | | | | | | 40613 | 2N4921 | | 06 |
| 2N6121 | | | | | | 2N5190 | 2N5295 | | 06 |
| 2N6122 | S | N | F | (BD439) | | 2N6292 | 2N6290 | | 06 |
| 2N6122 | | | | | | 40621 | 2N4922 | | 06 |
| | | | | | | | | | |
| 2N6122 | | | | | | 2N5297 | 2N5299 | | 06 |
| 2N6123 | S | N | F | BD2418 | (BD441) | 2N6292 | 2N4923 | | 06 |
| 2N6123 | | | | | | 2N5191 | 2N5496 | | 06 |
| 2N6123 | | | | | | 2N5497 | | | 06 |
| 2N6124 | S | P | F | (BD438) | | 2N6109 | 2N4918 | | 06 |
| | | | | | | | | | |
| 2N6124 | | | | | | 2N5193 | D41D | | 06 |
| 2N6124 | | | | | | MJE370 | | | 06 |
| 2N6125 | S | P | F | (BD440) | | 2N6107 | 2N6109 | | 06 |
| 2N6125 | | | | | | 2N5194 | 2N4919 | | 06 |
| 2N6125 | | | | | | TIP30A | 2N5191 | | 06 |
| | | | | | | | | | |
| 2N6126 | S | P | F | BD2428 | (BD442) | 2N6107 | 2N4920 | | 06 |
| 2N6126 | | | | | | 2N5195 | TIP40B | | 06 |
| 2N6126 | | | | | | TIP32C | | | 06 |
| 2N6129 | S | N | F | (BD437) | | 2N6290 | | | 06 |
| 2N6130 | S | N | F | (BD439) | | 2N6290 | | | 06 |
| | | | | | | | | | |
| 2N6131 | S | N | F | (BD441) | | 2N6292 | | | 06 |
| 2N6132 | S | P | F | (BD438) | | 2N6109 | | | 06 |
| 2N6133 | S | P | F | (BD440) | | 2N6107 | 2N6109 | | 06 |
| 2N6134 | S | P | F | BD2428 | (BD442) | 2N6107 | | | 06 |
| 2N6175 | S | N | RC | | | FT47 | 2N3440 | | 06 |
| | | | | | | | | | |
| 2N6176 | S | N | RC | | | FT48 | 2N3439 | | 06 |
| 2N6177 | S | N | RC | | | FT49 | 2N3439 | | 06 |
| 2N6218 | S | N | GE | (BF459) | | | | | |
| 2N6219 | S | N | GE | (BF458) | | | | | |
| 2N6220 | S | N | GE | (BF458) | | | | | |
| | | | | | | | | | |
| 2N6221 | S | N | GE | (BF457) | | | | | |
| 2N6222 | S | N | GE | BCY65EVII | | | | | |
| 2N6223 | S | P | GE | BCY77VII | | | | | |
| 2N6224 | S | N | GE | BCY65EVIII | | | | | |
| 2N6225 | S | P | GE | BCY77VIII | | | | | |
| | | | | | | | | | |
| 2N6229 | S | P | MO | | | 2N6248 | | | 06 |
| 2N6230 | S | P | MO | | | 2N6030 | 2N6292 | | 06 |
| 2N6231 | S | P | MO | | | 2N6031 | | | 06 |
| 2N6233 | S | N | F, MO | (BUY77) | | SE9331 | 2N3583 | | 16 |
| 2N6233 | | | | | | 2N6078 | | | 16 |
| | | | | | | | | | |
| 2N6234 | S | N | MO, F | (BUY78) | | 2N3584 | 2N6077 | | 16 |
| 2N6235 | S | N | MO, F | (BUY79) | | 2N3585 | 2N6079 | | 16 |
| 2N6246 | S | P | RC | | | 2N5879 | 2N3791 | | 06 |
| 2N6247 | S | P | RC | | | 2N5880 | 2N3792 | | 06 |
| 2N6248 | S | P | RC | | | 2N6020 | | | 06 |
| | | | | | | | | | |
| 2N6249 | S | N | RC | (BUY74) | | | | | 16 |
| 2N6250 | S | N | RC | (BUY75) | | | | | 16 |
| 2N6251 | S | N | RC | (BUY76) | | | | | 16 |
| 2N6253 | S | N | RC, SM, SF, PP | | | 2N5882 | 2N3055 | | 06 |
| 2N6254 | S | N | RC, SM, SF, PP | (2N4347) | | 2N5882 | | | 06 |
| | | | | | | | | | |
| 2N6257 | S | N | RC, SM, SF, PP | | | 2N5301 | (2N3055) | | 06 |
| 2N6257 | | | | | | 2N5882 | | | 06 |
| 2N6258 | S | N | RC, SF, SM, PP | | | 2N5886 | 2N5303 | | 06 |
| 2N6259 | S | N | RC, SM, SF, PP | | | 2N5631 | | | 06 |
| 2N6260 | S | N | RC, SF, PP | | | 2N3054 | 2N4231 | | 06 |

| TYPE | M/S | POL | MANUFAC | EUROPEAN | AMERICAN | | JAPANESE | USE |
|------|-----|-----|---------|----------|----------|--|----------|-----|
| 2N6261 | S | N | RC, SF, PP | (BDX25-6) | 2N3767 | 2N4233 | | 06 |
| 2N6262 | S | N | RC, SM, PP | | FT410 | (2N3442) | | |
| 2N6263 | S | N | RC, SF, PP | BDX25-6 | 2N6233 | | | 06 |
| 2N6264 | S | N | RC, SF, PP | (BDX25-6 | 2N6233 | | | 06 |
| 2N6270 | S | N | TX | | 2N5671 | | | 06 |
| | | | | | | | | 06 |
| 2N6271 | S | N | TX | | 2N5672 | | | |
| 2N6272 | S | N | TX | | 2N3265 | | | 06 |
| 2N6273 | S | N | TX | | 2N3265 | | | 06 |
| 2N6288 | S | N | RC | (BD437) | 2N6129 | | | 06 |
| 2N6289 | S | N | RC | (BD437) | 2N6129 | | | 06 |
| | | | | | | | | 06 |
| 2N6290 | S | N | RC | (BD439) | 2N6130 | | | |
| 2N6291 | S | N | RC | (BD439) | 2N6130 | | | 06 |
| 2N6292 | S | N | RC | (BD441) | 2N6131 | | | 06 |
| 2N6293 | S | N | RC | (BD441) | 2N6131 | | | 06 |
| 2N6294 | S | N | MO | | 2N6534 | | | 06 |
| | | | | | | | | 06 |
| 2N6295 | S | N | MO | | | | | |
| 2N6296 | S | P | MO | | 2N6534 | | | |
| 2N6297 | S | P | MO | | RCA8350A | | | 06 |
| 2N6298 | S | P | MO | | RCA8350B | | | 06 |
| 2N6299 | S | P | MO | | RCA8350A | | | 06 |
| | | | | | RCA8350B | | | 06 |
| 2N6300 | S | N | | | | | | 06 |
| 2N6301 | S | N | | | SE9303 | | | |
| 2N6302 | S | N | MO | | SE9304 | 2N6534 | | 06 |
| 2N6303 | S | P | MO | | 2N3773 | 2N6534 | | 06 |
| 2N6306 | S | N | MO | | 2N4234 | | | 16 |
| | | | | | TIP29A | | | 16 |
| 2N6307 | S | N | MO | | TIP298 | | | |
| 2N6308 | S | N | MO | | TIP30A | | | 16 |
| 2N6309 | S | P | MO | | TIP30A | | | 16 |
| 2N6312 | S | P | MO | | 2N5956 | 2N6308 | | 06 |
| 2N6313 | S | P | MO | | 2N5955 | | | 06 |
| | | | | | | | | |
| 2N6314 | S | P | MO | | 2N5954 | | | |
| 2N6315 | S | P | MO | | 2N5873 | | | 06 |
| 2N6316 | S | N | MO | | 2N5874 | | | 06 |
| 2N6317 | S | P | MO | | 2N5871 | | | 06 |
| 2N6318 | S | P | MO | | 2N5872 | | | 06 |
| | | | | | | | | 06 |
| 2N6326 | S | N | TX | | 2N5302 | 2N5881 | | |
| 2N6327 | S | N | TX | | 2N5806 | 2N5882 | | 06 |
| 2N6329 | S | P | TX | | 2N4399 | 2N3791 | | 06 |
| 2N6330 | S | P | TX | | 2N3792 | | | 06 |
| 2N6338 | S | N | TX, MO | | 2N5672 | | | 06 |
| | | | | | | | | 16 |
| 2N6339 | S | N | MO, TX | | 2N5672 | | | |
| 2N6354 | S | N | RC | | 2N5630 | (2N3442) | | 16 |
| 2N6359 | S | N | MO | | 2N5886 | 2N3773 | | 16 |
| 2N6360 | S | N | MO | | 2N4348 | | | 06 |
| 2N6371 | S | N | RC | | 2N3055 | | | 06 |
| | | | | | | | | 06 |
| 2N6372 | S | N | RC | BDX25-6 | | | | |
| 2N6373 | S | N | RC | BDX25-6 | | | | 06 |
| 2N6374 | S | N | RC | BDX25-6 | | | | 06 |
| 2N6384 | S | N | RC | | SE9303 | | | 06 |
| 2N6385 | S | N | RC | | SE9304 | | | 06 |
| | | | | | | | | 06 |
| 2N6386 | S | N | RC | | SE9300 | | | |
| 2N6387 | S | N | RC | | SE9300 | | | 06 |
| 2N6388 | S | N | RC | | SE9301 | | | 06 |
| 2N6406 | S | P | MO | | RCP700B | | | 06 |
| 2N6407 | S | P | MO | | RCP700C | | | 06 |
| | | | | | | | | 06 |
| 2N6408 | S | N | MO | | RCP701B | | | |
| 2N6409 | S | N | MO | | RCP701C | | | 06 |
| 2N6410 | S | N | MO | | | | | 06 |
| 2N6411 | S | P | MO | BD221 | | | | 06 |
| 2N6412 | S | N | MO | BD224 | | | | 06 |
| | | | | BD221 | RCP701A | | | 06 |
| 2N6413 | S | N | MO | BD222 | RCP701B | | | |
| 2N6414 | S | P | MO | BD224 | RCP700A | | | 06 |
| 2N6415 | S | P | MO | BD225 | RCP700B | 2N6701C | | 06 |
| 2N6416 | S | N | MO | | TIP298 | RCP701C | | 06 |
| 2N6417 | S | N | MO | | RCP701D | | | 06 |
| | | | | | | | | 06 |
| 2N6418 | S | P | MO | | TIP308 | RCP700C | | |
| 2N6419 | S | P | MO | | RCP700D | | | |
| 2N6420 | S | P | MO | | 2N6211 | | | |
| 2N6421 | S | P | MO | | 2N6212 | | | |
| 2N6422 | S | P | MO | | 2N6212 | | | |
| | | | | | | | | |
| 2N6423 | S | P | MO | | 2N6212 | | | |
| 2N6424 | S | P | MO | | 2N6211 | | | |
| 2N6425 | S | P | MO | | 2N6212 | | | |
| 2N6436 | S | P | MO | | 2N5671 | | | 16 |
| 2N6437 | S | P | MO | | 2N5672 | | | 16 |

| TYPE | M/S | POL | MANUFAC | EUROPEAN | | AMERICAN | | JAPANESE | USE |
|---|---|---|---|---|---|---|---|---|---|
| 2N6438 | S | P | MO | | | 2N5672 | | | 16 |
| 2N6461 | S | N | TX | | | 2N3439 | | | 01 |
| 2N6470 | S | N | RO | | | 2N6569 | | | |
| 2N6471 | S | N | RC | | | 2N3055 | | | |
| 2N6472 | S | N | RC | | | 2N5882 | | | |
| | | | | | | | | | |
| 2N6487 | S | N | RC | | | FT3055 | | | |
| 2N6490 | S | P | RC | | | FT2955 | | | |
| 2N6496 | S | N | RC | | | 2N5630 | | | 08 |
| 2N6515 | S | N | MO | | | | | | 08 |
| 2N6516 | S | N | MO | | | | | | 08 |
| 2N6517 | S | N | MO | | | | | | 08 |
| 2N6518 | S | P | MO | | | | | | 08 |
| 2N6519 | S | P | MO | | | | | | 08 |
| 2N6520 | S | P | MO | | | FT411 | 2N6510 | | |
| 2N6542 | S | N | MO | | | | | | |
| | | | | | | | | | |
| 2N6543 | S | N | MO | | | 2N6510 | | | |
| 2N6544 | S | N | MO | | | FT430 | 2N6510 | | |
| 2N6545 | S | N | MO | | | 2N6251 | 2N6510 | | |
| 2N6551 | S | N | MO | | | RCP701B | | | |
| 2N6552 | S | N | MO | | | RCP701C | | | |
| | | | | | | | | | |
| 2N6554 | S | P | MO | | | RCP700B | | | |
| 2N6555 | S | P | MO | | | RCP700C | | | |
| 2N6556 | S | P | RC | | | RCP700D | | | |
| 2N6557 | S | N | MO | | | RCP113B | | | |
| 2N6558 | S | N | MO | | | RCP113C | | | |
| | | | | | | | | | |
| 2N6559 | S | N | MO, SD | | | RCP113D | | | |
| 2N6563 | S | N | MO | | | RCP701D | | | |
| 2N6569 | S | N | MO | | | 2N6559 | 2N3055 | | |
| 2NJ5A | G | P | | AF185 | | | | | |
| 2NJ8A | G | P | | AF185 | | | | | |
| | | | | | | | | | |
| 2NJ9A | G | P | | AC128 | | 2N2431 | | | |
| 2NJ9D | G | P | | AC128 | | 2N2431 | | | |
| 2NJ50 | G | P | | AF185 | | | | | |
| 2NJ51 | G | P | | AF185 | | | | | |
| 2NU40 | G | P | | AC126 | | 2N2429 | | | |
| | | | | | | | | | |
| 2NU70 | G | P | | AC126 | | 2N2429 | | | |
| 2S001 | G | P | | AF178 | | 2N2495 | | | |
| 2S12 | G | P | TX | AF185 | | | | | |
| 2S13 | G | P | TX | AF185 | | | | | |
| 2S14 | G | P | TX | AC128 | | 2N2431 | | | |
| | | | | | | | | | |
| 2S15 | G | P | TX | AC128 | | 2N2431 | | | |
| 2S15A | G | P | TX | AC128 | | 2N2431 | | | |
| 2S22 | G | P | TX | AC128 | | 2N2431 | | | |
| 2S24 | G | P | TX | AC128 | | 2N2431 | | | |
| 2S25 | G | P | TX | AF185 | | | | | |
| | | | | | | | | | |
| 2S30 | G | P | | AF185 | | | | | |
| 2S31 | G | P | | AF185 | AF132 | 2N410 | 2N412 | | |
| 2S31 | | | | AF137 | | | | | |
| 2S32 | G | P | | AC128 | AC131 | 2N2431 | 2N611 | | |
| 2S32 | | | | AC153 | | | | | |
| | | | | | | | | | |
| 2S33 | G | P | TX | AC128 | AC131 | 2N2431 | 2N610 | | |
| 2S33 | | | | AC132 | AC153 | | | | |
| 2S34 | G | P | TX | AC128 | AC131 | 2N2431 | 2N568 | | |
| 2S34 | | | | AC153 | | | | | |
| 2S35 | G | P | TX | AF185 | AF133 | 2N111 | | | |
| | | | | | | | | | |
| 2S35 | | | | AF137 | | | | | |
| 2S36 | G | P | TX | AF185 | AF127 | 2N112 | | | |
| 2S36 | | | | ASY26 | | | | | |
| 2S37 | G | P | TX | AC128 | AC131 | 2N2431 | 2N106 | | |
| 2S37 | | | | AC132 | AC153 | | | | |
| | | | | | | | | | |
| 2S38 | G | P | | AC128 | AC131 | 2N2431 | 2N270 | | |
| 2S38 | | | | AC153 | | | | | |
| 2S39 | G | P | | AC128 | AC125 | 2N2431 | 2N115 | | |
| 2S39 | | | | AC163 | | | | | |
| 2S40 | G | P | | AC128 | ASY27 | 2N2431 | | | |
| | | | | | | | | | |
| 2S41 | G | P | | AD149 | AD150 | 2N2836 | 2N269 | | |
| 2S41 | | | | AF134 | AF135 | | | | |
| 2S41A | G | P | | AD149 | AD150 | 2N2836 | 2N268 | | |
| 2S41A | | | | AF135 | AF134 | | | | |
| 2S42 | G | P | | AD131 | ASZ15 | 2N387 | | | |
| | | | | | | | | | |
| 2S42 | | | | AUY28 | | | | | |
| 2S43 | G | P | | AC128 | AF132 | 2N2431 | 2N640 | | |
| 2S43 | | | | AF137 | AF134 | | | | |
| 2S44 | G | P | | AC128 | AC126 | 2N407 | 2N408 | | |
| 2S44 | | | | AC131 | | | | | |

| TYPE | M/S | POL | MANUFAC | EUROPEAN | | AMERICAN | | JAPANESE | USE |
|---|---|---|---|---|---|---|---|---|---|
| 2S45 | G | P | | AF185 | AF127 | 2N409 | 2N410 | | |
| 2S45 | | | | AF133 | AF137 | | | | |
| 2S46 | G | P | | AF185 | AF128 | | | | |
| 2S49 | G | P | | AF185 | AF133 | 2N410 | | | |
| 2S49 | | | | AF137 | | | | | |
| 2S52 | G | P | | AF185 | AF128 | 2N411 | 2N412 | | |
| 2S52 | | | | AC153 | | | | | |
| 2S53 | G | P | | AF185 | AF133 | 2N409 | 2N410 | | |
| 2S53 | | | | AF137 | | | | | |
| 2S54 | G | P | | AC126 | AC128 | 2N408 | 2N410 | | |
| 2S54 | | | | AC131 | AC132 | | | | |
| 2S54 | | | | AC153 | | | | | |
| 2S56 | G | P | | AC128 | AC131 | 2N2431 | 2N408 | | |
| 2S56 | | | | AC153 | | | | | |
| 2S60 | G | P | | AF185 | | 2N412 | | | |
| 2S60A | G | P | | AF185 | | 2N412 | | | |
| 2S91 | G | P | | AF185 | AC153 | 2N2700 | 2N370 | | |
| 2S91 | | | | AF136 | | | | | |
| 2S92 | G | P | | AF185 | | 2N411 | | | |
| 2S92A | G | P | | AF185 | | 2N411 | | | |
| 2S93 | G | P | | AF185 | | 2N140 | | | |
| 2S93A | G | P | | AF185 | | 2N412 | | | |
| 2S101 | S | P | TX | | | 2N726 | | | |
| 2S109 | G | P | | AF185 | AF135 | 2N360 | | | |
| 2S109 | | | | AF136 | | | | | |
| 2S110 | G | P | | AF185 | AF135 | 2N371 | 2N372 | | |
| 2S110 | | | | AF136 | | | | | |
| 2S112 | G | P | | AF185 | AF135 | 2N372 | | | |
| 2S112 | | | | AF136 | | | | | |
| 2S141 | G | P | | AF185 | AF134 | 2N372 | 2N371 | | |
| 2S141 | | | | AF136 | | | | | |
| 2S142 | G | P | | AF185 | AF135 | 2N370 | | | |
| 2S142 | | | | AF136 | | | | | |
| 2S143 | G | P | | AF185 | AF135 | 2N373 | 2N641 | | |
| 2S143 | | | | AF137 | | | | | |
| 2S144 | G | P | | AF185 | AF136 | 2N1108 | | | |
| 2S144 | | | | AF137 | | | | | |
| 2S145 | G | P | | AF185 | AF134 | 2N544 | 2N1110 | | |
| 2S145 | | | | AF136 | | | | | |
| 2S146 | G | P | | AF185 | AF126 | 2N219 | | | |
| 2S146 | | | | AF136 | | | | | |
| 2S148 | G | P | | AF126 | AF185 | | | | |
| 2S148 | | | | AF136 | | | | | |
| 2S155 | G | P | | AF185 | | | | | |
| 2S159 | G | R | | AF185 | AC162 | | | | |
| 2S159 | | | | AC170 | | | | | |
| 2S160 | G | P | | AF185 | | | | | |
| 2S163 | G | P | | AC128 | AC131 | 2N2431 | | | |
| 2S163 | | | | AC153 | AC132 | | | | |
| 2S178 | G | P | | AF185 | | 2N140 | | | |
| 2S179 | G | P | | AC128 | | 2N2431 | 2N217 | | |
| 2S301 | S | P | TX | BCY32 | | | | | |
| 2S302 | S | P | TX | BCY33 | BCZ10 | | | | |
| 2S303 | S | P | TX | BCY34 | BCZ11 | | | | |
| 2S304 | S | P | TX | BCZ10 | | | | | |
| 2S322 | S | P | TX | BCZ10 | | | | | |
| 2S323 | S | P | TX | BCZ11 | | | | | |
| 2SA12 | G | P | HI | (AF127) | AF127 | 2N4034 | 2N642 | 2SA240 | |
| 2SA12 | | | | ASY27 | AF185 | 2N412 | 2N483 | | |
| 2SA12 | | | | AFY131 | AF137 | | | | |
| 2SA12H | G | P | HI | (AF127) | | | | | |
| 2SA13 | G | P | HI | AF127 | AF185 | 2N4034 | 2N642 | 2SA240 | |
| 2SA13 | | | | AF137 | AF131 | | | | |
| 2SA14 | G | P | HI | (AF127) | AF185 | | | | |
| 2SA14 | | | | AF132 | AF137 | | | | |
| 2SA15 | G | P | HI | AF126 | AF185 | 2N641 | 2N411 | 2SA240 | |
| 2SA15 | | | | AFY15 | AF131 | 2N412 | | | |
| 2SA15 | | | | AF136 | | | | | |
| 2SA15H | G | P | HI | (AF126) | | | | | |
| 2SA16 | G | P | HI | AF185 | AF137 | 2N4034 | 2N642 | 2SA240 | |
| 2SA16 | | | | AF133 | | 2N411 | 2N412 | | |
| 2SA17 | G | P | HI | (AF127) | AF185 | 2N412 | 2N486 | | |
| 2SA17 | | | | AF134 | AF136 | | | | |
| 2SA17H | G | P | HI | (AF127) | | | | | |
| 2SA18 | G | P | HI | (AF126) | AF185 | 2N412 | 2N579 | | |

| TYPE | M/S | POL | MANUFAC | EUROPEAN | | AMERICAN | | JAPANESE | USE |
|------|-----|-----|---------|----------|--|----------|--|----------|-----|
| 2SA18 | | | | AF131 | AF136 | | | | |
| 2SA19 | G | P | NI | (AF127) | AF185 | | | | |
| 2SA20 | G | P | NI | (AF127) | AF185 | | | | |
| 2SA21 | G | P | NI | (AF127) | AF185 | | | | |
| 2SA22 | G | P | | AF185 | AF132 | 2N411 | | | |
| | | | | | | | | | |
| 2SA22 | | | | AF136 | | | | | |
| 2SA23 | G | P | | AF127 | AF185 | 2N4034 | 2N642 | 2SA240 | |
| 2SA23 | | | | AF137 | AF133 | 2N409 | | | |
| 2SA24 | G | P | | AF124 | AF178 | 2N2495 | 2N4034 | 2SA235 | |
| 2SA24 | | | | AF134 | AF194 | 2N346 | 2N370 | | |
| | | | | | | | | | |
| 2SA24 | | | | AF136 | | | | | |
| 2SA25 | G | P | | AF124 | AF178 | 2N2495 | 2N346 | 2SA235 | |
| 2SA25 | | | | AF134 | AF194 | | | | |
| 2SA25 | | | | AF131 | | | | | |
| 2SA26 | G | P | NI | (ASY26) | | | | | |
| | | | | | | | | | |
| 2SA27 | G | P | | AF125 | AF165 | 2N1110 | | 2SA156 | |
| 2SA27 | | | | AF135 | AF134 | | | | |
| 2SA28 | G | P | TO | AF127 | AF185 | 2N4034 | 2N642 | 2SA240 | |
| 2SA28 | | | | AF137 | AF134 | | | | |
| 2SA29 | G | P | TO | (AF127) | AF185 | | | | |
| | | | | | | | | | |
| 2SA29 | | | | AF125 | AF134 | | | | |
| 2SA30 | G | P | FU | AF126 | AF185 | 2N641 | 2N411 | 2SA240 | |
| 2SA30 | | | | AFY15 | AF132 | 2N412 | | | |
| 2SA30 | | | | AF136 | | | | | |
| 2SA31 | G | P | FU | AF127 | AF185 | 2N4034 | 2N646 | 2SA240 | |
| | | | | | | | | | |
| 2SA31 | | | | AFY15 | AF137 | 2N374 | 2N409 | | |
| 2SA31 | | | | AF133 | | | | | |
| 2SA32 | G | P | FU | (AF126) | | | | | |
| 2SA33 | G | P | FU | (AF126) | | | | | |
| 2SA35 | G | P | FU | AF126 | AF185 | 2N4034 | 2N646 | 2SA240 | |
| | | | | | | | | | |
| 2SA35 | | | | AF127 | AFY15 | 2N411 | 2N412 | | |
| 2SA35 | | | | AF132 | AF136 | | | | |
| 2SA36 | G | P | FU | (AF126) | AF185 | 2N411 | 2N412 | | |
| 2SA36 | | | | AF132 | AF136 | | | | |
| 2SA37 | G | P | TO | AF126 | AF185 | 2N4034 | 2N646 | 2SA240 | |
| | | | | | | | | | |
| 2SA37 | | | | AF127 | | | | | |
| 2SA38 | G | P | TO | AF126 | AF185 | 2N4034 | 2N646 | 2SA240 | |
| 2SA38 | | | | AF127 | AF137 | | | | |
| 2SA38 | | | | AF134 | | | | | |
| 2SA39 | G | P | TO | AF127 | AF185 | 2N4034 | 2N646 | 2SA240 | |
| | | | | | | | | | |
| 2SA39 | | | | AF137 | AF134 | | | | |
| 2SA40 | G | P | FU | (AF126) | AF185 | | | | |
| 2SA41 | G | P | HI | AF127 | AC150 | 2N4034 | 2N646 | 2SA240 | |
| 2SA41 | | | | AF137 | AF134 | | | | |
| 2SA42 | G | P | HI | (ASY48) | AF131 | | | | |
| | | | | | | | | | |
| 2SA42 | | | | AF134 | AF137 | | | | |
| 2SA43 | G | P | FU | AF125 | AF185 | 2N1110 | | 2SA156 | |
| 2SA43 | | | | AF135 | AF131 | | | | |
| 2SA44 | G | P | | AF185 | | | | | |
| 2SA44B | G | P | | AF185 | | | | | |
| | | | | | | | | | |
| 2SA45 | G | P | | AF185 | | | | | |
| 2SA48 | G | P | | AF125 | AF185 | 2N1110 | | 2SA156 | |
| 2SA48 | | | | AF135 | AF131 | | | | |
| 2SA48 | | | | AF134 | | | | | |
| 2SA49 | G | P | TO, DT, TJ | (AF127) | AF185 | 2N416 | 2N483 | | |
| | | | | | | | | | |
| 2SA49 | | | | AF135 | AF134 | | | | |
| 2SA49 | | | | AF126 | | | | | |
| 2SA50 | G | P | TO | AC152IVI | AC152IV | 2N4106 | 2N610 | 2S32 | |
| 2SA50 | | | | AF185 | AC124r | 2N1309 | 2N583 | | |
| 2SA50 | | | | AV128 | AF134 | | | | |
| | | | | | | | | | |
| 2SA51 | G | P | TO | AF127 | AF185 | 2N4034 | 2N646 | 2SA240 | |
| 2SA51 | | | | AF137 | AF134 | 2N212 | 2617 | | |
| 2SA51 | | | | AF136 | | | | | |
| 2SA52 | G | P | DT, TJ | AF126 | AF185 | 2N641 | 2N486 | 2SA240 | |
| 2SA52 | | | | AF137 | AF131 | 2N1058 | | | |
| | | | | | | | | | |
| 2SA52 | | | | AF134 | | | | | |
| 2SA53 | G | P | DT, TJ | AF127 | AF185 | 2N642 | 2N4034 | 2SA240 | |
| 2SA53 | | | | AF137 | AF134 | 2N482 | 2N614 | | |
| 2SA54 | G | P | NI | (AF106) | | | | | |
| 2SA56 | G | P | NI | (AC171IV) | | | | | |
| | | | | | | | | | |
| 2SA57 | G | P | TO | (AF127) | AF124 | 2N346 | 2N4035 | 2SA235 | |
| 2SA57 | | | | AF185 | AF134 | 2N370 | 2N384 | | |
| 2SA57 | | | | AF194 | AF136 | | | | |
| 2SA58 | G | P | TO | AF124 | AF127 | 2N346 | 2N4035 | 2SA235 | |
| 2SA58 | | | | AF185 | AF134 | 2N1110 | | | |

| TYPE | M/S | POL | MANUFAC | EUROPEAN | | AMERICAN | | JAPANESE | USE |
|------|-----|-----|---------|----------|--|----------|--|----------|-----|
| 2SA58 | | | | AF194 | AF136 | | | | |
| 2SA59 | G | P | TO | (AF127) | AF185 | 2N370 | 2N624 | | |
| 2SA59 | | | | AF134 | AF137 | | | | |
| 2SA60 | G | P | TO | AF124 | AF185 | 2N346 | 2N4035 | 2SA235 | |
| 2SA60 | | | | AF134 | AF194 | 2N371 | 2N393 | | |
| 2SA60 | | | | | | | | | |
| 2SA61 | G | P | TO | AF136 | | | | | |
| 2SA65 | G | P | TO | AF185 | | | | | |
| 2SA66 | G | P | TO | (RSY70V) | ASY27 | 2N36 | 2N302 | | |
| 2SA67 | G | P | TO | (ASY70V) | ASY27 | 2N36 | 2N302 | 2SA65 | |
| 2SA67 | | | | (ASY70V) | ASY27 | 2N36 | 2N302 | 2SA65 | |
| 2SA69 | G | P | MA | | | 2N1309 | | | |
| 2SA70 | G | P | CE, MA | (AF127) | AF118 | 2N2495 | 2N2707 | 2SA76 | |
| 2SA70 | | | | AF178 | AF136 | 2N2495 | | | |
| 2SA70 | | | | HFY15 | | 2N370 | | | |
| 2SA71 | G | P | CE, MA | (AF127) | AF124 | 2N2495 | 2N4035 | 2SA235 | |
| 2SA71 | | | | AF178 | AF134 | | | | |
| 2SA71 | | | | AF194 | AF131 | | | | |
| 2SA72 | G | P | TO | AF127 | AF185 | 2N4035 | 2N542 | 2SA240 | |
| 2SA72 | | | | AF136 | AF137 | | | | |
| 2SA72 | | | | | | | | | |
| 2SA73 | G | P | TO | AF134 | | | | | |
| 2SA73 | | | | AF127 | AF185 | 2N4035 | 2N642 | 2SA240 | |
| 2SA74 | G | P | TO | AF137 | AF134 | | | | |
| 2SA74 | | | | AF124 | AF185 | | | | |
| 2SA74 | | | | AF131 | AF134 | | | | |
| 2SA75 | G | P | TO | AF127 | AF185 | 2N4035 | 2N346 | 2SA235 | |
| 2SA75 | | | | AF124 | AF134 | | | | |
| 2SA75 | | | | AF194 | AF131 | | | | |
| 2SA76 | G | P | TO | AF126 | AF185 | 2N641 | 2N110 | 2SA240 | |
| 2SA76 | | | | AF137 | AF134 | | | | |
| 2SA76 | | | | | | | | | |
| 2SA77 | G | P | TO | AF136 | | | | | |
| 2SA77 | | | | AF124 | AF185 | 2N641 | | 2SA240 | |
| 2SA77 | | | | AF126 | AF137 | | | | |
| 2SA78 | G | P | TO | AF131 | AF134 | | | | |
| 2SA79 | G | P | TO | (AC121V) | ASY75 | | | | |
| 2SA80 | G | P | HI | AF124 | AF185 | 2N641 | 2N371 | 2SA240 | |
| 2SA80 | | | | AF126 | AF137 | | | | |
| 2SA80 | | | | AF134 | AF136 | | | | |
| 2SA81 | G | P | HI | (AF124) | AF185 | 2N1634 | 2N1638 | | |
| 2SA81 | | | | | | | | | |
| 2SA82 | G | P | HI | AF132 | AF136 | | | | |
| 2SA82 | | | | (AF124) | AF185 | 2N373 | | | |
| 2SA83 | G | P | HI | AF134 | AF136 | | | | |
| 2SA83 | | | | (AF127) | AF185 | 2N1634 | 2N1638 | | |
| 2SA83 | | | | AF134 | AF136 | | | | |
| 2SA84 | G | P | HI | (AF127) | AF185 | 2N1634 | 2N1638 | | |
| 2SA84 | | | | AF132 | AF136 | | | | |
| 2SA85 | G | P | HI | (AF127) | AF124 | 2N544 | | | |
| 2SA85 | | | | AF131 | AF136 | | | | |
| 2SA86 | G | P | HI | AF125 | AF126 | 2N641 | | 2SA240 | |
| 2SA86 | | | | | | | | | |
| 2SA87 | G | P | HI | AF137 | AF131 | | | | |
| 2SA87 | | | | AF134 | AF135 | | | | |
| 2SA88 | G | P | HI | (AF125) | | | | | |
| 2SA89 | G | P | HI | (AF127) | | | | | |
| 2SA89 | | | | (AF126) | AF131 | 2N481 | | | |
| 2SA89 | | | | | | | | | |
| 2SA90 | G | P | HI | AF134 | AF136 | | | | |
| 2SA90 | | | | (AF126) | AF131 | 2N499 | | 2SA90 | |
| 2SA92 | G | P | TO | AF135 | AF136 | | | | |
| 2SA92 | | | | AF125 | AF185 | 2N1110 | 2N345 | 2SA156 | |
| 2SA92 | | | | AF135 | AF132 | 2N374 | | | |
| 2SA92 | | | | | | | | | |
| 2SA93 | G | P | TO | AF136 | | | | | |
| 2SA93 | | | | AF126 | AF185 | 2N641 | 2N308 | 2SA240 | |
| 2SA94 | G | P | HI | AF136 | AF134 | 2N417 | | | |
| 2SA100 | G | P | MA | (AF126) | AF185 | | | | |
| 2SA100 | | | | AF127 | AF137 | 2N4034 | 2N642 | 2SA240 | |
| 2SA101 | G | P | MA | AF133 | AF136 | | | | |
| 2SA101 | | | | AF127 | AF185 | 2N4034 | 2N642 | 2SA240 | |
| 2SA101A | G | P | MR | AF137 | AF126 | | | | |
| 2SA102 | G | P | MA | AF127 | | | | | |
| 2SA102 | | | | AF127 | AF124 | 2N4034 | 2N642 | 2SA240 | |
| 2SA103 | G | P | MA | AF185 | AF137 | | | | |
| 2SA103 | | | | AF181 | ASZ20 | | | | |
| 2SA103 | | | | AF124 | AF127 | 2N642 | | 2SA240 | |
| 2SA103 | | | | AF185 | AF137 | | | | |
| 2SA103 | | | | AF181 | ASZ20 | | | | |

| TYPE | M/S | POL | MANUFAC | EUROPEAN | | AMERICAN | | JAPANESE | USE |
|------|-----|-----|---------|----------|---|----------|---|----------|-----|
| 2SA104 | G | P | MA | AF127 | AF185 | 2N4034 | 2N642 | 2SA240 | |
| 2SA104 | | | | AF137 | AF134 | | | | |
| 2SA104 | | | | AF135 | | | | | |
| 2SA105 | G | P | FU | (AF127) | AF178 | 2N2495 | 2N299 | | |
| 2SA105 | | | | AF130 | AF135 | | | | |
| 2SA106 | | | | (AF127) | AF185 | | | | |
| 2SA107 | G | P | FU | (AF127) | AF185 | | | | |
| 2SA108 | G | P | FU | AF125 | AF185 | 2N1110 | 2N374 | 2SA156 | |
| 2SA108 | | | | AF135 | AF136 | | | | |
| 2SA109 | G | P | FU | AF127 | AF185 | 2N4034 | 2N642 | 2SA240 | |
| 2SA109 | | | | AF137 | AF136 | 2N374 | 2N481 | | |
| 2SA110 | G | P | FU | AF126 | AF185 | 2N641 | 2N373 | 2SA240 | |
| 2SA110 | | | | AF136 | AF131 | 2N374 | | | |
| 2SA111 | G | P | FU | AF125 | AF185 | 2N1110 | 2N373 | 2SA156 | |
| 2SA111 | | | | AF135 | AF136 | 2N374 | | | |
| 2SA112 | G | P | FU | AF124 | AF185 | 2N4035 | 2N346 | 2SA235 | |
| 2SA112 | | | | AF134 | AF194 | 2N374 | 2N499 | | |
| 2SA112 | | | | AF131 | AF136 | | | | |
| 2SA113 | G | P | FU | (AF124) | AF185 | | | | |
| 2SA114 | G | P | FU | (AF124) | AF185 | | | | |
| 2SA115 | G | P | FU | (AF124) | AF185 | | | | |
| 2SA116 | G | P | FU | AF124 | AF178 | 2N2495 | 2N4035 | 2SA235 | |
| 2SA116 | | | | AF134 | AF194 | 2N384 | 2N346 | | |
| 2SA116 | | | | AF135 | | | | | |
| 2SA117 | G | P | FU | AF124 | AF178 | 2N2495 | 2N4035 | 2SA235 | |
| 2SA117 | | | | AF134 | AF194 | 2N1178 | 2N346 | | |
| 2SA117 | | | | AF130 | AF135 | | | | |
| 2SA118 | G | P | FU | AF124 | AF178 | 2N2495 | 2N4035 | 2SA235 | |
| 2SA118 | | | | AF134 | AF194 | 2N1179 | 2N346 | | |
| 2SA118 | | | | AF130 | AF136 | | | | |
| 2SA121 | G | P | SO | AF125 | AF185 | 2N1110 | 2N1117 | 2SA156 | |
| 2SA121 | | | | AF178 | AF135 | 2N1180 | | 2T201 | |
| 2SA121 | | | | AF136 | | | | | |
| 2SA122 | G | P | SO | (AF125) | AF178 | 2N1178 | 2N1180 | 2T201 | |
| 2SA122 | | | | AF185 | AFZ12 | | | | |
| 2SA123 | G | P | SO | AF125 | AF178 | 2N1110 | 2N1179 | 2SA156 | |
| 2SA123 | | | | AF185 | | | | | |
| 2SA124 | G | P | SO | AF124 | AF178 | 2N2435 | 2N4035 | 2SA235 | |
| 2SA124 | | | | AF134 | AF194 | 2N1180 | | 2T203 | |
| 2SA124 | | | | AF135 | AFZ12 | | | | |
| 2SA125 | G | P | SO | AF124 | AF178 | 2N2495 | 2N346 | 2SA235 | |
| 2SA125 | | | | AF134 | AF194 | 2N4035 | 2N1180 | 2T205A | |
| 2SA125 | | | | AFZ12 | | | | | |
| 2SA126 | G | P | NI | (AC121V) | | | | | |
| 2SA127 | G | P | TO | (ASY70) | | | | | |
| 2SA128 | G | P | TO | (ASY48IV) | AF185 | | | | |
| 2SA129 | G | P | TO | (ASY48V) | AF185 | | | | |
| 2SA130 | G | P | HI | (AF125) | AF185 | | | | |
| 2SA131 | G | P | HI | (AF125) | AF185 | | | | |
| 2SA132 | G | P | HI | (AF125) | AF185 | | | | |
| 2SA133 | G | P | HI | (AF125) | AF185 | | | | |
| 2SA134 | G | P | HI | (AF125) | AF178 | 2N2495 | | | |
| 2SA135 | G | P | HI | (AF125) | AF178 | 2N2495 | | | |
| 2SA136 | G | P | FU | (AC121VII) | AF185 | | | 2SA52 | |
| 2SA136 | | | | AF126 | AFY15 | | | | |
| 2SA137 | G | P | FU | (AC121V) | AF185 | | | | |
| 2SA138 | G | P | FU | (AC121VIII) | AF185 | | | | |
| 2SA139 | G | P | FU | (AC121IV) | AF185 | | | | |
| 2SA141 | G | P | MT | (AC121V) | ASY26 | 2N799 | 2N218 | 2SA55 | |
| 2SA141 | | | | AF185 | AFY15 | | | | |
| 2SA141 | | | | AF133 | AF137 | | | | |
| 2SA142 | G | P | MT | (AC121V) | ASY27 | 2N799 | 2N135 | | |
| 2SA142 | | | | AF127 | AF185 | | | | |
| 2SA142 | | | | AFY15 | AF133 | | | | |
| 2SA142 | | | | AF137 | | | | | |
| 2SA142A | G | P | MT | (ASY48V) | | | | | |
| 2SA143 | G | P | MT | AF126 | AF185 | 2N137 | | | |
| 2SA143 | | | | AF131 | AF136 | | | | |
| 2SA144 | G | P | MA | HF124 | AF185 | 2N346 | 2N4035 | 2SA235 | |
| 2SA144 | | | | AF134 | AF195 | 2N113 | 2N624 | | |
| 2SA144 | | | | AF130 | | | | | |
| 2SA145 | G | P | MA | AF185 | AF130 | | | | |
| 2SA146 | G | P | | AF185 | AF133 | 2N409 | | | |
| 2SA146 | | | | AF136 | | | | | |
| 2SA147 | G | P | | AF185 | AF133 | | | | |

| TYPE | M/S | POL | MANUFAC | EUROPEAN | | AMERICAN | | JAPANESE | USE |
|------|-----|-----|---------|----------|--|----------|--|----------|-----|
| 2SA147 | | | | AF137 | | | | | |
| 2SA148 | G | P | | AF185 | AF132 | | | | |
| 2SA148 | | | | AF137 | | | | | |
| 2SA149 | G | P | | AF185 | AF132 | | | | |
| 2SA149 | | | | AF137 | | | | | |
| 2SA151 | G | P | HI | (AF127) | AF185 | | | | |
| 2SA152 | G | P | HI | (AC121V) | AF185 | | | | |
| 2SA152 | | | | AF132 | AF136 | | | | |
| 2SA153 | G | P | NI | (AF127) | AF178 | 2N2495 | | | |
| 2SA153 | | | | AF185 | AF134 | | | | |
| 2SA154 | | | | (AF127) | AF185 | | | | |
| 2SA154 | | | | AF132 | AF137 | | | | |
| 2SA155 | G | P | NI | (AF127) | AF185 | 2N267 | | | |
| 2SA155 | | | | AP134 | AF137 | | | | |
| 2SA156 | G | P | NI | (AF127) | AF185 | 2N384 | | | |
| 2SA156 | | | | AF135 | AF136 | | | | |
| 2SA157 | G | P | NI | (AF127) | AF178 | 2N2495 | | | |
| 2SA157 | | | | AF185 | AF134 | | | | |
| 2SA159 | G | P | NI | (AF127) | AF178 | 2N2495 | | | |
| 2SA159 | | | | AF185 | AF134 | | | | |
| 2SA160 | G | P | NI | (AF127) | AF185 | | | | |
| 2SA161 | G | P | SO | (AF139) | AF106 | 2N2495 | | 2SA230 | |
| 2SA161 | | | | AF178 | AF190 | | | | |
| 2SA161 | | | | AG102 | | | | | |
| 2SA162 | G | P | SO | (AF139) | | | | | |
| 2SA163 | G | P | SO | (AF139) | | | | | |
| 2SA164 | G | P | SO | (AF139) | | | | | |
| 2SA165 | G | P | SO | (AF139) | | | | | |
| 2SA166 | G | P | SO | (AF139) | | | | | |
| 2SA167 | G | P | NI | (ASY26) | AF127 | 2N410 | | | |
| 2SA167 | | | | AF185 | AF133 | | | | |
| 2SA167 | | | | AF136 | | | | | |
| 2SA168 | G | P | NI | AF185 | AF132 | 2N135 | | | |
| 2SA168 | | | | AF137 | | | | | |
| 2SA168A | G | P | NI | AF185 | AF116 | 2N397 | | | |
| 2SA168A | | | | AF127 | | | | | |
| 2SA169 | G | P | NI | (ASY26) | | | | | |
| 2SA171 | G | P | NI | (ASY27) | | | | | |
| 2SA173 | G | P | NI | (ASY26) | | | | | |
| 2SA175 | G | P | TO | (AF125) | AF178 | 2N2495 | 2N304 | | |
| 2SA175 | | | | AF185 | AF134 | | | | |
| 2SA176 | G | P | | AF185 | AF131 | | | | |
| 2SA178 | G | P | | AF185 | AF131 | | | | |
| 2SA178 | | | | AF134 | | | | | |
| 2SA180 | G | P | SN | (AC121VI) | AF185 | | | | |
| 2SA180 | | | | AF131 | AF136 | | | | |
| 2SA181 | G | P | SN | (AC121V) | AF185 | 2N427 | | | |
| 2SA181 | | | | AF133 | AF137 | | | | |
| 2SA182 | G | P | SN | (AC121IV) | AF185 | 2N254 | | | |
| 2SA182 | | | | AF133 | AF137 | | | | |
| 2SA183 | G | P | SN | (AC121IV) | AF185 | 2N78 | | 2SA52 | |
| 2SA183 | | | | AC121 | AFY15 | | | | |
| 2SA183 | | | | AF126 | AF132 | | | | |
| 2SA183 | | | | AF137 | | | | | |
| 2SA184 | G | P | | AF185 | AF133 | 2N292 | | | |
| 2SA184 | | | | AF137 | | | | | |
| 2SA186 | G | P | | AF126 | AFY15 | | | 2SA52 | |
| 2SA186 | | | | AF185 | | | | | |
| 2SA188 | G | P | FU | (AC121VI) | AF185 | | | | |
| 2SA189 | G | P | FU | (AC121VI) | AF185 | | | | |
| 2SA190 | G | P | | AF185 | | | | | |
| 2SA191 | G | P | | AF185 | | | | | |
| 2SA192 | G | P | | AF185 | AF131 | 2N411 | | | |
| 2SA192 | | | | AF136 | | | | | |
| 2SA193 | G | P | | AF185 | AF133 | 2N313 | | | |
| 2SA193 | | | | AF137 | | | | | |
| 2SA194 | G | P | | AF185 | | | | | |
| 2SA195 | G | P | | AF185 | AF131 | 2N135 | | | |
| 2SA195 | | | | AF137 | | | | | |
| 2SA196 | G | P | | AF185 | AF127 | 2N136 | | | |
| 2SA196 | | | | AF133 | | | | | |
| 2SA197 | G | P | | AF185 | AF132 | | | | |
| 2SA197 | | | | AF137 | | | | | |
| 2SA198 | G | P | | AF185 | AF131 | | | | |
| 2SA198 | | | | AF137 | | | | | |

| TYPE | M/S | POL | MANUFAC | EUROPEAN | | AMERICAN | | | JAPANESE | USE |
|------|-----|-----|---------|----------|---|----------|---|---|----------|-----|
| 2SA199 | G | P | | AF185 | | | | | | |
| 2SA199 | | | | AF137 | AF132 | | | | | |
| 2SA200 | G | P | | AF185 | AF137 | | | | | |
| 2SA200 | | | | AF131 | | | | | | |
| 2SA201 | G | P | SN, TS | (AC121IV) | AF121 | | | | 2SA52 | |
| 2SA201 | | | | AF185 | AF126 | | | | | |
| 2SA201 | | | | AFY15 | | | | | | |
| 2SA202 | G | P | SN, TS | (AC121V) | AF121V | | | | 2SA52 | |
| 2SA202 | | | | AF185 | AFY15 | | | | | |
| 2SA202 | | | | AF126 | | | | | | |
| 2SA203 | G | P | SN, TS | (AC121V) | AF185 | | | | 2SA52 | |
| 2SA203 | | | | AF126 | AFY15 | | | | | |
| 2SA203 | | | | AF133 | AF137 | | | | | |
| 2SA204 | G | P | NI | (AC151V) | | | | | | |
| 2SA205 | G | P | NI | (AC151IV) | | | | | | |
| 2SA206 | G | P | NI | (AC151V) | AF185 | 2N252 | 2N1305 | | | |
| 2SA206 | | | | AF133 | AF137 | | | | | |
| 2SA207 | G | P | NI | (AC151VI) | | | | | | |
| 2SA208 | G | P | HI | ASY26 | AF126 | 2N799 | 2N146 | | 2SA155 | |
| 2SA208 | | | | AF130 | AF136 | | | | | |
| 2SA208H | G | P | HI | ASY26 | | 2N799 | | | 2SA155 | |
| 2SA209 | G | P | HI | ASY26 | AF127 | 2N799 | 2N412 | | 2SA155 | |
| 2SA209 | | | | AF133 | AF137 | | | | | |
| 2SA209H | | | | ASY26 | | | | | | |
| 2SA210 | G | P | HI | ASY27 | ASY26 | 2N799 | 2N307 | | 2SA155 | |
| 2SA210H | G | P | HI | ASY27 | | 2N799 | | | 2SA155 | |
| 2SA211 | G | P | HI | ASY26 | | 2N799 | | | 2SA155 | |
| 2SA212 | G | P | HI | ASY26 | | | | | | |
| 2SA212H | G | P | HI | ASY26 | | | | | | |
| 2SA213 | G | P | NI | (AF125) | AF178 | 2N2495 | | | | |
| 2SA213 | | | | AF129 | AF134 | | | | | |
| 2SA214 | G | P | NI | (AF125) | AF178 | 2N2495 | | | | |
| 2SA214 | | | | AF130 | AF135 | | | | | |
| 2SA215 | G | P | NI | (AF125) | AF185 | | | | | |
| 2SA215 | | | | AF135 | AF137 | | | | | |
| 2SA216 | G | P | NI | (AF125) | AF178 | 2N2495 | | | | |
| 2SA216 | | | | | AF127 | | | | | |
| 2SA217 | G | P | HI | ASY26 | | | | | | |
| 2SA217H | G | P | HI | ASY26 | | | | | | |
| 2SA218 | G | P | SN, TS | (AF127) | AF185 | | | | | |
| 2SA218 | | | | AF126 | AF134 | | | | | |
| 2SA219 | G | P | SN, TS | (AF127) | AF185 | | | | | |
| 2SA219 | | | | AF126 | | | | | | |
| 2SA220 | G | P | SN | (AF127) | AF185 | | | | | |
| 2SA220 | | | | AF134 | AF136 | | | | | |
| 2SA221 | G | P | SN, TS | (AF127) | AF185 | | | | | |
| 2SA221 | | | | AF126 | AF134 | | | | | |
| 2SA222 | G | P | SN, TS | (AF127) | AF185 | | | | | |
| 2SA222 | | | | AF134 | AF136 | | | | | |
| 2SA223 | G | P | SN, TS | (AF127) | AF185 | | | | | |
| 2SA223 | | | | AF126 | AF134 | | | | | |
| 2SA224 | G | P | FU | (AF127) | AF185 | | | | | |
| 2SA224 | | | | AF134 | AF135 | | | | | |
| 2SA225 | G | P | FU | (AF126) | | | | | | |
| 2SA226 | G | P | FU | (AF125) | AF185 | | | | | |
| 2SA226 | | | | AF134 | AF135 | | | | | |
| 2SA227 | G | P | FU | (AF124) | AF178 | 2N2495 | | | | |
| 2SA227 | | | | AF126 | AF134 | | | | | |
| 2SA229 | G | P | TO | AF139 | AF178 | 2N2495 | 11M139 | | M9031 | |
| 2SA229 | | | | AF186 | | | | | | |
| 2SA230 | G | P | TO | AF139 | AF178 | 2N2495 | 11M139 | | M9031 | |
| 2SA230 | | | | AF186 | | | | | | |
| 2SA231 | G | P | HI | (AUY18) | | | | | | |
| 2SA232 | G | P | HI | (AUY18) | | | | | | |
| 2SA233 | G | P | HI | (AF127) | AF185 | 2N136 | | | | |
| 2SA233 | | | | AF117 | AF126 | | | | | |
| 2SA234 | G | P | HI | (AF127) | AF106 | | | | 2SA230 | |
| 2SA234 | | | | AF185 | AF190 | | | | | |
| 2SA234 | | | | AF136 | AFZ12 | | | | | |
| 2SA235 | G | P | HI | (AF127) | AF106 | 2N2495 | 2N299 | | 2SA230 | |
| 2SA235 | | | | AF178 | AF190 | | | | | |
| 2SA235 | | | | AF135 | AFZ12 | | | | | |
| 2SA235H | G | P | HI | (AF127) | | | | | | |
| 2SA236 | G | P | TO | (AF127) | AF185 | | | | | |
| 2SA236 | | | | AF127 | | | | | | |

| TYPE | M/S | POL | MANUFAC | EUROPEAN | | AMERICAN | | JAPANESE | USE |
|---|---|---|---|---|---|---|---|---|---|
| 2SA237 | G | P | TO | (AF127) | AF185 | | | | |
| 2SA238 | G | P | NI | (AF139) | AF186 | | | | |
| 2SA239 | G | P | TO | AF106 | AF190 | | | | |
| 2SA240 | G | P | TO | AF106 | AF178 | 2N2495 | | 2SA230 | |
| 2SA240 | | | | AF185 | AF190 | | | 2SA230 | |
| 2SA241 | G | P | MA | AF118 | AF178 | 2N2495 | 2N2207 | 2SA76 | |
| 2SA242 | G | P | MA | (AF106) | AF178 | 2N2495 | | | |
| 2SA242 | | | | AF118 | | | | | |
| 2SA243 | G | P | MA | (AF106) | AF178 | 2N2495 | | | |
| 2SA243 | | | | AF118 | | | | | |
| 2SA244 | G | P | NI | (AF139) | | | | | |
| 2SA245 | G | P | NI | (AF139) | | | | | |
| 2SA246 | G | P | HI | AF106 | | | | | |
| 2SA247 | G | P | HI | (AF106) | | | | | |
| 2SA248 | G | P | TO | (AC151IV) | | | | | |
| 2SA250 | G | P | MA | (AF127) | AF185 | | | | |
| 2SA251 | G | P | FU | (AF127) | | | | | |
| 2SA252 | G | P | FU | (AF127) | | | | | |
| 2SA253 | G | P | FU | (AF139) | AF185 | | | | |
| 2SA254 | G | P | FU | (AC121IV) | AF185 | 2N1058 | | | |
| 2SA254 | | | | AF136 | AF186 | | | | |
| 2SA255 | G | P | FU | (AC121IV) | AC162 | 2N27 | 2N211 | 2SB459 | |
| 2SA255 | | | | AC170 | AF137 | | | | |
| 2SA255 | | | | AF133 | AF127 | | | | |
| 2SA256 | G | P | FU | (AF126) | AF185 | 2N370 | | | |
| 2SA256 | | | | AF135 | AF136 | | | | |
| 2SA257 | G | P | FU | (AF126) | AF185 | | | | |
| 2SA257 | | | | AF130 | AF134 | | | | |
| 2SA258 | G | P | FU | (AF126) | AF185 | | | | |
| 2SA258 | | | | AF130 | AF134 | | | | |
| 2SA259 | G | P | FU | (AF126) | AF185 | 2N247 | 2N374 | | |
| 2SA259 | | | | AF134 | AF137 | | | | |
| 2SA259 | | | | AF135 | AF136 | | | | |
| 2SA260 | G | P | SN, TS | (AF106) | | | | | |
| 2SA261 | G | P | SN, TS | (AF106) | | | | | |
| 2SA262 | G | P | SN, TS | (AF106) | | | | | |
| 2SA263 | G | P | SN, TS | (AF106) | | | | | |
| 2SA264 | G | P | SN, TS | (AF106) | | | | | |
| 2SA265 | G | P | SN, TS | (AF106) | | | | | |
| 2SA266 | G | P | FU | AF124 | AF185 | 2N4035 | 2N346 | 2SA235 | |
| 2SA266 | | | | AF134 | | | | | |
| 2SA267 | G | P | FU | AF125 | AF185 | 2N1110 | | 2SA156 | |
| 2SA267 | | | | AF135 | AF131 | | | | |
| 2SA268 | G | P | FU | AF126 | AF185 | SET316 | 2N641 | 2SA240 | |
| 2SA268 | | | | AF136 | AF132 | | | | |
| 2SA269 | G | P | FU | AF127 | AF185 | 2N4034 | 2N642 | 2SA240 | |
| 2SA269 | | | | AF137 | AF133 | 2N248 | | | |
| 2SA270 | G | P | FU | AF125 | AF185 | 2N1110 | 2N299 | 2SA156 | |
| 2SA270 | | | | AF135 | AF133 | | | | |
| 2SA271 | G | P | FU | (AF127) | AF124 | 2N4034 | 2N642 | 2SA240 | |
| 2SA271 | | | | AF185 | AF137 | | | | |
| 2SA271 | | | | AF132 | | | | | |
| 2SA272 | G | P | FU | AF127 | AF185 | 2N4034 | 2N642 | 2SA240 | |
| 2SA272 | | | | AF137 | AF133 | | | | |
| 2SA273 | G | P | FU | AF126 | AF185 | SET316 | 2N641 | 2SA240 | |
| 2SA273 | | | | AF136 | | | | | |
| 2SA274 | G | P | FU | AF127 | AF185 | 2N4034 | 2N642 | 2SA240 | |
| 2SA274 | | | | AF137 | | | | | |
| 2SA275 | G | P | FU | AF125 | AF185 | 2N1110 | | 2SA156 | |
| 2SA275 | | | | AF135 | | | | | |
| 2SA276 | G | P | TO | (AF127) | | | | | |
| 2SA277 | G | P | TO | (ASY26) | | | | | |
| 2SA278 | G | P | TO | (ASY27) | | | | | |
| 2SA280 | G | P | MA | (AF126) | | | | | |
| 2SA281 | G | P | MA | (AF126) | | | | | |
| 2SA282 | G | P | TO | ASY27 | | | | 2SA311 | |
| 2SA283 | G | P | TO | ASY27 | | | | 2SA312 | |
| 2SA284 | G | P | TO | ASY27 | AF185 | | | 2SA538 | |
| 2SA285 | G | P | NI | (AF127) | AF134 | | | | |
| 2SA285 | | | | AF132 | | | | | |
| 2SA286 | G | P | NI | (AF127) | AF185 | | | | |
| 2SA286 | | | | AF134 | AF135 | | | | |
| 2SA287 | G | P | NI | (AF127) | AF185 | | | | |
| 2SA287 | | | | AF134 | AF135 | | | | |
| 2SA288 | G | P | HI | (AF139) | | | | | |

| TYPE | M/S | POL | MANUFAC | EUROPEAN | | | AMERICAN | | | JAPANESE | USE |
|------|-----|-----|---------|----------|---|---|----------|---|---|----------|-----|
| 2SA289 | G | P | HI | (AF139) | | | | | | | |
| 2SA290 | G | P | HI | (AF139) | | | | | | | |
| 2SA291 | G | P | FU | (AF127) | | | | | | | |
| 2SA292 | G | P | FU | (AF106) | | | | | | | |
| 2SA293 | G | P | FU | (AF106) | AF126 | | SE316 | 2N641 | | 2SA240 | |
| 2SA293 | | | | AF137 | AF132 | | 2N267 | | | | |
| 2SA293 | | | | AF136 | | | | | | | |
| 2SA294 | G | P | FU | (AF106) | | | | | | | |
| 2SA295 | G | P | FU | (AC151IV) | | | | | | | |
| 2SA296 | G | P | Y | (AC121IV) | AF126 | | SE1316 | 2N641 | | 2SA52 | |
| 2SA296 | | | | AFY15 | | | | | | | |
| 2SA297 | G | P | Y | (AC121V) | AF126 | | SE1316 | 2N641 | | 2SA52 | |
| 2SA297 | | | | AFY15 | | | | | | | |
| 2SA298 | G | P | Y | (AF127) | AF185 | | | | | | |
| 2SA301 | G | P | MA | (AF127) | | | | | | | |
| 2SA302 | G | P | MA | (AC121IV) | | | | | | | |
| 2SA303 | G | P | MA | (AC121IV) | | | | | | | |
| 2SA304 | G | P | TO | (AC152I) | AF185 | | | | | | |
| 2SA304gn | G | P | TO | (AC152VI) | | | | | | | |
| 2SA304r | G | P | TO | (AC152IV) | | | | | | | |
| 2SA304ve | G | P | TO | (AC152V) | | | | | | | |
| 2SA305 | G | P | TO | (AC152I) | AF185 | | | | | 2SA373 | |
| 2SA305gn | G | P | TO | (AC152VI) | | | | | | | |
| 2SA305r | G | P | TO | (AC152IV) | | | | | | | |
| 2SA305ve | G | P | TO | (AC152V) | | | | | | | |
| 2SA306 | G | P | | (AF127) | | | | | | | |
| 2SA306 | G | P | | (AF127) | | | | | | | |
| 2SA307 | G | P | | (AF127) | AF185 | | | | | | |
| 2SA308 | G | P | MA | (AF139) | | | | | | | |
| 2SA309 | G | P | MA | (AF139) | | | | | | | |
| 2SA310 | G | P | MA | (AF139) | | | | | | | |
| 2SA311 | G | P | TO | (ASY27) | AF185 | | | | | | |
| 2SA311 | | | | AUY10 | | | | | | | |
| 2SA312 | G | P | TO | (ASY26) | AF185 | | | | | | |
| 2SA313 | G | P | TO | (AF127) | AF185 | | | | | | |
| 2SA313 | | | | AF125 | AF134 | | | | | | |
| 2SA313bl | G | P | TO | (AF127) | | | | | | | |
| 2SA313gn | G | P | TO | (AF127) | | | | | | | |
| 2SA313r | G | P | TO | (AF127) | | | | | | | |
| 2SA313ve | G | P | TO | (AF127) | | | | | | | |
| 2SA314 | G | P | TO | (AF127) | AF185 | | | | | | |
| 2SA314 | | | | AF125 | AF134 | | | | | | |
| 2SA314gn | G | P | TO | (AF127) | | | | | | | |
| 2SA314r | G | P | TO | (AF127) | | | | | | | |
| 2SA314ve | G | P | TO | (AF127) | | | | | | | |
| 2SA315 | G | P | TO | (AF127) | AF125 | | 2N1110 | | | 2SA156 | |
| 2SA315 | | | | AF185 | AF135 | | | | | | |
| 2SA315 | | | | AF134 | | | | | | | |
| 2SA315gn | G | P | TO | (AF127) | | | | | | | |
| 2SA315r | G | P | TO | (AF127) | | | | | | | |
| 2SA315ve | G | P | TO | (AF127) | | | | | | | |
| 2SA316 | G | P | TO | (AF127) | AF185 | | | | | 2SA316 | |
| 2SA316 | | | | AF125 | AF135 | | | | | | |
| 2SA316 | | | | AF134 | | | | | | | |
| 2SA316gn | G | P | TO | (AF127) | | | | | | | |
| 2SA316r | G | P | TO | (AF127) | | | | | | | |
| 2SA316ve | G | P | TO | (AF127) | | | | | | | |
| 2SA321 | G | P | TS | AF127 | AF137 | | 2N4034 | 2N642 | | 2SA240 | |
| 2SA322 | G | P | SN, TS | (AF126) | AF185 | | 2N4035 | 2N436 | | 2SA235 | |
| 2SA323 | G | P | TS | AF124 | AF185 | | | | | | |
| 2SA323 | | | | AF134 | | | | | | | |
| 2SA324 | G | P | TS | AF125 | AF185 | | 2N1110 | | | 2SA156 | |
| 2SA324 | | | | AF135 | | | | | | | |
| 2SA325 | G | P | Y | (AC121IV) | | | | | | | |
| 2SA326 | G | P | Y | (AC121IV) | | | | | | | |
| 2SA327 | G | P | Y | (AF127) | | | | | | | |
| 2SA329 | G | P | TS | AC125 | | | | | | | |
| 2SA340 | G | P | MA | AF124 | AF127 | | 2N1110 | | | 2SA156 | |
| 2SA340 | | | | AF85 | AF125 | | | | | | |
| 2SA340 | | | | AF135 | | | | | | | |
| 2SA341 | G | P | MA | AF124 | AF185 | | 2N4035 | 2N346 | | 2SA235 | |
| 2SA341 | | | | AF121 | AF194 | | | | | | |
| 2SA342 | G | P | MA | AF124 | AF178 | | 2N2495 | 2N4035 | | 2SA235 | |
| 2SA342 | | | | AF185 | AF121 | | 2N346 | | | | |
| 2SA342 | | | | AF194 | | | | | | | |

| TYPE | M/S | POL | MANUFAC | EUROPEAN | | AMERICAN | | JAPANESE | USE |
|------|-----|-----|---------|----------|---|----------|---|----------|-----|
| 2SA343 | G | P | MA | (AF106) | | | | | |
| 2SA344 | G | P | MA | (AF106) | | | | | |
| 2SA345 | G | P | MT | (AF106) | | | | | |
| 2SA346 | G | P | MT | (AF106) | | | | | |
| 2SA347 | G | P | MT | (AF106) | | | | | |
| | | | | | | | | | |
| 2SA348 | G | P | MT | (AF106) | | | | | |
| 2SA349 | G | P | MT | (AF127) | | | | | |
| 2SA350 | G | P | HI | AF126 | AF127 | SET316 | 2N641 | 2SA240 | |
| 2SA350 | | | | AF135 | AF125 | | | | |
| 2SA350 | | | | AF130 | | | | | |
| | | | | | | | | | |
| 2SA350H | | P | HI | (AF127) | | | | | |
| 2SA351 | G | P | HI | (AF126) | | | | | |
| 2SA352 | G | P | HI | (AF125) | AF126 | SET316 | 2N641 | 2SA240 | |
| 2SA352 | | | | AF137 | AF124 | | | | |
| 2SA352 | | | | AF129 | AF134 | | | | |
| | | | | | | | | | |
| 2SA353 | G | P | HI | AF124 | AF137 | SET316 | 2N641 | 2SA240 | |
| 2SA353 | | | | AF130 | AF134 | | | | |
| 2SA353A | G | P | HI | (AF124) | | | | | |
| 2SA354 | G | P | HI | (AF124) | | | | | |
| 2SA354A | G | P | HI | (AF124) | | | | | |
| | | | | | | | | | |
| 2SA355 | G | P | HI | (AF125) | | | | | |
| 2SA355A | G | P | HI | (AF125) | | | | | |
| 2SA356 | G | P | HI | (AF127) | | | | | |
| 2SA357 | G | P | HI | (AF126) | | | | | |
| 2SA360 | G | P | HI | (AF127) | | | | | |
| | | | | | | | | | |
| 2SA361 | G | P | MT | (AF127) | | | | | |
| 2SA362 | G | P | MT | (AF106) | | | | | |
| 2SA363 | G | P | MT | (AF125) | | | | | |
| 2SA364 | G | P | MT | (AF124) | | | | | |
| 2SA365 | G | P | MT | (AF124) | | | | | |
| | | | | | | | | | |
| 2SA366 | G | P | MT | (AF124) | | | | | |
| 2SA367 | G | P | MT | (AF127) | | | | | |
| 2SA368 | G | P | MT | (AF127) | | | | | |
| 2SA369 | G | P | MT | (AF127) | | | | | |
| 2SA371 | G | P | MT | (AC121V) | | | | | |
| | | | | | | | | | |
| 2SA374 | G | P | MA | (AF124) | | | | | |
| 2SA375 | G | P | MT | (AF124) | | | | | |
| 2SA377 | G | P | MA | AF106 | AF190 | | | 2SA230 | |
| 2SA378 | G | P | MA | (AF106) | | | | | |
| 2SA380 | G | P | Y | (AF127) | AF185 | | | | |
| | | | | | | | | | |
| 2SA381 | G | P | Y | (AF127) | AF185 | | | | |
| 2SA382 | G | P | Y | (AF125) | AF185 | | | | |
| 2SA383 | G | P | Y | (AF124) | AF185 | | | | |
| 2SA384 | G | P | Y | (AF126) | AF185 | | | | |
| 2SA385 | G | P | MA | (AF127) | | | | | |
| | | | | | | | | | |
| 2SA400 | G | P | FU | (AF127) | AF185 | | | | |
| 2SA401 | G | P | HI | (AF106) | | | | | |
| 2SA402 | S | P | SN, TS | (BC107B) | | | | | |
| 2SA403 | G | P | NI | (AF106) | | | | | |
| 2SA404 | G | P | NI | (AF139) | | | | | |
| | | | | | | | | | |
| 2SA406 | G | P | NI | (ASY26) | | | | | |
| 2SA407 | G | P | NI | (ASY27) | | | | | |
| 2SA408 | G | P | FU | (AC121VII) | | | | | |
| 2SA409 | G | P | FU | (AC121VII) | | | | | |
| 2SA412 | G | P | HI | (AF127) | | | | | |
| | | | | | | | | | |
| 2SA414 | G | P | MA | (ASY26) | | | | | |
| 2SA415 | G | P | MA | (ASY26) | | | | | |
| 2SA419 | G | P | SN, TS | (AF139) | | | | | |
| 2SA420 | G | P | TS | AF139 | | 2N2244 | IIN139 | M9031 | |
| 2SA421 | G | P | SN, TS | (AF139) | | | | | |
| | | | | | | | | | |
| 2SA422 | G | P | SN, TS | (AF139) | | 2N2244 | IIN139 | M9031 | |
| 2SA427 | G | P | SN, TS | (AF126) | | | | | |
| 2SA428 | G | P | SN, TS | (AF127) | | | | | |
| 2SA430 | G | P | TO | (AF139) | | | | | |
| 2SA431 | G | P | TO | (AF139) | | | | | |
| | | | | | | | | | |
| 2SA431A | G | P | TO | (AF139) | | | | | |
| 2SA432 | G | P | TO | (AF139) | | | | | |
| 2SA432A | G | P | TO | (AF139) | | | | | |
| 2SA433 | G | P | TO | AF126 | AF136 | SET316 | 2N641 | 2SA240 | |
| 2SA434 | G | P | HI | (AF106) | | | | | |
| | | | | | | | | | |
| 2SA435 | G | P | HI | (AF106) | | | | | |
| 2SA436 | G | P | HI | (AF106) | | | | | |
| 2SA437 | G | P | HI | (AF106) | | | | | |
| 2SA438 | G | P | HI | (AF106) | | | | | |
| 2SA440 | G | P | SN, TS | (AF139) | | | | | |

| TYPE | M/S | POL | MANUFAC | EUROPEAN | | AMERICAN | | JAPANESE | USE |
|------|-----|-----|---------|----------|---|----------|---|----------|-----|
| 2SA440A | G | P | SN, TS | (AF139) | | | | | |
| 2SA447 | G | P | MA | (AF139) | | | | | |
| 2SA454 | G | P | SO | AF139 | | 2N2244 | IIN139 | M9031 | |
| 2SA455 | G | P | SO | AF139 | | 2N2244 | IIN139 | M9031 | |
| 2SA456 | G | P | SO | AF139 | | 2N2244 | IIN139 | M9031 | |
| 2SA457 | G | P | TO | (AF127) | | | | | |
| 2SA458 | G | P | MT | (AC121VI) | | | | | |
| 2SA459 | G | P | MT | (AC121VII) | | | | | |
| 2SA463 | G | P | MT | (AF106) | | | | | |
| 2SA467 | S | P | TO | (BC327-16) | | | | | |
| 2SA467or | S | P | TO | (BC327-16) | | | | | |
| 2SA467ye | S | P | TO | (BC327-16) | | | | | |
| 2SA468 | G | P | TO | (AF127) | | | | | |
| 2SA469 | G | P | TO | (AF126) | | | | | |
| 2SA470 | G | P | TO | (AF124) | | | | | |
| 2SA471 | G | P | TO | AF127 | AF137 | 2N4034 | 2N642 | 2SA240 | |
| 2SA471 | | | | AF126 | AF132 | | | | |
| 2SA471 | | | | AF136 | | | | | |
| 2SA472 | G | P | TO | (AF127) | | | | | |
| 2SA473 | S | P | TO | (BD438) | | | | | |
| 2SA473gn | S | P | TO | (BD438) | | | | | |
| 2SA473or | S | P | TO | (BD438) | | | | | |
| 2SA473r | S | P | TO | (BD438) | | | | | |
| 2SA473ye | S | P | TO | (BD438) | | | | | |
| 2SA474 | G | P | TO | | | | | 2SA472 | |
| 2SA475 | G | P | TO | (AF127) | | | | | |
| 2SA476 | G | P | TO | (AF106) | | | | | |
| 2SA477 | G | P | TO | (AF126) | | | | | |
| 2SA478 | G | P | TO | (ASY48V) | | | | | |
| 2SA479 | G | P | TO | (ASY48V) | | | | | |
| 2SA482 | S | P | TO | BC160-6 | | | | | |
| 2SA484 | S | P | TO | (BSV17) | | | | | |
| 2SA484bl | S | P | TO | (BSV17-10) | | | | | |
| 2SA484r | S | P | TO | (BSV17-6) | | | | | |
| 2SA484ye | S | P | TO | BSV17-10 | | | | | |
| 2SA485 | S | P | TO | BSV17 | | | | | |
| 2SA485bl | S | P | TO | BSV17-10 | | | | | |
| 2SA485r | S | P | TO | (BSV17-6) | | | | | |
| 2SA486 | S | P | TO | BSV16 | | | | | |
| 2SA486bl | S | P | TO | BSV16-16 | | | | | |
| 2SA486r | S | P | TO | BSV16-6 | | | | | |
| 2SA486ye | S | P | TO | BSV16-10 | | | | | |
| 2SA489 | S | P | TO | (BD442) | | 2N6107 | | | |
| 2SA489or | S | P | TO | (BD442) | | | | | |
| 2SA489r | S | P | TO | (BD442) | | | | | |
| 2SA489ye | S | P | TO | (BD442) | | | | | |
| 2SA490 | S | P | TO | (BD438) | | 2N6109 | | | |
| 2SA490or | S | P | TO | (BD438) | | | | | |
| 2SA490r | S | P | TO | (BD438) | | | | | |
| 2SA490ye | S | P | TO | (BD438) | | | | | |
| 2SA493 | S | P | TO | (BC416) | | | | | |
| 2SA493gn | S | P | TO | (BC416B) | | | | | |
| 2SA493or | S | P | TO | (BC416A) | | | | | |
| 2SA493ye | S | P | TO | (BC416A) | | | | | |
| 2SA494 | S | P | TO | (BC415) | | | | | |
| 2SA494gn | S | P | TO | (BC415B) | | | | | |
| 2SA494or | S | P | TO | (BC415A) | | | | | |
| 2SA494ye | S | P | TO | (BC415A) | | | | | |
| 2SA495 | S | N | TO | BC257 | | | | 2SA495G | |
| 2SA495or | S | F | TO | BC257A | | | | | |
| 2SA495r | S | P | TO | BC257A | | | | | |
| 2SA495ye | S | P | TO | BC257A | | | | | |
| 2SA496 | S | P | TO | BD138 | | | | | |
| 2SA496or | S | P | TO | BD138-10 | | | | | |
| 2SA496r | S | P | TO | BD138-6 | | | | | |
| 2SA496ye | S | P | TO | BD138-10 | | | | | |
| 2SA497 | S | P | TO | BSV17 | | 2N4940 | | | |
| 2SA497or | S | P | TO | BSV17-10 | | | | | |
| 2SA497r | S | P | TO | BSV17-6 | | | | | |
| 2SA497ye | S | P | TO | BSC17-10 | | | | | |
| 2SA498 | S | P | TO | BSV16 | | | | 2SA497 | |
| 2SA498or | S | P | TO | BSV16-10 | | | | | |
| 2SA498r | S | P | TO | BSV16-6 | | | | | |
| 2SA498ye | S | P | TO | BSV16-16 | | | | | |
| 2SA499 | S | P | TO | BC177 | | 2N4940 | | | |

| TYPE | M/S | POL | MANUFAC | EUROPEAN | AMERICAN | JAPANESE | USE |
|---|---|---|---|---|---|---|---|
| 2SA499or | S | P | TO | BC177A | | | |
| 2SA499r | S | P | TO | BC177A | | | |
| 2SA499ye | S | P | TO | BC177A | | | |
| 2SA500 | S | P | TO | BC178 | 2N4940 | | |
| 2SA500or | S | P | TO | BC178A | | | |
| 2SA500r | S | P | TO | BC178A | | | |
| 2SA500ye | S | P | TO | BC178A | | | |
| 2SA501 | S | P | TO | (BC177A) | | | |
| 2SA503 | S | P | TO | BSV16 | 2N5314 | 2SA504 | |
| 2SA503gn | S | P | TO | BSV16-16 | | | |
| 2SA503or | S | P | TO | BSV16-6 | | | |
| 2SA503ve | S | P | TO | BSV16-10 | | | |
| 2SA504 | S | P | TO | BSV15   BCW93K | 2N4037 | | |
| 2SA504gn | S | P | TO | BSV15-16 | | | |
| 2SA504or | S | P | TO | BSV15-6 | | | |
| 2SA505ye | S | P | TO | BSC15-10 | | | |
| 2SA505 | S | P | TO | BD136 | | | |
| 2SA505or | S | P | TO | BD136-10 | | | |
| 2SA505r | S | P | TO | BD136-6 | | | |
| 2SA505ye | S | P | TO | BD136-16 | | | |
| 2SA506 | G | P | TO | (AF106) | | | |
| 2SA506r | G | P | TO | (AF106) | | | |
| 2SA506ye | G | P | TO | (AF106) | | | |
| 2SA507 | G | P | TO | (AF106) | | | |
| 2SA507r | G | P | TO | (AF106) | | | |
| 2SA507ye | G | P | TO | (AF106) | | | |
| 2SA508 | G | P | TO | (AF106) | | | |
| 2SA509 | S | P | TO | (BC327-16) | | | |
| 2SA509or | S | P | TO | (BC327-16) | | | |
| 2SA509ye | S | P | TO | (BC327-16) | | | |
| 2SA510 | S | P | TO | (BSV17)   BFS90A | | | |
| 2SA510or | S | P | TO | (BSV17-10) | | | |
| 2SA510r | S | P | TO | (BSV17-6) | | | |
| 2SA511 | S | P | TO | BSV17 | | | |
| 2SA511or | S | P | TO | BSV17-10 | | 2SA510 | |
| 2SA511r | S | P | TO | BSV17-6 | | | |
| 2SA512 | S | P | TO | BSV17 | 2N5314 | 2SA511 | |
| 2SA512or | S | P | TO | BSV17-10 | | | |
| 2SA512r | S | P | TO | BSV17-6 | | | |
| 2SA513 | S | P | TO | BSV16 | | 2SA512 | |
| 2SA513or | S | P | TO | BSV16-10 | | | |
| 2SA513r | S | P | TO | BSV16-6 | | | |
| 2SA517 | G | P | TO | (AF126) | | | |
| 2SA518 | G | P | TO | (AF126) | | | |
| 2SA522 | S | P | TO | BC178A | | | |
| 2SA522A | S | P | TO | BC177A | | | |
| 2SA525 | G | P | TO | (AF106) | | | |
| 2SA530H | S | P | HI | BC177A | | | |
| 2SA532 | S | P | SN, TS | (BC177A) | | | |
| 2SA537 | S | P | HI | BSV16-10 | | | |
| 2SA537A | S | P | HI | BSV17-10 | | | |
| 2SA537AH | S | P | HI | BSV17-10 | | | |
| 2SA537H | S | P | HI | BSV16-10 | | | |
| 2SA538 | G | P | TO, DT | (AC151VI) | 40359 | | |
| 2SA539 | S | P | NI | BC257A | | | |
| 2SA544 | S | P | NI | (BC177A) | | | |
| 2SA545 | S | P | NI | (BC257A) | | | |
| 2SA546 | S | P | MA | BSV17-10 | | | |
| 2SA546A | S | P | MA | BSV17-10 | | | |
| 2SA549 | S | P | HI | BC178A | | | |
| 2SA549A | S | P | HI | BC177A | | | |
| 2SA549AH | S | P | HI | BC177A | | | |
| 2SA549H | S | P | HI | BC178A | | | |
| 2SA550 | S | P | MA | BC178B | | | |
| 2SA552 | S | P | NI | (BC177A) | | | |
| 2SA560 | S | P | TO | | 2N4314 | | |
| 2SA561 | S | P | TO | BC257 | | | |
| 2SA561gn | S | P | TO | BC257B | | 2SA659 | |
| 2SA561or | S | P | TO | BC257A | | | |
| 2SA561r | S | P | TO | BC257A | | | |
| 2SA561ve | S | P | TO | BC257A | | | |
| 2SA562 | S | P | TO | (BC327-16) | | | |
| 2SA562gn | S | P | TO | (BC327-25) | | 2SA561 | |
| 2SA562or | S | P | TO | (BC327-16) | | | |
| 2SA562r | S | P | TO | (BC327-16) | | | |

| TYPE | M/S | POL | MANUFAC | EUROPEAN | AMERICAN | JAPANESE | USE |
|---|---|---|---|---|---|---|---|
| 2SA562ye | S | P | TO | (BC327-16) | | | |
| 2SA564 | S | P | MA | BC258B | | | |
| 2SA564A | S | P | MA | BC257B | | | |
| 2SA565 | S | P | HI | (BC327-16) | | | |
| 2SA565K | S | P | HI | (BC327-16) | | | |
| 2SA567 | S | P | HI | (BC178B) | | | |
| 2SA571 | S | P | NI | BSV16-6 | | | |
| 2SA578 | S | P | NI | BC177B | | | |
| 2SA579 | S | P | NI | BC177B | | | |
| 2SA594 | S | P | TO | (BSY34) | | | |
| 2SA594or | S | P | TO | (BSY34) | | | |
| 2SA594r | S | P | TO | (BSY34) | | | |
| 2SA594ye | S | P | TO | (BSU34) | | | |
| 2SA597 | S | P | TO | BC161 | 2N4037 | | |
| 2SA603 | S | P | NI | BCY77VII | | | |
| 2SA604 | S | P | NI | (BF457) | | | |
| 2SA605 | S | P | NI | (BF458) | | | |
| 2SA606 | S | P | NI | BSV17-6 | | | |
| 2SA608 | S | P | SN, TS | BC257A | | | |
| 2SA609 | S | P | SN, TS | (BC257A) | | | |
| 2SA617K | S | P | HI | (BC177A) | | | |
| 2SA618K | S | P | HI | (BC177A) | | | |
| 2SA623 | S | P | MT | (BD136) | | | |
| 2SA624 | S | P | MT | (BD136) | | | |
| 2SA628 | S | P | MT | BC258A | | | |
| 2SA628A | S | P | MT | (BC257A) | | | |
| 2SA629 | S | P | MT | BC258B | | | |
| 2SA634 | S | P | NI | BD136 | | | |
| 2SA636 | S | P | NI | BD138 | | | |
| 2SA637 | S | P | MA | (BF457) | | | |
| 2SA639 | S | P | NI | (BF457) | | | |
| 2SA640 | S | P | NI | BC257A | | | |
| 2SA641 | S | P | NI | BC257A | | | |
| 2SA642 | S | P | NI | BC258A | | | |
| 2SA643 | S | P | NI | (BC327-16) | | | |
| 2SA659 | S | P | SN, TS | (BC257A) | | | |
| 2SA661 | S | P | TO | (BC257) | | | |
| 2SA661gn | S | P | TO | (BC257B) | | | |
| 2SA661or | S | P | TO | (BC257A) | | | |
| 2SA661r | S | P | TO | (BC257A) | | | |
| 2SA661ye | S | P | TO | (BC257A) | | | |
| 2SA670 | S | P | HI | (BD440) | | | |
| 2SA671 | S | P | HI | (BD440) | | | |
| 2SA671K | S | P | HI | (BD440) | | | |
| 2SA672 | S | P | HI | (ASY48VI) | | | |
| 2SA673 | S | P | HI | (BC327-16) | | | |
| 2SA673A | S | P | HI | (BC327-16) | | | |
| 2SA673K | S | P | HI | (BC327-16) | | | |
| 2SA675 | S | P | NI | (BF457) | | | |
| 2SA677 | S | P | SO | (BC258B) | | | |
| 2SA678 | S | P | SO | (BC257B) | | | |
| 2SA682 | S | P | TO | BD140 | | | |
| 2SA682or | S | P | TO | BD140-10 | | | |
| 2SA682ye | S | P | TO | BD140-16 | | | |
| 2SA685 | S | P | MA | (BF457) | | | |
| 2SA699 | S | P | MA | (BD136) | | | |
| 2SA699A | S | P | MA | (BD136) | | | |
| 2SA701 | S | P | SN, TS | (BC257A) | | | |
| 2SA702 | S | P | SN, TS | (BC257A) | | | |
| 2SA704 | S | P | SO | (BC258B) | | | |
| 2SA705 | S | P | SO | (BC258B) | | | |
| 2SA708 | S | P | NI | BSV17-10 | | | |
| 2SA708A | S | P | NI | BSV17-10 | | | |
| 2SA715 | S | P | HI | BD436 | | | |
| 2SA719 | S | P | MA | (BC327-16) | | | |
| 2SA720 | S | P | MA | (BC327-16) | | | |
| 2SA733 | S | P | NI | BC257B | | | |
| 2SA738 | S | P | HI | BD136 | | | |
| 2SA741H | S | P | HI | BC177A | | | |
| 2SA743 | S | P | HI | BD138 | | | |
| 2SA748 | S | P | MA | (BD140) | | | |
| 2SA749 | S | P | MA | (BF457) | | | |
| 2SA754 | S | P | HI | (BD440) | | | |
| 2SA755 | S | P | HI | (BD440) | | | |
| 2SA814 | S | P | TO | | 2N6476 | | |

| TYPE | M/S | POL | MANUFAC | EUROPEAN | | AMERICAN | | JAPANESE | USE |
|------|-----|-----|---------|----------|---|----------|---|----------|-----|
| 2SA815 | S | P | TO | | | 2N6475 | | | |
| 2SA1018 | G | P | | AF185 | | | | | |
| 2SB12 | | P | | AC122 | AC125 | 2N76 | | | |
| 2SB12 | | | | AC163 | | | | | |
| 2SB13 | G | P | | AC116 | AC128 | 2N407 | | | |
| 2SB13 | | | | AC153 | | | | | |
| 2SB14 | G | P | | AC131 | AC152 | 2N467 | | | |
| 2SB14 | | | | OC76 | | | | | |
| 2SB16 | G | P | FU | AD148 | AD149 | 2N155 | | | |
| 2SB16 | | | | OC30 | | | | | |
| 2SB17 | G | P | FU | AD148 | AD149 | 2N351 | | | |
| 2SB17 | | | | OC30 | | | | | |
| 2SB22 | G | P | FU, TS | (AC151VI) | AC152V | 2N1924 | 2N238 | 2SB156 | |
| 2SB22 | | | | AC152 | AC128 | | | | |
| 2SB22 | | | | AC131 | | | | | |
| 2SB23 | G | P | SN, TS | (AC121IV) | | | | | |
| 2SB24 | G | P | SN, TS | (AC121V) | | | | | |
| 2SB25 | G | P | TO | (AD131V) | AUY22 | | | | |
| 2SB25 | | | | AD138/50 | ASZ18 | | | | |
| 2SB25 | | | | AD139 | AD150 | | | | |
| 2SB25 | | | | ASZ16 | | | | | |
| 2SB26 | G | P | TO | (AD130V) | AD148 | 2N2836 | 2N1022A | 2SB151 | |
| 2SB26 | | | | AD149 | AD138 | 2N561 | | | |
| 2SB26 | | | | AD139 | AD150 | | | | |
| 2SB26A | G | P | TO | (AD131V) | | | | | |
| 2SB27 | G | P | SO | (AD130III) | AD148 | 2N2836 | 2N376 | | |
| 2SB27 | | | | AD149 | AD150 | | | | |
| 2SB28 | G | P | SO | (AD130IV) | AD148 | 2N2836 | 2N351 | | |
| 2SB28 | | | | AD149 | AD150 | | | | |
| 2SB29 | G | P | SO | (AD130V) | AD148 | 2N2836 | 2N351 | | |
| 2SB29 | | | | AD149 | AD150 | | | | |
| 2SB30 | G | P | SO | AD148 | AD149 | 2N2836 | 2N255 | | |
| 2SB30 | | | | OC30 | | | | | |
| 2SB31 | G | P | SO | AD148 | AD149 | 2N2836 | 2N256 | | |
| 2SB31 | | | | AD150 | | | | | |
| 2SB32 | G | P | FU | (AC121IV) | AC151 | 2N2429 | 2N238 | 2SB459 | |
| 2SB32 | | | | AC126 | AC122 | 2N680 | | | |
| 2SB32 | | | | AC132 | AC152 | | | | |
| 2SB32 | | | | AC163 | | | | | |
| 2SB33 | G | P | FU | (AC121VI) | AC151 | 2N2431 | 2N238 | 2SB459 | |
| 2SB33 | | | | AC128 | AC122 | 2N680 | | | |
| 2SB33 | | | | AC126 | AC131 | | | | |
| 2SB33 | | | | AC153V | | | | | |
| 2SB34 | G | P | FU | (AC121VI) | AC151 | 2N2431 | 2N1381 | | |
| 2SB34 | | | | AC128 | AC124 | | | | |
| 2SB34 | | | | AC153 | | | | | |
| 2SB37 | G | P | FU | (AC151VI) | AC151 | 2N2431 | 2N238 | 2SB459 | |
| 2SB37 | | | | AC128 | AC131 | 2N680 | | | |
| 2SB37 | | | | AC126 | AC152 | | | | |
| 2SB38 | G | P | FU | (AC151VI) | AC151 | 2N2431 | 2N238 | 2SB459 | |
| 2SB38 | | | | AC153 | AC128 | 2N1381 | | | |
| 2SB38 | | | | AC131 | AC126 | | | | |
| 2SB39 | G | P | FU | (AC121V) | AC151 | 2N2429 | 2N238 | 2SB459 | |
| 2SB39 | | | | AC126 | AC122 | | | | |
| 2SB40 | G | P | TO | (ASY48VI) | AC151 | 2N238 | | 2SB459 | |
| 2SB40 | | | | AC122/30 | AC126 | | | | |
| 2SB41 | G | P | FU | (AD131V) | AD131 | 2N2836 | T13029 | 2SB471 | |
| 2SB41 | | | | AD148 | AD149 | 2N2065 | 2N301 | | |
| 2SB42 | G | P | FU | (AD131V) | AD132 | 2N2065 | | 2SB472 | |
| 2SB42 | | | | AD149 | ASZ15 | | | | |
| 2SB43 | G | P | TP | (ASY48V) | AC151 | 2N238 | | 2SB459 | |
| 2SB43 | | | | AC122 | | | | | |
| 2SB43A | G | P | TO | (ASY48V) | | | | | |
| 2SB44 | G | P | TO | (AC151VII) | AC128 | 2N2431 | | | |
| 2SB46 | G | P | TO | (AC151VII) | AC126 | 2N2429 | 2N217 | | |
| 2SB46 | | | | AC152 | AC162 | | | | |
| 2SB46 | | | | AC170 | | | | | |
| 2SB47 | G | P | TO | (AC151VII) | AC126 | 2N2429 | | | |
| 2SB47 | | | | AC132 | AC152IV | | | | |
| 2SB47 | | | | ASY80 | | | | | |
| 2SB48 | G | P | SO | (ASY26) | AC126 | 2N2429 | 2N1145 | 2T312 | |
| 2SB48 | | | | AC125 | AC163 | | | | |
| 2SB49 | G | P | SO | (ASY27) | AC126 | 2N2429 | 2N2433 | | |
| 2SB49 | | | | AC131 | AC153 | | | | |
| 2SB50 | G | P | SO | (ASY27) | AC126 | 2N2429 | 2N1605 | 2T315 | |

| TYPE | M/S | POL | MANUFAC | EUROPEAN | | AMERICAN | | JAPANESE | USE |
|------|-----|-----|---------|----------|---|----------|---|----------|-----|
| 2SB50 | | | | AC131 | AC152 | | | | |
| 2SB50 | | | | AC153 | | | | | |
| 2SB51 | G | P | SO | (ASY26) | AC128 | 2N2431 | 2N1383 | 2T322 | |
| 2SB51 | | | | AC131 | AC153 | | | | |
| 2SB52 | G | P | SO | (ASY27) | AC128 | 2N2431 | 2N1413 | 2T324 | |
| 2SB52 | | | | AC131 | AC153 | | | | |
| 2SB53 | G | P | SO | (ASY27) | AC128 | 2N2431 | 2N1307 | 2T383 | |
| 2SB53 | | | | AC131 | AC153 | | | | |
| 2SB54 | G | P | TO, DT | AC128 | AC151VII | 2N2431 | 2N408 | 2SB43 | |
| 2SB54 | | | | AC128 | AC122 | | | | |
| 2SB54 | | | | AC*25 | AC152 | | | | |
| 2SB855 | G | P | TO | (AC151V) | AC151 | 2N2431 | 2N238 | 2SB459 | |
| 2SB855 | | | | AC128 | AC131/30 | | | | |
| 2SB855 | | | | AC124 | AC153 | | | | |
| 2SB56 | G | P | TO, DT | AC128 | AC151V | 2N2431 | 2N680 | | |
| 2SB56 | | | | AC126 | AC153 | | | | |
| 2SB56A | G | P | TO | AC151V | | | | | |
| 2SB57 | G | P | FU | (AC151V) | AC151 | 2N2431 | | | |
| 2SB57 | | | | AC128 | AC126 | | | | |
| 2SB57 | | | | AC152V | | | | | |
| 2SB58 | G | P | FU | AC128 | | 2N2431 | | | |
| 2SB59 | G | P | FU | (AC151V) | AC151VI | 2N2429 | | | |
| 2SB59 | | | | AC126 | AC122gr | | | | |
| 2SB59 | | | | AC125 | | | | | |
| 2SB60 | G | P | FU | (AC151V) | AC126 | 2N2429 | | | |
| 2SB60A | G | P | FU | AC151V | AC151VI | 2N2429 | | | |
| 2SB60A | | | | AC126 | AC131 | | | | |
| 2SB60A | | | | AC128 | | | | | |
| 2SB61 | G | P | FU | AC151VI | AC126 | 2N2429 | 2N680 | | |
| 2SB61 | | | | AC125 | AC122gr | | | | |
| 2SB61 | | | | AC117 | AC153 | | | | |
| 2SB62 | G | P | TO | (AD131V) | AD139 | | | | |
| 2SB62 | | | | ASZ16 | | | | | |
| 2SB63 | G | P | TO | (AD130V) | AD149 | 2N2836 | | | |
| 2SB63 | | | | AD139 | | | | | |
| 2SB64 | G | P | TO | (AD163V) | AC131 | 2N422 | 2N467 | | |
| 2SB64 | | | | AC152 | OC76 | | | | |
| 2SB65 | G | P | FU | AC151V | AC122 | 2N36 | 2N1394 | | |
| 2SB65 | | | | AC128 | AC131 | | | | |
| 2SB65 | | | | AC152 | AC126 | | | | |
| 2SB66 | G | P | HI | (AC151V) | AC151VI | 2N2429 | 2N2431 | | |
| 2SB66 | | | | AC151VII | AC126 | | | | |
| 2SB66 | | | | AC128 | AC131 | | | | |
| 2SB66 | | | | AC125 | | | | | |
| 2SB66H | G | P | HI | (AC151V) | | | | | |
| 2SB67 | G | P | HI | (ASY48V) | AC153 | 2N467 | | 2SB222 | |
| 2SB67 | | | | AC124 | AC128 | | | | |
| 2SB67A | G | P | HI | (ASY48V) | | | | | |
| 2SB67AH | G | P | HI | (ASY48VI) | | | | | |
| 2SB67H | G | P | HI | (ASY48VI) | | | | | |
| 2SB68 | G | P | HI | AC122/30 | AC122 | | | 2SB460 | |
| 2SB68 | | | | ASY48 | ASY77 | | | | |
| 2SB68 | | | | ASY81 | | | | | |
| 2SB69 | G | P | TO | (AD131V) | | | | | |
| 2SB70 | G | P | | AC126 | | 2N2429 | | | |
| 2SB71 | G | P | | AC126 | AC152IV | 2N2429 | | | |
| 2SB71 | | | | AF126 | | | | | |
| 2SB73 | G | P | HI | (AC121V) | AC126 | 2N2429 | | 2SB459 | |
| 2SB73 | | | | AC151 | AC122 | | | | |
| 2SB74 | G | P | HI | (AC121V) | AC126 | 2N2429 | 2N105 | | |
| 2SB74 | | | | AC125 | AC163 | | | | |
| 2SB75 | G | P | HI | (AC151V) | AC126 | 2N2429 | 2N34 | | |
| 2SB75 | | | | AC162 | AC163 | | | | |
| 2SB75 | | | | AC170 | | | | | |
| 2SB75A | G | P | HI | AC151V | AC122 | | | 2SB459 | |
| 2SB75AH | G | P | HI | (ASY48VI) | | | | | |
| 2SB75H | G | P | HI | (ASY70V) | | | | | |
| 2SB76 | G | P | HI | (AC121IV) | AC126 | 2N2429 | 2N408 | | |
| 2SB76 | | | | AC151 | AC152 | | | | |
| 2SB77 | G | P | HI | (ASY70VI) | AC128 | 2N2431 | 2N41 | | |
| 2SB77 | | | | AC151IV | AC125 | | | | |
| 2SB77 | | | | AC131 | AC163 | | | | |
| 2SB77A | G | P | HI | (ASY48VI) | AC151VI | | | | |
| 2SB77AH | G | P | HI | (ASY48V) | | | | | |
| 2SB77H | G | P | HI | (ASY70V) | | | | | |

| TYPE | M/S | POL | MANUFAC | EUROPEAN | | AMERICAN | | JAPANESE | USE |
|------|-----|-----|---------|----------|--|----------|--|----------|-----|
| 2SB78 | G | P | HI | (AC121V) | AC128 | 2N2431 | 2N43 | | |
| 2SB78 | | | | AC152 | AC153 | | | | |
| 2SB79 | G | P | | AC128 | AC117 | 2N2431 | 2N178A | | |
| 2SB79 | | | | AC153 | | | | | |
| 2SB80 | G | P | HI | (AD130V) | AD149 | 2N2836 | | | |
| | | | | | | | | | |
| 2SB80 | | | | | | | | | |
| 2SB81 | G | P | HI | AD139 | | | | | |
| 2SB82 | G | P | HI | (AD132V) | | | | | |
| 2SB83 | G | P | HI | (AD163IV) | AD149 | 2N2836 | 2N1295 | | |
| 2SB83 | | | | (AD131IV) | AD150 | | | | |
| | | | | AD131 | | | | | |
| 2SB84 | G | P | HI | (AD131IV) | AC149 | | | | |
| 2SB84 | | | | AD150 | | | | | |
| 2SB85 | G | P | HI | (AUY21III) | | | | | |
| 2SB86 | G | P | HI | (AUY21III) | AD148 | 2N1291 | | | |
| 2SB86 | | | | CTP1104 | OC30 | | | | |
| 2SB87 | G | P | HI | (AUY22III) | AD131 | 2N387 | | | |
| 2SB87 | | | | CTP1313 | OC28 | | | | |
| 2SB89 | G | P | HI | (ASY70V) | AC151VI | 2N2431 | 2N1381 | | |
| 2SB89 | | | | AC128 | AC122gr | | | | |
| 2SB89 | | | | AC125 | AC152IV | | | | |
| | | | | | | | | | |
| 2SB89 | | | | AC153 | | | | | |
| 2SB89A | G | P | HI | (ASY48V) | | | | | |
| 2SB89AH | G | P | HI | (ASY48V) | | | | | |
| 2SB89H | G | P | HI | (ASY70V) | | | | | |
| 2SB90 | G | P | TO | (AC121V) | AC126 | 2N2429 | | | |
| | | | | | | | | | |
| 2SB90 | | | | AC162 | AC170 | | | | |
| 2SB91 | G | P | TO | (AC121V) | AC128 | 2N2431 | | | |
| 2SB91 | | | | AC131 | AC132 | | | | |
| 2SB91 | | | | AC153 | | | | | |
| 2SB92 | G | P | | AC128 | | 2N2431 | | | |
| | | | | | | | | | |
| 2SB94 | G | P | TO | (AC151VI) | AC128 | 2N2431 | 2N2447 | 2SB459 | |
| 2SB94 | | | | AC151 | AC122 | 2N44A | | | |
| 2SB94 | | | | AC131 | AC152 | | | | |
| 2SB94 | | | | AC153 | | | | | |
| 2SB95 | G | P | | AC128 | | 2N2431 | | | |
| | | | | | | | | | |
| 2SB97 | G | P | TO | (AC121V) | AC126 | 2N2429 | | | |
| 2SB98 | G | P | HI | (ASY27) | ASY26 | 2N2431 | 2N799 | 2SA155 | |
| 2SB98 | | | | AC123 | AC125 | 2N46 | | | |
| 2SB98 | | | | AC153 | | | | | |
| 2SB99 | G | P | NI | (ASY27) | AC128 | 2N2431 | 2N633 | | |
| | | | | | | | | | |
| 2SB99 | | | | AC152 | AC153 | | | | |
| 2SB100 | G | P | NI | (ASY27) | ASY26 | 2N2429 | 2N799 | 2SA155 | |
| 2SB100 | | | | AC126 | AC122 | 2N130 | | | |
| 2SB100 | | | | AC162 | AC163 | | | | |
| 2SB101 | G | P | NI | (ASY27) | ASY26 | 2N2431 | 2N799 | 2SA155 | |
| | | | | | | | | | |
| 2SB101 | | | | AC128 | AC131 | 2N43 | | | |
| 2SB101 | | | | AC152 | | | | | |
| 2SB102 | G | P | NI | AC128 | AC117 | 2N2431 | 2N188 | | |
| 2SB102 | | | | AC153 | | | | | |
| 2SB103 | G | P | NI | (ASY27) | AC128 | 2N2431 | 2N190 | | |
| | | | | | | | | | |
| 2SB103 | | | | AC152 | AC153 | | | | |
| 2SB104 | G | P | NI | AC128 | AC152 | 2N2431 | 2N188A | | |
| 2SB104 | | | | AC153 | | | | | |
| 2SB105 | G | P | NI | AD149 | AC152 | 2N2836 | 2N241 | | |
| 2SB105 | | | | AC153 | | | | | |
| | | | | | | | | | |
| 2SB106 | G | P | NI | AD149 | | 2N2836 | 2N352 | | |
| 2SB106 | | | | OC30 | | | | | |
| 2SB107 | G | P | NI | AD148 | CTP1104 | 2N353 | | | |
| 2SB107 | | | | OC30 | | | | | |
| 2SB107A | G | P | NI | (AD131V) | AD166 | TI156 | 2N456 | 2SB471 | |
| | | | | | | | | | |
| 2SB107A | | | | AD148 | AD149 | 2N68 | | | |
| 2SB107A | | | | OC30 | CTP1104 | | | | |
| 2SB108 | G | P | NI | AD149 | | 2N2836 | | | |
| 2SB109 | G | P | NI | AD149 | | 2N2836 | | | |
| 2SB110 | G | P | NI | (AC151VI) | AC151 | 2N2429 | 2N46 | | |
| | | | | | | | | | |
| 2SB110 | | | | AC126 | AC122 | | | | |
| 2SB110 | | | | AC162 | AC163 | | | | |
| 2SB110 | | | | ASY26 | | | | | |
| 2SB111 | G | P | NI | (AC151V) | AC151IV | 2N2429 | 2N77 | | |
| 2SB111 | | | | AC126 | AC122 | | | | |
| | | | | | | | | | |
| 2SB111 | | | | AC125 | AC152 | | | | |
| 2SB111 | | | | AC163 | | | | | |
| 2SB112 | G | P | NI | AC151V | AC126 | 2N2429 | 2N79 | | |
| 2SB112 | | | | AC122 | AC125 | | | | |
| 2SB112 | | | | AC131 | AC152IV | | | | |

262

| TYPE | M/S | POL | MANUFAC | EUROPEAN | | AMERICAN | | JAPANESE | USE |
|---|---|---|---|---|---|---|---|---|---|
| 2SB113 | G | P | NI | AC151V | AC126 | 2N2429 | 2N96 | | |
| 2SB113 | | | | AC122 | AC125 | | | | |
| 2SB113 | | | | AC163 | | | | | |
| 2SB114 | G | P | NI | (AC151V) | AC128 | 2N2431 | 2N36 | | |
| 2SB114 | | | | AC122 | | | | | |
| 2SB114 | | | | AC151 | AC125 | | | | |
| 2SB114 | | | | AC163 | | | | | |
| 2SB115 | G | P | NI | (AC151V) | AC151VI | 2N2431 | 2N37 | | |
| 2SB115 | | | | AC151VII | AC128 | | | | |
| 2SB115 | | | | AC122 | AC125 | | | | |
| 2SB115 | | | | AC163 | | | | | |
| 2SB116 | G | P | NI | (AC151VI) | AC151VII | 2N2431 | 2N38 | | |
| 2SB116 | | | | AC128 | AC122 | | | | |
| 2SB116 | | | | AC125 | AC163 | | | | |
| 2SB117 | G | P | NI | (AC151VI) | AC151VII | 2N2431 | 2N3RA | | |
| 2SB117 | | | | AC128 | AC122 | | | | |
| 2SB117 | | | | AC125 | AC163 | | | | |
| 2SB118 | G | P | | AC149 | AC149 | 2N2836 | | | |
| 2SB119 | G | P | MA | (AD130III) | AC149 | 2N2836 | | | |
| 2SB119A | G | P | MA | (AD131III) | | | | | |
| 2SB120 | G | P | FU | AC151V | AC126 | 2N2429 | 2N951 | | |
| 2SB120 | | | | AC122ye | AC125 | | | | |
| 2SB120 | | | | AC163 | | | | | |
| 2SB121 | G | P | FU | AC125 | | 2N398 | | | |
| 2SB122 | G | P | TO | (AD132V) | ASZ15 | | | | |
| 2SB122 | | | | AUY28 | AUY22 | | | | |
| 2SB123 | G | P | TO | (AUY21V) | | | | | |
| 2SB124 | G | P | TO | (AUY29V) | ASZ15 | 2N1100 | | | |
| 2SB124 | | | | AUY28 | AUY22 | | | | |
| 2SB125 | G | P | TO | (AUY29V) | ASZ16 | | | | |
| 2SB125 | | | | AUY21 | | | | | |
| 2SB126 | G | P | MA | (AUY19III) | | | | | |
| 2SB127 | G | P | MA | (AUY19V) | ADZ11 | 2N1022A | 2N561 | 2SB151 | |
| 2SB127 | | | | AD133 | AD138 | | | | |
| 2SN128 | G | P | MA | (AUY22III) | ASZ18 | | | | |
| 2SB128 | | | | AUY22 | AUY28 | | | | |
| 2SB128A | G | P | MA | (AUY22III) | | | | | |
| 2SB129 | G | P | MA | (AUY22IV) | | | | | |
| 2SB129A | G | P | MA | (AUY22IV) | | | | | |
| 2SB130 | G | P | MA | AD148 | OC30 | 2N155 | | | |
| 2SB131 | G | P | FU | (AUY19V) | AD149 | 2N2836 | | | |
| 2SB131A | G | P | FU | (AUY19V) | | | | | |
| 2SB132 | G | P | FU | (AUY19V) | | | | | |
| 2SB132A | G | P | FU | (AUY19V) | | | | | |
| 2SB134 | G | P | MT | (ASY70V) | AC126 | 2N2429 | 2N82 | | |
| 2SB134 | | | | AC125 | AC163 | | | | |
| 2SB135 | G | P | MT | (ASY70V) | AC151V | 2N2429 | 2N138 | | |
| 2SB135 | | | | AC126 | AC122ye | | | | |
| 2SB135 | | | | AC125 | AC131 | | | | |
| 2SB135 | | | | AC153 | | | | | |
| 2SB136 | G | P | MT | AC151VII | AC128 | 2N2431 | | | |
| 2SB136 | | | | AC122ye | AC125 | | | | |
| 2SB136 | | | | AC131 | AC153 | | | | |
| 2SB137 | G | P | MT | (AUY21IV) | AD149 | 2N2836 | | | |
| 2SB138 | G | P | MT | (AUY21IV) | | | | | |
| 2SB138A | G | P | MT | (AUY22IV) | | | | | |
| 2SB138B | G | P | MT | (AUY22IV) | | | | | |
| 2SB140 | G | P | SO | (AD131V) | AD149 | 2N2837 | 2N301 | 2T3011 | |
| 2SB140 | | | | ASZ16 | AUY21 | | | | |
| 2SB141 | G | P | SO | (AD132V) | ASZ15 | 2N301A | | 2T3021 | |
| 2SB141 | | | | AUY22 | AUY28 | | | | |
| 2SB142 | G | P | SO | (AD130III) | AD149 | 2N2836 | 2N301 | 2T3030 | |
| 2SB142 | | | | AD139 | AD150 | | | | |
| 2SB143 | G | P | SO | (AD130IV) | AD149 | 2N2836 | 2N660 | 2T3032 | |
| 2SB143 | | | | AD139 | AD150 | | | | |
| 2SB143P | G | P | SO | (AD130V) | | | | | |
| 2SB144 | G | P | SO | (AD130V) | AD149 | 2N2836 | 2N669 | 2T3032 | |
| 2SB144 | | | | AD139 | AD150 | | | | |
| 2SB144P | G | P | SO | (AD130V) | | | | | |
| 2SB145 | G | P | SO | (AD130IV) | AD149 | 2N2836 | | 2T30423 | |
| 2SB145 | | | | AD150 | | | | | |
| 2SB146 | G | P | SO | (AD130V) | AD149 | 2N2836 | | 2T3043 | |
| 2SB146 | | | | AD150 | | | | | |
| 2SB147 | G | P | SO | (AD132V) | | | | | |
| 2SB148 | G | P | | ASZ16 | ASZ18 | | | | |

| TYPE | M/S | POL | MANUFAC | EUROPEAN | | AMERICAN | | JAPANESE | USE |
|---|---|---|---|---|---|---|---|---|---|
| 2SB148 | | | | AUY21 | | | | | |
| 2SB149 | G | P | TO | (AUY21IV) | | | | | |
| 2SB150 | G | P | TO | | | 2N398 | | | |
| 2SB151 | G | P | FU | (AUY22IV) | AUY22 | 2N561 | | | |
| 2SB151 | | | | AD138 | ASZ18 | | | | |
| 2SB151 | | | | AD131 | CDT1313 | | | | |
| 2SB151 | | | | OC28 | | | | | |
| 2SB152 | G | P | FU | (AUY22IV) | AD131 | 2N157A | | | |
| 2SB152 | | | | OC28 | OD605 | | | | |
| 2SB153 | G | P | HI | (AC121V) | AC126 | 2N2429 | | | |
| 2SB153 | | | | AC152 | AC162 | | | | |
| 2SB154 | G | P | HI | (AC121V) | AC128 | 2N2431 | 2N408 | | |
| 2SB154 | | | | AC131 | AC132 | | | | |
| 2SB154 | | | | AC153 | | | | | |
| 2SB155 | G | P | HI | (AC121IV) | AC128 | 2N2431 | 2N249 | 2SB370A | |
| 2SB155 | | | | AC117 | AC153 | | | | |
| 2SB156 | G | P | HI | (AC121V) | AC128 | 2N2431 | 2N1307 | | |
| 2SB156 | | | | AC131 | AC153 | | | | |
| 2SB156A | G | P | HI | AC121V | AC117 | 2N1307 | 2N2431 | 2SB156A | |
| 2SB156A | | | | AC128 | AC131 | | | | |
| 2SB156A | | | | AC153 | | | | | |
| 2SB157 | G | P | HI | (AC121IV) | AC126 | 2N2429 | | | |
| 2SB157 | | | | OC58 | OC59 | | | | |
| 2SB158 | G | P | MA | (AC121V) | AC126 | 2N2429 | | | |
| 2SB158 | | | | OC58 | OC59 | | | | |
| 2SB159 | G | P | MA | (AC121V) | AC126 | 2N2429 | | | |
| 2SB159 | | | | OC59 | OC60 | | | | |
| 2SB160 | G | P | MA | (AC121V) | AC126 | 2N2429 | | | |
| 2SB160 | | | | OC60 | | | | | |
| 2SB161 | G | P | NI | (ASY26) | AC128 | 2N2431 | 2N367 | | |
| 2SB161 | | | | AC151 | AC122 | | | | |
| 2SB161 | | | | AC152 | AC163 | | | | |
| 2SB162 | G | P | NI | AC128 | AC122 | 2N2431 | 2N319 | | |
| 2SB162 | | | | AC151 | AC124 | | | | |
| 2SB162 | | | | AC153 | | | | | |
| 2SB163 | G | P | NI | (ASY26) | AC128 | 2N2431 | 2N320 | | |
| 2SB163 | | | | AC124 | AC153 | | | | |
| 2SB164 | G | P | NI | AC128 | AC124 | 2N2431 | 2N321 | | |
| 2SB164 | | | | AC153 | | | | | |
| 2SB165 | G | P | NI | (ASY27) | AC128 | 2N2431 | 2N323 | | |
| 2SB165 | | | | AC125 | AC153 | | | | |
| 2SB166 | G | P | NI | AC128 | AC124 | 2N2431 | | | |
| 2SB166 | | | | AC153 | | | | | |
| 2SB167 | G | P | FU | AC152V | AC122 | | | | |
| 2SB167 | | | | AC128 | | | | | |
| 2SB168 | G | P | FU | (AC121V) | AC151V | 2N2429 | | | |
| 2SB168 | | | | AC126 | AC122 | | | | |
| 2SB168 | | | | AC125 | OC331 | | | | |
| 2SB168 | | | | OC622 | | | | | |
| 2SB169 | G | P | FU | (AC121VI) | AC151VI | 2N2431 | | | |
| 2SB169 | | | | AC128 | AC122 | | | | |
| 2SB169 | | | | AC126 | OC343 | | | | |
| 2SB169 | | | | OC624 | | | | | |
| 2SB170 | G | P | MA | (AC151IV) | AC151 | 2N2431 | 2N76 | | |
| 2SB170 | | | | AC128 | AC122 | | | | |
| 2SB170 | | | | AC126 | AC162 | | | | |
| 2SB170 | | | | AC163 | | | | | |
| 2SB171 | G | P | MA | AC151V | AC128 | 2N2431 | 2N81 | | |
| 2SB171 | | | | AC122 | AC126 | | | | |
| 2SB171 | | | | AC162 | AC163 | | | | |
| 2SB172 | G | P | MA | AC151V | AC128 | 2N2431 | 2N505 | | |
| 2SB172 | | | | AC122 | AC126 | | | | |
| 2SB172 | | | | AC132 | AC153 | | | | |
| 2SB173 | G | P | MA | (AC121V) | AC151V | 2N2529 | | | |
| 2SB173 | | | | AC126 | AC125 | | | | |
| 2SB173 | | | | AC162 | | | | | |
| 2SB174 | G | P | MA | (AC121V) | AC128 | 2N2431 | 2N223 | | |
| 2SB174 | | | | AC117 | AC153 | | | | |
| 2SB175 | G | P | MA | AC151VI | AC128 | 2N2431 | 2N132 | | |
| 2SB175 | | | | AC122 | AC126 | | | | |
| 2SB175 | | | | ASY77 | | | | | |
| 2SB176 | G | P | MA | (AC151VI) | AC129 | 2N2431 | 2N4106 | 2SB222 | |
| 2SB176 | | | | AC153 | AC131 | 2N4607 | 2N505 | | |
| 2SB176 | | | | AC152 | | | | | |
| 2SB177 | G | P | MA | (ASY48V) | ACY77 | | | | |

| TYPE | M/S | POL | MANUFAC | EUROPEAN | | AMERICAN | | JAPANESE | USE |
|---|---|---|---|---|---|---|---|---|---|
| 2SB178 | G | P | MA | (ASY70V) | AC152V | 2N2431 | 2N610 | 2SB222 | |
| 2SB178 | | | | AC128 | AC124r | | | | |
| 2SB178 | | | | AC125 | | | | | |
| 2SB178A | G | P | MA | (ASY48V) | ASY80 | | | | |
| 2SB179 | G | P | | AC128 | ASY80 | 2N2431 | | | |
| 2SB180 | G | P | FU | AD148 | AD149 | 2N2836 | 2N301 | | |
| 2SB180 | | | | OC30 | | | | | |
| 2SB181 | G | P | FU | AD148 | AD149 | 2N307 | | | |
| 2SB182 | G | P | FU | AF185 | | | | | |
| 2SB183 | G | P | HI | (AC121V) | AC126 | 2N2429 | 2N132A | | |
| 2SB183 | | | | AC122 | AC163 | | | | |
| 2SB183A | | | | OC60 | | | | | |
| 2SB184 | G | P | HI | (AC121VI) | AC128 | 2N2431 | 2N63 | | |
| 2SB184 | | | | AC125 | AC163 | | | | |
| 2SB185 | G | P | SN, TS | (AC151IV) | AC151V | 2N107 | | | |
| 2SB185 | | | | AC126 | AC128 | | | | |
| 2SB185 | | | | AC122 | AC125 | | | | |
| 2SB185 | | | | AC163 | | | | | |
| 2SB186 | G | P | SN, TS | (AC151VII) | AC152VI | 2N2429 | 2N4106 | 2S32 | |
| 2SB186 | | | | AC122 | AC126 | 2N610 | 2N240 | | |
| 2SB186 | | | | AC128 | AC125 | | | | |
| 2SB186 | | | | AC163 | | | | | |
| 2SB187 | G | P | SN, TS | (AC151VI) | AC152VI | 2N2429 | 2N4106 | 2S32 | |
| 2SB187 | | | | AC126 | AC122 | 2N610 | 2N1144 | | |
| 2SB187 | | | | AC128 | AC131 | | | | |
| 2SB187 | | | | AC152 | | | | | |
| 2SB188 | G | P | SN, TS | (AC151VI) | AC152VI | 2N2431 | 2N610 | 2S32 | |
| 2SB188 | | | | AC128 | AC117r | | | | |
| 2SB188 | | | | AC126 | AC152 | | | | |
| 2SB189 | G | P | TO, DT | AC128 | AC117 | 2N2431 | 2N610 | 2S32 | |
| 2SB189 | | | | AC152VI | AC131 | 2N1036 | | | |
| 2SB189 | | | | AC153 | ASY30 | | | | |
| 2SB190 | G | P | | AC128 | AC125 | 2N2431 | 2N322 | | |
| 2SB190 | | | | AC163 | | | | | |
| 2SB191 | G | P | | AC122 | AC125 | 2N47 | | | |
| 2SB191 | | | | AC163 | | | | | |
| 2SB192 | G | P | | AC128 | AC125 | 2N2431 | 2N48 | | |
| 2SB192 | | | | AC163 | | | | | |
| 2SB193 | G | P | | AC128 | AC116 | 2N2431 | 2N324 | | |
| 2SB193 | | | | AC153 | | | | | |
| 2SB194 | G | P | | AC128 | AC131 | 2N2431 | 2N1145 | | |
| 2SB194 | | | | AC152 | | | | | |
| 2SB195 | G | P | | AC128 | AC117 | 2N2431 | 2N1097 | | |
| 2SB195 | | | | AC153 | | | | | |
| 2SB196 | G | P | | AC128 | AC124 | 2N2431 | 2N225 | | |
| 2SB196 | | | | AC153 | | | | | |
| 2SB197 | G | P | | AC128 | AC124 | 2B2431 | 2N226 | | |
| 2SB197 | | | | AC153 | | | | | |
| 2SB198 | G | P | | AC128 | AC124 | 2N2431 | 2N227 | | |
| 2SB198 | | | | AC153 | | | | | |
| 2SB199 | G | P | FU | (AC121VI) | AC128 | 2N2431 | 2N1388 | | |
| 2SB199 | | | | AC124 | AC153 | | | | |
| 2SB200 | G | P | TO | (ASY70IV) | AC128 | 2N2431 | 2N4106 | 2SB222 | |
| 2SB200 | | | | AC153V | AC124 | 2N467 | | | |
| 2SB200 | | | | AD139 | AD149 | | | | |
| 2SB200 | | | | AC153VI | | | | | |
| 2SB200A | G | P | TO | (ASY48IV) | | | | | |
| 2SB201 | G | P | TO | AC117 | AC128 | 2N4106 | 2N467 | 2SB222 | |
| 2SB201 | | | | AC153V | AC122 | | | | |
| 2SB201 | | | | AD149 | AC162 | | | | |
| 2SB202 | G | P | TO | (ASY70VII) | AC153VII | 2N2431 | 2N4106 | 2SB222 | |
| 2SB202 | | | | AC128 | AC117 | | | | |
| 2SB202 | | | | AC153 | AD139 | | | | |
| 2SB202 | | | | AD149 | AD149 | | | | |
| 2SB208 | G | P | SA | AC124 | AC128 | | | | |
| 2SB208 | | | | AC152 | | | | | |
| 2SB215 | G | P | SN, TS | (AD163V) | AD163 | | | 2SB341 | |
| 2SB215 | | | | ASZ15 | | | | | |
| 2SB216 | G | P | SN, TS | (AD131V) | AD131 | TI3029 | 2N2065 | 2SB471 | |
| 2SB216 | | | | AD138/50 | AD149 | | | | |
| 2SB217 | G | P | SN, TS | (AD130V) | AD150 | TI156 | 2N456 | 2SB4026 | |
| 2SB218 | G | P | NI | AC122 | AC163 | 2NG1 | 2N524 | | |
| 2SB218 | | | | OC70 | | | | | |
| 2SB219 | G | P | NI | (ASY70IV) | AC128 | 2N2431 | 2N41 | | |
| 2SB219 | | | | AC153 | AC163 | | | | |

| TYPE | M/S | POL | MANUFAC | EUROPEAN | | AMERICAN | | JAPANESE | USE |
|------|-----|-----|---------|----------|---|----------|---|----------|-----|
| 2SB220 | G | P | NI | (ASY70V) | AC128 | 2N2431 | 2N43 | | |
| 2SB220 | | | | AC124 | AC153 | | | | |
| 2SB221 | G | P | NI | (ASY70V) | AC128 | 2N2431 | 2N524 | | |
| 2SB221 | | | | AC124 | AC153 | | | | |
| 2SB222 | G | P | NI | (ASY70VI) | AC128 | 2N2431 | 2N220 | | |
| | | | | | | | | | |
| 2SB222 | | | | AC124 | AC153 | | | | |
| 2SB223 | G | P | NI | (ASY70VI) | AC128 | 2N2431 | | | |
| 2SB224 | G | P | NI | (ASY48IV) | AC152 | 2N284 | 2N524 | | |
| 2SB224 | | | | AC153 | AC131 | | | | |
| 2SB225 | G | P | NI | (ASY48IV) | AC117 | 2N43 | 2N525 | | |
| | | | | | | | | | |
| 2SB225 | | | | AC128 | AC153 | | | | |
| 2SB226 | G | P | NI | (ASY48V) | AC124 | 2N408 | 2N526 | | |
| 2SB226 | | | | AC128 | AC153 | | | | |
| 2SB227 | G | P | NI | (ASY48VI) | AC124 | 2N223 | 2N527 | | |
| 2SB227 | | | | AC128 | AC153 | | | | |
| | | | | | | | | | |
| 2SB228 | G | P | HI | (AUY22III) | | | | | |
| 2SB229 | G | P | HI | (AUY22III) | | | | | |
| 2SB230 | G | P | HI | (AUY22III) | | | | | |
| 2SB235 | G | P | TO | AFZ11 | | | | | |
| 2SB236 | G | P | TO | | | | | | |
| | | | | | | | | | |
| 2SB237 | G | P | TO | | | | | | |
| 2SB240 | G | P | NI | AD148 | CTP1104 | 2N68 | | | |
| 2SB240 | | | | OC30 | | | | | |
| 2SB240A | G | P | NI | AD148 | CTP1104 | 2N141 | | | |
| 2SB240A | | | | OC30 | | | | | |
| | | | | | | | | | |
| 2SB242 | G | P | NI | AUY18 | ASZ15 | 2N1183 | | | |
| 2SB242 | | | | AD148 | CTP1104 | | | | |
| 2SB242 | | | | OC30 | | | | | |
| 2SB242A | G | P | NI | AUY18 | AD146 | 2N141 | | | |
| 2SB242A | | | | CTP1104 | OC30 | | | | |
| | | | | | | | | | |
| 2SB246 | G | P | NI | (AUY21IV) | AD133V | | | | |
| 2SB247 | G | P | NI | (AUY21IV) | AD138 | | | | |
| 2SB247 | | | | AD133V | AD138 | | | | |
| 2SB247 | | | | ADZ11 | | | | | |
| 2SB248 | G | P | NI | (AUY21IV) | AC124 | 2N1502 | | | |
| | | | | | | | | | |
| 2SB248 | | | | AC128 | AC153 | | | | |
| 2SB248A | G | P | NI | (AUY21IV) | AD133IV | 2N1501 | | | |
| 2SB248A | | | | AD133V | AD138 | | | | |
| 2SB248A | | | | ADZ11 | AC105 | | | | |
| 2SB248A | | | | AC117 | | | | | |
| | | | | | | | | | |
| 2SB249 | G | P | NI | (AUY22V) | AC128 | 2N457 | | | |
| 2SB249 | | | | AC153 | ASZ18 | | | | |
| 2SB250 | G | P | NI | (AUY21V) | AD133V | 2N176 | | | |
| 2SB250 | | | | AD138 | ADZ11 | | | | |
| 2SB250 | | | | AD148 | AD149 | | | | |
| | | | | | | | | | |
| 2SB250 | | | | OC30 | | | | | |
| 2SB250A | G | P | NI | (AUY21V) | AC117 | 2N1245 | | | |
| 2SB250A | | | | AC128 | AC153 | | | | |
| 2SB251 | G | P | NI | (AUY21V) | AD133V | 2N1246 | | | |
| 2SB251 | | | | AD138 | ADZ11 | | | | |
| | | | | | | | | | |
| 2SB251 | | | | AC128 | AC153 | | | | |
| 2SB251 | | | | AD149 | | | | | |
| 2SB251A | G | P | NI | (AUY21IV) | | | | | |
| 2SB252 | G | P | NI | (AUY22IV) | AD133V | | | | |
| 2SB252 | | | | AD138/50 | ADZ11 | | | | |
| | | | | | | | | | |
| 2SB252A | G | P | NI | AD148 | ASZ18 | 2N1437 | | | |
| 2SB252A | | | | OC30 | | | | | |
| 2SB253 | G | P | NI | (AUY22IV) | AC129 | 2N1263 | | | |
| 2SB253 | | | | AC153 | ASZ18 | | | | |
| 2SB254 | G | P | SN, TS | (AD149V) | AC128 | 2N2431 | | | |
| | | | | | | | | | |
| 2SB254 | | | | AC125 | | | | | |
| 2SB255 | G | P | SN, TS | (AD149V) | AC128 | 2N2431 | | | |
| 2SB256 | G | P | SN, TS | (AD149V) | | | | | |
| 2SB257 | G | P | TO | (AC151) | | | | | |
| 2SB261 | G | P | FU | (AC121IV) | AC126 | 2N2429 | 2N406 | 2SA305 | |
| | | | | | | | | | |
| 2SB261 | | | | AC125 | AC163 | | | | |
| 2SB262 | G | P | FU | (AC121VII) | AC126 | 2N2429 | 2N407 | | |
| 2SB262 | | | | AC125 | AC153 | | | | |
| 2SB263 | G | P | FU | (AC121V) | AC124 | 2N2431 | 2N270 | | |
| 2SB263 | | | | AC153 | | | | | |
| | | | | | | | | | |
| 2SB264 | G | P | NI | (AC151V) | AC126 | 2N2429 | 2N133 | | |
| 2SB264 | | | | AC125 | AC153 | | | | |
| 2SB265 | G | P | TO | (ASY70V) | ASY26 | | | | |
| 2SB266 | G | P | Y | (AC151V) | AC125 | | | | |
| 2SB266 | | | | AC152 | AC170 | | | | |

| TYPE | M/S | POL | MANUFAC | EUROPEAN | | AMERICAN | | JAPANESE | USE |
|---|---|---|---|---|---|---|---|---|---|
| 2SB267 | G | P | Y | (AC151V) | AC128 | | | | |
| 2SB267 | | | | AC131 | AC153 | | | | |
| 2SB268 | G | P | MT | (ASY48V) | | | | | |
| 2SB269 | G | P | Y | (AC151V) | | | | | |
| 2SB271 | G | P | SN, TS | (AC151V) | | | | | |
| 2SB272 | G | P | SN, TS | (AC151VII) | | | | | |
| 2SB273 | G | P | SN, TS | (AC151VII) | | | | | |
| 2SB276 | G | P | HI | AU103 | | | | | |
| 2SB282 | G | P | MA | (AUY22III) | | | | | |
| 2SB283 | G | P | MA | (AUY21IV) | | | | | |
| 2SB284 | G | P | MA | (AUY22III) | | | | | |
| 2SB285 | G | P | MA | (AUY21IV) | | | | | |
| 2SB290 | G | P | TO | ASY26 | AC122 | 2N799 | | 2SA155 | |
| 2SB290gn | G | P | TO | (ASY26) | | | | | |
| 2SB290ve | G | P | TO | (ASY26) | | | | | |
| 2SB291 | G | P | TO | ASY26 | AC131 | 2N799 | | 2SA155 | |
| 2SB291gn | G | P | TO | (ASY26) | | | | | |
| 2SB291r | G | P | TO | (ASY26) | | | | | |
| 2SB291ve | G | P | TO | (ASY26) | | | | | |
| 2SB292 | G | P | TO | (ASY70IV) | ASY26 | 2N799 | | 2SA155 | |
| 2SB292 | | | | AC131 | | | | | |
| 2SB292bl | G | P | TO | (ASY70V) | | | | | |
| 2SB292gn | G | P | TO | (ASY70VI) | | | | | |
| 2SB292r | G | P | TO | (ASY70VI) | | | | | |
| 2SB292ve | G | P | TO | (ASY70VI) | | | | | |
| 2SB292A | G | P | TO | (ASY48IV) | | | | | |
| 2SB292Abl | G | P | TO | (ASY48V) | | | | | |
| 2SB292Agn | G | P | TO | (ASY48VI) | | | | | |
| 2SB292Aor | G | P | TO | (ASY48VI) | | | | | |
| 2SB292Ar | G | P | TO | (ASY48VI) | | | | | |
| 2SB292Ave | G | P | TO | (ASY48VI) | | | | | |
| 2SB293 | G | P | Y | AC121V | | | | | |
| 2SB294 | G | P | Y | AC121IV | | | | | |
| 2SB295 | G | P | FU | (AD163IV) | | | | | |
| 2SB299 | G | P | Y | AC121V | | | | | |
| 2SB300 | G | P | TO | (AUY21IV) | | | | | |
| 2SB301 | G | P | TO | (AUY21IV) | | | | | |
| 2SB302 | G | P | HI | AF124 | AF134 | | | 2SB235 | |
| 2SB303 | G | P | SN, TS | (AC151V) | AC163 | | | 2SB73 | |
| 2SB303 | | | | AC150 | AC125 | | | | |
| 2SB304 | G | P | FU | (AC152V) | | | | | |
| 2SB304A | G | P | FU | (AC152V) | | | | | |
| 2SB306 | G | P | TO | | | | | 2SB425 | |
| 2SB309 | G | P | MA | (AUY22IV) | | | | | |
| 2SB315 | G | P | MT | AC121IV | | | | | |
| 2SB316 | G | P | MT | AC121V | | | | | |
| 2SB317 | G | P | MT | (AC121V) | | | | | |
| 2SB318 | G | P | FU | (AD131IV) | | | | | |
| 2SB319 | G | P | FU | (AD163IV) | | | | | |
| 2SB321 | G | P | TO | (AC151VI) | | | | | |
| 2SB322 | G | P | TO | (AC151V) | | | | | |
| 2SB323 | G | P | TO | (AC151VII) | | | | | |
| 2SB324 | G | P | MA | AC152VI | AC128 | | | | |
| 2SB326 | G | P | NI | (ASY26) | | | | | |
| 2SB327 | G | P | NI | (ASY27) | | | | | |
| 2SB328 | G | P | NI | AC121V | NKT274 | | | | |
| 2SB329 | G | P | NI | AC121VII | NKT374 | | | | |
| 2SB335 | G | P | MA | (AC121V) | | | | | |
| 2SB336 | G | P | MA | (AC121V) | | | | | |
| 2SB337 | G | P | HI | (AUY21IV) | | | | | |
| 2SB337H | G | P | HI | (AUY21IV) | | | | | |
| 2SB338 | G | P | HI | (AUY22IV) | | | | | |
| 2SB338H | G | P | HI | (AUY22IV) | | | | | |
| 2SB345 | G | P | MA | AC162 | AC151VII | 2N2429 | | | |
| 2SB345 | | | | AC126 | AC122VI | | | | |
| 2SB345 | | | | AC125 | | | | | |
| 2SB346 | G | P | MA | AC163 | AC151VII | 2N2429 | | | |
| 2SB346 | | | | AC126 | AC131/50 | | | | |
| 2SB347 | G | P | MA | AC162 | AC126 | 2N2429 | | | |
| 2SB348 | G | P | MA | AC163 | AC126 | 2N2429 | | | |
| 2SB349 | G | P | SN | AC121VII | | | | | |
| 2SB350 | G | P | SN | AC151VI | | | | | |
| 2SB355 | G | P | MT | (AD130V) | | | | | |
| 2SB356 | G | P | MT | (AD132V) | | | | | |
| 2SB357 | G | P | MT | (AD163IV) | | | | | |

| TYPE | M/S | POL | MANUFAC | EUROPEAN | | | AMERICAN | | JAPANESE | USE |
|------|-----|-----|---------|----------|---|---|----------|---|----------|-----|
| 2SB361 | G | P | HI | (AUY22IV) | | | | | | |
| 2SB362 | G | P | HI | (AUY22IV) | | | | | | |
| 2SB364 | G | P | TO | AC152VI | AC128 | 2N1924 | 2N2431 | | 2SB370A | |
| 2SB364 | | | | AC131 | AC131 | | | | | |
| 2SB364 | | | | AC163 | | | | | | |
| 2SB365 | G | P | TO | AC152V | AC128 | 2N1924 | 2N2431 | | | |
| 2SB365 | | | | AC131 | AC153 | | | | | |
| 2SB367 | G | P | HI | (AD148V) | | | | | | |
| 2SB367H | G | P | HI | (AD148V) | | | | | | |
| 2SB368 | G | P | HI | (AD148V) | | | | | | |
| 2SB368H | G | P | HI | (AD148V) | | | | | | |
| 2SB370 | G | P | HI | AC152VI | AC128 | | | | | |
| 2SB370A | G | P | HI | AC152VI | AC128 | | | | | |
| 2SB371 | G | P | MA | AC162 | AC151VI | | | | | |
| 2SB371 | | | | AC122gr | AC125 | | | | | |
| 2SB372 | G | P | SN, TS | (AC153VI) | | | | | | |
| 2SB373 | G | P | SN, TS | (AC153VII) | | | | | | |
| 2SB374 | G | P | SN, TS | (AS153VIII) | | | | | | |
| 2SB376 | G | P | MA | (AC121IV) | | | | | | |
| 2SB378 | G | P | SO | (AC121IV) | AC121 | 2N2431 | | | 2SB156A | |
| 2SB378 | | | | AC131 | AC128 | | | | | |
| 2SB379 | G | P | SO | (AC121V) | AC121 | 2N2431 | | | 2SB156A | |
| 2SB379 | | | | AC131 | AC128 | | | | | |
| 2SB381 | G | P | SO | AC151VI | AC122r | 2N238 | | | 2SB459 | |
| 2SB381 | | | | AC126 | | | | | | |
| 2SB383 | G | P | SO | AC124 | | | | | | |
| 2SB384 | G | P | Y | (AC151V) | | | | | | |
| 2SB386 | G | P | Y | (AC151IV) | | | | | | |
| 2SB386 | G | P | MT | AC152V | | | | | | |
| 2SB389 | G | P | FU | (AF126) | | | | | | |
| 2SB390 | G | P | SN, TS | (AUY22IV) | | | | | | |
| 2SB391 | G | P | SN, TS | (AUY21IV) | AUY21 | 2N352 | | | 2S339 | |
| 2SB391 | | | | AUY28 | ASZ18 | | | | | |
| 2SB400 | G | P | SN, TS | (AC151VII) | AC121VI | | | | | |
| 2SB400 | | | | AC160 | | | | | | |
| 2SB401 | G | P | MA | (ASY48IV) | | | | | | |
| 2SB402 | G | P | MA | (ASY48IV) | | | | | | |
| 2SB403 | G | P | MA | (ASY48IV) | | | | | | |
| 2SB405 | G | P | SN, TS | AC153VI | | | | | | |
| 2SB407 | G | P | SN, TS | (AUY21IV) | | | | | | |
| 2SB413 | G | P | TO | (AD131IV) | | | | | | |
| 2SB414 | G | P | TO | (AD130IV) | | | | | | |
| 2SB415 | G | P | TO, DT | AC153V | | | | | | |
| 2SB422 | G | P | | AC122 | AC126 | | | | | |
| 2SB422 | | | | AC151 | | | | | | |
| 2SB424 | G | P | TO | (AD132V) | | | | | | |
| 2SB425 | G | P | TO | (AD131V) | | | | | | |
| 2SB426 | G | P | TO | AD130V | | | | | 2SB426 | |
| 2SB427 | G | P | FU | (ASY48V) | | | | | 2SB425 | |
| 2SB428 | G | P | FU | (ASY48VI) | | | | | | |
| 2SB431 | G | P | FU | (AC152VI) | | | | | | |
| 2SB434 | S | P | TO | (BD440) | | | | | 2SB435 | |
| 2SB434or | S | P | TO | (BD440) | | | | | | |
| 2SB434r | S | P | TO | (BD440) | | | | | | |
| 2SB434ve | S | P | TO | (BD440) | | | | | | |
| 2SB435 | S | P | TO | (BD438) | | | | | 2SB434 | |
| 2SB435or | S | P | TO | (BD438) | | | | | | |
| 2SB435r | S | P | TO | (BD438) | | | | | | |
| 2SB435ve | S | P | TO | (BD438) | | | | | | |
| 2SB439 | G | P | TO | AC163 | AC171 | 2N2907 | 2N506 | | 2SB459 | |
| 2SB439 | | | | AC128 | | | | | | |
| 2SB440 | G | P | TO | AC163 | AC171 | 2N2907 | 2N506 | | 2SB459 | |
| 2SB440 | | | | AC128 | | | | | | |
| 2SB443 | G | P | FU | (AC163) | AC121VI | | | | | |
| 2SB443A | G | P | HI | AC121VI | | | | | | |
| 2SB443B | G | P | HI | AC121VI) | | | | | | |
| 2SB444 | G | P | FU | (AC163) | AC121VI | | | | | |
| 2SB444A | G | P | HI | AC121VI | | | | | | |
| 2SB444B | G | P | HI | AC121VI | | | | | | |
| 2SB445 | G | P | FU | (AD131V) | | | | | | |
| 2SB446 | G | P | FY | (AD131V) | | | | | | |
| 2SB448 | G | P | MA | AD148V | | | | | | |
| 2SB449 | G | P | MA | AD131IV | | | | | | |
| 2SB450 | G | P | MT | AC152VI | | | | | | |
| 2SB450A | G | P | MT | AC152VI | | | | | | |

| TYPE | M/S | POL | MANUFAC | EUROPEAN | AMERICAN | | JAPANESE | USE |
|---|---|---|---|---|---|---|---|---|
| 2SB451 | G | P | MT | (AC153VII) | | | | |
| 2SB452 | G | P | MT | (AC153VII) | | | | |
| 2SB452A | G | P | MT | (AC153VII) | | | | |
| 2SB453 | G | P | MT | (AC153VI) | | | | |
| 2SB454 | G | P | MT | (AC153VI) | | | | |
| | | | | | | | | |
| 2SB455 | G | P | MT | (AC153VI) | | | | |
| 2SB457 | G | P | MT | AC152VI | | | | |
| 2SB457A | G | P | MT | AC152VI | | | | |
| 2SB458 | G | P | MT | (AD130IV) | | | | |
| 2SB458A | G | P | MT | (AD131IV) | | | | |
| | | | | | | | | |
| 2SB458B | G | P | MT | (AD163IV) | | | | |
| 2SB459 | G | P | HI | AC163 | | | | |
| 2SB461 | G | P | TO | (ACY33) | | | 2SB463 | |
| 2SB462 | G | P | TO | AD131V | | | | |
| 2SB462bl | G | P | TO | AD131V | | | | |
| | | | | | | | | |
| 2SB462r | G | P | TO | AD131V | | | | |
| 2SB462ve | G | P | TO | AD131V | | | 2SB462 | |
| 2SB463 | G | P | TO | AD130V | | | | |
| 2SB463bl | G | P | TO | AD130IV | | | | |
| 2SB463r | G | P | TO | AD130V | | | | |
| | | | | | | | | |
| 2SB463ve | G | P | TO | AD130V | | | | |
| 2SB464 | G | P | TO | (AUY34V) | | | | |
| 2SB465 | G | P | TO | (AUY20) | | | | |
| 2SB466 | G | P | TO, FU | (AD131IV) | | | | |
| 2SB467 | G | P | FU | (AD131V) | | | | |
| | | | | | | | | |
| 2SB470 | G | P | FU | AUY22IV | | | | |
| 2SB471 | G | P | HI | (AUY22IV) | | | | |
| 2SB471A | G | P | HI | (AUY22IV) | | | | |
| 2SB471B | G | P | HI | (AUY22IV) | | | | |
| 2SB472 | G | P | HI | (AUY22IV) | | | | |
| | | | | | | | | |
| 2SB472A | G | P | HI | (AUY22IV) | | | | |
| 2SB472B | G | P | HI | (AUY22IV) | | | | |
| 2SB473 | G | P | MA | (AD148V) | AD162VII | | 2SB367 | |
| 2SB474 | G | P | SN, TS | AD130V | | | | |
| 2SB475 | G | P | MA | AC121V | AC121VI | | | |
| | | | | | | | | |
| 2SB476 | G | P | MA | (AC188K) | | | | |
| 2SB481 | G | P | MA | (AD148V) | | | | |
| 2SB482 | G | P | TO | (AC151VII) | | | 2SB486 | |
| 2SB486 | G | P | TO | (AC151VII) | | | 2SB482 | |
| 2SB492 | G | P | SN, TS | (AC188K) | | | | |
| | | | | | | | | |
| 2SB494 | G | P | MT | AC153VII | | | | |
| 2SB495 | G | P | MT | AC153VII | | | | |
| 2SB495A | G | P | MT | AC153VII | | | | |
| 2SB496 | G | P | HI | AC152VI | | | | |
| 2SB497 | G | P | FU | (AC121VI) | | | | |
| | | | | | | | | |
| 2SB502A | S | P | TO | | 2N5954 | | | |
| 2SB503A | S | P | TO | | 2N5955 | | | |
| 2SB507 | S | P | SN, TS | (BD440) | | | | |
| 2SB508 | S | P | SN, TS | (BD440) | | | | |
| 2SB510 | S | P | NI | (BSV17-10) | | | | |
| | | | | | | | | |
| 2SB511 | S | P | SN, TS | (BD438) | | | | |
| 2SB512 | S | P | MA | (BD440) | | | | |
| 2SB512A | S | P | MA | (BD442) | | | | |
| 2SB513 | S | P | MA | (BD440) | | | | |
| 2SB513A | S | P | MA | (BD442) | | | | |
| | | | | | | | | |
| 2SB514 | S | P | SN, TS | (BD440) | | | | |
| 2SB515 | S | P | SN, TS | (BD440) | | | | |
| 2SB530 | S | P | TO | | 2N6248 | | | |
| 2SB531 | S | P | TO | | 2N6247 | | | |
| 2SB534 | G | P | HI | AC152VI | | | | |
| | | | | | | | | |
| 2SB535 | G | P | HI | | | | | |
| 2SB558 | S | P | TO | | 2N6248 | | | |
| 2SB595 | S | P | TO | | 2N6475 | | | |
| 2SB596 | S | P | TO | | 2N6107 | | | |
| 2SC11 | G | N | TO | (AC127) | ASY29 | | | |
| | | | | | | | | |
| 2SC11 | S | N | TO | ASY73 | | | | |
| 2SC12 | S | N | TO | (BCY65EVII) | | | | |
| 2SC15 | S | N | SO | (BCY65EVII) | 2N1753 | 2N1754 | | |
| 2SC15-1 | S | N | SO | (BCY65EVII) | | | | |
| 2SC15-2 | S | N | SO | (BCY65EVII) | | | | |
| | | | | | | | | |
| 2SC15-3 | S | N | SO | (BCY65EVII) | | | | |
| 2SC16 | S | N | TO | BC107A | | | | |
| 2SC16A | S | N | TO | BC107A | | | | |
| 2SC17 | S | N | TO | BC107A | | | | |
| 2SC17A | S | N | TO | BC107A | | | | |

| TYPE | M/S | POL | MANUFAC | EUROPEAN | | AMERICAN | | JAPANESE | USE |
|------|-----|-----|---------|----------|--|----------|--|----------|-----|
| 2SC18 | S | N | TO | BC107A | | | | | |
| 2SC19 | S | N | TO | (BC337-16) | | | | | |
| 2SC20 | S | N | TO | (BC337-16) | | | | | |
| 2SC23C | S | N | | BD137 | | | | | |
| 2SC26 | S | N | FU | (BCY65EVII) | | | | | |
| 2SC27 | S | N | FU | (BCY65EVII) | | | | | |
| 2SC28 | S | N | FU | (BC107A) | | | | | |
| 2SC29 | S | N | FU | (BC107A) | | | | | |
| 2SC30 | S | N | NI | (BCY65EVII) | | | | | |
| 2SC31 | S | N | NI | (BCY65EVII) | BC140 | 2N2218A | | | |
| 2SC32 | S | N | NI | (BC107A) | BFY13 | | | | |
| 2SC32 | S | | | BFY13 | | | | | |
| 2SC32A | S | N | NI | (BC107A) | BFX55 | | | | |
| 2SC33 | S | N | NI | (BC107A) | BFX55 | | | | |
| 2SC37 | S | N | NI | (BC107A) | | | | | |
| 2SC38 | S | N | NI | (BC107A) | BFX55 | | | | |
| 2SC39 | S | N | FU | (BF198) | | | | | |
| 2SC39A | S | N | FU | (BF198) | | | | | |
| 2SC40 | S | N | FU | (BF198) | | | | | |
| 2SC41 | S | N | SO | (BU310) | BU110 | | | | |
| 2SC42 | S | N | SO | (BU310) | | | | | |
| 2SC42A | S | N | SO | (BU311) | | | | | |
| 2SC43 | S | N | SO | (BU310) | BU110 | | | | |
| 2SC44 | S | N | SO | (BU310) | BU110 | 2N1490 | | | |
| 2SC45 | S | N | NI | (BC107A) | BFX55 | | | | |
| 2SC46 | S | N | FU | BSX46-6 | | | | | |
| 2SC47 | S | N | FU | BSX45-6 | | | | | |
| 2SC48 | S | N | FU | BSX47-6 | | | | | |
| 2SC49 | S | N | NI | BSX47-6 | | | | | |
| 2SC50 | S | N | MA | (BU312) | BU110 | | | | |
| 2SC51 | S | N | FU | (BSX46-6) | | | | | |
| 2SC52 | S | N | FU | (BSY34) | | | | | |
| 2SC53 | S | N | FU | (BC107A) | BFX55 | | | | |
| 2SC54 | S | N | FU | (BSX49) | | | | | |
| 2SC55 | S | N | FU | (BSX48) | | | | | |
| 2SC57 | S | N | NI | (BSX45-6) | | | | | |
| 2SC58 | S | N | MA | (BF457) | | | | | |
| 2SC58A | S | N | MA | (BF457) | | | | | |
| 2SC59 | S | M | FU, NI | BSX47-6 | | | | | |
| 2SC60 | G | N | SN, TS | (AC127) | | | | | |
| 2SC61 | S | N | FU | (BSX46-6) | | | | | |
| 2SC62 | S | N | HI | BSY63 | | | | | |
| 2SC63 | S | N | NI | BSY63 | | | | | |
| 2SC64 | S | N | SN, TS | (BCY65EVII) | BSX45 | 2N4231 | 2N3252 | | |
| 2SC65 | | | | BSX22 | | | | | |
| 2SC66 | S | N | SN, TS | (BF457) | | | | | |
| 2SC68 | S | N | NI | BSY63 | | | | | |
| 2SC69 | S | N | NI | BSX47-6 | | | | | |
| 2SC70 | S | N | TO | (BF458) | | | | 2SC499 | |
| 2SC71 | S | N | TO | | | | | | |
| 2SC72 | S | N | TO | | | | | | |
| 2SC73 | G | N | SO | | | 2N168A | 2N1086 | 2T73R | |
| 2SC74 | S | N | TO | (BC108A) | BFX55 | | | | |
| 2SC74gn | S | N | TO | (BC108B) | | | | | |
| 2SC74or | S | N | TO | (BC108A) | | | | | |
| 2SC74r | S | N | TO | (BC108A) | | | | | |
| 2SC74ye | S | N | TO | (BC108B) | | | | | |
| 2SC75 | G | N | SO | | | 2N169 | 2N293 | 2T75R | |
| 2SC76 | G | N | SO | | | 2N169 | 2N293 | 2T75R | |
| 2SC77 | G | N | SO | | | 2N169 | 2N293 | 2T77R | |
| 2SC78 | G | N | SO | ASY14 | | 2N1109 | 2N1121 | 2T78R | |
| 2SC79 | S | N | FU | (BF199) | BF173 | | | 2SC464 | |
| 2SC80 | S | N | NI | (BF199) | | | | | |
| 2SC84 | G | N | MT | (AC127) | | | | | |
| 2SC85 | G | N | MT | (AC127) | | | | | |
| 2SC86 | G | N | MT | (AC127) | | | | | |
| 2SC87 | S | N | FU | BC107A | | | | | |
| 2SC89 | G | N | HI | ASY14 | | | | | |
| 2SC90 | G | N | HI | (AC127) | | 2N1304 | | | |
| 2SC91 | G | N | HI | (AC127) | | 2N1306 | | | |
| 2SC92 | S | N | NI | (BSX46-6) | | | | | |
| 2SC93 | S | N | NI | (BSX45-6) | | | | | |
| 2SC94 | S | N | NI | (BSX46-6) | | | | | |
| 2SC95 | S | N | TO | (BSX47-6) | | | | | |
| 2SC97 | S | N | NI | (BSY34) | BC140 | 2N3036 | 2N2218A | | |

| TYPE | M/S | POL | MANUFAC | EUROPEAN | | AMERICAN | | | JAPANESE | USE |
|------|-----|-----|---------|----------|--|----------|--|--|----------|-----|
| 2SC97A | S | N | NI | (BSY34) | | | | | | |
| 2SC98 | S | N | MA | (BSY62) | | | | | | |
| 2SC99 | S | N | MA | (BSY62) | | | | | | |
| 2SC100 | S | N | NI | (BSY63) | | | | | | |
| 2SC101 | S | N | TO | | | | | | 2SC782 | |
| 2SC103 | S | N | TO | BC107A | BDY91 | | | | | |
| 2SC103A | S | N | TO | BC107A | | | | | | |
| 2SC104 | S | N | TO | BC107A | | | | | | |
| 2SC105 | S | N | TO | BC109B | BC169 | MPS6521 | | | | |
| 2SC105 | | | | BC169B | BC173 | | | | | |
| 2SC106 | S | N | TO | | | | | | 2SA474 | |
| 2SC106 | | | | | | | | | 2SA472 | |
| 2SC107 | S | N | TO | | | | | | 2SB216 | |
| 2SC108 | S | N | TO | (BSY34) | | | | | 2SC400 | |
| 2SC108A | S | N | TO, TS | (BC141-6) | | | | | | |
| 2SC109 | S | N | TO | (BSY34) | | | | | 2SC393 | |
| 2SC109A | S | N | TO, TS | (BC140-6) | | | | | | |
| 2SC110 | S | N | HI | (BSY34) | | | | | | |
| 2SC111 | S | N | HI | (BSY34) | | | | | | |
| 2SC112 | S | N | HI | (BSY34) | | | | | | |
| 2SC113 | S | N | HI | (BSY34) | | | | | | |
| 2SC114 | S | N | HI | (BSY34) | | | | | | |
| 2SC117 | S | N | HI | BSX46-6 | | | | | | |
| 2SC118 | S | N | HI | BSX46-6 | | | | | | |
| 2SC119 | S | N | HI | BSX46-6 | | | | | | |
| 2SC120 | S | N | NI | (BC107A) | BC140VI | 2N2218A | 2N3036 | | 2SC708 | |
| 2SC120 | | | | BSY46 | | | | | | |
| 2SC121 | S | N | NI | (BC107A) | BC140VI | 2N2218A | 2N3036 | | 2SC708 | |
| 2SC121 | | | | BSY46 | | | | | | |
| 2SC122 | S | N | NI | (BC107A) | BC140X | 2N2218A | 2N3036 | | 2SC708 | |
| 2SC122 | | | | BSY46 | | | | | | |
| 2SC123 | S | N | NI | (BC107A) | BC140XVI | 2N2218A | 2N3036 | | 2SC708 | |
| 2SC123 | | | | BSY46 | | | | | | |
| 2SC124 | S | N | NI | (BC107A) | BC140VI | 2N2218A | 2N3036 | | 2SC708 | |
| 2SC124 | | | | BSY46 | | | | | | |
| 2SC125 | G | N | HI | (AF139) | | | | | | |
| 2SC127 | S | N | NI | (BC107A) | BC140XVI | 2N2218A | 2N3036 | | 2SC708 | |
| 2SC127 | | | | BSY46 | | | | | | |
| 2SC128 | G | N | MA | (AC127) | | | | | | |
| 2SC129 | G | N | MA | (AC127) | | | | | | |
| 2SC130 | S | N | FU, CE | (BSX45-6) | | | | | | |
| 2SC131 | S | N | FU, CE | BSX49 | | | | | | |
| 2SC132 | S | N | FU, CE | BSX48 | | | | | | |
| 2SC133 | S | N | FU, CE | BSX48 | | | | | | |
| 2SC134 | S | N | FU, CE | BSX49 | | | | | | |
| 2SC135 | S | N | FU, CE | BSX48 | | | | | | |
| 2SC136 | S | N | FU, CE | BSX49 | | | | | | |
| 2SC137 | S | N | FU, CE | BSX48 | | | | | | |
| 2SC138 | S | N | NI | BSY34 | | | | | | |
| 2SC138A | S | N | NI | BSY34 | | | | | | |
| 2SC139 | S | N | NI | BSY34 | | | | | | |
| 2SC140 | S | N | SO | (BSX46-6) | | | | | | |
| 2SC147 | S | N | SO | (BSX45-6) | | 2N2196 | | | | |
| 2SC149 | S | N | NI | BSX47-6 | | | | | | |
| 2SC150 | S | N | HI, CE | (BC107A) | | | | | | |
| 2SC154 | S | N | HI | (BF457) | | | | | | |
| 2SC154C | S | N | HI | (BF457) | | | | | | |
| 2SC154H | S | N | HI | (BF458) | | | | | | |
| 2SC157 | S | N | HI | (BC107A) | | | | | | |
| 2SC158 | S | N | HI | (BC107A) | | | | | | |
| 2SC159 | S | N | HI | (BC107A) | | | | | | |
| 2SC160 | S | N | HI | (BC107A) | | | | | | |
| 2SC166 | S | N | HI | (BC107A) | | | | | | |
| 2SC167 | S | N | HI | (BC107A) | | | | | | |
| 2SC170 | S | N | FU | BC108A | BC108 | 2N3391 | | | 2SC458 | |
| 2SC170 | | | | BC183 | | | | | | |
| 2SC171 | S | N | FU | BC108A | | | | | | |
| 2SC172 | S | N | FU | BC108A | | | | | | |
| 2SC172A | S | N | FU | BC107A | | | | | | |
| 2SC174 | S | N | FU | (BC167A) | BC167 | MPS6566 | | | 2SC458 | |
| 2SC174 | | | | BC183 | BC171A | | | | | |
| 2SC182 | S | N | NI | (BC238A) | | | | | | |
| 2SC183 | S | N | NI | BF115 | | | | | | |
| 2SC184 | S | N | NI | BF115 | | | | | | |
| 2SC185 | S | N | NI | BF115 | | | | | | |
| | | | | (BC108A) | | | | | | |

| TYPE | M/S | POL | MANUFAC | EUROPEAN | | | AMERICAN | | JAPANESE | USE |
|---|---|---|---|---|---|---|---|---|---|---|
| 2SC186 | S | N | FU | (BC108A) | | | | | | |
| 2SC187 | S | N | FU | (BC108A) | | | | | | |
| 2SC188 | S | N | FU, CE | (BC337-16) | | | | | | |
| 2SC189 | S | N | FU, CE | (BC337-16) | | | | | | |
| 2SC190 | S | N | FU | (BC337-16) | | | | | | |
| 2SC191 | S | N | SO | (BCY65EVII) | | | 2N1074 | 2N1075 | | |
| 2SC192 | S | N | SO | (BCY65EVII) | | | 2N1074 | 2N1075 | | |
| 2SC193 | S | N | SO | (BCY65EVII) | | | 2N336 | 2N337 | | |
| 2SC194 | S | N | SO | (BCY65EVII) | | | 2N1074 | 2N1075 | | |
| 2SC195 | S | N | SO | (BC108A) | | | 2N1278 | 2N1279 | | |
| 2SC196 | S | N | SO | (BC108A) | | | 2N1278 | 2N1279 | | |
| 2SC197 | S | N | SO | (BC108A) | | | 2N1277 | 2N1278 | | |
| 2SC199 | S | N | TO | BSY34 | BSX73 | | 2N2218B | | 2SC458 | |
| 2SC199 | | | | BSX61 | | | | | | |
| 2SC200 | S | N | FU | (BSY34) | BFX55 | | | | | |
| 2SC201 | S | N | FU | (BSY34) | BFX55 | | | | | |
| 2SC202 | S | N | FU | (BSY34) | BFX55 | | | | | |
| 2SC203 | S | N | FU, CE | (BSX49) | | | | | | |
| 2SC204 | S | N | FU, CE | (BSX48) | | | | | | |
| 2SC205 | S | N | FU | (BSX49) | | | | | | |
| 2SC206 | S | N | FU | (BF198) | BF184 | | | | 2SC460 | |
| 2SC206 | | | | BF234 | | | | | | |
| 2SC210 | S | N | FU | (BSX46-6) | BSY34 | | 2N2218 | | 2SC479 | |
| 2SC210 | | | | BSX61 | BSX73 | | | | | |
| 2SC211 | S | N | FU | (BSX45-6) | BSY34 | | 2N2218 | | 2SC479 | |
| 2SC211 | | | | BSX61 | BSX73 | | | | | |
| 2SC212 | S | N | FU | (BSX47-6) | BSX45 | | 2N4231 | 2N3252 | | |
| 2SC212 | | | | BSX22 | | | | | | |
| 2SC213 | S | N | FU | (BSX46-6) | | | | | | |
| 2SC214 | S | N | FU | (BSX45-6) | | | | | | |
| 2SC215 | S | N | FU | (BSX47-6) | | | | | | |
| 2SC216 | S | N | FU, CE | (BSX46-6) | | | | | | |
| 2SC217 | S | N | FU | (BSX45-6) | | | | | | |
| 2SC218 | S | N | FU, CE | (BSX47-6) | | | | | | |
| 2SC220 | S | N | FU | (BSX46-6) | | | | | | |
| 2SC221 | S | N | FU | (BSX45-6) | | | | | | |
| 2SC222 | S | N | FU | (BSX47-6) | | | | | | |
| 2SC223 | S | N | FU | (BSX46-6) | | | | | | |
| 2SC224 | S | N | FU | (BSX45-6) | | | | | | |
| 2SC225 | S | N | FU | (BSX47-6) | | | | | | |
| 2SC226 | S | N | FU | (BSX46-6) | | | | | | |
| 2SC227 | S | N | FU | (BSX45-6) | | | | | | |
| 2SC228 | S | N | FU | (BSX47-6) | | | | | | |
| 2SC229 | S | N | FU | (BSX47-6) | | | | | | |
| 2SC230 | S | N | FU | BSX49 | | | 2N222A | | | |
| 2SC231 | S | N | FU | (BSX46-6) | | | | | | |
| 2SC232 | S | N | FU | (BSX45-6) | | | | | | |
| 2SC233 | S | N | FU | (BSX47-6) | BSX63 | | | | | |
| 2SC234 | S | N | FU | (BSX46-6) | | | | | | |
| 2SC235 | S | N | FU | (BSX46-6) | | | | | | |
| 2SC236 | S | N | FU | (BSX46-6) | | | | | | |
| 2SC237 | S | N | FU | (BSX48) | | | | | | |
| 2SC238 | S | N | FU | (BSY58) | | | | | | |
| 2SC239 | S | N | FU | (BSX48) | | | | | | |
| 2SC240 | S | N | FU, NI | (BU310) | | | | | | |
| 2SC244 | S | N | NI | BU310 | | | | | | |
| 2SC245 | S | N | NI | BU311 | | | | | | |
| 2SC246 | S | N | NI | BU312 | | | | | | |
| 2SC247 | S | N | FU | (BSX46-6) | | | | | | |
| 2SC248 | S | N | FU | (BCY65EVII) | | | | | | |
| 2SC249 | S | N | FU | (BCY65EVII) | | | | | | |
| 2SC250 | S | N | FU | (BF198) | BFY12 | | 2N3568 | | | |
| 2SC251 | S | N | NI | (BFX89) | | | | | | |
| 2SC251A | S | N | NI | (BFX89) | | | | | | |
| 2SC252 | S | N | NI, CE | (BFX89) | | | | | | |
| 2SC253 | S | N | NI, CE | (BFX89) | | | | | | |
| 2SC270 | S | N | SO | BU312 | | | | | | |
| 2SC281 | S | N | HI | (BC108A) | BC107A | | 2N2821 | | 2SC458 | |
| 2SC281 | | | | BC182A | | | | | | |
| 2SC281H | S | N | HI | (BC108A) | | | | | | |
| 2SC282 | S | N | HI | (BC108A) | BC108 | | 2N3391 | | 2SC458 | |
| 2SC282 | | | | BC183A | | | | | | |
| 2SC182H | S | N | HI | (BC108A) | | | | | | |
| 2SC283 | S | N | HI | (BC107A) | BCY65 | | 2N2484 | 2N2483 | 2SC648 | |
| 2SC283 | | | | BC107B | | | | | | |

| TYPE | M/S | POL | MANUFAC | EUROPEAN | | AMERICAN | | JAPANESE | USE |
|---|---|---|---|---|---|---|---|---|---|
| 2SC283H | S | N | HI | (BC107A) | | | | | |
| 2SC284 | S | N | HI | (BCY65EVII) | BSX49 | 2N2222A | | | |
| 2SC284H | S | N | HI | (BCY65EVII) | | | | | |
| 2SC285 | S | N | NI, FU | (BSY34) | | | | | |
| 2SC291 | S | N | SO | BSX63 | BSW65 | 2N1893 | | | |
| 2SC300 | S | N | MT | (BSX49) | BSX48 | 2N222A | | | |
| 2SC301 | S | N | MT | (BSX49) | BSX48 | 2N222A | | | |
| 2SC302 | S | N | MT | BSX49 | | | | | |
| 2SC303 | S | N | MT | BSX45-6 | | | | | |
| 2SC304 | S | N | MT | BSX45-6 | | | | | |
| 2SC305 | S | N | MT | BSX47-6 | | | | | |
| 2SC306 | S | N | MT | BSX45-6 | | | | | |
| 2SC307 | S | N | MT | BSX45-6 | | | | | |
| 2SC308 | S | N | MT | BSX46-6 | | | | | |
| 2SC309 | S | N | MT | BSX47-6 | | | | | |
| 2SC310 | S | N | MT | BSX47-6 | | | | | |
| 2SC313 | S | N | MT, NS | (BFX89) | BC108A | 2N3391 | | 2SC458 | |
| 2SC313 | | | | BC183A | | | | | |
| 2SC316 | S | N | MA | BCY58IX | BC109 | MPS6521 | | 2SC458- | |
| 2SC316 | | | | BC184B | | | | | |
| 2SC318 | S | N | SO | BC107A | BC182A | 2N2921 | | 2SC458 | |
| 2SC318A | S | N | MA, SO | BC107A | | | | | |
| 2SC319 | S | N | NI | BSY58 | BSX48 | 2N2221 | | | |
| 2SC320 | S | N | NI | BSY58 | | | | | |
| 2SC321H | S | N | HI | BSY63 | | | | | |
| 2SC323 | S | N | TO | BCY59VII | | | | | |
| 2SC350 | S | N | HI | BC107B | BC128B | 2N3568 | | | |
| 2SC352 | S | N | HI, SO | (BC107A) | | | | | |
| 2SC352A | S | N | SO | (BC107A) | | | | | |
| 2SC353 | S | N | SO | (BCY65EVII) | | | | | |
| 2SC353A | S | N | SO | (BCY65EVII) | | | | | |
| 2SC354 | S | N | FU | (BSX45-6) | | | | | |
| 2SC356 | S | N | NI | (BSX48) | | | | | |
| 2SC360 | S | N | TO | BC108A | | | | | |
| 2SC361 | S | N | TO | BC167A | | | | | |
| 2SC362 | S | N | TO | BC167B | | | | | |
| 2SC363 | S | N | TO | BC167B | | | | | |
| 2SC366 | S | N | TO | (BC337-16) | BSY77 | | | 2SC499 | |
| 2SC366or | S | N | TO | (BC337-16) | | | | | |
| 2SC366r | S | N | TO | (BC337-16) | | | | | |
| 2SC366ye | S | N | TO | (BC337-16) | | | | | |
| 2SC366G | S | N | TO | (BC336-16) | | | | | |
| 2SC367 | S | N | TO | (BC337-16) | | 2N930 | | | |
| 2SC367gn | S | N | TO | (BC337-25) | | | | | |
| 2SC367or | S | N | TO | (BC337-16) | | | | | |
| 2SC367r | S | N | TO | (BC337-16) | | | | | |
| 2SC367ye | S | N | TO | (BC337-16) | | | | | |
| 2SC367G | S | N | TO | (BC337-16) | | | | | |
| 2SC368 | S | N | TO | BC168B | BC107B | 2N3568 | | | |
| 2SC368 | | | | BC182B | | | | | |
| 2SC369 | S | N | TO | BC169C | BC168 | MPS6520 | | 2SC371 | |
| 2SC369 | | | | BC183 | | | | | |
| 2SC369bi | S | N | TO | BC169C | | | | | |
| 2SC369gn | S | N | TO | BC169B | | | | | |
| 2SC369G | S | N | TO | BC168B | | | | | |
| 2SC369bi | S | N | TO | BC168C | | | | | |
| 2SC369gn | S | N | TO | BC168B | | | | | |
| 2SC370 | S | N | TO | BC167A | BC168A | MPS6520 | | 2SC458 | |
| 2SC370 | | | | BC183A | BC172A | | | | |
| 2SC370G | S | N | TO | BC167A | | | | | |
| 2SC371 | S | N | TO | BC167A | BC168A | MPS6520 | | 2SC458 | |
| 2SC371 | | | | BC183A | BC172A | | | | |
| 2SC371or | S | N | TO | BC167A | | | | | |
| 2SC371r | S | N | TO | BC167A | | | | | |
| 2SC371G | S | N | TO | BC167A | | | | | |
| 2SC372 | S | N | TO | BC167 | BC168A | MPS6520 | | 2SC458 | |
| 2SC372 | | | | BC168B | BC183A | | | | |
| 2SC372 | | | | BC172A | | | | | |
| 2SC372or | S | N | TO | BC167A | | | | | |
| 2SC372ye | S | N | TO | BC167A | | | | | |
| 2SC372G | S | N | TO | BC167A | | | | | |
| 2SC373 | S | N | TO | BC167B | BC168A | MPS6520 | | 2SC458 | |
| 2SC373 | | | | BC168B | BC168C | | | | |
| 2SC373 | | | | BC183A | BC172A | | | | |
| 2SC373G | S | N | TO | BC167A | | | | | |

| TYPE | M/S | POL | MANUFAC | EUROPEAN | | AMERICAN | | JAPANESE | USE |
|---|---|---|---|---|---|---|---|---|---|
| 2SC374 | | | | BC167B | BC168C | | | | |
| 2SC374 | S | N | TO | BC183C | BC172C | | | | |
| 2SC374bl | S | N | TO | BC167B | | | | | |
| 2SC374r | S | N | TO | (BC167B) | | | | | |
| 2SC376 | S | N | TO | (BC167A) | | | | | |
| | | | | | | | | | |
| 2SC377 | S | N | TO | (BF198) | BC167A | MPS6566 | | 2SC458 | |
| 2SC377 | S | N | TO | BC182A | BC171A | | | | |
| 2SC377br | S | N | TO | (BF198) | | | | | |
| 2SC377or | S | N | TO | BF198 | | | | | |
| 2SC377r | S | N | TO | (BF198) | | | | | |
| | | | | | | | | | |
| 2SC378 | S | N | TO | (BF198) | BC167A | MPS6566 | | 2SC458 | |
| 2SC378 | S | N | TO | BC182A | BC171A | | | | |
| 2SC378or | S | N | TO | (BF198) | | | | | |
| 2SC378r | S | N | TO | (BF198) | | | | | |
| 2SC378ve | S | N | TO | (BF198) | | | | | |
| | | | | | | | | | |
| 2SC379 | S | N | TO | BC167A | BC169 | MPS6521 | | | |
| 2SC379 | | | | BC169B | BC184B | | | | |
| 2SC379 | | | | BC173B | | | | | |
| 2SC380 | S | N | TO | (BF198) | BC167 | MPS5566 | | | |
| 2SC380 | | | | BC167A | BC182A | | | 2SC458 | |
| | | | | | | | | | |
| 2SC380 | | | | BC172A | | | | | |
| 2SC380r | S | N | TO | (BF198) | | | | | |
| 2SC380ve | S | N | TO | (BF198) | | | | | |
| 2SC380A | S | N | TO | (BF198) | | | | | |
| 2SC380Aor | S | N | TO | (BF198) | | | | | |
| | | | | | | | | | |
| 2SC380Ar | S | N | TO | (BF198) | | | | | |
| 2SC380Aye | S | N | TO | (BF198) | | | | | |
| 2SC381 | S | N | TO | (BF198) | BC168 | MPS5520 | | 2SC458 | |
| 2SC381 | | | | BC168A | BC183A | | | | |
| 2SC381 | | | | BC173A | | | | | |
| | | | | | | | | | |
| 2SC381or | S | N | TO | (BF198) | | | | | |
| 2SC381or | S | N | TO | (BF198) | | | | | |
| 2SC381r | S | N | TO | (BF198) | | | | | |
| 2SC382 | S | N | TO | (BF198) | BF173 | | | | |
| 2SC382 | | | | BF224 | | | | 2SC464 | |
| | | | | | | | | | |
| 2SC382or | S | N | TO | (BF198) | | | | | |
| 2SC382r | S | N | TO | (BF198) | | | | | |
| 2SC382G | S | N | TO | BF232 | BF198 | | | | |
| 2SC382R | S | N | TO | BF232 | BF198 | | | | |
| 2SC384 | S | N | TO | (BF255) | BF232 | | | 2SC464 | |
| | | | | | | | | | |
| 2SC384 | | | | BF173 | BF224 | | | | |
| 2SC384or | S | N | TO | (BF254) | | | | | |
| 2SC384ve | S | N | TO | (BF255) | | | | | |
| 2SC385 | S | N | TO | (BFY90) | BF232 | | | 2SC464 | |
| 2SC385 | | | | BF224 | BF173 | | | | |
| | | | | | | | | | |
| 2SC385A | S | N | TO | (BFY90) | | | | | |
| 2SC386 | S | N | TO | (BF199) | BF173 | | | 2SC464 | |
| 2SC386 | | | | BF224 | | | | | |
| 2SC386A | S | N | TO | (BF199) | | | | | |
| 2SC387 | S | N | TO | (BFY90) | BFX59 | | | 2SC707 | |
| | | | | | | | | | |
| 2SC387A | S | N | TO | (BFY90) | | | | | |
| 2SC388 | S | N | TO | (BF199) | BF173 | | | 2SC464 | |
| 2SC388 | | | | BF224 | | | | | |
| 2SC388A | S | N | TO | (BF199) | | | | | |
| 2SC389 | S | N | TO | (BF199) | BF173 | | | 2SC464 | |
| | | | | | | | | | |
| 2SC389 | | | | BF224 | | | | | |
| 2SC390 | S | N | TO | (BFX59) | | | | | |
| 2SC391 | S | N | TO | (BFX59) | | | | | |
| 2SC392 | S | N | TO | (BFX59) | | | | 2SC551 | |
| 2SC392A | S | N | TO | (BFX59) | | | | | |
| | | | | | | | | | |
| 2SC393 | S | N | | BF224 | | | | | |
| 2SC394 | S | N | TO | (BF198) | BC167 | MPS6566 | | 2SC395A | |
| 2SC394 | | | | BC182A | BC171A | | | 2SC458 | |
| 2SC394gn | S | N | TO | (BF198) | | | | | |
| 2SC394or | S | N | TO | (BF198) | | | | | |
| | | | | | | | | | |
| 2SC394r | S | N | TO | (BF198) | | | | | |
| 2SC394ye | S | N | TO | (BF198) | | | | | |
| 2SC395 | S | N | TO | (BF198) | | | | | |
| 2SC395A | S | N | TO | (BSY18) | | | | 2SC391 | |
| 2SC396 | S | N | TO | (BSY63) | | 2N3794 | | | |
| | | | | | | | | | |
| 2SC397 | S | N | TO | (BFX59) | BF185 | | | | |
| 2SC398 | S | N | TO | (BF254) | BF185 | | | | |
| 2SC398 | | | | BF237 | BF125 | | | 2SC535 | |
| 2SC399 | S | N | TO | (BF254) | BF185 | | | 2SC535 | |
| 2SC399 | | | | BF237 | BF125 | | | | |

| TYPE | M/S | POL | MANUFAC | EUROPEAN | | | AMERICAN | | JAPANESE | USE |
|------|-----|-----|---------|----------|--|--|----------|--|----------|-----|
| 2SC400 | S | N | TO, TS | BC107 | | | | | | |
| 2SC400gn | S | N | TO | BC107A | | | | | | |
| 2SC400or | S | N | TO | BC107A | | | | | | |
| 2SC400r | S | N | TO | BC107A | | | | | | |
| 2SC400ve | S | N | TO | BC107A | | | | | | |
| 2SC401 | S | N | SO, NI | BC167B | BC182A | MPS6566 | | | 2S458 | |
| 2SC401 | | | | BC171A | | | | | | |
| 2SC402 | S | N | SO, NI | BC167B | BC182A | MPS6566 | | | 2SC458 | |
| 2SC402 | | | | BC171A | | | | | | |
| 2SC403 | S | N | SO | (BC167B) | BC167A | MPS6566 | | | 2SC458 | |
| 2SC403 | | | | BC182A | BC171A | | | | | |
| 2SC403A | S | N | SO | (BC167A) | BC171A | | | | | |
| 2SC404 | S | N | SO | BC167A | BC167B | MPS6566 | | | 2SC458 | |
| 2SC404 | | | | BC182A | BC171A | | | | | |
| 2SC405 | G | N | MT, NI | (AC127) | | | | | | |
| 2SC406 | G | N | MT, NI | (AC127) | | | | | | |
| 2SC407 | S | N | SH, NI | BUY55 | | | | | | |
| 2SC408 | S | N | SH, NI | BUY55 | | | | | | |
| 2SC409 | S | N | SH, NI | BUY56 | | | | | | |
| 2SC410 | S | N | SH, NI | BUY56 | | | | | | |
| 2SC411 | S | N | SH, NI | BUY72 | | | | | | |
| 2SC412 | S | N | SH, NI | BUY72 | | | | | | |
| 2SC423 | S | N | SN | BSY58 | | | | | | |
| 2SC425 | S | N | SN, TO | BSY58 | | | | | | |
| 2SC429 | S | N | NI | (BF199) | BF173 | | | | 2SC464 | |
| 2SC429 | | | | BF224 | | | | | | |
| 2SC430 | S | N | NI | (BF199) | | | | | | |
| 2SC431 | S | N | SH | (BUY57) | | | | | | |
| 2SC432 | S | N | SH | (BUY57) | | | | | | |
| 2SC433 | S | N | SH | (BUY58) | | | | | | |
| 2SC434 | S | N | SH | (BUY58) | | | | | | |
| 2SC435 | S | N | SH | (BUY73) | | | | | | |
| 2SC436 | S | N | SH | (BUY73) | | | | | | |
| 2SC437 | S | N | MT | (BSX63-6) | | | | | | |
| 2SC438 | S | N | MT | (BSX63-6) | | | | | | |
| 2SC440 | S | N | MT | (BSY58) | | | | | | |
| 2SC441 | S | N | MT | (BSY58) | | | | | | |
| 2SC442 | S | N | MT | (BSY34) | | | | | | |
| 2SC443 | S | N | MT | (BSX45-6) | | | | | | |
| 2SC444 | S | N | MT | (BSX45-6) | | | | | | |
| 2SC445 | S | N | MT | (BSX47-6) | | | | | | |
| 2SC454 | S | N | HI | (BC163A) | BC148 | 2N3568 | MPS6520 | 2SC281 | | |
| 2SC454 | | | | BC148A | BC172A | | | | | |
| 2SC456 | S | N | MA | (BSY34) | BSY58 | 2N2218 | | 2SC479 | | |
| 2SC456 | | | | BSX73 | | | | | | |
| 2SC458 | S | N | HI, MA | (BC167A) | BC148A | 2N3568 | MPS6520 | 2SC281 | | |
| 2SC458 | | | | BC183A | BC172A | | | | | |
| 2SC458K | S | N | HI | (BC167A) | | | | | | |
| 2SC458LG | S | N | HI | (BC167A) | | | | | | |
| 2SC460 | S | N | HI | (BC167A) | BC148 | 2N3568 | MPS6520 | 2SC281 | | |
| 2SC460 | | | | BC148A | BC183A | | | | | |
| 2SC460 | | | | BC172A | | | | | | |
| 2SC461 | S | N | HI | (BC167A) | BC148 | 2N3568 | MPS6520 | 2SC281 | | |
| 2SC461 | | | | BC148A | BC183A | | | | | |
| 2SC463H | S | N | HI | (BF199) | | | | | | |
| 2SC464 | S | N | HI | (BF199) | BF173 | | | | | |
| 2SC464 | | | | BF224 | | | | | | |
| 2SC465 | S | N | HI | (BF199) | BF173 | | | | 2SC464 | |
| 2SC465 | | | | BF224 | | | | | | |
| 2SC466 | S | N | HI | (BF199) | BF173 | | | | 2SC464 | |
| 2SC466 | | | | BF224 | | | | | | |
| 2SC468H | S | N | HI | (BSY63) | | | | | | |
| 2SC470 | S | N | SO | (BF457) | BF178 | | | | 2SC856 | |
| 2SC470 | | | | BF140D | | | | | | |
| 2SC475 | S | N | NI | | | | | | | |
| 2SC476 | S | N | NI | | | | | | | |
| 2SC477 | S | N | MA | BCY58VII | | | | | | |
| 2SC478 | S | N | MA | BCY59VII | BC107 | 2N3568 | 2N2921 | 2SC458 | | |
| 2SC478 | | | | BC1B2A | | | | | | |
| 2SC479H | S | N | HI | BSY34 | | | | | | |
| 2SC481 | S | N | TO | | | 2N699 | | 2SD237 | | |
| 2SC482 | S | N | TO | BSX45 | | 2N1613 | | 2SC485 | | |
| 2SC482gn | S | N | TO | BSX45-16 | | | | | | |
| 2SC482or | S | N | TO | BSX45-6 | | | | | | |
| 2SC482ye | S | N | TO | BSX45-10 | | | | | | |

| TYPE | M/S | POL | MANUFAC | EUROPEAN | AMERICAN | JAPANESE | USE |
|------|-----|-----|---------|----------|----------|----------|-----|
| 2SC484 | S | N | TO | (BSX47) | | 2SD110 | |
| 2SC484bl | S | N | TO | (BSX47-10) | | | |
| 2SC484r | S | N | TO | (BSX47-6) | | | |
| 2SC484ye | S | N | TO | (BSX47-10) | | | |
| 2SC485 | S | N | TO | BSX47 | 2N1893 | 2SC489 | |
| | | | | | | | |
| 2SC485bl | S | N | TO | BSX47-10 | | | |
| 2SC485r | S | N | TO | BSX47-6 | | | |
| 2SC485ye | S | N | TO | BSX47-10 | | | |
| 2SC486 | S | N | TO | BSX46 | | 2SC490 | |
| 2SC486bl | S | N | TO | BSX46-16 | | | |
| | | | | | | | |
| 2SC486r | S | N | TO | BSX46-6 | | | |
| 2SC486ye | S | N | TO | BSX46-10 | | | |
| 2SC487 | S | N | TO | (BDY13) | | 2SC791 | |
| 2SC488 | S | N | TO | (BDY13) | | | |
| 2SC489 | S | N | TO | (BDY13) | | 2SC485 | |
| | | | | | | | |
| 2SC489bl | S | N | TO | (BDY13-16) | | | |
| 2SC489r | S | N | TO | (BDY13-6) | | | |
| 2SC489ye | S | N | TO | (BDY13-10) | | | |
| 2SC490 | S | N | TO | BDY13 | | 2SC486 | |
| 2SC490bl | S | N | TO | BDY13-16 | | | |
| | | | | | | | |
| 2SC490r | S | N | TO | BDY13-6 | | | |
| 2SC490ye | S | N | TO | BDY13-10 | | | |
| 2SC491 | S | N | TO | BDY12 | | 2SC482 | |
| 2SC491bl | S | N | TO | BDY12-16 | | | |
| 2SC491r | S | N | TO | BDY12-6 | | | |
| | | | | | | | |
| 2SC491ye | S | N | TO | BDY12-10 | | | |
| 2SC492 | S | N | TO | BU310 | | | |
| 2SC493 | S | N | TO | BU310 | | 2SC497 | |
| 2SC493bl | S | N | TO | BU310 | | | |
| 2SC493r | S | N | TO | BU310 | | | |
| | | | | | | | |
| 2SC493ye | S | N | TO | BU310 | | | |
| 2SC494 | S | N | TO | BU310 | | 2SC498 | |
| 2SC494bl | S | N | TO | BU310 | | | |
| 2SC494r | S | N | TO | BU310 | | | |
| 2SC494ye | S | N | TO | BU310 | | | |
| | | | | | | | |
| 2SC495 | S | N | TO | BD139 | | 2SC490 | |
| 2SC495or | S | N | TO | BD139-10 | | | |
| 2SC495r | S | N | TO | BD139-6 | | | |
| 2SC495ye | S | N | TO | BD139-10 | | | |
| 2SC496 | S | N | TO | BD135 | | 2SC491 | |
| | | | | | | | |
| 2SC496or | S | N | TO | BD136-10 | | | |
| 2SC496r | S | N | TO | BD135-6 | | | |
| 2SC496ye | S | N | TO | BD135-16 | | | |
| 2SC497 | S | N | TO | BSX47 | | 2SC493 | |
| 2SC497or | S | N | TO | BSX47-10 | | | |
| | | | | | | | |
| 2SC497r | S | N | TO | BSX47-6 | | | |
| 2SC497ye | S | N | TO | BSX47-10 | | | |
| 2SC498 | S | N | TO | BSX46 | | 2SC486 | |
| 2SC498or | S | N | TO | BSX46-10 | | | |
| 2SC498r | S | N | TO | BSX46-6 | | | |
| | | | | | | | |
| 2SC498ye | S | N | TO | BSX46-16 | | | |
| 2SC499 | S | N | TO | (BF457) | | 2SC500 | |
| 2SC500 | S | N | TO | (BF457) | | 2SC499 | |
| 2SC501 | S | N | TO | (BSY34) | | 2SC504 | |
| 2SC502 | S | N | TO | | | 2SC481 | |
| | | | | | | | |
| 2SC503 | S | N | TO | BSX46 | | 2SC504 | |
| 2SC503gn | S | N | TO | BSX46-16 | | | |
| 2SC503or | S | N | TO | BSX46-6 | | | |
| 2SC503ye | S | N | TO | BSX46-10 | | | |
| 2SC504 | S | N | TO | BSX45 | 2N1711 | 2SC503 | |
| | | | | | | | |
| 2SC504gn | S | N | TO | BSX45-16 | | | |
| 2SC504or | S | N | TO | BSX45-6 | | | |
| 2SC504ye | S | N | TO | BSX45-10 | | | |
| 2SC506 | S | N | TO | | | 2SC5019 | |
| 2SC508 | S | N | TO | | | 2SC50 | |
| | | | | | | | |
| 2SC509 | S | N | TO | (BC337-16) | | | |
| 2SC509or | S | N | TO | (BC337-16) | | | |
| 2SC509ye | S | N | TO | (BC337-16) | | | |
| 2SC510 | S | N | TO | (BSX47) | | 2SC13 | |
| 2SC510or | S | N | TO | (BSX47-10) | | | |
| | | | | | | | |
| 2SC510r | S | N | TO | (BSX47-6) | | | |
| 2SC511 | S | N | TO | BSX47 | | 2SC12 | |
| 2SC511or | S | N | TO | BSX47-10 | | | |
| 2SC511r | S | N | TO | BSX47-6 | | | |
| 2SC512 | S | N | TO | BSX46 | 2N699 | 2SC513 | |

| TYPE | M/S | POL | MANUFAC | EUROPEAN | | AMERICAN | | JAPANESE | USE |
|------|-----|-----|---------|----------|--|----------|--|----------|-----|
| 2SC512or | S | N | TO | BSX46-10 | | | | | |
| 2SC512r | S | N | TO | BSX46-6 | | | | | |
| 2SC513 | S | N | TO | BSX45 | | | | 2SC510 | |
| 2SC513or | S | N | TO | BSX45-10 | | | | | |
| 2SC513r | S | N | TO | BSX45-6 | | | | | |
| 2SC515 | S | N | TO | | | | | 2SC485 | |
| 2SC516 | S | N | TO | (BSX46-6) | | | | | |
| 2SC516A | S | N | TO | (BSX47-6) | | | | | |
| 2SC517 | S | N | TO | | | (2N3054) | | | |
| 2SC518 | S | N | TO | BU312 | | | | | |
| 2SC518A | S | N | TO | BU312 | | | | | |
| 2SC519 | S | N | TO | BUY55 | | | | | |
| 2SC519A | S | N | TO | BUY55 | | | | 2SC101 | |
| 2SC520 | S | N | TO | BUY55 | | | | 2SC101 | |
| 2SC520A | S | N | TO | BUY55 | | | | | |
| 2SC521 | S | N | TO | BUY55 | | | | 2SC101 | |
| 2SC521A | S | N | TO | BUY55 | | | | 2SC525 | |
| 2SC522 | S | N | TO | | | | | 2SC525 | |
| 2SC523 | S | N | TO | | | | | 2SC525 | |
| 2SC524 | S | N | TP | | | | | | |
| 2SC525 | S | N | TO | | | | | 2SC522 | |
| 2SC528 | S | N | HI | BC168A | | | | | |
| 2SC529 | S | N | HI | BC167A | | | | | |
| 2SC529A | S | N | HI | BC167A | | | | | |
| 2SC529B | S | N | HI | BC167A | | | | | |
| 2SC530 | S | N | HI | BC167 | | | | | |
| 2SC530A | S | N | HI | BC167A | | | | | |
| 2SC530B | S | N | HI | BC167A | | | | | |
| 2SC530C | S | N | HI | BC167B | | | | | |
| 2SC531 | S | N | HI | BC167A | | | | | |
| 2SC531A | S | N | HI | BC167A | | | | | |
| 2SC531B | S | N | HI | BC167A | | | | | |
| 2SC532 | S | N | HI | BC167A | | | | | |
| 2SC532A | S | N | HI | BC167A | | | | | |
| 2SC532B | S | N | HI | BC167A | | | | | |
| 2SC533 | S | N | HI | BC167A | | | | | |
| 2SC533A | S | N | HI | BC167A | | | | | |
| 2SC533B | S | N | HI | BC167A | | | | | |
| 2SC533C | S | N | HI | BC167A | | | | | |
| 2SC535 | S | N | HI, NS | (BF 255) | BF232 | | | | |
| 2SC535 | | | | BF234 | BF184 | | | | |
| 2SC538 | S | N | MA | BCY58VIII | BC108 | | | | |
| 2SC538 | | | | BC108A | BC108B | | | | |
| 2SC538A | S | N | MA | BCY59VIII | | | | | |
| 2SC539 | S | N | MA | BCY58VIII | BF254 | | | | |
| 2SC539 | | | | BF229 | BF194 | | | | |
| 2SC547 | S | N | TO | | | | | 2SC597 | |
| 2SC548 | S | N | TO | | | | | 2SC909 | |
| 2SC549 | S | N | TO | | | | | 2SC547 | |
| 2SC550 | S | N | TO | | | | | 2SC549 | |
| 2SC551 | S | N | TO | | | | | 2SC555 | |
| 2SC552 | S | N | TO | | | | | 2SC555 | |
| 2SC553 | S | N | TO | | | | | 2SC555 | |
| 2SC555 | S | N | TO | | | 2N497A | | | |
| 2SC556 | S | N | TO | | | 2N497A | | | |
| 2SC558 | S | N | TO | BUX17A | BU312 | | | 2SC508 | |
| 2SC560 | S | N | TO | BSX46-6 | | 2N2405 | | | |
| 2SC561 | S | N | FU | (BF198) | BC108 | 2N3391 | | 2SC458 | |
| 2SC561 | | | | BC183A | | | | | |
| 2SC562 | S | N | MA, NS | (BF198) | | | | | |
| 2SC563 | S | N | MA, NS | (BF198) | | | | | |
| 2SC567 | S | N | NI | (BFX89) | | | | | |
| 2SC568 | S | N | NI | (BFY90) | | | | | |
| 2SC580 | S | N | NI | (BCW77-16) | | | | | |
| 2SC586 | S | N | MA | BU312 | | | | | |
| 2SC587 | S | N | MA, SO, TO | BC107B | | | | | |
| 2SC587A | S | N | MA, SO, TO | BC107B | | | | | |
| 2SC588 | S | N | SO | (BSY58) | | | | | |
| 2SC590 | S | N | NI | BSX47-6 | | | | | |
| 2SC593 | S | N | MA | (BF198) | | | | | |
| 2SC594 | S | N | NI, TO | BSY34 | | | | | |
| 2SC594or | S | N | TO | BSY34 | | | | | |
| 2SC594r | S | N | TO | BSY34 | | | | | |
| 2SC594ve | S | N | TO | BSY34 | | | | | |
| 2SC595 | S | N | NI, TO | BSX49 | BSX48 | 2N2221 | | 2SC495 | |

| TYPE | M/S | POL | MANUFAC | EUROPEAN | | AMERICAN | JAPANESE | USE |
|------|-----|-----|---------|----------|--|----------|----------|-----|
| 2SC596 | S | N | NI | BSY34 | | | | |
| 2SC597 | S | N | FU, MA, TO | (BSX49) | | | | |
| 2SC601 | S | N | MA | (BSY63) | BFX59 | | | |
| 2SC605 | S | N | NI | BF173 | BF224 | | 2SC707 | |
| 2SC606 | S | N | NI | (BF199) | | | 2SC464 | |
| | | | | | | | | |
| 2SC611 | S | N | MA, NI, TO | (BFX89) | BFX59 | | | |
| 2SC612 | S | N | MA, NI, TO | (BFY90) | | | 2SC707 | |
| 2SC613 | S | N | NI | (BSY63) | | | | |
| 2SC614 | S | N | SN | (BSX45-6) | | | | |
| 2SC615 | S | N | SN | (BSX45-6) | | | | |
| | | | | | | | | |
| 2SC619 | S | N | MT | BC168A | | | | |
| 2SC620 | S | N | MT | BC167A | | | | |
| 2SC622 | S | N | MT | BC108B | BC183A | 2N3391 | | |
| 2SC631 | S | N | SO | (BC168A) | BC107B | | 2SC458 | |
| 2SC631 | | | | BC182B | | | | |
| | | | | | | | | |
| 2SC631A | S | N | SO | (BC168A) | | | | |
| 2SC632 | S | N | SO | (BC167A) | BC108C | | | |
| 2SC632 | | | | BC183C | | | | |
| 2SC632A | S | N | SO | (BC167A) | | | | |
| 2SC633 | S | N | SO | (BC168A) | BC107A | | | |
| | | | | | | | | |
| 2SC633 | | | | BC182A | | | | |
| 2SC633A | S | N | SO | (BC168A) | | | | |
| 2SC634 | S | N | SO | (BC167A) | BC107A | | | |
| 2SC634 | | | | BC182A | | | 2SC633 | |
| 2SC634A | S | N | SO | (BC167A) | | | | |
| | | | | | | | | |
| 2SC640 | S | N | NI | BC108C | BC183C | | | |
| 2SC641H | S | N | HI | (BSY63) | | | | |
| 2SC641K | S | N | HI | (BSY63) | | | | |
| 2SC642 | S | N | TO | (BUY79) | | | 2SC487 | |
| 2SC642A | S | N | TO | (BUY79) | | | | |
| | | | | | | | | |
| 2SC643 | S | N | TO | (BUY79) | | | 2SC558 | |
| 2SC643A | S | N | TO | (BUY79) | | | | |
| 2SC644 | S | N | MA | (BC168B) | BC167B | MPS6566 | | |
| 2SC644 | | | | BC182B | BC171B | | | |
| 2SC646 | S | N | MA | (BU310) | | | | |
| | | | | | | | | |
| 2SC647 | S | N | MA | | | | (2N3442) | |
| 2SC648H | S | N | HI | | | | | |
| 2SC649 | S | N | HI | (BC108B) | BC107A | 2N2921 | 2SC458 | |
| 2SC649 | | | | BC182A | | | | |
| 2SC650 | S | N | HI | (BC108B) | BC107B | | | |
| | | | | | | | | |
| 2SC650 | | | | BC182B | | | | |
| 2SC654 | S | N | NI | (BFX55) | | | | |
| 2SC657 | S | N | SO | (BF199) | BF173 | | 2SC464 | |
| 2SC657 | | | | BF224 | | | | |
| 2SC658 | S | N | MT | (BF199) | BF173 | | 2SC464 | |
| | | | | | | | | |
| 2SC658 | | | | BF224 | | | | |
| 2SC659 | S | N | MT | (BF199) | BF173 | | 2SC464 | |
| 2SC659 | | | | BF224 | | | | |
| 2SC660 | S | N | MT | (BF199) | | | | |
| 2SC661 | S | N | MT | (BF199) | | | | |
| | | | | | | | | |
| 2SC662 | S | N | MT | (BF199) | | | | |
| 2SC664 | S | N | HI | (BUY55) | | | | |
| 2SC665 | S | N | HI | (BUY55) | | | | |
| 2SC668 | S | N | SN, TS | (BF199) | | | | |
| 2SC674 | S | N | SN, TS | (BF199) | | | | |
| | | | | | | | | |
| 2SC680 | S | N | HI | (BUY56) | | | | |
| 2SC680A | S | N | HI | (BUY56) | | | | |
| 2SC681 | S | N | HI | (BUY56) | | | | |
| 2SC681A | S | N | HI | (BUY56) | | | | |
| 2SC682 | S | N | HI, NS | (BF199) | BF173 | | 2SC464 | |
| | | | | | | | | |
| 2SC682 | | | | BF224 | | | | |
| 2SC683 | S | N | HI | (BF199) | BF173 | | 2SC464 | |
| 2SC683 | | | | BF224 | | | | |
| 2SC685 | S | N | HI | (BUY78) | | | | |
| 2SC685A | S | N | HI | (BUY78) | | | | |
| | | | | | | | | |
| 2SC686 | S | N | NI | (BF457) | | | | |
| 2SC687 | S | N | MA | (BUY76) | | | | |
| 2SC689A | S | N | MA | BC107A | BC182A | 2N2921 | | |
| 2SC689H | S | N | HI | (BSY63) | BC107A | | 2SC458 | |
| 2SC693 | S | N | SN | (BC167B) | | | | |
| | | | | | | | | |
| 2SC694 | S | N | SN | (BC168B) | | | | |
| 2SC696 | S | N | MA | BSX46-6 | | | | |
| 2SC696A | S | N | MA | BSX47-6 | | | | |
| 2SC708 | S | N | HI | BSX46-6 | | | | |
| 2SC708A | S | N | HI | BSX47-6 | | | | |

| TYPE | M/S | POL | MANUFAC | EUROPEAN | | AMERICAN | | JAPANESE | USE |
|------|-----|-----|---------|----------|--|----------|--|----------|-----|
| 2SC708AH | A | N | HI | BSX47-6 | | | | | |
| 2SC708H | S | N | HI | BSX46-6 | | | | | |
| 2SC709 | S | N | MT | (BC108A) | | | | | |
| 2SC710 | S | N | MT | BC167A | | | | | |
| 2SC711 | S | N | MT | BC167B | | | | | |
| 2SC711A | S | N | MT | BC167B | | | | | |
| 2SC712 | S | N | MT | BC167A | BC168 | | | 2SC712A | |
| 2SC712 | | | | BF173 | | | | | |
| 2SC712A | S | N | MT | BC167A | BC168A | | | | |
| 2SC712A | | | | BC173 | | | | | |
| 2SC713 | S | N | MT | (BC167A) | | | | | |
| 2SC714 | S | N | MT | (BC167A) | | | | | |
| 2SC715 | S | N | SN, TS | (BC167A) | | | | | |
| 2SC716 | S | N | SN, TS | (BC168A) | | | | | |
| 2SC727 | S | N | FU | (BF457) | | | | | |
| 2SC728 | S | N | FU | (BF458) | | | | | |
| 2SC730 | S | N | MT | (BFX55) | | | | | |
| 2SC732 | S | N | TO | (BC413B) | | | | 2SC733 | |
| 2SC732 | S | N | TO | | | | | | |
| 2SC732bl | S | N | TO | (BC413C) | | | | | |
| 2SC732gn | S | N | TO | (BC413B) | | | | 2SC732 | |
| 2SC733 | S | N | TO | BC167 | | | | | |
| 2SC733bl | S | N | TO | BC167B | | | | | |
| 2SC733gn | S | N | TO | BC167B | | | | | |
| 2SC733or | S | N | TO | BC167A | | | | | |
| 2SC733ve | S | N | TO | BC167A | | | | | |
| 2SC734 | S | N | TO | (BC167) | BC107B | 2N3508 | | | |
| 2SC734 | | | | BC182B | | | | | |
| 2SC734gn | S | N | TO | (BC167B) | | | | | |
| 2SC734or | S | N | TO | (BC167A) | | | | | |
| 2SC734r | S | N | TO | (BC167A) | | | | | |
| 2SC734ve | S | N | TO | (BC167B) | | | | | |
| 2SC735 | S | N | TO | (BC337) | | | | 2SC649 | |
| 2SC735gn | S | N | TO | (BC337-25) | | | | | |
| 2SC735or | S | N | TO | (BC337-16) | | | | | |
| 2SC735r | S | N | TO | (BC337-16) | | | | | |
| 2SC735ve | S | N | TO | (BC337-16) | | | | | |
| 2SC736 | S | N | NI | (BUY55) | | | | | |
| 2SC738 | S | N | MT | (BF255) | | | | | |
| 2SC739 | S | N | MT | (BF255) | | | | | |
| 2SC740 | S | N | MT | (BF255) | | | | | |
| 2SC741 | S | N | MT | (BFX55) | | | | | |
| 2SC752 | S | N | TO | (BSY63) | | | | 2SC505 | |
| 2SC752or | S | N | TO | (BSY63) | | | | | |
| 2SC752r | S | N | TO | (BSY63) | | | | | |
| 2SC752ve | S | N | TO | (BSY63) | | | | | |
| 2SC752G | S | N | TO | (BSY63) | | | | | |
| 2SC761 | S | N | MA | (BFX59) | | | | | |
| 2SC762 | S | N | MA | (BFX59) | | | | | |
| 2SC763 | S | N | MT | (BF198) | | | | | |
| 2SC765 | S | N | MT | (BUY55) | | | | | |
| 2SC766 | S | N | MT | (BUY55) | | | | | |
| 2SC767 | S | N | MT | (BUY56) | | | | | |
| 2SC768 | S | N | MT | (BUY55) | | | | | |
| 2SC769 | S | N | MT | (BUY55) | | | | | |
| 2SC770 | S | N | MT | (BUY56) | | | | | |
| 2SC771 | S | N | MT | (BUY56) | | | | | |
| 2SC772 | S | N | SN | (BF198) | | | | | |
| 2SC773 | S | N | MT | BC167 | | | | | |
| 2SC779 | S | N | TO | (BUY77) | | 2N3584 | | | |
| 2SC779or | S | N | TO | (BUY77) | | | | | |
| 2SC779r | S | N | TO | (BUY77) | | | | | |
| 2SC779ve | S | N | TO | (BUY77) | | | | | |
| 2SC780 | S | N | TO | (BF457) | BSX21 | | | | |
| 2SC780or | S | N | TO | (BF457) | | | | | |
| 2SC780r | S | N | TO | (BF457) | | | | | |
| 2SC780ve | S | N | TO | (BF457) | | | | | |
| 2SC780A | S | N | TO | (BF457) | | | | | |
| 2SC780Aor | S | N | TO | (BF457) | | | | | |
| 2SC780Ar | S | N | TO | (BF457) | | | | | |
| 2SC782 | S | N | TO | (BUY77) | | | | 2SC783 | |
| 2SC782or | S | N | TO | (BUY77) | | | | | |
| 2SC782r | S | N | TO | (BUY77) | | | | | |
| 2SC782ve | S | N | TO | (BUY77) | | | | | |
| 2SC782A | S | N | TO | | | 2N3585 | | | |

| TYPE | M/S | POL | MANUFAC | EUROPEAN | | AMERICAN | | JAPANESE | USE |
|---|---|---|---|---|---|---|---|---|---|
| 2SC783 | S | N | TO | (BUY77) | | 2N3583 | | | |
| 2SC783or | S | N | TO | (BUY77) | | | | | |
| 2SC783r | S | N | TO | (BUY77) | | | | | |
| 2SC783ye | S | N | TO | (BUY77) | | | | | |
| 2SC784 | S | N | TO | (BF198) | | | | 2SC785 | |
| 2SC784br | S | N | TO | (BF198) | | | | | |
| 2SC784or | S | N | TO | (BF198) | | | | | |
| 2SC784r | S | N | TO | (BF198) | | | | | |
| 2SC784ye | S | N | TO | (BF198) | | | | | |
| 2SC785 | S | N | TO | (BF196) | | | | 2SC784 | |
| 2SC785br | S | N | TO | (BF198) | | | | | |
| 2SC785or | S | N | TO | (BF198) | | | | | |
| 2SC785r | S | N | TO | (BF198) | | | | | |
| 2SC785ye | S | N | TO | (BF198) | | | | | |
| 2SC786 | S | N | TO | (BF198) | | | | | |
| 2SC787 | S | N | TO | (BFX59) | | | | | |
| 2SC789 | S | N | TO | BD439 | | 2N6292 | | | |
| 2SC789or | S | N | TO | BD439 | | | | | |
| 2SC789r | S | N | TO | BD439 | | | | | |
| 2SC789ye | S | N | TO | BD439 | | | | | |
| 2SC790 | S | N | TO | BD437 | | 2N6290 | | | |
| 2SC790or | S | N | TO | BD437 | | | | | |
| 2SC790ye | S | N | TO | BD437 | | | | | |
| 2SC791 | S | N | TO | | | (2N3054) | | 2SC642 | |
| 2SC792 | S | N | TO | BUX16B | BUY79 | | | | |
| 2SC793 | S | N | TO | BUY55 | | | | 2SC556 | |
| 2SC793bl | S | N | TO | BUY55 | | | | | |
| 2SC793r | S | N | TO | BUY55 | | | | | |
| 2SC793ye | S | N | TO | BUY55 | | | | | |
| 2SC796 | S | N | FU | (BSX45-6) | | | | | |
| 2SC797 | S | N | FU | (BSX45-6) | | | | | |
| 2SC798 | S | N | FU | (BSX45-6) | | | | | |
| 2SC799 | S | N | NI | (BSX63-6) | | | | | |
| 2SC802 | S | N | FU | (BSX45-6) | | | | | |
| 2SC803 | S | N | FU | (BSX45-6) | | | | | |
| 2SC805 | S | N | SO | (BF457) | | | | | |
| 2SC806 | S | N | SO | (BUY76) | | | | | |
| 2SC806A | S | N | SO | (BUY76) | | | | | |
| 2SC807 | S | N | SO | (BUY58) | | | | | |
| 2SC807A | S | N | SO | (BUY58) | | | | | |
| 2SC815 | S | N | NI | BC167A | | | | | |
| 2SC816 | S | N | MT | BSX45-6 | | | | | |
| 2SC817 | S | N | MT | (BF457) | | | | | |
| 2SC818 | S | N | MT | (BF457) | | | | | |
| 2SC823 | S | N | NI | (BFX55) | | | | | |
| 2SC824 | S | N | NI | (BFX55) | | | | | |
| 2SC825 | S | N | FU | (BUY79) | | | | | |
| 2SC826 | S | N | FU | BSX46-10 | | | | | |
| 2SC827 | S | N | FU | BSX46-10 | | | | | |
| 2SC828 | S | N | MA | BC167A | BC167 | MPS6566 | | | |
| 2SC828 | S | N | | BC182A | BC171A | | | | |
| 2SC828 | | | | BC547 | | | | | |
| 2SC828A | S | N | MA | BC167A | | | | | |
| 2SC829 | S | N | MA | (BF254) | BF494 | | | | |
| 2SC830 | S | N | HI | | | (2N3054) | | | |
| 2SC833 | S | N | TO | (BUY79) | | | | | |
| 2SC838 | S | N | NI | (BC167A) | | | | | |
| 2SC839 | S | N | NI | (BC167A) | BC167 | MPS6566 | | 2SC458 | |
| 2SC839 | | | | BC182A | BC171A | | | | |
| 2SC840 | S | N | MA | (BUY55) | | | | | |
| 2SC840A | S | N | MA | (BUY55) | | | | | |
| 2SC841H | S | N | HI | (BSY63) | | | | | |
| 2SC847 | S | N | FU | BC108A | | | | | |
| 2SC848 | S | N | FU | BC108A | | | | | |
| 2SC849 | S | N | FU | BC338-16 | | | | | |
| 2SC850 | S | N | FU | BC337-16 | | | | | |
| 2SC854 | S | N | FU | (BFX55) | | | | | |
| 2SC855 | S | N | FU | (BFX55) | | | | | |
| 2SC856 | S | N | HI | (BF457) | BF178 | | | | |
| 2SC857H | S | N | HI | (BC177A) | | | | | |
| 2SC857K | S | N | HI | (BC177A) | | | | | |
| 2SC858 | S | N | SN, TS | (BC168B) | | | | | |
| 2SC859 | S | N | SN, TS | (BC168B) | | | | | |
| 2SC864 | S | N | TO | (BF198) | BF167 | MPS6566 | | 2SC458 | |
| 2SC864 | | | | BC182A | BC171A | | | | |

| TYPE | M/S | POL | MANUFAC | EUROPEAN | | AMERICAN | JAPANESE | USE |
|------|-----|-----|---------|----------|--|----------|----------|-----|
| 2SC867 | S | N | SO | (BUY78) | | | | |
| 2SC869 | S | N | MT | (BF457) | | | | |
| 2SC875 | S | N | SN, TS | (BSX47-10) | | | | |
| 2SC876 | S | N | SN, TS | (BSX46-10) | | | | |
| 2SC881 | S | N | NI | BC167A | | | | |
| | | | | | | | | |
| 2SC894 | S | N | SO | (BC108A) | BC108 | | | |
| 2SC894 | | | | BC182A | | | | |
| 2SC895 | S | N | SO | (BUY77) | | | | |
| 2SC896 | S | N | NI | BC107A | | | | |
| 2SC897 | S | N | HI | BUY55 | BDY90 | | | |
| | | | | | | | | |
| 2SC898 | S | N | HI | BUY55 | | | | |
| 2SC900 | S | N | NI | (BC167B) | | | | |
| 2SC901 | S | N | MA | (BUY77) | | | | |
| 2SC901A | S | N | MA | (BUY77) | | | | |
| 2SC907 | S | N | HI | (BSX48) | | | | |
| | | | | | | | | |
| 2SC907A | S | N | HI | (BSX49) | | | | |
| 2SC907AH | S | N | HI | (BSX49) | | | | |
| 2SC907H | S | N | HI | (BSX48) | | | | |
| 2SC912 | S | N | MT | BC108A | BC182A | | | |
| 2SC913 | S | N | NI | (BSX49) | | | | |
| | | | | | | | | |
| 2SC914 | S | N | NI | (BSX49) | | | | |
| 2SC915 | S | N | NI | (BSX49) | | | | |
| 2SC917 | S | N | HI | (BC197A) | BF177 | | | |
| 2SC918 | S | N | SO | (BF198) | | | | |
| 2SC923 | S | N | NI | (BC167B) | | | | |
| | | | | | | | | |
| 2SC926 | S | N | SO | (BF457) | | | | |
| 2SC927 | S | N | SN, TS | (BFX89) | | | | |
| 2SC928 | S | N | SN, TS | (BFX89) | | | | |
| 2SC929 | S | N | SN, TS | (BF198) | | | | |
| 2SC930 | S | N | SN, TS | (BF198) | | | | |
| | | | | | | | | |
| 2SC935 | S | N | HI | BUY78 | | | | |
| 2SC936 | S | N | HI | (BUY79) | | | | |
| 2SC937 | S | N | HI | (BUY79) | | | | |
| 2SC939 | S | N | NI | (BUY55) | | | | |
| 2SC940 | S | N | NI | (BUY55) | | | | |
| | | | | | | | | |
| 2SC941 | S | N | TO | (BC413) | BC168 | MPS6520 | | |
| 2SC941 | | | | BC168A | BC183A | | | |
| 2SC941 | | | | BC172A | | | | |
| 2SC941or | S | N | TO | (BC413B) | | | | |
| 2SC941r | S | N | TO | (BC413B) | | | | |
| | | | | | | | | |
| 2SC941ye | S | N | TO | (BC413B) | | | | |
| 2SC943 | S | N | NI | (BCY65EVII) | BC107 | | | |
| 2SC943 | | | | BC182A | | | | |
| 2SC944 | S | N | NI | (BC167A) | | | | |
| 2SC945 | S | N | NI | (BC167B) | | | | |
| | | | | | | | | |
| 2SC947 | S | N | MA | (BFX59) | | | | |
| 2SC948 | S | N | MA | (BFX59) | | | | |
| 2SC959 | S | N | NI | (BSX47-6) | | | | |
| 2SC960 | S | N | NI | (BSX47-10) | | | | |
| 2SC979 | S | N | TO | BCY65E | | | | |
| | | | | | | | | |
| 2SC979or | S | N | TO | (BCY65EVII) | | | | |
| 2SC979r | S | N | TO | BCY65EVII | | | | |
| 2SC979ye | S | N | TO | BCY65EVII | | | | |
| 2SC979A | S | N | TO | (BCY65E) | | | | |
| 2SC979Aor | S | N | TO | (BCY65EVII) | | | | |
| | | | | | | | | |
| 2SC979Ar | S | N | TO | (BCY65EVII) | | | | |
| 2SC980 | S | N | TO | (BC167) | | | | |
| 2SC980or | S | N | TO | (BC167A) | | | | |
| 2SC980r | S | N | TO | (BC167A) | | | | |
| 2SC980ye | S | N | TO | (BC167A) | | | | |
| | | | | | | | | |
| 2SC980A | S | N | TO | (BC167) | | | | |
| 2SC980Aor | S | N | TO | (BC167A) | | | | |
| 2SC980Ar | S | N | TO | (BC167A) | | | | |
| 2SC983 | S | N | TO | (BF458) | | | | |
| 2SC983or | S | N | TO | (BF458) | | | | |
| | | | | | | | | |
| 2SC983r | S | N | TO | (BF458) | | | | |
| 2SC983ye | S | N | TO | (BF458) | | | | |
| 2SC984 | S | N | HI | BC337-16 | | | | |
| 2SC988 | S | N | NI | (BFR15) | | | | |
| 2SC988A | S | N | NI | (BFR15) | | | | |
| | | | | | | | | |
| 2SC988B | S | N | NI | (BFR15) | | | | |
| 2SC989 | S | N | NI | (BFR34) | | | | |
| 2SC994 | S | N | TO | (BFX55) | | | | |
| 2SC995 | S | N | TO | (BF459) | | | | |
| 2SC996 | S | N | TO | (BF459) | | | | |

| TYPE | M/S | POL | MANUFAC | EUROPEAN | | AMERICAN | JAPANESE | USE |
|------|-----|-----|---------|----------|---|----------|----------|-----|
| 2SC997 | S | N | TO | (BF 199) | | | | |
| 2SC998 | S | N | TO | (BFX55) | | | | |
| 2SC999 | S | N | TO | (BUY79) | | | | |
| 2SC999A | S | N | TO | (BUY79) | | | | |
| 2SC1000 | S | N | TO | BC167B | | | | |
| | | | | | | | | |
| 2SC1000bl | S | N | TO | BC167B | | | | |
| 2SC1001 | S | N | TO | (BFX55) | | | | |
| 2SC1004 | S | N | TO | (BUY79) | | | | |
| 2SC1004A | S | N | TO | (BUY79) | | | | |
| 2SC1005 | S | N | SN, TO | (BUY79) | | | | |
| | | | | | | | | |
| 2SC1005A | S | N | SN, TO | (BUY79) | | | | |
| 2SC1006 | S | N | NI | BCY59X | | | | |
| 2SC1008 | S | N | NI | BSX46-16 | | | | |
| 2SC1010 | S | N | NI | BCY59X | BC110 | | | |
| 2SC1010 | S | N | NI | BC1771 | BC174 | | 2SC856 | |
| | | | | | | | | |
| 2SC1012 | S | N | MA | (BF458) | | | | |
| 2SC1012A | S | N | MA | (BF458) | | | | |
| 2SC1013 | S | N | MT | (BD135) | | | | |
| 2SC1014 | S | N | MT | (BD135) | | | | |
| 2SC1017 | S | N | MT | (BD139) | | | | |
| | | | | | | | | |
| 2SC1018 | S | N | MT | (BD139) | | | | |
| 2SC1024 | S | N | SN, TS | | | 2N3054 | | |
| 2SC1025 | S | N | SN, TS | | | (2N3054) | | |
| 2SC1030 | S | N | HI | BUY55 | | | | |
| 2SC1031 | S | N | NI, FU | (BUY79) | | | | |
| | | | | | | | | |
| 2SC1033 | S | N | MA | (BF458) | | | | |
| 2SC1033A | S | N | MA | (BF458) | | | | |
| 2SC1034 | S | N | SO | (BUY79) | | | | |
| 2SC1035 | S | N | SN, TS | (BFX89) | | | | |
| 2SC1036 | S | N | SN, TS | (BFX89) | | | | |
| | | | | | | | | |
| 2SC1047 | S | N | MA | (BF254) | | | | |
| 2SC1050 | S | N | SN, TS | BUY79 | | | | |
| 2SC1051 | S | N | SN, TS | BUY55 | | | | |
| 2SC1056 | S | N | SO | (BF459) | | | | |
| 2SC1059 | S | N | HI | (BF459) | | | | |
| | | | | | | | | |
| 2SC1060 | S | N | HI | (BD439) | | | | |
| 2SC1061 | S | N | HI | (BD439) | | | | |
| 2SC1061K | S | N | HI | (BD439) | | | | |
| 2SC1062 | S | N | NI | (BF458) | | | | |
| 2SC1071 | S | N | NI | (BSX49) | | | | |
| | | | | | | | | |
| 2SC1072 | S | N | NI | (BSX49) | | | | |
| 2SC1072A | S | N | NI | (BSX49) | | | | |
| 2SC1079 | S | N | SN, TO | | | 2N3442 | | |
| 2SC1079r | S | N | TO | | | 2N3442 | | |
| 2SC1079ve | S | N | TO | | | 2N3442 | | |
| | | | | | | | | |
| 2SC1080 | S | N | SN, TO | | | 2N4347 | | |
| 2SC1080r | S | N | TO | | | 2N4347 | | |
| 2SC1080ve | S | N | TO | | | 2N4347 | | |
| 2SC1088 | S | N | MT | (BF459) | | | | |
| 2SC1089 | S | N | MT | (BF459) | | | | |
| | | | | | | | | |
| 2SC1096 | S | N | NI | (BD135) | | | | |
| 2SC1098 | S | N | NI | (BD139) | | | | |
| 2SC1101 | S | N | NI | (BUY79) | | | | |
| 2SC1104 | S | N | NI | (BUY79) | | | | |
| 2SC1106 | S | N | NI | (BUY77) | | | | |
| | | | | | | | | |
| 2SC1111 | S | N | SA | BUY55 | | | | |
| 2SC1112 | S | N | SA | BUY55 | | | | |
| 2SC1114 | S | N | SA | BUY77 | | | | |
| 2SC1115 | S | N | SA | BUY55 | | | | |
| 2SC1116 | S | N | SA | BUY56 | | | | |
| | | | | | | | | |
| 2SC1117 | S | N | HI | (BFX59) | | | | |
| 2SC1123 | S | N | SO | (BF199) | | | | |
| 2SC1124 | S | N | SO | (BF458) | | | | |
| 2SC1127 | S | N | SO | (BF458) | | | | |
| 2SC1129 | S | N | SO | (BF198) | | | | |
| | | | | | | | | |
| 2SC1160 | S | N | NL | (BUY56) | | | | |
| 2SC1161 | S | N | NI | (BUY56) | | | | |
| 2SC1162 | S | N | HI | (BD135) | | | | |
| 2SC1165 | S | N | TO | (BFX55) | | | | |
| 2SC1166 | S | N | TO | (BC167) | | | | |
| | | | | | | | | |
| 2SC1166gn | S | N | TO | (BC167B) | | | | |
| 2SC1166or | S | N | TO | (BC167A) | | | | |
| 2SC1166r | S | N | TO | (BC167A) | | | | |
| 2SC1166ve | S | N | TO | (BC167A) | | | | |
| 2SC1167 | S | N | TO | (BUY79) | | | | |

| TYPE | M/S | POL | MANUFAC | EUROPEAN | | AMERICAN | | JAPANESE | USE |
|------|-----|-----|---------|----------|---|----------|---|----------|-----|
| 2SC1168 | S | N | TO | (BF459) | | | | | |
| 2SC1170 | S | N | TO | (BUY79) | | | | | |
| 2SC1170B | S | B | TO | (BUY79) | | | | | |
| 2SC1171 | S | N | TO | (BUY79) | | | | | |
| 2SC1172 | S | N | TO | (BUY79) | | | | | |
| 2SC1172A | S | N | TO | (BUY79) | | | | | |
| 2SC1173 | S | N | TO | (BD437) | | 2N6288 | | | |
| 2SC1173gn | S | N | TO | (BD437) | | | | | |
| 2SC1173or | S | N | TO | (BD437) | | | | | |
| 2SC1173r | S | N | TO | (BD437) | | | | | |
| 2SC1173ye | S | N | TO | (BD437) | | | | | |
| 2SC1174 | S | N | HI | (BUY79) | | | | | |
| 2SC1175 | S | N | SN, TS | (BC167A) | | | | | |
| 2SC1180 | S | N | SN, TS | (BFX59) | | | | | |
| 2SC1187 | S | N | NI | (BF198) | | | | | |
| 2SC1195 | S | N | TO | BUX16 | (BUY72) | | | | |
| 2SC1204 | S | N | HI | (BF240) | | | | | |
| 2SC1205 | S | N | HI | (BF241) | | | | | |
| 2SC1212 | S | N | HI | (BD137) | | | | | |
| 2SC1212A | S | N | HI | (BD139) | | | | | |
| 2SC1213 | S | N | HI | (BC337-16) | | | | | |
| 2SC1213A | S | N | HI | (BC337-16) | | | | | |
| 2SC1213K | S | N | HI | (BC337-16) | | | | | |
| 2SC1214 | S | N | HI | (BC337-16) | | | | | |
| 2SC1215 | S | N | MA | (BFX59) | | | | | |
| 2SC1222 | S | N | NI | BC167B | | | | | |
| 2SC1226 | S | N | MA | (BD135) | | | | | |
| 2SC1226A | S | N | MA | (BD135) | | | | | |
| 2SC1235 | S | N | SN, TS | (BF459) | | | | | |
| 2SC1268 | S | N | NI | (BFR14A) | | | | | |
| 2SC1269 | S | N | NI | (BFR14A) | | | | | |
| 2SC1270 | S | N | NI | (BFR14A) | | | | | |
| 2SC1271 | S | N | NI | (BFR14A) | | | | | |
| 2SC1272 | S | N | NI | (BFR14A) | | | | | |
| 2SC1275 | S | N | NI | (BFY90) | | | | | |
| 2SC1279 | S | N | NI | (BF458) | | | | | |
| 2SC1285 | S | N | SN | (BC167A) | | | | | |
| 2SC1293 | S | N | SN, TS | (BF198) | | | | | |
| 2SC1295 | S | N | SN, TS | (BUY79) | | | | | |
| 2SC1296 | S | N | SN | (BUY79) | | | | | |
| 2SC1303 | S | N | MA | BSX45-6 | | | | | |
| 2SC1306 | S | N | NI | (BD139) | | | | | |
| 2SC1308 | S | N | SN, TS | (BUY79) | | | | | |
| 2SC1316 | S | N | SO | (BUY79) | | | | | |
| 2SC1317 | S | N | MA | (BC338-16) | | | | | |
| 2SC1318 | S | N | MA | (BC337-16) | | | | | |
| 2SC1325 | S | N | NI | (BUY79) | | | | | |
| 2SC1335 | S | N | HI | (BF240) | | | | | |
| 2SC1336 | S | N | NI | (BFR14A) | | | | | |
| 2SC1343 | S | N | HI | BUY55 | | | | | |
| 2SC1343H | S | N | HI | BUY55 | | | | | |
| 2SC1344 | S | N | HI | (BC237A) | | | | | |
| 2SC1345 | S | N | HI | (BC237A) | | | | | |
| 2SC1358 | S | N | NI | (BUY79) | | | | | |
| 2SC1359 | S | N | MA | (BF254) | | | | | |
| 2SC1367 | S | N | HI | (BUY79) | | | | | |
| 2SC1367A | S | N | HI | (BUY79) | | | | | |
| 2SC1368 | S | N | HI | (BD135) | | | | | |
| 2SC1380 | S | N | TO | BC414B | | | | | |
| 2SC1380bl | S | N | TO | BC414C | | | | | |
| 2SC1380gn | S | N | TO | BC414B | | | | | |
| 2SC1380A | S | N | TO | BC414B | | | | | |
| 2SC1380Abl | S | N | TO | BC414C | | | | | |
| 2SC1380Agn | S | N | TO | BC414B | | | | | |
| 2SC1381 | S | N | TO | (BF457) | | | | | |
| 2SC1382 | S | N | TO | BD139 | | | | | |
| 2SC1382or | S | N | TO | BD139-10 | | | | | |
| 2SC1382ye | S | N | TO | BD139-10 | | | | | |
| 2SC1385H | S | N | HI | (BSY34) | | | | | |
| 2SC1386H | S | N | HI | (BSY34) | | | | | |
| 2SC1398 | S | N | MA | (BD441) | | | | | |
| 2SC1402 | S | N | SA | (BUY55) | | | | | |
| 2SC1403 | S | N | SA | (BUY55) | | | | | |
| 2SC1413 | S | N | HI | (BUY79) | | | | | |
| 2SC1413A | S | N | HI | (BUY79) | | | | | |

| TYPE | M/S | POL | MANUFAC | EUROPEAN | | AMERICAN | | JAPANESE | USE |
|---|---|---|---|---|---|---|---|---|---|
| 2SC1416 | S | N | TO | (BC107B) | | | | | |
| 2SC1416A | S | N | TO | (BC107B) | | | | | |
| 2SC1418 | S | N | HI | (BD439) | | | | | |
| 2SC1419 | S | N | HI | (BD439) | | | | | |
| 2SC1424 | SI | N | NI | (BFY90) | | | | | |
| 2SC1433 | S | N | TO | BUY79 | | | | | |
| 2SC1434 | S | N | TO | BUY76 | | | | | |
| 2SC1436 | S | N | SA | (BUY72) | | | | | |
| 2SC1440 | S | N | SA | BUY56 | | | | | |
| 2SC1441 | S | N | SA | BUY72 | | | | | |
| 2SC1444 | S | N | SA | (BUY55) | | | | | |
| 2SC1445 | S | N | SA | (BUY55) | | | | | |
| 2SC1447 | S | N | TO | (BF459) | | | | | |
| 2SC1448A | S | N | TO | | | | | | |
| 2SC1449 | S | N | NI | (BD135) | | TA8863 | | | |
| 2SC1450 | S | N | MA | (BUY77) | | | | | |
| 2SC1453 | S | N | TO | (BCY65EVII) | | | | | |
| 2SC1454 | S | N | SA | BUY77 | | | | | |
| 2SC1456 | S | N | NI | (BF459) | | | | | |
| 2SC1458 | S | N | NI | (BFR14A) | | | | | |
| 2SC1466 | S | N | SH | (BUY79) | | | | | |
| 2SC1467 | S | N | SH | (BUY79) | | | | | |
| 2SC1468 | S | N | SH | (BUY76) | | | | | |
| 2SC1469 | S | N | SH | (BUY76) | | | | | |
| 2SC1504 | S | N | SA | (BUY78) | | | | | |
| 2SC1505 | S | N | NI | (BF459) | | | | | |
| 2SC1506 | S | N | NI | BF459 | | | | | |
| 2SC1507 | S | N | NI | (BF459) | | | | | |
| 2SC1514 | S | N | HI | (BF459) | | | | | |
| 2SC1515K | S | N | HI | (BF458) | | | | | |
| 2SC1516K | S | N | HI | (BD135) | | | | | |
| 2SC1517AK | A | N | HI | (BD139) | | | | | |
| 2SC1520 | S | N | NI | (BF458) | | | | | |
| 2SC1521 | S | N | NI | (BF458) | | | | | |
| 2SC1576 | S | N | TO | BUX16 | | | | | |
| 2SD11 | G | N | NI | (AC127) | | | | | |
| 2SD15 | S | N | HI, SA | | | | | | |
| 2SD16 | S | N | HI, SA | | | (2N3055) | | | |
| 2SD17 | S | N | SA | | | (2N3055) | | | |
| 2SD18 | S | N | SA | (BUY56) | | (2N3442) | | | |
| 2SD19 | G | N | NI | (AC127) | | | | | |
| 2SD20 | G | N | NI | (AC127) | | | | | |
| 2SD21 | G | N | NI | (AC127) | | | | | |
| 2SD22 | G | N | NI | (AC127) | | | | | |
| 2SD23 | G | N | NI | (AC127) | | | | | |
| 2SD24 | S | N | SN, TS | (BF459) | | | | | |
| 2SD25 | G | N | NI | (AC127) | | | | | |
| 2SD28 | S | N | SO | | | (2N3054) | | | |
| 2SD29 | S | N | SO | | | (2N3054) | | | |
| 2SD30 | G | N | TS | AC127 | AC179 | 2N2430 | | 2SD96 | |
| 2SD31 | G | N | MA | AC127 | AC179 | 2N2430 | | 2SD96 | |
| 2SD32 | G | N | MA | AC127 | AC179 | 2N2430 | | 2SD96 | |
| 2SD33 | G | N | FU | AC127 | AC179 | 2N2430 | | 2SD96 | |
| 2SD34 | G | N | FU | AC127 | AC179 | 2N2430 | | 2SD96 | |
| 2SD35 | G | N | | AC127 | AC179 | 2N2430 | | 2SD96 | |
| 2SD36 | G | N | | AC127 | AC179 | 2N2430 | | 2SD96 | |
| 2SD37 | G | N | FU | AC127 | AC179 | 2N2430 | | 2SD96 | |
| 2SD38 | G | N | FU | AC127 | AC179 | 2N2430 | | 2SD96 | |
| 2SD41 | S | N | TO | (BUY57) | | | | | |
| 2SD43 | G | N | TO | (AC127) | | | | | |
| 2SD43A | G | N | TO | AC127 | AC179 | 2N2430 | | 2SD96 | |
| 2SD44 | G | N | TO | AC127 | AC179 | 2N2430 | | 2SD96 | |
| 2SD45 | S | N | SO | BU110 | | | | | |
| 2SD46 | S | N | SO | BD130 | AM291 | 2N3055 | | | |
| 2SD47 | S | N | HI, SO, CE | (BU114) | BD130 | 2N3059 | | | |
| 2SD47 | | N | | BD109 | AM291 | | | 2SD46 | |
| 2SD48 | S | N | FU | BUY46 | | (2N3054) | | | |
| 2SD49 | S | N | SO | BUY46 | | (2N3054) | | | |
| 2SD50 | S | N | FU | BD130 | AM291 | 2N3055 | | | |
| 2SD51 | S | N | TO, SO | BD130 | AM291 | 2N3055 | | | |
| 2SD51A | S | N | SO, TO | | | (2N3055) | | | |
| 2SD53 | S | N | TO, FU | | | | | | |
| 2SD54 | S | N | FU | BD130 | AM291 | 2N3055 | | | |
| 2SD55 | S | N | TO | BD130 | AM291 | 2N3055 | | | |
| 2SD55A | S | N | TO | (BUY57) | | | | | |
| | | | | (BUY58) | | | | | |

| TYPE | M/S | POL | MANUFAC | EUROPEAN | | AMERICAN | | JAPANESE | USE |
|------|-----|-----|---------|----------|--|----------|--|----------|-----|
| 2SD56 | S | N | SO | BU110 | | (2N3054) | | | |
| 2SD57 | S | N | MT | BUY43 | | (2N3054) | | | |
| 2SD58 | S | N | MT | BUY43 | | 2N3055 | | | |
| 2SD59 | S | N | MT, CE | BD130 | AM291 | 2N3055 | | | |
| 2SD60 | S | N | MT | BD130 | AM291 | 2N3055 | | | |
| 2SD61 | G | N | SO | AC127 | AC179 | 2N2430 | 2N647 | 2SD96 | |
| 2SD61 | | | | ASY28 | | | | 2T682 | |
| 2SD62 | G | N | SO | AC127 | AC179 | 2N2430 | 2N647 | 2SD96 | |
| 2SD62 | | | | ASY28 | | | | 2T681 | |
| 2SD63 | G | N | SO | AC127 | AC179 | 2N2430 | 2N647 | 2SD96 | |
| 2SD63 | | | | | | | | 2T69 | |
| 2SD64 | G | N | SO | AC127 | AC179 | 2N2430 | 2N647 | 2SD96 | |
| 2SD64 | | | | | | | | 2T648 | |
| 2SD65 | G | N | SO | AC127 | AC179 | 2N2430 | 2N647 | 2SD96 | |
| 2SD65 | | | | | | | | 2T65R | |
| 2SD66 | G | N | SO | AC127 | AC179 | 2N2430 | 2N647 | 2SD96 | |
| 2SD67 | S | N | SN, TS | BU114 | | | | | |
| 2SD68 | S | N | SN, HI, TS | BU114 | | | | | |
| 2SD69 | S | N | SO | (BUY55) | | | | | |
| 2SD70 | S | N | NI | (BDY12-10) | BD109 | 2N3054 | | | |
| 2SD70 | | | | BDY34 | BD124 | | | | |
| 2SD70 | | | | BD107 | | | | | |
| 2SD71 | S | N | NI | (BDY13-10) | BUY46 | | | | |
| 2SD72 | G | N | SN. TS | (AC127) | AM291 | | | | |
| 2SD73 | S | N | NI | BD130 | | 2N3055 | | | |
| 2SD74 | S | N | NI | BU110 | | 2N3442 | | | |
| 2SD75 | G | N | HI | AC127 | AC176 | 2N2430 | | | |
| 2SD75 | | | | AC186 | AC187K | | | | |
| 2SD75A | G | N | HI | (AC127) | | | | | |
| 2SD75AH | G | N | HI | (AC127) | | | | | |
| 2SD75H | G | N | HI | (AC127) | | | | | |
| 2SD77 | G | N | HI | AC127 | ASY29 | 2N2430 | | | |
| 2SD77A | G | N | HI | (AC127) | | | | | |
| 2SD77AH | G | N | HI | (AC127) | | | | | |
| 2SD77H | C | N | HI | (AC127) | | | | | |
| 2SD78 | S | N | NI | BSX63 | BSX63-10 | | | | |
| 2SD79 | S | N | NI | BUY46 | | (2N3054) | | | |
| 2SU80 | S | N | SA | (BU114) | BD130 | 2N3055 | | | |
| 2SD80 | | | | AM291 | | | | | |
| 2SD81 | S | N | SA | (BU114) | BD130 | 2N3055 | | | |
| 2SD81 | | | | AM291 | | | | | |
| 2SD82 | S | N | SA | (BU114) | BD130 | 2N3055 | | | |
| 2SD82 | | | | AM291 | | | | | |
| 2SD83 | S | N | SA | (BU114) | BD130 | 2N3055 | | | |
| 2SD83 | | | | AM291 | | | | | |
| 2SD84 | S | N | SA | (BU114) | BU110 | | | | |
| 2SD88 | S | N | SO | BUY77 | | | | | |
| 2SD88A | A | N | SO | BUY74 | | | | | |
| 2SD90 | S | N | SA | | | (2N3054) | | | |
| 2SD91 | S | N | SA | | | (2N3054) | | | |
| 2SD92 | S | N | SA | | | (2N3054) | | | |
| 2SD96 | G | N | HI | AC187K | AC175K | | | | |
| 2SD96 | | | | (AC127) | | | | | |
| 2SD102 | S | N | TO | BU110 | | 2N6261 | (2N3054) | | |
| 2SD102r | S | N | TO | | | (2N3054) | | | |
| 2SD102t | S | N | TO | | | (2N3054) | | | |
| 2SD102ve | S | N | TO | | | (2N3054) | | | |
| 2SD103 | S | N | TO | | | 2N3054 | | | |
| 2SD103or | S | N | TO | | | 2N3054 | | | |
| 2SD103r | S | N | TO | | | 2N3054 | | | |
| 2SD103ve | S | N | TO | | | (2N3054) | | | |
| 2SD104 | G | N | TO. | AC127 | AC179 | 2N2430 | | 2SD96 | |
| 2SD105 | G | N | TO. | AC127 | AC179 | 2N2430 | | 2SD96 | |
| 2SD110 | S | N | TO | BUY55 | | | | 2SD111 | |
| 2SD110or | S | N | TO | BUY55 | | | | | |
| 2SD110r | S | N | TO | BUY55 | | | | | |
| 2SD110ve | S | N | TO | BUY55 | | | | | |
| 2SD111 | S | N | TO | BUY55 | | | | 2SD113 | |
| 2SD111or | S | N | TO | BUY55 | | | | | |
| 2SD111r | S | N | TO | BUY55 | | | | | |
| 2SD111ve | S | N | TO | BUY55 | | | | 2SD111 | |
| 2SD113 | S | N | TO | (BUY57) | | | | | |
| 2SD113or | S | N | TO | (BUY57) | | | | | |
| 2SD113ve | S | N | TO | (BUY57) | | | | 2SD113 | |
| 2SD114 | S | N | TO | (BUY57) | | | | | |

| TYPE | M/S | POL | MANUFAC | EUROPEAN | | AMERICAN | | JAPANESE | USE |
|------|-----|-----|---------|----------|--|----------|--|----------|-----|
| 2SD114or | S | N | TO | (BUY57) | | | | | |
| 2SD114r | S | N | TO | (BUY57) | | | | | |
| 2SD114ye | S | N | TO | (BUY57) | | | | | |
| 2SD118 | S | N | TO | BUY55 | BU110 | | | | |
| 2SD118bl | S | N | TO | BUY55 | | | | | |
| | | | | | | | | | |
| 2SD118r | S | N | TO | BUY55 | | | | | |
| 2SD118ye | S | N | TO | BUY55 | | | | | |
| 2SD119 | S | N | TO | BUY55 | BU110 | | | | |
| 2SD119bl | S | N | TO | BUY55 | | | | | |
| 2SD119r | S | N | TO | BUY55 | | | | | |
| | | | | | | | | | |
| 2SD119ye | S | N | TO | BUY55 | | | | | |
| 2SD120 | S | N | HI | (BSX45-6) | | | | | |
| 2SD120H | S | N | HI | (BSX45-6) | | | | | |
| 2SD121 | S | N | HI | (BSX46-6) | | | | | |
| 2SD121H | S | N | HI | (BSX46-6) | | | | | |
| | | | | | | | | | |
| 2SD122 | S | N | HI | | | 2N3054 | | | |
| 2SD123 | S | N | HI | | | 2N3054 | | | |
| 2SD124 | S | N | HI | BD130 | AM291 | 2N3055 | MJD3055 | | |
| 2SD124A | S | N | HI | BD130 | AM291 | 2N3055 | | | |
| 2SD125AH | S | N | HI | | | (2N4347) | (2N3055) | | |
| | | | | | | | | | |
| 2SD124H | S | N | HI | BD130 | | | | | |
| 2SD125 | S | N | HI | BD130 | AM291 | 2N3055 | MJD3055 | | |
| 2SD125A | S | N | HI | BD130 | AM291 | 2N3055 | | | |
| 2SD125H | S | N | HI | BD130 | | | | | |
| 2SD126H | S | N | HI | BU110 | | (2N3442) | | | |
| | | | | | | | | | |
| 2SD128A | G | N | SO | (AC127) | | | | | |
| 2SD129 | S | N | TO | | | 2N6372 | (2N3054) | | |
| 2SD129bl | S | N | TO | | | (2N3054) | | | |
| 2SD129r | S | N | TO | | | (2N3054) | | | |
| 2SD129ye | S | N | TO | | | (2N3054) | | | |
| | | | | | | | | | |
| 2SD130 | S | N | TO | | | 2N3054 | | | |
| 2SD130bl | S | N | TO | | | 2N3054 | | | |
| 2SD130r | S | N | TO | | | 2N3054 | | | |
| 2SD130ye | S | N | TO | | | 2N3054 | | | |
| 2SD132 | S | N | NI | (BUY57) | | | | | |
| | | | | | | | | | |
| 2SD141 | S | N | NI, HI | (BDY12-16) | BUY43 | | | | |
| 2SD142 | S | N | NI | (BDY12-16) | BUY43 | | | | |
| 2SD143 | S | N | NI | (BDY13-16) | BUY46 | | | | |
| 2SD144 | S | N | NI | (BDY13-16) | BD109 | 2N3054 | | 2SC830 | |
| 2SD144 | | | | BDY34 | BD124 | | | | |
| | | | | | | | | | |
| 2SD144 | | | | BD107 | | | | | |
| 2SD146 | S | N | FU | BD109 | BDY34 | 2N3054 | | 2SC830 | |
| 2SD146 | | | | BD124 | BD107 | | | | |
| 2SD147 | S | N | FU, HI, CE | BDY13 | | 2N3054 | | | |
| 2SD150 | S | N | NI | | | 2N3054 | | | |
| | | | | | | | | | |
| 2SD151 | S | N | NI | BD130 | AM291 | 2N3055 | | | |
| 2SD152 | S | N | NI | BY110 | | | | | |
| 2SD154 | S | N | NI | (BDY13-10) | BDY13 | | | | |
| 2SD155 | S | N | NI | (BDY13-10) | | | | | |
| 2SD156 | S | N | FU | (BUY77) | | | | | |
| | | | | | | | | | |
| 2SD157 | S | N | FU | (BUY79) | | | | | |
| 2SD158 | S | N | FU | (BUY77) | | | | | |
| 2SD159 | S | N | FU | (BUY79) | | | | | |
| 2SD162 | G | N | FU | (AC127) | | | | | |
| 2SD163 | S | N | SA | | | 2N3055 | | | |
| | | | | | | | | | |
| 2SD164 | S | N | SA | | | 2N3055 | | | |
| 2SD165 | S | N | SA | | | 2N3442 | | | |
| 2SD166 | S | N | SA | (BUY56) | | | | | |
| 2SD167 | G | N | FU | (AC127) | | | | | |
| 2SD170 | G | N | HI | (AC127) | | | | | |
| | | | | | | | | | |
| 2SD170A | G | N | HI | AC127 | | | | | |
| 2SD171 | S | N | SO | (BUY77) | | | | | |
| 2SD172 | S | N | FU | BD130 | AM291 | 2N3055 | | | |
| 2SD173 | S | N | FU | BD130 | AM291 | 2N3055 | | | |
| 2SD174 | S | N | FU, HI, CE | BUY46 | | 2N3055 | | | |
| | | | | | | | | | |
| 2SD175 | S | N | FU, CE | BD130 | AM291 | 2N3055 | | | |
| 2SD176 | S | N | FU | BD130 | AM291 | 2N3055 | | | |
| 2SD177 | S | N | FU | | | 2N4347 | | | |
| 2SD178 | G | N | MA | (AC127) | | | | | |
| 2SD178A | G | N | MA | (AC127) | | | | | |
| | | | | | | | | | |
| 2SD180 | S | N | NI | BD130 | AM291 | 2N3055 | | | |
| 2SD182 | S | N | FU | (BSX45-6) | BUY43 | | | | |
| 2SD183 | S | N | FU | (BSX46-6) | BUY46 | | | | |
| 2SD184 | S | N | FU | (BSX45-6) | BUY46 | | | | |
| 2SD185 | S | N | FU | (BSX46-6) | BUY46 | | | | |

| TYPE | M/S | POL | MANUFAC | EUROPEAN | | AMERICAN | JAPANESE | USE |
|---|---|---|---|---|---|---|---|---|
| 2SD186 | G | N | TS | AC127 | AC179 | 2N2430 | | |
| 2SD187 | G | N | TS | AC127 | AC179 | 2N2430 | | |
| 2SD188 | S | N | NI | (BU114) | | | | |
| 2SD189 | S | N | MA | BUY55 | BU110 | | | |
| 2SD189A | S | N | MA, HI | BUY55 | BU110 | | | |
| 2SD191 | G | N | TO | (AC127) | | | | |
| 2SD192 | G | N | TO | (AC127) | | | | |
| 2SD193 | G | N | TO | (AC127) | | | | |
| 2SD194 | G | N | TO | (AC127) | | | | |
| 2SD195 | G | N | FU, CE | AC127 | AC179 | 2N2430 | | |
| 2SD196 | S | N | FU | BUY55IV | | | | |
| 2SD197 | S | N | FU | BUY55IV | | | | |
| 2SD198 | S | N | MA | (BUY78) | BU111 | | | |
| 2SD199 | S | N | MA | (BUY79) | | | | |
| 2SD200 | S | N | SA, MA | (BUY79) | | | | |
| 2SD201 | S | N | SA | (BU114) | | | | |
| 2SD202 | S | N | SA | (BU114) | | | | |
| 2SD203 | S | N | SA | (BU114) | | | | |
| 2SD204 | S | N | NI | (BSX45) | | | | |
| 2SD211 | S | N | SA | (BUY55) | | | | |
| 2SD212 | S | N | SA | (BUY55) | | | | |
| 2SD213 | S | N | SA | (BUY55) | | | | |
| 2SD214 | S | N | SA | (BUY55) | | | | |
| 2SD217 | S | N | HI, NI | | | 2N3442 | | |
| 2SD218 | S | N | NI | | | 2N4347 | | |
| 2SD219 | S | N | SA | (BSX45-6) | | | | |
| 2SD220 | S | N | SA | (BSX46-6) | | | | |
| 2SD221 | S | N | SA | (BSX47-6) | | | | |
| 2SD222 | S | N | SA | (BU114) | | | | |
| 2SD223 | S | N | SA | (BU114) | | | | |
| 2SD224 | S | A | SA | (BU114) | | | | |
| 2SD226 | S | N | MA | BUY43 | | (2N3054) | | |
| 2SD226A | S | N | MA | BUY46 | | (2N3054) | | |
| 2SD226B | S | N | MA | | | (2N3054) | | |
| 2SD227 | S | N | NI | (BC168A) | | | | |
| 2SD234 | S | N | TO | (BD439) | BUY46 | RCA3054 | | |
| 2SD234or | S | N | TO | (BD439) | | | | |
| 2SD234r | S | N | TO | (BD439) | | | | |
| 2SD234ye | S | N | TO | (BD439) | | | | |
| 2SD235 | S | N | TO | (BD437) | BUY43 | RCA3054 | | |
| 2SD235or | S | N | TO | (BD437) | | | | |
| 2SD235r | S | N | TO | (BD437) | | | | |
| 2SD235ye | S | N | TO | (BD437) | | | | |
| 2SD236 | S | N | SA | | | (2N3054) | | |
| 2SD237 | S | N | SA | | | (2N3054) | | |
| 2SD238 | S | N | SA | | | (2N3054) | | |
| 2SD254 | S | N | NI | | | 2N3054 | | |
| 2SD255 | S | N | NI | | | 2N3054 | | |
| 2SD256 | S | N | SA | (BU114) | | | | |
| 2SD257 | S | N | SA | (BU114) | | | | |
| 2SD258 | S | N | SA | (BU114) | | | | |
| 2SD259 | S | N | SA | (BU114) | | | | |
| 2SD287 | S | N | NI | BUY58 | | | | |
| 2SD288 | S | N | NI | (BD441) | | | | |
| 2SD289 | S | N | NI | (BD441) | | | | |
| 2SD291 | S | N | SO | | | 2N3054 | | |
| 2SD292 | S | N | SO | | | 2N3054 | | |
| 2SD297 | S | N | NI | (BU114) | | | | |
| 2SD312 | S | N | MA | (BUY79) | | | | |
| 2SD313 | S | N | SN, TS | (BD439) | | | | |
| 2SD314 | S | N | SN, TS | (BD439) | | | | |
| 2SD315 | S | N | SN, TS | | | 2N3054 | | |
| 2SD316 | S | N | SO | BUY55 | | | | |
| 2SD317 | S | N | MA | (BD439) | | | | |
| 2SD317A | S | N | MA | (BD441) | | | | |
| 2SD318 | S | N | MA | (BD439) | | | | |
| 2SD318A | S | N | MA | (BD441) | | | | |
| 2SD319 | S | N | MA | (BUY57) | | | | |
| 2SD320 | S | N | SN, TS | BUY77 | | | | |
| 2SD321 | S | N | MA | (BUY74) | | | | |
| 2SD324 | S | N | MA | (BUY79) | | | | |
| 2SD325 | S | N | SN, TS | (BD439) | | | | |
| 2SD327 | S | N | NI | (BC337-16) | | | | |
| 2SD328 | S | N | NI | BSX46-10 | | | | |
| 2SD330 | S | N | SN, TS | (BD439) | | | | |

| TYPE | M/S | POL | MANUFAC | EUROPEAN | | AMERICAN | | JAPANESE | USE |
|------|-----|-----|---------|----------|--|----------|--|----------|-----|
| 2SD331 | S | N | SN, TS | (BD439) | | | | | |
| 2SD334 | S | N | MA | | | 2N4347 | | | |
| 2SD334A | S | N | MA | | | 2N3442 | | | |
| 2SA335 | S | N | NI | (BU114) | | | | | |
| 2SD341 | S | N | HI | | | 2N3055 | | | |
| 2SD351 | S | N | MA | BUY78 | | | | | |
| 2SD352 | G | N | MA | (AC176) | | | | | |
| 2SD362 | S | N | NI | (BUY55) | | | | | |
| 2SD367 | G | N | MA | (AC127) | | | | | |
| 2SD369 | S | N | TO | | | 2N3055 | | | |
| 2SD370 | S | N | TO | (BUY55) | | | | | |
| 2SD371 | S | N | TO | BU114 | | 2N6254 | | | |
| 2SD375 | S | N | NI | BUY57 | | | | | |
| 2SD376 | S | N | NI | BUY73 | | | | | |
| 2SD376A | S | N | NI | BUY74 | | | | | |
| 2SD377 | S | N | NI | BUY76 | | | | | |
| 2SD383 | S | N | HI | BUY77 | | | | | |
| 2SD388 | S | N | NI | BUY57 | | | | | |
| 2SD404C | S | N | TO | | | 2N6288 | | | |
| 2SD424 | S | S | N | TO | | | 2N6262 | | | |
| 2SD425 | S | N | TO | | | 2N3442 | | | |
| 2SD427 | S | N | TO | | | 2N4347 | | | |
| 2SD428 | S | N | TO | | | 2N4348 | | | |
| 2SD523 | S | N | TO | | | 2N6384 | | | |
| 2SD524 | S | N | TO | | | 2N6385 | | | |
| 2SD526 | S | N | TO | | | 2N6292 | | | |
| 2SD552 | S | N | TO | BUX17A | | | | | |
| 2SK13 | S | N | TO | | | 2N5457 | | | |
| 2SK17gr | S | N | TO | | | 2N5457 | | | |
| 2SK17or | S | N | TO | | | 2N5457 | | | |
| 2SK17r | S | N | TO | | | 2N5457 | | | |
| 2SK17ye | S | N | TO | | | 2N5457 | | | |
| 2SK19bl | S | N | TO | | | 2N5485 | | | |
| 2SK19gr | S | N | TO | | | 2N5485 | | | |
| 2SK19ye | S | N | TO | | | 2N5486 | | | |
| 2SK23 | S | N | SO | | | 2N5486 | | | |
| 2SK32 | S | N | SO | | | 2N5486 | | | |
| 2SK35 | S | N | SO | | | 2N5485 | | | |
| 2T11 | G | P | | AC128 | AC131 | 2N2431 | 2N322 | 2SD48 | |
| 2T11 | | | | AC153 | | | | | |
| 2T12 | G | P | | AC128 | AC131 | 2N2431 | 2N322 | 2SB48 | |
| 2T12 | | | | AC153 | | | | | |
| 2T13 | G | P | | AC128 | AC131 | 2N2431 | 2N223 | 2S849 | |
| 2T13 | | | | AC153 | | | | | |
| 2T14 | G | P | | AC128 | AC131 | 2N2431 | 2N324 | 2SB49 | |
| 2T14 | | | | AC153 | | | | | |
| 2T15 | G | P | | AC128 | AC131 | 2N2431 | 2N232 | 2SB48 | |
| 2T15 | | | | AC153 | | | | | |
| 2T16 | G | P | | AC128 | AC131 | 2N2431 | 2N322 | 2S848 | |
| 2T16 | | | | AC153 | | | | | |
| 2T17 | G | P | | AC128 | AC131 | 2N2431 | 2N322 | 2S848 | |
| 2T17 | | | | AC153 | | | | | |
| 2T18 | | P | | | | 2N526 | | | |
| 2T20 | G | P | | AC128 | | 2N2431 | | 2SB63 | |
| 2T21 | G | P | | AC128 | AC153 | 2N2431 | 2N319 | 2SB51 | |
| 2T22 | G | P | | AC128 | AC131 | 2N2431 | 2N320 | 2SB51 | |
| 2T22 | | | | AC153 | | | | | |
| 2T23 | G | P | | AC128 | AC131 | 2N2431 | 2N321 | 2SB52 | |
| 2T23 | | | | AC153 | | | | | |
| 2T24 | G | P | | AC128 | AC131 | 2N2431 | 2N321 | 2SB52 | |
| 2T24 | | | | AC153 | | | | | |
| 2T25 | G | P | | AC128 | AC131 | 2N2431 | 2N320 | 2SB51 | |
| 2T25 | | | | AC153 | | | | | |
| 2T26 | G | P | | AC128 | AC131 | 2N2431 | 2N319 | 2SB51 | |
| 2T26 | | | | AC153 | | | | | |
| 2T51 | G | N | | AC127 | ASY73 | 2N2430 | 2N169 | 2SC76 | |
| 2T52 | G | N | | ASY73 | | 2N169 | | 2SC77 | |
| 2T53 | G | N | | ASY74 | | 2N169 | | 2SC73 | |
| 2T54 | G | N | | ASY74 | | | | 2T524 | |
| 2T61 | G | N | | AC127 | ASY73 | 2N2430 | 2N647 | 2SD65 | |
| 2T62 | G | N | | AC127 | ASY73 | 2N2430 | 2N647 | 2SD66 | |
| 2T63 | G | N | | AC127 | ASY74 | 2N2430 | 2N647 | 2SD63 | |
| 2T64 | G | N | | AC127 | | 2N2430 | 2N1251 | 2SD64 | |
| 2T64R | G | N | | AC127 | ASY74 | 2N2430 | 2N647 | 2SD64 | |
| 2T65 | G | N | | AC127 | ASY74 | 2N2430 | 2N649 | 2SD65 | |

| TYPE | M/S | POL | MANUFAC | EUROPEAN | | AMERICAN | | JAPANESE | USE |
|------|-----|-----|---------|----------|--|----------|--|----------|-----|
| 2T65R | G | N | | AC127 | | 2N2430 | 2N647 | 2SD65 | |
| 2T66 | G | N | | AC127 | ASY75 | 2N2430 | 2N647 | 2SD66 | |
| 2T66R | G | N | | AC127 | | 2N2430 | 2N647 | 2SD66 | |
| 2T67 | G | N | | AC127 | ASY75 | 2N2430 | 2N647 | | |
| 2T67 | | | | ASY73 | | | | | |
| 2T69 | G | N | | AC127 | | 2N2430 | 2N647 | 2SD63 | |
| 2T71 | G | N | | ASY73 | | 2N169 | | 2SC75 | |
| 2T72 | G | N | | ASY73 | | 2N169 | | 2SC75 | |
| 2T73 | G | N | | | | 2N168 | 2N1058 | 2SC73 | |
| 2T73R | G | N | | ASY14 | | 2N168A | 2N1086 | 2SC73 | |
| 2T74 | G | N | | ASY14 | | 2N168 | | 2T73 | |
| 2T75 | G | N | | | | 2N169 | | 2SC75 | |
| 2T75R | G | N | | ASY73 | | 2N169 | 2N293 | 2SC75 | |
| 2T76 | G | N | | ASY75 | | 2N169 | 2N233A | 2SC76 | |
| 2T76R | G | N | | | | 2N169 | 2N293 | 2SC76 | |
| 2T77 | G | N | | | | 2N169 | | 2SC77 | |
| 2T77R | G | N | | ASY73 | | 2N169 | | 2SC77 | |
| 2T78 | G | N | | ASY73 | | 2N1109 | 2N1121 | | |
| 2T78R | G | N | | ASY73 | | 2N1109 | 2N1121 | 2SC78 | |
| 2T82 | G | N | | | | 2N576 | | 2SD63 | |
| 2T83 | G | N | | | | 2N576 | | 2SD63 | |
| 2T84 | G | N | | | | 2N576 | 2N1101 | 2SD63 | |
| 2T85 | G | N | | AC127 | ASY73 | 2N2430 | 2N1251 | 2SD63 | |
| 2T86 | G | N | | AC127 | | 2N2430 | 2N1101 | 2SD63 | |
| 2T89 | G | N | | AC127 | ASY73 | 2N2430 | 2N649 | | |
| 2T201 | G | N | | AF178 | AF185 | 2N2495 | 2N384 | 2SA122 | |
| 2T201 | | | | AF135 | | | | | |
| 2T203 | G | P | | AF178 | AF185 | 2N2495 | 2N370 | 2SA124 | |
| 2T203 | | | | AF134 | | | | | |
| 2T204 | G | P | | AF178 | AF134 | 2N2495 | 2N284 | | |
| 2T204A | G | P | | AF178 | | 2N2495 | | | |
| 2T205 | G | P | | AF124 | AF134 | 2N384 | | 2SA125 | |
| 2T205A | G | P | | AF178 | | 2N2495 | | | |
| 2T311 | G | P | | AC128 | AC132 | 2N322 | 2N2431 | 2SB51 | |
| 2T311 | | | | AC153 | | | | | |
| 2T312 | G | P | | AC128 | AC132 | 2N2431 | 2N322 | 2SB51 | |
| 2T312 | | | | AC153 | | | | | |
| 2T313 | G | P | | AC128 | AC131 | 2N2431 | 2N323 | 2SB52 | |
| 2T313 | | | | AC153 | AC132 | | | | |
| 2T314 | G | P | | AC128 | AC131 | 2N2431 | 2N324 | 2SB52 | |
| 2T314 | | | | AC132 | AC153 | | | | |
| 2T315 | G | P | | AC128 | AC131 | 2N2431 | 2N508 | 2SB50 | |
| 2T315 | | | | AC132 | AC153 | | | | |
| 2T321 | G | P | | AC128 | AC131 | 2N2431 | 2N319 | 2SB51 | |
| 2T321 | | | | AC153 | | | | | |
| 2T322 | G | P | | AC128 | AC131 | 2N2431 | 2N320 | 2SB51 | |
| 2T322 | | | | AC153 | | | | | |
| 2T323 | G | P | | AC128 | AC131 | 2N2431 | 2N321 | 2SB52 | |
| 2T323 | | | | AC153 | | | | | |
| 2T324 | G | P | | AC128 | | 2N2431 | 2N321 | 2SB52 | |
| 2T383 | G | P | | AC131 | AC132 | 2N526 | | 2SB53 | |
| 2T383 | | | | AC153 | | | | | |
| 2T501 | G | N | | | | 2N326 | | | |
| 2T511 | G | N | | ASY73 | | 2N169 | | 2SC77 | |
| 2T512 | G | N | | ASY73 | | 2N169 | | 2SC77 | |
| 2T513 | G | N | | ASY73 | | 2N169 | 2N194 | 2SC77 | |
| 2T520 | G | N | | ASY73 | | 2N169 | 2N233A | 2SC77 | |
| 2T521 | G | N | | ASY73 | | | | 2SC76 | |
| 2T522 | G | N | | ASY73 | | | | 2SC77 | |
| 2T523 | G | N | | ASY73 | | | | 2SC77 | |
| 2T524 | G | N | | | | 2N216 | | | |
| 2T551 | G | N | | ASY74 | | | | 2SC73 | |
| 2T552 | G | N | | ASY73 | | | | 2SC75 | |
| 2T681 | G | N | | AC127 | | 2N2430 | 2N647 | 2SD61 | |
| 2T682 | G | N | | ASY73 | | | | 2SD62 | |
| 2T701 | G | N | | ASY74 | | 2N168 | | 2SC73 | |
| 2T2001 | G | P | | AF178 | AF124 | 2N2495 | 2N384 | 2SA121 | |
| 2T2001 | | | | AF134 | | | | | |
| 2T3011 | G | P | | AS716 | AUY21 | 2N301 | | 2SB140 | |
| 2T3011 | | | | AUY28 | | | | | |
| 2T3021 | G | P | | ASZ15 | AUY22 | 2N301 | | 2SB141 | |
| 2T3021 | | | | AUY28 | | | | | |
| 2T3030 | G | P | | AD149 | AD150 | 2N2836 | 2N301 | 2SB142 | |
| 2T3031 | G | P | | AD149 | AD150 | 2N2836 | 2N301 | 2SB143 | |
| 2T3032 | G | P | | AD149 | AD150 | 2N2836 | 2N301 | 2SB144 | |

| TYPE | M/S | POL | MANUFAC | EUROPEAN | | AMERICAN | | JAPANESE | USE |
|------|-----|-----|---------|----------|---|----------|---|----------|-----|
| 2T3033 | G | P | | AD149 | AD150 | 2N2836 | 2N301 | 2SB144 | |
| 2T3041 | G | P | | AD149 | AD150 | 2N2836 | | 2SB145 | |
| 2T3042 | G | P | | AD149 | AD150 | 2N2836 | | 2SB146 | |
| 2T3043 | G | P | | AD149 | AD150 | 2N2836 | | 2SB146 | |
| 3G2 | J | N | | | | 2N5457 | | | |
| | | | | | | | | | |
| 3MC | G | P | | AF185 | | | | | |
| 3N25/501 | G | P | | AF185 | OC71 | | | | |
| 3N62 | S | N | TR | | | | | | |
| 3N63 | S | N | TR | | | 3N79 | | | |
| 3N64 | S | N | TR | | | 3N78 | 3N79 | | |
| | | | | | | 3N77 | 3N79 | | |
| 3N65 | S | N | TR | | | 3N79 | | | |
| 3N66 | S | N | TR | | | 3N78 | | | |
| 3N67 | S | N | TR | | | 3N77 | | | |
| 3N68 | S | N | TR | | | 3N79 | 3N79 | | |
| 3N68A | S | N | TR | | | 3N79 | | | |
| | | | | | | | | | |
| 3N69 | S | N | TR | | | 3N78 | 3N79 | | |
| 3N70 | S | N | TR | | | 3N77 | 3N78 | | |
| 3N71 | S | N | TR | | | 3N77 | 3N79 | | |
| 3N72 | S | N | TR | | | 3N78 | 3N79 | | |
| 3N73 | S | N | TR | | | 3N79 | | | |
| | | | | | | | | | |
| 3N74 | S | N | TX, TR | | | 3N79 | | | |
| 3N75 | S | N | TX, TR | | | 3N79 | | | |
| 3N76 | S | N | TX, TR | | | 3N79 | | | |
| 3N77 | S | N | TX, TR | | | 3N79 | | | |
| 3N78 | S | N | TX, TR | | | 3N79 | | | |
| | | | | | | | | | |
| 3N79 | S | N | TX, TR | | | | | | |
| 3N87 | S | N | | | | 3N77 | 3N79 | | |
| 3N88 | S | N | | | | 3N78 | 3N79 | | |
| 3N90 | S | P | SP | | | 3N110 | 3N111 | | |
| 3N91 | S | P | SP | | | 3N110 | 3N111 | | |
| | | | | | | | | | |
| 3N92 | S | P | SP | | | 3N111 | | | |
| 3N93 | S | P | SP | | | 3N108 | 3N111 | | |
| 3N94 | S | P | SP | | | 3N108 | 3N111 | | |
| 3N95 | S | P | SP | | | 3N109 | 3N111 | | |
| 3N98 | M | N | | | | MFE3004 | | | |
| | | | | | | | | | |
| 3N99 | M | N | | | | MFE3004 | | | |
| 3N100 | S | P | SP | | | 3N108 | 3N111 | | |
| 3N101 | S | P | SP | | | 3N108 | 3N111 | | |
| 3N102 | S | P | SP | | | 3N108 | 3N111 | | |
| 3N103 | S | P | SP | | | 3N108 | 3N111 | | |
| | | | | | | | | | |
| 3N104 | S | P | SP | | | 3N108 | 3N111 | | |
| 3N105 | S | P | SP | | | 3N108 | 3N111 | | |
| 3N106 | S | P | SP | | | 3N108 | 3N111 | | |
| 3N107 | S | P | SP | | | 3N108 | 3N111 | | |
| 3N108 | S | P | TX, SP | | | 3N311 | | | |
| | | | | | | | | | |
| 3N109 | S | P | TX, SP | | | 3N111 | | | |
| 3N110 | S | P | TX, SP | | | 3N111 | | | |
| 3N111 | S | P | TX, SP | | | | | | |
| 3N112 | S | P | | | | | | | |
| 3N113 | S | P | | | | 3N108 | 3N111 | | |
| | | | | | | 3N108 | 3N111 | | |
| 3N114 | S | P | SP | | | 3N110 | 3N111 | | |
| 3N115 | S | P | SP | | | 3N110 | 3N111 | | |
| 3N116 | S | P | SP | | | 3N111 | | | |
| 3N117 | S | P | SP | | | 3N110 | | | |
| 3N118 | S | P | SP | | | 3N110 | 3N111 | | |
| | | | | | | | | | |
| 3N119 | S | P | SP | | | 3N111 | | | |
| 3N121 | S | P | | | | 3N111 | | | |
| 3N123 | S | P | SP | | | 3N111 | | | |
| 3N127 | S | N | | | | 3N79 | | | |
| 3N128 | M | N | MO, RC, TX, GI | | | MFE3004 | 3N142 | | |
| | | | | | | | | | |
| 3N129 | S | P | | | | 3N108 | 3N111 | | |
| 3N130 | S | P | | | | 3N108 | 3N111 | | |
| 3N131 | S | P | | | | 3N108 | 3N111 | | |
| 3N132 | S | P | | | | 3N108 | 3N111 | | |
| 3N133 | S | P | | | | 3N108 | 3N111 | | |
| | | | | | | | | | |
| 3N134 | S | P | | | | 3N108 | 3N111 | | |
| 3N135 | S | P | | | | 3N108 | 3N111 | | |
| 3N136 | S | P | | | | 3N108 | 3N111 | | |
| 3N138 | M | N | RC, GI | | | MFE3004 | 3N139 | | |
| 3N139 | M | N | RC, GI | | | MFE3004 | 3N128 | | |
| | | | | | | | | | |
| 3N140 | M | N | MO, RC, GI | | | | | | |
| 3N141 | M | N | RC, GI | | | 3N141 | | | |
| 3N142 | M | N | RC, GI | | | MFE130 | | | |
| 3N143 | M | N | RC, GI | | | MFE3004 | 40486 | | |
| 3N145 | M | P | GI; IL | | | MFE3004 | | | |
| | | | | | | 2N4352 | 3N174 | | |

| TYPE | M/S | POL | MANUFAC | EUROPEAN | | AMERICAN | | JAPANESE | USE |
|------|-----|-----|---------|----------|---|----------|---|----------|-----|
| 3N146 | M | P | GI, IL | | | 3N157A | 3N174 | | |
| 3N147 | M | P | GI, IL | | | 2N4067 | | | |
| 3N148 | M | P | GI, IL | | | 2N4067 | | | |
| 3N149 | M | P | IL | | | 3N157A | 3N158A | | |
| 3N149 | | | | | | 3N161 | | | |
| 3N150 | M | P | IL | | | 3N157A | 3N158A | | |
| 3N150 | | | | | | 3N161 | | | |
| 3N151 | M | P | GI, IL | | | 2N4067 | | | |
| 3N152 | M | N | RC, GI | | | MFE3004 | 3N143 | | |
| 3N153 | M | N | GI, RC, TX | | | MFE3004 | 3N138 | | |
| 3N154 | M | N | RC, GI | | | MFE3004 | MFE3005 | | |
| 3N154 | | | | | | 40467A | | | |
| 3N158 | M | P | MO, GI, IL, TX | | | SFC4047 | | | |
| 3N158A | M | P | MO, GI, IL, TX | | | SFC4047 | | | |
| 3N159 | M | N | GI, RC | | | MFE131 | 3N140 | | |
| 3N160 | M | P | TX, GI, IL | | | MFE3003 | 3N161 | | |
| 3N161 | M | P | TX, GI, IL | | | MFE3003 | 3N160 | | |
| 3N162 | M | P | GI | | | MFE3003 | 3M161 | | |
| 3N163 | M | P | SD, GI, IL, SX, TX | | | 3N158 | | | |
| 3N164 | M | P | SD, GI, IL, SX, TX | | | 3N158 | | | |
| 3N165 | M | P | SD, GI, IL | | | 2N4067 | | | |
| 3N166 | M | P | SD, GI, IL | | | 2N4067 | | | |
| 3N167 | M | P | SX, GI | | | MFE3003 | | | |
| 3N168 | M | P | SX, GI | | | MFE3003 | | | |
| 3N172 | M | P | SD, GI, IL | | | | | | |
| 3N173 | M | P | SD, GI, IL | | | | | | |
| 3N174 | M | P | TX, GI | | | 2N4352 | | | |
| 3N175 | M | N | GI | | | 2N4351 | | | |
| 3N176 | M | N | GI | | | 2N4351 | | | |
| 3N177 | M | N | GI | | | 2N4351 | | | |
| 3N178 | M | P | GI | | | 3N155 | | | |
| 3N179 | M | P | GI | | | 3N155 | | | |
| 3N180 | M | P | GI, IL | | | 3N155 | | | |
| 3N181 | M | P | GI | | | 3N155 | | | |
| 3N182 | M | P | GI | | | 3N155 | | | |
| 3N183 | M | P | GI | | | 3N155 | | | |
| 3N184 | M | P | GI | | | 3N155 | | | |
| 3N185 | M | P | GI | | | 3N155 | | | |
| 3N186 | M | P | GI | | | 3N155 | | | |
| 3N187 | M | N | RC, GI, SX | | | MFE132 | | | |
| 3N200 | M | N | RC, GI | | | 3N201 | | | |
| 3N201 | J | N | TX, GI, SX | | | | | | |
| 3N202 | J | N | TX, GI, SX | | | | | | |
| 3N203 | J | N | TX, GI, SX | | | | | | |
| 3N204 | J | N | TX | | | | | | |
| 3N212 | J | N | RC, TX | | | 3N223 | | | |
| 3NU40 | G | P | | AC126 | | 2N2429 | | | |
| 3NU70 | G | P | | AC126 | | 2N2429 | | | |
| 3SK20H | M | N | HI | | | 2N5457 | | | |
| 3SK21H | M | N | HI | | | 2N5457 | | | |
| 3SK22 | J | N | TO | | | 2N5485 | | | |
| 3SK23 | J | N | TO | | | 2N5485 | | | |
| 3SK28 | J | N | TO | | | 2N5485 | | | |
| 4G2 | J | N | | | | 2N5485 | | | |
| 4JDI17 | G | P | | AC128 | | 2N2431 | | | |
| 4JX1E850 | G | N | | AC127 | | 2N2430 | | | |
| 4JX2A601 | G | N | | AC127 | | 2N2430 | | | |
| 4JX2A816 | G | N | | AC127 | | 2N2430 | | | |
| 4JX16A567 | S | N | | | | 2N4401 | 2N3566 | | |
| 4JX16A667 | S | N | | | | 2N4400 | 2N4401 | | |
| 4JX16A667 | | | | | | SE6001 | SE6002 | | |
| 4JX16A668 | S | N | | | | 2N4401 | 2N3566 | | |
| 4JX16A669 | S | N | | | | 2N4401 | 2N3566 | | |
| 4NU40 | G | P | | AC126 | | 2N2429 | | | |
| 4NU70 | G | P | | AC126 | | 2N2429 | | | |
| 5G2 | J | N | | | | 2N5485 | | | |
| 6MC | G | P | | AC126 | | | | | |
| 6XT2 | G | P | | AC126 | | 2N2429 | | | |
| 8D | G | P | | AF185 | OC45 | | | | |
| 8E | G | P | | AF185 | OC45 | | | | |
| 8F | G | P | | AF185 | OC45 | | | | |
| 12HO1 | G | P | | AF185 | | | | | |
| 12MC | G | P | | AF185 | | | | | |
| 14T | J | N | | | | TIS14 | 2N4224 | | |
| 16G2 | S | N | | | | 2N5770 | 2N3563 | | |

| TYPE | M/S | POL | MANUFAC | EUROPEAN | AMERICAN | | JAPANESE | USE |
|---|---|---|---|---|---|---|---|---|
| 16J1 | S | N | | | 2N5772 | 2N4275 | | |
| 16J2 | S | N | | | 2N5772 | 2N4275 | | |
| 16K1 | S | N | | | SE5002 | | | |
| 16K2 | S | N | | | SE5002 | | | |
| 16K3 | S | N | | | SE5003 | | | |
| 16L42 | S | N | | | 2N4123 | EN4123 | | |
| 16L43 | S | N | | | 2N4123 | EN4123 | | |
| 16L44 | S | N | | | 2N4123 | EN4123 | | |
| 20MC | G | P | | AF185 | | | | |
| 25TI | G | P | | AF185 | | | | |
| 26TI | G | P | RC | AF185 | | | | |
| 29 | S | N | RC | (BD437) | | | | |
| 29A | S | N | RC | (BD439) | | | | |
| 29B | S | N | RC | (BD441) | | | | |
| 29C | S | N | RC | (BD441) | | | | |
| 30 | S | P | RC | (BD438) | | | | |
| 30A | S | P | RC | (BD440) | | | | |
| 30B | S | P | RC | (BD442) | | | | |
| 30C | S | P | RC | (BD442) | | | | |
| 31 | S | N | RC | (BD437) | | | | |
| 31A | S | N | RC | (BD439) | | | | |
| 31B | S | N | RC | (BD441) | | | | |
| 31C | S | N | RC | (BD441) | | | | |
| 31TI | G | P | | AF185 | | | | |
| 32 | S | P | RC | (BD438) | | | | |
| 32A | S | P | RC | 'BD440) | | | | |
| 32B | S | P | RC | (BD442) | | | | |
| 32C | S | P | RC | (BD442) | | | | |
| 32TI | G | P | | AF185 | | | | |
| 33TI | G | P | | AF185 | | | | |
| 34TI | G | P | | A⁵185 | | | | |
| 34-6000 | G | P | | AC128 | 2N2431 | | | |
| 34-6000-3 | G | P | | AF185 | | | | |
| 34-6000-16 | G | P | | AC128 | 2N2431 | | | |
| 34-6000-18 | G | P | | AF185 | | | | |
| 34-6000-19 | G | P | | AF185 | | | | |
| 34-6000-28 | G | P | | AC128 | 2N2431 | | | |
| 34-6000-33 | G | P | | AC128 | 2N2431 | | | |
| 34-6009 | G | P | | AC128 | 2N2431 | | | |
| 35TI | G | P | | AF185 | | | | |
| 36TI | G | P | | AF185 | | | | |
| 37TI | G | P | | AF185 | | | | |
| 41 | S | N | RC | (BD437) | | | | |
| 41A | S | N | RC | (BD439) | | | | |
| 41B | S | N | RC | (BD441) | | | | |
| 41C | S | N | RC | (BD441) | | | | |
| 42 | S | P | RC | (BD438) | | | | |
| 42A | S | P | RC | (BD440) | | | | |
| 42B | S | P | RC | (BD442) | | | | |
| 42C | S | P | RC | (BD442) | | | | |
| 42T | J | N | | | SX42 | U1898E | | |
| 44TI | G | P | | AC128 | 2N2431 | | | |
| 58T | J | N | | | 2N5953 | 2N4302 | | |
| 59T | S | N | SE, NU, ML | | 2N5951 | U1873E | | |
| 73T2 | | | | | 40392 | | | |
| 74T2 | S | N | SE, NU, ML | | 40628 | | | |
| 82T1 | G | P | SE | AD149 | 2N2836 | | | |
| 99AT6 | G | P | | AC128 | 2N2431 | | | |
| 99B5 | G | P | | AC128 | 2N2431 | | | |
| 99A6 | G | P | | AF185 | | | | |
| 99B6 | G | P | | AF185 | | | | |
| 99L6 | G | N | | AC127 | 2N2430 | | | |
| 99Q7 | G | N | | AC127 | 2N2430 | | | |
| 100S | J | N | | | 2N5950 | E100 | | |
| 100T2 | S | N | SE | | 2N4347 | | | |
| 101 | S | P | RC | (BD438) | | | | |
| 101S | J | N | | | 2N3460 | E101 | | |
| 102 | S | P | RC | (BD440) | | | | |
| 102M | J | N | | | 2N5950 | 2N5486 | | |
| 102S | J | N | | | 2N5953 | E102 | | |
| 103 | S | P | RC | (BD440) | | | | |
| 103M | J | N | | | 2N5953 | 2N5457 | | |
| 103S | J | N | | | 2N5949 | E103 | | |
| 104 | S | P | RC | (BD442) | | | | |
| 104M | J | N | | | 2N5953 | 2N5458 | | |

| TYPE | M/S | POL | MANUFAC | EUROPEAN | | AMERICAN | | JAPANESE | USE |
|------|-----|-----|---------|----------|---|----------|---|----------|-----|
| 104T2 | S | N | SE | | | 2N6253 | | | |
| 105 | S | P | RC | (BD440) | | | | | |
| 105M | J | N | | | | 2N5951 | 2N5459 | | |
| 105U | J | N | | | | 2N3458 | | | |
| 106M | J | N | | | | 2N5245 | 2N5485 | | |
| | | | | | | | | | |
| 107M | J | N | | | | 2N5247 | 2N5486 | | |
| 108T2 | S | N | SE | | | 2N5039 | | | |
| 109T2 | S | N | SE | | | 2N6354 | | | |
| 110U | J | N | | | | 2N3821 | | | |
| 115U | J | N | | | | 2N3459 | | | |
| | | | | | | | | | |
| 102U | J | N | | | | 2N3821 | | | |
| 121-19 | G | P | | AC128 | | 2N2431 | | | |
| 121-27 | G | P | | AC128 | | 2N2431 | | | |
| 121-34 | G | P | | AC128 | | 2N2431 | | | |
| 121-44 | G | P | | AF185 | | | | | |
| | | | | | | | | | |
| 121-45 | G | P | | AF185 | | | | | |
| 121-46 | G | P | | AC128 | | 2N2431 | | | |
| 121-47 | G | P | | AC128 | | 2N2431 | | | |
| 121-48 | G | P | | AF185 | | | | | |
| 121-49 | G | P | | AF185 | | | | | |
| | | | | | | | | | |
| 121-51 | G | P | | AF185 | | | | | |
| 121-52 | G | P | | AC128 | | 2N2431 | | | |
| 121-53 | G | P | | AF185 | | | | | |
| 121-54 | G | P | | AF185 | | | | | |
| 121-61 | G | P | | AC128 | | 2N2431 | | | |
| | | | | | | | | | |
| 121-62 | G | P | | AF185 | | | | | |
| 121-63 | G | P | | AF185 | | | | | |
| 121-64 | G | P | | AC128 | | 2N2431 | | | |
| 121-65 | G | P | | AF185 | | | | | |
| 121-66 | G | P | | AF185 | | | | | |
| | | | | | | | | | |
| 121-67 | G | P | | AF185 | | | | | |
| 121-68 | G | P | | AC128 | | 2N2431 | | | |
| 121-69 | G | P | | AC128 | | 2N2431 | | | |
| 121-72 | G | P | | AF185 | | | | | |
| 121-73 | G | P | | AF185 | | | | | |
| | | | | | | | | | |
| 121-74 | G | P | | AF185 | | | | | |
| 121-75 | G | P | | AF185 | | | | | |
| 121-76 | G | P | | AF185 | | | | | |
| 121-78 | G | P | | AF185 | | | | | |
| 121-83 | G | P | | AF185 | | | | | |
| | | | | | | | | | |
| 121-91 | G | P | | AF185 | | | | | |
| 121-92 | G | P | | AF185 | | | | | |
| 121-93 | G | P | | AF185 | | | | | |
| 121-95 | G | P | | AC128 | | 2N2431 | | | |
| 121-96 | G | P | | AC128 | | 2N2431 | | | |
| | | | | | | | | | |
| 121-100 | G | P | | AF185 | | | | | |
| 121-102 | G | P | | AF185 | | | | | |
| 121-103 | G | P | | AF185 | | | | | |
| 121-104 | G | P | | AF185 | | | | | |
| 121-105 | G | P | | AF185 | | | | | |
| | | | | | | | | | |
| 121-106 | G | P | | AC128 | | 2N2431 | | | |
| 121-107 | G | P | | AC128 | | 2N2431 | | | |
| 121-120 | G | P | | AC128 | | 2N2431 | | | |
| 121-128 | G | P | | AF185 | | | | | |
| 121-161 | G | P | | AF185 | | | | | |
| | | | | | | | | | |
| 121-162 | G | P | | AF185 | | | | | |
| 121-164 | G | P | | AC128 | | 2N2431 | | | |
| 121-179 | G | P | | AF185 | | | | | |
| 121-180 | G | P | | AF185 | | | | | |
| 121-190 | G | P | | AC128 | | 2N2431 | | | |
| | | | | | | | | | |
| 121-191 | G | P | | AC128 | | 2N2431 | | | |
| 121-192 | G | P | | AC128 | | 2N2431 | | | |
| 121-1032 | G | P | | AC128 | | 2N2431 | | | |
| 121-1033 | G | P | | AC128 | | 2N2431 | | | |
| 121-1034 | G | P | | AC128 | | 2N2431 | | | |
| | | | | | | | | | |
| 121-1035 | G | P | | AC128 | | 2N2431 | | | |
| 121-1036 | G | P | | AC128 | | 2N2431 | | | |
| 125U | J | N | | | | 2N3460 | | | |
| 126TI | G | P | | AC128 | | 2N2431 | | | |
| 127TI | G | P | | AC128 | | 2N2431 | | | |
| | | | | | | | | | |
| 130U | J | N | | | | TN4338 | | | |
| 135U | J | N | | | | 2N3460 | | | |
| 153TI | G | P | | AF185 | | | | | |
| 154TI | G | P | | AF185 | | | | | |
| 155TI | G | P | | AF185 | | | | | |

| TYPE | M/S | POL | MANUFAC | EUROPEAN | | AMERICAN | | JAPANESE | USE |
|---|---|---|---|---|---|---|---|---|---|
| 155U | J | N | | | | | | | |
| 156TI | G | P | | | | 2N4416 | | | |
| 157TI | G | P | | AF185 | | | | | |
| 159TI | G | P | | AF185 | | 2N2495 | | | |
| 160TI | G | P | | AF178 | | | | | |
| 161TI | G | P | | AF178 | | 2N2495 | | | |
| 162T | G | P | | AF178 | | 2N2495 | | | |
| 182S | J | N | | | | | | | |
| 182T2A | S | N | SE | BUX16 | | 2N3970 | | | |
| 182T2B | S | N | SE | BUX16 | | | | | |
| 182T2C | S | N | SE | BUX16 | | | | | |
| 183S | J | N | | | | | | | |
| 183T2A | S | N | SE | BUX16 | | SFB9448 | 2N3823 | | |
| 183T2B | S | N | SE | BUX16 | | | | | |
| 183T2C | S | N | SE | BUX16 | | | | | |
| 184T2A | S | N | SE | BUX16 | | | | | |
| 184T2B | S | N | SE | BUX16 | | | | | |
| 184T2C | S | N | SE | BUX16 | | | | | |
| 185T2A | S | N | SE | BUX16A | | | | | |
| 185T2B | S | N | SE | BUX16A | | | | | |
| 185T2C | S | N | SE | BUX16A | | | | | |
| 197S | J | N | | | | | | | |
| 198S | J | N | | | | 2N3460 | TN4338 | | |
| 199S | J | N | | | | 2N3459 | TN4340 | | |
| 200S | J | N | | | | 2N3458 | TN4341 | | |
| 200U | J | N | | | | 2N3458 | 2N4092 | | |
| 201 | S | N | RC | (BD437) | | 2N5549 | 2N4393 | | |
| 201S | J | N | | | | | | | |
| 202 | S | N | RC | (BD439) | | 2N3492 | 2N4091 | | |
| 202S | J | N | | | | 2N3491 | 2N4092 | | |
| 203 | S | N | RC | (BD439) | | | | | |
| 203S | J | N | | | | | | | |
| 204 | S | N | RC | (BD441) | | 2N3821 | | | |
| 204S | J | N | | | | | | | |
| 205 | S | N | RC | (BD439) | | 2N3821 | | | |
| 210U | J | N | | | | | | | |
| 222 | G | P | | AF185 | OC45 | 2N4416 | 2N3822 | | |
| 225 | G | P | | AF185 | OC45 | | | | |
| 228 | G | P | | AF185 | OC44 | | | | |
| 231S | J | N | | | | 2N5545 | 2N3954 | | |
| 232S | J | N | | | | 2N5546 | 2N3955 | | |
| 233S | J | N | | | | 2N5547 | 2N3956 | | |
| 234 | G | P | | AF185 | | | | | |
| 234S | J | N | | | | 2N5045 | 2N3957 | | |
| 235S | J | N | | | | 2N5045 | 2N3958 | | |
| 241U | J | N | | | | 2N3822 | | | |
| 250U | J | N | | | | 2N4859 | 2N3970 | | |
| 251U | J | N | | | | 2N4861 | 2N3971 | | |
| 300 | G | P | | OC72 | | | | | |
| 301 | G | P | | OC72 | | | | | |
| 302 | G | P | | OC72 | | | | | |
| 310 | G | P | | AC126 | OC72 | 2N2429 | | | |
| 350 | G | P | | AC128 | OC72 | 2N2431 | | | |
| 352 | G | P | | AC128 | OC72 | 2N2431 | | | |
| 353 | G | P | | AC128 | OC72 | | | | |
| 370 | S | P | RC | (BD438) | | | | | |
| 371 | S | P | RC | (BD438) | | | | | |
| 410 | S | N | RC | BUY73 | | | | | |
| 411 | S | N | RC | BUY75 | | | | | |
| 413 | S | N | RC | BUY76 | | | | | |
| 421TI | G | P | | | | | | | |
| 423 | S | N | RC | AC128 | | 2N2431 | | | |
| 431 | S | N | RC | BUY76 | | | | | |
| 486TI | G | P | | AC128 | | 2N2431 | | | |
| 501TI | G | P | | AF178 | | 2N2495 | | | |
| 503TI | G | P | | AF178 | | 2N2495 | | | |
| 520 | S | N | RC | (BD437) | | | | | |
| 521 | S | N | RC | (BD437) | | | | | |
| 570C | G | P | | OC58 | | | | | |
| 588U | J | N | | | | 2N5245 | U1994E | | |
| 641TI | G | P | | AC128 | | 2N2431 | | | |
| 665TI | G | P | SE | AC126 | | 2N2429 | | | |
| 687TI | G | P | SE | AC126 | | 2N2429 | | | |
| 688TI | G | P | SE | AC126 | | 2N2429 | | | |
| 689TI | G | P | SE | AC126 | | 2N2429 | | | |

| TYPE | M/S | POL | MANUFAC | EUROPEAN | | AMERICAN | | JAPANESE | USE |
|---|---|---|---|---|---|---|---|---|---|
| 690TI | G | P | SE | AC126 | | 2N2429 | | | |
| 691TI | G | P | SE | AC126 | | 2N2429 | | | |
| 692T2 | G | P | | AC126 | | 2N2429 | | | |
| 703U | J | N | | | | 2N3822 | | | |
| 704U | J | N | | | | 2N3822 | | | |
| 705U | J | N | | | | 2N3824 | | | |
| 707U | J | N | | | | 2N4091 | | | |
| 714U | J | N | | | | 2N3823 | | | |
| 734EU | J | N | | | | U1994E | | | |
| 734U | J | N | | | | 2N4416 | | | |
| 751U | J | N | | | | TN4340 | | | |
| 752U | J | N | | | | TN4341 | | | |
| 753U | J | N | | | | 2N3459 | 2N4092 | | |
| 754U | J | N | | | | 2N3459 | TN4340 | | |
| 755U | J | N | | | | 2N3458 | TN4341 | | |
| 756U | J | N | | | | 2N3458 | 2N4224 | | |
| 760 | G | P | | AF185 | | | | | |
| 761 | G | P | | AF185 | | | | | |
| 941TI | G | P | SE | AC126 | | 2N2429 | | | |
| 965TI | G | P | SE | AC126 | | 2N2429 | | | |
| 987TI | G | P | SE | AC128 | | 2N2431 | | | |
| 988TI | G | P | SE | AC128 | | 2N2431 | | | |
| 989TI | G | P | | AC126 | | 2N2429 | | | |
| 990TI | G | P | | AC126 | | 2N2429 | | | |
| 991TI | G | P | | AC126 | | 2N2429 | | | |
| 992TI | G | P | | AC126 | | 2N2429 | | | |
| 1032 | G | P | | AC128 | OC72 | 2N2431 | | | |
| 1033 | G | P | | AC128 | OC72 | 2N2431 | | | |
| 1034 | G | P | | AC128 | OC72 | 2N2431 | | | |
| 1035 | G | P | | AC128 | OC72 | 2N2431 | | | |
| 1036 | G | P | | AC128 | OC72 | 2N2431 | | | |
| 1277A | J | N | | | | 2N3822 | | | |
| 1278A | J | N | | | | 2N3821 | | | |
| 1279A | J | N | | | | 2N3821 | | | |
| 1280A | J | N | | | | 2N3822 | 2N4224 | | |
| 1281A | J | N | | | | 2N3458 | 2N3822 | | |
| 1292A | J | N | | | | 2N3458 | TN4341 | | |
| 1283A | J | N | | | | 2N3459 | TN4340 | | |
| 1284A | J | N | | | | 2N3458 | 2N3069 | | |
| 1285A | J | N | | | | 2N3821 | 2N3453 | | |
| 1286A | J | N | | | | 2N3459 | 2N3069 | | |
| 1320 | G | P | | AC128 | OC72 | 2N2431 | | | |
| 1325A | J | N | | | | 2N4222 | | | |
| 1330 | G | P | | AC128 | OC72 | 2N2431 | | | |
| 1340 | G | P | | AC128 | OC72 | 2N2431 | | | |
| 1350 | G | P | | AC128 | OC72 | 2N2431 | | | |
| 1360 | G | P | | AC128 | OC72 | 2N2431 | | | |
| 1390 | G | P | | AF185 | OC45 | | | | |
| 1400 | G | P | | AF185 | OC45 | | | | |
| 1410 | G | P | | AF185 | OC45 | | | | |
| 1714A | J | N | | | | 2N3459 | TN4340 | | |
| 2000M | J | N | | | | 2N4416 | 2N3823 | | |
| 2001M | J | N | | | | 2N4416 | 2N3823 | | |
| 2078A | J | N | | | | 2N5546 | 2N4083 | | |
| 2079A | J | N | | | | 2N5547 | 2N4083 | | |
| 2080A | J | N | | | | 2N5547 | 2N4085 | | |
| 2081A | J | N | | | | 2N5045 | 2N4085 | | |
| 2093M | J | N | | | | 2N5647 | | | |
| 2094M | J | N | | | | 2N5648 | | | |
| 2095M | J | N | | | | 2N5649 | | | |
| 2098A | J | N | | | | 2N5545 | SU2098 | | |
| 2099A | J | N | | | | 2N5546 | SU2099 | | |
| 2130U | J | N | | | | 2N5546 | 2N3954 | | |
| 2132U | J | N | | | | 2N5546 | 2N3955 | | |
| 2134U | J | N | | | | 2N5547 | 2N3956 | | |
| 2136U | J | N | | | | 2N5045 | 2N3958 | | |
| 2138U | J | N | | | | 2N5046 | 2N3958 | | |
| 2139U | J | N | | | | 2N5047 | 2N3958 | | |
| 2147U | J | N | | | | 2N5047 | 2N3958 | | |
| 2148U | J | N | | | | 2N5047 | 2N3958 | | |
| 2149U | J | N | | | | 2N5047 | 2N3958 | | |
| 3435 | G | P | | AF185 | | | | | |
| 3504 | G | P | | AC126 | | 2N2429 | | | |
| 6100-35 | G | P | | AC128 | | 2N2431 | | | |
| 09390 | G | P | | AC128 | | 2N2431 | | | |

| TYPE | M/S | POL | MANUFAC | EUROPEAN | | AMERICAN | | JAPANESE | USE |
|---|---|---|---|---|---|---|---|---|---|
| 09391 | G | P | | AC128 | | 2N2431 | | | |
| 12119 | G | P | | AC128 | | 2N2431 | | | |
| 12152 | G | P | | AC128 | | 2N2431 | | | |
| 12153 | G | P | | AC128 | OC44 | 2N2431 | | | |
| 12161 | G | P | | AC128 | | | | | |
| 12163 | G | P | | | | 2N2431 | | | |
| 12165 | G | P | | AF185 | | | | | |
| 12166 | G | P | | AF185 | OC45 | | | | |
| 12173 | G | P | | AF185 | OC45 | | | | |
| 12178 | G | P | | AF185 | OC45 | | | | |
| | | | | AF185 | | | | | |
| 40022 | G | P | RC, St | AUY21IV | | 40050 | | | |
| 40050 | G | P | RC, St | AUY21IV | | 40051 | | | |
| 40051 | S | N | RC, St | AUY22IV | | 2N3715 | | | |
| 40080 | S | N | RC, St, SM | | | 40081 | | | |
| 40081 | S | N | RC, St, SM | | | 40080 | | | |
| 40082 | J | N | RC, St, SM | | | 40081 | | | |
| 40084 | S | N | RC, SM, SQ, St | (BSX49) | | 2N2897 | | | |
| 40231 | S | N | SM, RC, St | BC108A | | 40232 | | | |
| 40232 | S | N | SM, RC, St | BC108B | | 40233 | | | |
| 40233 | S | N | SM, RC, St | BC108B | | 2N718A | | | |
| 40234 | S | N | SM, RC, St | BC108A | | 40233 | | | |
| 40235 | S | N | RC, SM, NS | | | 40472 | | | |
| 40236 | S | N | RC, SM, NS | | | 40235 | | | |
| 40237 | S | N | RC, SM, NS | | | 40474 | | | |
| 40238 | S | N | RC, SM, NS | | | 40239 | 40240 | | |
| 40239 | S | N | RC, SM, NS | | | | | | |
| 40240 | S | N | RC, SM, NS | | | 40240 | | | |
| 40242 | S | N | RC, SM, NS | | | 40239 | | | |
| 40243 | S | N | RC, SM, NS | | | 40478 | | | |
| 40244 | S | N | RC, SM, NS | | | 40478 | | | |
| 40245 | S | N | RC, SM, NS | | | 40480 | | | |
| 40246 | S | N | RC, SM, NS | | | 40481 | 40246 | | |
| 40250 | S | N | RC, AT, St, KE, PP | | | 40481 | 40245 | | |
| 40250 | | | | | | 2N4913 | 2N3054 | | |
| 40250V1 | S | N | RC | | | 40250V1 | TIP31 | | |
| | | | | | | (2N3054) | 40250 | | |
| 40251 | S | N | RC, AT, PP, BL, St | | | 2N6569 | 2N3055 | | |
| 40251 | | | | | | 2N3771 | 2N5881 | | |
| 40254 | G | P | RC, St | | | 40051 | 40022 | | |
| 40261 | G | P | RC | AUY21IV | | 40487 | | | |
| 40262 | G | P | RC | | | 40488 | | | |
| 40263 | G | P | RC | | | | | | |
| 40279 | S | N | RC, SQ | | | 40490 | 40395 | | |
| 40280 | S | N | RC, SM, St | | | 2N3375 | | | |
| 40281 | S | N | RC, SM, St | | | 2N4427 | | | |
| 40282 | S | N | RC, SM, St | | | 2N3632 | | | |
| 40290 | S | N | RC, SQ, St | | | 40291 | | | |
| 40291 | S | N | RC, SQ, St | | | 40290 | | | |
| 40292 | S | N | RC, SQ, St | | | 40282 | | | |
| 40294 | S | N | RC, SQ | (BFY90) | | 2N2857 | | | |
| 40295 | S | N | RC | | | 2N2708 | | | |
| 40296 | S | N | RC | (BFY90) | | | | | |
| 40305 | S | N | RC, SS, St | | | 2N3839 | | | |
| 40306 | S | N | RC, SS, St | | | 2N3553 | | | |
| 40307 | S | N | RC, SS, St | | | 2N3375 | | | |
| 40309 | S | N | RC, SS, St | BSX45-16 | | 2N3632 | | | |
| 40309 | | | | | | 2N5321 | 40311 | | |
| 40309J1 | S | N | RC | | | 40315 | | | |
| 40309J2 | S | N | RC | | | 40309 | | | |
| 40310 | S | N | RC, SS, St | | | 40309 | | | |
| 40310 | | | | | | 2N3054 | 40314 | | |
| | | | | | | 40324 | TIP31 | | |
| 40310V1 | S | N | RC, St | | | | | | |
| 40311 | S | N | RC, SS, St | BSX45-16 | | 40310 | 40314 | | |
| 40311V1 | S | N | RC, St | | | 2N5321 | 40314 | | |
| 40311V2 | S | N | RC, St | | | 40311 | 40314 | | |
| 40312 | S | N | RC, SS, St | | | 40311 | 40314 | | |
| | | | | | | 40316 | TIP31A | | |
| 40312 | | | | | | | | | |
| 40313 | S | N | RC, SS, St | (BUY78) | | 2N3054 | | | |
| 40313 | | | | | | 40318 | TIP48 | | |
| 40314 | S | N | RC, SS, St | BSX45-16 | | SE9331 | | | |
| 40314V1 | S | N | RC, St | | | 2N5321 | 40315 | | |
| | | | | | | 40314 | 40315 | | |
| 40314V2 | S | N | RC, SS, St | | | | | | |
| 40315 | S | N | RC, SS, St | BSX45-16 | | 40314 | 40315 | | |
| 40315V1 | S | N | RC, St | | | 2N5321 | 40314 | | |
| 40315V2 | S | N | RC, St | | | 40315 | 40314 | | |
| 40316 | S | N | RC, SS, St | | | 40315 | 40314 | | |
| | | | | | | 2N3054 | 40312 | | |

| TYPE | M/S | POL | MANUFAC | EUROPEAN | AMERICAN | | JAPANESE | USE |
|---|---|---|---|---|---|---|---|---|
| 40316 | | | | | TIP31 | | | |
| 40317 | S | N | RC, SS, St | BSX45-10 | 2N5321 | 40320 | | |
| 40317V1 | S | N | RC, St | | 40317 | 40320 | | |
| 40317V1 | | | | | 40326 | | | |
| 40317V2 | S | N | RC, SS, St | | 40317 | 40320 | | |
| 40317V2 | | | | | 40326 | | | |
| | | | | | SE9331 | 40322 | | |
| 40318 | S | N | RC, St | (BUY78) | TIP48 | | | |
| 40318 | | | | BSV15-6 | 2N5323 | 40362 | | |
| 40319 | S | P | RC, SS, St | | 40319 | | | |
| 40319V1 | S | P | RC, St | | | | | |
| 40319V2 | S | P | RC, SS, St | | 40319 | | | |
| 40320 | S | N | RC, SS, St | BSX45-10 | 2N5321 | 40317 | | |
| 40320V1 | S | N | RC, St | | 40320 | 40317 | | |
| 40320V2 | S | N | RC, SS, St | | 40320 | 40317 | | |
| 40321 | S | N | RC, SS, St | | 2N3440 | 40327 | | |
| 40321V1 | S | N | RC, St | | 40321 | | | |
| 40321V2 | S | N | RC, SS, St | | 40321 | | | |
| 40322 | S | N | RC, SS, St | (BUY78) | SE9331 | 40318 | | |
| 40322 | | | | | TIP48 | | | |
| 40323 | S | N | RC, SS, St | BSX45-16 | 2N5321 | 40309 | | |
| 40323V1 | S | N | RC, St | | 40323 | | | |
| 40323V2 | S | N | RC, SS, St | | 40323 | 40309 | | |
| 40324 | S | N | RC, SS, St | | 2N3064 | 40316 | | |
| 40324 | | | | | TIP31 | | | |
| 40325 | S | N | RC, SS, St | | 2N6669 | 2N3055 | | |
| 40325 | | | | | 2N3715 | 2N5877 | | |
| 40326 | S | N | RC, SS, St | BSX45-10 | 2N5321 | 40317 | | |
| 40326V1 | S | N | RC, St | | 40326 | 40320 | | |
| 40326V1 | | | | | 40317 | | | |
| 40326V2 | S | N | RC, SS, St | | 40326 | 40320 | | |
| 40326V2 | | | | | 40317 | | | |
| 40327 | S | N | RC, SS, St | | 2N3440 | 40385 | | |
| 40327V1 | S | N | RC, St | | 40327 | | | |
| 40327V2 | S | N | RC, SS, St | | 40327 | | | |
| 40328 | S | N | RC, St | (BUY78) | SE9331 | 2N4240 | | |
| 40328 | | | | | TIP48 | | | |
| 40329 | G | P | RC | | | | | |
| 40340 | S | N | RC, SS | | 40341 | | | |
| 40341 | S | N | RC, SS | | 40340 | | | |
| 40346 | S | N | RC, SS, St | | 2N3440 | 40412 | | |
| 40346V1 | S | N | RC, St | | 40346 | | | |
| 40346V2 | S | N | RC, SS, St | | 40412 | | | |
| 40347 | S | N | RC, SS, St | (BSX62-6) | 2N5321 | 40348 | | |
| 40347V1 | S | N | RC, St | | 40347 | | | |
| 40347V2 | S | N | RC, SS, St | | 40347 | | | |
| 40348 | S | N | RC, SS, St | (BSX63-6) | 2N4238 | 40349 | | |
| 40348V1 | S | N | RC, St | | 40348 | | | |
| 40348V2 | S | N | RC, SS, St | | 40348 | | | |
| 40349 | S | N | RC, SS, St | | 40348 | | | |
| 40349V1 | S | N | RC, St | | | | | |
| 40349V2 | S | N | RC, SS, St | | 40348 | | | |
| 40354 | S | N | RC | | 40355 | | | |
| 40355 | S | N | RC | | 40354 | | | |
| 40359 | G | P | RC, St | | 40263 | | | |
| 40360 | S | N | RC, SS, St, SM | BSX46-10 | 2N5320 | 40361 | | |
| 40360V1 | S | N | RC, St | | 40360 | | | |
| 40360V2 | S | N | RC, SS, St | | 40360 | | | |
| 40361 | S | N | RC, SS, St, SM | BSX46-16 | 2N5320 | 40360 | | |
| 40361V1 | S | N | RC, St | | 40361 | | | |
| 40361V2 | S | N | RC, SS, St | | 40361 | | | |
| 40362 | S | P | RC, St, SM | BSV16-10 | 2N5322 | 40319 | | |
| 40362V1 | S | P | RC, St | | 40362 | | | |
| 40362V2 | S | P | RC, SS, St | | 40362 | | | |
| 40363 | S | N | RC, SZ, SS, PP, St | | 2N3055 | 2N3715 | | |
| 40363 | | | | | 2N5877 | | | |
| 40364 | S | N | RC, SZ, SS, PP, St | PDX25-6 | TIP31A | | | |
| 40366 | S | N | RC, SS, St, SQ | BSX47-6 | 2N5320 | 2N2405 | | |
| 40366V1 | S | N | RC, St | | 40366 | | | |
| 40366V2 | S | N | RC, SS, St | | 40366 | | | |
| 40367 | S | N | RC, SS, St, SQ | (BSX63-6) | 2N4238 | 40366 | | |
| 40367V1 | S | N | RC, St | | 40367 | | | |
| 40367V2 | S | N | RC, SS, St | | 40367 | | | |
| 40368 | S | N | RC, St | | 2N1486 | | | |
| 40369 | S | N | RC, SS, St, PP, SQ | | 2N5873 | 2N4914 | | |
| 40369 | | | | | 2N3713 | | | |

| TYPE | M/S | POL | MANUFAC | EUROPEAN | | AMERICAN | | JAPANESE | USE |
|---|---|---|---|---|---|---|---|---|---|
| 40372 | S | N | RC, St | | | (2N3055) | 2N3054 | | |
| 40372 | | | | | | TIP31A | | | |
| 40373 | S | N | RC, St, PP | | | 2N3441 | | | |
| 40374 | S | N | RC, St | | | 2N3683 | | | |
| 40375 | S | N | RC, St | | | 2N5873 | TIP47 | | |
| | | | | | | | 2N3879 | | |
| 40375 | | | | | | | | | |
| 40385 | S | N | RC, SS, SM, St, SQ | | | TIP31A | | | |
| 40385V1 | S | N | RC, St | | | 2N3439 | 2N4063 | | |
| 40385V2 | S | N | RC, SS, St | | | 40385 | 2N4063 | | |
| 40389 | S | N | RC, St | | | 40392 | 2N4063 | | |
| | | | | | | | 2N3053 | | |
| 40390 | S | N | RC, St | | | 2N3440 | | | |
| 40391 | S | P | RC, St | | | 2N5323 | 40394 | | |
| 40391 | | | | | | 2N4037 | | | |
| 40392 | S | N | RC, St | | | 40389 | | | |
| 40394 | S | P | RC, St | | | 2N5323 | 2N4037 | | |
| 40395 | G | P | RC, SM, St, NP | | | | | | |
| 40396/N | G | N | RC, St | AC127 | | 40263 | | | |
| 40396/P | G | P | RC, St | AC152 | | | | | |
| 40397 | S | N | RC, St | | | | | | |
| 40398 | S | N | RC, SM, St | | | 40453 | | | |
| | | | | | | 40454 | | | |
| 40399 | S | N | RC, SM, St | | | 40455 | | | |
| 40400 | S | N | RC, SM, St | | | 40456 | | | |
| 40405 | S | N | RC, SM, St, SQ | | | 50419 | | | |
| 40406 | S | P | RC, SM, St | BSV16-10 | | | | | |
| 40407 | S | N | RC, SM, St, SQ | BSX46-10 | | 40408 | | | |
| 40408 | S | N | RC, SM, St, SS, SQ | BSX47-10 | | | | | |
| 40409 | S | N | RC, St | | | 2N5053 | | | |
| 40410 | S | P | RC | | | 2N4038 | | | |
| 40411 | S | N | RC, PP, SF, SQ, St | | | MJ802 | 2N3715 | | |
| 40411 | | | | | | 2N5878 | | | |
| 40412 | S | N | RC, SS, St, SQ | | | 2N3440 | 40412V1 | | |
| 40412 | | | | | | 40412V2 | | | |
| 40412V1 | S | N | RC, St | | | 40412 | | | |
| 40412V2 | S | N | RC, SS, St, SQ | | | 40412 | | | |
| 40413 | S | N | RC | | | TIP33 | | | |
| 40414 | S | N | RC | (BFY90) | | TIP33 | | | |
| 40421 | G | N | RC, St | AUY221V | | 2N2147 | | | |
| 40439 | G | P | RC, SS | | | 2N3731 | | | |
| 40440 | G | P | RC, SS | | | 2N3731 | | | |
| 40446 | S | N | RC, St | | | 40582 | | | |
| 40450 | S | N | RC | | | 2N3241A | | | |
| 40451 | S | N | RC | | | 2N3242A | | | |
| 40452 | S | N | RC | | | 2N4074 | | | |
| 40453 | S | N | RC | | | 2N3242A | | | |
| 40454 | S | N | RC | | | 2N3242A | | | |
| 40455 | S | N | RC | | | 40398 | 40399 | | |
| 40456 | S | N | RC | | | 40400 | | | |
| 40457 | S | N | RC | | | | | | |
| 40458 | S | N | SM, RC, St | (BSX45-10) | | | | | |
| 40459 | S | N | RC, St | (BSX45-10) | | 40459 | 2N3241A | | |
| | | | | | | 2N3241A | | | |
| 40460 | M | N | | | | | | | |
| 40461 | M | N | | | | | | | |
| 40462 | G | P | RC, GP, St | AUY211V | | MFE3004 | MFE3005 | | |
| 40464 | S | N | SM, RC, PP | (BU310) | | MFE3004 | MFE3005 | | |
| 40465 | S | N | SM, RC, PP | (BU310) | | 40421 | | | |
| 40466 | S | N | SM, RC, PP | (BU310) | | | | | |
| 40467 | M | N | RC | | | | | | |
| 40467A | M | N | RC | | | MFE3004 | | | |
| 40468 | M | N | RC | | | MFE3004 | 3N154 | | |
| 40468A | S | N | RC | | | MFE3004 | 40468A | | |
| | | | | | | MFE3004 | 40559 | | |
| 40468A | | | | | | | | | |
| 40472 | S | N | RC, NS, SM | | | 3N201 | | | |
| 40473 | S | N | RC, NS, SM | | | 40473 | | | |
| 40474 | S | N | RC, NS, SM | | | 40472 | | | |
| 40475 | S | N | RC, NS, SM | | | 40237 | | | |
| | | | | | | 40476 | 40477 | | |
| 40476 | S | N | RC, NS, SM | | | 40475 | 40477 | | |
| 40477 | S | N | RC, NS, SM | | | 40475 | 40476 | | |
| 40478 | S | N | RC, NS, SM | | | 40479 | | | |
| 40479 | G | N | RC, NS, SM | | | 40478 | | | |
| 40480 | S | N | RC, NS, SM | | | 40474 | | | |
| 40481 | S | N | RC, SM, NS | | | 40482 | | | |
| 40482 | S | N | RC, NS, SM | | | 40481 | | | |
| 40487 | G | P | RC | | | 40488 | 40261 | | |
| 40488 | G | P | RC | | | 40261 | | | |
| 40489 | G | P | RC | | | 40487 | | | |

| TYPE | M/S | POL | MANUFAC | EUROPEAN | | AMERICAN | | JAPANESE | USE |
|---|---|---|---|---|---|---|---|---|---|
| 40490 | G | P | RC | | | 40395 | 2N2963 | | |
| 40491 | S | N | RC, St, SM, SQ | | | | | | |
| 40500 | S | N | SM | BC107A | | | | | |
| 40513 | S | N | RC, PP | | | (2N3055) | 2N5035 | | |
| 40513 | | | | | | TIP33 | | | |
| 40514 | S | N | RC, PP, St | | | (2N3055) | 40513 | | |
| 40514 | | | | | | TIP33 | | | |
| 40517 | S | N | RC | | | 40518 | 2N3839 | | |
| 40517 | | | | | | 40296 | | | |
| 40518 | S | N | RC | | | 40517 | 2N3839 | | |
| 40518 | | | | | | 40296 | | | |
| 40519 | S | N | RC, SS, St, SQ | | | 40405 | | | |
| 40537 | S | P | RC, SS, SM, St, SQ | BSV16-16 | | 2N5322 | 40362 | | |
| 40538 | S | P | RC, SS, SM, St, SQ | BSV16-6 | | 2N5322 | | | |
| 40539 | S | N | RC, SS, SM, St | BSX46-6 | | 40635 | | | |
| 40542 | S | N | RC | | | (2N3055) | 40543 | | |
| 40543 | S | N | RC | | | (2N3055) | 40633 | | |
| 40544 | S | N | RC, SM, St | | | 40392 | | | |
| 40559 | M | N | RC | | | MFE3004 | 40468A | | |
| 40559A | M | N | RC | | | MFE3004 | 40467A | | |
| 40577 | S | N | RC, SS, SQ | | | 2N3118 | | | |
| 40578 | S | N | RC, St, KE | | | 2N3866 | | | |
| 40581 | S | N | RC, SM | | | 40582 | | | |
| 40582 | S | N | RC, SM | | | 40581 | | | |
| 40594 | S | N | RC, SM | (BSX47-10) | | 2N5338 | | | |
| 40595 | S | P | RC, SS, SM, St, SQ | (BSV17-10) | | | | | |
| 40600 | J | N | RC | | | MFE130 | MFE132 | | |
| 40600 | | | | | | 40673 | 3N201 | | |
| 40601 | J | N | RC | | | MFE130 | MFE132 | | |
| 40601 | | | | | | 3N202 | | | |
| 40602 | J | N | RC | | | MFE130 | MFE132 | | |
| 40602 | | | | | | 40603 | 40203 | | |
| 40603 | J | N | RC | | | MFE130 | MFE132 | | |
| 40603 | | | | | | 40602 | 3N201 | | |
| 40604 | J | N | RC | | | MFE130 | MFE132 | | |
| 40604 | | | | | | 40603 | 3N202 | | |
| 40608 | S | N | RC, SM | | | 2N5108 | | | |
| 40611 | S | N | RC, SS, SM, St, SQ | BSX45-16 | | 40616 | | | |
| 40612 | G | P | RC, St | AUY21IV | | 40623 | | | |
| 40613 | S | N | RC, SM, St, NP, PP | (BD437) | | TIP29 | 2N6121 | | |
| 40613 | | | | | | TIP31 | | | |
| 40616 | S | N | RC, SS, SM, St | BSX45-16 | | | | | |
| 40618 | S | N | RC, SS, St, SQ | BD221 | (BD437) | 2N6121 | TIP31 | | |
| 40621 | S | N | RC, SS, St, SQ, PP | BD221 | (BD437) | 2N6122 | TIP31 | | |
| 40622 | S | N | RC, SS, St, NP, SQ | BD221 | (BD437) | 2N6122 | TIP31 | | |
| 40623 | G | P | RC, St | AUY21IV | | 40626 | | | |
| 40624 | S | N | RC, SS, St, SQ, PP | (BD437) | | 2N6129 | 2N5629 | | |
| 40624 | | | | | | 2N6122 | TIP41 | | |
| 40625 | S | N | RC, SS, St | | | 40628 | | | |
| 40626 | G | P | RC, St | AUY22IV | | 40051 | | | |
| 40627 | S | N | RC, SS, SQ, PP | (BD439) | | 2N6130 | 2N6122 | | |
| 40627 | | | | | | TIP41A | | | |
| 40628 | S | N | RC, SS | | | 40625 | | | |
| 40629 | S | N | RC, SS, SQ, PP | (BD437) | | 2N6122 | 2N6121 | | |
| 40629 | | | | | | TIP31 | | | |
| 40630 | S | N | RC, SS, NP, SQ, PP | (BC437) | | 2N6122 | TIP31 | | |
| 40631 | S | N | RC, SS, NP, PP, SQ | (BD437) | | 2N6122 | 2N6121 | | |
| 40631 | | | | | | TIP31 | | | |
| 40632 | S | N | RC, SS, NP, PP, SQ | (BD439) | | 2N6131 | 2N6121 | | |
| 40632 | | | | | | TIP41A | | | |
| 40633 | S | N | RC, St, KE, PP | | | (2N3055) | 40543 | | |
| 40633 | | | | | | TIP33A | | | |
| 40634 | S | P | RC, SS, SM, St, SQ | BSV17-10 | | 2N4314 | 2N4036 | | |
| 40635 | S | N | RC, SS, SM, St, SQ | BSX45-16 | | 2N3053 | 2N3055 | | |
| 40636 | S | N | AT, RC, SS, St, PP | | | 2N5630 | 2N3055 | | |
| 40636 | | | | | | 4063 | 2N5878 | | |
| 40637 | S | N | RC, SM, SQ | BC107A | | | | | |
| 40673 | J | N | RC | | | 3N159 | 3N201 | | |
| 40819 | J | N | | | | MFE131 | | | |
| 40820 | J | N | RC | | | MFE131 | | | |
| 40821 | J | N | RC | | | MFE131 | | | |
| 40822 | J | N | | | | MFE131 | | | |
| 40823 | J | N | | | | MFE131 | | | |
| 40840 | S | N | RC | | | TIP52 | | | |
| 40850 | S | N | RC, SZ, St | (BUY78) | | FT401 | TIP48 | | |

| TYPE | M/S | POL | MANUFAC | EUROPEAN | AMERICAN | | JAPANESE | USE |
|------|-----|-----|---------|----------|----------|---|----------|-----|
| 40851 | S | N | RC, SZ, St | (BUY79) | 2N6251 | TIP49 | | |
| 40852 | S | N | RC, SZ, St | BUY76 | 2N6251 | TIP53 | | |
| 40853 | S | N | RC, SZ, St | BUY75 | FT430 | TIP53 | | |
| 40854 | S | N | RC, SZ, St | (BUY75) | | | | |
| 40871 | S | N | RC, PP | | | | | |
| 40872 | S | P | RC, PP | | TIP32C | | | |
| 40873 | S | N | RC, PP | | | | | |
| 40874 | S | P | RC, PP | | TIP32B | | | |
| 40875 | S | N | RC, PP | | | | | |
| 40876 | S | P | RC, PP | | TIP32A | | | |
| 40884 | S | N | RC | | TIP41A | | | |
| 40885 | S | N | RC | | FT47 | | | |
| 40886 | S | N | RC | | FT48 | | | |
| 40887 | S | N | RC | | FT49 | | | |
| 40894 | S | N | RC, SM | (BFW30) | | | | |
| 40895 | S | N | RC, SM | (BFW30) | | | | |
| 40896 | S | N | RC, SM | (BFW30) | | | | |
| 40897 | S | N | RC, SM | (BFW30) | | | | |
| 40910 | S | N | RC | | 2N4231 | (2N3054) | | |
| 40911 | S | N | RC | (BDX25-6) | 2N5233 | | | |
| 40912 | S | N | RC | (BDX25-6) | | | | |
| 40915 | S | N | RC, SM | (BFY90) | | | | |
| 41500 | S | N | RC | | TIP31 | | | |
| 41501 | S | P | RC | | TIP32 | | | |
| 41502 | S | N | RC | | 2N4237 | | | |
| 41503 | S | P | RC | | 2N4234 | | | |
| 41504 | S | N | RC | BD224 | | | | |
| 41505 | S | N | RC | | FT47 | | | |
| 41506 | S | N | RC | | 2N5838 | | | |
| 43104 | S | N | RC | | 2N5631 | | | |
| 45190 | S | N | RC | (BD437) | | | | |
| 45191 | S | N | RC | (BD439) | | | | |
| 45192 | S | N | RC | (BC441) | | | | |
| 45193 | S | N | RC | (BD438) | | | | |
| 45194 | S | P | RC | (BD440) | | | | |
| 45195 | S | P | RC | (BD442) | | | | |
| 814044A | G | P | | AC128 | 2N2431 | | | |
| 815020 | G | P | | AF185 | | | | |
| 815021 | G | P | | AF185 | | | | |
| 815023 | G | P | | AC128 | 2N2431 | | | |
| 815024 | G | P | | AC128 | 2N2431 | | | |
| 815025 | G | P | | AF185 | | | | |
| 815025A | G | P | | AF185 | | | | |
| 815027 | G | P | | AF185 | | | | |
| 815028 | G | P | | AF185 | | | | |
| 815029 | G | P | | AC128 | 2N2431 | | | |
| 815030 | G | P | | AC128 | 2N2431 | | | |
| 815031 | G | P | | AC128 | 2N2431 | | | |
| 815034 | G | P | | AC128 | 2N2431 | | | |
| 815036 | G | P | | AF185 | | | | |
| 815037 | G | P | | AF185 | | | | |
| 815038 | G | P | | AC128 | 2N2431 | | | |
| 815041 | G | P | | AF185 | | | | |
| 815043 | G | P | | AF185 | | | | |
| 815068 | G | P | | AC128 | 2N2431 | | | |
| 815070A | G | P | | AC128 | 2N2431 | | | |
| 815075 | G | N | | AC127 | 2N2430 | | | |
| 815076 | G | N | | AC127 | 2N2430 | | | |
| 815103 | G | P | | AF185 | 2N2431 | | | |
| 815104 | G | P | | AC128 | | | | |
| 815105 | G | P | | AF185 | | | | |
| 825065 | G | P | | AF185 | | | | |

*Notes*

*Notes*

*Notes*

*Notes*

*Notes*

*Notes*

*Notes*

# OTHER BOOKS OF INTEREST

## BP108: INTERNATIONAL DIODE EQUIVALENTS GUIDE
### A. Michaels

This book is designed to help the user in finding possible substitutes for a large user-orientated selection of the many different types of semiconductor diodes that are available today.

Besides simple rectifier diodes, also included are zener diodes, LEDs, diacs, triacs, thyristors, OCIs, photo diodes and display diodes.

Wherever possible material type, function or type of diode and country of origin are shown and equivalents are sub-divided into European, and American and in some cases, Japanese types.

An extremely useful addition to the bookshelf of all those interested in electronics, be they technicians, designers, engineers or hobbyists.

| | |
|---|---|
| 144 pages | 1982 |
| 0 85934 083 X | **£2.25** |

## BP140: DIGITAL EQUIVALENTS AND PIN CONNECTIONS
### Adrian Michaels

Shows equivalents and pin connections of a popular user-orientated selection of digital integrated circuits.

Also shows details of packaging, families, functions, country of origin and manufacturer.

Includes devices manufactured by Fairchild, Ferranti, Harris, ITT, Motorola, National, Philips, R.C.A., Signetics, Sescosem, SGS-Ates, Siemens, SSSI, Stewart Warner, AEG-Telefunken, Texas Instruments, Teledyne.

Companion volume to book No. BP141: *Linear IC Equivalents and Pin Connections.*

| | |
|---|---|
| 320 pages | 1984 |
| 0 85934 115 1 | **£3.95** |

## BP141: LINEAR IC EQUIVALENTS AND PIN CONNECTIONS
### Adrian Michaels

Shows equivalents and pin connections of a popular user-orientated selection of linear integrated circuits.

Also shows details of families, functions, country of origin and manufacturer.

Includes devices manufactured by Analog Devices, Advance Micro Devices, Fairchild, Harris, ITT, Motorola, Philips, R.C.A., Raytheon, Signetics, Sescosem, SGS-Ates, Siemens, AEG-Telefunken, Texas Instruments, Teledyne.

Companion volume to book No. BP140: *Digital IC Equivalents and Pin Connections.*

| | |
|---|---|
| 320 pages | 1984 |
| 0 85934 116 X | **£3.95** |

Please note overleaf is a list of other titles that are available in our range of Radio, Electronics and Computer Books.

These should be available from all good Booksellers, Radio Component Dealers and Mail Order Companies.

However, should you experience difficulty in obtaining any title in your area, then please write directly to the publisher enclosing payment to cover the cost of the book plus adequate postage.

If you would like a complete catalogue of our entire range of Radio, Electronics and Computer Books then please send a Stamped Addressed Envelope to:

BERNARD BABANI (publishing) LTD
The Grampians
Shepherds Bush Road
London W6 7NF
England